John Lindley, Thomas Moore

The Treasury of Botany

A Popular Dictionary of the Vegetable Kingdom with which is incorporated a Glossary of

Botanical Terms

John Lindley, Thomas Moore

The Treasury of Botany
A Popular Dictionary of the Vegetable Kingdom with which is incorporated a Glossary of Botanical Terms

ISBN/EAN: 9783348014458

Printed in Europe, USA, Canada, Australia, Japan

Cover: Foto ©berggeist007 / pixelio.de

More available books at **www.hansebooks.com**

THE

TREASURY OF BOTANY:

A Popular Dictionary

OF

THE VEGETABLE KINGDOM;

WITH WHICH IS INCORPORATED

A GLOSSARY OF BOTANICAL TERMS

EDITED BY

JOHN LINDLEY, PH.D., F.R.S., F.L.S.

Late Emeritus Professor of Botany in University College, London;
Author of 'The Vegetable Kingdom'

AND

THOMAS MOORE, F.L.S.

Curator of the Chelsea Botanic Garden; Author of 'Index Filicum;' and,
Co-Editor of 'The Gardeners' Chronicle.'

ASSISTED BY NUMEROUS CONTRIBUTORS.

ILLUSTRATED BY NUMEROUS WOODCUTS BY FITCH AND BRANSTON
AND STEEL ENGRAVINGS BY ADLARD.

IN TWO PARTS.—PART II.

LONDON:

LONGMANS, GREEN, AND CO.

1866.

HISINGER. *Xylosma.*

HISPID. Covered with long stiff hairs.

HITCHENIA. A genus of Indian herbaceous plants of the order *Zingiberaceæ.* They have tuberiform rootlets; a stem destitute of leaves at its upper part, a spicate inflorescence, with white flowers, having a tubular three-toothed calyx, a corolla with a long slender tube, and a somewhat two-lipped limb, a short filament, channelled to receive the threadlike style, which is surmounted by a funnel-shaped stigma. The capsule is membranous, three-valved, and contains a number of seeds provided with a large star-like arillus.   [M. T. M.]

HOCHSTETTERIA. A genus of *Compositæ,* represented by *H. Schimperi,* a much-branched herb found in Arabia Petræa and Scind, whose wiry stems are furnished with distant serrated leaves, and each twig is terminated by a single orange-coloured flower-head. The genus differs from its allies of the fleabane group, in the florets being all tubular, perfect, and seated on a frilled receptacle.   [A. A. B.]

HOCK-HERB. *Althæa;* also *Malva.*

HOCKINIA. An annual gentianaceous plant of Brazil. The flowers are blue, with a five-parted cylindrical calyx, a bell-funnel-shaped corolla, five stamens having the connective prolonged into a lance-shaped point, and a hairy stigma divided into two plates. The fruit is capsular, bursting by two valves.   [M. T. M.]

HODGSONIA. A magnificent cucurbitaceous plant, very common in many parts of Eastern Bengal. The stems are described by Dr. Hooker as slender, frequently one hundred feet long, climbing the forest trees, and having their branching ends matted together and covered with leaves, which sometimes form a dense hanging screen of bright green foliage. The large flowers, yellow outside and white inside, remarkable for the long filiform twisted appendages hanging from their lobes, appear in May, and are very deciduous; they may often be seen strewing the ground in abundance in the forest, when the plant itself cannot be recognised amidst the canopy of vegetation above the traveller's head. The great melon-like fruit, called *Kathlor-pot* by the Lepchas, ripens in autumn and winter. Its coarse hard green pulp exudes a gummy fluid in great abundance, but is austere and uneatable.

HOFFMANNIA. The name of a West Indian cinchonaceous herb, with hairy branches, ovate rough leaves, and axillary many-flowered peduncles. The parts of the flower are in fours; the corolla salver-shaped; the anthers sessile; the stigma blunt on the end of a simple style; the fruit two-celled, many-seeded. [M. T. M.]

HOFFMANSEGGIA. A genus of *Leguminosæ,* nearly related to *Cassia,* but differing from it in the calyx segments being united by their margins so as to form a

five-toothed cup. It consists of about fifteen species distributed over California, Mexico, the temperate parts of Peru and Chili, extending nearly to the extreme south. They are neat little plants, with bipinnate leaves often marked with black dots; and the pretty yellow flowers are arranged in racemes which arise from opposite the leaves.   [A. A. B.]

HOFMEISTERELLA *eumicroscopica* is a little epiphytal orchid of Peru, belonging to the *Vandeæ,* nearly related to *Telipogon,* and remarkable for the very long beak hanging down in front of the stigma. The plant is stemless, with a few fleshy roots, a tuft of lance-shaped leaves, and a short flexuous spike bearing a few small yellow flowers.   [A. A. B.]

HOGMEAT. *Boerhaavia decumbens.*

HOGWEED. *Heracleum Sphondylium;* also *Polygonum aviculare,* and *Boerhaavia.* —, POISONOUS. *Aristolochia grandiflora.*

HOHENACKERIA. A genus of umbellifers characterised by having the styles awl-shaped and bent back, and the fruit compressed laterally, somewhat pear-shaped, and having a cylindrical beak crowned by the five persistent sharp teeth of the calyx; each half of the fruit has five obtuse strong ridges and narrow grooves between. The only species is a small annual (or biennial?) plant, *H. bupleurifolia,* a native of Armenia, with very short decumbent stems, long serrulate leaves, and small greenish flowers. [G. D.]

HOHENBERGIA. A genus of Brazilian bromeliaceous herbs, distinguished from *Billbergia* and other genera by the perianth, the outer segments of which are unequal, the two posterior segments being somewhat pyramidal winged and keeled, the anterior one convex outwardly and shorter, while the inner segments are longer, petal-like, occasionally provided with a minute scale at the base, and ultimately spirally twisted, as also are the three linear stigmas.   [M. T. M.]

HOITZIA. A genus of *Polemoniaceæ,* containing seven species, natives of Mexico. They are rigid or herbaceous under-shrubs with alternate leaves, and axillary flowers crowded at the tops of the branches, with many bracts below the calyx. The calyx is tubular and five-cleft; the corolla funnel-shaped, with the limb divided into five unequal laciniæ, and the stamens exserted. There are but few ovules in each of the three cells of the ovary.   [W. C.]

HOLACANTHA. A name expressive of the thorny character of the shrub to which it is applied, and which forms a genus of *Simarubaceæ.* It is a native of the deserts of Mexico and California, has no leaves, but is beset with strong spines. The flowers are small and unisexual, with a seven or eight-parted calyx, and seven or eight petals.   [M. T. M.]

HOLARRHENA. A genus of dogbanes,

having the calyx in five deep divisions, which are very narrow and acute; and five stamens attached to the lower part of the tube of the corolla, their anthers perfect. The species are Indian shrubs, erect and smooth; the leaves opposite, stalked and of thin texture; the flowers in terminal and lateral bunches. [G. D.]

HOLBŒLLIA. A small genus of *Lardizabdaceæ*, consisting of scandent shrubs, natives of India, and having digitate leaves, and axillary corymbiform racemes of purple or greenish flowers, which are monœcious, with six petaloid sepals and six minute petals. In the male flowers there are six free fertile stamens, and in the female six small sterile ones and three ovaries, which become oblong indehiscent berries. [T. M.]

HOLOOSORUS. A peculiar Bornean fern, referred by some botanists to *Grammitis* and *Polypodium*, but by others considered to form a distinct genus of the *Tænitideæ*. The fronds are solid and bluntly pentangular, with three grooves on the upper and two on the lower surface, the oval-oblong naked sori lying in the latter. The venation is reduced to a simple costa, imbedded in the centre of the narrow wiry fronds. *H. pentagonus* is the *Grammitis bisulcata* of Hooker. [T. M.]

HOLCUS. A genus of grasses, mostly European, belonging to the tribe *Phalareæ*, and distinguished by its somewhat open panicle with numerous crowded two-flowered spikelets. The upper flower is male, and has a shortly-awned glume, and the lower one is hermaphrodite, with the glume usually awnless. The outer glumes are boat-shaped, enclosing the flowers. Two species are natives of Britain, but they have soft woolly herbage, and are of little value. [T. M.]

HOLEWORT. *Corydalis bulbosa.*

HOLIGARNA. A genus of lofty Indian trees, belonging to the *Anacardiaceæ*, and distinguished by the parts of the flower being arranged in fives; the petals oblong, hairy, spreading, attached to the five-toothed calyx; the ovary united to the tube of the calyx, and containing a single ovule at its upper part; and the fruit fleshy, with a one-seeded stone. From the stem of *H. longifolia*, a lofty tree, occasionally cultivated in our stoves, the natives of Malacca are said to extract an acrid juice, which is used as a varnish. The stone of the fruit likewise contains an acrid resinous juice, while the investing pulp contains a glutinous fluid made use of by painters, and for fixing colours on linen. The fruit and the bark are used medicinally, but require to be employed with caution, as they are apt to give rise to dangerous symptoms. [M. T. M.]

HOLLOWROOT. *Adoxa Moschatellina.*

HOLLOWWORT. *Corydalis bulbosa.*

HOLLY. *Ilex* —. CAPE. *Crocoxylon excelsum.* —, KNEE. *Ruscus aculeatus.*

—; MOUNTAIN. *Nemopanthes.* —, SEA. *Eryngium maritimum.*

HOLLYHOCK. *Althæa rosea, chinensis,* and *ficifolia.* Sometimes written Hollihock, or Holy Hoke.

HOLLYWORTS. Lindley's name for the *Aquifoliaceæ.*

HOLM. The Holly, *Ilex Aquifolium.* —, KNEE. *Ruscus aculeatus.* —, SEA. *Eryngium maritimum.*

HOLOGRAPHIS. A genus of *Acanthaceæ*, containing a single Mexican species, a branching undershrub, with oblong-ovate obtuse leaves, and axillary flowers in pairs. The calyx is equally five-parted, and the corolla ringent, with a very short tube. It has four didynamous stamens. [W. C.]

HOLOLACHNE *soongarica* is a plant of the *Reaumuria* family, which grows in saline places on the shores of lakes in Soongaria and Mongholia. It is a few inches high, much-branched, with white wiry stems furnished with numerous minute linear clustered fleshy leaves, bearing inconspicuous white flowers in their axils. The few (eight to ten) stamens, and the absence of scales at the base of the petals, are the chief characters. [A. A. B.]

HOLOSERICEOUS. Silky; so covered with hairs that it feels soft to the touch, although the naked eye may fail to detect the presence of hairs.

HOLOSTEMMA. A small genus of *Asclepiadaceæ*, from tropical Asia, consisting of twiners with largish flowers, deeply coloured inside and arranged in shortly pedunculate interpetiolar umbels or racemes. The corolla is rotate with a short tube, and the limb divided into five broadly ovate lobes. [W. C.]

HOLOSTEUM. A small genus of *Caryophyllaceæ*, with the styles usually three and the capsule valves twice as many. They are small annuals found in Europe, North Africa, and temperate Asia, with simple stems, smooth oblong leaves in pairs, sometimes united at the base, and terminal umbels of small chickweed-like flowers. *H. umbellatum* is found in a few of the eastern counties of England, but is far from common. [J. T. S.]

HOLY GHOST. *Angelica sylvestris.* — FLOWER. *Peristeria elata.*

HOLY-HERB. *Verbena officinalis.*

HOLY-ROPE. *Eupatorium cannabinum.*

HOMALIACEÆ. (*Homaliads.*) A natural order of monochlamydeous dicotyledons included in Lindley's cactal alliance of epigynous Exogens. Trees or shrubs with alternate leaves; perianth funnel-shaped, with five to fifteen gland-bearing divisions and alternating petaloid scales, the latter considered by some as petals, and hence Lindley places the order between *Loasaceæ* and *Cactaceæ*; stamens inserted on the perianth, either singly or in bundles of three or six; ovary adherent, one-celled; ovules numerous, pendulous; placentas three to five parietal; styles three to five; fruit a capsule or berry; seeds albuminous. Tropical plants of India, Africa, and America, having astringent qualities. There are nine known genera and thirty-six species. Examples: *Homalium, Blackwellia, Nisa, Cordylanthus.* [J. H. B.]

HOMALIUM. Tropical American shrubs, forming the typical genus of *Homaliaceæ*. The principal characters reside in the stamens, which vary in number, and are attached to the perianth in groups of three or four placed opposite to the inner segments of the perianth, and alternate with fleshy glands placed in front of the outer or calycine segments; and in the capsule, which is one-celled, containing a few seeds and opening partially by three valves. The roots of some of the species are astringent. [M. T. M.]

HOMALONEMA. A genus of *Araceæ*, consisting of Indian herbaceous plants, with heart or arrow-shaped leaves; an expanded aromatic spathe; a spadix covered with flowers over the whole of its surface, and having rudimentary flowers mixed with the ovaries; numerous sessile anthers, and three-celled detached ovaries; and a three-cleft stigma. *H. cordatum*, with a white spathe, is cultivated in greenhouses. *H. aromaticum*, a native of Chittagong, has an agreeable aromatic smell, and its root is deemed by the natives to possess medicinal virtues. [M. T. M.]

HOMBAC D'ARABIE. (Fr.) *Sodada decidua.*

HOMBRONIA. A name given to two species of *Pandanaceæ*, figured in the *Voyage de la Bonite*, but not yet described.

HOMERIA. The name of a few species of Cape bulb-tuberous plants, sometimes separated from *Moræa*, from which they differ in having nearly regular flowers. The perianth has a very short tube, and six divisions, of which the three alternate or inner ones are rather but not conspicuously smaller than the others, the three stamens are monadelphous, and the stigma is trifid, with two-cleft fringed branches. They are rather handsome plants, with linear-ensiform leaves, and leafy branching scapes bearing several showy enduring flowers, usually orange-red, copper-coloured, or yellow. [T. M.]

HOMINY. A meal prepared from Indian corn.

HOMOCARPOUS. Having all the fruits of a flower-head exactly alike.

HOMODROMAL. Having all the spires turned the same way; or the spires of a lateral organ the same as those on a central organ.

HOMOGAMOUS. When all the florets of a capitulum, &c., are hermaphrodite.

HOMOGENS. A name given by Lindley to a division of Exogens characterised by the wood being arranged in the form of

wedges, and not in concentric circles or zones. It is seen in the case of *Piperaceæ*, the shrubby *Aristolochiaceæ, Nepenthaceæ, Lardizabalaceæ*, and *Menispermaceæ*. The term is not now used. [J. H. B.]

HOMOGYNE. A small genus of stemless composite herbs, found in Alpine situations in South Europe. They have long stalked root-leaves with kidney-shaped toothed or angled blades, and flower-scapes three inches to a foot in length, furnished with one or two distant leaves, and terminating in a single white or purple flower-head, having all the florets tubular. Related to *Petasites*, they differ in the heads being solitary instead of numerous on each scape. *H. alpina* and *H. discolor* are sometimes seen in collections of Alpine plants. [A. A. B.]

HOMOIOS, or HOMO. In Greek compounds = alike or similar.

HOMOLOGUE. Organs are called homologous when they have the same analytical relations, or, in other words, correspondence of structure and origin, though the functions may be different; analogous when they resemble each other in outward form or in functions. Affinity, on the contrary, expresses a close relation of one species, genus, or order to another. The several external parts of a water-lily, for instance, are perfectly homologous with those of a common white lily, but there is no affinity between them. Pollen-grains and the spores of many of the higher cryptogams resemble each other in origin and germination. They are, therefore, homologous with each other, though their functions are totally different. [M. J. B.]

HOMOMORPHUS. Uniform. All shaped alike.

HOMONEMEÆ. A name given by Fries to the lower cryptogams as propagated by spores which send out threads of the same nature with the perfect plant, and do not produce anything like a false cotyledon as in ferns. [M. J. B.]

HOMORANTHUS. A genus of *Chamælauciaceæ*, consisting of small Australian shrubs, and bearing opposite linear sharp-pointed leaves, and axillary racemes of flowers. The tubular calyx has five ribs, and five elongated hair-like teeth; there are ten stamens and a long bearded style. The seed-vessel is indehiscent and single-seeded. [R. H.]

HOMORGANA. A term applied to cryptogamic plants, as consisting of cells only, without vessels. It is synonymous with Cellulares, and is liable to the same objections. [M. J. B.]

HOMOTHALAMUS. Resembling the thallus; a term employed among lichens only.

HOMOTROPAL. Having the same direction as the seed, but not straight.

HONAY. An Indian name for *Calophyllum Inophyllum*.

HONESTY. *Lunaria biennis.*

HONEWORT. *Sison Amomum*; also *Trinia vulgaris*, and *Cryptotænia canadensis.*

HONEYBERRY. The name in modern Greece of the berries of *Celtis australis*; also *Melicocca bijuga.*

HONEYDEW. A sugary secretion from the leaves of plants in hot weather, usually attributed to aphides, because they secrete a similar matter. When the secretion is extreme, as is sometimes the case in unusual heat, it drips from the leaves in little drops, which are sometimes so abundant that they may be swept up in considerable quantities. The secretion is then called Manna, though it is not intended by the term to identify it with the manna of the ash. The affection is ranked in vegetable pathology under the genus Apostaxis, and is generally harmless. [M. J. B.]

HONEY-FLOWER, or HONEY-PLANT. *Melianthus.*

HONEYSUCKLE. *Lonicera*; also applied amongst agriculturists to meadow clover, *Trifolium pratense.* — of Australia. *Banksia serrata.* — of Jamaica. *Passiflora laurifolia.* —, BUSH. *Diervilla.* —, DWARF. *Cornus suecica.* —, FLY. *Halleria*; also *Lonicera Xylosteum.* —, FRENCH. *Hedysarum coronarium.* —, HEATH. *Banksia serrata.* —, WHITE. *Azalea viscosa.*

HONEYSUCKLE TREE. *Banksia australis.*

HONEYWARE. *Alaria esculenta*; also *Laminaria saccharina.*

HONEYWORT. *Cerinthe.*

HONGHEL-BUSH. *Adenium Honghel.*

HONKENYA, or HONKENEJA. A genus of *Caryophyllaceæ*, allied to *Alsine*, but distinguished by its few large pear-shaped seeds, beaked at the end and having an indentation on the opposite side. They are all littoral plants found in the northern hemisphere, in the temperate and arctic zones. *H. peploides* is very common on the shores of the British Islands, its rhizome creeping in the sand, and throwing up numerous low stems with fleshy leaves and small white flowers. [J. T. S.]

HOODED. The same as Cucullate.

HOODIA. A remarkable genus of *Asclepiadaceæ*, containing two branching South African herbs, with fleshy many-angled cactus-like stems, thickly covered at the angles with strong prickles, which are dilated at the base. The flowers have a very large corolla, and are on short peduncles near the apex of the stem; the calyx five-parted; the corolla rotate with a very short tube and a large dilated faintly five-lobed limb, each lobe terminating in an aristate tooth. The staminal crown is double, the outer whorl consisting of five deeply emarginate lobes, with the margins incurved, the inner of five alternating leaflets bent downwards. [W. O.]

HOOKED-BACK. Curved in a direction from the apex to the base; as the side lobes of the leaf of the dandelion.

HOOKERIEI. A natural order of mosses, distinguished by the flat creeping irregularly-branched stems, with reticulated leaves, a cernuous succulent capsule on a succulent elongated footstalk, a campanulate smooth veil and double peristome. *Hookeria lucens* is one of our most beautiful mosses, and remarkable for its large pale shining loosely reticulated leaves. It is not uncommon in Devonshire. Most of the species are extra-European, and inhabitants of warm regions. A few have not flattened stems, and two or three species included in the Antarctic Flora have erect capsules, but these are distinguished from *Leucodontei* by their mitræform veil. Occasionally the base of the veil is laciniate, as in the Irish *H. lætevirens.* [M. J. B.]

HOOKHEAL. *Prunella vulgaris.*

HOOP-PETTICOAT. *Corbularia.*

HOP. *Humulus Lupulus.* —, WILD. *Bryonia dioica.*

HOPEA. A genus of *Dipterocarpaceæ*, consisting of resin-bearing trees natives of Borneo, whose flowers differ from those of *Shorea* only in the number and disposition of the stamens. [M. T. M.]

HOPKIRKIA. A genus of *Compositæ*, peculiar to Mexico, represented by a single species, *H. anthemoidea*, a smooth branching herb, with pinnately-parted leaves, and small terminal flower-heads with yellow florets. The involucre consists of four or five obovate scales, and encloses three tubular four or five-toothed florets, whose silky achenes are crowned with a pappus of eight chaffy one-nerved scales, three-toothed at top, the nerve prolonged into an awn. [A. A. B.]

HOPPIA. A small genus of Brazilian cyperaceous plants, belonging to the tribe *Caricinæ.* The inflorescence is in heads which are composed of compound imbricated spikes. [D. M.]

HORANINOVIA. A genus of *Chenopodiaceæ* closely allied to *Salsola*, but differing in habit, and in the perianth being longer than the filaments, in the segments having a smaller wing not produced till much later, after flowering, and in the minute styles looking like a simple stigma. They are rough annual herbs of temperate Asia. [J. T. S.]

HORARIOUS. Enduring for an hour or two only; as the petals of *Cistus.*

HORDEUM. The Barley: one of the most valuable of the genera of grasses (*Graminaceæ*). As a corn plant, Barley is perhaps one of the most early cultivated, and its different varieties can be grown under a wider range of climatal differences than almost any other variety of cereal; but which wild species is the true parent of the cultivated form is a matter involved in obscurity, though in all probability one of the wild forms of the more temperate parts of India may be made to yield a good grain by cultivation. The genus may be distinguished by its spikelets being in threes arranged on opposite sides of the rachis, hence forming a bilateral spike.

The species consist of—I. Cereal Barleys: *H. hexastichum*, the six-rowed, in which all three flowers of the spikelets are perfect and fertile; *H. distichum*, the two-rowed, in which only the central floret is fertile, and the two lateral abortive. 2. Wild Barleys: *H.murinum, pratense*, and *maritimum*.

Of the many varieties of cultivated Barley, those known as distichous or two-rowed Barley are those more commonly cultivated, for in them the seed is tolerably uniform in size, and so a better sample is produced, and we believe that it is even more productive than the six-rowed form. This latter, however, is frequently attempted to be employed in farming; but as the lateral florets are seldom so plump as the central one, a very uneven sample is the result. This is one of the causes of the greater coarseness of the varieties of the six-rowed barley when compared with the two-rowed—a fact perhaps more observable in the black variety than in any other.

In this group we must notice a naked six-rowed variety, the grain of which separates from the chaff scales after the manner of wheat: the difference being that in ordinary barley we have the grain + the chaff scales, which adhere and form what is usually called the skin of the barley, which is described as coarse or fine according to its degree of thickness; whilst in the naked barley we have the grain—the chaff scales. This latter is not a good malting kind, and therefore,though interesting from a botanical point of view, is never likely to become extensively cultivated.

Of the Meadow Barleys, *H. pratense* only is of any importance. Its herbage is sweet and nutritious, and when the field is constantly depastured it is an exceedingly good species to encourage; but its long awns, rough as they are with little spiculæ or projections for their whole length, render them highly prejudicial in hay, for being very brittle they readily break up into small lengths which stick beneath the tongue or in the gums, the spiculæ acting like barbs in preventing their removal, and so creating great irritation, swelling of the mouth, and inability to eat, which often result in serious derangements to the animals partaking of it. This effect would be even more conspicuous if the Wall Barley, *H.murinum*, formed part of a meadow, but it particularly affects old walls and waste places. Still, however, it not unfrequently occurs in waste corners of sandy fields, and when this is so the contents of such spots should never be included in the hay-rick. We all remember how in our youth we put inverted spikes of the Wall Barley

up our sleeves and found them travel to our shoulders, where they were difficult to dislodge without disarranging them. This was caused by the parts of the spikelets being compressible, so that by a gentle motion they progressed upwards with a kind of spring; but the spiculæ or barbs, on pulling the spike the contrary way, stuck into the clothes, and so it could not easily be dislodged from its position.

Both the Wall and the Seaside Barleys are denizens of sandy soils—the former everywhere, the latter on the seashore. The Wall Barley is thus a remarkable agrarian indicator of the nature of land. On the sands of the tertiaries it is a common weed, so on the more sandy deposits of the new and old red sandstones. A curious instance of the partiality of this grass for sand occurs in the Cotswold hills; these are composed of oolitic freestones and chalk, both calcareous rocks, and there, as in the clays of the Oxford clay and lias, it is universally absent; but in the lias hollows of the valley of the Severn, as at Gloucester and Cheltenham in the former county, and Bredon in the latter, where are thick beds of sand varying to as much as thirty feet in depth, the wall barley so abounds, as to become a most exact indicator of the boundary lines of the arenaceous deposit. See CRITHO. [J. B.]

HOREHOUND. *Marrubium vulgare.* —, BLACK. *Ballota nigra.* —, STINKING. *Ballota.* —, WATER. *Lycopus.* —, WHITE. *Marrubium.* —, WILD. *Eupatorium teucrifolium.*

HORESTRANG. *Peucedanum officinale.*

HORKELIA. A genus of the rose family peculiar to Oregon and California, and numbering about a dozen species. They are perennial herbs one to two feet high, with pinnatifid root-leaves, the stems terminating in crowded cymes of minute white or pink flowers. From *Potentilla* they differ in the small flowers, and in the definite number of stamens (ten in two series). [A. A. B.]

HORMIDIUM. A section of the genus *Epidendrum.*

HORMIN. (Fr.) *Salvia Horminum.*

HORMINUM. A small genus of labiate plants. The calyx is bell-shaped and two-lipped, the upper lip with three teeth, the lower with two; the tube of the corolla much longer than the calyx, and the corolla itself imperfectly two-lipped, the upper lip being very short and notched, the lower three-lobed. The anthers cohere in pairs. *H. pyrenaicum* is a tufted perennial herb, with numerous root-leaves, simple almost leafless stems, and purplish-blue flowers which grow in whorls of six, all turned the same way. It is a native of the temperate parts of Europe, on the mountains. [C. A. J.]

HORMOGYNE. A name applied to an Australian shrub belonging to the order *Sapotaceæ.* It may be recognised by the anthers, all of which burst inwardly; and by the jointed ring which surmounts the ovary—whence the name, from *ormos*, a necklace. [M. T. M.]

HORNBEAM. *Carpinus Betulus.* —, HOP. *Ostrya vulgaris.*

HORNEMANNIA *pinnata* is a slender prostrate creeping Nepalese herb, with ovate pinnately divided leaves and small flowers, forming a genus of *Scrophulariaceæ* nearly allied to *Sibthorpia*, and differing chiefly in the corolla, which is more distinctly contracted at the base into a short tube. The name *Hornemannia* had been previously applied to a species of *Thibaudia*, and to *Mazus rugosus.*

HORN OF PLENTY. *Fedia Cornucopiæ.*

HORN PLANT. *Ecklonia buccinalis.*

HORNSCHUCHIA. A Brazilian genus of doubtful affinity, placed by Von Martius in the ebony family. *H. bryotrophe*, so called from the moss growing on its leaves, is said to be a scrambling shrub, with three to five-nerved oblong unequal-sided leaves, and small white flowers in racemes arising from the lower naked shoots, each flower with a cup-shaped nearly entire calyx, six petals, six stamens, and a three-celled ovary which developes into a fruit of three cylindrical carpels each about an inch long. [A. A. B.]

HORNUS. Anything the produce of the same year ; thus *Rami horni* are branches not a year old.

HORNWORT. *Ceratophyllum.* Hornworts is Lindley's name for the *Ceratophyllaceæ.*

HORNY. Hard and close in texture, but not brittle, as the albumen of many plants.

HOROLOGIUM FLORÆ. A time-paper of flowers ; a table explaining the time at which the same flowers expand in different latitudes.

HORSEBANE. *Œnanthe Phellandrium.*

HORSECHIRE. *Teucrium Chamædrys.*

HORSE-FLOWER. *Melampyrum sylvaticum.*

HORSEHEAL, or HORSHELE. *Inula Helenium.*

HORSEHOOF. *Tussilago Farfara.*

HORSEKNOB. *Centaurea nigra.*

HORSE-MUSHROOM. A term commonly applied to the larger kinds of mushroom, as *Agaricus arvensis*, to the exclusion of the true pink-gilled *A. campestris.* Though the latter is doubtless the more delicate and makes the finest ketchup, the horse-mushroom need not be excluded on account of its supposed unwholesomeness. It is largely consumed in London and all our greater towns, and when eaten in moderation is an excellent article of food. The species is distinguished from *A. campestris* by its paler gills and generally double ring,

but especially by its turning yellow when bruised. A variety of this species, commonly known as the Hedge Mushroom, with a yellower scaly pileus, is an object of suspicion, as is also one which occurs in woods and has a bell-shaped pileus which instantly becomes of a deep yellow when touched. A closely allied species or variety is known by the name of Springers. It is observable that in Italy this species is considered far safer than the common mushroom. In France, also, it is highly esteemed, and is known under the name of Boule de Neige. [M. J. B.]

HORSEPIPE. *Equisetum.*

HORSERADISH. *Cochlearia Armoracia.*

HORSERADISH-TREE. *Moringa pterygosperma.*

HORSETAIL. *Equisetum.* —, SHRUBBY. *Ephedra.* — TREE. *Casuarina equisetifolia.*

HORSEWEED. *Erigeron canadense*; also *Collinsonia.*

HORSEWOOD, JAMAICA. *Calliandra comosa.*

HORSFIELDIA. A genus of umbellifers having the fruit flat and covered with wool, each half of it with three ribs on the back. The genus was founded in honour of Dr. Horsfield, well known for his researches in the natural history of Java. The only species is a Javanese prickly shrub, having some of the leaves heart-shaped and five-lobed, the upper three-lobed and densely hairy. The genus is of interest to the botanist, as in some measure connecting umbellifers and ivyworts, having the fruit of the former and the general habit of the latter. [G. D.]

HORTENSIA. (Fr.) *Hydrangea Hortensia.*

HORTENSIS. Of or belonging to a garden.

HORTIA. A Brazilian shrub forming a genus of *Rutaceæ.* The flowers are arranged in a corymbose manner on thick stalks ; they have a cup-shaped calyx ; five lance-shaped petals much longer than the sepals, hairy at the base on their inner surface, and with their points turned inwards like a hook; five stamens inserted on a disk with the petals, the filaments glandular and flattened; and a thick style surmounting a five-lobed ovary. The fruit is a capsule with one or two-seeded compartments. *H. brasiliana* is said to possess febrifugal properties. [M. T. M.]

HORTONIA. A genus of *Schizandraceæ*, consisting of smooth shrubs with entire leaves, axillary cymose inflorescence, and pale yellow flowers. The sepals and petals number about thirty, in many rows ; the stamens seven to ten, their filaments having two glands at their base. There are from fifteen to twenty ovaries, and the stigma is sessile. The fruit consists of dry closely-agglomerated drupes. There is but one species, *H. floribunda*, found in Ceylon.   [J. H. B.]

HORTUS SICCUS. The same as Herbarium.

HOSACKIA. A genus of pretty dwarf pea-flowered annual or perennial herbs, found in Oregon, California, and Mexico. Though allied to, and having much the appearance of, *Lotus*, they differ in the minute (not foliaceous) stipules. The leaves are in many species unequally pinnate, in others trifoliolate; the flowers are mostly yellow mixed with white and purple, usually disposed in umbels, which are often stalked. Upwards of twenty species are known.   [A. A. B.]

HOTTENTOT BREAD. *Testudinaria Elephantipes.*

HOTTONIA. Aquatic herbaceous plants distinguished among the *Primulaceæ* by their capsules, which, when ripe, split into five valves connected at the base and summit. *H. palustris*, the Water Violet, is a singular and beautiful plant found in ditches and pools in many parts of England, and is not unfrequently cultivated. The roots are long and silvery, and are either suspended in the water or strike deep into the muddy bottom. The leaves, wholly submersed, are finely pinnated or pectinated, and grow in tufts, from the midst of which rises a long cylindrical solitary stalk, bearing a pyramid of handsome light purple and white flowers, which are disposed in whorls. French, *Plume d'eau*; German, *Wasserviole*.   [C. A. J.]

HOUBLON. (Fr.) *Humulus.*

HOULLETIA. The name of a few epiphytal orchids of tropical America, having ovate or conical pseudobulbs with one long membranaceous plaited leaf at the apex, and from the base of the bulb erect or drooping spikes, ending in a raceme of rather large and handsome nodding flowers. In *H. Brocklehurstiana*, the erect flower-scape is a foot and a half high, and the individual flower two inches in diameter, and deliciously sweet; the sepals and petals spreading, nearly equal, yellow, mottled with blood-red; the lip purple at the apex, and furnished with two horn-like processes directed towards the column. The genus is related to *Stanhopea*, differing, according to Brongniart, in the spreading sepals and petals, and in the lip being articulate in the middle, with two horns on its lower half directed towards the column. It has been named after M. Houllet, a French gardener.   [A. A. B.]

HOUND'SBERRY, or **HOUND'S-TREE.** The Dogwood, *Cornus sanguinea.*

HOUND'S-TONGUE. *Cynoglossum officinale.*

HOUQUE. (Fr.) *Holcus.*

HOUSELEEK. *Sempervivum tectorum.*

HOUSELEEK-TREE. *Æonium arboreum.*

HOUSTONIA. *Hedyotis.*

HOUTTEA. One of the generic or sub-generic groups, separated from GESNERA: which see.

HOUTTUYNIA. A genus of marsh plants, inhabiting Japan and tropical Asia, and belonging to the *Saururaceæ*. They have a creeping jointed rhizome, a wavy herbaceous stem, heart-shaped leaves, with a large sheathing stipule above them, and flowers placed on a spike surrounded at its base by a ring of a few white bracts. Perianth none; stamens three, adherent for some distance to the ovary; fruit capsular, of three carpels, with three parietal placentæ and numerous seeds. *H. cordata*, a curious and not inelegant plant, is occasionally met with in cultivation; its leaves are accounted serviceable as a medicine in Cochin China.   [M. T. M.]

HOUX. (Fr.) *Ilex Aquifolium.* — DE MAHON. *Ilex balearica.* — FRAGON, FRÉLON, or PETIT. *Ruscus aculeatus.*

HOVE. *Nepeta Glechoma*, sometimes called *Glechoma hederacea.*

HOVEA. A genus of handsome blue-flowered evergreen bushes, belonging to the *Leguminosæ*, differing from its allies in having turgid nearly orbicular pods as large as good-sized peas. Of about twenty known species, the greater part are confined to Western Australia, the rest occurring in South-eastern Australia and Tasmania. The leaves are mostly lance-shaped or linear, with the margins entire and rolled back, and both surfaces smooth, or the lower clothed with rusty down, *H. ilicifolia*, sometimes called *Plagiolobium ilicifolium*, has holly-like leaves. *H. Celsi* is one of the best known, and a very common and beautiful greenhouse plant, flowering like most of the species in spring. This plant exhibits ' the peculiarity of the flower-buds of the preceding year appearing at the base of those expanded during the present—a common condition of leaf-buds, which are always visible the season preceding their expansion, but not frequently so with flower-buds, which, though they may be formed several years before their development externally, generally remain concealed till the period of their unfolding.' The genus bears the name of M. Hove, a Polish botanist.   [A. A. B.]

HOVENIA. A genus of *Rhamnaceæ*, nearly allied to *Ceanothus*, from which it is readily recognised by the short footstalks of the minute whitish flowers (which are in axillary or terminal forked panicles) becoming much thickened after the flower withers. Two species are known, *H. dulcis* and *inæqualis*, the former found in Japan, the latter in the Himalaya. Both are trees with alternate heart-shaped serrated leaves. The round fruits about the size of a pea, are seated on the end of the recurved fleshy peduncle, which is cylindrical, about an inch long, and contains a sweet red pulp which is eaten.   [A. A. B.]

HOWARDIA. A genus of trees or shrubs inhabiting tropical America, belonging to the *Cinchoniaceæ*, and named in honour of Mr. Howard, an eminent English pharmacologist. The flowers are remarkable, in that one of the sepals of the calyx is expanded into a large heart-shaped stalked leaf. The corolla is tubular and hairy; the stamens originate from a densely hairy ring; the ovary is surmounted by a cushion-like disk; and the fruit is capsular, girt at the top by the remains of the calyx, and bursting from above downwards.

H. (*Chrysoxylon*) *febrifuga* furnishes a bitter tonic bark, first detected by Mr. Howard, who likewise found that its medicinal qualities depended on two chemical principles, one an alkaloid called *howardine*, the other a bitter principle. With reference to the leafy calyx of these and some allied plants, as *Mussænda*, &c., it may be remarked, that the arrangement of the veins of the leafy sepal is different from that of the true leaves, a fact which has, apparently, been generally overlooked. [M. T, M.]

HOYA. A genus of *Asclepiadaceæ*, containing, besides one African species, a large number of species dispersed over tropical Asia. They are herbaceous plants with twining or creeping stems, which throw out roots at the lower nodes. The

Hoya imperialis.

leaves are opposite, often, but not in all the species, thick and fleshy; and the flowers are in lateral umbels. The corolla is rotate, the five lobes of the limb are ovate and valvate in the bud. The staminal corona consists of five scales inserted on the gynostegium, and usually spreading horizontally like a star in the centre of the corolla; the inner angle bears a small tooth incumbent on the anther. The pollen-masses are erect, oblong, and attached in pairs. The stigma is not beaked. The follicles are smooth or with wing-like appendages. The genus contains some of the most ornamental among the plants cultivated in our hothouses. [W. C.]

HUACSARO. A Peruvian fern, *Elaphoglossum Ruizianum*.

HUCKBERRY. *Celtis crassifolia*.

HUCKLEBERRY. *Gaylussacia*.

HUDSONIA. Small tufted heath-like North American plants belonging to the *Cistaceæ*, among which they are distinguished by the calyx of five equal sepals, and the one-celled three-valved capsule, containing one to three seeds. Most of the species are downy, with somewhat shrubby, erect stems, closely invested with small narrow imbricated leaves; the flowers are yellow. [C. A. J.]

HUGELIA. A genus of Californian annuals belonging to the *Polemoniaceæ*, and allied to *Gilia*, from which it is distinguished by having a short tube to the corolla, and linear arrow-shaped anthers. All the species are more or less clothed with white down, the leaves alternate, and the flowers disposed in heads surrounded at the base with dense wool. Some of the species have blue and yellow flowers.

The name has also been given to an Australian genus of *Rutaceæ*, which is said to differ from its congeners in its ten-cleft calyx, its ten petals, and its indefinite perigynous stamens. [O. A. J.]

HUGONIACEÆ. A name given by Arnott to a group of plants now included under *Oxalidaceæ*. [J. H. B.]

HUGONIA. A genus of *Oxalidaceæ*, considered the type of a special order by Planchon and others. They are Indian shrubs, with alternate oval leathery leaves, and single-flowered axillary peduncles, often changed into a circinate spine. The flowers have the parts in fives, the stamens being twice as many. The fruit is a fleshy berry or drupe, with five pips. The roots of *H. Mystax* smell like violets, and are said to act on the kidneys and skin; they are used in reducing inflammation, and as a remedy for the bite of snakes. [J. T. S.]

HUILE ANTIQUE DE LAVANDE. (Fr.) A perfumery oil, forming one of the ingredients of Eau de Cologne. — DE CADE. A tarry oil obtained from *Juniperus Oxycedrus*. — DE CÉDRAT. An essential oil obtained from the citron. — DES MARMOTTES. An oil obtained from the kernel of *Prunus Brigantiaca*.

HULDEE. An Indian name for *Curcuma longa*.

HULST. *Ilex Aquifolium*.

HULVER. *Ilex Aquifolium*. —, KNEE. *Ruscus aculeatus*. —, SEA. *Eryngium maritimum*.

HUMATA. A small genus of creeping davallioid ferns, sometimes referred indeed to *Davallia* itself, but having more of the technical character of *Cystopteris*. They are variable in character, having simple, lobed, pinnatifid, pedately pinnatifid, or subternate rigid leathery fronds. The sori, which are covered by suborbicular-reniform or transversely oblong reniform indusia, affixed only by their broad base, are usually vertical at the apex of the veins, but sublateral in *H. Gaimardiana*. The species are mostly natives of India and the Indian and Eastern Islands, one or two being also found in the Mascaren Islands, and in the Feejees. [T. M.]

HUMBERTIA. A genus of *Convolvulaceæ*, containing a single species from Madagascar. It is a tree with obovate petiolate leaves, and single-flowered peduncles. The calyx consists of five sepals, the corolla is five-cleft, the five stamens are much exserted, and the ovary is surmounted by a curved style, and a flat hollowed-out stigma. The baccate ligneous capsule is two-celled, with two seeds in each cell. [W. C.]

HUMBLE PLANT. *Mimosa pudica.*

HUMBOLDTIA. A genus of the *Cæsalpinia* group of *Leguminosæ*, consisting of two elegant scrambling shrubs, found in Malabar and Ceylon. They have curiously tumid branchlets, furnished with unequally-pinnate leaves, at the base of which are remarkable leaf-like stipules, transversely dilated at their point of attachment. The numerous scarlet flowers are disposed in axillary racemes, and have a four-toothed tubular calyx supported by two bracts, three or five petals and stamens, and an ovary which becomes an oblong compressed pod, with numerous seeds. From *Jonesia* it differs in the presence of petals, and from other allied genera in the nature of the stipules. The name of the illustrious Humboldt is perpetuated in the genus. [A. A. B.]

HUMEA *elegans*, so well known and so frequently cultivated in gardens, is the only species of this genus, which belongs to the *Compositæ*, and is remarkable for its minute and extremely numerous flower-heads, each of which contains but three or four tubular and perfect florets. This plant, found in a wild state in South-east Australia, is in our gardens an erect unbranched biennial, attaining a height of four to eight feet, the stems furnished below with ample dock-like leaves, and terminating in a beautiful pyramidal panicle, consisting of myriads of drooping rose-coloured heads, not much larger than the flowers of some grasses. The whole plant is somewhat glutinous, and, especially when bruised, emits a strong and peculiar balsamic odour. [A. A. B.]

HUMIFUSE. Spread over the surface of the ground.

HUMILIS. Low. When the stature of a plant is not particularly small, but much smaller than that of kindred species; thus, a tree twenty feet high may be called low, if the other species of its genus are forty or fifty feet high.

HUMIRIACEÆ. (*Humiriads.*) A natural order of thalamifloral dicotyledons included in Lindley's erical alliance of hypogynous Exogens. Balsamic trees or shrubs with alternate simple exstipulate leaves; calyx in five divisions; petals five, imbricate; stamens numerous, monadelphous;

the anthers two-celled with a membranous connective, extended beyond the lobes; disk often present; ovary five-celled. Fruit a drupe; seed albuminous; embryo orthotropal. They are natives of tropical America. The genera are: *Vantanea, Humirium,* and *Saccoglottis*. [J. H. B.]

HUMIRIUM. This and two other genera of small trees or shrubs form the order *Humiriaceæ*, all the species of which belong to tropical South America. *Humirium* is distinguished by its flowers being small and arranged in cymes; by their stamens being twenty in number, either all bearing a single anther, or, in a few species, five of them larger with three-forked filaments bearing three anthers; and by the disk being ten-lobed. About a dozen species are described.

H. balsamiferum, the Houmiri of French Guiana, is a tree growing about forty feet high, and having smooth, egg-shaped or oval-oblong, stalkless leaves, with the base half clasping round the stem. It produces a red-coloured wood, useful for house-building; and its bark, when wounded, yields a reddish balsamic juice, possessing an odour like that of storax, and which after a time becomes hard and brittle, and is then burnt as a perfume. An ointment is also prepared from it, and used for pains in the joints, besides which it is given internally as a remedy for tape-worm and other complaints. *H. floribundum* is a small tree common in Brazil, where it is called 'Umiri,' and its wood is used for the rafters of houses. Its bark is greatly esteemed as a perfume by the Brazilians, and when wounded a fragrant yellow balsam, termed balsam of Umiri, flows from it. [A. S.]

HUMMING-BIRD BUSH. *Æschynomene montevidensis.*

HUMULUS. The common Hop (*H. Lupulus*), belonging to the *Cannabinaceæ*, is the sole representative of this genus. It is a perennial, producing annually long, weak, roughish twining stems, and lobed coarsely-toothed leaves, which bear a general resemblance to those of the vine, but are harsh to the touch; each pair of leaves has two forked curved stipules between them. The male and female flowers are produced on separate plants. The males grow in loose, drooping panicles from the axils of the leaves, and have five sepals and five stamens; while the females form green scaly cones or catkins, which are produced either singly or in clusters, and are composed of a number of broad concave scales, partly overlapping, each having two inconspicuous flowers at its base. After flowering and during the period of ripening, these cones increase in size, and when full grown constitute the well known 'hops' used by brewers. The scales also become covered with small grains of a resinous substance, called *lupuline*; and the ovary changes into a small nut which is enveloped in the enlarged sepal, and is the true fruit.

The Hop was well known to the Romans, and is mentioned by Pliny under the name of *Lupus salictarius*. It gradually spread through Europe during the middle ages, but was not cultivated in England till the year 1524, when it was introduced from Flanders, though not without violent opposition, petitions against it being presented to Parliament, in which it was stigmatised as ' a wicked weed that would spoil the drink, and endanger the people.' At the present day, the principal hop-producing countries are England, Belgium, Bavaria, and the United States. In England about 50,000 acres are devoted to it, chiefly in Kent, Sussex, Hampshire, Worcestershire, and Herefordshire, and more sparingly in Essex, Suffolk, Surrey, Yorkshire, &c. Several varieties are known, the finest of which are the White Bines, the *Goldings*, and the Grapes. The plants are supported during growth upon stout poles varying in height from ten to twenty feet. When the hop-picking season arrives, usually early in September, the stems are cut through at about a yard from the ground, and the poles pulled up, so that the hops may readily be picked off by hand. As soon as possible after picking, they are conveyed to the oast houses, where they are spread upon hair cloths and thoroughly dried by means of hot air, and afterwards pressed into large hempen bags called pockets, in which they are brought to market.

The hop crop is a very fluctuating one. In 1859 it amounted to 68,496,727 lbs., but in 1860 it was only 11,162,717 lbs.; whilst the imports of foreign hops in the same years were respectively 248,640 lbs., and 7,718,816 lbs. The Excise duty of 1¾d. per lb., and the Customs duty of 2l. 5s. per cwt. (now reduced to 1l.), yielded in 1860 a total revenue of 79,439l.

Hops serve three important purposes in brewing; 1st, they impart an agreeable flavour to the beer; 2nd, they check acetous fermentation and thus render the beer capable of being kept; 3rd, their tannin helps to clarify the beer by precipitating the albumen of the barley. Their active qualities reside principally in the golden yellow grains of *lupuline* with which they are covered. Besides their use in brewing they are sometimes prescribed as a tonic; and, on account of their narcotic odour, pillows stuffed with them are employed to induce sleep.   [A. S.]

HUNGERWEED. *Ranunculus arvensis.*

HUNNEMANNIA. An erect-growing perennial belonging to the *Papaveraceæ*, and allied to *Eschscholtzia*, from which it is distinguished by its single peltate four-furrowed stigma, by its ten-ribbed pod-like seed-vessel, and by the absence of a disk-like receptacle. *H. fumariæfolia*, the only species, is a native of Mexico; it grows to the height of two or three feet, with glaucous leaves resembling those of the fumitories, and bears large solitary terminal flowers like those of *Eschscholtzia*.   [C. A. J.]

HUNTERIA. A genus of dogbanes, having a funnel-shaped corolla with a border of five oblique divisions; five stamens attached to the upper part of the tube of the corolla; and a fruit consisting of twin berries with two seeds. The species are natives of Asia, and attain considerable size; the leaves are in pairs or threes, entire and smooth; and the flowers are small in terminal or axillary clusters.   [G. D.]

HUNTLEYA. A small genus of epiphytal orchids of tropical America, related to *Zygopetalum*, from which, according to Dr. Lindley, there is nothing to distinguish them except the excessively enlarged column, and the union of the sepals at the base as in *Maxillaria*. *H. violacea*, from Demerara, has large flowers, of an intense violet colour, which is not at all usual amongst orchids. The plant consists of a short stem with a few wiry roots, a tuft of strap-shaped leaves, and one-flowered drooping stalks from the axils of the lower leaves. The sepals and petals are oblong and crisped, the lip kidney-shaped, with a naked brown grooved crest, and the column boat-shaped as large as the lip. *Bollea violacea* is another name for it. *H. Meleagris* is of somewhat similar habit, but with an erect flower-stalk, pointed sepals and petals of a pale yellow at the base and claret-coloured towards the apex, and a nearly white lip. This plant is called *Batemannia Meleagris* by Reichenbach.   [A. A. B.]

HUNTSMAN'S CAP. *Sarracenia purpurea.*

HURA. A genus of the spurgewort family, differing from all others in the many-celled ovary, and the peculiar structure of the sterile flowers. *H. crepitans*, the Sand-box tree, indigenous in tropical America, known as Javilla in Panama, Acupa and Habillo in New Granada, and commonly cultivated in most tropical countries, is the only species. It is a branching tree of thirty to forty feet high, often planted for the sake of its shade, for which it is well adapted, having a great abundance of glossy poplar-like leaves. The reddish inconspicuous flowers are sterile, and fertile on different plants; the former in stalked catkin-like heads, each flower with a cup-shaped calyx, and a central column around which are one or many rows of scale-like bodies, each supporting on its concave face a stamen; the latter, solitary and stalked in the axils of the leaves, with a like calyx and a rounded ovary terminated by a singularly long trumpet-shaped style, the terminal cup-like portion of which has a reflexed many-toothed border. The curious, rounded, hard-shelled fruits are about the size of an orange, and have as many deep furrows as there are cells, each cell containing a single flattened seed. When the fruit is ripe and exposed to the action of a dry atmosphere, it bursts with great force, accompanied by a loud sharp crack like the report of a pistol, for which reason it is often called the Monkey's Dinner-bell. The seeds are emetic, in a green state violently purgative, but when dry, according to Lunan, they lose this

Hura crepitans.

property. An oil is extracted from them and sometimes used as a purgative, about twenty drops of it being equal in action to a table-spoonful of castor-oil, and less nauseous. A venomous milky juice is abundant in all parts of the plant, and if it be applied to the eye causes almost immediate blindness. The wood is extremely brittle, and the hollowed trunks are said to be used in the West Indies as vats for containing cane juice.   [A. A. B.]

HURDA, HURRAH, or HURITUKEE. Indian names for the Myrobalans, *Terminalia Chebula*, and *citrina*.

HUREEK. An Indian name for *Paspalum scrobiculatum*.

HURRBURR. *Arctium Lappa*.

HURRYALEE. *Cynodon Dactylon*.

HURSINGHOR. An Indian name for the flowers of *Nyctanthes arbor-tristis*.

HURSTBEECH. *Carpinus Betulus*.

HURTLEBERRY. *Vaccinium Myrtillus*.

HURTSICKLE. *Centaurea Cyanus*.

HUSSEIA. A curious genus of puff-balls, named after the late Mrs. Hussey, distinguished by a cylindrical stem, supporting a globose peridium with a plicate terminal mouth, clothed with a gelatinous veil, which ultimately is turned back from the pileus and top of the stem. The only species grows on the naked soil, and has hitherto been found nowhere except in Ceylon.   [M. J. B.]

HUTCHINSIA. A genus of *Cruciferæ*, allied to *Lepidium*, but differing in having two seeds in each cell of the pouch, which is elliptical, with compound keeled valves without any ring or notch at the summit. They are small annuals with pinnately parted leaves, and small white flowers. One species, *H. petræa*, occurs in the western part of England.   [J. T. S.]

HUTTIA *conspicua*, a small rush-like plant with numerous branches, but without leaves, or with the leaves reduced to very minute scales, is the only species of this genus of *Dilleniaceæ*; a native of the sandy plains lying between the Hutt and

Murchison rivers on the western coast of Australia. The flowers have five egg-shaped sepals, five roundish petals with their bases contracted into short claws, and stamens arranged in two series with their bases united, the inner consisting of two broad ones, and the outer of ten, seven only of which bear anthers. They have two single-celled free ovaries crowned by thread-like styles.   [A. S.]

HYACINTH. *Hyacinthus*. — of Peru. *Scilla peruviana*. —, CAPE. *Scilla corymbosa*, and *brachyphylla*. —, FEATHERED. *Muscari comosum monstrosum*. —, GRAPE. *Muscari*. —, LILY. *Scilla Lilio-Hyacinthus*. —, MISSOURI. *Hesperoscordum*. —, SPANISH. *Hyacinthus amethystinus*. —, STARCH. *Muscari racemosum*. —, TASSEL. *Muscari comosum*. —, WILD. *Hyacinthus non scriptus*. —, of America. *Scilla esculenta*. —, STAR. *Scilla amœna*.

HYACINTHORCHIS *variabilis*. The name of a pretty terrestrial Japanese orchid, having one or two lance-shaped ribbed radical leaves a foot in length, and a flower scape exceeding the leaves and bearing a number of narrow-petaled pink blossoms, each about an inch long. This seems almost identical with the *Cremastra Wallichiana* of the Himalaya. [A. A. B.]

HYACINTHUS. A well-known genus of very handsome liliaceous bulbs, of which large numbers of garden varieties are grown in Holland for exportation. The original of the common Hyacinth, *H. orientalis*, is a native of the East about Aleppo, Bagdad, &c., and is a stout bulb with fleshy linear oblong leaves, and a loose spike of drooping flowers, of which the perianth is bell-shaped with a six-parted regular limb of oblong nearly equal recurved segments, and encloses six equal stamens, and a sub-globose three-celled ovary, crowned by a short erect style, and a three-cornered obtuse stigma. From this the various-coloured, full-spiked single and double varieties of the garden Hyacinth have been produced. A smaller flowered species, *H. amethystinus*, found in the south of Europe, has the flowers of a bright blue, and is exceedingly pretty.   [T. M.]

HYÆNA POISON. *Hyænanche capensis*.

HYÆNANCHE. A genus of *Euphorbiaceæ*, containing only one species, *H. capensis*, a native of the Cape of Good Hope, where it is called Wolveboon by the Dutch and Hyæna-poison by the English. It is a tree-like shrub, with smooth, feathery leaves arranged in whorls, and the small flowers of separate sexes on the same plant. This shrub has acquired the name of Hyæna-poison bush from its fruits, which are exceedingly poisonous, being used to destroy those animals, the powder being sprinkled upon raw flesh, which is left in places frequented by them. Dr. Pappe supposes it to contain strychnine.   [A. S.]

HYA HYA. *Tabernæmontana utilis*, one

of the innocuous milky plants called Cow trees in South America.

HYALINE. Transparent, or nearly so.

HYALIS. A genus belonging to the *Mutisia* group of the composite family, differing from its allies in the smooth style, the nature of the pappus, and the ten-ribbed achenes. *H. argentea*, the only species, is found on the salt plains of North Patagonia, where, according to Tweedie, it grows in patches to the extent of acres, and to the exclusion of almost everything else. It is a perennial stiff-branched plant, covered with short white hairs, the stems clothed with grassy leaves, and terminating in corymbs of small white flower-heads. The pappus hairs are white, rough, and in three series.　　　[A. A. B.]

HYALISMA. A small slender leafless annual, a native of Ceylon, forming a genus of the curious little order or tribe *Triuridaceæ*.

HYALOLEPIS. The generic name of a pigmy annual found in South and West Australia, and belonging to the cudweed group of the composite family. It has very short stems, with grassy leaves surrounding a sessile cluster of small white flower-heads, each head containing a single floret, and the whole surrounded by a common involucre of very thin scales so as to form a compound head. The generic name has reference to the hyaline scales, and the specific *rhizocephala* to the heads which arise from the collar of the plant in close proximity to the root.　　　[A. A. B.]

HYALOSTEMMA. The name of an Indian shrub of the anonaceous family, now referred to the genus *Miliusa* by Drs. Hooker and Thomson.　　　[M. T. M.]

HYAWABALLI. The Zebra wood of Guiana.

HYBERNACULUM. The same as Hibernaculum.

HYBERNAL. Of or belonging to the winter.

HYBRIDS, HYBRIDÆ. Plants obtained by applying the pollen of one species to the stigma of another.

HYDNEI. A natural order of hymenomycetous *Fungi*, distinguished by the hymenium being broken up into flat teeth, or variously flattened into spines, tubercles, granules, &c. *Irpex*, which has flat teeth, is sometimes with difficulty distinguished from certain states of *Polyporei*, but in the more genuine members of the order which on the other side is confluent with *Auricularini*, the peculiar characters are at once evident. *Hydnum gelatinosum* has the substance and nearly the structure of *Tremella*. The species are mostly inhabitants of the northern hemisphere, though a few have been found in Australia and the southern regions.　　　[M. J. B.]

HYDNOCARPUS. One of the four genera belonging to the poisonous order *Pan-

giaceæ*. It consists of six species, all of which are trees, sometimes attaining a large size, and natives of India. The leaves are alternate, oblong lance-shaped, generally somewhat unequal-sided; and the flowers are of separate sexes borne on distinct trees: in both having five sepals and five petals, with an equal number of scales opposite them. The fruit is one-celled, with a hard corky rind, and contains numerous irregularly angled seeds, with thick roughish shells, lying in pulp.

H. venenata (or *H. inebrians*, as it is sometimes called) is a large tree, native of Ceylon (where it is called Makooloo) and of the Malabar coast of India. Its fruit, which is about the size of an apple and covered with a brown velvety down, is very poisonous, and is used by the Singhalese for intoxicating fish, but the fish taken thus are not fit for human food. The seeds contain a quantity of fatty oil, which is expressed and used by the native Indian doctors as a cure for leprosy and other cutaneous complaints, for which purpose it is greatly esteemed.　　　[A. S.]

HYDNOPHYTUM. A genus of cinchonaceous shrubs, inhabiting the Molucca Islands. They are described as being of parasitic habit and frequently dilated at the base, so as to form a cavity, made use of by ants as a nest. The flowers have an inferior calyx with an undivided margin, a four-lobed corolla, with a short tube, into the throat of which the stamens are inserted. The fruit is fleshy with two one-seeded stones.　　　[M. T. M.]

HYDNORA. A genus of curious fungus-like leafless plants of the order *Cytinaceæ*, found in South Africa, parasitical on the roots of succulent euphorbias and other plants. *H. africana*, called Jackal's kost, is said to smell like decaying roast-beef or some fungus, and to be eaten, when roasted, by the African savages. The plant consists of a large succulent hermaphrodite solitary, tubulose, trifid flower, borne on a creeping rhizome; and this flower is succeeded by a globose, baccate, many-seeded fruit. The plant may be compared with *Geaster*, or some such half-buried fungus.　　　[T. M.]

HYDNUM. A genus of hymenomycetous *Fungi*, varying greatly in substance, but distinguished by the hymenium consisting of prickles projecting from the pileus. These differ very much in length. Occasionally they are variously cleft or laciniate. Many of the species are of a large size, and supported by a central stem, or much branched with the divisions connate, so as to make a kind of coarse network. *H. repandum*, which is common in woods, where it sometimes occurs in scattered patches, and sometimes in large rings, affords an excellent article of food if carefully dressed, and is scarcely exceeded in delicacy by any fungus. The specimens must be quite fresh and free from insects, and after being sliced into hot water, and gently pressed, should either be carefully stewed or rubbed down into a purée. Other species are occasionally eaten abroad. *H. auriscalpium* is one of our most elegant *Fungi*, and not uncommon on fir cones. The spongy and corky species are only slightly represented in Great Britain, though numerous elsewhere. Of the resupinate forms we have many good examples.   [M. J. B.]

HYDRANGEACEÆ. (*Hydrangeads, Baueraceæ.*) A natural order of calycifloral dicotyledons, included in Lindley's saxifragal alliance of perigynous Exogens. Shrubs with opposite simple exstipulate leaves. Flowers in cymes, the central ones complete, the outer ones with large petals and often barren; calyx more or less adherent to the ovary, four to six-toothed; petals four to six, deciduous; stamens eight to twelve in two rows, or numerous, attached to the calyx; ovary of two to five carpels united; ovules numerous, anatropal; styles two to five with kidney-shaped stigmas. Fruit a capsule crowned by the persistent styles, two to five-celled: seeds albuminous, minute. Natives of the temperate part of Asia and America. About one half are found in China and Japan. Some species of *Hydrangea* are used for tea. There are ten genera and nearly fifty species.   [J. H. B.]

HYDRANGEA. Showy shrubs, referred by some to the *Saxifragaceæ*, by others to *Hydrangeaceæ*. The distinctive characters are: calyx superior five-toothed; petals five; stamens five; pistils two; capsule two-beaked, two-celled, opening by a hole between the beaks. The best known species is *H. hortensis*, introduced from China by Sir Joseph Banks in 1790. It is distinguished by its broad, smooth, strongly veined leaves, which are toothed, and taper to a point, and yet more strongly marked by its almost globular clusters of large flowers, the colour of which varies in the same plant, from white to blue or pink, according to the soil in which it is grown. The part of the flower which appears to be the corolla, is not so in reality, but a monstrous expansion of the calyx leaves, the rest of the flower being generally abortive. The similarity between the balls of flowers of this plant and those of the guelder rose is obvious; and it is worthy of remark that the resemblance is owing to precisely the same irregularity in each — an undue development of the floral envelope to the detriment of the essential parts of the flower—stamens and pistils. These organs are found only in a few flowers, which of course are the only ones that can produce seeds.   [C. A. J.]

HYDRANGELLE. (Fr.) *Hydrangea.*

HYDRANTHELIUM. A genus of *Scrophulariaceæ*, consisting of small aquatic annuals, with the habit of *Callitriche* or of *Elatine.* The leaves are opposite and cuneate or obovate, the flowers very minute and axillary, with a three-cleft corolla, and three stamens. There are two species, natives of the mountainous districts of tropical America, one of which has also been found in tropical Africa.

HYDRASTIS *canadensis* is the only species of a genus of *Ranunculaceæ*, found in damp places in woods, in the Northern United States and Canada, where it is called Yellow Puccoon, Orange root, or Canadian Yellow root. It is an herbaceous perennial, with a thick knotty yellow underground stem, or root as it is more frequently called, which in early spring sends up a simple stem, about a foot high, bearing near the top two (or rarely three) rounded hand-shaped leaves, the upper leaf growing close upon the stem, while the lower one has a longish stalk. At the top of the stem is a solitary small greenish-white inconspicuous flower, entirely destitute of petals; the three-leaved calyx quickly falls away, leaving only the stamens and pistils. The fruit is about the size of and greatly resembles a raspberry in its appearance, having juicy flesh of a bright crimson colour. The yellow root of this plant was formerly employed by the American aborigines for dyeing a bright yellow colour, and it is occasionally employed for the same purpose at the present day. It has a strong narcotic odour, with a bitter pungent taste, and possesses tonic properties, on which account it is sometimes used medicinally; it was at one time supposed to be a remedy for cancer. [A. S.]

HYDRILLA. A genus of *Hydrocharidaceæ*, allied to *Anacharis.* A slender-stemmed aquatic herb, with whorled sessile leaves, growing in the rivers of India, China, and America. The spathes are axillary and single-flowered, with a six-cleft reflexed perianth, and three stamens which become detached and float on the surface. The female, with a spreading perianth, has a long thread-like tube adhering to the ovary, permitting the stigmas to reach the top of the water. [J. T. S.]

HYDROCERA. A genus of *Balsamineæ*, consisting of aquatic Indian herbs, with alternate linear or lanceolate glaucous leaves, and solitary axillary two or three-flowered peduncles, the pedicels longer than the common peduncle. They have a calyx of five coloured unequal sepals, the two lateral smaller, and the lowest larger and gibbous at the base, unequal petals, and five stamens, with the filaments united at the apex. The fruit is a drupe, with a five-celled hard interior, each cell containing one seed. [J. T. S.]

HYDROCHARIDACEÆ, (*Vallisneriaceæ, Anacharideæ, Hydrocharads, Frogbits.*) A natural order of epigynous monocotyledons belonging to Lindley's hydral alliance of Endogens. Aquatic plants with flowers in spathes, often incomplete; perianth of six leaves, the three inner petaloid; ovary one-celled, or spuriously three to nine-celled; stigmas three to nine; placentas parietal. Fruit dry or fleshy, and opening; seeds albuminous; embryo straight, orthotropal. Natives chiefly of Europe, Asia, and North America, and growing generally in fresh water. Movements of granules may be seen in the cells of many of the plants. *Vallisneria spiralis* is found in the south of Europe. Two species of this genus occur in New Holland. The leaves of *Hydrocharis morsus ranæ* are mucilaginous and astringent. *Anacharis Alsinastrum* has become naturalised in many parts of Britain. There are nineteen genera, and about thirty-six species. Examples: *Udora*, *Vallisneria*, *Stratiotes*, *Hydrocharis*.　　　[J. H. B.]

HYDROCHARIS. A small floating aquatic, giving name to the order *Hydrocharidaceæ*, and distinguished by the following characters: ovary six-celled; stigmas six, wedge-shaped, two-cleft; stamens six to nine. *H. morsus ranæ*, or Frogbit, is an elegant little plant, inhabiting ditches, ponds, and the still back waters of rivers. It increases by floating horizontal runners which shoot out to a considerable length; from the joints descend tufts of long, scarcely branched roots, which penetrate deep into the mud. From the same points issue pendulous leaf-buds, supported on long footstalks; each of these buds is composed of two leaf-like scales, folded together and curiously enveloping the embryo leaves of the future plant. The leaves are stalked, kidney-shaped, entire; the flowers of three delicate white petals, rise several in succession, from a pellucid membranous sheath, and bear the stamens and pistils on separate plants. This is one of the most desirable plants for the fresh-water aquarium. French, *Morene*; German, *Froschbiss.*　　　[C. A. J.]

HYDROCHLOA. A genus of grasses belonging to the *Oryzeæ*. *H. carolinensis*, with *Zizania aquatica*, the Canada rice, constitute the genus *Hydropyrum*. The name is also given to another group of grasses synonymous with *Glyceria.*　　　[D. M.]

HYDROCLEIS. A genus of aquatic plants, belonging to the *Butomaceæ*, growing in tropical America. They have the leaves all radical, cordate ovate. The flowers are on simple scapes, large, yellow, with the three inner perianth segments petaloid and deciduous; the three outer green and persistent; they have numerous stamens, and from six to nine carpels. *Limnocharis*, as now restricted to *L. Plumieri*, differs in having fifteen to twenty carpels, and an umbel of flowers.　　　[J. T. S.]

HYDROCOTYLE. An extensive genus of umbelliferous plants, mostly herbaceous and of humble growth, but some approaching shrubs in habit, difficult of discrimination, and possessing little interest except for the scientific botanist. The only native species, *H. vulgaris*, common Pennywort, is one of the few British plants which have peltate leaves. The plant bears an ill name from being considered, in conjunction with one or three other bog plants, the fruitful cause of rot in sheep, an unfounded accusation, for it possesses no noxious properties, and sheep more-

over refuse to eat it. German, *Wassernabel.*　　　[C. A. J.]

HYDRODICTYEÆ, HYDRODICTYON. An order and genus of green-spored *Algæ*, remarkable at once for beauty and singularity of structure. The plant, when full-grown, resembles a long purse, consisting of a beautiful regular network of threads. These threads contain a mass of endochrome which is ultimately resolved into minute zoospores; these arrange themselves, within the articulation which gave them birth, into polygons, in such a way as, when united, to form a network, which gradually increases till it resembles the parent plant; each joint, therefore, of the network gives rise to a new individual. This singular mode of development is without example in other orders. The other genera usually ascribed to this order are probably related to *Anadyomene*. *Hydrodictyon utriculatum* is found in fresh water, though rarely, in several parts of Europe, and has long been known as growing every year in the pond in the Old Botanic Gardens at Cambridge. It has also been found in the United States. [M. J. B.]

HYDROGLOSSUM. A genus of climbing ferns of the *Schizæa* group, the exact analogues of *Lygodium* in habit and fructification, but differing therefrom in having netted instead of free veins, the venules anastomosing in from two to four series of unequal obliquely-elongated hexagonal areoles. The species are but few, and are found in the Pacific Isles, Madagascar, and Mexico.　　　[T. M.]

HYDROLEACEÆ. A name given by Brown to the plants now included in the order *Hydrophyllaceæ*.　　　[J. H. B.]

HYDROLEA. A genus of *Hydrophyllaceæ*, containing several species common in America, and rare in Asia and Africa. They are marsh plants, often armed with axillary spines, and bearing alternate entire leaves, and axillary or terminal blue flowers, which have a calyx of five persistent sepals, a rotate campanulate corolla, five stamens inserted in the tube of the corolla, and a two-celled ovary with many anatropal ovules, attached to fungous placentæ. The capsule is two-celled with numerous small striated seeds. The leaves of *H. zeylanica* are bitter; in India they are beaten into pulp, and applied as a poultice to ill-conditioned sores with a beneficial effect.　　　[W. C.]

HYDROGERA VASA. The spiral threads inside a spiral vessel; formerly supposed to be tubes conveying fluid.

HYDROPELTIS. A genus deriving its name of Water-buckler from the shape of the leaves. It is included among the *Cabombaceæ*, and differs from *Cabomba* in the numerous thread-like stamens, and the equally numerous whorled, somewhat fleshy carpels. *H. purpurea*, called also *Brasenia peltata*, is a curious little water plant, with floating peltate oval leaves, and purple flowers, on the end of somewhat thickened flower-stalks. The submerged portions are covered with a mucilaginous substance, formed by the rapid formation and rupture of the cells on the outer surface of the plant. The wide distribution of this plant is hardly less remarkable than its structure, for it has been found in the United States, Canada, Australia, and the Himalaya mountains. In America it is esteemed nutritious, possibly from the large-grained starch it contains. The leaves are somewhat astringent, and have been employed in phthisis and dysentery. [M. T. M.]

HYDROPHYLAX. A genus of *Cinchonaceæ*, represented by a creeping herb, native of the sandy sea-shores of India. The corolla, like the leaves, is somewhat fleshy, bell-shaped, with a hairy throat into which the four stamens are inserted. Fruit succulent, four-cornered, with a single seed in each of its two compartments. *H. maritima* is used for dyeing purposes. [M. T. M.]

HYDROPHYLLACEÆ. (*Hydroleaceæ*.) A natural order of corollifloral dicotyledons belonging to Lindley's cortusal alliance of perigynous Exogens. Herbs or small trees, usually with alternate and lobed hispid leaves. Calyx five-cleft, persistent; corolla regular, somewhat bell-shaped; stamens five, alternating with the corolla lobes; ovary superior with two parietal placentas; styles two. Fruit a two-valved one-celled or spuriously two-celled capsule, filled with a large placenta; seeds reticulated; embryo small, in hard albumen. Natives chiefly of the temperate and cold portions of America. A few are found in the East Indies, and some at the Cape of Good Hope: some are cultivated on account of their showy flowers. *Hydrolea* has bitter qualities. There are eighteen known genera, and about eighty species. Examples: *Hydrophyllum, Nemophila, Eutoca, Phacelia, Hydrolea, Whitlavia.* [J. H. B.]

HYDROPHYLLUM. A genus of American herbaceous perennials, giving name to the order *Hydrophyllaceæ*. The corolla is five-cleft and furnished with as many corolline scales, which are attached by the back, but free at the margins and point; the stamens exceed in length the tube of the corolla, and the stigma is two-cleft. The flowers of these plants resemble those of the borage tribe, not only in the structure of the corolla, but in their curled arrangement while in bud; but the seeds are enclosed in a single one-celled or half-two-celled capsule, and the leaves are always more or less divided. The species grow among moist shady rocks, and derive their name (which means Water-leaf) from their having in the spring a small quantity of water in the cavity of each leaf. In North America the leaves of *H. virginicum* are eaten under the name of Shawanese salad. French, *Hydrophylle;* German, *Wasserblatt.* [C. A. J.]

HYDROPIPER. *Polygonum Hydropiper;* also *Elatine Hydropiper.*

HYDROPYRUM. A genus of aquatic grasses, distinguished by the spikelets being monœcious, the male and female florets in the same panicle. Male flowers without glumes; pales two, membranous, the lower acute and mucronate, five-nerved, concave, the upper three-nerved; stamens six. Females with rudiments of glumes; pales two, membranous, the lower three-nerved, ending in a long awn; styles two, short and spreading. *H. esculentum,* the Canada Rice, is a well-known plant of North America, where the large seeds yield a considerable amount of food to the wandering tribes of Indians, and feed immense flocks of wild swans, and other aquatic birds. It grows well in Britain when it is once established, but it is liable to die away if not cared for. [D. M.]

HYDROSTACHYS. Aquatic herbs, natives of Madagascar, constituting a genus of *Podostemaceæ*. They are of little general interest, but are known by their unisexual naked flowers, and by their fruit, which consists of two carpels, forming a single cavity, and bursting by two pieces or valves. [M. T. M.]

HYDROTÆNIA. A genus of bulbous *Iridaceæ* allied very closely to *Sisyrinchium,* from which it differs in having the anthers opposite the sepaline divisions; it has, moreover, quite a different habit, imitating rather the liliaceous genus *Fritillaria.* The perianth is bell-shaped with the parts almost isomerous, the petaline divisions clawed, and marked above the claw with a triangular zone which glitters as if constructed of rock crystal; there are three monadelphous stamens, and a trifid style whose branches divide into three erect stigmas of a remarkable character, each parting into two arms which are rolled up as if to form a gutter, and bear a dense mass of bright papillæ at the end, and a single tooth on the inner edge, while between the arms stands a short mucro free from glands, and forming a minute horn. The name refers to the glittering dewy or watery band on the petaline segments. *H. Meleagris,* the only species, is a native of Mexico, and has a single plaited ensiform leaf, and fugacious campanulate purple flowers, pendulous on slender footstalks. [T. M.]

HYEMAL. Of or belonging to winter. Usually applied to plants that bloom in winter.

HYGROPHILA. A genus of *Acanthaceæ,* containing about two dozen species, which are widely distributed over the tropical and sub-tropical regions of the world. They are erect or decumbent herbs, growing in moist localities. The flowers are in sessile axillary clusters, and have a calyx of five or rarely four sepals; a two-lipped corolla, with the upper lip notched, and the lower three-lobed, the lobes contorted in the bud; and four didynamous stamens. The oblong or linear capsule has seeds along its whole length. [W. C.]

HYGROPHORUS. A genus of *Fungi,*

separated from *Agaricus* on account of their peculiar habit, their waxy not membranaceous gills, and granular intermediate substance. Though the characters seem rather indefinite, there is no difficulty in recognising the genus at the first glance. Many of the species are extremely beautiful and exhibit the most brilliant colours, but these are often not characteristic, the same species presenting frequently very different hues. A great many of them grow in open pastures, and abound in the fields in autumn, the woodland species generally exhibiting a different type. All of them readily imbibe and part with their moisture, and several are covered all over with a glutinous coat. Few, if any, are admitted into our kitchens, though there can be no doubt some are wholesome. *H. conicus* is one of the commonest and most variable species, exhibiting every shade between yellow and scarlet; it may, however, always be known by its turning black when bruised. *H. psittacinus* presents various tints even in the same specimen; it is often extremely beautiful, its variety of colours vying with those of parrots. The genus is little known out of Europe and the United States.   [M. J. B.]

HYGRORYZA. A genus of grasses, belonging to the tribe *Oryzeæ*, distinguished by the spikelets being hermaphrodite, oneflowered; glumes two, the lower terminating in a tail-like bristle, the upper acute; pales slender, toothed at the apex; stamens three; styles one. *H. aristata* is a native of the West Indies.   [D. M.]

HYGROSCOPICITY. The property of extending or shrinking upon the application or removal of water.

HYMEN. In Greek compounds = a membrane, or membranous.

HYMENIUM. That part of hymenomycetous fungals on which the spores are borne—plates in *Agaricus*, tubes in *Boletus*, &c.

HYMENODES. Having a membranous texture.

HYMENOPHORUM. The pileus of certain fungals.

HYMENULUM. A disk or shield containing asci, but without excipulum.

HYMENÆA. A genus of leguminous plants of the section *Cæsalpiniæ*, so named from Hymen, the god of marriage, in consequence of the leaves being composed of a pair of leaflets. Its flowers have a woody tubular calyx with two bracts at its base, and divided into five deciduous segments, the two lower of which are sometimes joined together; and five unequal petals, inserted along with the ten distinct stamens into the summit of the calyx tube. The fruit is a pod with a hard woody shell containing several seeds imbedded in a fibrous pulpy substance, which eventually becomes dry and mealy, and is commonly eaten by Indians.

H. Courbaril, the common West Indian Locust tree, called Algarroba in Panama, Jatai in Brazil, and Simiri in Guiana, is a common tree in most parts of tropical South America. It grows to an enormous size, and, according to some calculations, lives to a very great age, some of the trees at present existing in the forests of Brazil being supposed to have been of considerable size at the commencement of the Christian era. Most of these old trees are supported at the base by immense buttresses, and at this part some have been measured no less than eighty-four feet in circumference, while even at the top of

Hymenæa Courbaril.

the buttresses, where the trunk assumes the usual cylindrical form, the circumference is as much as sixty feet. The timber is of a fine brown colour, hard and closegrained; it is used for building and other purposes in South America, and is occasionally exported to this country. It is covered with a very thick but light bark, which is used by the Indians for making canoes. A valuable resin, resembling the anime of Africa, exudes from the trunk, and large lumps of it are found about the roots of old trees.   [A. S.]

HYMENANDRA. A genus of *Myrsineæ*, consisting of a single species found in the Silhet district of India, and differing from the other genera in the anthers being united to each other by their margins, and in the ovaries containing numerous ovules. *H. Wallichii* is a stout evergreen shrub often cultivated in plant stoves for the sake of its handsome leathery and glossy leaves, which are shortly stalked, and in form and size a good deal like the leaflet of a horse-chestnut. The pretty pink flowers disposed in compound lateral umbels have wheel-shaped five-parted corollas half an inch across. The fruit is a berry about the size of a pea.   [A. A. B.]

HYMENANTHERA. A genus of Australian shrubs, belonging to the violet family. The leaves have no stipules; the flowers are regular: the five short stamens are alternate with the petals, the anthers being connected by the long crest which surmounts their lobes. The fruit is succulent, surrounded by the persistent outer whorls of the flower, either one or two-celled. From other genera this differs in its nearly regular flowers, and in its five stamens which are united into a tube, having at their base scale-like appendages prolonged beyond the anthers. [M. T. M.]

HYMENIDIUM. A genus of umbellifers, distinguished chiefly by each half of the fruit being provided with five ridges prolonged into wing-like membranes. The genus comprehends herbaceous plants natives of Kashmir, having the leaves much divided, and membranous bracts longer than the flowers. [G. D.]

HYMENIUM. The fructifying surface in *Fungi*, more properly applied where the spores are naked, but used also to express the same condition in such genera as *Helvilla* and *Peziza*. It is not used where the fructifying cells are contained in a distinct perithecium, the word *nucleus* being then more generally substituted. [M. J. B.]

HYMENOCALLIS. A genus of beautiful pancratiform *Amaryllidaceæ*, consisting of bulbous plants, with usually persistent lorate leaves and flattened two-angled solid scapes, bearing an umbel of from one to a score of flowers, which are white and very fragrant. The perianth has a straight elongated tube scarcely widened at the throat, a six-parted limb of subequal linear segments, a funnel-shaped or rotate spreading coronet on the edge of which the six stamens are developed, and a long flaccid declinate style with a roundish minutely fimbriated stigma. There are some score or more of species inhabiting the West Indies and South America. [T. M.]

HYMENOCARDIA. A genus of the *Antidesmia* family, differing from the others in having samaroid (somewhat maple-like) fruits. Of four known species three belong to West Africa, and one to the Malay peninsula. They are deciduous shrubs or small trees, with ovate oblong or elliptical leaves covered with glandular dots underneath, and minute reddish flowers, the sterile and fertile borne on different plants, the former in short axillary spikes, the latter solitary or in racemes. These are succeeded by two-celled two-winged fruits. *Samaropyxis* is the name applied to the Malayan species by Miquel. [A. A. B.]

HYMENOCYSTIS. A name proposed by Meyer for the Caucasian *Woodsia fragilis*.

HYMENODICTYON. A genus of Indian trees closely related to *Cinchona*. The distinguishing features are the projecting style, terminated by a lobed, somewhat club-shaped stigma; and the fruit, which is not surmounted by a limb of the calyx, forming a capsule, bursting by two valves. The seeds are numerous, surrounded by a membranous netted wing, whence the name. *H. excelsum* a native of Ceylon and the peninsula of India, and *H. utile* a native of Malabar, have soft mahogany-coloured wood. The bark of the first-named is very astringent, as much so as that of the true cinchonas. This bark is used for tanning purposes. [M. T. M.]

HYMENODIUM. The principal species of this genus of acrostichoid ferns is a coarse simple-fronded West Indian plant, with large oblong-ovate fronds, sprinkled over rather thickly with long black hairs. The fertile fronds are of the same form, but smaller, and entirely covered with spore-cases on the under surface. The veins are uniformly reticulated in coarse hexagonal or elongated meshes, without free veinlets. Also called *Dictyoglossum*. [T. M.]

HYMENOGLOSSUM. A name proposed by Presl for the *Hymenophyllum cruentum* of Chili.

HYMENOLÆNA. A genus of umbellifers, having the fruit ovate or oblong, each half with five nearly equal winged ribs, and two oil-cells in the commissure. The species are smooth perennial herbs, natives of Nepal, having much-divided leaves, and terminal many-rayed umbels, each surrounded by a many-leaved involucre, the pieces of which are membranous, often toothed or cut. [G. D.]

HYMENOLEPIS. A small and well-marked genus of polypodiaceous ferns, referable to the tribe *Pleurogrammeæ*. The fronds are simple opaque and linear lanceolate or lorate, with the apex very much contracted, usually spike-like and fertile, so much contracted, indeed, that the continuous line of spore-cases which lies on each side the costa is in the early stages covered by the revolute margin, as in the fertile parts of *Lomaria*. The veins are compoundly anastomosing, forming crowded irregular areoles, in which occur variously directed free veinlets. The species are found in India and the islands of the Pacific and Indian Oceans. [T. M.]

HYMENOMYCETES. The highest of the six great divisions of *Fungi*, containing those naked-spored genera, in which the fructifying surface or hymenium is at length completely exposed. In a few of the agarics and boleti, there is at first a common wrapper (volva), or a partial veil covering the hymenium, but in far the greater part it is exposed even in infancy. The hymenium literally applies to the fruit-bearing stratum only, the organs on which it is spread being called the hymenophorum, but in general it is applied to the whole apparatus, whether consisting of gills, wrinkles, tubes or pores, spines or tubercles, or if all inequalities in the surface cease and it becomes perfectly even. In the higher species, the hymenium is horizontal and turned away from the light, but in those of an inferior dignity it is often resupinate, though in such cases there is frequently a tendency to attain the usual position by the turning over of the border. In a few rare cases, on the contrary, amongst agarics, where a species was in the first instance stipitate, the pileus is at length turned over, the stem becoming gradually lateral, while it ceases to increase in length ; and in a little species from Borneo, the stem is completely torn off, and remains like a little style in the centre.

The *Hymenomycetes* are for the most part either soft and fleshy, or by various transitions hard and compact, but a few species are gelatinous, and some of these when dried up recover their form on the application of moisture. They pass by almost imperceptible degrees into *Hyphomycetes*, by means of *Typhula* and *Isaria* ; into *Gasteromycetes*, by means of *Agaricus* and *Montagnites* ; and into *Coniomycetes* by means of *Tremella* and *Podisoma*. The transition into the sporidiferous fungi is not so acutely marked, the relation of *Clavaria* to *Geoglossum* being rather one of analogy than affinity. They are fungi of great importance as containing the greater number of the larger species, and supplying an immense quantity of excellent food, besides answering other domestic ends. In the organised world their use is to decompose more rapidly such structures as have answered their immediate purpose. The largest trees, when once attacked, soon acquire a condition which is favourable to other causes of decay. The hymenium being the prominent element in these plants affords the readiest mode of their classification. The following natural orders depend, therefore, on its conformation :—

Agaricini : those which bear gills or gill-like wrinkles.

Polyporei : those with pores or tubes.

Hydnei : those with spines or tubercles.

Auricularini : those destitute of inequalities.

Clavariei : pileus club-shaped.

Tremellini : substance gelatinous ; fertile threads not fastigiate ; hymenium convolute.

The *Hymenomycetes* occur in all parts of the world, extending southwards as far as Campbell's Island, and northwards to Spitzbergen. They abound, however, most in warm and moist temperate regions, as in Sweden, which is perhaps the richest and most prolific country in the world for these fungi. There are no certain traces of them in any geological formation older than ancient peat mosses. [M. J. B.]

HYMENOPAPPUS. A genus of annual or perennial North American herbs of the composite family, with angular stems, pinnately lobed or cut leaves, usually clothed with lax white wool, and white or yellow flower-heads in corymbs at the ends of the branches. From its allies the genus differs in the florets being all tubular and perfect, and in the involucral scales being white and petal-like at the tips, thus giving the heads a ragged appearance. [A. A. B.]

HYMENOPHORUM. The cellular or filamentous structure in hymenomycetous *Fungi*, on which the hymenium or fructifying surface is spread like wax upon a mould. In the *Agaricini* and *Polyporei*, it is identical with what is called the trama or

inner substance of the gills or partitions of the pores. [M. J. B.]

HYMENOPHYLLUM. A genus of film ferns, of which one or two species occur in Britain, and many others are scattered over the hot damp forests of the tropics, both insular and continental, as well as the moist ravines of New Zealand and Chili. The fronds vary greatly in size and character, some being minute and others of considerable size and length, some simple and others decompound ; but all, or nearly all of them, filmy pellucid in substance, and with creeping thread-like rhizomes. The spore-cases are collected around free projecting bodies formed of the ends of the veins which traverse the fronds, and are contained within oblong or suborbicular two-valved marginal cysts. *Hymenophyllum* differs from *Trichomanes*, the other principal genus of film ferns, by the two valves of the involucres being separate, and not blended into a cup. [T. M.]

HYMENOPHYSA. A genus of *Cruciferæ* closely related to *Lepidium*, and differing chiefly in the little fruits—the size of mustard seed—being globular instead of compressed. There are two species known, *H. fenestrata*, found in Persia, and *H. pubescens*, in the Altai. The latter is a perennial branching, leafy-stemmed herb, whose branches terminate in racemes of numerous small white flowers. [A. A. B.]

HYMENOPYRAMIS *brachiata*, the only species of the genus, is a scandent East Indian shrub of the *Verbena* family, with quadrangular stems, opposite entire ovate leaves, hoary underneath, and terminal leafy panicles of very minute flowers, with tubular corollas, having four-toothed borders. The calyx, at first of four minute teeth, enlarges when the flowers wither, and encloses the small ripe hairy nut, in the form of a four-winged bladder. This character serves to distinguish the genus from its allies. [A. A. B.]

HYMENOXYS. A genus belonging to the corymbiferous tribe of compound flowers. The scales of the involucre are in two rows, the inner largest, all rigid and pressed close to the flower ; the receptacle is chaffy, and furnished with small glands ; and the fruit is downy with chaffy pappus. *H. californica*, an annual species, grows to the height of about a foot, with slender branched stems, smooth narrow pinnatifid leaves, and large yellow flowers on very slender stalks. [C. A. J.]

HYOBANCHE. A genus of fleshy and woolly plants, parasitical on various roots, found in the flat lands of the Cape of Good Hope. The stem is closely covered with ovate appressed scales. The flowers are in a dense ovate spike, and have an unequally five-cleft calyx, a clavate corolla slightly curved and vaulted, with a very narrow oblique mouth, and obsolete limb, four stamens of nearly equal length, the anthers by abortion one-celled, and a more or less completely two-celled ovary. The capsule is sub-globose, fleshy, containing numerous minute round seeds. The habit and structure of this genus seem to place it in *Orobanchaceæ*, where it would, without doubt, remain, but for its two-celled ovary, and axile placentæ, characteristics of the *Scrophulariaceæ*. [W. C.]

HYOPHORBE. Palms inhabiting the island of Bourbon and Mauritius, and having tall cylindrical stems marked with circular scars, and a crown of graceful pinnate leaves. The male and female flowers grow on distinct trees, or a few males are occasionally interspersed among the females, the flower-spikes being simply branched and growing out from beneath the leaves, with a single spathe at their base. Both sexes have a three-sided three-lobed bell-shaped calyx, and a three-parted corolla. The fruit has a fibrous fleshy rind, and contains a single seed.

H. *Commersoniana*, frequently called H. *indica*, or *Areca lutescens* in English gardens, a native of Bourbon, has a smooth trunk thirty or forty feet high, and from four to six inches in diameter, almost cylindrical, except at the base where it swells out to nearly double its usual diameter. Its leaflets are about two feet long, and two inches wide, divided at the top into two sharp points. It has a nearly round fruit covered with rough tubercles. H. *amaricaulis*, a native of the Mauritius, much resembles this, but is taller, and its leaflets are narrower, and more densely covered with chaffy scales; its fruit, also, is smooth and olive-shaped. [A. S.]

HYOSCYAMUS. This name is the Latinised version of the ancient Greek name for the common Henbane, and literally signifies hog-bean. It is applied to a genus of *Atropaceæ* or *Solanaceæ*, characterised especially by the corolla, which is funnel-shaped, and by the fruit which is enclosed within the persistent calyx, and consists of a capsule which opens by means of a transverse valve, like the lid of a tankard or pix.

The most interesting species of this genus is H. *niger*, the Henbane, an annual or biennial plant, widely distributed throughout Europe and Western Asia, frequently found by roadsides, or in other localities, whither it has most probably been brought by the agency of man, the plant having been long cultivated for its medicinal qualities. In this country the Henbane is found growing spontaneously in the vicinity of old ruins, on rubbish heaps, and not unfrequently by the sea-shore. The whole plant is densely covered with thickly woven hairs, and by a sticky heavy-smelling exudation. The stem attains a height of one to two feet, and has oblong sessile, irregularly lobed leaves, the upper ones clasping the stem. The flowers are borne on very short stalks in the axils of the leaves, and look all in the same direction; the calyx enlarges as the fruit ripens; the corolla is funnel-shaped, of a dull yellow colour, traversed by a network of purple veins. A variety sometimes oc-

curs in which the corolla is not marked with these veins, but the above-mentioned characteristics are amply sufficient for the determination of the plant. The leaves of this plant are employed in the form of extract, &c., for the purpose of tranquillising and allaying irritability of the nervous system, to alleviate pain and procure sleep. It is chiefly given in cases where circumstances render it undesirable to employ opium. Other species are grown in gardens or in greenhouses, all possessing more or less of the same properties as the common henbane. [M. T. M.]

HYOSERIS. A small genus of annual composite weeds, having the habit and foliage of *Taraxacum*. The flower-scape is thickened and club-shaped upwards, and bears a single yellow flower-head. From their near allies they differ in the achenes being of two sorts in each head; the outer corky and cylindrical, the inner with membranous wings, or *vice versa*. The pappus is biserial, and consists of narrow chaffy and unequal scales. The three known species are confined to the Mediterranean region. [A. A. B.]

HYOSPATHE. The only species belonging to this genus of palms, H. *elegans*, is a native of the forests in the vicinity of Pará, where it is called Ubim by the natives. It is one of the reed-like palms common in the underwood of tropical forests, its stem being about an inch in thickness, marked with rings, and growing five or six feet high. The leaves are from three to four feet long, nearly entire when young, having only a division at the point, but when full-grown they are more or less divided, and become irregularly pinnate. The flower-spikes are produced below the leaves, and bear both male and female flowers. The fruit contains a single seed and resembles an olive in shape, but is of a violet colour. The only part of the plant applied to a useful purpose is the leaves, which are used for thatching, their large size and entire form rendering them peculiarly suitable for that purpose. [A. S.]

HYPANTHIUM. The fleshy enlarged hollow of the end of a flower-stalk, such as occurs in the rose, apple, or myrtle. It was formerly regarded as the tube of a calyx.

HYPECOUM. Small annual herbs of the order *Papaveraceæ*, allied to *Chelidonium*, from which they are distinguished by their four stamens and two stigmas. As in *Chelidonium*, the seed-vessel simulates the pod of a cruciferous plant, and the juice, which is yellow, is said to have the same properties as opium. The root leaves are smooth glaucous and pinnate, and the stem leaves much divided; the flowers are small and yellow. The species occur in sandy places in the south of Europe and some parts of Asia. French, *Cumin cornu*; German, *Lappenblume*. [C. A. J.]

HYPERBÆNA. A genus of South American and Mexican plants, belonging to the *Menispermaceæ*, and differing but little from *Cocculus* save by the anthers which are two-lobed, and originally four-celled, and by the styles which are cylindrical and hooked.   [M. T. M.]

HYPERBOREAN. Inhabiting northern regions.

HYPERICACEÆ. (*Eucryphieæ, Tutsans.*) A natural order of thalamifloral dicotyledons, belonging to Lindley's guttiferal alliance of hypogynous Exogens. Herbs, shrubs, or trees with a resinous juice, opposite entire exstipulate leaves, usually with transparent dots and blackish glands, and regular flowers. Sepals four to five, persistent, two outer often smaller; petals four to five, unequal-sided, twisted in bud, often bordered with black dots ; stamens generally numerous and polyadelphous ; carpels three to five, partially united. Fruit a capsule opening at the septa; seeds numerous and exalbuminous. The plants of the order are generally distributed over the world, both in temperate and warm climates. Many species of *Hypericum* yield a yellow juice, and an essential oil. Some of the plants are purgative, others tonic and astringent. Some species of *Vismia* yield a gum resin similar to gamboge. There are 19 genera, and nearly 300 species. Examples: *Hypericum, Elodea, Vismia, Cratoxylon.*   [J. H. B.]

HYPERICUM. An extensive genus of herbaceous or shrubby plants giving name to the order *Hypericaceæ*. The sepals and petals are each five in number ; stamens collected into three to five bundles ; styles three to five ; seeds without wings, in a dry capsule. The best known example of the genus is *H. calycinum*, a somewhat shrubby plant one to two feet high, with large almost evergreen leaves, which, like those of most others in the genus, are curiously sprinkled with pellucid dots. The flowers are very large, terminal, solitary. This is commonly planted in shrubberies or extensive rockeries, where it is valued not only on account of its handsome flowers, but because it affords excellent shelter for game. *H. Androsæmum* (by some authors made a distinct genus on account of its berry-like capsules) is in the west of England a common hedge or woodland plant, growing to the height of one and a half feet. The stem is two-edged, the leaves large glaucous, ovate, sessile, with a strong resinous smell ; the flowers, which grow in terminal corymbs, are yellow, but less conspicuous than the elliptical capsules, which as they ripen turn red and finally black. The leaves were formerly applied to fresh wounds, which they were supposed to heal ; hence the plant was called in French *toute saine*, corrupted into Tutsan, its common English name. The pellucid dots and black glands in all the species contain an essential oil. *H. pulchrum* is the badge of the M'Kinnons. French, *Millepertuis* ; German, *Johanniskraut.*   [C. A. J.]

HYPERTROPHIA. An excessive de-velopment of one part of a plant to the deterioration of others. Where parts of plants possess valuable properties, art steps in to produce an hypertrophy of those parts, as in the turnip, radish, &c. Sometimes the vegetative powers of a plant are so strong as to prevent the formation of flower-buds and fruit. This is called rankness, and is to be suppressed by the withdrawal of nutriment and by root-pruning. Galls produce hypertrophy on every part of plants. The roots of melons are sometimes gouty from the attacks of a minute vibrio. The disease called clubbing, which is a form of hypertrophy, has been already noticed. Some curious transformations of plants, a few of which are encouraged by gardeners, are also referable to the same category.   [M. J. B.]

HYPHA. The mycelium, or spawn of certain fungals ; also the filamentous fleshy watery thallus of certain fungoid plants.

HYPHÆNE. A small genus of African palms confined to and widely distributed throughout that continent, more particularly upon the eastern side, extending from Egypt as far south as Natal. The genus is remarkable for having the stem branched, a peculiarity not frequent among palms, each branch terminating in a tuft of large fan-shaped leaves, from amongst which the branching catkin-like spikes of flowers are produced, the different sexes being borne on separate trees. The fruit is about the size of an apple, and has a thick mealy fibrous rind with a smooth polished skin, enclosing a single hollow seed of a horny consistence.

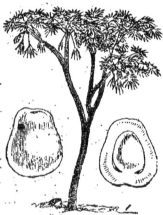

Hyphæne thebaica.

H. thebaica, the Doum or Doom Palm, or Gingerbread tree of Egypt, grows also in Nubia, Abyssinia and Arabia. It seldom exceeds twenty-five or thirty feet in height, and its stem is frequently three or four times forked or branched in old trees,

Plate 18

HYPHÆNE OR DOUM PALM IN UPPER EGYPT

though when young it is always simple. The fruits, which are produced in long clusters, each containing between one and two hundred, are beautifully polished, of a rich yellowish-brown colour, and of irregular form. In Upper Egypt they form part of the food of the poorer classes of inhabitants, the part eaten being the fibrous mealy husk, which tastes almost exactly like gingerbread, but its dry husky nature renders it unpalatable. The hard tough wood is used for making various domestic utensils; and rosaries are cut out of the horny seed. See Plate 18.　　[A. S.]

HYPHASMA. A name applied to the mycelium of moulds, as subiculum is often given to the same growth in *Sphæria*. In neither case is it absolutely necessary, though, like many other needless terms, consecrated by habit.　　[M. J. B.]

HYPHOMYCETES. One of the great divisions of *Fungi*, containing those species which have naked spores borne on free or only fasciculate threads. In the two first divisions only are the threads at all compacted, and it is by these that they are connected with *Hymenomycetes*. Care must be taken not to confound them with the vesicular moulds which have a similar habit. As they are plants of an extremely simple structure, it is not surprising that some conditions of more compound forms should occasionally exhibit their characters, exactly as the organs of which phænogams are composed have their analogues amongst the simpler cryptogams. Accordingly the early stage of certain species of *Hypoxylon* and *Sphæria* cannot be distinguished from them, and the young of *Erysiphe* exhibits all the characters of *Oidium*. A few, moreover, either produce a second subsidiary fruit, as some species of *Aspergillus* or *Peronospora*, but whether they should be removed into the sporidiiferous series is at present matter of doubt. A great portion of the moulds which act so prominent a part in the decomposition of organised bodies belong to this section, and some of them, as *Peronospora infestans*, are of immense importance as affecting substances of extensive use to man. As objects of interest for the observer of nature, they exhibit an endless variety of forms, which are frequently most attractive. Most of them, however, require the assistance of the microscope, even for the inspection of their outward form, and they are difficult to observe when moistened on account of their retaining so much air about them. They occur in all parts of the world, and in the shape of yeast some of them perform a most important part in domestic economy. A few have been detected in amber. Like many other fungi they have immense powers of penetration, and accordingly they are found in situations apparently removed from all external access. They occur in the most deep-seated tissues, occasionally producing fruit though removed from the direct influence of light and air, and this not only in the vegetable kingdom. Amongst animals they are the

source of many cutaneous disorders, and sometimes, as in the case of silk worms, they produce death. A case is even mentioned by Mr. Beale, as reported in the *Lancet* of January 1861, in which a few threads seemed to have formed the nucleus of a large calculus. They occur in all climates where there is sufficient moisture, and some of the more common species appear to be complete cosmopolites. The following natural orders have been proposed to include the species:—

Isariacei : stem compound; spores dry, easily dispersed.
Stilbacei : stem compound; spores forming a diffluent gelatinous mass.
Dematiei : fertile threads more or less carbonised; spores often compound.
Mucedineæ : fertile threads hyaline or coloured; spores mostly simple.
Sepedoniei : fertile threads scarcely distinct from the spawn; spores very abundant.

These latter pass evidently into *Coniomycetes*.　　[M. J. B.]

HYPHOSTROMA. The mycelium or spawn of fungals.

HYPNÆI. A natural order of pleurocarpous mosses, with a nodding capsule, elongated footstalk, and mostly cylindrical stems, with imbricated leaves; and distinguished from *Leucodontei* by the cernuous not erect capsules. In a very few species the stem is flat, and the leaves two-ranked. The species for the most part creep over trees, rocks, or shady banks, though sometimes growing in exposed pastures, forming frequently thick tufts. A few are pinnate, but are easily distinguished from *Neckera* by their nodding capsules. *Hypnum* is the principal genus.　　[M. J. B.]

HYPNUM. One of the largest and most important genera of mosses belonging to the division which has lateral fruit, numbering above ninety species in Great Britain alone. It has been divided into various genera dependent on slight differences of habit and condition of the leaf-cells, but if capable of accurate discrimination, they are rather to be considered as subgenera. The peristome in all is double, consisting of an outer row of sixteen equidistant lanceolate acuminate teeth, the inner of a membrane divided halfway down into sixteen keeled, often perforated processes, alternating with the outer teeth, with intermediate cilia which are either solitary or two or three together. The capsule is more or less curved or irregular. It differs from *Leskea* in the nodding capsule and the cilia of the inner peristome, and from *Isothecium* in the curved not straight and symmetrical capsule, and straggling not dendroid habit. Many of the species are very large and ornamental. They occur in all parts of the world. *H. tamariscinum* is much used by the makers of artificial flowers in the construction of moss roses. [M. J. B.]

HYPO. In Greek compounds = under.
HYPOBLASTUS. The flat dorsal cotyledon of a grass.

HYPOCALYMMA. A genus of myrtaceous shrubs, indigenous at the Swan River. The leaves are narrow with a sharp spine at their extremity; and the flowers are rose-coloured, in heads, the tube of the calyx bell-shaped, the petals five with short stalks, and the stamens numerous attached like the petals to the throat of the calyx. [M. T. M.]

HYPOCALYPTUS. A South African genus of *Leguminosæ*, consisting of a single species, *H. obcordatus*, a handsome bush or small tree with angular stems, trifoliolate leaves, having obversely heart-shaped leaflets, and stiff erect racemes of numerous purple pea-flowers terminating the twigs. The standard, which has a white spot at its base, is longer than the keel; and the narrow and smooth many-seeded pod is about two inches long. The two latter characters distinguish it from *Loddigesia* and its other allies. [A. A. B.]

HYPOCHÆRIS. A family of herbaceous plants belonging to the cichoraceous division of compound flowers. The characters of the genus are: pappus feathery; receptacle with chaffy scales; involucre unequally imbricated; fruit striated, often beaked. *H. radicata*, the long-rooted Cat's-ear, is a very common weed in pastures, rising to about the height of the crop among which it grows; the leaves are runcinate and very rough, and the stems generally bear several large yellow flower-heads, which are sometimes so abundant as to give a tint to the field in which it grows. It is a weed of no interest, rather mischievous than otherwise, from usurping the places of more nutritious fodder. *H. maculata*, a more robust plant found on the magnesian rocks of the Lizard Point, on the limestone of Ormeshead, and a few other places on chalk, generally bears a single very large flower-head. French, *Porcelle*; German, *Saukraut*. [C. A. J.]

HYPOCHIL, HYPOCHILIUM. The lower part of the lip of certain orchids.

HYPOCRATERIFORM. Having a long slender tube and a flat limb; as in the flower of the primrose.

HYPOCYRTA. A genus of *Gesneraceæ*, containing a few species, natives of South America. They are procumbent, sometimes erect, undershrubs, throwing out roots from below the origin of the opposite and fleshy leaves. The flowers are axillary, and solitary or several together, with a deeply five-parted calyx, and an urn-shaped corolla gibbous behind at the base, the limb unequally five-lobed or five-toothed; there are four stamens, and the ovary is surrounded by a disk which swells on one side into a gland. The fruit is a one-celled berry. [W. C.]

HYPODEMATIUM. *Lastrea.*

HYPODERMIS. The inner layer of the spore-case of an urn-moss.

HYPODERRIS. A genus of polypodiaceous ferns, allied to *Woodsia*, with which it agrees in having globose involucrato sori, and in the involucre being membranaceous, calyciform, and fringed at the edge. It is, however, at once distinguished by its compoundly anastomosing venation. In its aspect, moreover, it is quite dissimilar to *Woodsia*, the only species, *H. Brownii*, being a West Indian plant with simple or three-lobed coarse-looking fronds, having much more the appearance of some *Aspidium*. The venal areoles enclose free divaricate sterile veinlets; and the sori are conital, i.e. seated at the points where several veins meet. [T. M.]

HYPODISCUS. A genus of *Restiaceæ*, allied to *Willdenowia*, differing in having the male spikes many-flowered. The disk of the female flowers (in one-flowered spikes) is crenated or waved. They are natives of the Cape of Good Hope. [J. T. S.]

HYPOËSTES. A considerable genus of *Acanthaceæ*, dispersed over Africa, tropical Asia, and Australia, and remarkably abundant in Madagascar. They are shrubs or small trees with entire or dentate leaves, and large purple or rose-coloured flowers in axillary clusters or short spikes, often numerous and forming a terminal leafy thyrse. The flowers are contained in a calyx-like involucre of four more or less united bracts; the calyx is five-lobed; the corolla is two-lipped, with the upper lip entire or notched and the lower three-lobed; there are two stamens with one-celled anthers; and the capsule is compressed and seedless below, but towards the apex enlarged and two-celled, containing four tuberculated seeds. Nearly forty species have been described. [W. C.]

HYPOGÆI. A natural order of gasteromycetous *Fungi*, distinguished by their hymenium resembling the crumb of bread, and by their subterranean habit. Some have a distinct peridium, while others are totally destitute of any covering, and depart from the characters of the tribe to which they belong. They differ from real truffles in the fruit consisting of naked spores. The genera and species are numerous, and confined to temperate regions. Australia and North America produce two or three species. *Melanogaster ambiguus* is used as a substitute for truffles, and is sold in the market at Bath. Several have an extremely offensive smell. These and other fungi of a similar habit have been most exquisitely illustrated in a separate work by the Messrs. Tulasne. [M. J. B.]

HYPOGÆOUS. Growing under the earth.

HYPOGYNOUS. Growing from below the base of the ovary.

HYPOLÆNA. A genus of *Restiaceæ* from South Australia, with the habit of *Restio*. Stems branched, with the male flowers amentaceous; female plants with the flowers in an imbricated spike, terminal and solitary; style two or three-parted, deciduous. [J. T. S.]

HYPOLEPIS. A genus of polypodiaceous ferns, belonging to the *Cheilantheæ*, and not very well distinguished technically from *Cheilanthes* itself, though obviously distinct in habit and aspect, in the large herbaceous fronds and long creeping rhizomes, and also generally distinguishable by the axillary position of the sori in respect to the segments of the fronds. The fronds are twice, thrice, or four times pinnated, with free veins, and punctiform sori at the apex of the veins, covered by reflexed marginal, sometimes herbaceous, indusia. The species are widely dispersed, being found in New Zealand and the Pacific Isles, India, Bourbon, and Mauritius, South Africa, South America, and the West Indies. [T. M.]

HYPOLYTRUM. A genus of cyperaceous plants, characteristic of the tribe *Hypolytreæ*. It is distinguished by the inflorescence being in fascicled or corymbose roundish panicles, which are many-flowered. Scales imbricated on all sides, none of the lower without flowers; proper scales two, keeled and compressed, the exterior one largest; calyx none; stamens two to three; styles cleft. The majority of the species are natives of Brazil and the West Indies, but some occur in the East Indies. [D. M.]

HYPOMENOUS. Free, not adherent; arising from below an organ, without adhering to it.

HYPOPHYLLIUM. A small abortive leaf, like a scale, placed below a cluster of leaf-like branches, or leaves.

HYPOPHYLLOUS. Growing on the under side of a leaf.

HYPOPITHYS. A genus of fir-rapes, distinguished by having the calyx three to five-parted, and the style slender and hollow, ending in a round stigma, bearded at the margin. The species are parasites, on firs and beeches, with leaves in the form of scales, the entire plant pale in colour, and often with an odour of musk. [G. D.]

HYPOPODIUM. The stalk of the carpels.

HYPOPTERIES. A wing growing from below anything, as the seed of a fir-tree.

HYPOPTERATE. Having a wing produced at the base or below.

HYPOPTERYGEI. An order of pleurocarpous mosses, with three-ranked leaves, the third row being mostly smaller than the others. The accessory leaves remind one of the appendages in *Jungermanniaceæ*. The capsules are mostly lateral, beneath the proper leaves, but sometimes axillary. The genera of this order belong principally to warm temperate regions in either hemisphere. [M. J. B.]

HYPOSATHRIA. A condition assumed by the tissues of certain fruits, commonly called bletting. It is a partial decomposition, accompanied by the formation of sugar, and is sometimes promoted artificially with a view to improve the flavour of harsh fruits, and, indeed, to render them eatable as medlars, services, &c. [M. J. B.]

HYPOSPORANGIUM. The indusium of ferns, when it grows from below the sporecases.

HYPOSTASIS. The suspensor of an embryo.

HYPOSTROMA. The mycelium of certain fungals.

HYPOTHALLUS. Delicate filaments which constitute the vegetation of coniomycetous fungals. The inferior stratum of the thallus of lichenals.

HYPOTHECIUM. The cellular stratum below the thalamium of lichenals.

HYPOXIDACEÆ. (*Hypoxids.*) A natural order of epigynous monocotyledons belonging to Lindley's narcissal alliance of Endogens. Herbs with a tuberous or fibrous perennial root, radical linear dry leaves, and trimerous flowers on scapes. Perianth petaloid, adherent to the ovary, six-parted; stamens six, attached to the perianth, the anthers introrse; ovary three-celled; ovules numerous, attached to a central placenta. Fruit dry or berried, one to two or three celled, not opening, with a lateral hilum, and a peculiar beak-like appendage. Natives of the Cape of Good Hope, the East Indies, New Holland, and the tropical parts of America. The roots of some of them are bitter and aromatic, and the tubers of a few are eaten. There are five genera, and upwards of sixty species. Examples: *Hypoxis, Curculigo.* [J. H. B.]

HYPOXIS. A genus of herbaceous plants, forming the type of the *Hypoxidaceæ.* They are known by their six stamens being inserted into a disk surmounting the ovary, by the style being detached from the corolla, and by the three-celled capsular fruit. These plants are, for the most part, natives of the Cape of Good Hope, and have much of the appearance of some amaryllidaceous plants, but they are not bulbous: several are in cultivation. *H. erecta,* a North American species, is used as an application to ulcers. [M. T. M.]

HYPOXYLON. An important genus of sphæriaceous *Fungi,* distinguished by the stroma, in which the perithecia or fruit-bearing cysts are sunk, being free from the wood on which it grows. They are found in all parts of the world. *H. concentricum,* which is common in this country on ash-trees, looking like lumps of cobbler's wax, is a perfect cosmopolite, assuming several forms. The allied *H. vernicosum,* which, though marked like the last with concentric layers within, is loosely cellular, is eaten by the inhabitants of Bhotan. [M. J. B.]

HYPSEOCHARIS. A genus referred to *Geraniaceæ,* and found on the Andes at above 10,000 feet elevation. The plant has root leaves resembling those of *Pimpinella Saxifraga,* and axillary peduncles, with three or four subsessile flowers, fifteen united stamens, and a five-lobed ovary, with several ovules in each cell. [J. T. S.]

HYPTIS. A genus of labiates, having the calyx with five nearly equal teeth, which are very acute; and the corolla about as long as the calyx, the upper lip with four entire lobes, the lower undivided. The species are herbs or undershrubs, varying much in general aspect; they are chiefly natives of the warmer parts of South America. [G. D.]

HYSSOP. *Hyssopus officinalis.* — of Scripture. *Capparis spinosa.* —, BASTARD. *Teucrium Pseudo-hyssopus.* —, HEDGE. *Gratiola officinalis.*

HYSSOPUS. A genus of *Labiatæ*, consisting of small bushy herbs, with lance-shaped leaves, rolled under at the margin, a calyx marked with fifteen ribs, and four fertile diverging stamens. *H. officinalis*, the common Hyssop, of Southern Europe, was once much employed as a carminative in flatulence and hysterical complaints, but is now seldom employed. [M. T. M.]

HYSTERANTHIUS. When leaves appear after flowers; as in the almond.

HYSTERIA. *Corymbis.*

HYSTERIUM. A genus of pyrenomycetous *Fungi*, distinguished by a hard more or less linear dark perithecium, opening by an elongated narrow aperture. The species grow on naked wood, bark, leaves, &c., and are sometimes so similar to lichens that it is difficult to distinguish them when the crust is worn away or obsolete. *H. Fraxini* and *Rosæ* are to be found commonly on fallen twigs of ash and rose. The species are numerous, and occur in all parts of the world. [M. J. B.]

IANTHE. A genus of *Scrophulariaceæ* closely allied to *Verbascum*, and only differing from the *Blattaria* section of that genus by the stamens, of which two only bear anthers, two being reduced to barren filaments, and there being no rudiment of the fifth. *I. buguifolia*, the only known species, grows in the neighbourhood of Constantinople. It has the habit of the more glabrous species of *Verbascum* or *Celsia*, with the leaves chiefly radical, and greenish-yellow flowers, remarkable for their almost metallic appearance when fresh.

IANTHINUS. Pure blue stained with red, so as to be intermediate between the two colours.

IBÉRIDE DE PERSE. (Fr.) *Iberis sempervirens.*

IBERIDELLA. A genus of *Cruciferæ*, allied to *Hutchinsia*, differing principally in the truncate pouch, with a long slender style. They are small undershrubs, with white or rose-coloured flowers. [J. T. S.]

IBERIS. A genus of *Cruciferæ*, containing numerous species from Europe, Eastern Asia, and Northern Africa. They are easily known from most of their allies, by their flat corymbs of flowers with the two exterior petals larger than the others, so that the inflorescence is radiant. These Candytufts are nearly smooth annuals, or small undershrubs, with oblong or linear leaves (pinnatifid in many of the annual kinds), and white pink or purple flowers, fragrant in some of the species. The seed-pouch is oval or roundish, flattened so that the partition is in the narrowest diameter, and the valves compressed, with an expanded wing on the keel. The seed is solitary in each of the two cells, with the radicle bent over the edges of the flat cotyledons, on one side. The most common species is *I. amara*, which is found wild in the south of England as a weed in cultivated grounds, and many of the other species are common in gardens. [J. T. S.]

ICACINACEÆ. (*Icacineæ.*) A natural order of thalamifloral dicotyledons, consisting of evergreen trees and shrubs, allied to *Olacaceæ*, and differing from that order in the calyx not enlarging with the fruit; in the stamens being alternate with the petals; in the ovary being normally many-celled, with axile placentation, and one-celled only by abortion; and in the ovules being suspended below the summit of the cell. The plants are chiefly tropical, and there are about thirteen genera and seventy known species. Nothing is known regarding their properties. Bentham makes them a tribe of *Olacineæ*. Lindley places the order under his berberal alliance of hypogynous Exogens. [J. H. B.]

ICACINA. A genus of *Icacinaceæ*, with shrubby ascending or twining branches, smooth leaves, panicled flowers, and scarlet fruit. Calyx small, five-cleft; petals five, valvate villous; stamens five, alternate with petals, hypogynous; ovary one-celled, with two pendulous ovules. Fruit indehiscent, the seed pendulous with a prominent raphe. There are three or four known species, natives of the western parts of tropical Africa. [J. H. B.]

ICACO. *Chrysobalanus Icaco.*

ICE-PLANT. *Mesembryanthemum crystallinum.*

ICHNANTHUS. A genus of grasses, belonging to the tribe *Paniceæ*, and now generally included in *Panicum*. The only species described, *I. panicoides*, is a native of Brazil and Guiana. [D. M.]

ICHNOCARPUS. A genus of dogbanes, having the stamens five in number, their anthers distinct from the stigma, which is ovate acuminate; and the seed-vessels very slender. The name is indicative of the slender capsules. *I. frutescens* is an ornamental stove shrub, a native of the East Indies, with oval lanceolate leaves, and small flowers. [G. D.]

ICICA. A genus of *Amyridaceæ*, found chiefly in the tropics of the western hemisphere, only two or three out of the twenty species described occurring in the eastern.

They are mostly large trees, sometimes a hundred feet in height, and nearly all abound in balsamic or resinous-juice. Their leaves are either pinnate with a terminal leaflet, or ternate, the leaflets being of a leathery texture, and without the dots usual in some plants of the same order. The flowers are small, usually white or yellowish-green, and borne in racemes or crowded heads at the angles of the leaves; they have a small four or five-toothed calyx, and an equal number of petals, which, along with the eight or ten stamens, are inserted under the cup-shaped fleshy disk. The fruit is a berry containing from one to five hard stones covered with pulp, and containing one seed each.

I. altissima, attaining, in the forests of Guiana, a height of one hundred feet, is preferred by the Indians for making their canoes, not only from its large size but on account of its durability and the facility with which it is worked. It is called Cedar-wood in consequence of its fragrant odour, and is used for the inside fittings of houses, for book-cases, &c., its odour preserving books from injury by insects. The balsam obtained from the trunks of many of the species is highly odoriferous, and is commonly used as a perfume in South America. That of *I. heptaphylla*, called Hyawa in Guiana, is used as a remedy against dysentery, and also for coughs. Balsam of Acouchi, yielded by *I. heterophylla*, is employed as a vulnerary. These balsams remain fluid for a considerable time, but ultimately harden, and are then commonly used for burning as incense in churches. So highly charged with resin are the trees, that the branches of one species are used in British Guiana for torches; and the wood of *I. heptaphylla* is called Incense wood.   [A. S.]

ICONES. Pictorial representations of plants.

ICOS. In Greek compounds = twenty.

ICOSAÉDRAL. Having twenty sides; as the pollen of *Tragopogon*.

ICTERUS. A name given to the yellow condition assumed by wheat and some other plants, under the influence of prolonged wet and cold. More genial weather generally improves the condition of the plants. The disease is, therefore, distinct from chlorosis, which is more frequently constitutional, and, in consequence, past cure. Vine leaves become yellow from their roots being placed under unfavourable circumstances; the remedy, therefore, must be directed to the point from whence the evil is derived. Yellowness is sometimes produced by *Fungi*, and is then irremediable. The golden hues of autumn belong clearly to another category.   [M. J. B.]

IDES, or IDEUS. In terminating Greek compounds = similar: as *petaloideus*, like a petal.

IDIOGYNOUS. Not having a pistil.

IDIOTHALAMUS. Having a different colour or texture from the thallus; a term used among lichens.

IDOTHEA. A genus of *Liliaceæ*, from the Cape of Good Hope, allied to *Drimia*, but differing in the perianth being deciduous. It is also near *Uropetalum* and *Urginea*, but is distinguished from the former by the sepals being united at the base, forming a bell-shaped tube, and from the latter by the deciduous one-nerved perianth segments. They are herbs with scaly or more rarely coated bulbs. [J. T. S.]

IF   (Fr.)   *Taxus baccata*. — NUCIFÈRE,   *Podocarpus nucifer*

IFE, An Indian name for *Sanseviera cylindrica*.

IGNAME. (Fr.) *Dioscorea sativa*.

IGNATIA. A genus described by the younger Linnæus as belonging to the *Strychnos* family, but since suppressed by Mr. Bentham, who has shown it to be composed of the leaves and flowers of a species of *Posoqueria*, and the fruits of a *Strychnos*, the former a plant of Guiana, the latter from the Philippines. The seeds are called by old writers, St. Ignatius' Beans, and are held up by them as a remedy against cholera. They are supposed to belong to *Strychnos multiflora*, but are quite unknown to modern botanists.   [A. A. B.]

IGNEUS. Very lively scarlet, fiery red.

ILEODICTYON. A genus of phalloid *Gasteromycetes*, nearly allied to *Clathrus*, but distinguished from it by the hollow branches of the receptacle, which are, moreover, not porous. The gelatinous volva of *I. cibarium* was formerly eaten in New Zealand, before the English habits had gained ground, and was known by a name equivalent to Thunder-dirt.   [M. J. B.]

ILEX. A genus of shrubs and trees belonging to the *Aquifoliaceæ*, inhabiting Europe, Asia, and America, and characterised by having an inferior calyx with small teeth; a corolla which is monopetalous but scarcely so, it being divided into deep spreading concave segments; stamens inserted upon the corolla and alternate with its segments; a four or five-celled ovary, with nearly sessile stigmas; and a berried fruit containing one-seeded nuts, the parts being all in fours or fives. The species are very numerous. *I. Aquifolium*, common Holly, employed so much for purposes of decoration at Christmas, and *I. paraguayensis*, Paraguay Tea, are the most remarkable.

I. Aquifolium is distinguished from other species by its peculiar smooth, wavy, shining, spinous leaves, and its short axillary, many-flowered peduncles. The leaves are stated on good authority to be equal to Peruvian bark in the cure of intermittent fevers. The root and bark are said to be deobstruent, expectorant, and diuretic, agreeably to which Haller recommends the juice of the leaves in jaundice. The berries

are purgative and emetic, six or eight being
sufficient, it is said, to produce the latter
effect. The beautiful white wood is much
used for inlaying, and birdlime is obtained
from the bark. It has been stated recently by M. J. Pierre, that the young stems
are gathered in Morbihan by the peasants,
and made use of as a cattle-food from the
end of November to April with great success. The stems are dried, and having
been bruised are given as food to cows
three times a day. They are found to be
very wholesome and very productive of
good milk, and the butter made from it is
excellent. The common Holly is the badge
of the Drummonds.

I. *paraguayensis* is characterised as a
species by its perfectly smooth, ovate,
lanceolate unequally-serrated leaves, and
by having much-branched racemes of flowers, the subdivisions of which are somewhat umbellate, and by its slightly hairy
calyx. The leaves of the Maté, the name
by which it is known in South America,
are from four to five inches long. The
Maté occupies the same important position in the domestic economy of South
America, as the Chinese tea does in this
country, and it is calculated that it is consumed in that country to the extent of
about 8,600,000 lbs. annually. It has been
in use for about a century and a half, the
practice having been adopted from the
aboriginal people. The leaves are prepared
by drying and roasting, not in the manner
of Chinese teas, but large branches are cut
off the plants and placed on hurdles over
a wood fire until sufficiently roasted; the

Ilex paraguayensis.

branches are then placed on a hard floor
and beaten with sticks; the dried leaves
are thus knocked off and reduced to a
powder, which is collected, made into
packages, and is ready for use. There are
three sorts known in the South American
markets: the Caa-Cuys, which is the half-
expanded leaf-buds; the Caa-Miri, the leaf
torn from its midrib and veins, without

roasting; and the Caa-Guaza or Yerva de
Palos of the Spaniards, the whole leaf with
the petioles and small branches roasted. It
is prepared for drinking by putting a small
quantity, about a teaspoonful, into a gourd
or cup, with a little sugar; the drinking
tube is then inserted, and boiling water
poured on the Maté; when sufficiently cool,
the infusion is sucked up through the
tube. It has an agreeable, slightly aromatic odour, is rather bitter to the taste,
and very refreshing and restorative to the
human frame, after enduring great fatigue.
It is almost impossible for those accustomed to it to leave it off. It acts in some
degree as an aperient and diuretic, and if
taken in over-doses, it occasions diseases
similar to those produced by strong
liquors. It contains the same active principle as tea and coffee, called theine, but
not their volatile and empyreumatic oils.

It is stated that *I. Gongonha* and *I. theezans* are also employed in Brazil as tea,
and they are described in common with
I. paraguayensis as being valuable diuretics and diaphoretics. The leaves of *I.
paraguayensis* and several others are used
by dyers; the unripe fruits of *I. Macoucua*
abound in tannin, and, bruised in a ferrugineous mud, are used in dyeing cotton, acting something like galls.　　　[B. C.]

ILLAIREA. A genus of *Loasaceæ* from
central America, of which the only species
I. canarinoides is a climber, with much the
habit and aspect of *Caiophora lateritia*, but
having the ovate oblong keeled petals so
arranged as to form a bell-shaped flower, bearing considerable resemblance to
that of *Canarina.* The leaves are cordate
or fiddle-shaped, deeply pinnatifid with
toothed lobes, and furnished, as are the
stems, with virulent stinging hairs; the
flowers are nodding, borne on long axillary peduncles, and of a cinnabar or brick-
red colour, with blue stamens. There are
five concave half-boatshaped nectary scales
alternating with the petals, bearing on
their back a couple of setæ, and standing
in front of the scales, two before each,
long filiform staminodia, converging in a
cone over the style, which has five hemispherical corpuscules at its base. Beyond this there is little besides the campanulate form of the corolla to separate
Illairea from *Caiophora.*　　　[T. M.]

ILLECEBRACEÆ. (*Paronychieæ, Her-
niariæ, Knotworts.*) A natural order of
dicotyledons belonging to Lindley's silenal
alliance of hypogynous Exogens. Herbaceous or somewhat shrubby plants with
opposite or alternate often clustered sessile stipuled leaves, and minute flowers;
sepals three to five, distinct or ovuled;
petals small, sometimes none; stamens
opposite the sepals, if equal to them in
number; ovary superior; styles two to
five; seeds either numerous and attached
to a free central placenta, or solitary and
pendulous from a cord attached to a basal
placenta; embryo curved in albumen. Natives of barren places chiefly in Europe
and the north of Africa. Their properties

are astringent. There are thirty-one known genera, and about one hundred and twenty-five species. Examples : *Illecebrum, Paronychia, Spergula.*   [J. H. B.]

ILLECEBRUM. A genus of *Illecebraceæ* containing a single species, *I. verticillatum*, found over the greater part of Europe, though very rare in Britain, and only occurring in the extreme south-west. It is a small branched prostrate smooth annual, with ascending branches, crowded with pairs of obovate leaves, and bearing axillary clusters of flowers forming false whorls; these are small, white, and shining, from the dry white thickened calyx segments.   [J. T. S.]

ILLICIUM. A limited genus of *Magnoliaceæ*, found in the south-eastern parts of the United States, Japan, Southern China, and the Khasia mountains. They are evergreen shrubs or low trees, with smooth entire leaves, exhaling when bruised a strong odour of aniseed, owing to the volatile oil contained in minute pellucid dots, which may be seen by means of a lens. Their flowers are borne singly or in threes from the sides of the branches, usually of a yellowish colour, except in one species where they are dark purple; they have a calyx of three or six sepals, coloured in the same manner as, and scarcely distinguishable from, the petals, which vary in number from nine to thirty, and are arranged in several series, the innermost ones being the smallest; the stamens are numerous, and the ovaries, varying from six to eighteen, are crowded together in a circle. The fruit resembles a star, consisting of a variable number of one-seeded flattened cells arranged round a central axis.

Illicium anisatum.

I. anisatum, the Star or Chinese Anise, the Badiane of the French, is a shrub growing eight or ten feet high. It is found in China, and derives its name of Star Anise from the stellate form and odour of its fruit, which is about an inch in diameter. This fruit forms a considerable article of commerce amongst Asiatic nations, and is likewise sent to Europe, though not in very large quantities. In China, Japan, India, and elsewhere in Asia, it is commonly used by cooks as a condiment in the preparation of food, and it is also chewed in small quantities after each meal, both for the purpose of sweetening the breath and as a promoter of digestion, while the native physicians prescribe it as a stomachic and carminative. In France it is reputed to be employed as the flavouring ingredient of *Anisette de Bordeaux.* Its pungent aromatic flavour and odour, which bear a strong resemblance to those of the common anise but rather sweeter and softer, is due to the presence of a volatile oil, which is obtained from it by distillation, and is said to be substituted for genuine oil of anise.

I. religiosum, a Japanese species, was formerly confounded with the Chinese. It is a small tree about the size of a cherry tree, and is held sacred by the Japanese, who form wreaths of it with which to decorate the tombs of their deceased friends, and they also burn the fragrant bark as incense before their deities. Their watchmen likewise use the powdered bark for burning in graduated tubes in order to mark the time, the bark consuming slowly and uniformly. The leaves are said to possess poisonous properties; while in Alabama those of *I. floridanum* have the same reputation, and the plant has hence acquired the name of Poison-bay. [A. S.]

ILLIGERA. An apetalous genus of Exogens, regarding the station of which much difference of opinion has been entertained. It consists of climbing shrubs, natives of Java, having alternate coriaceous leaves which are ternate. The flowers are hermaphrodite in axillary panicles; the calyx superior, coloured, ten-lobed, the lobes being disposed in two rows; the stamens five, opposite the outer row, having glands at their bases; the anthers open by valves which turn upwards; and the ovary is one-celled. The fruit is four-sided with four unequal wings at the angles, and the single pendulous seed has the cotyledons spirally twisted together. The nearest affinity of this genus is with *Gyrocarpus*, from which it differs in its climbing stem, and in having wings on the sides of its fruit. These two genera have been considered as the type of a distinct family under the name of *Illigereæ* or *Gyrocarpeæ*, but are very near both *Combretaceæ* and *Lauraceæ*, with the former of which they have been combined.   [B. C.]

ILLIGEREÆ. A suborder of *Combretaceæ*, from which the plants referred to it are distinguished mainly by their recurved anther valves, in which respect they resemble laurels. The group also receives the name of *Gyrocarpeæ*.   [J. H. B.]

ILLUPIE TREE. *Bassia longifolia.*

IMANTOPHYLLUM. This name, under the form of *Imatophyllum*, subsequently changed by Sprengel to *Himantophyllum*, was originally applied to the amaryllidaceous plant called *Cliria*, which latter name has superseded it; and its author, Sir W. J. Hooker, has since transferred it to a related Natal plant of great beauty, which he calls *I. miniatum*. This plant forms a stemless herb, with thick fleshy roots, ample distichous lorate leaves embracing each other at the base, and a tall piano-convex scape bearing an umbel of many large showy flowers of a bright orange-tipped vermilion. These consist of a six-leaved perianth, with a very short tube and broad obovate-lanceolate nearly equal segments, spreading into a broadly campanulate form; there are six stamens with thickish subulate filaments, and a thick slightly decurved style with a trifid stigma. The seeds are bulbiform, about the size of a horsebean. [T. M.]

IMBERBIS. Having no hairs.

IMBRICATED. When bodies overlap each other like tiles on a roof.

IMBRICARIA. A genus of sapotaceous trees natives of Bourbon, Mauritius, &c. The flowers have eight sepals in two rows; a corolla divided into several segments, arranged in three rows; sixteen stamens, eight of them fertile and eight sterile; and a fleshy fruit, with eight one-seeded cells. The fruits of *I. malabarica* and *I. maxima* are edible. [M. T. M.]

IMHOFIA. A genus of *Amaryllidaceæ*, allied to *Brunsvigia*, and consisting of Cape bulbs characterised by the flowers having a very short straight tube and a spreading or reflexed limb of six nearly equal segments, six stamens with equal filaments enlarged at the base, and a straight style with an obtuse three-cornered stigma. They have filiform leaves, and a solid scape bearing at top a many-flowered umbel of white flowers, often marked with red. The name was originally intended for *Amaryllis marginata*, a plant which is now referred to *Nerine*. [T. M.]

IMMARGINATE. Having no rim or edge.

IMMEDIATE. Proceeding directly from a part, without the intervention of any other part; as the flower-stalks of a raceme.

IMMOBILE, IMMOBILIS. Immovable; that is to say, not having a free motion on the part which bears it; as many anthers.

IMMORTAL FLOWER. A name applied to the various common species of *Helichrysum, Antennaria, Gnaphalium,* &c.

IMMORTELLE (Fr.) *Xeranthemum*; also *Helipterum* and *Helichrysum*, especially *H. orientale*; also the wood of *Erythrina glauca*. — BLANCHE or DE VIRGINIE. *Antennaria margaritacea*. — DE LA MAL-MAISON. *Helichrysum bracteatum*. — JAUNE. *Helichrysum orientale*. — VIO-LETTE. *Gomphrena globosa*.

IMPARIPINNATE. When the petiole of a pinnate leaf is terminated by a single leaflet.

IMPATIENS. A genus of *Balsaminaceæ*, chiefly found in India, though a few species occur in Europe and North America. They are generally glabrous herbs with thick succulent stems enlarged at the joints, where the alternate undivided leaves are given off. The flowers are axillary, often handsome, and so very irregular that considerable difference of opinion exists as to which parts belong to the calyx and which to the corolla. The view taken by Kunth is by far the most probable, namely, that two outer small scale-like leaves, a large h od-shaped and spurred coloured lower sepal, and an upper coloured portion composed of two united together so as to appear but one, form an irregular imbricated calyx of five sepals. Within this there are two pairs of petals, unequally cleft, nearly to the base. The stamens are five in number, with the filaments united above; and in the centre is the five-celled ovary with a sessile lobed stigma. The capsule is oblong, subcylindrical, or with five blunt angles. The valves separate and roll up when touched after the seeds are ripe. *I. Balsamina* is the much-cultivated Garden Balsam, which readily becomes double, and of which the flowers are very variable in colour, a native of India. *I. Noli-tangere*, the Touch-me-not, is found apparently wild in Britain, and is frequent in Europe; the flowers in this species are yellow. [J. T. S.]

IMPERATORIA. *Peucedanum.*

IMPÉRIALE. (Fr.) *Fritillaria imperialis.*

IMPLEXOUS. Entangled, interlaced.

IMPREGNATION. The fertilisation of the ovule by the pollen-tubes.

IMPUBERA (ÆTAS). The period of maturity in fruit anterior to the fertilisation of the ovules.

INÆQUALIS. Of unequal or dissimilar size.

INÆQUILATERAL, INÆQUILATERUS. When the two sides of a figure are not symmetrical; as the leaf of a *Begonia*.

INANIS. Empty, not containing anything; or merely filled with a loose spongy substance.

INANTHERATE. Bearing no anther; applied to sterile filaments or abortive stamens.

INAPERTOUS. Not opened, although its habit is to open.

INCANESCENT. Having a hoary or grey aspect, because of the presence of hairs upon the surface.

INCANUS. The same as Canus; hoary.

INCARNATUS. The same as Carneus.

INCARVILLEA. A genus of *Bignoniaceæ* containing now only a single species, the plants formerly referred to it being placed in new or neighbouring genera. It is an erect glabrous herb from China, having the habit of *Argylia*, with alternate bipinnatisect leaves, and large scarlet flowers in terminal racemes. [W. C.]

INCENSE. Frankincense, the modern Olibanum.

INCENSE TREE. *Icica guianensis.*

INCENSE WOOD. *Icica heptaphylla.*

INCISED, INCISUS. Regularly divided by deep incisions. Hence *inciso-serratus,* having deep slashed serratures ; *inciso-dentatus,* having slashed toothings, &c.

INCLINING. Falling back considerably from the horizontal line.

INCLUDED. Enclosed in anything.

INCOMPLETE. Deficient in some of its parts, as a flower without corolla, or a calyx with only a part of its sepals.

INCONSPICUOUS. Small in size, not readily observed.

INCRASSATE. Thicker than usual in proportion to its area ; as the leaves of the houseleek.

INCRUSTATE. A term applied to seeds which grow so firmly to their pericarp as to appear to have but one integument. Also coated with earthy matter.

INCUBOUS. A name employed in descriptions of *Jungermanniaceæ* in contradistinction to succubous, to indicate that the leaves are imbricated over each other from the base towards the apex, whereas in succubous leaves they are imbricated in a contrary direction. [M. J. B.]

INCUMBENT. Said of an embryo when its radicle is folded down upon the back of the cotyledons.

INCURVED, INCURVUS, INCURVATE Curved inwards.

INDEHISCENT. Not splitting in a definite manner when ripe.

INDIAN HEART. *Cardiospermum Corindum.*

INDIAN RUBBER. The inspissated juice of *Ficus elastica, Siphonia elastica,* and other plants : see CAOUTCHOUC.

INDIAN SHOT. *Canna.*

INDIGO. A blue dye yielded by several plants, as *Indigofera tinctoria* and *argentea, Wrightia tinctoria, Marsdenia tinctoria, Gymnema tingens.* —, BASTARD. *Amorpha fruticosa.* —, CHINESE. *Isatis indigotica.* —, EGYPTIAN. *Tephrosia Apollinea.* —, FALSE. An American name for *Baptisia.* —, INDIAN. *Indigofera tinctoria.* —, NATIVE. *Isatis tinctoria.* —, WEST INDIAN. *Indigofera Anil.* —, WILD. *Baptisia tinctoria.*

INDIGO-BERRY. *Randia latifolia.*

INDIGOFERA. A very extensive tropical or subtropical genus of leguminous plants, valuable on account of the blue colouring material, called Indigo, afforded by several of the species, of which upwards of two hundred are described, the greater number belonging to the African continent, but abounding also in both America and Asia, and a few extending to Australia. They are either annual or perennial herbaceous plants or shrubs, and have pinnate leaves, which, however, are occasionally reduced to three or one leaflet only. The flowers are usually of a rose-purplish or bluish colour or white, and are borne in racemes from the angles of the leaves ; they have a broad five-toothed calyx, a papilionaceous corolla having the upper petal curved backwards ; and ten stamens, one of which is free. The fruit is a cylindrical or four-sided, straight or curved pod, containing numerous (rarely one or two) angular seeds.

I. tinctoria, the species most commonly cultivated, is a native of the East Indies and other parts of Asia, but it has been introduced into and become naturalised in Africa and America. It is a shrubby plant growing about three or four feet high, having oval or inversely egg-shaped leaflets, and long narrow pods. *I. Anil,* the

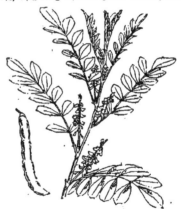

Indigofera tinctoria.

West Indian Indigo, is a larger plant, attaining a height of five or six feet, and is a native of the West Indies and America, from Carolina to Brazil, but has become naturalised in Asia and Africa. Its leaflets are of a spathulate form, and its pods short and thick.

The use of Indigo as a dye is of great antiquity. It is mentioned by Dioscorides and by Pliny, and is supposed to have been employed by the ancient Egyptians. It was not, however, much used in Europe till about three centuries ago, and for a long time it experienced considerable opposition on account of its interference with the domestic manufacture of woad (see ISATIS), and in several European countries edicts were issued prohibiting its use by dyers, and stigmatising it as the devil's dye. As met with in commerce at the present day, Indigo usually consists of cubical cakes, measuring between two and three inches. It is prepared by throwing bundles of the fresh-cut plants into shallow vats and covering them with water, care being taken to keep them under the surface. After steeping for ten or twelve hours the liquid is run off into another vat and beaten with sticks or bamboos from one and a half to three hours, in order to promote the formation of the blue colouring matter, which does not exist ready formed in the tissues of the plant, but is formed by the oxidation of other substances contained in them. The colouring matter is then allowed to settle, the precipitation being accelerated by the addition of a small quantity of clean cold water or lime-water, and the supernatant liquor drawn off and thrown away, while the deposited matter is put into a boiler and kept at the boiling point for five or six hours. After this it is spread upon frames covered with cloth, and allowed to drain for twelve or fourteen hours, and when it is sufficiently solid it is pressed, cut into cubes, stamped and dried for the market. Our imports of Indigo average about 68,000 cwt. annually, the greatest part coming from the East Indies, but a large portion is re-exported to various European countries, the consumption in the United Kingdom not being more than about 13,000 cwt. per annum.   [A. S.]

INDIGOTICUS. The deepest blue.

INDIGOTIER. (FR.) *Indigofera.*

INDIVISUS. Not separated into other parts.

INDRAJOW, INDURJAW. Indian names for the bitter seeds of *Wrightia antidysenterica.*

INDUGA. An Indian name for the Clearing-nut, *Strychnos potatorum.*

INDUMENTUM. The hairy covering of plants, of whatever kind.

INDUPLICATE, INDUPLICATIVE. Having the margins bent abruptly inwards, and the external face of these edges applied to each other without any twisting.

INDURASCENT. Hardening by degrees, as the permanent petioles of a tragacanth bush.

INDUSIUM. A name given to the immediate covering of the tuft of capsules or sporangia in ferns. Sometimes the sori are quite naked, the cuticle being simply ruptured by the protrusion of the young fruit. Sometimes, however, the cuticle is lifted up, and forms a covering of various shapes, being sometimes lateral, sometimes target-shaped, sometimes spherical, &c. In other cases the indusium appears to be a distinct growth arising from the tip or side of a vein. The border is either entire or ciliate. The indusium may be variously

seated even in the same genus, or again it may be almost obsolete, or, as in *Hypolepis tenuifolia,* be quite membranous or herbaceous, and in the latter case partaking more of the nature of the frond itself. In *Pleopeltis,* the indusium is replaced by a number of peltate scales, which, however, have no real relation to a true indusium. In genera like *Hymenophyllum,* where the fruit is produced at the tip of the protruding costa, the bivalvate or cup-shaped indusium is either formed of the frond itself, or springs from the excurrent costa. Sometimes the sori are covered, not only with an indusium, but with a portion of the turned-up edge of the leaf. The annulus of some fungals also bears the same name.   [M. J. B.]

INDUVIÆ (adj. INDUVIATE). Withered leaves remaining upon a stem, and clothing it.

INENCHYMA. Fibro-cellular tissue, that is to say, cells having the appearance of spiral vessels.

INERMIS. Destitute of any kind of spines or prickles.

INFERIOR. Growing below some other organ ; thus, an inferior calyx grows below the ovary, whilst an inferior ovary grows, or seems to grow, below a calyx.

INFLATED. Thin, membranous, slightly transparent, swelling equally, as if inflated with air.

INFLORESCENCE. The manner in which the flowers are arranged.

INFOSSOUS. Sunk in anything, as veins in some leaves, leaving a channel, however.

INFRACTOUS. Curved inwards.

INFUNDIBULAR, INFUNDIBULIFORM. Funnel-shaped.

INFUNDIBULI-CAMPANULATE. Between funnel-shaped and bell-shaped.

INGA. A very extensive genus of leguminous plants, of the section *Mimoseæ,* comprising nearly one hundred and fifty species, all of which are natives of the warmer parts of South America, principally of Brazil and Guiana. They form large shrubs or trees, sometimes growing fifty or sixty feet high, and have pinnate leaves composed of from two to five or six pairs of largish leaflets, bearing a gland on the stalk between each pair, the stalk being frequently winged or leaf-like. The flowers are usually white or yellowish, and borne in variously shaped spikes or in nearly globular heads, growing singly or in clusters from the angles of the leaves. They are generally all perfect, and have a tubular calyx, and a tubular or funnel-shaped corolla, enclosing an indefinite number of stamens, which are twice or several times the length of the corolla, and joined together at the bottom. The pods are flattened or roundish, with thickened edges, and the seeds are enveloped in a sweet, generally white pulp.

I. Feuillei, a native of Peru, is cultivated in the gardens about Lima, where the inhabitants call it Pacay, and commonly eat the white pulp of its pods. Its leaves have winged stalks, and are composed of three or four pairs of oval-oblong leaflets, which are smooth, and tapered towards both ends. Its pods are sometimes as much as two-feet long.

I. spectabilis is a large showy tree, called Guavo real in the Isthmus of Panama, where it is commonly cultivated on account of its eatable pods, as it also is in some parts of New Grenada. The leaves consist of two pairs of smooth and shining, egg-shaped, pointed leaflets, the upper pair being much the largest. The flowers are pure white, succeeded by numerous large pods, two or more feet long, and three inches broad, which, in consequence of their weight, are pendulous from the branches. The white pulp surrounding the seeds in the pods of this and other species of the genus, has a pleasant sweet flavour, and is much eaten by the inhabitants of Panama.

I. vera, a West Indian tree, common in Jamaica and Trinidad, has leaves with winged stalks, and four or five pairs of elliptical lance-shaped leaflets. Its pods are curved like a reaper's sickle, and measure about six inches long; the pulp contained in these is sweet, but like that of several other species, it possesses purgative properties.   [A. S.]

INGENHOUZIA. A name applied to a Mexican shrub, described as being like a *Gossypium*, and with yellow flowers, passing into red, and numerous stamens in one parcel. It is not perfectly known, but is evidently allied to the *Malvaceæ*. [M. T. M.]

INK-BERRY. An American name for *Prinos glaber*.

INNATE. Adhering to the apex of a thing, as the anther to the apex of a filament.

INNOVATIONS. A name given to the new branches of mosses, which are produced after the fructification has been perfected, or after the first complete growth where the plants remain barren. A difference of habit may arise from their suppression or peculiar growth. In *Bryum*, for example, the innovations are produced from the floral apex, but in *Leptobryum* none are produced. The little bud-like tufts which bear the male organs in some species of *Hypnum* and *Dicranum*, which are attached very slightly to the stem, must be distinguished from true innovations.   [M. J. B.]

INOCARPUS. This genus consists of but one species, a large tree, native of Asia and the islands of the tropics, having alternate entire subcordate leaves, and yellow flowers in axillary spikes. They have a tubular calyx, arched at the back, and bifid; five petals united to form a short tube; ten stamens in two rows, the upper attached to the mouth of the corolla tube and the lower to its base; and a one-celled ovary with a nearly sessile stigma. The fruit is a fibrous pod with one seed. The genus was for some time referred to the daphnaceous family, its petals being regarded as a calyx, but it is now known to belong to *Cæsalpinieæ*, a section of the leguminous family. The seeds of *I. edulis* are much prized by the natives of the Indian Archipelago, and in Machian they almost live upon them. They are, however, not palatable food, but when boiled or roasted in ashes are sweet. They are less agreeable than the chestnut, and are not suited to weak stomachs. [B. C.]

INOSCULATIO. The operation of grafting or budding.

INSECT FUNGI. Many animals are subject to attacks of fungi, but none more so than insects, whether in a perfect state or in the condition of caterpillar or chrysalis. Some of these fungi are very minute, and often of little interest except from the ravages they commit amongst bees, silkworms, &c.; but others, on the contrary, are large and sometimes brilliantly coloured, and attract notice from the proportion which they bear to the insect on which they grow. These belong to the genus *Cordiceps*, to which head we refer for particulars. Amongst them one of the most remarkable is the species which is so often brought home from New Zealand, where it is produced in abundance on the caterpillar of *Hepialus virescens*. The white mould which oozes out as it were between the abdominal wings in autumn, is in all probability a form of one of the curious productions which we shall notice under *Saprolegnia*.   [M. J. B.]

INSERTION. The manner in which one part is inserted into or adheres to, or originates from another.

INTEGER. Properly speaking, this means having no kind of marginal or other division; but sometimes it has been used to indicate not pinnatifid, and also nearly destitute of marginal division.

INTEGERRIMUS. Perfectly free from division of the margin or other part.

INTEGRA VAGINA. A sheathing petiole which forms a continuous tube, not slit on one side, as in sedges.

INTEGUMENTA FLORALIA. The calyx and corolla.

INTER. In composition = between: as *interfoliaceus*, placed between leaves.

INTERCELLULAR. Anything interposed between the cells or tubes of tissue.

INTERMEDIUS. Standing between two bodies in a different row, as petals when they alternate with sepals. Also half-way between one thing and another.

INTERNODE. The space which intervenes between two nodes.

INTERRUPTED. When any symmetrical arrangement is destroyed by local causes; a leaf is interruptedly pinnated when some of the pinnæ are much smaller than the others, or wholly wanting.

INTERVENIUM. The space of parenchyma between the veins.

INTEXINE. That coating of the pollen which is next the extine or outer crust, and above the intine or inner lining.

INTINE. The innermost lining of the shell of a pollen grain.

INTORTUS. Twisted upon itself.

INTRA. Placed within anything; as *intrafoliaceus*, placed within the axil of a leaf.

INTRARIUS. Turned inwards; that is to say, towards the centre of a flower

INTRAVALVULAR. Placed within valves, as the dissepiments of many crucifers.

INTRICATE. Entangled.

INTROCURVUS, INTROFLEXUS, INTROFLEXED. Curved inwards.

INTRORSE. Turned towards the axis to which it appertains; as an anther when its valves face the centre of a flower.

INTROVENIUM. Hidden-veined: when veins are so much buried in parenchyma that they are not visible on external inspection.

INTRUSUS. Pushed inwards; as when the base of a fruit is so concave as to seem as if pushed inwards by the peduncle.

INULA. A genus of composite plants, having the outer or ray florets strap-shaped and containing pistils only, while the central florets are tubular and contain both pistils and stamens; the anthers have two bristles at their base: the pappus consists of rather rough hairs, arranged in a single row; and the involucre consists of numerous overlapping scales, but the receptacle is devoid of scales. The species are numerous and occur throughout Europe and central Asia. *I. Helenium*, Elecampane, occurs spontaneously in this country, but having long been cultivated in herb gardens, it is considered that it may originally have been derived from such a source. It is a perennial plant with a stem from three to five feet high; large saw-toothed leaves tapering to a stalk, the upper ones smaller, and embracing the stem; and large heads of yellow flowers. The root has an aromatic camphor-like taste, due to the presence of a crystalline substance called helenin, allied in chemical constitution to creosote. It also contains a quantity of starchy material, called inulin, which differs from ordinary starch in being coloured yellow by iodine. Elecampane was formerly much used as an aromatic tonic, and as a stimulant of all the secreting organs, likewise in coughs, dyspepsia, &c. *I. Conyza*, a common hedge plant in some parts of England, grows to the height of two to three feet, and has rough leaves, and numerous small flower-heads disposed in a corymb. This plant, called Ploughman's Spikenard, has a somewhat aromatic odour. Its leaves are occasionally gathered in place of those of *Digitalis*, from which they may be distinguished by their roughness and their smell. [M. T. M.]

INUNCANS. Said of surfaces covered with little hooked hairs, as the leaves of some species of *Galium*.

INUNDATE. Flooded. Sometimes covered with water, sometimes dry.

INUS. A termination expressing the quality of resemblance, as *calycinus*, like a calyx in position, in colour, &c.; it also expresses augmentation, as *calycinus*, having a large calyx.

INVERTED. Having the apex in an opposite direction to that of some other thing; as many seeds.

INVERTENTIA FOLIA. Leaflets which in their sleep hang downwards, but touch by their upper surfaces.

INVOLUCEL, INVOLUCELLUM. A diminutive involucre; a secondary involucre usually not containing more than one or two flowers.

INVOLUCRAL. Of or belonging to an involucre.

INVOLUCRATE. Having an involucre.

INVOLUCRE, INVOLUCRUM. A ring or rings of bracts surrounding several flowers. Also the peridium, volva, or annulus of some fungals. Also the cup-formed external indusia of some ferns.

INVOLUCRARIA. A genus of *Cucurbitaceæ*, consisting chiefly of Indian species, nearly allied to *Trichosanthes*, but having the segments of the corolla entire, and the bracts of the racemes of male flowers large, leafy, concealing the flowers before their expansion. [M. T. M.]

INVOLUTE, INVOLUTIVE. When edges are rolled inwards on each side, as the leaf of the apple.

IOCHROMA. A genus of South American shrubs belonging to the *Solanaceæ*, deriving its name from the handsome violet or purple-coloured flowers. The calyx is tubular, somewhat distended, with five unequal teeth, and becomes larger as the fruit ripens. The corolla is tubular, much longer than the calyx, and conceals the stamens. The fruit is succulent, two-celled, many-seeded, and enclosed within the bladdery calyx. *I. tubulosum* and *I. lanceolatum* are handsome greenhouse shrubs. [M. T. M.]

IODINA. A genus of *Olacaceæ*, a South American shrub with rhomboid leathery leaves, spinous at the angles and apex, and subsessile flowers in axillary glomerules, having a five-cleft calyx, five petals on a fleshy disk, five stamens, and a two-celled ovary immersed in the disk. [J. T. S.]

IONE. A genus of epiphytal orchids from the Himalayas, numbering seven species. They are tufted plants, three to nine inches high, with pseudobulbs bearing a single coriaceous leaf, and a radical flower-scape ending in a spike of small white or violet flowers. The lip is narrow like the sepals, and there are four pollen-masses attached to two distinct glands. Dr. Lindley remarks that with the habit of *Bolbophyllum*, this genus unites the glands and pollen-masses of *Angræcum*. Its long membranous two-lipped calyx, dwarf petals, and large lip with fleshy axis usually extended into a dagger-shaped point, are very unlike anything belonging to the neighbouring genera. He also notes that it forms a transition from *Vandeæ* to *Malaxideæ*. [A. A. B.]

IONIDIUM. An extensive genus of *Violaceæ*, whose species are natives for the most part of subtropical America. Their flowers are characterised by the sepals not being extended at the base; by the five unequal petals, one of which is much larger than the rest; and by the detached stamens. The roots of some of the species contain emetin, and may be used, therefore, instead of ipecacuanha. What is called White Ipecacuanha consists of the roots of *I. Ipecacuanha*. Another species, famed in Peru for the cure of tubercular elephantiasis, is *I. microphyllum*, whose roots act powerfully as emetics and purgatives. The root of *I. suffruticosum*, an Indian plant, is likewise used medicinally in diseases of the urinary organs, and the leaves as external applications. [M. T. M.]

IONOPSIDIUM. A genus of *Cruciferæ*, containing extremely small Portuguese and Algerian annual plants, with scarcely any stem, numerous long-stalked roundish root leaves, and scape-like flower-stalks, each bearing a small white or purplish flower. The pouch is roundish, laterally compressed, slightly notched at the apex, with keeled wingless valves more turgid than is usual among the genera, in which the partition is in the narrowest diameter of the pouch, whence the plant used to be placed in *Cochlearia* though really allied to *Capsella*. [J. T. S.]

IONOPSIS. A small genus of elegant little epiphytal orchids of tropical America. They are stemless plants, having small pseudobulbs emitting wiry roots, a few lance-shaped leaves, and an erect slender flower-scape, ending in a panicle of numerous small pink or white flowers, resembling those of a violet in form—whence the generic name. The sepals and petals are small and connivent; the lip large, fan-shaped, two-lobed at the apex, and slightly spurred at the base; and there are two pollen-masses attached to the end of a linear caudicle with an oblong gland at the base. Their delicate flowers remain for a long time expanded without fading. [A. A. B.]

IPÉBRANCO. *Patagonula vulneraria.*

IPESAC. AMERICAN. *Gillenia stipulacea.* —, WILD. *Euphorbia Ipecacuanha.*

IPECACUANHA. The root of *Cephaëlis Ipecacuanha.* —, BASTARD. *Asclepias curassavica.* —, BLACK, or PERUVIAN. *Psychotria emetica.* —, FALSE BRAZILIAN. *Ionidium Ipecacuanha.* —, GUIANA. *Boerhaavia decumbens.* —, STRIATED. *Psychotria emetica.* —, UNDULATED. *Richardsonia scabra.* —, VENEZUELA. *Sarcostemma glaucum.* —, WHITE. *Ionidium Ipecacuanha*; also *Richardsonia scabra.* —, WILD. *Asclepias curassavica.*

IPECACUANHA DES ALLEMANDS. (Fr.) *Vincetoxicum officinale.*

IPE-TABACCO, or IPEUNA. Names given to certain hard-wooded species of *Bignonia*, in Brazil.

IPHIGENIA. A genus of *Liliaceæ* from India, with the habit of the Australian genus *Anguillaria*, from which it differs by its introrse anthers, and styles united at the base. They are glaucous herbs, with coated bulbs, erect leafy stems, and a three-flowered or racemose inflorescence; the perianth deciduous coloured with linear divisions spreading like a star, the filaments hairy, the style with three stigmas. [J. T. S.]

IPIE. *Bassia latifolia.*

IPO. A Malay name for the Upas poison.

IPOMÆA. A large genus of *Convolvulaceæ*, widely distributed over all warm climates, with a few species extending into North America, and into extratropical Africa and Australia. They are twining prostrate creeping or rarely low and erect

Ipomæa batatoides.

herbs, occasionally woody at the base, very rarely shrubby, with entire, lobed, or divided leaves, and generally large and showy flowers in the axils of the leaves, in small cymes, rarely solitary. The flowers have a calyx of five sepals; a campanulate or tubular corolla with a spreading entire or angular limb, rarely deeply lobed; five included stamens; a two or three-celled ovary with two ovules in each cell; and a slender style with a bilobed stigma, the lobes capitate.

Ipomœa is frequently cultivated as an ornamental plant because of its showy flowers, but it derives its chief importance from the medicinal properties which many of its species possess. These depend chiefly on an acrid juice which abounds in their roots, and which has a strongly purgative quality arising from the presence of a peculiar resin. Sometimes sugar and starch replace the resin, and a valuable edible root is obtained; this is remarkably the case in the allied genus *Batatas*, the root of one species of which is the sweet potato. Although the best jalap is obtained from *Exogonium purga*, yet many species of *Ipomœa* supply it, though of an inferior quality. *I. Turpethum*, a native of India and the islands of the Pacific Ocean, is employed by the natives as a common purgative, and although the resin is more diluted than in the true jalap, it is free from the nauseous taste and smell of that drug. The Mechameck of the North American Indians is *I. pandurata*. Its powdered root acts like rhubarb, and has also some reputation as a diuretic. The root of the South American *I. batatoides* has sufficient of the purgative resin to cause it to be employed. Scammony, it is said, can be obtained from *I. tuberosa*, the Spanish Arbour Vine of Jamaica. *I. sensitiva* is remarkable for the irritability of its corolla. [W. C.]

IPOMOPSIS. A subgenus of *Gilia*, comprising those species which have alternate divided leaves, flowers solitary or somewhat clustered, and a corolla tube very much longer than the calyx. See GILIA. [C. A. J.]

IRESINE. A genus of *Amaranthaceœ*, natives of tropical and subtropical America (a single species reaching as far north as Ohio), and also of Australia. They are herbs with opposite stalked leaves, and small scarious white flowers in lax panicles, or dense heads, or spikes. The flowers are often polygamous, or diœcious by abortion. The fruit is a globular indehiscent utricle. [J. T. S.]

IRIARTEA. A genus of palms, from which have recently been separated *Socratea*, *Iriartella*, *Catoblastus*, &c. The wax palm (*Ceroxylon*), which has been combined with it by some botanists, is here kept distinct. As now defined, *Iriartea* consists of five species, one of which is a native of Peru, and the others of the banks of the Amazon river. All of them are tall-growing plants, some of them attaining a height of sixty or eighty feet, or even higher, and they are frequently elevated above the conical mass of cylindrical roots, which gives them a most remarkable appearance. The stems are smooth, and marked with distant circular scars, generally almost cylindrical, but occasionally swollen or bulged out towards the top. They bear a

crown of large pinnate leaves, the lower part of the stalks of which form a cylindrical sheath round the top of the stem; the leaflets are somewhat trapezoid in form, and jagged on one side. The flower-spikes are pendulous from below the leaves, and have several spathes, the innermost of which completely encloses them while young, but eventually splits open; both sexes of flowers are borne on the same spike. The fruit is roundish or egg-shaped, and contains a single seed.

I. exorrhiza, the Pashiubá or Paxiubá palm of Brazil, is the tallest-growing species, and its cone of roots is sometimes so high that a man can stand in the centre, with the tall tree above his head. These aerial roots, being covered with little asperities, are commonly used by the Indians as graters, whilst the hard outer wood of the stem is employed for various portions of their houses, and likewise exported to the United States for making umbrella handles. [A. S.]

IRIARTELLA. A small South American palm, formerly called *Iriartea setigera*. It differs greatly in general appearance from the *Iriarteas*, which are all tall stout-growing palms, whilst this seldom grows higher than eighteen or twenty feet, and has a perfectly straight cylindrical trunk scarcely more than an inch thick. The flowers also differ in the males having a small rudimentary pistil in the centre of the fifteen stamens, whilst the females have no sterile stamens, containing only a three-celled ovary. The Indians on the Amazon and Rio Negro, where this palm grows in the underwood of the forests, use its slender stems for making their gravatánas, or blow-pipes, the weapon commonly employed by them in the pursuit of game, and through which they blow small poisoned arrows with unerring accuracy and to a considerable distance. These gravatánas are usually from eight to twelve feet long, and have a bore of about a quarter of an inch. The stems, being soft and spongy in the centre, are easily bored by pushing a rod of hard wood through them, but in order to have the bore perfectly smooth, the Indians prefer splitting them in halves and carefully working a groove in each half, afterwards neatly reuniting and binding them round with the smooth shining bark of a creeping plant. [A. S.]

IRIDACEÆ. (*Ensatæ*, *Irids.*) A natural order of monocotyledonous plants, belonging to Lindley's narcissal alliance of Endogens. Herbs with corms, rhizomes, or fibrous roots, and mostly with equitant leaves, and flowers in sheaths. Perianth six-parted, in two rows, sometimes irregular; stamens three, inserted at the base of the outer row of the perianth; anthers innate, opening on the back; style dividing into three petal-like portions, which bear the stigmas. Capsular fruit three-celled, three-valved, opening in a loculicidal manner; seeds with hard albumen. The plants are found both in warm and temperate regions; they abound at the Cape of Good

Hope. They have fragrant, stimulant, and acrid qualities. The stigmatic processes of *Crocus sativus* yield saffron; the rhizomes of *Iris florentina* have the odour of violets. Upwards of 500 species in some fifty genera are known. Examples: *Iris, Gladiolus, Crocus, Ixia.* [J. H. B.]

IRIDÆA. A genus of the rose-spored *Algæ*, belonging to the natural order *Cryptonemtaceæ*, distinguished by its flat frond, which is simple or loosely divided, bearing compound capsules, immersed in its substance. It is closely allied to *Gigartina*, and distinguished principally by the different position of the capsules, and the frond being less regularly cleft. *I. edulis*, which is easily known by its tough obovate dark-red frond, wedge-shaped at the base, is sometimes eaten like the common dulse, *Rhodomenia palmata*, and has been employed in the preparation of a dye, which is probably fugitive. The genus contains many species, most of which inhabit the Southern seas. [M. J. B.]

IRIDINE. (Fr.) *Vieusseuxia.*

IRIO. *Sisymbrium Irio.*

IRIS. A beautiful and extensive genus of perennial plants, giving its name to the order *Iridaceæ*. They are very common in gardens, and one or two rank amongst our native wild flowers. The greater part have fleshy rhizomes, and sword-shaped leaves of greater or less breadth, but some few are tufted plants, with fibrous roots, and a few others bulbous. The flowers are, in

Iris florentina.

many of the species, large and very showy, being of bright or well-contrasted colours. The perianth is six-parted, with a short tube, but of the six segments the three outer are reflexed, and very frequently bearded at the base, and the three inner erect and very frequently smaller than the outer; there are three stamens inserted at the base of the outer segments, and having the anthers turned outwards; and

a triquetrous style with three petaloid dilated stigmas, each opposite the stamens, keeled above, and hollow beneath, having a transverse fold towards the front. The capsule is three or six-angled, and three-celled, containing numerous seeds. The species are found chiefly in the south of Europe and north of Asia, a few extending to North America and North Africa. Orris root, which has the odour of violets, and so much used for perfumery powders, &c., is the rhizome of *I. florentina*, a species with large white flowers. The root possesses cathartic and emetic properties; it is also sometimes chewed by persons who have offensive breath. The common native species, *I. Pseud-acorus*, found by the margins of ponds and streams, possesses astringent properties, and it is said that it may be used as a substitute for galls in making ink, as well as for dyeing black. Another species, *I. versicolor*, has purgative rhizomes. As garden flowers, the species of *Iris* rank amongst the most ornamental of hardy perennials. [T. M.]

IRIS, PEACOCK. *Vieusseuxia.* — SCORPION. *Iris alata.* —. SNAKE'S-HEAD. *Hermodactylus tuberosus.*

IRIS. (Fr.) The Fleur-de-lis, the emblem of France. — D'ALLEMAGNE. *Iris germanica.* — DES MARAIS. *Iris Pseud-acorus.* — DES PRÉS. *Iris sibirica.* — DEUIL. *Iris susiana.* — GIGOT. *Iris fœtidissima.* — JAUNE. *Iris Pseud-acorus.* — NAINE. *Iris pumila.* — PLUMEUSE. — *Moræa virgata.* — TIGRÉE. *Moræa sinensis.*

IRIS-ROOT. The same as Orris-root.

IRONBARK-TREE. *Eucalyptus resinifera*, and *Sideroxylon.*

IRONHEADS. *Centaurea nigra.*

IRON-TREE. *Siderodendron.*

IRON-WEED. *Vernonia.*

IRONWOOD. *Sideroxylon*; also the timber of several species of *Diospyrus*, and of *Metrosideros vera.* — of Bourbon. *Cupania Sideroxylon.* — of Dutch East Indies. *Eusideroxylon Zuageri*; also *Namia vera, Intsia amboinensis, Cassia florida, Memecylon ferreum, Stadmannia Sideroxylon, Dodonæa Waitziana*, and *Sloëtia Sideroxylon.* — of Morocco. *Argania Sideroxylon.* — of New South Wales. *Argyrodendron trifoliatum.* — of Norfolk Island. *Notelæa longifolia*, and *Olea apetala.* —of North America. *Ostrya virginica*, and *Carpinus americana.* — of South Africa. *Olea undulata* and *capensis.* — of S. Sea Islands. *Casuarina equisetifolia.* — of Tasmania. *Notelæa ligustrina.* —, BASTARD. *Xanthoxylon Pterota.* —, BLACK. *Olea undulata.* —, JAMAICA. *Erythroxylon areolatum.* —, WHITE. *Vepris lanceolata.*

IRONWORT. *Sideritis*; also *Galeopsis Ladanum.* —, YELLOW. *Galeopsis villosa.*

IRREGULAR. Having the parts which

constitute one series of a flower dissimilar in size or form.

IRUPÉ. *Victoria regia.*

IRVINGIA. A genus of *Simarubaceæ*, allied to *Soulamea* and *Amaroria*, but differing in habit, in the large disk under the ovary, and in several other characters. It consists of tropical African trees, entirely glabrous, with alternate entire leaves convolute in the bud, and leaving prominent rings on the branches as they fall off. The flowers are small and yellow, in terminal or axillary panicles. The drupaceous fruits of two at least of the three species known are edible, and known under the name of Wild Mangos.

ISACANTHUS. A genus of *Acanthaceæ*, containing a single species from Africa. It is a branching shrub, with entire leaves, and white flowers in few-flowered terminal spikes. The calyx is five-parted, the corolla has a slender tube, and a limb consisting of a single unequally five-lobed lip, and there are four exserted stamens. [W. C.]

ISACHNE. A genus of grasses belonging to the tribe *Paniceæ*, now included by Steudel in *Panicum*. [D. M.]

ISANTHERA. A genus of *Cyrtandraceæ*, containing a single species a native of India. It is an herbaceous plant, with an erect stem, obovate-cuneiform acute leaves, and flowers in axillary clusters. The flowers are polygamous. The hermaphrodite ones have a five-cleft calyx, a rotate corolla, four or five stamens, and one-celled ovary. The female flowers want the corolla. This genus has the flowers of *Platystemma* conjoined to the habit of *Cyrtandra*. [W. C.]

ISANTHUS. A genus of labiates, having the calyx bell-shaped, with five equal lobes, enlarging as the fruit ripens; and the corolla slightly longer than the calyx, with five nearly equal lobes. The only species, *I. cœruleus*, is a small annual, covered with clammy hairs, the flowers minute, pale blue. It is a native of the southern parts of the United States, and is called False Pennyroyal. [G. D.]

ISARIA. An important genus of filamentous moulds, connecting them very closely with the lower club-shaped *Hymenomycetes*. The genus is divisible into two distinct groups, in one of which all the species grow upon insects, and principally upon *Hymenoptera*. It is, however, suspected that all of these are mere conditions of different species of *Cordiceps*. The species of the second group grow upon various vegetable substances, and a few of these must be considered as mere sporiferous forms of other fungi. Some good species, however, remain, which are known by their threads being compacted with a solid mass, which may be either simple or branched, the free tips of which bear the spores. The limits between some of these and *Pistillaria* are so indefinite, that it is not always possible to say posi-

tively to which genus a species should be referred. [M. J. B.]

ISARIEI. A natural order of filamentous moulds containing those genera in which the fertile threads are compacted, and have deciduous pulverulent spores at their free apices. It must be observed, however, that the order contains two sets of species which are connected on the one hand with *Mucedines*, and on the other hand with *Dematiei*, in which order the threads are more or less dark and carbonised. Little is known of exotic species. *Ceratium*, however, which, from its texture, would perhaps be better referred to *Hymenomycetes*, occurs in Ceylon, and we have one of the darker series in India. North America, as might be expected, has some in common with Europe, besides an admixture of distinct forms. [M. J. B.]

ISATIS. A genus of *Cruciferæ*, consisting of erect annual or biennial plants, natives of Southern Europe and Western Asia, one being found in China. They have undivided leaves, with a bluish bloom, the lower stalked, the upper clasping the stem; and the small yellow flowers are borne in long loose erect terminal panicles, and produce flat pendulous pods of an elliptical form, with a strong rib along each side.

I. tinctoria, the Dyer's Woad, is said to have been originally a native of Southeastern Europe, from whence it has spread by means of cultivation and become naturalised in most parts of Europe as far north as Sweden, and also in some parts of Asia. It is a biennial, growing from eighteen inches to three or four feet high, with a smooth straight stem, branched towards the top, the root-leaves stalked, inversely egg-shaped or oblong, and coarsely toothed, the upper ones narrow lance-shaped, with prominent auricles at the base. The pods are rather more than half an inch long, broad, and very blunt at the top, but tapering to the base.

Before the use of indigo became common among European dyers, the blue colouring matter called Woad, obtained from this plant, was an article of great importance, and the plant was extensively cultivated; but the introduction of indigo has almost entirely superseded it, and it is now only grown to a limited extent, and used chiefly by woollen dyers for mixing with indigo, in order to excite fermentation. It is generally prepared by grinding the leaves into a paste, which is then carefully fermented in heaps, and afterwards made into balls or bricks for sale. Small quantities of these balls are annually imported from the continent, amounting in 1859 to 200 cwt. The use of woad as a dye dates from very early times. Dioscorides, Pliny, and others, mention its use for dyeing wool; and Cæsar relates that the ancient Britons used it for staining their bodies—the word Britain being derived from the Celtic *brith* or *brit*, 'painted,' in reference to this custom.

I. indigotica is cultivated as a tinctorial

plant in the north of China, where it is called Tein-ching. It is a small half-shrubby plant, with a decumbent stem, bearing at its extremity several long drooping racemes of small yellow flowers, and smooth black fiddle-shaped pods about half an inch long. The lower leaves are rather fleshy, on long stalks, oval, lance-shaped, and pointed, with the edges slightly toothed, the upper ones very much

Isatis indigotica.

narrower and smaller. In the north of China, this plant takes the place of the indigo of the south, and its colouring matter is obtained by a process closely analogous to that employed in the preparation of indigo, but instead of being thoroughly inspissated, so as to form solid cakes, it is used by the Chinese dyers in a semi-liquid or pasty state. It is commonly employed for dyeing cotton cloth, to which it imparts a dark-blue colour.   [A. S.]

ISAUXIS. A genus of Indian trees, belonging to the *Dipterocarpaceæ*, and distinguished from *Vateria*, by the flowers being arranged in short axillary panicles, the segments of the calyx increasing in size as the fruit ripens, by the petals which are sickle-shaped and larger than the sepals; by the fifteen stamens, which have oblong anthers; and by the short style and club-shaped stigma.   [M. T. M.]

ISCHÆMUM. A genus of grasses belonging to the tribe *Andropogoneæ*, now included in *Andropogon*.   [D. M.]

ISCHARUM. *Biarum.*

ISCHNIA. A genus of *Pedaliaceæ*, containing a single species, a native of Mexico. It is an erect herb, with opposite petiolate ovate acute leaves, and pale violet flowers on long opposite and axillary peduncles, arranged in loose racemes. The calyx is five-toothed and persistent; the corolla tube slightly curved, and its spreading limb obscurely five-cleft. The nut-like fruit is indehiscent, and furnished with four long divaricate horns. This genus has an herbaceous flower, but the fruit is that of *Pedalium.*

ISERTIA. A genus of Central American shrubs or small trees, belonging to the *Cinchonaceæ*. The flowers have a long tubular corolla, the limb of which is divided into six woolly segments; the anthers are six, sessile, concealed within the corolla; the ovary has six compartments, each containing several ovules. The species have handsome scarlet flowers.   [M. T. M.]

ISIDIUM. A corolla-like elevation of the thallus of a lichen, bearing a globule at its end.

ISKEEL. *Scilla indica.*

ISMENE. A small genus of pancratiform *Amaryllidaceæ*, consisting of bulbous plants of South America, mostly Peruvian. They have lanceolate leaves sheathing at the base, and tall scapes bearing at top an umbel of few or many flowers, the perianth of which has an elongated three-cornered tube curved in the upper part, and broader in the throat, a six-parted limb with narrow spreading segments, and a funnel-shaped six-lobed lacerately-toothed coronet, each lobe deeply emarginate and having an antheriferous filament projected inwards from the sinus. The ovary is three-celled with two ovules in each cell, and supporting a filiform declinate style with a globose stigma; and the seeds are few, green, and bulb-like. *I. Amancaes* is the Peruvian Daffodil, and the name of Sea Daffodil is given to *I. calathina*, both very beautiful plants.   [T. M.]

ISNARDIA. A genus of aquatic or marsh herbs belonging to the order *Onagraceæ*, of which the characters are: stamens four; calyx four-parted persistent; capsule not tapering to a point; seeds many, destitute of any feathery or hairy appendage. *I. palustris* is remarkable only for having been found growing in the south of England about the middle of the seventeenth century, and for having been subsequently lost sight of until it was rediscovered in 1827. It is frequent in the continent of Europe, in North America, and the temperate parts of Asia.   [C. A. J.]

ISOBRIOUS, ISODYNAMOUS. Growing with equal force; two of the names of the dicotyledonous embryo.

ISOCARPHA. A genus of tropical American plants of the composite family, nearly related to *Ageratum*, but differing in the achenes being destitute of pappus, and having interspersed among them on the conical receptacle numerous chaffy scales like those composing the involucre. They are branching weeds, with lance-shaped or linear leaves, and solitary or corymbose flower-heads.   [A. A. B.]

ISOCHILUS. A few epiphytal orchids of tropical America, usually with slender erect stems, twelve to eighteen inches long, furnished with broadly linear two-ranked leaves, and terminating in a very short bracted spike of small dingy purple or white flowers. The relationship of the genus is with *Epidendrum*, but the lip is free, not connate with the column. The sepals and petals are free, nearly equal, and connivent; the column semiterete with two or three horns, and the anthers four-celled, with four pollen-masses, each with a recurved caudicle. [A. A. B.]

ISOËTES. A genus of *Lycopodiaceæ*, with subulate fronds, a globose rhizome, the apex of which is sunk, so that the bases of the older leaves are higher than those of the younger. The axillary capsules are incorporated with the base of the leaves, producing either antheridia in the shape of small oblong spores, or larger four-sided spores, which germinate by cell-division of the apex in which archegonia are formed, from whence ultimately the new plant is produced. Most of the species are strictly aquatic, but *I. Hystrix*,* which has lately been found in the Channel Islands, grows in sandy places. The rhizome is often rough, with dark horny processes which are supposed to be abortive leaves, to which the name of phyllopods has been given. The leaves are studded with stomates, and the rhizome and roots contain annular vessels like those of *Equisetum*. The genus occurs in all the four quarters of the globe. [M. J. B.]

ISOËTOPSIS. The generic name of an annual plant of the composite family found in South and West Australia. It gets this name from the great outward resemblance it bears to our common *Isoëtes*. It has numerous small sessile flower-heads, arising from the crown of the plant, and surrounded by a few grassy leaves, whence the specific name *graminifolia*. [A. A. B.]

ISOGYRUS. Forming a complete spire.

ISOLEPIS. A genus of cyperaceous plants, belonging to the tribe *Scirpeæ*. Distinguished by the inflorescence being in spikes, two or three together or solitary; scales imbricated on all sides, all floriferous, or more rarely the exterior scales empty; stamens three, rarely fewer; styles three. Steudel describes two hundred species, mostly natives of the warm temperate zones of both hemispheres. The British representatives are only two species, namely *I. setaceus*, and *I. Savii*, which with most British authors simply form a section of *Scirpus*. [D. M.]

ISOLOMA. *Lindsæa.*

ISOMERIS. The name of a Californian shrub, forming a genus of *Capparidaceæ*. The flowers are yellow, with four equal sessile petals; stamens six, upon a fleshy receptacle which is prolonged into a narrow appendage; ovary stalked; capsule large, terminated by the short style. The plant has a disagreeable odour. [M. T. M.]

* The sculpture of the small spores or antheridia is not, however, precisely the same, but more like that of *I. Duriæi*, in the only specimen we have seen. It may possibly, therefore, be a species distinct from either.

ISOMEROUS. Equal in number; an isomerous flower is one all whose parts are equal to each other in number.

ISONANDRA. The inspissated milky juice of one of the species of this genus of *Sapotaceæ* constitutes the well-known Gutta Percha, and ten other species are known. They are all inhabitants of Southern India, Ceylon, Malaya, and the adjacent islands, forming lofty forest trees. The leaves are entire and leathery. The flowers small and inconspicuous, produced in little clusters, either in the angles of the leaves or at the ends of the young branches. They have a four or six-parted calyx and corolla enclosing double as many stamens, which are all fertile. The ovary has four or six cells, and eventually becomes a fleshy fruit containing one or two oily seeds.

I. Gutta, the species which yields Gutta Percha, is a large forest tree growing sixty or seventy feet high, with a trunk two or three feet in diameter. Its leaves are inversely egg-shaped and entire, of a pale green on the upper side, but covered beneath with short reddish-brown shining down. The flowers grow in clusters of three or more in the axils of the leaves.

The Gutta Percha (or Gutta Taban) tree, and its now famous product, was first brought into notice about twenty years ago by Dr. Montgomery at Singapore,

Isonandra Gutta.

where the tree was then common, but the Malays having adopted the extravagant method of felling the trees in order to obtain the milky juice, it is now quite extinct in that island, though it fortunately exists in Borneo, Sumatra, and other eastern islands. The average quantity yielded by each tree is 20 lbs.; and as 18,593 cwt. were imported into this country in 1859, it follows that 104,120 trees would have to be sacrificed for the supply of the English market alone. The raw Gutta Percha arrives in this country in lumps weighing from five to six pounds, which are cut into slices, softened in hot water, then torn into shreds by rapidly revolving cylinders set with sharp teeth, and thrown into cold water, when the impurities sink and the Gutta Percha floats on the surface. The shreds are then transferred to hot water, and are made into solid masses which are afterwards kneaded by machinery, in order to expel the extraneous moisture.

One of the first uses to which Gutta Percha was applied in this country was for the soles of boots, its imperviousness to water and great durability recommending it for such purposes. From its property of becoming plastic by heat, it is valuable for modelling and moulding, and it is used for making a variety of useful articles, such as door-handles, pipes, plates, buckets, ear-trumpets, &c.; but its most important use is owing to its being a non-conductor of electricity, which, combined with its indestructibility in sea-water, renders it applicable for coating the wires employed for submarine telegraphs. Alkalies, vegetable acids, and weak mineral acids, also, do not act injuriously upon it, but strong sulphuric, nitric, and hydrochloric acids corrode it, and turpentine, benzole, chloroform, &c., completely dissolve it.　　[A. S.]

ISONEMA. A genus of dogbanes, having the corolla salver-shaped with a five-parted border, its tube without scales; the filaments of the anthers simple at the apex; and the base of the ovary without scales. *I. Smeathmanni* is the only species; it is a small hairy shrub, native of tropical Africa, with opposite leaves, and terminal clusters of flowers.　　[G. D.]

ISOPAPPUS. A genus of composite plants, found in Texas. The two known species are hirsute annual herbs, with numerous lance-shaped leaves, and an abundance of small yellow-rayed flower-heads, supported on slender stalks, and disposed in loose much-branched panicles. From *Stenotus*, and other allies, they differ in the narrow scales of the involucre, and in the pappus being composed of a single series of capillary nearly equal bristles: whence the name.　　[A. A. B.]

ISOPHOROUS. Transformable into something else. Thus, *Actinia* is an isophorous form of *Dendrobium*, *Paxtonia* of *Spathoglottis*, and, according to Morren, *Anguloa* and *Lycaste* of *Maxillaria*.

ISOPHYSIS. A genus of *Melanthaceæ*, also called *Hewardia*. It consists of a single Tasmanian species, *I. tasmanica*, with dry rigid, distichous, equitant, narrow, sword-shaped leaves, and purple flowers on bracteated scapes, taller than the leaves. The perianth is six-leaved, spreading in a star-like form, the segments acuminate; there are three stamens, with short broadly subulate filaments; and a pyramidate, bluntly three-cornered, three-celled, many-seeded ovary, with a short style, and three thick recurved stigmas. The spathes which terminate the scapes are one or two-flowered.　　[T. M.]

ISOPLEXIS. A genus of *Scrophulariaceæ*,

consisting of two species, formerly included under *Digitalis*, but distinguished by Lindley on account of their shrubby habit, and their corolla, of which the upper lobes are reflexed. Both the *I. Sceptrum*, from Madeira, and *I. canariensis*, from the Canary Islands, have been in cultivation in our greenhouses; they are handsome plants, with terminal racemes of showy yellow or orange-coloured flowers.

ISOPOGON. An extensive genus of *Proteaceæ*, forming large shrubs or small trees, natives of the extra-tropical parts of Australia, principally in the south-west portions of it. The foliage is harsh and rigid, the leaves being of various forms, simple or much divided. They are filiform and sharp-pointed in *I. petrophiloides*, *I. teretifolius*. &c.; lanceolate and leathery in texture in *I. attenuatus*, *I. longifolius*, &c.; wedge-shaped and deeply toothed in *I. tripartitus*, *I. Baxteri*, &c.; and broadly ovate in *I. latifolius*. The flowers grow in globose, generally terminal heads, and have a regularly four-cleft calyx bearing on each of its concave segments a nearly sessile anther, a filiform style with a cylindrical or spindle-shaped stigma. The nut contains a single wingless seed.　　[R. H.]

ISOPTERYX. A genus of *Begoniaceæ*, and the type of one of the sections of that order, according to Klotzsch. Its characters are: petals of staminate flowers, four, ciliately toothed at the apex; anther oval, short; filaments very long, not united; branches of the styles bipartitely multifid, and papillose, with slender somewhat terete lobes; fruit top-shaped, of a somewhat cartilaginous and papery consistence, three-horned above, attenuated at the base, shortly lengthened out at the apex. The horns are short cuspidate erect incurved. The one species referred hither is a native of New Grenada.　　[J. H. B.]

ISOPYRUM. A genus of *Ranunculaceæ*, with the habit of *Thalictrum*, but really more nearly allied to *Helleborus*. They are natives of Europe and temperate Asia, and are slender herbs, with the leaves ternately divided, and with the leaflets again ternate or three-lobed. The flowers are stalked, without involucres, white, with five rather large petaloid sepals, and five or ten minute petals, tubular at the base, two-lipped; stamens ten or more; ovary of two to twenty carpels, which become follicles, containing several seeds each. *I. thalictroides* is not uncommon in central and southern Europe. [J. T. S.]

ISOS. In Greek compounds = equal. Placed before the name of an organ, it indicates that it is equal in number to that of some other which is understood: thus, *isostemonous* is said of plants the stamens of which are equal in number to the petals.

ISOTOMA. A genus of lobeliaceous herbs, distinguished principally by the salver-shaped corolla, the segments of which are spreading and nearly equal.

I. longiflora, a native of the West Indies, is a most venomous plant, producing dangerous cathartic symptoms. It proves fatal to horses that eat it. Others of the species are natives of Australia.　　[M. T. M.]

ISOTROPIS. The generic name of a few erect or decumbent leguminous herbs, found in South-west Australia. They mostly have slender rush-like stems six inches to a foot high, with alternate spathulate leaves about an inch long, usually bilobed at the apex; and solitary and long-stalked or racemed pea-flowers, the standard yellow with purple lines, and the keel and wings purple. The flowers are much like those of *Chorozema*, so often seen in greenhouses, and have a deeply four-cleft calyx, and orbicular bilobed standard, free stamens, and an oblong membranaceous pod.　　[A. A. B.]

ISOTYPUS. A genus of South American two-lipped composites. The present name supersedes CALOSERIS; which see.　-

ISPRUK. An Indian powder made from a species of *Delphinium*.

ISTHMIA. One of the finest genera of *Diatomaceæ*, distinguished by its trapezoid or rhomboid articulations, which are compressed and cellular, marked with a transverse zone, composed of smaller cells, and supported at one corner by a short stem. We have two native species which form most interesting objects for the microscope, and are very instructive as exhibiting, most distinctly, the peculiar mode in which cell-division takes place in these algæ. The new frustules are either attached alternately as in *Diatoma*, or united to each other by means of a very short blunt stem, springing from one corner and fixed to different points of the older frustules.　　[M. J. B.]

ITAKA WOOD. A cabinet wood produced from *Machærium Schomburgkii*.

ITÉA *virginica*, the only representative of this genus of *Escalloniaceæ*, is a North American shrub, with clusters of white flowers, which open in summer. The calyx is bell-shaped; petals five, lance-shaped; stamens five, attached with the petals to the calyx; ovary with two compartments; fruit capsular, compressed. This shrub is frequently cultivated in shrubberies in this country, and derives its name from the Greek name for the willow, which it resembles in its mode of growth. [M. T. M.]

ITOUBOU. *Ionidium Ituba.*

IVA. The generic name of a few rank-growing annual or biennial weeds of the composite family, found in marshy or maritime places in North America. The stems have nettle or willow-like leaves, opposite below, and alternate above; and the greenish-white flower-heads, somewhat like those of *Artemisia*, are arranged in racemes, or placed singly in the axils of the upper leaves or bracts. The florets are all tubular, inconspicuous.　　[A. A. B.]

IVETTE. (Fr.) *Ajuga Chamæpitys.* —MUSQUÉE. *Ajuga Iva.*

IVRAIE. (Fr.) *Lolium temulentum.*

IVORY, VEGETABLE. The hard albumen of the nuts of *Phytelephas macrocarpa.*

IVY. *Hedera Helix.* —, AMERICAN. *Ampelopsis hederacea.* —, GERMAN. A garden name for *Senecio scikanoides.* —, GROUND. *Nepeta Glechoma.* —, POISON. *Rhus Toxicodendron.*

IVYWORTS. Lindley's name for the *Araliaceæ.*

IXERBA. A genus of *Brexiaceæ*, represented by a single species, *I. brexioides*, which is an elegant evergreen tree of New Zealand, growing to the height of twenty feet, and having lance-shaped leaves, and terminal panicles of few large white flowers. The leaves are glossy, leathery, and toothed; and the flowers consist of five calyx leaves, five petals, five stamens, and a lobed disk surrounding a five-celled ovary. The name *Ixerba* is an anagram of *Brexia.*　　[A. A. B.]

IXIA. A genus of beautiful Cape iridaceous bulb-tuberous plants, with narrow ensate leaves, and slender simple or slightly branched stems bearing spikes of large showy flowers, various in colour, and exceedingly attractive when fully expanded by sunshine. These flowers have a salver-shaped perianth, with a slender tube, and six-parted spreading equal limb, three stamens inserted in the throat, with filiform filaments and versatile anthers, and a three-celled ovary with numerous ovules, terminating in a filiform style, and three narrow linear conduplicate recurved stigmas. *I. viridiflora*, which has large sea-green flowers with black markings at the base of the segments, is a very singular-looking as well as beautiful plant. There are a great many species, and some garden varieties.　　[T. M.]

IXIANTHES *retzioides* is an erect South African shrub, with lanceolate whorled leaves, and very viscid flowers, growing singly or two or three together on axillary peduncles. It forms a genus of *Scrophulariaceæ* of the tribe *Cheloneæ*, distinguished by a two-lipped calyx, by the corolla which has a short broad tube, a short erect upper lip, and a longer three-lobed spreading lower lip, and by the stamens, of which two only bear anthers.

IXIANTHUS. A genus of the gentian family, represented by a perennial plant, native of Teneriffe, with sticky leaves and yellow flowers. The calyx is provided with exterior triangular bracts; the corolla is wheel-shaped, with a four-cleft limb; there are four stamens; and the capsule is partly two-celled, two-valved. [M. T. M.]

IXIOLÆNA. A few annual Australian herbs compose this genus, which belongs to the same group of the composite family as the everlastings. They have glutinous smooth or woolly stems, six inches to a foot high, furnished with lance-shaped or linear leaves, and terminating in one or many white or yellow flower-heads about half an inch across. These contain numerous tubular and perfect florets, enclosed in an involucre of many narrow scales which are slightly bent out at the apex so as to resemble ray florets. From their allies they differ in the achenes being seated on a frilled receptacle, and crowned with a pappus of numerous long rough hairs, as well as in the nature of the involucre. [A. A. B.]

IXIOLIRION. The name of a few pretty bulbous amaryllidaceous plants of Asia Minor and Northern Asia. They have tunicated bulbs, and simple erect stems with

Ixiolirion montana.

leafy bracts, smaller upwards, and bearing a few flowers near the top. The leaves are narrow linear, channelled, glaucous, and sheathing at the base : and the flowers are erect long-stalked, blue or violet, with a six-parted funnel-shaped or subrotate perianth having narrow lanceolate divisions, six erect stamens, and a somewhat top-shaped ovary, with a filiform style and three narrow channelled stigmas. [T. M.]

IXIONANTHES. A genus of the flax family, comprising five species which are found in the Malay peninsula and islands, and one in Hong Kong. They are smooth trees or bushes with obovate or elliptical leaves; and numerous small generally green flowers disposed in axillary forked corymbs usually longer than the leaves. The flowers have a calyx of five to six rounded sepals, a like number of rounded petals, ten to twenty long stamens, and an ovary which, when ripe, is a somewhat woody five-celled capsule. [A. A. B.]

IXODIA. A genus of *Compositæ*, comprising two erect glutinous herbs of South-east Australia, with slightly-winged stems furnished with linear hyssop-like leaves, and numerous white flower-heads, disposed in corymbs at the ends of the twigs. They have much the appearance of *Achillea*, with this difference, that what gives the rayed appearance to the heads here is the

white tips of the involucral scales, while in milfoils it is an outer row of strap-shaped florets. The achenes being destitute of pappus, each enveloped by a chaffy scale, distinguishes the genus from its near allies. [A. A. B.]

IXORA. A genus of Indian and tropical African shrubs, with corymbs of handsome flowers of a scarlet pink or white colour, and frequently having an agreeable fragrance. The corolla is salver-shaped with a long slender tube, into the throat of which the four or five anthers are inserted by means of very short filaments. The fruit is succulent, crowned by the calyx, containing two one-seeded stones.

Several of these elegant flowering shrubs are grown in stoves in this country. *I. coccinea* is used in India by the natives for various medicinal purposes. The name of the genus is supposed to be derived from the Hindoo deity, Iswarra, to whom the beautiful scarlet flowers of these plants are offered in the temples. [M. T. M.]

JABOROSA. A genus of South American herbs, belonging to the *Solanaceæ*, and differing from *Himeranthus*, principally in the funnel-shaped corolla, and the very short filaments of the stamens. [M. T. M.]

JABÚTI. The edible fruit of *Psidium albidum.*

JACARANDA. A considerable genus of *Bignoniaceæ*, natives of tropical America, consisting of trees with opposite abruptly bipinnate leaves, the pinnæ themselves imparipinnate. They have bluish flowers in terminal (rarely lateral) panicles. The calyx is five-toothed or five-parted; the corolla tubular at the base, dilated at the throat with an unequally five-lobed limb; there are four included didynamous stamens with a rudimentary fifth; and the capsule is roundish, compressed, two-celled, with many flattened winged seeds. Decandolle has divided the genus into two sections ; *Monolobos*, characterised by having a single-celled anther and abruptly pinnate leaves ; and *Dilobos*, with perfect two-celled anthers and imparipinnate leaves. Some species, especially *J. procera*, have the character of being useful in syphilitic affections. [W. O.]

JACA, or JACK-TREE. *Artocarpus integrifolia.*

JACÉE. (Fr.) *Lychnis dioica.* — DES PRÉS. *Centaurea Jacea.* — DU MONTAGNE. *Centaurea montana.*

JACINTH. Another name for the Hyacinth.

JACINTHE. (Fr.) *Hyacinthus.* — DE SIENNE. *Muscari monstrosum.* — DES JARDINIERS. — *Scilla italica.* — DU PÉROU. *Scilla peruviana.* — ÉTOILÉE. *Scilla amœna.* — MONSTRUEUSE. *Muscari monstrosum.* — MUSQUÉE. *Muscari moschatum.* PANICULÉE. *Muscari monstrosum.* PETITE. *Hyacinthus non scriptus.*

JACKAL'S KOST. *Hydnora africana.*

JACK-BY-THE-HEDGE. *Sisymbrium Alliaria,* or *Alliaria officinalis.*

JACK-IN-A-BOX. *Hernandia sonora.*

JACK-OF-THE-BUTTERY. *Sedum acre.*

JACKIA. The name of a tree of Southern India, forming a genus of *Cinchonaceœ.* The flowers have an irregular calyx, divided into three segments; the corolla is funnel-shaped, with a slender tube and five-lobed limb; the anthers are sessile on the throat of the corolla; the style is very long, hairy in the middle; and the fruit is capsular, one-seeded, and surmounted by the three large sepals. [M. T. M.]

JACKSONIA. A genus of Australian undershrubs, belonging to that group of *Leguminosœ* in which the ten stamens are free, and the pods two-seeded; and distinguished from *Daviesia* and other allies by the deeply and equally five-parted calyx, the absence of a carunculus or swollen excrescence to the seeds, and the want of stipules. Of upwards of thirty species a goodly proportion are leafless and have flattened stems which perform the functions of leaves; others have rush-like stems with juniper-like leaves; and some have the aspect of furze or broom bushes, with leaves like them, and branches often terminating in spiny points. The flowers are small and yellow. *J. scoparia,* the Dogwood of New South Wales, grows twelve or fifteen feet high, with a diameter of four to six inches, and furnishes a tolerably hard wood which takes a good polish, but is not applied to any particular purpose; when burning it emits an offensive smell, whence its local name. [A. A. B.]

JACKWOOD. A wood obtained from *Artocarpus integrifolia.*

JACOBÉE. {Fr.} *Senecio Jacobœa.*

JACOBINIA. A genus of *Acanthaceœ,* containing seven species, natives of Central America. They are erect shrubs with subcoriaceous leaves, and large flowers with a large herbaceous deeply five-cleft calyx, a ringent corolla with an erect oblong linear bidentate upper lip, and a three-cleft lower one, two stamens, a capitate two-lobed stigma, and a two-celled capsule. [W. C.]

JACOB'S LADDER. *Polemonium cœruleum.*

JACQUEMONTIA. A small genus of *Convolvulaceœ* of tropical America, with a single species from Asia. They are mostly twining herbs, sometimes woody at the base, with entire or slightly lobed leaves, and rather small flowers in axillary pedunculate cymes, the corolla usually broadly campanulate, and angular or broadly five-lobed. The ovary is two-celled with two ovules in each cell. This genus, separated from *Convolvulus,* is intermediate between that genus and *Ipomœa* in the shape of the oblong two-lobed stigma. [W. C.]

JACQUINIA. A genus of handsome evergreen bushes, of the *Myrsine* family, peculiar to America, where they range from Florida to Brazil, and are usually found near the coast. They have alternate entire glossy leaves, and terminal racemes or umbels of vermilion flowers, having a five-parted calyx, a bell-shaped corolla with a flat border, five stamens with five alternating scales, and a one-celled ovary. The fruits are bright yellow, containing from one to three seeds imbedded in a mucilaginous placenta, which feature chiefly serves to distinguish the genus from *Clavija* and *Theophrasta. J. armillaris* is known to French settlers in the West Indies as Bracelet-wood, it being their custom to string its shining brown and yellow seeds into bracelets. The genus bears the name of N. I. de Jacquin, an eminent botanist, once professor at Leyden. [A. A. B.]

JAGERY or JAGGERY. A coarse kind of sugar made from the juice of the Cocoanut, and other palms.

JAGONG. The Malay name for Maize.

JALAP. A well-known drug, of which the best kind is obtained from *Exogonium Purga,* but other species are also collected under the same name. —, INDIAN. *Ipomœa Turpethum.* —, MALE. *Ipomœa batatoides.*

JALAP-PLANT. *Mirabilis Jalapa.*

JALOUSIE. (Fr.) *Dianthus barbatus;* also *Amaranthus tricolor.*

JAMAICA-PEPPER. One of the names given to Allspice.

JAMALGHOTA. The Hindoo name for Croton oil and seed.

JAMBIRA. A Sanscrit name for the Lemon, *Citrus Limonum.*

JAMBOLAN-TREE. *Calyptranthes Jambolana.*

JAMBOLIER. (Fr.) *Cyminosma.*

JAMBON DES JARDINIERS. (Fr.) *Œnothera biennis.*

Jambosa malaccensis.

JAMBOSA. A group of myrtaceous

plants, belonging to *Eugenia*, from which it is sometimes separated on account of the throat of the calyx being drawn out beyond the ovary, and by the latter being many-celled. They are Indian trees, with large edible fruit, the most esteemed being the Malay Apple, *J. malaccensis*, and the Rose Apple, *J. vulgaris*, also called *Eugenia Jambos*.   [T. M.]

JAMBOSIER. (Fr.) *Eugenia* or *Jambosa*.

JAMESIA. A genus of *Hydrangeaceæ*, from the vicinity of the Rocky Mountains, consisting of a shrub with opposite serrated leaves, and small few-flowered axillary and terminal cymes, the flowers small, with a downy bell-shaped five-cleft calyx, and five petals.   [J. T. S.]

JAMESTOWN-WEED. An American name for *Datura*.

JAMROSADE. The Rose Apple, *Eugenia Jambos* or *Jambosa vulgaris*.

JAN. (Fr.) *Ulex europæus*.

JANAPA. An Indian name for Sunn Hemp, *Crotalaria juncea*.

JANCA-TREE. *Amyris toxifera*.

JANGI. The Indian *Vallisneria alternifolia*.

JANIPHA. A name sometimes applied to a genus of euphorbiaceous plants, otherwise called *Manihot*. *Janipha Manihot*, and *Jatropha Manihot*, are other names for *Manihot utilissima*, the Mandioc plant, which yields cassava and tapioca.

JANOOL. An Indian wood, *Lagerstræmia macrocarpa*.

JANSONIA. A genus of *Leguminosæ*, peculiar to Western Australia, and represented by a single species, *J. formosa*, an erect branching bush of myrtle-like habit, with opposite smooth ovate-oblong leaves, and nodding heads of (apparently) scarlet pea-flowers, terminating the lateral twigs. The heads are surrounded by four ovate bracts, clothed externally with silky hairs. The plant agrees with *Brachysema*, in the great length of the keeled petal, compared with the very short standard which is here almost wanting, but it differs in the capitate inflorescence, and the great length of the lower lip of the calyx with respect to the upper. On account of the small standard the plant has also been named *Cryptosema*.   [A. A. B.]

JANTONG. The Malay name for a Plantain leaf.

JANUSIA. A genus of Brazilian *Malpighiaceæ*, mostly climbing shrubs, with flowers of two kinds (whence the name), as in *Gaudichaudia*, from which they differ principally in the fruit, consisting of three or fewer carpels, which have a dorsal wing thickened along one edge.   [M. T. M.]

JAPAN LACQUER. A black hard varnish, obtained from *Stagmaria verniciflua*

JAQUIER. (Fr.) *Artocarpus*.

JARAT. (Fr.) *Lathyrus Cicera*.

JARBÃO. *Stachytarpha jamaicensis*.

JAREE. An Indian name for the Jujube.

JAROOL. *Lagerstræmia reginæ*.

JAROSSE. (Fr.) *Lathyrus Cicera*. — D'AUVERGNE. *Ervum monanthos*.

JARRAH. A durable West Australian wood, like mahogany, the produce of *Eucalyptus rostrata*.

JASIONE. A genus of dwarf herbaceous plants of the order *Campanulaceæ*, bearing their flowers in terminal heads, with much of the habit of the compound flowers, and yet more of the scabious family. The most obvious character of the flowers is that the anthers are united by their bases so as to form a ring, and contain blue or purplish pollen. The species inhabit mountainous and sandy places in various parts of Europe and the north of Africa. *J. montana*, Sheep's Scabious, the only British species, bears numerous tufted root leaves, which are oblong, and hairy simple stems which are almost leafless, each surmounted by a head of bright blue flowers, all enclosed by a whorl of bracts. It is abundant in many heathy and moorland districts of Britain, and appears to have derived its name from its resemblance to a scabious, and from its abundance in sheep-walks.   [O. A. J.]

JASMIN. (Fr.) *Jasminum officinale*. — BLANC. *Jasminum officinale*. — D'AFRIQUE. *Lycium afrum*. — D'AMÉRIQUE. *Quamoclit coccinea*. — D'ARABIE. *Jasminum Sambac*. — D'ESPAGNE. *Jasminum grandiflorum*. — D'ITALIE. *Jasminum humile*. — DE VIRGINIE. *Bignonia radicans*. — DU CAP. *Gardenia florida*. — JONQUILLE. *Jasminum odoratissimum*. — ODORANT DE LA CAROLINE. *Gelsemium nitidum*. — ROUGE DE L'INDE. *Quamoclit coccinea*. — TROMPETTE. *Bignonia radicans*.

JASMINACEÆ. (*Jasmineæ*, *Bolivarieæ*, *Jasminworts*.) A natural order of corollifloral dicotyledons, belonging to Lindley's echial alliance of perigynous Exogens. Shrubs, often twining, with opposite or alternate, usually compound leaves; calyx and corolla regular, with five to eight divisions; stamens two, included within the salver-shaped corolla; ovary two-celled. Fruit a double berry or capsule; seeds with little or no albumen, and a straight embryo. Found chiefly in the tropical parts of India. The fragrant oil of jasmin is procured from several species of *Jasminum*. There are half a dozen genera, and above 100 species. Examples: *Jasminum*, *Nyctanthes*.   [J. H. B.]

JASMINANTHES. A genus of *Asclepiadaceæ*, containing a single species from the Indian Archipelago. It is a twining shrub, with opposite oblong acuminate leaves, and yellowish flowers growing in few or many-flowered interpetiolar cymes.

The calyx is five-parted; the corolla is salver-shaped, with a long tube distended below, and a spreading five-cleft limb; and the staminal crown is wanting.　[W. C.]

JASMINE. *Jasminum.* —, AMERICAN. *Quamoclit coccinea.* —, CAPE. *Gardenia florida.* —, CAROLINA. *Gelsemium nitidum.* —, GROUND. *Passerina Stelleri.* —, WHITE. *Jasminum officinale.* —, WILD, of Jamaica. A species of *Paretta.*

JASMINOÏDE. (Fr.) *Lycium barbarum.*

JASMINUM. A considerable genus of *Jasminaceæ*, dispersed over the warmer regions of the Old World, and containing one or two South American species. They are shrubs or climbers, with pinnate leaves or apparently simple, consisting of one leaflet — when the petiole is articulate. The white or yellow flowers are in axillary or terminal panicles, and have a tubular five or eight-cleft calyx, a cylindrical corolla tube and spreading limb, two included stamens, and a two-lobed ovary. Jasmines are of little economic value, but they are prized as ornamental shrubs, on account of the fragrance of their flowers. The most universally cultivated is *J. officinale*, common throughout the centre and south of Europe, where it is thoroughly acclimatised, though certainly not native.

Some species are used medicinally. The bitter leaves of *J. floribundum* have a very powerful action, and are employed in Abyssinia against the tape-worm. The bitter root of *J. angustifolium*, ground small, and mixed with the powdered root of *Acorus Calamus*, is considered in India as a valuable external application for ringworm. The fragrant essential oil of Jasmin is obtained from *J. officinale* and *grandiflorum*; and an inferior oil is produced from the flowers of other species, as *J. Sambac*, &c.　[W. C.]

JASMINWORTS. Lindley's name for the *Jasminaceæ*.

JASONIA. A small genus of erect, branching, perennial, often glutinous composite herbs, confined to the Mediterranean region, nearly allied to *Pulicaria*, and technically distinguished from it by the nature of the pappus, which consists of a double series of rough hairs, the outer row like the inner but shorter, not crown-like as in *Pulicaria*. The stems have linear or lance-shaped leaves; and small yellow flower-heads, solitary at the ends of the twigs,　[A. A. B.]

JATAI. A Brazilian name for *Hymenæa Courbaril.*

JATAMANSI. An Indian name for Spikenard, *Nardostachys Jatamansi.*

JATEE. The common Indian name for *Jasminum grandiflorum.*

JATEORHIZA. This genus of *Menispermaceæ*, so called on account of the root of one of the species which is used in medicine, is closely allied to *Cocculus*, but the flowers have concave petals, enclosing the six stamens, which have thick filaments,

ending in a large fleshy connective, separating the lobes of the anthers, these opening by transverse slits. In the female flowers are three ovaries, densely hairy externally, and placed on a short stalk; and a three-parted stigma, with reflected segments. The fruit is clothed with long glandular hairs.

J. palmata, or *Cocculus palmatus*, furnishes the root known as Calumba-root, so called from a false impression that it was supplied from Ceylon. The plant is now

Jateorhiza palmata.

known to be indigenous in the forests of Mozambique, and the roots to be imported from thence. This drug is much esteemed as a bitter tonic, where a stimulant or astringent effect is not required; it is hence frequently employed in cases of indigestion, dependent upon languor and want of tone in the stomach, and attended by nausea and flatulence. It has likewise the effect of alleviating vomiting. [M. T. M.]

JATIPATRI. An Eastern name for Mace.

JATIPHALI. A Sanscrit name for the Nutmeg.

JATROPHA. A genus of *Euphorbiaceæ*, consisting of woody plants, with alternate

Jatropha podagrica.

stipulate leaves, and flowers in cymes, the central flower female, and the outer ones male. The males have a calyx with five divisions, five petals, and ten stamens, five long and five short, with the anthers united together around a central disk; the females have ten barren stamens, and a three-celled ovary.

J. glauca, an East Indian plant, known also under the name of *J. glandulifera*, furnishes an oil which is obtained by crushing the seeds, and which is used as an external application in rheumatism, &c. *J. podagrica* is a curious gouty-stemmed plant. See CURCAS, CNIDOSCOLUS, MANIHOT. [M. T. M.]

JAU, JO. Indian names for Barley.

JAUBERTIA. An Arabian spiny shrub, with very small leaves, forming a genus of *Cinchonaceæ*. The segments of the calyx and corolla are hairy, the latter organ is funnel-shaped, with the stamens inserted into its throat; the ovary has two one-seeded compartments; and the style is terminated by two spoon-shaped stigmatic divisions. [M. T. M.]

JAUNDICE BERRY. *Berberis vulgaris.*

JAURSA. An Affghan name for *Alhagi Maurorum.*

JAWA-WUT. A Javanese name for *Panicum miliaceum.*

JAWATRI. An Indian name for Mace.

JEANNARETTIA. A genus of *Pandaneæ*, figured in the *Voyage de la Bonite*, but not yet described.

JEANNETTE. (Fr.) *Narcissus poeticus.*

JEDWAR. *Curcuma Zedoaria.*

JEEAPOOTRA. An Indian name for the nuts of *Putranjiva Roxburghii.*

JEERA. An Indian name for Cumin.

JEFFERSONIA. A genus of *Berberidaceæ* with the habit of *Sanguinaria*, a small glabrous perennial North American herb, with a horizontal rhizome, a simple naked one-flowered scape, and long-stalked root-leaves divided into two half-ovate leaflets. The flowers are large white, with four petaloid sepals, eight oblong flat narrow petals, and eight stamens. The capsule is pear shaped and one-celled. *J. diphylla*, the only species, occurs from New York to the mountains of the Southern States; it is called Rheumatism-root in some places. [J. T. S.]

JELLY-PLANT of Australia. *Eucheuma speciosum.*

JENEQUEN. A Mexican name for the *Agave*, from the fibres of which cordage, sacks, &c., are made.

JENKINSIA. A genus of polypodiaceous ferns, allied to the *Acrosticheæ* through *Pæcilopteris*, of which it is by some regarded as an abnormal form. The sori form linear submarginal patches, with an areolate instead of universal attachment, which is the principal feature to separate them from the *Acrosticheæ*. The receptacle consists usually of the three outer series of arcuate venules with three excurrent veinlets, and are hence compound, from which artificial characters it has been referred to the *Platycerieæ*, though having no natural affinity with *Platycerium* itself. The plant is a native of India, with much the general character of *Pæcilopteris*. [T. M.]

Also a genus of *Olacaceæ*, now referred to *Miquelia*, consisting of climbing or twining shrubs, with alternate leaves, and diœcious five-petaled flowers collected into heads. The fruit is a drupe. There are two or three species, natives of tropical Asia. [J. H. B.]

JERCATCHREE. An Indian name for Nux-vomica seeds.

JERDONIA. A genus of *Cyrtandraceæ*, containing a single species, a native of India, a small herbaceous stemless plant, with petiolate ovate leaves, and erect terminal scapes, terminating in a few-flowered umbel of funnel-shaped four-lobed flowers, with four stamens, all fertile, and an ovary surrounded at the base by a cup-shaped disk. [W. C.]

JERMAEE. An Indian name for *Cocculus indicus.*

JEROOGOO. *Caryota urens.*

JÉROSE. (Fr.) *Anastatica.*

JERSEY LIVELONG. *Gnaphalium luteo-album.*

JERUSALEM CROSS. *Lychnis chalcedonica.*

JERUSALEM STAR. *Tragopogon porrifolius.*

JESSAMINE. A popular corruption of Jasmine.

JESSENIA. A solitary palm, inhabiting moist woods in New Grenada, and attaining a height of sixty feet, with a trunk a foot in diameter, bearing a spreading crown of pinnate leaves, each of which measures twenty-four feet in length, and has numerous opposite leaflets, about four feet long by six inches broad, whitish underneath. The flower-spikes hang down from amongst the leaves, and are enclosed within two spathes, the outer one being a foot and a half, and the inner five feet long, bursting open along the back at the time of flowering. The flowers are arranged in threes (two males and one female) upon the lower, and in pairs (both males) upon the upper, part of the spikes. The fruit is about the size of a pigeon's egg, violet-coloured, having a thin, oily, eatable flesh, surrounding a fibrous husk which encloses a single horny seed. It is named *Jessenia polycarpa*, on account of the large number of fruits produced by a single flower-spike. [A. S.]

JETEE. An Indian name for *Marsdenia tenacissima*, whose fibres are made into bowstrings.

JETERUS. A yellowness of the green parts. Vegetable jaundice.

JETTIMUD. An Indian name for Liquorice root.

JEWBUSH. *Pedilanthus tithymaloides.*

JEWEL-WEED. An American name for *Impatiens.*

JEW'S-EAR. The popular name of *Hirneola* (or *Exidia*) *Auricula Judæ*, a tough but gelatinous fungus, belonging to the natural order *Tremellini.* The plant is cup-shaped, velvety without and wrinkled within, and more or less rufous. It was formerly in reputation as an ingredient in gargles, but its virtues probably rest on no better foundation than a certain resemblance which the hymenium bears to the fauces. It is still to be met with in the shops of the herbalists. It grows principally on elder, but occasionally on elm. It is sometimes called the Jew's Ear *Peziza*, but the whole structure is totally different from that of that genus.　　　[M. J. B.]

JEWUL, JINGUN. Indian names for the gum-resin of the bark of *Odina Wodier.*

JIM CROW'S NOSE. A West Indian name for *Phyllocoryne.*

JIPIJAPA. A South American name for *Carludovica palmata.*

JIQUILITE. The native name for the Indigo plant in Central America.

JIRA. The Indian name for Cumin.

JITO. A Brazilian purgative, supposed to be a species of *Guarea.*

JOAN SILVER-PIN. *Papaver Rhœas.*

JOAR, JOWARREE, JONDLA. Indian names for *Sorghum vulgare.*

JOB'S TEARS. *Coix Lachryma.*

JOCASTE. A genus of *Liliaceæ* from India, founded on *Smilacina purpurea.* It has a horizontal rhizome, a simple leafy stem, scattered leaves, and a terminal raceme of violet-purple flowers, with the perianth leaves elliptical united at the base, six stamens with awl-shaped filaments, and a three-celled ovary.　　　[J. T. S.]

JOE-PYE WEED. An American name for *Eupatorium purpureum.*

JOHANNIS-BROD. A German name for the pod of the Carob tree.

JOHNSONIA. A genus of *Liliaceæ*, allied to *Aphyllanthes*, founded on a South Australian plant, with fibrous roots, two-ranked linear leaves, and a simple scape terminating in an oblong nodding spike, with imbricated coloured bracts, the lower ones small and sterile, the rest one-flowered. The flowers are small sessile, with a six-parted connivent perianth, three stamens, and a membranous capsule.　[J. T. S.]

JOINTED. Falling in pieces at the joints, or separating readily there, or furnished with a distinct joint. Also applied to bodies having the appearance of being jointed, as the stem and leaves of *Juncus articulatus.*

JOINTWEED. An American name for *Polygonum articulatum.*

JOLI-BOIS. (Fr.) *Daphne Mezereum.*

JONC. (Fr.) *Juncus.* — À BALAIS, *Phragmites communis.* — DES CHAISIERS, *Scirpus lacustris.* — DES JARDINIERS, *Juncus glaucus.* — DES TONNELIERS, *Scirpus lacustris.* — ÉTALÉ, *Juncus effusus.* — FLEURI, *Butomus umbellatus.* —, MARIN, *Ulex europæus.* — ODORANT, *Andropogon Schœnanthus.*

JONCINELLE. (Fr.) *Eriocaulon.*

JONCIOLE. (Fr.) *Aphyllanthes.*

JONESIA. The generic name of a few pinnated-leaved trees of the leguminous family, found in the Malayan peninsula and the adjacent islands. They are large shrubs or trees of twenty to forty feet in height, with the habit and leaves of *Brownea*, to which they are nearly allied, but they differ from them and others in the flowers being destitute of petals. The glossy leaves, a foot or more long, are made up of three to six pairs of oblong or lance-shaped leaflets, and the bright scarlet flowers are in terminal rounded clusters, having much superficial resemblance to those of the scarlet *Ixora.* Each flower consists of a tubular calyx supported by two rounded bracts, and having a four-parted petal-like border, and six to eight long protruding stamens. The ripe pod is cimiter-shaped. The Ushoka of the Bengalese, *J. Asoca*, is very commonly planted throughout India, and is also cultivated in the Mauritius for the beauty of its flowers and foliage. Some Japanese species have flower clusters six to eight inches across. The genus bears the name of Sir William Jones, the eminent lawyer and scholar. [A. A. B.]

JONNA. An Indian name for grain.

JONQUIL. *Narcissus Jonquilla.* —, QUEEN ANNE'S. *Narcissus pusillus plenus.*

JONQUILLE. (Fr.) *Narcissus Jonquilla.*

JORDANIA. A genus of *Caryophyllaceæ*, consisting of herbs from Asia Minor, with the habit of *Queria*, or of the aggregate-flowered *Arenariæ.* The leaves are setaceous, united at the base; the flowers small, in dense cymes, with squarrose bracts, a tubular calyx of five united sepals with two bracts at the base, five petals, two styles, and four-valved capsules. [J. T. S.]

JOSEPHIA *lanceolata*, and *latifolia*, are the names given to two epiphytal vandeous orchids of Malabar and Ceylon. They are stemless herbs, with a tuft of stalked, lance-shaped, coriaceous leaves, four to six inches in length, and slender scapes bearing panicles of minute flowers of a whitish colour, tinged with pink. The flowers are said to be renewed annually on the old scapes. The anther has four parallel club-shaped pollen-masses, attached to a dilated shield-like gland. Named after Dr. Joseph D. Hooker, a well-known English botanist.　　　[A. A. B.]

JOSEPHINIA. A genus of *Pedaliaceæ*,

containing a single species from New Holland and the East Indian Archipelago. It is an erect or diffuse herb, with sub-opposite petiolate elliptical or lanceolate leaves, and reddish, shortly-stalked, solitary, axillary flowers. The calyx is unequally five-parted and persistent; the corolla has a short tube, a large campanulate throat, and a spreading five-lobed limb; there are four didynamous stamens, with a rudimentary fifth; and the nut-like four to eight-celled fruit is covered with numerous simple spines. [W. C.]

JOSEPH'S OAT. An American name for *Amaranthus tricolor*.

JOSEPH'S-FLOWER. *Tragopogon pratensis*.

JOTTE. (Fr.) *Sinapis arvensis*.

JOUBARBE. (Fr.) *Sempervivum*. DES TOITS. *Sempervivum tectorum*.

JOUTAY. *Outea guianensis*.

JOVELLANA. *Calceolaria*.

JOVE'S-BEARD. *Hydnum Barba Jovis*; also *Anthyllis Barba Jovis*.

JOVE'S-FRUIT. *Lindera melissæfolia*.

JOWAR, JOAR. Indian names for *Sorghum vulgare*.

JUANULLOA. A Peruvian shrub, with pendulous racemes of red flowers, constituting a genus of *Atropaceæ (Solanaceæ)*, and distinguished by its distended coloured calyx, and its tubular corolla contracted at the throat, concealing the five stamens. The fruit is succulent, many-seeded, enclosed within the inflated calyx. *J. parasitica* is in cultivation. [M. T. M.]

JUBA. A loose panicle, such as is often found in grasses.

JUBÆA. The Coquito Palm of Chili, *J. spectabilis*, is the sole species of this genus of palms. It is very abundant in central Chili, between the latitudes of 33° and 35°, and is one of the most southern of American palms, existing only in a cultivated state in warmer latitudes. It has a tall straight trunk, bearing a crown of large pinnate leaves, and branching spikes of dark yellow distinct male and female flowers, enclosed in a double spathe. The fruit is roundish or egg-shaped, and has a thick fibrous husk, enclosing a hard one-seeded nut which has three small holes or pores at the bottom.

In Chili, a sweet syrup, called Miel de Palma, or Palm-honey, is prepared by boiling the sap of this tree to the consistency of treacle, and it forms a considerable article of trade, being much esteemed for domestic use as sugar. The sap is obtained by the very wasteful method of felling the trees, and cutting off the crown of leaves, when it immediately begins to flow, and continues for several months until the tree is exhausted, providing a thin slice is shaved off the top every morning, each tree yielding about ninety gallons. The nuts are used by the Chilian confectioners in the preparation of sweetmeats, and by the boys as marbles. A quantity of them were brought to this country a few years ago, and sold under the name of Little Coker-nuts; they had a pleasant nutty taste. The leaves are used for thatching, and the trunks, being soft inside, and extremely hard towards the outside, are hollowed out, and converted into water-pipes, &c. [A. S.]

JUBELINA. A climbing shrub of Guiana, forming a genus of *Malpighiaceæ*. The flowers have a glandular calyx, ten stamens all fertile, and partly-united ovaries. The dorsal wing of the fruit hardly exceeds the lateral ones in size. [M. T. M.]

JUDAS-TREE. *Cercis*.

JUDIEGA. Inferior Spanish olives, used for making oil.

JUEPHUL. An Indian name for the Nutmeg.

JUGA. The ridges on the fruit of umbellifers.

JUGEOLINE. (Fr.) *Sesamum brasiliense*.

JUGLANDACEÆ. (*Juglands*.) An order of monochlamydeous dicotyledonous plants, belonging to Lindley's quernal alliance of diclinous Exogens. Trees with alternate pinnate stipulate leaves, and unisexual flowers. Male flowers in catkins; perianth two to three or six-parted, with a scaly bract; stamens three or more. Female flowers in terminal clusters, or in loose racemes, with distinct or united bracts; perianth adherent, three to five-parted; ovary two to four-celled at the base, one-celled at the apex; ovule solitary, orthotropal; styles one or two. Fruit drupaceous, with a stony and often two-valved endocarp; seed exalbuminous, two to four-lobed at the base. Chiefly natives of North America. *Juglans regia* is the common walnut. *Carya alba* yields the American hickory nut. There are five genera, and about thirty species. [J. H. B.]

JUGLANS. The typical genus of *Juglandaceæ*, composed of the Common Walnut, and two or three other species, all of which form noble trees, and are natives of the temperate regions of Asia and North America. They have deciduous pinnate leaves, and bear flowers of separate sexes upon the same tree, and appearing in early spring before the leaves. The male flowers have a calyx of five or six scales, surrounding from eighteen to thirty-six stamens; whilst the calyx of the females closely envelopes the ovary, which bears two or three fleshy stigmas. The fruit has a fleshy husk, which does not split into regular divisions when ripe, but bursts irregularly, allowing the escape of the hard-shelled two-valved nut.

J. regia, the common Walnut tree, serves various useful purposes. The wood, particularly that of old trees, is valued by cabinet-makers on account of its beautiful veining and dark colour; and in consequence of its strength, lightness, and elasticity, it is extensively employed for gunstocks. In Circassia, sugar is made from the sap, in the same way that the Canadians prepare that from the sugar-maple. The leaves are used medicinally in domestic practice; and an infusion of them is recommended as a vehicle for the administration of cod-liver oil, in order to overcome its nauseous taste. The husk of the fruit yields a dark brown dye; and the seeds a fine oil, which is suitable either for salad oil, or as a drying oil for painters. [A. S.]

It was said that in the golden age, when men lived upon acorns, the gods lived upon Walnuts, and hence the name of *Juglans*, *Jovis glans*, or Jupiter's nuts. The Romans called the walnut *Nux persica*, *Nux regia*, *Nux euboea*, *Jovis glans*, *Djuglans*, *Juglans*. Greek authors mention it under the names of *Carya*, *Carya persica*, and *Carya basilike*, or Royal Nut. We are not aware that the common English name of Walnut has been satisfactorily explained. On the contrary, we think an erroneous derivation has been given. Walnut, they say, is from Gaul-nut, presuming at the same time that the tree had been introduced from France into this country. But our ancestors, in their ordinary language, and that of the common people, did not use the classic name of Gaul in their designations of the things introduced from France in comparatively modern times. Walnut is doubtless of German derivation. In that language we find it is sometimes written *Watnuss*, sometimes *Wälschenuss*; the latter appears to have been the original. *Wälsch* simply means foreign; hence, Wälschenuss, a foreign nut, properly applied to the walnut, as regarded Germany, as well as the rest of the continent of Europe. In Dutch it is called *Walnoot*, and its English, Danish, and Swedish names are modifications of this and of the original German term.

According to Dr. Royle (*Illustrations of the Botany, etc. of the Himalayan Mountains*), *J. regia* extends from Greece and Asia Minor, over Lebanon and Persia, probably all along the Hindoo Koosh to the Himalayas. It is abundant in Kashmir, and is found in Sirmore, Kumaon, and Nepal. The walnuts imported into the plains of India are chiefly from Kashmir. Dr. Hooker states that in the Sikkim Himalaya, the walnut inhabits the mountain slopes at 4,000 to 7,000 feet elevation. Professor Targioni says that it is a native of the mountains of Asia from the Caucasus almost to China. According to Pliny, it was introduced into Italy from Persia, and this must have been at an early date, for it is mentioned as existing in Italy by Varro, who was born B.C. 116. There is no certain account of the time it was brought into this country. Some say 1562, 300 years ago; but Gerard, writing only about thirty years later, mentions the walnut as being very common in the fields near common highways, and in orchards, and that being the case, its introduction in all probability had taken place at a much earlier period.

The nut, well known to every one, is covered with a green fleshy bark, which is very bitter, like the leaves. The tree grows to the height of forty or sixty feet, with a large spreading top, and thick massive stem. One accurately measured by Professor du Breuil, in Normandy, was upwards of twenty-three feet in circumference; and in some parts of France there are walnut trees 300 years old, with stems of much greater thickness. In the southern parts of England, the trees grow vigorously and bear abundantly, when not injured by late frosts in spring.

The timber of the walnut is light, a cubic foot, when dry, weighing about forty-seven pounds. Formerly, it was in much request for cabinet work, but since the introduction of mahogany it is less esteemed for that purpose. It is still, however, preferred to all other woods for gun-stocks, being light, yet tough and strong, and, with this desirable combination, it takes a good polish. The fruit is used for pickling in a green state, whilst the shell is still tender and can be easily pierced with a pin. The fruit becomes mature in the end of September, or in October; then, to bring it down, the trees are threshed with poles, and many of the shoots are consequently broken; but an opinion has long been entertained, that this has the effect of making the trees more productive. It is, in fact, a rude mode of pruning.

Some varieties of the walnut are hard, and others tender-shelled. One of the latter is called the Titmouse Walnut (*Noyer mésange*), because the shell is so thin that birds, and especially the titmouse, can break it, and eat the kernel. Another variety, called the double walnut (*Noyer à bijoux*), is large, of a square form, and when the shell is polished and hinged, it is fitted up so as to contain such presents as a pair of gloves, trinkets, &c. A variety called the Highflyer Walnut is considered the best English variety. In many parts, large quantities of oil are extracted from the fruit; indeed the walnut furnishes one-third of the oil made in France, and when well purified it is little inferior to olive oil; whilst, for some purposes in the arts, it is superior. Altogether, the Walnut is a tree of great importance—for its fruit as an edible product, for its oil, and for its timber. Trees of choice quality of wood have been sold for 600*l.* each. Its plantation, therefore, should not be neglected, but not too near dwellings, as some persons are affected by the powerful aroma of its foliage. [R. T.]

JUGUM. A pair of leaflets: thus, *unijugus* is one pair; *bijugus* two pairs, &c.

JUJUBE. *Zizyphus vulgaris*, and *Z. Jujuba.*

JUJUBIER. (Fr.) *Zizyphus.*

JULIANA. A genus consisting of two trees, one from Mexico, the other from Peru, which, as far as can be judged from the specimens known, appears to belong to the *Juglandaceæ*. The leaves are pinnate, the flowers diœcious; the males in short loose racemes very much like those of an oak; the females two or three together, imbedded in the summit of a broad flat peduncle having the appearance of a samara. The name of *Juliania* was also originally given by Llave to a Mexican shrub, which afterwards proved to be the *Choisya* of Kunth.

JULIENNE. (Fr.) *Hesperis.* — DE MAHON. *Malcolmia maritima.* — DES JARDINS. *Hesperis matronalis.* — JAUNE. *Barbarea vulgaris.*

JULLALYA. An Indian name for hard wheat.

JULOCROTON. A genus of spurgeworts, numbering about ten species, peculiar to tropical America, and ranging from Mexico to Buenos Ayres. They are branching undershrubs, having all their parts more or less clothed with white or rusty-coloured starry hairs, such as those seen in *Verbascum*. The alternate long-stalked leaves have ovate or heart-shaped blades; and the small green flowers are disposed in axillary or terminal bracted spikes, the lower flowers on which are fertile, the upper sterile. From *Croton* they differ in having irregular fertile flowers. [A. A. B.]

JULUS. The same as Amentum.

JULY-FLOWER. *Prosopis juliflora.* Also sometimes applied to the Stock Gilliflower.

JUNCTURE. A joint or articulation; the place where a body spontaneously separates into two parts.

JUNCACEÆ. (*Junci, Kingiaceæ, Xerotideæ, Rushes.*) A natural order of petaloid monocotyledonous plants, belonging to Lindley's juncal alliance of Endogens. Herbs with fasciculate or fibrous roots, hollow or flat and grooved leaves, and glumaceous (sometimes petaloid) flowers in clusters, cymes, or heads. Perianth dry, greenish or brownish, six-parted; stamens six or three, perigynous; anthers introrse; ovary one to three-celled; ovules one to three, or many in each cell; style one; stigmas often three. Fruit a three-valved loculicidal capsule, or indehiscent and one-seeded; seeds with a thin testa, which often becomes gelatinous when moistened. Natives chiefly of temperate or cold regions. The leaves are used for mats and the bottoms of chairs; the central cellular tissue for wicks of candles. There are upwards of 200 species distributed in about eighteen genera, of which *Juncus, Luzula,* and *Narthecium* are examples. [J. H. B.]

JUNCAGINACEÆ. (*Potamogetoneæ, Arrow-grasses.*) A natural order of petaloid monocotyledonous plants, belonging to Lindley's alismal alliance of Endogens. Marsh plants, with narrow radical leaves, and hermaphrodite flowers in spikes or racemes. Perianth greenish; stamens six; anthers introrse; carpels three to six, united or distinct; ovules one or two, erect. Fruit dry, one to two-seeded; albumen none; embryo straight, with a lateral cleft. Natives of temperate or cold regions. *Triglochin* and *Aponogeton* are examples of the few genera. [J. H. B.]

JUNCUS. The Rush, a very extensive and almost universally distributed genus of *Juncaceæ*, with a peculiar rigid habit, and small greenish or brown flowers, arranged in heads or panicles. The flowers have two bracts and a six-leaved perianth resembling in texture the glumes of *Cyperaceæ*; six (rarely three) stamens; and a three-celled capsule, with numerous seeds. The soft pith of the stems of several species is used to form candle-wicks, and the stems themselves are made into mats. These plants are generally found in bogs or wet places, especially in sandy soil, and the great majority of the species occur in the temperate and arctic zones. Of these twenty are included in the British flora. Of those with the inflorescence apparently lateral from the lowest bract resembling a prolongation of the stem, and having many leaf-like barren stems, *J. acutus, effusus,* and *glaucus* are examples; while of those with the inflorescence evidently terminal and without barren stems, *J. obtusiflorus, acutiflorus, bufonius,* and *squarrosus,* furnish illustrations. [J. T. S.]

JUNE-BERRY. An American name for *Amelanchier.*

JUNERA. An Indian name for *Sorghum vulgare.*

JUNGERMANNIACEÆ. The principal division of the liverworts (*Hepaticæ*), distinguished by the solitary capsules which, for the most part, split into a definite number of valves, and are filled with a mass of spiral elaters and spores. A few have a horizontal frond without any distinct leaves, but the greater part have distinct leaves, which assume the most grotesque forms, and are often folded or furnished below with a curious lobe. The leaves are arranged on two separate plans, the upper edge either resting upon the hinder edge of the one which succeeds it, in which case they are called incubous, or placed beneath it, when they are styled succubous. The leaves are mostly two-ranked, and there are frequently stipules on the under-side of the stem. As in mosses, the base of the fruit is often surrounded with leaves of a different form from those on the stem, besides which there are one or more membranes immediately surrounding the peduncle. The elaters which accompany the spores are distinct spiral vessels, and the outer cells of the capsules often contain rings, while the walls of succeeding cells are studded with deep broad pits, like those in punctate tissue. The spores germinate like those of mosses, producing a mass of threads from which the plants grow. The archegonia, which are sometimes solitary, are produced upon the stems, and the young plant is developed exactly as in mosses.

This large group is divisible into two natural sections of very unequal size, the one of which contains those genera which have a one or two-valved capsule, and in part of these it is threaded like a columella; the other comprises the multitudes of species in which the capsule opens with four equal valves. These again are divided into frondose and foliose sub-orders, while the foliose are arranged in two sets, according as the leaves are incubous or succubous. Very rarely the capsule opens irregularly as in *Petalophyllum Ralfsii*, and as rarely more than one capsule is developed within the same calyx, as in *Jungermannia emarginata*.

Jungermanniaceæ are found in all parts of the world, and are quite as abundant in the south as in the northern hemisphere. None of them seem to be of any economical value. One or two incubous species are found in amber.   [M. J. B.]

JUNGERMANNIA. Almost all the *Jungermanniaceæ* were originally referred to this genus, which is now, however, restricted to such succubous species as have a free terminal perianth, plicato-angular above, and cleft. It is the only one of its peculiar group which has its maximum in Europe, neighbouring genera, which contain many of the finest species, resembling small film-ferns, occurring in New Zealand, where they luxuriate more perhaps than in any other country.   [M. J. B.]

JUNGIA. A genus of erect or climbing perennial herbs, belonging to the *Nassauviæ*, a tribe of *Compositæ*, and differing from its allies in the chaffy receptacle of the flower-heads, the uniserial feathery or rough pappus, and the simple-lobed leaves. The ten known species are all South American. They have stalked five or seven-lobed leaves, usually clothed underneath with dense white or rusty down, and the twigs terminate in panicles or cymes of small white flower-heads of numerous perfect two-lipped florets.   [A. A. B.]

JUNGLE-BENDY. *Tetrameles*.

JUNGLE-NAIL. *Acacia tomentosa*.

JUNIPER. *Juniperus*; also applied in Nova Scotia to the Hackmatack Tamarack, or American Larch, *Abies pendula*.

JUNIPERUS. A genus of dicotyledons belonging to the *Gymnospermæ*, and placed in the order *Coniferæ*. The characters of the genus are:—Male flowers in catkins; anthers four to seven, one-celled, inserted on the lower edge or the scales. Female flowers few, in a small catkin, erect; scales of the catkin imbricate, lower ones barren; ovules three, surrounded by a three-cleft baccate involucre. The species have subulate leaves; and the fruit is berry-like, although in reality a reduced fleshy cone. There are forty or fifty known species. *J. communis* is the common Juniper; *J. Sabina*, the Savin; *J. bermudiana*, Pencil Cedar; *J. virginiana*, Red Cedar. The Juniper is the badge of the Murrays. One of the species is shown at Plate 11 b.   [J. H. B.]

JUNO'S TEARS. *Verbena officinalis*.

JUPITER'S BEARD. *Anthyllis Barba Jovis*; also *Sempervivum tectorum*.

JURINEA. A genus of perennial herbs belonging to the thistle group of the *Compositæ*, numbering about forty species, found chiefly in south Europe and Asia Minor, extending north to Siberia and east to Persia. A goodly number are neat little stemless plants, with a rosette of pinnatifid or entire hoary leaves, lying close on the ground, and surrounding a sessile thistle-like flower-head, consisting of many purple florets. Others differ from these in having the flower-heads borne on long naked stalks; and a few are branching plants, with stem as well as root leaves, which are either pinnatifid with linear divisions, or oblong or lance-shaped; while the flowers are numerous, disposed in corymbs. From *Serratula*, and other allies, this genus differs in the four-sided, somewhat top-shaped achenes being crowned with a pappus of unequal rough hairs, which arises from within the minute cup-shaped and elevated border, and falls off in one piece, thus having the appearance of a painter's brush.   [A. A. B.]

JURUMU. A Brazilian variety of Squash.

JUSQUIAME. (Fr.) *Hyoscyamus niger*.

JUSSIÆA. An extensive genus of *Onagraceæ*, consisting of herbs or more rarely shrubs, growing in marshes or ponds throughout the tropics, a few species reaching to sub-tropical regions. They have alternate leaves, and axillary yellow or rarely white, sessile or very shortly stalked flowers, with a persistent four-parted (rarely five to six-parted) calyx tube, as many petals, and twice as many stamens. Some of the species are astringent, as *J. villosa* from India, and *J. Caparossa* and *scabra* from Brazil, where also occurs *J. pilosa* which yields a yellow dye. *J. decurrens* reaches north to Virginia. [J. T. S.]

JUSTICIA. A genus of *Acanthaceæ*, occurring in tropical and sub-tropical regions, chiefly in India and Southern Africa. They are herbs or shrubs with red flowers in terminal spikes, furnished with large herbaceous bracts, or opposite and solitary flowers with small subulate bracteoles. The small calyx consists of five sepals; the corolla has a long tube and is two-lipped, the upper lip being concave and entire or notched, and the lower three-lobed, convex, and veined or rugose in the centre; there are two stamens, and two ovules in each cell of the ovary; while the capsule is laterally compressed below the seed-bearing part.   [W. C.]

JUTE. The fibre of *Corchorus capsularis* and *C. olitorius*.

JUVANEE. An Indian name for *Ptychotis Ajowan*.

JUVIA. The Brazil Nut; *Bertholletia excelsa*.

JUWANSA. The Camel's Thorn, *Alhagi Maurorum*.

JUXTAPOSITION. The manner in which organs are placed with respect to each other.

JYNTEE. An Indian name for *Sesbania ægyptiaca*, from which gunpowder charcoal is made.

KABONG. A Malayan name for *Arenga saccharifera*.

KADI-KANE. An Indian name for *Panicum miliaceum.*

KADSURA. A genus of dicotyledonous plants belonging to the *Schizandraceæ*. They are climbing mucilaginous shrubs, with white or reddish unisexual flowers; sepals three; petals six to nine; stamens fifteen or more, the filaments distinct or united; ovaries numerous, the style lateral; carpels berried, distinct, forming a globular capitulum. There are about half a dozen species, natives of tropical Asia.   [J. H. B.]

KADUA. A genus of cinchonaceous undershrubs, natives of the Sandwich islands. The flowers have a leathery salver-shaped corolla, with a long tube and a four-parted limb. The fruit is capsular and adherent below to the calyx which is sometimes fleshy, while at the upper part it is detached from it.   [M. T. M.]

KÆMPFERIA. A genus of tropical East Indian herbs, included among the *Zingiberaceæ*. The flowers have a tubular calyx; a corolla with a slender tube, narrow equal outer lobes of the limb, much larger inner ones, and a flat lip; the filament short, prolonged beyond the anther into a two-lobed crest; the style thread-like, with a cup-shaped stigma. The roots or stocks of some of these plants are purple on the exterior, white within, and have an aromatic fragrance. Those of *K. Galanga* are used medicinally in India, and also as a perfume; those of *K. rotunda* are used for similar purposes. The flowers are curious, appearing before the leaves, from a very short stem.   [M. T. M.]

KAGENECKIA. A genus of the rose family, differing from most of the others in the unisexual flowers and winged seeds, and from its nearest allies in the calyx segments overlapping each other in the bud. Of three known species two are found in Chili, and one in the Andes of Peru. They are trees with alternate, often gummy, ovate or lance-shaped leaves, and white flowers, much like those of the hawthorn. *K. oblonga*, known in Chili as Lyday, furnishes a wood used for building purposes, while the 'leaves being very bitter are used by the inhabitants to cure intermittent fevers.'   [A. A. B.]

KAHOO. An East Indian name for the Lettuce.

KAIMAILEE. *Rottlera tinctoria.*

KAJU GARU. A fragrant Malayan wood obtained from *Gonystylus Miquelianus.*

KAKATERRO. The New Zealand *Dacrydium taxifolium.*

KAKOON. An Indian name for *Setaria italica.*

KALADANA. *Pharbitis Nil.*

KALAF. A medicated water obtained from the male catkins of *Salix ægyptiaca.*

KALA KANGNEE. An Indian name for *Setaria italica.*

KALANCHOË. A genus of succulent plants, natives of tropical Asia, Brazil, and Africa, belonging to the order *Crassulaceæ*. The flowers are four-parted; the corolla salver-shaped, with a four-parted limb; stamens eight; capsules four, detached, many-seeded. They have yellow or pinkish flowers.   [M. T. M.]

KALE. *Brassica oleracea acephala*, an open-leaved variety of Cabbage. '—, INDIAN. *Caladium esculentum.* —, SEA. *Crambe maritima.*

KALLYMENIA. A genus of rose-spored *Algæ*, belonging to the order *Cryptonemiaceæ*, distinguished by its compound capsule, and its flat nearly sessile indefinite frond, composed internally of threads sometimes combined with cells, and externally of cells. *K. reniformis* occurs on our southern coasts at extreme low-water mark, but is more common on the Atlantic coasts of France, though it occurs as high as Orkney. At first it forms a roundish or kidney-shaped frond with a very short stem; this becomes proliferous and produces from the edge a crop of similar expansions, which, however, are frequently torn by the waves, and as they grow after the laceration the ultimate appearance is very different from that of younger plants. Occasionally the fronds assume a longer outline. The species of the genus are at present ill-defined, and consequently their geographical distribution is doubtful. One, for instance, at the Cape, which was considered identical with our own, is now held by Agardh to be distinct.   [M. J. B.]

KALMIA. A genus of heathworts, characterised by the border of the corolla having on the upper surface cavities in which the stamens are partly concealed. The name was given by Linnæus in honour of Peter Kalm, a Swedish professor. The species are evergreen shrubs, natives of North America. Like many others of the heathwort order, they are deservedly favourites. In some species the flowers are in clusters more or less dense; in *K. hirsuta* they are solitary; in *K. latifolia* they are large and showy; in *K. angustifolia* smaller. The regular form of the corolla between wheel-shaped and bell-shaped, the depressions or small pouches in which the stamens lie, and the delicacy of texture and colour, render these plants objects of interest. In size of the whole plant there is considerable range, and even in the same species according to locality. *K. glauca* and *K. hirsuta* are shrubs of a foot in height; *K. latifolia*, in the more northern parts of the

United States, varies from four to eight feet, while farther south it attains from ten to twenty feet, and when in full flower the dense thickets which it forms render it a prominent object. The flowers of this last species yield a honey said to be deleterious, and its leaves and shoots are certainly so to cattle; *K. angustifolia*, probably for the same reason, has received the name Lambkill. The powdered leaves of some are used as a local remedy in some skin diseases. The hard wood of *K. latifolia* is used in the manufacture of various useful articles. The Canadian partridge is said to become poisonous as human food after feeding on *Kalmia* berries. [G. D.]

KALOSANTHES. *Rochea.*

KALUMBA-ROOT. *Jateorhiza palmata.*

KAMALA. A down which covers the capsules of *Rottlera tinctoria*, and is used for dyeing orange.

KAMBOU. A name in the Kurile Islands for the *Fucus saccharinus.*

KAMMA. A Russian name for birch oil.

KANARI. The oil-producing Java Almond, *Canarium commune.*

KANDELIA. A Malabar tree, constituting a genus of *Rhizophoraceæ*. The flowers are remarkable for their five petals, which are inserted into a fleshy rim lining the interior of the tube of the calyx; they are divided beyond the middle into two segments, each of which is again broken up into a number of hairlike divisions; stamens indefinite; fruit one-celled, with only one seed. The species, like others of the mangrove family, present the curious phenomenon of the seed germinating within the fruit. The bark of *K. Rheedii* is used medicinally in India. [M. T. M.]

KANGAROO'S-FOOT PLANT. *Anigozanthus Mangiesii.*

KANILIA. A genus of *Rhizophoraceæ*, consisting of trees and shrubs, natives of tropical Asia, and whose flowers are distinguished by their calyx having a limb divided into eight segments, shorter than the tube; and by the eight two-lobed convolute petals, inserted into a disk lining the throat of the calyx, into which are likewise inserted sixteen stamens. The ovary is two to three-celled. [M. T. M.]

KANTEN. *Fucus cartilagineus.*

KAPAS. An Eastern name for the Cotton plant.

KAPITIA. A resin obtained in Ceylon from *Croton lacciferum.*

KAPOK. An eastern name for the cottony down of *Bombax pentandrum.*

KARBI. An Indian name for *Sorghum vulgare.*

KARELINIA. A genus of *Compositæ*, represented by a single species, *K. caspica*, found in littoral places on the borders of the Caspian Sea, and in Siberia. It is a smooth erect woody-stemmed herb, having oblong lanceolate entire leaves, and corymbs of cylindrical purple flower-heads terminating the twigs, each head containing numerous tubular florets, the outer ones with pistil only, and their achenes crowned with a single series of soft white hairs, while the inner ones are perfect and have many series of pappus hairs to their achenes, which are cylindrical—not one series of pappus hairs and flattened achenes as in *Conyza* to which this plant is most nearly related. The genus is named in honour of M. Karelin, a Russian botanist. [A. A. B.]

KA-RI-SHUTUR. An Afghan name for *Alhagi Maurorum.*

KAROO-VAILUM. An Indian name for the gum of *Acacia arabica.*

KARWINSKIA. A Mexican genus of the buckthorn family, containing two or three species which have much the aspect of *Rhamnus*, and chiefly differ from them in having two instead of one ovule in each cell of the ovary. *K. Humboldtiana*, the most common species, has the smooth leaves marked underneath with prominent parallel nerves, and the minute greenish flowers in clusters in their axils, succeeded by little black berries. [A. A. B.]

KASSOU-KHAYE. The Senegal name for *Khaya senegalensis*, African Mahogany.

KASSAB. An Arab name for the Sugar Cane.

KASSU. A kind of Catechu, prepared from *Areca Catechu.*

KAT, or KHÂT. *Catha edulis.*

KATHERINE'S-FLOWER. *Nigella damascena.*

KATUMBAR. A Malay name for Coriander.

KANKOOR. *Cucumis utilissimus.*

KAULFUSSIA. A very distinct genus of marattiaceous ferns, found in India and Java, with thick rhizomes and coarse ternate fronds, but most remarkable for the structure of the sori, which are dorsal, sessile globose crenate fleshy cotiaceous concave hemispherical bodies, consisting of ten or twelve spore-cases arranged in a single concrete cyclose series, each sporecase bursting on the inner face by a vertical oblong or obovate cleft. The veins are compoundly anastomosing, with free included veinlets, and compital receptacles. On the under surface of the fronds are found curious cavities which are supposed to be secreting organs. [T. M.]

KAVA, KAWA. Other names for Ava, *Macropiper methysticum.*

KAVAROO. The Tamil name for *Eleusine coracana.*

KAWRIE TREE. *Dammara australis.*

KAYEA. A genus of *Clusiaceæ*, differing from most others in its one-celled ovary, and from its nearest ally, *Calophyllum*, in having four ovules instead of one. *K. oribunda*, found in Silhet, is a large handsome evergreen tree, with opposite narrow laurel-like leaves, and terminal panicles of numerous white flowers tinged with pink: each flower consisting of four calyx leaves, four petals, numerous stamens, and a simple style four-cleft at top. The fruits are rounded yellow drupes. *K. stylosa*, from Ceylon, is said to yield a useful timber, and to have very fragrant flowers. The genus bears the name of Dr. R. Kaye Greville of Edinburgh. [A. A. B.]

KAYLA. A Hindoo name for the Banana.

KAYU-MANIS. A Malay name for *Cinnamomum zeylanicum*.

KECKS, KECKSIES, KIXES. Country names for the dried fistulous stalks of cow parsley, hemlock, and various other wild umbellifers.

KEDLOCK. *Sinapis arvensis*.

KEELED. Formed in the manner of the keel of a boat; that is to say, with a sharp projecting ridge, arising from a flat or concave central plate, as the glumes of grasses.

KEESLIP. A Scotch name for *Galium verum*.

KEFERSTEINIA. A small genus of epiphytal stemless bulbless orchids of New Grenada, with a few lance-shaped leaves, and from the lower axils solitary bracted peduncles, bearing a single flower at the apex. The sepals and petals are spreading, lance-shaped; the lip larger, fan-shaped, jointed to the base of the column, which has a keeled crest, extending from the stigma halfway down in front; the anther has four unequal pollen-masses, attached to a strap-shaped caudicle as long as the gland to which it is fixed. [A. A. B.]

KEITHIA. A genus of the labiate order, having the calyx with five nearly equal teeth; the lower lip of the corolla with three nearly equal lobes; and the fruit dry and ovoid. The species are natives of Brazil. The genus was named after the Rev. P. Keith, a botanical author. [G. D.]

KELINGOO. An Indian name for *Batatas edulis*.

KELLETTIA. A name given by Dr. Seemann to *Prockia crucis*.

KELP. The ashes produced by burning sea-weeds, consisting principally of the common *Fuci* and *Laminariæ*. They contain carbonate of soda and salts of potash, and were formerly used in the manufacture of coarse soap and glass, and returned a considerable revenue on rocky shores, or where large stones had been purposely placed to encourage the growth of sea-weed. Modern improvements in chemistry, by which carbonate of soda was more profitably obtained from common salt, and the removal of the high duty from barilla, put an end to the manufacture, and the benefit resulting in consequence to the public was unhappily in some measure counterbalanced by the ruin of many proprietors who had reaped a rich temporary harvest from what was supposed to be a permanent source of revenue. [M. J. B.]

KEMPS. *Plantago media*.

KENDOO. An Indian name for *Diospyros Melanoxylon*.

KENGUEL. The seeds of *Gundelia Tournefortii*, used as coffee in Asia Minor and Scinde.

KENKERIG. The Welsh name for a variety of *Parmelia saxatilis*, called *omphalodes*, which is much gathered for dyeing amongst the mountains. [M. J. B.]

KENNEDYA. A genus of prostrate or twining *Leguminosæ*, peculiar to Australia, with the exception of *K. prostrata*, which grows also in Tasmania. They have wiry stems, with alternate, trifoliolate, stipulate leaves, and axillary racemes of large handsome pea-flowers, bright red, pink, or almost black in colour. These have a two-lipped calyx; an obovate standard, the wings and keel nearly equalling it in length; ten stamens, one only of which is free; and an ovary tipped with a thread-like incurved style. They are distinguished from the allied *Hardenbergia* by their much larger and fewer flowers, which are never blue or white. *K. nigricans*, a Swan River species, is remarkable for its nearly black flowers. The genus is named in honour of Mr. Kennedy, once a nurseryman of Hammersmith. [A. A. B.]

KENTIA. A genus of palms, separated from *Areca*, chiefly on account of their ovary having only one cell, and their seed being solid and homogeneous, not having the nutmeg-like structure of the seed of true *Areca*, under which name, however, many botanists still retain them. They are natives of the islands of the Malayan Archipelago, Norfolk Island, and New Zealand; and have slender unarmed stems, marked with circular scars, supporting a cluster of large pinnate leaves, and branched flower-spikes, which bear numerous flowers of distinct sexes, each female being seated between two males.

K. sapida is the most southern known palm, being found in New Zealand as far south as lat. 38° 22', which is between two and three degrees further south than any representative of the order is found upon the Australian, African, or American continents. The New Zealanders call this palm Nikau, and use the young flower-spikes, just as they emerge from among the leaves, as an article of food. [A. S.]

KENTROPHYLLUM. A genus of *Compositæ*, containing about a dozen species, distributed over the Mediterranean region, extending eastward to Kashmir, and west and south to the Canary Isles. They are mostly annual slightly branched thistle-like plants, with hard lance-shaped spiny-toothed leaves, and yellow, white, or purple flower-heads, each surrounded by a number of prickly scales, which are like the stem leaves. *K. lanatum*, one of the most widely distributed species, is remarkable for the loose white wool which hangs from the stems and flower-heads, giving them the appearance of distaffs loaded with wool. *K. arborescens*, a Spanish plant, grows eight or ten feet high. According to Boissier, this plant gives quite a character to the lower warm regions in Granada, and is popularly known as Cardo Santo, or Cardo lechero. [A. A. B.]

KERAMIDIUM. The same as Cysto-carp.

KERMESINUS. Carmine-coloured.

KERNELWORT. *Scrophularia nodosa.*

KEROBETA. An Abyssinian name for *Balsamodendron Myrrha.*

KERRIA. An evergreen shrub, with long slender branches, invested with smooth green bark, lanceolate acuminated leaves, which are coarsely and unequally serrated, and numerous buff-yellow flowers. The double-flowered form is commonly cultivated under the name of *Corchorus japonicus.* The structure of its flowers approaches that of *Spiræa*, near which it is placed in the system. French : *Corète du Japon.* [C. A. J.]

KESHOOR. A Bengal name for *Rottlera tinctoria.*

KESTING, KESLING. The Bullace Plum.

KETCHUP, or CATSUP. A name originally of Eastern origin, now applied to a favourite condiment prepared from various *Fungi*, as mushrooms, morels, champignons, &c. It is usually made by sprinkling the fungi when broken up with salt, and boiling the expressed juice with spice. The best way, however, is to let the juice drain without squeezing, and after standing for twelve hours to rack it off clear, and bottle it, filling the top of the bottle up with alcohol in which the proper spices have been previously steeped. Prepared in this way it retains its peculiar aroma much more perfectly than when boiled. Ketchup is often prepared for sale from agarics collected almost indiscriminately, no care being taken to discard notoriously poisonous species. The mass, moreover, frequently becomes putrid before it is boiled, and the ketchup is in consequence disgusting in flavour, and if taken largely very unwholesome. The best ketchup is prepared from *Agaricus campestris*, but a very good quality may be obtained from an admixture of other species, especially *A. procerus*, if care is used. [M. J. B.]

KÉTIMONS DES INDIENS (Fr.) *Cucumis sativus.*

KETMIE. (Fr.) *Hibiscus.* — MUSQUÉE *Abelmoschus moschatus.*

KHAIR-TREE. *Acacia Catechu.*

KHÂT. *Catha edulis.*

KHAYA. The name of a lofty Senegambian tree, forming a genus of *Cedrelaceæ*, closely allied to *Swietenia*, but distinguished from it by the parts of the flower being in fours, and by the fruit bursting from above downwards. The bark of *senegalensis* is used as a febrifuge on the banks of the Gambia river, while the wood is like mahogany. [M. T. M.]

KHEU. *Melanorrhœa usitatissima.*

KHISMIS. A Malay name for Raisins.

KHORMA. A Malay name for the Date.

KHUJJOOR. *Phœnix sylvestris.*

KHUS. An Indian name for *Andropogon muricatus.*

KHYAR. An Egyptian name for *Cucumis sativus.*

KIBARA. A genus of but one species, *K. coriacea*, belonging to the *Monimiaceæ*, and differing from the other genera in the sterile flowers having but five to seven instead of many stamens. It is a large tree of Malacca and Java, having large opposite ovate oblong leaves, and small yellow flowers borne in axillary cymes. The fertile flowers, supported by two bracts, have the mouth of the calyx nearly closed by two or three series of scales enclosing a number of ovaries, which when ripe are oblong stalked drupes about half an inch in length. [A. A. B.]

KIBI. The Japanese name for Millet.

KIDAR-PATRI. An Indian name for *Limonia laureola.*

KIDNEY-BEAN TREE. *Wistaria frutescens.*

KIDNEY-SHAPED. Resembling the figure of a kidney ; that is to say, crescent-shaped, with the ends rounded, as the leaf of *Asarum europæum.*

KIDNEY-WORT. *Umbilicus pendulinus*; also *Saxifraga stellaris.*

KIELMEYERA. A genus of resinous shrubs or small trees of Brazil, belonging to *Ternströmiaceæ*, and related to *Camellia*, from which they differ in the petals being twisted instead of simply overlapping each other in the bud, and from others of their allies in their very numerous flattened and winged seeds. They have alternate, glossy, lance-shaped or elliptical leaves, with numerous nerves running at right angles to the midrib, and racemes or panicles of white or rose-coloured flowers, which in some species are small, but in others large and rose-like, thus suggesting the name Roso do Campo, by which some of the species are known in Brazil. *K. speciosa*, called by the Brazilians Malvo do Campo, from the resemblance of its flowers to those of some mallows, has an abundance of mucilage in its leaves, which in decoctions are used by them for fomentations. M. St. Hilaire remarks as a curious circumstance, that we have soothing properties in the leaves of this plant, while in those of the tea, to which it is related, we have stimulating properties. The Malvo do Campo is a tortuous tree eight to fifteen feet high, with short thick branches, corky bark, and elliptical leaves, the shoots terminating in a few rose-coloured flowers as large as camellias, with six curiously unequal-sided petals, and very numerous stamens. [A. A. B.]

KIERA. An Indian name for the seeds of *Amaranthus frumentaceus.*

KIGELIA *pinnata*, an African tree, found in Nubia, Abyssinia, Mozambique, to as far south as Natal on the eastern side, and in Senegal and Guinea on the western, is the only representative of this genus of *Crescentieæ*. It is of large size, with whitish bark and spreading branches, bearing opposite pinnate leaves, and long-stalked panicles of flowers, hanging down from the trunk or old branches : each flower being turned upwards, and having a two-lipped calyx with the lobes irregularly cut ; a broad bell-shaped corolla divided at the mouth into five nearly equal lobes, enclosing two long and two short perfect stamens and five sterile ones ; and a single-celled smooth ovary with a two-plated stigma. The fruit is often two or more feet long by from five to eight inches broad, hanging from a stalk several feet in length ; it has a whitish corky rind, and is filled with pulp containing numerous roundish seeds. In Nubia this tree is held sacred ; the negroes celebrate their religious festivals under it by moonlight, and poles made of its wood are erected as symbols of special veneration before the houses of their great chiefs. The fruits, cut in half and slightly roasted, are employed as an outward application in rheumatic and other complaints. [A. S.]

KIGELLARIA. A genus of *Flacourtiaceæ*, having for its chief distinguishing features a calyx of five distinct segments ; the presence of scales at the base of the petals; and anthers opening at top by small round pores, instead of by longitudinal slits. The three known species are bushes or small trees of South Africa, with willow-like leaves clothed underneath with white starry down ; in their axils grow the inconspicuous white unisexual flowers, the sterile ones in stalked cymes, and the fertile solitary, on different plants. [A.A.B.]

KING-CUPS, or **KING'S CUP** or **COB.** *Ranunculus bulbosus,* and the allied species.

KINGIA. A genus of *Juncaceæ* from South Australia, with the habit of *Xanthorrhæa* (grass tree), having an erect arborescent stem with crowded linear three-edged leaves at the top. The peduncles are shorter than the leaves ; at first terminal and erect, but afterwards, as the stem elongates, lateral and reflexed, terminating in dense globose heads of flowers with a six-parted glumaceous perianth, six stamens, and a three-celled ovary becoming an indehiscent one-seeded pericarp. [J. T. S.]

KING-PLANT. Anœctochilus setaceus.

KING'S-SPEAR. *Asphodelus albus.*

KING'S-TREE. The name among the Zulu Kaffirs of *Strychnos Atherstonei.*

KINGWOOD. A Brazilian wood believed to be derived from a species of *Triptolomœa*, but by some referred to *Brya Ebenus.*

KINO. The name of various astringent gums. —, AFRICAN. The gum of *Pterocarpus erinaceus.* —, AMBOYNA. The gum of *Pterocarpus Marsupium.* —, BOTANY BAY. The inspissated juice of *Eucalyptus resinifera.* —, BUTEA or DHAK. The gum of *Butea frondosa.* —, INDIAN. The gum of *Pterocarpus Marsupium.*

KIPPER. *Orobus tuberosus.*

KIRIAGHUNA. *Gymnema lactiferum.*

KIRIATHA. A Malabar name for *Andrographis paniculata.*

KIRILOVIA. A genus of *Chenopodiaceæ* from Siberia, consisting of woolly annuals with a slender stem, membraneous oblong or lanceolate entire leaves, and axillary sessile polygamous flowers in head-like spikes. The perianth has five (rarely four) small teeth ; stamens five, with long exserted filaments ; style two-cleft ; fruit utricular, included in the unchanged woolly perigone. [J. T. S.]

KIRIS. (Fr.) *Matthiola græca.*

KIRRITOCHEE. The fruit of *Terminalia angustifolia.*

KIRSCHENWASSER, KIRSCHWASSER. German names for a liqueur prepared from the cherry.

KISSMISS. A small kind of grape from which the Shiraz wine is made in Persia.

KISSING COMFITS. The candied roots of *Eryngium maritimum.*

KITAIBELIA. The name of a malvaceous plant peculiar to Hungary. The genus is distinguished by the outer calyx or involucel, which is cleft into seven or nine pieces ; and by the numerous one-seeded carpels, which are aggregated together into a five-lobed head. *K. vitifolia* is a mallow-like plant, sometimes seen in English gardens ; its leaves are employed in Hungary as a vulnerary. [M. T. M.]

KIT-JAP. The Japanese name of Ketchup.

KITTOOL, KITTUL. A Cinghalese name for *Caryota urens* ; also for the strong fibre obtained from its leaf-stalks.

KLAPA. A Malay name for the Cocoanut.

KLAPROTHIA. A genus of *Loasaceæ* readily distinguishable by having a four-toothed calyx and four petals to the flowers, instead of five which is the usual number, and by the sterile stamens having their apices dilated and fan-like. *K. mentzelioides*, the only known species, found in the Andes of Quito, is a twining annual herb, with rough nettle-like leaves, and corymbs of inconspicuous white flowers terminating the twigs. Klaproth, whose name the genus bears, was a distinguished chemist of Berlin. [A. A. B.]

KLEINHOVIA. A genus of *Sterculaceæ*, consisting of a single species, *K. hospita*, a low branching tree with alternate heart-shaped leaves, and terminal panicles of small pink flowers, which are succeeded by top-shaped, bladdery, five-winged fruits, with five cells having a single seed in each. These curious fruits are sufficient to distinguish the genus. The calyx is five-parted: the corolla consists of five narrow unequal petals; and the staminal tube bears on its apex five parcels of anthers, three in each parcel. The plant is a native of the Malay Archipelago, extending eastwards to the Solomon Isles. Its bruised leaves are said by Burmann to smell like violets. M. Kleinhoff was once director of the botanic garden at Batavia. [A. A. B.]

KLEINIA. From the extensive genus *Senecio* a number of African species are severed by some authors who give to them the name of *Kleinia*, distinguishing them from true groundsels more by habit than anything else. *K. neriifolia* will serve to show what sort of plants they are. Growing on maritime rocks through all the Canary Islands, this plant is commonly known as Berode by the inhabitants; it is a fleshy-stemmed bush three to eight feet high, with thick candelabra-like branches, covered with scars of old leaves, and furnished at the apex with a rosette of pale-green lance-shaped leaves, somewhat like those of the oleander but fleshy in texture; and the numerous flower-heads are disposed in stalked corymbs arising from the axils of, and shorter than, the leaves. The achenes are ten-ribbed, surmounted by a white pappus of rough hairs. Most of the remaining species are South African; a few only Arabian; almost all having the stems (when present) fleshy, and leaves like those of that noted above. [A. A. B.]

KLOPSTOCKIA. A name sometimes given to the Wax Palm of the Andes and a few allied species, referred by others to *Ceroxylon.* [A. S.]

KLOTZSCHIA. A genus of umbellifers, having the fruit compressed from behind, each half with three dorsal approximate ribs but no oil-cells, and the lateral ribs small with single oil-cells. The genus was named in honour of Klotzsch, a well-known German botanist. The only species is an herb of the warmer parts of Brazil, having the stem leaves stalked, shield-shaped, five-lobed, and finely veined. [G. D.]

KLUGIA. A small genus of *Cyrtandraceæ*, natives of India and Mexico. They are annual herbs with alternate leaves, and blue flowers in subsecund racemes. They have a five-cleft calyx; a two-lipped corolla, the upper lip being the smaller and bi-lobed, the lower entire; four included stamens, without trace of a fifth; and a

one-celled ovary surrounded by a disk, and crowned by a cup-shaped stigma. [W. C.]

KNAPBOTTLE. *Silene inflata.*

KNAPWEED, or KNOPWEED. *Centaurea nigra*; also *C. Jacea* and *C. Scabiosa.*

KNAURS. Knobs or tumours formed on the stems or roots of plants : see EXOSTOSIS.

KNAUTIA. A genus of herbaceous plants belonging to the *Dipsacaceæ*, and allied to *Scabiosa*, from which it is distinguished by having its fruit invested with a toothed, not awned, calyx. *K. arvensis*, the only British species, is a common but graceful weed in cornfields; it grows to the height of two feet or more, with divided hairy leaves, and large handsome terminal lilac flowers, which are collected into convex heads, the outer florets much the largest, and having their outer segments larger than the inner, so as to assume the appearance of a ray, like that of the compound flowers. This is a favourite plant for showing the effect of burning tobacco on vegetable colour, for the flowers, immediately on being touched by a lighted cigar, assume a brilliant green hue. A similar effect may be produced by thus experimenting with other flowers of a reddish tinge, but none show so bright a green as this *Knautia*. [C. A. J.]

KNAWEL. *Scleranthus.*

KNEE-JOINTED. The same as Geniculate.

KNEEPAN-SHAPED. Broad, round, thick, convex on the lower surface, concave on the other; the same as Meniscoid, but thicker. See PATELLIFORM.

KNEIFFIA. A genus of hydnoid *Fungi*, in which the hymenium consists of minute granules, surmounted by a little bristle-like point. It is very close to *Grandinia*. *K. setigera* is not uncommon in our woods on decayed sticks. [M. J. B.]

KNEMA. A genus of trees nearly allied to the nutmeg, and belonging to the *Myristicaceæ*. The points of distinction lie in the three-lobed hairy calyx, and the stamens forming a column dilated at the top into a disk bearing the anthers at the margin. In the female flowers the stigma is provided with many teeth at its margin. The rigid leaves and the contracted inflorescence also form points of distinction. The trees are natives of India and other parts of tropical Asia. [M. T. M.]

KNESEBECKIA. A genus of *Begoniaceæ*. Its characters are : anthers obovate, truncately tumid at the apex, with oblique chinks; filaments umbellately monadelphous; stigmas bipartite, dilated anteriorly at the base; placentas bilamellar, with the lamellæ distinct, not united into a pedicel. There are thirteen species, found chiefly in Mexico and central America. The plants are more generally regarded as *Begonias*, as are all those proposed to be separated from it by Klotzsch. [J. H. B.]

KNIGHTIA. A genus of *Proteaceæ*, containing a single species, *K. excelsa*, native of the northern island of New Zealand. It is distinguished by having a calyx of four sepals; four stamens with very long anthers and short filaments, one inserted on each sepal a little below the middle; and a long slender style thickened at the end. The fruit is a woody downy capsule, an inch in length with the long style still attached, containing four seeds, which are winged at the apex. The leaves are four to six inches long, very harsh, linear oblong, coarsely and rather bluntly toothed;

Knightia excelsa.

and the flowers grow in axillary racemes, nearly as long as the leaves, densely covered with a reddish-brown velvety down, as are also the flowers and their stalks. It forms a large tree about 100 feet high, erect and very narrow for its height, and consequently very conspicuous. The wood is much prized for its colour, which is a mottled red and brown; it is also useful as readily splitting for shingles. *Embothrium strobolinum*, a native of New Caledonia, has latterly been provisionally placed in this genus under the name of *K. integrifolia*, but the structure of the matured seeds has not been ascertained. [R. H.]

KNIGHTS SPURS. *Delphinium.*

KNIGHTS STAR. *Hippeastrum.*

KNIGHTSWORT. *Stratiotes aloides.*

KNIPHOFIA. *Tritoma.*

KNIPNÉE. *Melicocca bijuga.*

KNITBACK. *Symphytum officinale.*

KNOBTANG. *Fucus nodosus.*

KNOL KOHL. *Brassica oleracea caulorapa.*

KNOLLES. *Brassica Rapa.*

KNOPPERN. A curious kind of gall, formed on some species of oak in Hungary and other parts of Europe.

KNOTBERRY. *Rubus Chamæmorus.*

KNOTTED. Cylindrical, uneven on the surface, as the pod of *Chelidonium.*

KNOTWORT. *Polygonum aviculare.*

KNOTWORTS. Lindley's name for the *Illecebraceæ.*

KNOWLTONIA. A genus of herbaceous plants of the *Ranunculaceæ*, having, nevertheless, in outward aspect, much the appearance of umbellifers. The flowers have a green five-leaved calyx, several petals, and numerous stamens and carpels. The fruits are somewhat succulent, with a deciduous style, and are placed on a convex receptacle. These are acrid Cape plants, whose leaves are used to produce blisters. [M. T. M.]

KNOXIA. The name of a genus of cinchonaceous plants, consisting of Indian undershrubs, whose flowers have a four-parted calyx; and a salver-shaped corolla with lance-shaped segments, and a hairy throat, into which the stamens are attached. The fruit is a two-celled capsule, crowned by the calyx, and consisting of two halves, which separate from a slender central column. The species have pink or white flowers. [M. T. M.]

KOARY. An Indian grass used for making mats.

KOBRESIA. A genus of cyperaceous plants, belonging to the tribe *Caricineæ.* Distinguished by the inflorescence being in spikes together, or what is termed aggregate; lower flowers female or pistilliferous, the upper ones male or staminiferous; without any perianth; perigone of one scale, enclosing the germen and covered by the glume. Steudel describes four species, which are natives of high mountains or northern latitudes. The British species, *K. caricina*, is a rare plant, which has hitherto only been observed to grow on the bleak moors of the north of England and Scotland. [D. M.]

KOCHIA. A genus of *Chenopodiaceæ* allied to *Chenopodium*, but with an urceolate perigone, the five segments of which at length send out from their backs transverse membranous wings. They are herbs or undershrubs from the temperate regions of the old world, with sessile, linear, or cylindrical leaves (rarely absent), and axillary flowers. [J. T. S.]

KODDA-PAIL. *Pistia.*

KODOYA BIKH. *Aconitum ferox.*

KODRO. An Indian name for *Paspalum scrobiculatum.*

KŒLERIA. A genus of grasses belonging to the tribe *Festuceæ.* It is distinguished by the inflorescence being in crowded spike-like panicles; glumes unequal, two or three-ribbed; spikelets compressed, two to five-flowered; lower pale keeled, acuminate, or with a straight subterminal bristle; nut free. There are about three dozen species, which have a wide range, mostly inhabiting temperate climates. One of them, *K. cristata*, is a native of Britain, and is a beautiful grass, as it grows on dry sandy plains, or on dry hills.　　　[D. M.]

KŒLREUTERIA. A small-sized deciduous tree belonging to the *Sapindaceæ*. The generic characters are: calyx of five sepals; petals four with two scales at the base of each; stamens eight; ovary three-celled; capsule three-valved; seeds without an arillus. A native of China, first introduced into this country in 1793, and being handsome in regard to both leaf and flower, and hardy withal, it is much cultivated. The leaves are pinnate with an odd leaflet, the leaflets ovate coarsely toothed; the flowers yellow, disposed in terminal spreading clusters, and succeeded by large bladdery capsules which render the tree conspicuous till late in the autumn.　　　[C. A. J.]

KŒNIGIA. A genus of *Polygonaceæ*, consisting of an exceedingly small annual found in Iceland and Lapland, with alternate obovate, somewhat succulent leaves, short ochreate stipules, and terminal three-leaved flowers in small clusters with membranous bracts.　　　[J. T. S.]

KOHAUTIA. A genus of cinchonaceous herbaceous plants, of no great beauty or interest. The corolla is salver-shaped with a long slender tube and pointed lobes; anthers sessile, within the corolla; capsule globular.　　　[M. T. M.]

KOHL. A German name for Cabbage or Colewort. — ·RABI. *Brassica oleracea caulo-rapa*.

KÖHLERIA. A genus of handsome *Gesneraceæ*, represented by *K. hondensis* and *K. Seemanni*. They have squamose stolons, upright stems with opposite leaves, and numerous axillary flowers having the corolla slightly deflexed, with a cylindrical somewhat tumid tube, and a narrow spreading limb; the stigma is bifid; and there are five nearly equal hypogynous glands.　　　[T. M.]

KOKOONA. The Kokoon of the Cinghalese, a large forest tree growing sixty feet or upwards in height, in the central provinces of Ceylon, is the only species of this genus, which belongs to the small order *Hippocrateaceæ*, from all the other genera of which it differs in having five stamens instead of three, the anthers splitting open longitudinally. The leaves are narrow at the base, but broad, rounded and with a small notch at the top, spotted beneath with numerous very small dark red dots. The fruit is three-sided and three-celled, each cell containing numerous seeds with broad wings. The Cinghalese use the yellow corky bark in the preparation of a kind of cephalic snuff, which they mix with ghee (vegetable butter) and introduce into the nostrils in order to relieve severe headache by encouraging a copious secretion from the nose. They also express an oil from the seeds and use it for burning in their lamps.　　　[A. S.]

KOKRA. *Lepidostachys Roxburghii*, the hard wood of which is used for making musical instruments.

KOLA. *Cola* or *Sterculia acuminata*, an tomentosa.

KOLBIA. The name of a trailing plant belonging to the *Papayaceæ*. The inner flowers alone are known: they have an outer involucel of a bell-like shape, five-cleft; the perianth is bell-shaped, its limb divided into ten segments, the outer ones glandular, saw-toothed, the inner ones feathery; stamens five, united below. The plant is a native of western tropical Africa.　　　[M. T. M.]

KOLGAS. *Colocasia antiquorum*.

KOLKOUAL. *Euphorbia abyssinica*. ·

KÖLLIKERIA. A small genus of *Gesneraceæ*, separated from *Achimenes*. *K. ærgyrostigma* is a dwarf New Grenada herb with squamose stolons, rather large opposite leaves spotted with white, and racemes of small white flowers, mottled with red, the lower lip fimbriate.　　　[T. M.]

KOME. A Japanese name for Rice.

KÖNIGA. The generic name sometimes given to the Sweet Alyssum, referred by Lindley to GLYCE: which see.

KOOL. The fruit of *Zizyphus Jujuba*.

KOOLINGAN. An Indian name for the Galanga root.

KOOLLAH-I-HUZAREH. The Cabul name of various species of *Statice*.

KOOLTOO. An Indian name for *Fagopyrum esculentum*.

KOOMUGGI. A Japanese name for wheat.

KOONGOONIE. An Indian name for *Setaria italica*.

KOONGOO-TARO. An Indian name for the flowers of a *Tamarix* used in dyeing.

KOORINGA. An Indian fibre obtained from *Tylophora asthmatica*.

KOOROOMBA. ·A name in Ceylon for the young Cocoa-nut.

KOOSHA. An Indian name for *Eragrostis cynosuroides*.

KOOSUM, KOOSUMBA. Indian names for Safflower; also for *Schleichera trijuga*.

KOOT. The Indian Costus root.

KOPEH. The Tara, *Colocasia macrorhiza*.

KOPSIA. A genus belonging to the order of dogbanes, distinguished by having the corolla salver-shaped, its tube swollen above, the border of five spreading or reflexed lobes; the style ending in an oblong undivided hairy stigma; and the fruit of two drupes, one often abortive. The name was given in honour of Professor Kops, author of a botanical dictionary. The species are natives of Japan, usually having milky juice, opposite leaves, and flowers resembling those of *Vinca*, and of handsome appearance. [G. D.]

KORA KANG. An Indian name for *Setaria italica*.

KORARIMA, KURARIMA. A large kind of Abyssinian Cardamom, the fruit of *Amomum angustifolium*.

KOROUMB. An Egyptian name for Cabbage.

KORRAS. An Arabic name for Leek.

KORTHALSIA. A small genus of palms bearing a general resemblance to *Calamus*, having long flexible cane-like stems which climb up and become entangled among the branches of trees. Their pinnate leaves, also, terminate in long prickly tails like those of the *Calami*, and the lower part of their leaf-stalks forms a sheath round the stem; the leaflets being broad and shaped like a wedge or somewhat trapeziform, plaited, and irregularly toothed or torn at the top. The flower-spikes grow from the sides of the stem and have branches resembling catkins, bearing numerous flowers of separate sexes, the base of each branch being sheathed in an incomplete spathe. The males have a three-cut calyx, a deeply three-parted corolla, and six stamens; the females a similar calyx, a tubular corolla trifid at the top, six sterile stamens, and a one-celled ovary. The fruit contains a solitary seed. There are five species, all natives of moist places in the forests of the Indian Archipelago. [A. S.]

KOSHEL. *Andropogon Nardus.*

KOUBANKA. A kind of wheat grown in Russia.

KOUKOU. A Tartar name for *Strychnos Ignatii*, the *Ignatia amara* of authors.

KOUKOUNARIA. *Abies cephalonica.*

KOUSSO, KOSSO. An Abyssinian medicinal plant, *Brayera anthelmintica*; also called Cusso.

KOYFUL. An Indian name for wild Nutmegs.

KRAMERIA. An anomalous genus so nearly allied on the one hand to *Leguminosæ*, and on the other to *Polygalaceæ*, that its station is considered as doubtful, and it has even been separated as a distinct family, the *Krameriaceæ*. It consists of much-branched spreading undershrubs, indigenous to America, having alternate simple or trifoliolate leaves, and flowers in racemes. The calyx consists of four or five irregular coloured sepals, and the corolla of four or five petals, the three inner of which are very small and unguiculate; the stamens are four or fewer, unequal, and open at the end by pores; the ovary is one-celled with two suspended ovules; and the one-seeded fruit is covered with hooked prickles. On careful examination the irregularity of the flower proves to be of the same kind as that of *Leguminosæ*, one of the petals being superior or directly next the stem from which

the flower-stalk springs, on which account it appears undoubtedly preferable to refer it to *Leguminosæ*. In *Polygalaceæ* a sepal occupies that position, so that neither of the petals which are alternate with it can be directly superior. The sepals of *Krameria* are, however, sometimes partially displaced from crowding or inequality, so that one of them may appear superior.

K. triandra, remarkable for its entire obovate acuminate leaves, covered on both sides with silky hairs, is one of the species most known as yielding the Rhatany roots of commerce, but all the species, as far as known, are intensely astringent. In Peru an extract is made from this species which is a mild, easily assimilated, astringent medicine, possessed of great power in passive, bloody, or mucous discharges; it acts as a tonic in weakness of the digestive organs and muscular debility, and is even useful in intermittent and putrid fevers. It is also styptic, and restores tone to relaxed parts, and when applied in plaisters is said to correct and cure all kinds of ulcers. An infusion is used as a gargle and wash, and the powder forms along with charcoal an excellent tooth-powder. The colour of the infusion of the roots of the *Krameria* is blood-red, on which account advantage is taken of it to adulterate port wine. [B. C.]

KRAUSIA. The name of a genus of *Cinchonaceæ*, consisting of a Natal shrub, whose flowers have a calyx with a short five-cleft limb; a funnel-shaped corolla with a short tube and a five-cleft limb; anthers placed on very short stalks on the hairy throat of the corolla; and an ovary crowned by a large fleshy disk, and a large spindle-shaped stigma which is divided into two lobes; fruit fleshy, two-celled, two seeded. [M. T. M.]

KRAUT. A German name for Colewort or Cabbage.

KREAT or CREAT. A tonic infusion of the root of *Andrographis paniculata*.

KREYSIGIA. A genus of *Melanthaceæ* from New Holland, with a roughish simple stem, ovate lanceolate amplexicaul leaves, smooth above and rough below, and axillary, solitary, one-flowered peduncles, with an involucel of three bracts below the middle. The flowers are pale lilac with a six-leaved spreading deciduous perianth, having glandular appendages, six stamens, and three stigmas. The capsule is somewhat fleshy. [J. T. S.]

KRYNITZKIA. A genus of *Boraginaceæ* from New California, allied to *Echinospermum*, but having the nuts quite smooth. They are hispid annuals with sessile leaves, and small flowers with a very hispid calyx, and a white salver-shaped corolla, having yellow scales in the throat. [J. T. S.]

KUCHOO. An Indian name for the tubers of *Colocasia antiquorum*, *Arum maculatum*, &c.

KUCHOORA. *Curcuma Zerumbet.*

KUDUMBA. *Nauclea Cadamba.*

KUENI. The Indian name for Butea Kino.

KUEPHUL. An Indian name for the aromatic bark of *Myrica sapida.*

KUHNIA. A small genus of *Compositæ*, differing from its allies in the many striate achenes, seated on a naked receptacle, and crowned with a single series of capillary and feathery pappus hairs. The species of De Candolle excluded by Torrey and Gray, have, like our own *Eupatorium*, five-angled not faintly streaked achenes. [A. A. B.]

KUJOOR. An Indian name for Dates.

KUMBOO. The Tamil name for spiked Millet, *Penicillaria spicata.*

KUMERA. A New Zealand name for *Batatas edulis.*

KUMKUMA. An aromatic drug and perfume obtained from *Didymocarpus aromaticus*; also the Malay name for Saffron.

KUMLA. An Indian name for *Citrus Aurantium.*

KUMMEL. A German name for Cumin or Caraway seeds.

KUMOON. An Indian name for Cumin.

KUMNYIAN. The Malay name for Frankincense.

KUM-QUAT. A variety of *Citrus japonica.*

KUNDALOO. A large kind of Indian Nettle.

KUNDEL. An Indian name for Sagapenum.

KUNGOO. An Indian name for *Setaria italica.*

KUNKIRZEED. An Arabian name for the gum of *Cynara Scolymus.*

KUNTHIA. A genus of palms, containing but one species, *K. montana*, a reedy plant, with a ringed stem about an inch in thickness, and twenty feet high or more, inhabiting the temperate mountain-regions of New Grenada, where the natives call it Cana de la Vibora, i.e. Snake Cane, from the resemblance of its stem to a snake, and they consider its juice to be a remedy against the bite of that reptile. It has a terminal tuft of pinnate leaves, three or four feet long, beneath which the flower spikes, which are enclosed in several spathes, and bear both male and female flowers, are produced. The fruit is about the size of a sloe, of a green colour, containing a single seed. Besides the use of its juice for curing snake bites, the Indians hollow out the reedy stems of this palm for the purpose of making blowpipes, through which they expel poisoned arrows to a considerable distance. [A. S.]

KURBEE. An Indian name for the cut stalks and straw of the *Sorghums*, used as fodder for cattle.

KURDEH, CURDEE. Indian names for Safflower.

KURPAH. A kind of Indigo.

KURRAJONG. A native Australian name for several fibrous plants. BROWN. *Commersonia platyphylla.* GREEN. *Hibiscus heterophyllus.* —. TASMANIAN. *Plagianthus sidoides.*

KURTAU. A Malay name for the Mulberry.

KURUNDA. An Indian name for *Carissa Carandas.*

KUSHMUT. An Indian name for the root of *Costus speciosus.*

KUSHNEEZ. The Persian name for Coriander seed.

KUTCHOORA. An Indian name for the roots of *Curcuma.*

KUTEERA, KUTERA. A gum obtained from *Cochlospermum Gossypium*; also from *Sterculia urens.*

KUTH. An Indian name for *Acacia Catechu.*

KUTHAR-CHARA. An Indian name for *Limonia laureola.*

KUTKARANGA, KUTKULEGA. Indian names for the tonic seeds of *Cæsalpinia Bonducella.*

KUTKEY. An Indian name for Hellebore.

KYABOOCA. An ornamental wood obtained in the Eastern Archipelago, from the excrescences or burrs of *Pterospermum indicum*; the same as Amboyna wood.

KYLLINGIA. A genus of cyperaceous plants, belonging to the tribe *Cypereæ.* Distinguished principally by the inflorescence being in solitary heads, rarely two to three together; spikes compressed, one to two-flowered, the upper flowers male; stamens one to three; styles cleft. There are upwards of fifty species, the greater part natives of Brazil and South Africa, with a few from Australia. [D. M.]

LABARIA PLANT of Demerara. *Dracontium polyphyllum.*

LABATIA. A genus of tropical American trees belonging to the *Sapotaceæ.* The flowers have a four-parted calyx, whose segments are arranged in two rows; five fertile stamens inserted at the base of the tube of the corolla, alternating with five scale-like abortive stamens placed on its throat; a four-celled ovary surmounted by a style that does not project beyond the corolla; and a fleshy fruit. [M. T. M.]

LABEL, LABELLUM. The third petal of an orchid, usually turned towards the lower front of the flower, and very different in form from the remainder. Also a similar petal in other flowers.

LABIATÆ. (*Lamiaceæ, Labiates.*) A natural order of dicotyledonous plants belonging to Lindley's echial alliance of perigynous Exogens. Herbs or undershrubs with square stems, opposite and exstipulate leaves, and flowers in verticillasters. Calyx tubular, persistent, five to ten-toothed or bilabiate; corolla bilabiate; stamens four didynamous, or by abortion two: anthers two-celled, or one-celled by abortion; ovary deeply four-lobed on a disk; style basilar; stigma bifid. Fruit one to four achenes enclosed by the calyx; seeds erect with little or no albumen. Natives of temperate climates. Many of them are carminative, and yield volatile oils. Mint, sage, lavender, rosemary, hyssop, patchouly, marjoram, horehound, thyme, basil, savory, belong to the order. There are upwards of one hundred genera, and about 2,500 species.   [J. H. B.]

LABIATE. A term applied to a monopetalous calyx or corolla which is separated into two unequal divisions, the one anterior, and the other posterior, with respect to the axis.

LABIATIFLOROUS. A term applied to composites whose corolla is labiate.

LABICHEA. A genus of *Leguminosæ* of the suborder *Cæsalpinieæ*, allied to *Cassia*, but the sepals and petals are occasionally reduced to four, and the stamens are usually two only, unequal and dissimilar, or rarely three and equal. The pod is also short, and has only two seeds. There are three or four species, all from Western Australia, and two at least have been introduced into our gardens. They are glabrous shrubs, with pinnate leaves consisting of one conspicuous terminal usually lanceolate and sharply pointed leaflet, and two or more small ones at its base. The flowers are yellow, in short axillary racemes, and rather showy.

LABIOSE. A polypetalous corolla having the appearance of being labiate.

LABISIA *pothoina* is the name given by Lindley to the *Ardisia pumila*, a native of the Eastern Archipelago, which differs from the rest of the genus in the more induplicate æstivation of the corolla, in the almost spicate inflorescence, and in the shape and venation of the leaves, which are almost those of some monocotyledonous plants. It was thus mistaken for a *Pothos* in the garden of the Horticultural Society until it flowered; and for the same reason it was proposed by A. De Candolle as a section of *Ardisia* under the name of *Marantoides*.

LABIUM. The lower lip of a labiate corolla.

LABLAB. A genus of tropical pulse formerly included in *Dolichos*. The two recognised species are natives of India, but they have been so widely spread by cultivation that they are now found naturalised in most tropical countries. They are twining herbaceous plants, with trifoliolate leaves, and long-stalked racemes composed of alternate clusters of short-stalked flowers seated upon glandular knobs. The calyx is tubular or bell-shaped, cut into four segments, the upper one broad and blunt; the corolla has the spreading upper petal channeled, with four callosities or swellings at its base, the two lower ones being bent inwards at a right angle, but not twisted as in *Phaseolus*; and nine of the stamens are united. The pods are flat, marked along the edges with rough tubercles or warts, and containing usually four oval seeds. *L. vulgaris* and *L. cultratus* are greatly cultivated in tropical countries, the young pods taking the place of our kidney beans, while the seeds or pulse, on account of their nitrogenous qualities, afford nutritive and wholesome food. There are several varieties, some of which yield better-flavoured pulse than others. [A. S.]

LABORDIA. An evergreen shrub from the Sandwich Islands, described and figured by Gaudichaud as a genus of *Loganiaceæ*, but the specimens were very imperfect, and the plant has not been again found, so that its affinities are as yet doubtful.

LABOUCHERIA. A name given by Dr. Mueller to a North Australian tree of the tribe *Mimoseæ* of *Leguminosæ*, but which is probably scarcely sufficiently distinct as a genus from the African *Erythrophlœum*.

LABURNUM. *Cytisus Laburnum.* —, **SCOTCH.** *Cytisus alpinus.*

LABYRINTHIFORM. Marked by sinuous intricate lines: the same as Dædaleus.

LAC. A fluid having an opaque appearance, and either white, orange, or some such colour, occurring in many plants. Also the name of a gummy substance produced by *Erythrina monosperma*, *Aleurites laccifera*, &c.

LACÆNA. A genus of epiphytal orchids with the habit of *Acineta*, and approaching very nearly to it in structure, but differing in having the lip articulated with the column as well as in the middle, and in having but two pollen-masses instead of four, these being attached to a long slender caudicle. *L. bicolor*, the original species, is a native of Guatemala, and has long pendulous racemes of flowers of a greenish-yellow colour, the three-lobed lip marked with purple about the centre.   [T. M.]

LACAUSSADEA. *Polybotrya.*

LACE-BARK. The inner bark of *Lagetta lintearia.*

LACEPEDEA. A Mexican shrub, described by Kunth as a distinct genus, but which has since proved to be a species of *Turpinia.*

LACE-LEAF PLANT. *Ouvirandra.*

LACERATE, LACERUS. Irregularly divided by deep incisions.

LACHENALIA. A genus of lilywort, of which several beautiful species are cultivated in our gardens. They are natives of the Cape of Good Hope, and consist of bulbous plants, with lanceolate lorate often spotted leaves, and erect flower-scapes bearing a raceme of pendulous flowers, the yellow colour being predominant among them. The perianth is six-parted, with the segments connivent into a cylindrical tube, the three exterior ones shorter than the others; there are six stamens, and a three-celled many-ovuled ovary which becomes a membranaceous three-winged capsule, containing but few seeds. *L. pendula*, *luteola*, *tricolor*, And *quadricolor* are familiar inhabitants of our greenhouses, and very ornamental in the spring months. [T. M.]

LACHNÆA. Cape shrubs of the *Thymelaceæ*, deriving their name from the woolly hairs that densely clothe their flowers. The inflorescence consists of terminal flower-heads frequently surrounded by bracts. The perianth is coloured, tubular, jointed below, the lower portion persistent, the limb divided into four segments, and having attached to it, at its junction with the tube, eight stamens in two rows, and as many scales (petals ?) inserted lower down than the stamens, and placed opposite to the divisions of the limb. [M. T. M.]

LACHNOCAULON. A genus of *Eriocaulaceæ*. They have fibrous roots, a very short stem, linear-lanceolate leaves, sheathed peduncles, and villous capitules of unisexual flowers. They are natives of Virginia, Carolina, Georgia, Florida, and other parts of North America. [J. H. B.]

LACHNOSTACHYS. An Australian genus of *Amaranthaceæ*, consisting of woolly shrubs with opposite rigid leaves and terminal and axillary cylindrical bracteated spikes of perfect flowers, with a six or eight-parted scarious perigone, densely woolly outside. [J. T. S.]

LACHRYMÆFORM. Tear-shaped; the same as Pear-shaped, except that the sides of the inverted cone are not contracted; as the seed of the Apple.

LACINIA (adj. LACINIATE). A slash. A deep taper-pointed incision.

LACINULA. A small lacinia or slash; also the inflected point of the petals of umbellifers.

LACIS. A genus of *Podostemaceæ*, consisting of small herbs, natives of Brazilian rivers, having a thick somewhat globular root-stock, numerous stalked palmately-divided leaves and racemose flowers, which differ from those of other genera of the order in their monadelphous stamens, and in their capsules which consist of two or three equal ribbed valves. [M. T. M.]

·LACISTEMACEÆ. (*Lacistemads.*) A natural order of dicotyledonous plants belonging to Lindley's violal alliance of hypogynous Exogens. They are shrubs with simple stipulate leaves, and hermaphrodite or unisexual flowers in axillary catkins. Perianth free, divided, with a large bract; stamen one, hypogynous, the connective separating the antherine lobes, which open transversely; disk often fleshy;

ovary one-celled; placentas parietal. Fruit a one-celled two to three-valved loculicidal capsule. Seeds numerous, albuminous, with an aril. Natives of the tropical woods of America. There are about half a dozen species in two genera. [J. H. B.]

LACISTEMA. A small genus of arborescent plants of tropical America, from which the order *Lacistemaceæ* derives its name. They have simple alternate leaves, polygamous catkin-like flowers, a calyx supported by a bract, no corolla, a solitary stamen surrounded by a somewhat fleshy disk, a capsular one-celled fruit, each cell bearing a solitary seed. In habit the species somewhat resemble pepperworts. Their properties are unknown. [B. S.]

LACTARIUS. A large genus of gill-bearing *Fungi*, distinguished by the cellular not filamentous substance of the gills, and the milky juice which is contained in distinct tubes. They are often extremely acrid and dangerous, but some of them, as *L. volemus* and *L. deliciosus*, are mild and form excellent articles of food. As, however, they are used when pickled in considerable quantities almost indiscriminately by the Russians, it would seem that the dangerous properties are neutralised by the acid. Dogs suffer dreadfully after biting such species as *L. vellereus*, and Dr. Badham had very unpleasant symptoms from simply tasting a few of the spores. The milk of this species leaves a burning sensation in the throat like that of *Euphorbia Lathyrus*. When collected it forms a cheesy mass which burns with a bright flame. The milk in many species, though originally white, changes colour when exposed to the air, and sometimes displays brilliant tints, as blue, orange, &c. One or two species have been found in the Himalayas, but Europe and North America are their principal habitats. [M. J. B.]

LACTESCENT. Containing lac, or milk.

LACTEUS. Milk-white; dull white verging to blue.

LACTUCA. A well-known genus of *Compositæ*, deriving its name from the milk-like juice which pervades the plants in their wild state. The genus belongs to that group, the *Cichoraceæ*, which is characterised by the presence of heads of strap-shaped florets only, and may be further distinguished by the following marks: involucre of a few overlapping bracts, including a few yellow or blue flowers, which are placed upon a scaleless receptacle; fruits somewhat flattened, surmounted by a thread-like beak, and a pappose calyx of silky hairs. The species are annual or perennial herbs, with erect branching stems, and smooth or spiny leaves, and are distributed over Southern Europe, Central Asia, and North America.

The Garden Lettuces have been so modified by long cultivation, that it is impossible to decide accurately from which species they have originated. Suffice it to say, that the narcotic and sedative principles that are so well known to exist in Lettuce do not occur except to an infinitesimal extent in the succulent young leaves that form so agreeable a salad, but when the flowering stem is thrown up, the sap becomes milky and bitter, and its narcotic properties are then more fully developed. The sedative effects of Lettuces appear to have been known from the earliest times of which we possess any record. Venus, after the death of Adonis, is reported to have found rest for her love-distracted mind by throwing herself upon a bed of Lettuces. Virgil and Columella both mention the Lettuce as proper to be eaten as a sequel to more savoury viands, at the end of a repast, as well as for their soporific qualities; and Pliny relates that Augustus was cured of an illness by the use of Lettuces, prescribed by his physician, Musa. The popular opinion respecting the properties of these plants is maintained in our own times by the doggrel that tells us

for want of rest
Lettuce and cowslip-wine probatum est.

Indeed, a substance called *Lactucarium* or Lettuce Opium is prepared from the dried juice of some of these plants, especially *L. virosa*, and is occasionally used as a mild narcotic or sedative where opium is inadmissible.

There are a few British species of this genus of which mention may be made, such as *L. muralis*, sometimes called *Prenanthes muralis*, distinguished from the other British species by its thin stalked leaves, and the short beak to the fruit. The name of this species would imply that its usual habitat was on walls, but it is also frequent on banks, and in hedgerows. *L. virosa* has sessile prickly leaves, and a spreading panicle; it occurs in hedgerows, and by roadsides, but not abundantly. *L. saligna* is yet more uncommon in this country; its panicle is so contracted as to resemble a spike.   [M. T. M.]

The Garden Lettuce, commonly called *L. sativa*, is a hardy annual, whose native country is unknown with certainty, although it is generally supposed to be Asia. It has been cultivated in England since 1562. The plant has large roundish or roundish-oblong entire slightly-toothed milky leaves, which in some varieties are of a deep green, while in others they are of a dingy brown colour. The flower-stem is round, about three feet high, the flowers pale yellow and corymbose. Lettuces appear to have been known and used for salads at a very early period. According to Herodotus, they were served to the royal tables of the Persian kings more than 400 years before the Christian era. It is also recorded that they formed the opium of Galen, the celebrated Greek physician, in A.D. 200, and it was probably the consideration of this historical fact which led to the discovery in our day, by the late Dr. Duncan of Edinburgh, of the drug called *Lactucarium*, prepared from the juice of the Lettuce. The ancient Romans knew but one sort of Lettuce, and this was a variety

with dark-coloured leaves, which they suspected of having an injurious effect on those who ate it; but after the Emperor Augustus was said to have been cured by the free use of Lettuces, suspicion of their deleterious qualities vanished, and great efforts were made not only to cultivate them, but to blanch them so as to remove their bitterness, and thus render them more palatable.

The first English writer on gardening who has noticed the Lettuce is Gerarde in 1597. He describes eight varieties as being then cultivated. The number has since greatly increased, and year after year new and improved sorts are brought forward to supply the places of those which have degenerated and are considered unworthy of further cultivation. The whole have been arranged in two divisions or groups, namely, *Cabbage Lettuces*, comprising all those which have round leaves, and form a compact head resembling a cabbage; and *Cos Lettuces*, those having firm and crisp upright oblong leaves, folded over one another. The latter are preferred for salads, while the cabbage kinds, from being more flaccid and milder, are preferred for soups. Although containing but little nourishment, Lettuces are universally esteemed for their emollient and cooling properties, and they are always in great demand.   [W. B. B.]

LACUNA (adj. **LACUNOSE**). A large deep depression or excavation.

LACUNOSO-RUGOSE. Marked by deep broad irregular wrinkles, as the shell of the walnut, or stone of the peach.

LACUSTRIS. Growing in lakes.

LADANUM, or **LABDANUM.** A resinous product of *Cistus creticus*, and other species.

LADENBERGIA. A genus of *Cinchonaceæ*, consisting of trees inhabiting Peru. The characteristics of the genus reside in the limb of the calyx, which is very small, somewhat bell-shaped, with triangular teeth; and in the ovary which is surmounted by an eight-lobed disk.   [M. T. M.]

LADY'S BEDSTRAW. *Galium verum*; also *Pharnaceum Mollugo*.

LADY'S BOWER. *Clematis Vitalba*.

LADY'S COMB. *Scandix Pecten-Veneris*.

LADY'S CUSHION. *Armeria vulgaris*.

LADY'S FINGERS. *Anthyllis Vulneraria*.

LADY'S GARTERS. *Digraphis arundinacea variegata*.

LADY'S GLOVE. *Digitalis purpurea*.

LADY'S HAIR. *Briza media*.

LADY'S LACES. *Cuscuta*.

LADY'S LOOKING-GLASS. *Specularia hybrida*.

LADY'S MANTLE. *Alchemilla vulgaris*.

LADY'S NAVEL. *Umbilicus pendulinus*.

LADY'S NIGHTCAP, *Calystegia septum.*

LADY'S SEAL. *Convallaria Polygonatum.*

LADY'S SLIPPER. *Cypripedium Calceolus.*

LADY'S SMOCK. *Cardamine pratensis.*

LADY'S THIMBLE. *Campanula rotundifola.*

LADY'S THISTLE. *Carduus Marianus.*

LADY'S TRACES or TRESSES. *Neottia spiralis.*

LADY'S THUMB. An American name for *Polygonum Persicaria.*

LADLEWOOD. A Cape name for the wood of *Cassine Colpoon.*

LÆLIA. A beautiful genus of orchids, closely related to *Cattleya*, from which indeed it differs in little if anything, besides having eight pollen-masses instead of four. They are epiphytes, furnished with pseudobulbs which are often elongated clavate and stem-like, thick hard leaves, and terminal scapes of few or many flowers, which are for the most part extremely showy. *L. purpurata* and its allies, *L. superbiens, L. majalis,* and *L. præstans,* are some of the finest of the species, which are all South American, and come chiefly from Brazil and Mexico. [T. M.]

LÆLIOPSIS, The name of a few epiphytal orchids of the West Indies and South America. They agree with *Cattleya* in all respects except that the flowers are membranaceous, and the veins of the lip bearded. *L. domingensis,* the typical species, is a St. Domingo plant, with two-leaved pseudobulbs, and a slender terminal scape, bearing at the end a few showy flowers, of which the sepals and petals are rather erect than spreading, and the large lip is rolled up round the column, and two-lobed with wavy toothed recurved divisions. [T. M.]

LÆTIA. A genus of *Flacourtiaceæ* consisting of small trees inhabiting the woods of tropical America, with dotted or dotless, usually entire and leathery leaves; hermaphrodite or polygamous flowers, arranged in racemes; a highly imbricate calyx; either no corolla or one composed of five petals, yellow or white; an indefinite number of stamens, with very short anthers; and an ovate or three-cornered berry. *L. apetala,* of the Magdalena river, yields a balsamic resin which becomes white in contact with the air, like Sandarach. [B. S.]

LÆVIGATE. Having the appearance of being polished, as many seeds.

LÆVIS. Free from asperities or hairs, or any sort of unevenness.

LAFOENSIA. A genus of South American *Lythraceæ,* consisting of trees or shrubs, with opposite leaves, and flowers either solitary in the axils or in terminal racemes or panicles; they are large, white or pale red, with a bibracteolate eight to ten-toothed calyx, ten to twelve petals, and twenty to twenty-four stamens; and are succeeded by an incompletely two-celled capsule. [T. M.]

LAGAROSIPHON. A genus of aquatic herbs, inhabiting tropical rivers and lakes, and belonging to *Hydrocharidaceæ.* It has smooth parallel-veined leaves, and flowers enclosed in a spathe, and having three sepals and three petals, an indefinite number of stamens, and a succulent fruit. [B. S.]

LAGASCEA. A genus of *Compositæ* of the tribe *Vernoniaceæ,* distinguished by the doubly compound flower-heads, each separate floret being enclosed in a four or five-toothed tubular involucre, several of these partial involucres being collected in a general head, surrounded by imbricated leafy bracts. Each floret has a very slender tubular corolla, and a compressed four-angled achene crowned by a very short entire or toothed membranous pappus. There are about seven species, natives of Mexico, all coarse weedy herbs of little interest.

LAGENARIA. A genus of *Cucurbitaceæ,* consisting of annual pubescent musky plants, with alternate heart-shaped leaves, tendrils, clustered single-flowered axillary flower-stalks, and white monœcious flowers; the males with a bell-shaped five-

Lagenaria vulgaris.

parted calyx, five spreading petals, and five triadelphous stamens; and the females with a three-celled inferior ovary, becoming, when mature, a woody pepo. They are natives of the warm parts of Asia and Africa. [J. H. B.]

LAGENIFORM. Shaped like a Florence flask.

LAGENOCARPUS. The generic name of plants belonging to the order of heathworts; distinguished by having the corolla small, nearly globose, its border slightly five-cleft, the seed-vessel flagon-shaped and one-celled. The species are heath-like shrubs, natives of the Cape, with small leaves in whorls of three together, and small solitary flowers. The name indicates the flagon-like shape of the fruit. [G. D.]

LAGENOPHORA. A genus of *Compositæ*

of the tribe *Asteroideæ*, consisting of small daisy-like herbs, with the leaves mostly radical, and the small flower-heads growing singly on slender scapes. The numerous spreading ray-florets, either white or pale-blue, the numerous yellow tubular florets of the disk, and the flattened achenes without any pappus, are nearly those of *Bellis*, from which genus *Lagenophora* differs chiefly in the achenes being narrowed into a beak at the top. There are about ten species, all Australian, although one species, *L. Billardieri*, extends also into Southern Asia.

LAGERSTRÖMIA. A genus of *Lythraceæ*, of which about a dozen species are known, all natives of tropical Asia, and forming large trees or shrubs, with opposite entire leaves, and terminal panicles of purplish or white flowers. The bell-shaped calyx is cut into six equal-sized lobes, without any intermediate teeth; the corolla consists of six petals, furnished with long narrow claws or stalks; the stamens vary from eighteen to thirty; and the fruit is divided into three or six cells, containing numerous winged seeds. *L. indica* is a shrubby plant, growing eight or ten feet high, with elliptical smooth pale green leaves, and bright rose-coloured flowers, the petals of which are very much curved, having a crumpled but exceedingly beautiful appearance. It is a native of China, and flourishes in our greenhouses.

L. reginæ forms a magnificent timber tree, yielding a bloodred-coloured wood, which, though open in the grain and soft, is greatly used in India for boat-building, and for the knees of ships, on account of its great durability under water. It is called Jarool, and is common in the peninsula of India, and in Birmah. The native Indian physicians esteem various parts medicinal, the astringent root being used as a remedy for thrush, its bark and leaves as purgatives, and its seeds as a narcotic. [A. S.]

LAGETTA. The tree producing the well-known lace-bark of Jamaica is called in that island by the name Lagetto. The genus belongs to the *Thymelaceæ*, and is known by its perfect flowers; its tubular coloured perianth, with a distended tube, contracted throat, and four glands; eight stamens; and a small round hairy fruit, enclosed in the persistent base of the perianth.

The inner bark of *L. lintearia* consists of numerous concentric layers of fibres which interlace in all directions; and thus present a great degree of resemblance to lace, whence the common name of the tree. It is reported that Charles II. received, as a present from the governor of Jamaica, a cravat, frill, and pair of ruffles, made of this material; and to this day it is used for bonnets, collars, and other articles of apparel, specimens of which may be seen at the Kew museum, &c. The uses to which this natural lace is applied are not always so unobjectionable as those just mentioned, for it is likewise used in the manufacture of thongs and whips, with which, in former times at least, the negroes were beaten by their cruel taskmasters. The plant is cultivated in English hothouses as an object of curiosity. [M. T. M.]

LAGOECIA. The name of a genus of umbellifers, characterised by having one half of the fruit abortive, and a deep furrow on one side of that part which attains maturity. The only species is a small annual, a native of Eastern Europe, along the borders of the Mediterranean. [G. D.]

LAGOPUS. Hare-footed. A term applied to parts which are so closely covered with long hairs as to resemble a hare's foot; as the rhizome of some ferns, and the inflorescence of some grasses.

LAGUNARIA. The name of a malvaceous tree, native of Norfolk Island. The genus is allied to *Hibiscus*, but from it, and from other closely-related genera, it is distinguished by the small size and paucity of the bracts of the involucel; by the presence of a club-shaped style, terminated by a radiated stigma; as well as by the capsule, which is five-celled. The flowers are handsome, and of a pink hue. [M. T. M.]

LAGURUS. A genus of grasses belonging to the tribe *Agrostideæ*. It is distinguished by the inflorescence being in round spike-like panicles; glumes scarious, ending in a long-fringed bristle. The soft white silky spikes of flowers, with their protruded awns, give this pretty grass a very remarkable appearance. *L. ovatus*, the only species, is a native of the south of Europe, as well as of some parts of Asia. Though included in the British flora, it is only found in Guernsey. [D. M.]

LAITRON. (Fr.) *Sonchus.* —DE PLUMIER. *Mulgedium.*

LAITUE. (Fr.) *Lactuca sativa.*

LA-KAO. A Chinese green dye obtained from *Rhamnus catharticus.*

LAKE-WEED. *Polygonum Hydropiper.*

LALAGE. A genus of *Leguminosæ*, nearly allied to *Hovea*, but differing chiefly in the narrower and more deeply divided upper lip of the calyx, and in the flat pod. It consists of four or five shrubs, natives of South-west Australia, with alternate ovate lanceolate or linear leaves, and pretty axillary flowers, either yellow or mixed with orange-violet and crimson. *L. ornata* has been introduced into our greenhouses with other Swan River *Papilionaceæ.*

LALANG. A worthless Eastern grass, *Andropogon caricosus.*

LALO. The powdered leaves of *Adansonia digitata.*

LAMAN. (Fr.) *Solanum nigrum.*

LAMARCKIA. A genus of grasses belonging to the tribe *Festuceæ*. The inflorescence is in simple crowded panicles, the spikelets of which are stalked, two-flowered, one fertile and the other sterile. *L. aurea*, the only species of the genus, is a pretty

annual, sometimes cultivated in botanical
gardens. It is a native of the south of
Europe and north of Africa.   [D. M.]

LAMBERTIA. A proteaceous genus of
small shrubs, natives of extra-tropical
Australia, principally on the south and
south-west coasts. The flowers are regular,
solitary or in clusters, with a four-cleft
tubular calyx, the segments of which bear
each an anther; and a filiform style with a
pointed stigma. The prevailing colour is
dark red with occasionally an orange tint.
The seed-vessel is ovate, leathery, often
bristly, containing two winged seeds.
The leaves are entire or toothed, either
in threes or verticillate.   [R. H.]

LAMBKILL. An American name for
Kalmia angustifolia.

LAMBRUSQUE. (Fr.) Vitis Labrusca.

LAMB'S QUARTERS. Atriplex patula;
in America, Chenopodium album.

LAMB'S TOE. Anthyllis Vulneraria.

LAMB'S TONGUE. Plantago media.

LAMELLA (adj. LAMELLAR). A plate
or thin part such as is found at the end of
many styles.

LAMELLÆ, LAMINÆ, LAMELLULÆ.
The gills of fungals : vertical membranous radiating or branching plates belonging to a pileus.

LAMIACEÆ. Lindley's name for the
Labiatæ : which see.

LAMINA. The blade of a leaf; that expanded part which terminates the petiole,
if there be one.

LAMINARIACEÆ. A natural order of
dark-spored Algæ, consisting of olive-
coloured inarticulate sea-weeds, whose
spores are superficial and form indefinite
cloud-like patches, or cover the whole surface of the frond. Most of them are of considerable size, except Chorda which attains
a great length, and Adenocystis. Some,
like Lessonia, form submarine forests with
stems as thick as a man's thigh, while Macrocystis by repeated division attains a length
of hundreds of feet. One of the most remarkable is Nereocystis, which occurs on the
north-west coast of America, and has a stem
300 feet long, which bears above a huge
air-vessel six or seven feet long, shaped
like a great cask, and ending in a tuft of
upwards of fifty forked leaves. This is the
favourite resting-place of the sea-otter.
Ecklonia buccinalis, again, the Trumpet
Weed of the Cape colonists, has a stem
twenty feet high crowned with a fan-
shaped cluster of leaves more than half as
long. The stem, which is hollow above, is
often used as a siphon or converted into a
trumpet. These plants are mostly deep-sea
Algæ, and occur in either hemisphere, both
in colder and warmer seas.   [M. J. B.]

LAMINARIA. An important genus of
dark-spored Algæ, the type of the natural
order Laminariaceæ. It has no definite
leaves, but on the contrary a plane ribless

expansion, which is either simple or cloven.
The stem is either short or elongated, and
is sometimes of considerable thickness, and
either naked or fringed with a crisped expansion. Some of the species, as L. digitata
and L. bulbosa, attain an immense size, and
together with L. saccharina, which is commonly brought away from the coast to
answer the purpose of an hygrometer,
yield an enormous supply for the preparation of manure or kelp. One peculiarity
about these plants is that the old lamina annually falls off by means of a constriction,
and is replaced by a new frond formed
from the part beneath. The species delight
in the colder seas of the north, and are usually exposed only at low tides. [M. J. B.]

LAMINATING. Separating into several
plates or layers.

LAMIUM. A genus of herbaceous labiate
plants distinguished by having four stamens, of which the lower pair are longest ;
hairy anthers, the cells of which diverge
and burst longitudinally ; and a corolla of
two lips, of which the upper is arched and
entire, the lower spreading, two-lobed, and
mostly furnished with one or two teeth on
each side. The commonest species, L. album,
Dead-nettle, received its English name from
the resemblance borne by its leaves to
those of the true nettle, from which, however, it may be distinguished at any stage
of its growth by its square stem. L. purpureum is a common weed in hedges and
cultivated land. French, Lamier ; German,
Taubnessel.   [C. A. J.]

LAMOUROUXIA. A genus of Scrophulariaceæ, distinguished by a four-cleft calyx ;
by a corolla with an elongated somewhat
flattened tube, dilated below the throat,
and the small three-lobed lower lip shorter
than the concave upper one ; and by transverse hairy anthers with the cells unusually
mucronate. The species are natives of
Mexico or of the Andes of South America ;
they are all herbs, either erect or somewhat climbing, with opposite toothed or
divided leaves, rarely quite entire, and
handsome flowers, usually scarlet or pink,
in terminal spikes or racemes. There are
about eighteen species known, most of
them very showy plants. None have, however, been yet brought into cultivation,
and indeed it is probable that they are more
or less parasitical on the roots of other
plants, and therefore scarcely capable of
being cultivated.

LAMPOURDE. or L. GLOUTERON.
(Fr.) Xanthium Strumarium.

LAMPRA. A genus of Commelynaceæ
from Mexico. They have erect leafy stems,
with the lower leaves reduced to sheaths,
the upper numerous and lanceolate, and
numerous flowers in a sessile head among
the leaves.   [J. T. S.]

LAMPRETTE. (Fr.) Lychnis Flos-cuculi.

LAMPSANE. (Fr.) Lapsana.

LANA, LANUGO (adj. LANATE, LA-
NUGINOSE). Long, dense, curled, and

matted hairs, resembling wool, as in *Verbascum Thapsus.*

LANCEOLATE. Narrowly elliptical, tapering to each end. *Lanceolato-hastate* is hastate with the principal lobe lanceolate; and *Lanceolato-sagittate* is sagittate with the principal portion lanceolate.

LANCE-WOOD. The light elastic wood of *Duguetia quitarensis.* —, JAMAICA. A species of *Lycium.*

LANDE, or LANDIER. (Fr.) *Ulex europæus.*

LANGUE D'AGNEAU. (Fr.) *Plantago media.* — DE BŒUF. *Anchusa officinalis.* — DE CERF. *Scolopendrium vulgare.* — DE CHIEN. *Cynoglossum officinale.* — DE MOINEAU. *Passerina Stelleri.* — DE SERPENT. *Ophioglossum vulgatum.*

LANGUOR. A name given in vegetable Pathology to that condition of plants in which, from unwholesome food, bad drainage, frequent want of water, &c., they fall into a state of premature decrepitude. This is well known in French vineyards under the name of *Goupissure,* and is familiar to all fruit-growers when the subsoil is ungenial. When once this condition is set up, it is difficult of remedy, if not past cure altogether. The removal of the cause is the only rational treatment, and this is not always possible. [M. J. B.]

LANKESTERIA. A genus of *Acanthaceæ,* containing two species, natives of Central Africa. They are hairy shrubs with ovate entire leaves, and yellow flowers in short axillary spikes, having a calyx of equal linear sepals, subtended by two bracts; a long slender corolla-tube, and one-sided five-parted limb, two exserted stamens, and a simple capitate stigma. The genus is named after Dr. Lankester, a well-known English botanist. [W. C.]

LANSA, LANGSAT, or LANSÉH. The fruit of *Lansium domesticum.*

LANSBERGIA. A South American genus of *Iridaceæ,* related to *Phalocallis* and *Cypella,* from the first of which it differs in having the sepals all closed and converging, in the cells of the anther being adherent to the lobes of the style by their whole length, and in the stigmas being minutely crested and not petaloid; while the second is known from it by its stigmas being lobed, acute, and fringed at the upper side with acute horny crests. The outer divisions of the perianth are large and concave, the inner narrow and involute. *L. caraçasana* has tuberous roots, simple stems, equitant leaves, and yellow fugacious flowers, spotted with brown or black. [T. M.]

LANSIUM. A genus of *Meliaceæ,* confined to the East Indies, and consisting of trees with imparipinnate leaves, and axillary flowers arranged in panicles. The calyx is composed of five sepals; the corolla of five petals; the ten stamens are formed into a tube. The fruit is a corticate berry, having five cells, each cell containing one or two seeds. This berry has a cooling pleasant taste, and hence they are sometimes cultivated, and sold in the Canton markets. *L. domesticum* (known as Lansa, Langsat, Lanséh, Ayer-Ayer, or Bejetian, in the different languages of the East Indies) has a fruit as large as a pigeon's egg, of a yellowish colour without, and whitish within, which is highly esteemed, and eaten either fresh or variously prepared. The wood is used by the Malays. [B. S.]

LANTANA. A considerable genus of *Verbenaceæ,* containing upwards of fifty species, chiefly from tropical or sub-tropical America. They are shrubs, or rarely herbs, with flowers in pedunculate axillary heads, rarely lengthening into spikes. The calyx is small, truncate or sinuately four-toothed; the corolla tube slender, with a spreading four or five-lobed limb; there are four included stamens; the ovary is two-celled; and the fruit is a drupe, the kernel two-celled, or divided into two nuts. [W. C.]

LAPAGERIA. A genus of *Philesiaceæ,* consisting of twining undershrubs, with alternate cuspidate somewhat reticulate leaves, and solitary one-flowered peduncles, the perianth coloured, six leaved, and somewhat bell-shaped; and the stamens six, in-

Lapageria rosea.

serted at its base. The fruit is a one-celled berry, with numerous seeds. They are natives of Chili. *L. rosea,* with its single variety, are two of the most beautiful plants grown in modern greenhouses. [J. H. B.]

LAPEYROUSIA. A genus of *Iridaceæ,* consisting of half a dozen species from the Cape colony, allied to *Anomatheca,* in the long slender tube of their perianth, and spreading lobes, but these are much more equal, the stigmas are more deeply cleft, and the capsule is distinctly three-lobed. They have tuberous bulbs, simple stems, with sheathing leaves, and terminal elongated flower-spikes, each flower in the axil of a leafy bract. Three species, *L. fissifolia, L. anceps,* and *L. corymbosa,* were formerly cultivated among our Cape *Irideæ,* but are not near so showy as many other Ixia-like plants. The same genus has been described by Sprengel under the name of *Ovieda*; nnd the name of *Lapeyrousia* was also given by Thunberg to a genus of *Compositæ*, which De Candolle altered to *Peyrousia*.

LAPHAMIA. A genus of *Compositæ*, connected in many respects with the tribe *Asteroideæ*, but the leaves are usually opposite, and it has not exactly the style of that group. It consists of five species, low herbs or undershrubs, from Texas or New Mexico, with small discoid or radiating yellow flower-heads, and offering no particular interest except to botanists. It is in many respects very near *Perityle*.

LAPIDOSE. Growing in stony places.

LAPIEDRA. A small genus of pancratiform *Amaryllidaceæ*, consisting of a single species, *L. Placiana*, found in Spain. Its leaves are linear obtuse, striped longitudinally with white, and its flowers, white in a many-flowered umbel, have a spreading limb, an imperfect staminal cup, with the filaments short, and dentately winged on each side; a curved and tapering style, and a small trifid stigma. According to Herbert it is the same as *Vagaria parviflora*. [T. M.]

LAPLACEA. A name given by Kunth to a genus of *Ternströmiaceæ*, which has proved to be the same as *Hæmocharis*.

LAPPA. *Arctium.*

LAPPACEOUS. Having the appearance of a *lappa* or bur; that is to say, of a round body covered with small hooks.

LAPPAGO. A genus of grasses, belonging to the tribe *Paniceæ*. The inflorescence is in close bundles or heads; spikelets two to five-flowered, with the rudiments of neuter florets. There are three species, natives of the south of Europe and Africa. [D. M.]

LAPSANA. A genus of herbaceous plants mostly annual, belonging to the tribe *Cichoraceæ* of compound flowers, and distinguished by having compressed striated fruit destitute of pappus, a naked receptacle, and the involucre composed of a single row of erect scales, with smaller ones at the base. *L. communis*, a hedge weed, is our common Nipplewort. [C. A. J.]

LARANGA DA TERRA. A wild orange of Brazil.

LARBREA. A section of the caryophyllaceous genus *Stellaria*, of which *S. uliginosa*, the *Larbrea aquatica* of St. Hilaire, is the type; also a synonym of *Malachium*, *M. aquaticum* being the *Larbrea aquatica* of De Candolle. [J. T. S.]

LARCH. *Abies Larix.* —, CORSICAN. *Pinus Laricio.*

LARDIZABALACEÆ. (*Lardizabalads.*) A natural order of dicotyledons, belonging to Lindley's menispermal alliance of diclinous Exogens. Twining shrubs, with alternate exstipulate leaves, ternary symmetry, and unisexual flowers. They re-

semble *Menispermaceæ*, but differ in their compound leaves. Natives of the cooler parts of South America and China. The fruit of some of the plants is eaten. Examples: *Lardizabala, Holböllia.* [J. H. B.]

LARDIZABALA. One of the two American genera, belonging to the small order *Lardizabalaceæ*, and consisting of two species, both climbing shrubs, with rather large compound leaves, the six or nine leaflets disposed in two or three sets containing three each. The flowers are of separate sexes, borne on distinct plants, the males in many-flowered racemes, and the females solitary. Both sexes have a calyx of six fleshy egg-shaped sepals, arranged in a double series, the inner ones narrower than the outer. The ovaries ripen into many-seeded berries. Both species are found in Chili, extending as far south as Conception. One, *L. biternata*, which generally has leaves composed of six leaflets, is sufficiently hardy to withstand the cold of our winters, when trained against a wall, and its dark glossy evergreen foliage, and drooping spikes of deep purple flowers, render it very ornamental. In Chili, a very tough fibre is obtained from its stems and made into cordage; and its fruit, containing a sweet-tasted pulp, is sold in the markets. [A. S.]

LARIX. See ABIES, under which head information is given respecting the well-known European Larch; hence, it is here only necessary to add what is there omitted, viz. that the American Larch, *Abies* or *Larix pendula*, is the tree known to the Canadians as the Tamarack, and which furnishes an important feature in the appearance of the Canadian forests. [M. T. M.]

LARKSPUR, LARKHEEL, LARK'S-CLAW. *Delphinium.*

LARME DE JOB, or LARMILLE. (Fr.) *Coix Lachryma.*

LARNAX. Peruvian and Mexican herbs, constituting a genus of *Solanaceæ*, closely allied to *Physalis*, with which genus, among other things, they concur in the fact that, as the berry-like fruit ripens, the calyx increases in size and assumes the appearance of a bladder surrounding the fruit. The points of distinction are to be sought for in the shape of the calyx, which is here tubular, angular, and five-toothed; and in that of the corolla, whose limb is somewhat bell-shaped, and divided into five acute spreading lobes. [M. T. M.]

LAROCHEA. *Rochea.*

LARREA. A genus of *Zygophyllaceæ*, of which four species, three of them found in Chili and Paraguay, are known. They are strong-scented evergreen shrubs, with low branched stems, knotty jointed branchlets, opposite leaves, consisting usually of a single or rarely of several pairs of unequal-sided leaflets, and terminal flowers, with five sepals, five yellow petals, ten stamens, and a five-celled ovary, each cell maturing a single thin-shelled seed.

L. mexicana, the Creosote plant of the

Americans, is a shrub growing from four to six feet high, very abundant in some parts of Mexico, forming a dense and almost impassable scrub, particularly on the borders of the Colorado desert, where its luxuriant growth puts a stop to the drifting sand. It is a sure sign of a sterile soil, for wherever it flourishes little else can be found, and although it gives the scenery a beautifully verdant appearance, its strong creosote-like odour renders it so repulsive that no animal will touch it. Moreover, as it can scarcely be made to burn, it is useless even for the purpose of fuel. The resinous matter to which the odour is due abounds in all parts of the plant. The Pimos Indians collect and form it into balls which they kick before them as they journey from one point to the other of their trail. It is also used in rheumatism.   [A. S.]

LASEGUEA. A genus of dogbanes, distinguished by having the calyx five-parted, the divisions oblong, two glands at the base of each; the corolla shorter than the calyx, its border five-lobed; a ring of hairs at the point of origin of the stamens; and the glands of the nectary five. The species are shrubs or undershrubs, natives of Brazil, having opposite and shortly-stalked leaves, which are cordate and entire; the racemes of flowers are terminal, and the individual flowers are supported on stalks which are longer than the linear-lanceolate bracts.   [G. D.]

LASER. (Fr.) *Laserpitium.*

LASER CYRENAICUM. The Asa dulcis, *Thapsia garganica.*

LASERPITIUM. A genus of umbellifers, distinguished from its allies by the fruit having eight prominent wing-like appendages. The species are perennial herbs, chiefly found in South-eastern Europe. Some of them are employed as domestic remedies, on account of their possessing some degree of aroma.   [G. D.]

LASERWORT. *Laserpitium;* also *Thapsia Laserpitii.*

LASIA. A genus of orontiads, very closely allied to *Pothos,* but distinguished from that genus by its sessile spadix and its pendulous ovules. The species are Indian plants, with more or less of a creeping habit, thickly beset with strong spines; and the pinnately-divided leaves have sheathing leaf-stalks.   [M. T. M.]

LASIAGROSTIS. A genus of grasses belonging to the tribe *Stipeæ.* The species which were referred to it are described under *Stipa* by Steudel, who makes *Lasiagrostis* a section of that genus.   [D. M.]

LASIANDRA. A genus of *Melastomaceæ,* consisting of trees or shrubs with four-angled branches, opposite or verticillate entire ribbed leaves, and panicled showy flowers, with five petals and a capsular fruit. There are about forty species, natives of tropical America.   [J. H. B.]

LASIOLEPIS. This genus is stated to differ from *Harrisonia* in its five-parted flowers only, and therefore would be better merged therein. The name is applied to a shrub of the Philippine Islands, with wavy spiny branches and compound leaves, and refers to the hairy scales that are attached to the base of the stamens in this and other genera of *Simarubaceæ.*   [M. T. M.]

LASIOPETALUM. A genus of *Sterculiaceæ,* considered as the type of a tribe exclusively Australian, distinguished by hermaphrodite flowers with the petals either wanting or reduced to small scales; and by the stamens, of which five only bear anthers, and which are only shortly united at the base, or quite free. The genus is characterised in the tribe by anthers opening in terminal pores, and by the calyx not marked with the parallel prominent ribs of *Sarotes.* It consists of about twenty-five Australian species, low shrubs, more or less clothed with stellate hairs. The leaves are usually alternate, and more or less toothed or lobed, rarely entire or opposite; and the flowers are in short racemes, with the calyx at first herbaceous and downy, often enlarging as the flower advances, and coloured blue or reddish, so as to assume the appearance of a corolla. A few species occasionally occur in our collections of greenhouse plants.

LASIOSPERMUM. A genus of South African plants, belonging to the chamomile group of the *Compositæ,* and readily recognised by the dense rusty wool which completely envelopes the ripe achenes. The three species are erect branching herbs, with pinnatisect leaves, and solitary white-rayed flower-heads, having much resemblance to those of the feverfew. [A. A. B.]

LASIOSTOMA. The name of a cinchonaceous shrub, native of New Ireland. It has sessile flowers in axillary heads; a cup-shaped calyx limb; a short-tubed four-parted funnel-shaped corolla; four anthers; and a succulent two-celled fruit. The name is also synonymous with *Rouhamon,* a genus of *Loganiaceæ.*   [M. T. M.]

LASTHENIA. A genus of *Compositæ,* of the tribe *Heliantheæ,* consisting of three or four Californian or Chilian annuals, with opposite linear leaves, and small flower-heads, with a yellow ray or entirely discoid. The involucre is campanulate, of several united bracts, the receptacle without scales, and the achenes with a pappus of about ten chaffy scales or none at all. They grow in wet places, and appear to be uninteresting weeds.

LASTREA. A large genus of polypodiaceous ferns of the *Aspidium* group, including all those species in which the veins are free, and the indusium is kidney-shaped. It is one of the three great divisions into which the old genus *Aspidium* is broken up by modern pteridologists, the others being *Nephrodium* and *Polystichum.* The former, which also has reniform indusia, is known from it by the connivently anastomosing venation, that of *Lastrea* being quite free; while the other, which is free-veined; is separated by its peltate indusia. *Sagenia*, another group with reniform indusia, is separated by its compoundly anastomosing veins. The species are well represented in gardens, and consist principally of those whose veins are simple, as in *L. invisa*, and those whose veins are forked, as in *L. marginalis*. Several of our British species belong to this genus, of which, indeed, *L. Filix-mas* is the type. A similar name, *Lastræa*, was formerly given to certain species supposed to be allies of *Polypodium*, and this name is sometimes mistakenly used for the modern group, which was defined by Presl under the name of *Lastrea*. A fine Japanese species, *L. Sieboldii*, has several series of sori. [T. M.]

LATANIA. A small genus of African palms, forming trees of twenty or thirty feet high, their stems marked with circular scars, and bearing at the summit a tuft of fan-shaped leaves, from the lower part of which the branching flower-spikes, sheathed in incomplete spathes, emerge. The two sexes of flowers grow on separate trees, the males being disposed in many-flowered, the females in fewer-flowered, cylindrical catkins. Both have three sepals and three petals. The fruits contain three rough stones, covered with a bony network. The round or somewhat three-sided yellowish fruit of *L. Commersoni* is about the size of a small apple, covered with a tough rind, and containing a small quantity of pulp, which the negroes eat in spite of its very disagreeable flavour. It is a native of Bourbon and Mauritius, and is one of the palms cultivated in the hot-houses of European gardens. [A. S.]

LATERA. Sides; the two opposite sides of a stem or similar body.

LATERAL. Fixed near or upon the side of anything.

LATERINERVED. Straight-veined, like the leaves of grasses.

LATERITIUS. Red brick colour.

LATEX. The same as Lac (which see), but the term is extended to any kind of viscid fluid conveyed in laticiferous vessels, whether opaque or not. Latex granules are particles of starch or other matter, floating in the latex.

LATHRÆA. Toothwort, a curious herbaceous plant belonging to the *Orobanchaceæ*, and having the habit of an *Orobanche*, from which it may be distinguished by its four-cleft calyx. *L. Squamaria*, the only species, has a simple fleshy erect stem, about a foot high, leafless, but furnished with numerous fleshy scale-like bracts; and dull purple or flesh-coloured drooping flowers, which grow in two rows on the same side of the stem. The root, which is parasitic on the roots of various trees, is branched and clothed with numerous fleshy scales, which, from their resemblance to human front teeth, originated the English name. In accordance with the common fallacy of the old herbalists, its tooth-like roots were considered a specific for tooth-ache, but the plant has no known virtues. French, *Clandestine*; German, *Schuppenwurz*. [C. A. J.]

LATHYRUS. A genus of *Leguminosæ*, of the suborder *Papilionaceæ*, very nearly allied to *Vicia*, but distinguished by the style, which is flattened below the stigma, quite glabrous on the outer side, but more or less downy on the inner face for some way below the stigma. There are a considerable number of species, mostly known by the name of Peas. Indeed, the common pea (for which see PISUM) ought, strictly speaking, to be included in the same genus, the characters by which botanists have been in the habit of separating it being of very trifling value. The true *Lathyri* are dispersed over various parts of the globe, chiefly in temperate climates or in mountain ranges within the tropics. They are herbs with weak stems, sometimes climbing, the leaves usually pinnate, with fewer and larger leaflets than in the vetches, and often only one pair or even none at all, the common stalk always ending in a point or a tendril. The flowers are solitary or in racemes, purple, red, blue, white, or bright yellow, and often very handsome.

Several species are in cultivation. *L. odoratus*, the Sweet Pea of our gardens, an annual well known for its showy sweet-scented flowers, two or rarely three together on each peduncle, is a native of southern Sicily, where it is not uncommon wild, in cultivated as well as in bushy places. *L. latifolius*, cultivated in flower-gardens as the Everlasting Pea, is a slight variety of *L. sylvestris*, a species dispersed over the greater part of Europe, and known by its perennial root-stock, its single pair of lanceolate or rarely ovate leaflets, and its loose racemes of rather large reddish-purple scentless flowers. The garden variety has broader leaflets, and larger, more richly coloured, flowers. *L. sativus*, an annual with leaflets in single pairs, bluish flowers growing singly on each peduncle, and winged broad short pods, is extensively cultivated in Southern Europe, under the name of Jarosse or Gesse, for its seed, which is eaten in the same way as the chick pea (*Cicer*), but is of superior quality; the pod is also eaten green, and the whole plant is sometimes cut for forage, while the peas are much given to poultry. *L. Cicera*, an annual like the last but with red flowers, is also grown occasionally for its peas, under the names of Jarosse pois-carrés, or lesser chick pea, but is of a still inferior quality, and said to be sometimes very unwholesome. *L. tuberosus*, a very handsome perennial, with purplish-red often sweet-scented flowers, not uncommon in cornfields in several parts of Europe, has been recently detected in Essex. In countries where it is abundant, its tuberous roots are much sought after for eating, boiled, or baked like potatoes, but it is now much less common than it used to be. *L. pratensis*, common in our meadows, has short racemes of yellow flowers, and forms an excellent pasture. *L. Aphaca*, an annual with solitary small yellow flowers, is curious from the leaves, which have no real leaflets, but are reduced to a tendril between two large leaf-like stipules; and *L. Nissolia*, an annual with solitary pale red flowers, has neither leaflets nor stipules; but the leaf-stalk is flattened so as to resemble a linear grass-like leaf. The genus *Orobus*, distinguished only by the tendril being reduced to a short point, is now united with *Lathyrus*, and includes the British species *L. macrorhizus* (*Orobus tuberosus*) and *L.* (*Orobus*) *niger*.

LATICIFEROUS VESSELS. A continuous anastomosing tubular tissue in which latex is conveyed. It is probably a modification of cellular tissue, formed in a similar way to bothrenchyma.

LATIPES. A genus of grasses belonging to the tribe *Paniceæ*. *L. senegalensis*, the only species, is now included under *Lappago*.　　　　[D. M.]

LATOURIA. A section of *Leschenaultia* consisting of a North Australian herb, with alternate filiform leaves, and flowers opposite the leaves, having a tubular calyx and a partially two-lipped corolla. They are distinguished by the capsule which is slightly valvate, and by the seeds which are cylindraceous.　　　　[R. H.]

LATROBEA. The *Pultenæa Brunonis* and *P. genistoides*, two small-flowered Swan River species, have been separated by Meisner under the above name from the rest of the genus, on account of their minute membranous five-toothed calyx, and the total absence of stipules.

LATTICE-LEAF-PLANT. *Ouvirandra fenestralis*; also *O. Berneriana*.

LAURACEÆ. (*Laurineæ, Lauri, Laurels.*) A natural order of dicotyledons belonging to Lindley's daphnal alliance of perigynous Exogens. Trees with exstipulate, usually alternate, dotted leaves; perianth four or six-cleft in two rows; stamens often eight to twelve, the three or four innermost being abortive staminodia, and the outer fertile; filaments sometimes bearing glands; anthers two to four-celled, opening by recurved valves; ovary superior, one-celled, with one or two pendulous ovules. Fruit a berry or drupe; pedicle often thickened; seed solitary, exalbuminous; embryo with large cotyledons. They are tropical aromatic and fragrant plants, distributed over about fifty genera, and numbering between four and five hundred species. *Cinnamomum zeylanicum* yields cinnamon bark. *C. Cassia* supplies cassia bark. *Camphora officinarum*, a native of China, Japan, and Cochin China, yields camphor. *Persea gratissima* furnishes the fruit called avocado pear or alligator pear. *Nectandra Rodiæi* is the name of beheeru bark. *Sassafras officinale* is the sassafras tree of America. *Laurus nobilis*, a tree of the south of Europe and the Levant, is the victor's laurel or sweet-bay.　　　　[J. H. B.]

LAUREL. *Laurus*; also *Cerasus Laurocerasus*. — of Panama. *Cordia Gerascanthus*. — of New South Wales. *Cryptocarya glaucescens*. —, ALEXANDRIAN. *Ruscus racemosus*. —, AMERICAN. *Kalmia*. —, BAY. *Laurus nobilis*. —, CHERRY. *Cerasus Laurocerasus*. —, COPSE. *Daphne Laureola*. —, GREAT. An American name for *Rhododendron maximum*. —, GROUND. *Epigœa*. —, JAPAN. *Aucuba japonica*, —, MOUNTAIN. *Oreodaphne bullata*. —, PORTUGAL. *Cerasus lusitanica*. —, NATIVE, of Tasmania. *Anopterus glandulosa*. —, NEW ZEALAND. *Corynocarpus lævigata*. —, ROMAN. *Laurus nobilis*. —, SEASIDE. *Xylophylla latifolia*. —, SHEEP. *Kalmia angustifolia*. —, SPURGE. *Daphne Laureola*.

LAUREL-CHERRY. *Cerasus Laurocerasus*.

LAURELIA. A genus of *Atherospermaceæ*, one species of which is confined to Chili, and the other to New Zealand. They are tall trees, exhaling a powerful aromatic odour when bruised or broken. The leaves are ovate or oblong lanceolate serrated, and of smooth leathery texture; the flowers are small and inconspicuous, borne in short racemes, the two sexes being usually upon different trees, their calyx cut into from five to fifteen segments, arranged in several series, those of the males containing from seven to fourteen stamens, and those of the females numerous scales in the place of stamens, and several hairy ovaries.

L. Novæ Zelandiæ, called Pukatea by the natives, is one of the largest of the New Zealand trees, attaining a height of one hundred and fifty feet, with a trunk from three to seven feet in diameter, encircled at the base by huge buttresses fifteen feet thick. It affords a soft yellowish timber which is much used by the colonists for boat-building. The aromatic seeds of the Chilian species, *L. sempervirens*, are used as a spice in Peru, and are often called Peruvian Nutmegs.　　　　[A. S.]

LAURENCIACEÆ, LAURENCIA. A natural order and genus of rose-spored *Algæ* belonging to the series with tufted spore-threads. The capsules are external, and contain a distinct nucleus with a basal placenta, and the fruit is confined to the terminal joint of the spore-threads. The frond is inarticulate, solid or tubular, and septate, the cells on the surface minute, and the tetraspores scattered irregularly through the branchlets. The type of the order is *Laurencia*, which has a solid cartilaginous round or compressed inarticulate compound pinnate or rarely forked frond, studded with ovate capsules, opening by a terminal pore. This genus contains some of our more common *Algæ*, as *L. obtusa* and *pinnatifida*, the latter of which is sometimes eaten under the name of Pepper Dulse, while *L. obtusa* forms the greater part of what is now sold in the shops as Corsican Moss. Both of these are found equally in the north and south hemispheres. No *Algæ* are more subject to variation.   [M. J. B.]

LAURENTIA. A genus of *Lobeliaceæ*, consisting of low-growing annual plants, with tufted leaves, axillary or racemose inflorescence, and blue or rose-coloured flowers. They are natives of extra-tropical Australia, and of the Cape of Good Hope. The genus is mainly distinguished from its allies by the ovate calyx tube, and the straight tube of the corolla, whose limb is divided into five nearly equal segments, or is somewhat bilabiate.   [M. T. M.]

LAURÉOLE. (Fr.) *Daphne Laureola.*

LAURESTINE, or LAURUSTINUS. *Viburnum Tinus.*

LAURIER. (Fr.) *Laurus.* — ALEXANDRIN. *Ruscus racemosus.* — ALEXANDRIN DES ALPES. *Streptopus amplexifolius.* — AMANDIER. *Cerasus Laurocerasus.* — À SAUCE. *Laurus nobilis.* — AU LAIT. *Cerasus Laurocerasus.* — AUX CRÊMES, *Cerasus Laurocerasus.* — AVOCAT. *Persea gratissima.* — BENJOIN. *Benzoin odoriferum.* — CERISE. *Cerasus Laurocerasus.* — D'APOLLON. *Laurus nobilis.* — DE PORTUGAL. *Cerasus lusitanica.* — DE SAINT ANTOINE. *Epilobium spicatum.* DU MISSISSIPI. *Cerasus caroliniana.* — SASSAFRAS. *Sassafras officinalis.* — TIN. *Viburnum Tinus.* — TULIPIER. *Magnolia grandiflora.*

LAURIER-ROSE. (Fr.) *Nerium Oleander.* — DES ALPES. *Rhododendron ferrugineum.*

LAURINE. (Fr.) A kind of olive.

LAURUS. Under the common name of Laurel many very different plants are met with in gardens, but Bay or Noble Laurel, *L. nobilis*, is the only one which is properly so called. The genus *Laurus* gives its name to the order *Lauraceæ*, and is distinguished by the leaves, which have a single midrib, and by the twelve stamens all of which are fertile, with two-celled anthers, and two glands, one at each side. In the female flower the succulent fruit is surrounded by the persistent base of the calyx. The Bay Laurel, *L. nobilis*, is a native of the south of Europe, and is commonly cultivated in this country as an evergreen shrub, as it usually proves hardy enough to resist our winters. In its native countries it attains a height of thirty or forty or even sixty feet, but never loses its shrub-like character. Its leaves are evergreen, lance-shaped, with an agreeable aromatic slightly bitter taste; its flowers are yellowish and inconspicuous, and its fruits are succulent and of the size of a small cherry. From their agreeable flavour the leaves of the Bay are made use of by cooks and confectioners, and without the hazard that attends upon the use of the leaves of the cherry-laurel, which are frequently substituted for those of the Bay. The dried figs that are imported into this country are usually packed with these leaves. From the fruit is expressed a butter-like substance known as oil of Bays, which has been used as an external stimulant, and still finds a use in veterinary medicine.

The Laurel is one of the plants called *Daphne* by the ancients, and is figured under that name in the Rinuccini MS. of Dioscorides, now in the possession of Sir Thomas Phillips. The branches of this plant were likewise used to form the crowns placed on the heads of the heroes of antiquity, and on the statues of the gods: hence perhaps the name from *laus*, praise, and also the specific name 'noble.' See BENZOIN, CINNAMOMUM, CAMPHORA, PERSEA, and SASSAFRAS. One of the Laurels is figured in Plate 11 d. [M. T. M.]

LAVANDE MÂLE. (Fr.) *Lavandula Spica.*

LAVANDULA. A genus of *Labiatæ* known by its ovate ribbed calyx; its two-lipped corolla, the upper lip of which is two-lobed and the lower three-lobed; and its four stamens which are bent downwards. The common Lavender, *L. vera*, is a native of the south of Europe, but is largely cultivated in this country for the sake of its agreeable perfume, and for the oil on which this property depends. It is an undershrub two to three feet high, with ascending striated branches; linear hoary leaves, which in the young state are rolled under at the edges; and greyish-blue flowers which are borne in compact spikes. The flowers and leaves of this plant are stated to have been used by the ancients to perfume their baths, whence perhaps the name, from *lavare*, to wash. They are still used by housewives to perfume their stores of linen, and prevent the access of moth. The essential oil of Lavender is procured by distillation from the flowers, and is much prized for its agreeable odour; when dissolved in spirits of wine, and mixed with other perfumes, it forms the much-appreciated Lavender Water. The Red Lavender drops of the druggists consist merely of a spirituous solution of the oils of Lavender and Rosemary, mixed with certain aromatic and colouring materials. They are used frequently as a stimulant and cordial in cases of flatulence, hysteria, or faintness.

Another species, *L. Spica*, yields oil of Spike, which is of a darker colour and less agreeable perfume than true oil of Lavender. The oil procured from this plant, together with that from *L. Stœchas*, are used by painters on porcelain, and by artists in the preparation of varnishes. The last-named plant is employed as an expectorant and antispasmodic by the Arabs.

Besides these, other species natives of the Canary Isles, Madeira, &c., are cultivated in greenhouses; some of them are remarkable for the elegance of their leaves, which are more or less deeply divided in a pinnate manner. *L. Stœchas* is moreover remarkable for the large size of some of the uppermost bracts of the spike, which are of a beautiful violet colour.   [M. T. M.]

LAVANÈSE. (Fr.) *Galega officinalis.*

LAVATERA. A genus of *Malvaceæ* chiefly confined to Europe and Western Asia, abounding principally in the countries bordering on the Mediterranean, and apparently preferring the vicinity of the sea, one species extending as far north as the British Isles. They are shrubby plants, sometimes having woody stems two to three feet high, their leaves being roundish and lobed, and their flowers having a three to six-lobed involucre, a five-lobed true calyx, five or more carpels or ovaries arranged in a circle round a thick axis, and as many styles. *L. arborea*, the Sea or Tree Mallow, is a common southwest European plant, growing upon rocks on the sea-shores, occasionally found in a wild state on the south and west coasts of England and Ireland, and also on the Bass Rock in the Frith of Forth, but more frequently seen in places where it has escaped from cultivation, it being a common plant in sea-coast cottage gardens. In a wild state it is usually three or four feet high, but when cultivated it attains a height of eight or ten feet, and its stem is three or four inches thick. The pale purple-red flowers grow in long racemes at the ends of annual flowering branches. Like the rest of mallowworts the Tree Mallow contains an abundance of mucilaginous matter, and a large quantity of fibre. It has lately been recommended for cultivation as a fibre-yielding plant, but the quality of its fibre is not very good. [A. S.]

LAVATÈRE D'HYÈRES. (Fr.) *Lavatera Olbia.*

LAVENDER. *Lavandula vera.* —, FRENCH. *Lavandula Spica.* —, SEA. *Statice.*

LAVENDER COLOUR. Pale blue, with a slight mixture of grey.

LAVENDER-COTTON. *Santolina.*

LAVER. A condiment prepared from the common *Porphyra*, which is greatly esteemed by some, while to others it is an object of unmitigated disgust. The taste for it, like that for olives, is only acquired by use. The best way of preparing it for table is to mix the quantity required for immediate use with a few tablespoonfuls of stock, and a little lemon-juice. It is then to be made quite hot in a well-tinned or silver saucepan, and poured upon toast. Green Laver is *Ulva latissima.* [M. J. B.]

LAVOIR DE VÉNUS. (Fr.) *Dipsacus sylvestris.*

LAVOISIERA. A genus of *Melastomaceæ*, consisting of shrubs with dichotomous erect branches, opposite decussate sessile leaves, and terminal bracteated showy flowers, with a five to ten-toothed calyx, five to ten petals, and ten to twenty stamens, the anthers with a short beak, and a single pore. The fruit is a capsule covered by the calyx. There are about twenty species, natives of Brazil. [J. H. B.]

LAVRADIA. A genus of *Sauvagesiaceæ*, consisting of smooth undershrubs, with crowded alternate stipuled leaves, and white or rose-coloured panicles, bracteated flowers, having a five-parted calyx, five hypogynous convolute petals, hypogynous stamens, the outer ones petaloid staminodia, and a free ovary three-celled at the base and one-celled at the apex. The few species are natives of Brazil. [J. H. B.]

LAWRENCELLA *rosea* is a very pretty dwarf Swan River annual, described by Lindley as forming a genus of *Compositæ*, of the tribe *Gnaphalieæ*. It resembles *Rhodanthe*, but is said to be handsomer, and differs in the achenes being covered with long clavate glands, and in the pappus not being plumose. The leaves are said to be fragrant.

LAWRENCIA. The name of a small malvaceous herb of Tasmania, having small flowers arranged in densely-crowded spikes, provided with numerous bracts ; each flower has an involucel of three segments, and an inner bell-shaped five-cleft calyx, five lance-shaped petals, and reniform two-valved anthers ; and the fruit consists of five one-celled one-seeded indehiscent capsules. [M. T. M.]

LAWSONIA. The celebrated Henna of the East, *L. alba*, or as sometimes called *L. inermis*, the only species of this genus of *Lythraceæ*, is a dwarf shrub eight or ten feet high, bearing smooth oval lance-shaped entire leaves, and panicles of small white sweet-smelling flowers, which are used by Buddhists as offerings to their deities. These flowers have a four-parted persistent calyx without intermediate teeth, four spreading petals, eight stamens, and a four-celled ovary. The fruit is about as large as a pea.

This shrub is grown throughout India, Kurdistan, Persia, Syria, Egypt, and the north of Africa, and the use of its powdered leaves as a cosmetic is very general in all these countries, the practice having descended from very remote ages, as is proved by the evidence of Egyptian mummies, the parts dyed being usually the finger and toe nails, the tips of the fingers, the palms of the hands, and the soles of the feet, to all of which it imparts a reddish-orange colour, which is considered by the Oriental fair sex greatly to enhance their beauty ! It is also used by the men for colouring their beards, and by the Arabs for dyeing the manes and tails of their horses. The preparation of henna usually consists in simply reducing the leaves and young twigs to a fine powder, but sometimes powdered catechu or lucern leaves are mixed with it. When required for use, this powder is made into a pasty mass with hot water, and then spread upon the part to be dyed, being generally allowed to remain on for one night. Henna is the Persian name of the shrub, Khenna the Egyptian, Al Khanna the Arabic, and Mendee the Indian, while in England it is often called Egyptian Privet, and in the West Indies, where it is naturalised, it goes by the name of Jamaica Mignonette. [A. S.]

LAXMANNIA. A genus of Australian herbs, belonging to the *Liliaceæ*. They have the habit of *Polycarpæa*, with filiform procumbent stems, setaceous-acerose leaves, the radical ones crowded, and small purple or white flowers, arranged in sessile axillary or shortly-stalked terminal heads, the perianth being membranaceous, six-parted, and persistent. [J. T. S.]

LAX, LAXUS. Said of parts which are distant from each other, with an open arrangement, such as the panicle among the kinds of inflorescence.

LAYIA. A genus of *Compositæ*, of the tribe *Helianthea*, including *Madaroglossa* of De Candolle. It is near to *Madia*, differing chiefly in the achenes not being laterally compressed, and all, at least those of the disk, being crowned by a pappus of ten to twenty bristles, which are plumose or villous, with long hairs at the base. It consists of seven or eight annual or biennial herbs, natives of California or Oregon, usually pubescent or hirsute and often glandular, with alternate leaves, the lower ones often cut or lobed, and flower-heads more showy than in *Madia*, with white or yellow rays. The name of *Layia* has also been given to a Chinese leguminous tree, which has since been united with *Ormosia*.

LEAD-COLOURED. Slate-coloured, with a slight metallic lustre.

LEAD PLANT. An American name for *Amorpha canescens*.

LEADWORT. *Plumbago.*

LEADWORTS. Lindley's name for the *Plumbaginaceæ*.

LEAF. An expansion of the bark, placed symmetrically with regard to other leaves, and performing the offices of respiration and digestion when in its perfect condition. In an incomplete or modified state, it constitutes all the forms of the appendages of the axis. It is *simple* when not cut into separate parts, and *compound* when divided into other distinct parts.

LEAF-BUDS. Buds from which leaves only are produced; they are called *normal* when produced at the axils, *adventitious* when they occur in places not axillary, and *latent* when they are undiscoverable by the naked eye.

LEAFLET. One of the divisions of a compound leaf.

LEAF-LIKE. The same as Foliaceous.

LEAF-STALK. The (unexpanded) base of a leaf, connecting it with the stem.

LEAF-CUP. *Polymnia Uvedalia.*

LEAF, WALKING. *Camptosorus rhizophyllus.*

LEATHER-FLOWER. *Clematis Viorna;* also *Byrsanthes.*

LEATHER-WOOD. *Dirca.*

LEATHERY. The same as Coriaceous.

LEAVENWORTHIA. A genus of *Cruciferæ* from North America, formerly included in *Cardamine*, from which it differs by having the seed wing-margined and the embryo nearly straight, or with the radicle only slightly bent towards the edge of the cotyledons. The flowers also are yellow, which is never the case in *Cardamine* and *Dentaria*. [J. T. S.]

LEBECKIA. A South African genus belonging to the papilionaceous suborder of *Leguminosæ*. The species are shrubs with ternate leaves, or occasionally with one leaflet or with none, the leaf-stalk being then leafy and supplying the place of the true leaf. The flowers have a five-toothed calyx; an ovate standard bent downwards, and a rather sharp keel; ten monadelphous stamens; and a cylindrical many-seeded pod. [M. T. M.]

LEBO. The leaves of the Bread-fruit tree used in the Pacific Islands sewed together to cover food in cooking, in order to keep in the steam.

LECANIODISCUS. A name given by Planchon to a sapindaceous tree or shrub from tropical Africa, which appears, however, scarcely to differ generically from some species of the large genus *Cupania.*

LECANOPTERIS. A name proposed by Blume for a Javanese polypodiaceous fern, remarkable chiefly for its coriaceous pinnatifid fronds, with roundish ovate segments, having the sori immersed in the concave or cupuliform marginal teeth, which are turned back on the surface of the frond. It belongs to the series with the venation anastomosing, and has free included veinlets within the areoles. Sir W. Hooker and Mr. J. Smith both regard it as an abnormal form of *Pleopeltis lomarioides*. [T. M.]

LECANORA. A genus of crustaceous lichens belonging to the order *Parmeliaceæ*, resembling frequently *Lecidea* in appearance, but always distinguished by the border being formed from the thallus. *L. tartarea* affords the Cudbear of commerce; but the most remarkable species in the genus are *L. esculenta* and *affinis*, which are found in Armenia and Algeria, blown about and heaped up by the winds, and are ground up with corn in times of scarcity to eke out the scanty supply. They are, however, a bad substitute, as they contain 66 per cent. of oxalate of lime. These species are either slightly lobed like the brain, or composed of close-packed branches. Their early stage of growth has not been observed, but it is probable that they are attached when young, and become free by a sort of hypertrophy, which nourishes the plant everywhere except at the very base — at least an analogous form of *Parmelia saxatilis* has been described. The natives consider these lichens to be the Manna of the Israelites, and believe that they fall from heaven, as they see them occasionally borne by tempests from distant tracts. [M. J. B.]

LECHEA. A genus of *Cistaceæ*, differing from *Helianthemum* in the petals being reduced to three small ones or entirely deficient, in the fringed stigmas, the ovules two only to each placenta, and in the seeds having a straight embryo. There are four or five species, natives of North America, all low slender much-branched herbs or undershrubs, with numerous small flowers of no beauty.

LECHEGUANA HONEY. A dangerous kind of honey, supposed to be furnished by *Paullinia australis* and *Serjania lethalia.*

LECHENAULTIA. *Leschenaultia.*

LECIDEA. The typical genus of *Lecidinei*, consisting of crustaceous lichens, for the most part adhering closely to rocks or trunks of trees. The weather-stains on stones and the grey patches on trees belong principally to this genus, which is diffused over the whole face of the globe. The fruit-bearing shields have the border coloured like the disk, which is always well-defined in the young plant, though sometimes obliterated in age. [M. J. B.]

LECIDINEI. A natural order of lichens in which the open orbicular disk of the fruit is contained in a distinct proper receptacle. The disk sometimes in age obliterates the margin and becomes convex. The frond frequently consists of a mere crust adhering closely to the substance on which it grows, and scarcely separable from it. It becomes, however, by gentle degrees, foliaceous; and finally erect often branched bodies, as in the reindeer moss (*Cenomyce*) and cup moss, arise from the crust and bear the fruit. The order, in fact, contains some of the most obscure and some of the most beautiful of lichens. *Lecidea murorum* is one of the most common examples of the crustaceous group, and is conspicuous from its golden hue, which is, however, far surpassed by that of *L. elegans*, which flourishes in extreme latitudes. [M. J. B.]

LECYTHIDACEÆ. (*Lecyths.*) A natural order of dicotyledonous plants, belonging to Lindley's myrtal alliance of epigynous Exogens. Large trees, with stipulate leaves and showy flowers, allied to *Myrtaceæ*, but distinguished by the large almond-like seeds, the alternate dotless leaves, and by the stamens being in part collected into a hooded plate. The fruit is a woody capsule, often opening by a lid. They are natives of the warm regions of South America. The seed-vessels are used as cups and bowls. The seeds of *Bertholletia excelsa* are the Brazil or Castanha nuts of the shops. There are about forty species distributed among seven genera. [J. H. B.]

LECYTHIS. A genus of *Lecythidaceæ*, almost exclusively confined to Venezuela, Guiana, and Brazil, where most of the thirty or forty known species attain a large size, their gigantic trunks towering to a height of eighty or more feet, and expanding into large heads of glossy foliage. The flowers have a six-lobed calyx, and six nearly equal petals, the centre being hid by the curious

hood-shaped body to which the sterile stamens are attached, and which serves to protect the fertile stamens seated beneath it. In most species the fruit is very hard and woody, and often of a large size; it is furnished with a lid at the top, which, when the fruit is quite ripe, falls away, and thus permits the escape of the seeds.

Under the name of Sapucaia nuts, the seeds of *L. Zabucajo* are commonly sold in our fruit shops, and they will probably take the place of the closely-allied Brazil nuts, to which they are greatly superior in point of flavour and much easier of digestion. They are rather more than two inches long and one wide, covered with a longitudinally-furrowed corky shell, and grow in large hard woody fruits, shaped like urns, measuring about six inches in diameter, and having close-fitting lids at the top. Our supply comes from Pará, and is principally the produce of the Brazilian forests.

L. Ollaria is another species producing large fruits, commonly known as Monkey Pots, but its seeds are not so palatable as those of the last, leaving a bitter flavour in

Lecythis Ollaria.

the mouth. Its bark is composed of a great number (upwards of a hundred have been counted) of layers, not thicker than writing paper, which the Indians separate by beating, and employ, under the name of Tauaré, for the wrappers of cigarettes. [A. S.]

LEDEBOURIA. A genus of bulbous plants from India, referred to *Liliaceæ* by some authors, and to *Melanthaceæ* by others. They have broadly-lanceolate root-leaves, spotted like those of *Orchis maculata*, and scapes terminating in a raceme of bluish flowers, with a six-leaved bell-shaped deciduous perianth; six stamens with introrse anthers. The cells of the capsule are one-seeded. [J. T. S.]

LEDGERIA. *Cyrtosia.*

LEDOCARPUM. A genus of small Chilian shrubs belonging to *Oxalidaceæ*. They have alternate, rarely opposite, three-parted leaves, with linear revolute segments, and rather large yellow terminal solitary flowers on long peduncles. The flowers have five sepals, with as many linear bracts on the outside ; five petals, ten free stamens, and a five-celled capsule. [J. T. S.]

LÉDON, or **LÈDE.** (Fr.) *Ledum.*

LEDUM. A genus of heathworts, having the calyx five-toothed, and the seed-vessel with five cells, each containing numerous small seeds, the outer coat of which is soft and forms a wing-like border at each end. The species are small shrubs, natives of the colder parts of the northern hemisphere ; their leaves are of hard texture, usually with rust-coloured down on the lower surface. One of them, *L. palustre,* is known by the name of Labrador Tea, on account of its use. [G. D.]

LEEA. A genus of *Vitaceæ,* the type of the suborder *Leeæ,* distinguished by its petals being united at the base, by its monadelphous stamens, and by its three to six-celled ovaries, with the ovules solitary in each cell. The tendrils which are present in the true vines are absent in this suborder. They are rough shrubby plants (rarely trees) found in tropical Asia, Africa, and the Mauritius, and have opposite pinnate or bi-tri-pinnate leaves, and peduncles opposite the leaves, cymosely branched, with small greenish-yellow flowers, the petals united to the staminal cup, which is five-lobed, and has the five filaments adnate outside between the lobes. [J. T. S.]

LEE-CHEE, or **LITCHI** *Nephelium Litchi.*

LEEK. *Allium Porrum.* —, STONE. *Allium fistulosum.* —, VINE. *Allium Ampeloprasum.*

LEERSIA. A genus of grasses belonging to the tribe *Oryzeæ.* Most of the species have the inflorescence in lax panicles ; and the pales of the florets ribbed, thin, paper-like, of equal length, the outer somewhat boat-shaped. There are about a dozen species, which have an extensive range over some of the warmer parts of the globe ; only one extends so far north as the British Isles, namely, *L. oryzoides,* which is found in wet ditches through the counties of Sussex, Surrey, and Hampshire, though it seldom flowers there. [D. M.]

LEGNOTIDEÆ. (*Cassipoureæ.*) A tribe of *Rhizophoraceæ,* sometimes regarded as a distinct order. It consists of tropical trees or shrubs, with opposite entire stipulate leaves, and axillary solitary or clustered flowers, having the calyx bell-shaped, four to five-cleft ; the petals four to five, fringed ; and the stamens two or three times as many as the petals, distinct, with free filaments, and two-celled introrse anthers. The ovary is superior, three to five-celled ; ovules two or more in each cell ; style simple ; stigma blunt. Fruit baccate or capsular. Lindley considers them to be allied to *Loganiaceæ. Cassipourea* is the principal genus. [J. H. B.]

LEGUME. The fruit of leguminous plants, as the pod of the pea ; a solitary two-valved carpel, bearing its seeds on the ventral suture only.

LEGUMINOSÆ. (*Fabaceæ, Leguminous plants.*) A natural order of dicotyledons belonging to Lindley's rosal alliance of perigynous Exogens. Herbs, shrubs, or trees, with alternate usually compound stipulate leaves. Calyx five-parted, hypogynous, the odd segment inferior ; petals usually five, sometimes one or more abortive, papilionaceous or regular, the odd petal superior ; stamens definite or indefinite, perigynous, rarely hypogynous, distinct, or united in one or more bundles ; ovary superior, one-celled, one or many-seeded, sometimes consisting of one carpel, sometimes of two or five ; style and stigma simple. Fruit a legume or a drupe ; seeds with or without albumen ; embryo with large cotyledons.

This order is a large one, and the plants occur in all parts of the world, but are abundant in tropical countries. It has been divided into three suborders—1. *Papilionaceæ* : petals papilionaceous imbricate, upper one exterior ; 2. *Cæsalpinieæ* : petals imbricated, upper one interior ; 3. *Mimoseæ* : petals valvate in æstivation. Some of the plants are nutritious, others tonic and astringent, others purgative, and a few poisonous. They supply timber, fibres, gums, dyes, and various economical substances. Amongst the useful plants of the order may be noted, beans, peas, lentils, kidneybeans, and pulse of various kinds, lupins, clover, lucerne, medick, sainfoin, liquorice, tragacanth, indigo, and kino. Among the poisonous plants are *Coronilla varia, Cytisus Laburnum, Gompholobium uncinatum,* and *Physostigma venenosum,* the ordeal bean of Calabar. There are about 550 genera and 7,000 species. Examples : *Lotus, Pisum, Vicia, Phaseolus, Cæsalpinia, Cassia, Acacia.* [J. H. B.]

LEHMANNIA. A Peruvian undershrub constituting a genus of *Solanaceæ,* or of *Atropaceæ* according to Miers. It has decurrent lance-shaped leaves, and racemes of dull purple flowers, the corollas of which are funnel-shaped with a short tube and a bell-shaped somewhat oblique plaited and five-toothed limb. By these latter characters the genus is distinguished from *Nicotiana.* [M. T. M.]

LEIANTHUS. A genus of *Gentianaceæ,* very closely allied to *Lisianthus* and *Tachia.* The points of distinction reside in the corolla which is regular ; in the stamens which are bent downwards, and protrude beyond the corolla ; and in the fruit which is one-celled, with the margins of the valves bent inwards. The leaves are opposite, and have sheathing connate stalks. The species are natives of the West Indies and Mexico. *L. nigrescens* has pendent purplish flowers, which in outward appearance are somewhat like those of *Atragene. L. longiflorus* has yellow tubular flowers. Both are highly ornamental. [M. T. M.]

LEICHARDTIA. A genus of Australian *Asclepiadaceæ,* having a five-parted calyx, an urceolate corolla with the tube beardless within, and the throat with a thickened ring, a five-lobed staminal crown, with the leaflets undivided, erect pollen-masses, and a scarcely divided stigma. *L. australis* is a climbing shrub, with linear acute leaves, and flowers in fascicles.   [T. M.]

LEIOCARPUS. A genus of *Euphorbiaceæ*, established by Blume for two Javanese shrubs referred to the tribe of *Buxeæ*, but the precise affinities of which are as yet very imperfectly known.

✸LEIOPHYLLUM. A genus of heathworts, having the calyx in five deep divisions; and the capsule five-celled, opening by as many valves at the top, and containing numerous small ovate seeds. The only species is a native of New Jersey, where it is called Sand Myrtle.   [G. D.]

LEIOSPERMUM. A genus of *Cunoniaceæ*, allied to *Weinmannia*, differing in the deciduous calyx, and the flat (not urceolate) disk; the seeds also are glabrous, not hairy. They are New Zealand trees or shrubs, with opposite simple or pinnate leaves, having jointed leaf-stalks and caducous stipules; and the flowers are racemose.   [J. T. S.]

LEIOTHAMNUS. A genus of *Gentianaceæ*, represented by an Andean shrub, with opposite stalked leaves, axillary incurved flower-stalks provided with large bracts, a wingless calyx with five overlapping concave divisions, a salver-shaped deciduous corolla, its limb divided into five slightly unequal lobes, and five stamens inserted into a ring-like membrane, lining the base of the tube of the corolla, the anthers arrow-shaped, finally revolute.   [M. T. M.]

LEMAIREA. A genus of *Goodeniaceæ*, proposed by De Vriese for an Amboyna plant, resembling a *Scævola*, except that the style is said to be deprived of the indusium considered as characteristic of the order.

LEMANEA. A curious genus of green-spored *Algæ* belonging to the natural order *Batrachospermeæ*, consisting of one or two species which grow mostly in sub-Alpine torrents. The first growth is precisely that of a conferva, but the walls of the frond at length become cellular, and are coated within with two or three layers of colourless cells, which give off tufts of necklace-like threads, the ultimate joints of which are the spores. It is, in point of structure, like a *Batrachospermum*, turned inside out. *L. fluviatilis* and *torulosa* occur not unfrequently in this country, the latter also in North America.   [M. J. B.]

LEMMAPHYLLUM. *Drymoglossum.*

LEMNACEÆ. A synonym of *Pistiaceæ*.

LEMNA. The Duckweed, the typical genus of *Pistiaceæ*. The species have a membranous urn-shaped spathe or flower sheath; flowers proceeding from immediately below the edge of the frond; stamens one to two; anthers two-celled. The plants float on water, and are propagated chiefly by buds. The 'green mantle of the standing pool' is formed chiefly by *L. minor*. There are six species, natives of Britain.   [J. H. B.]

LEMONIA. A genus of *Rutaceæ*, named in honour of Sir Charles Lemon, an enlightened patron of science and of horticulture. *L. spectabilis* is a Cuban shrub with ternate leaves, and axillary clusters of beautiful rose-coloured flowers, recognised by the following characters: calyx of five sepals, the two outer much larger than the three inner ones; corolla salver-shaped, with an oblique five-parted limb; stamens five, attached to the hairy inner surface of the corolla tube, two fertile sessile, three sterile, projecting from the tube, horned, glandular; ovary five-celled, surrounded by a lobed disk: stigma five-lobed. Fruit of five two-valved carpels each with one seed.   [M. T. M.]

LEMON. The fruit of *Citrus Limonum*. There are many varieties, some of which bear the names of Citron, Cedrato, Genoa, or Wax Lemons. —, JAVA. *Citrus javanica.* —, MEDIAN. *Citrus Medica.* —, PEAR. A variety of *Citrus Limetta.* —, PEARL. *Citrus margarita.* —, SWEET. *Citrus Lumia.* —, WATER. *Passiflora laurifolia.* —, WILD. *Podophyllum peltatum.*

LEMON-COLOURED. The purest yellow, without any brightness; as in a lemon when ripe.

LENS-SHAPED. The same as Lenticular.

LENTIBULARIACEÆ. (*Utricularieæ, Utriculineæ, Butterworts.*) A natural order of dicotyledons, belonging to Lindley's bignonial alliance of perigynous Exogens. Herbs growing in water or in wet places, with radical leaves, which are either undivided or cut into filiform root-like segments, bearing little bladders; and producing irregular showy flowers. Calyx divided, persistent; corolla bilabiate, irregular; stamens two, included, with one-celled anthers; ovary superior, one-celled, with a free central placenta. Fruit a one-celled capsule; seeds exalbuminous. Most abundant in the tropics. There are four genera, and about 180 species. *Pinguicula* and *Utricularia* are familiar examples.   [J. H. B.]

LENTICELLÆ (adj. LENTICELLATE). Lenticular glands. Rudimentary roots appearing on the surface of the stems of many trees in the form of small conical swellings.

LENTICULÆ. The spore-cases of certain fungals.

LENTICULAR, LENTIFORM. Lens-shaped; resembling a double convex lens.

LENTIGINOSE. Covered with minute dots, as if dusted.

LENTILS. The seeds of *Ervum Lens*, from which Revalenta Arabica is prepared.

LENTILLE, or **L. COMMUNE.** (Fr.) *Ervum Lens.* — D'EAU. *Lemna minor.* — D'ESPAGNE. *Lathyrus sativus.*

LENTILLON. (Fr.) *Ervum Lens minor.*

LENTINUS. A large genus of gill-bearing *Fungi*, distinguished principally from *Agaricus* by their tough substance, and from *Panus* by their thin-toothed gills. Two or three species are found in this country, and a few more in Europe and North America, the maximum being attained in hot countries, where they are the ornaments of the woods from their beautiful forms, elegant sculpture, and various clothing. The tough substance renders them unfit for food, but easy of preservation, so that more is known of them than of most tropical *Agaricini*, as they are brought home by every collector, when the more watery and fleshy species are neglected.　　[M. J. B.]

LENTISCUS. *Pistacia Lentiscus.*

LENTISQUE. (Fr.) *Pistacia Lentiscus.*

LENZITES. A genus of gill-bearing *Fungi*, distinguished from *Agaricus* by its tough corky substance and gills. It leads in fact directly through *Dædalea* to the pore-bearing *Fungi*, the gills in certain states being so connected with transverse processes as almost to constitute pores. *L. betulina* is our commonest species, and is often very beautiful from the purity of its hymenium, and the zoned velvety pileus. It occurs on stumps of various trees, and on wrought wood. *L. scoparia* is often very rich in colouring, showing various tints of brown and reddish-yellow. It is sometimes abundant on imported deals, but is scarcely indigenous.　　[M. J. B.]

LEOCHILUS. A genus of South American epiphytes of the orchid family, allied to *Oncidium*, from which it is distinguished by the arms of the column being placed below the stigma, and by the presence of a honey-pore at the base of the lip. The species, which are not numerous, are pseudo-bulbous, and produce small, often yellowish flowers in racemes.　　[T. M.]

LEONIA. This genus, referred by Mr. Bentham to the *Violaceæ*, consists of two species, one found in Peru, the other in Brazil. They form moderately high trees, and have alternate entire leaves, full of pellucid dots, with small deciduous stipules at their base. The flowers are small, full of dots, with a five-parted calyx of round fringed lobes; five petals slightly cohering, but ultimately free; and four stamens, with their filaments united into a short tube. *L. glycycarpa* produces edible fruit, greatly relished by the Peruvians, who call the tree Achocon. It is of a roundish form, about the size of a peach, with a rough yellow rind, marked with a kind of network, and contains from six to ten seeds, and a soft whitish pulp or flesh possessing an agreeable sweet taste.　　[A. S.]

LEONOTIS. A genus of herbaceous or somewhat shrubby plants belonging to the *Labiatæ*, well distinguished among its congeners by the elongated concave entire upper lip of the corolla, and the very short lower lip which is nearly equally three-cleft.

The species inhabit the southern hemisphere, and are cultivated in English conservatories for the sake of their handsome orange flowers, which grow in dense whorls, with numerous very narrow bracts. The Greek name *Leonotis* (or Lion's ear) was given from some fancied resemblance of the corolla to a lion's ear. One species, *L. Leonurus*, a native of the Cape of Good Hope, received its second systematic, and its popular name Lion's tail, from the assumed resemblance of the inflorescence to a lion's tail, an infelicitous combination of not very apposite terms. French, *Queue de lion*; German, *Löwenschwanz.*　　[C. A. J.]

LEONTICE. A small genus of *Berberidaceæ*, of Southern and Eastern Europe, and Western and Northern Asia, consisting of smooth herbaceous plants with tuberous roots, which annually send up several variously-cut leaves, and stems about a foot or a foot and a half high, bearing smaller leaves, and racemes of small yellow flowers. The calyx consists of six coloured sepals; the corolla of six smaller stalked petals, bearing scales at the bottom on the inside. The fruits are inflated or bladder-like, of a thin texture, marked with netted veins. *L. Leontopetalum* is a strong-growing herbaceous plant, having large long-stalked leaves, composed of six inversely egg-shaped stalked leaflets arranged in threes. It is commonly called Lion's leaf, on account of a fancied resemblance between the leaves and the imprint of a lion's foot. Its tuberous roots, sometimes called Lion's turnips, are pounded and used at Aleppo, instead of soap, for washing woollen garments, and more particularly for taking out spots or stains from Cashmere shawls. Medicinal properties were formerly ascribed to them, Dioscorides attributing to them the power of allaying the pain caused by snake-bites; and the Turks of the present day employ them as an antidote to the effects of overdoses of opium.　　[A. S.]

LEONTODON. A genus of *Compositæ*, having a perennial rootstock, from which proceed, near to the ground, a number of spreading toothed leaves. The flower-stalks are usually leafless, the flowers yellow, all strap-shaped, surrounded by several rows of overlapping bracts, but the receptacle on which the flowers are immediately placed is destitute of bracts. The fruits taper above into a short beak, and are surmounted by a pappus of feathery hairs, which latter circumstance serves to separate the genus from the nearly-allied *Taraxacum*. The species are widely spread over Europe and central Asia. Three of them, according to Mr. Bentham, are British, viz. *L. hispidus, autumnalis* (formerly ranged under *Apargia*), and *hirtus* (which has been also called *Thrincia*). *L. hispidus* is covered with short hairs that are frequently stellate.　　[M. T. M.]

LEONTOPODIUM. A genus established by Cassini and adopted by De Candolle for the *Gnaphalium Leontopodium* from the Alps of Europe, and two closely-allied species of varieties from the mountains of Asia, which differ slightly in the pappus from other species. They are also remarkable for their dense clusters of flower-heads surrounded by a kind of radiating general involucre of floral leaves, all densely clothed with a close white cotton.

LEONURUS. A small genus of *Labiatæ*, consisting of erect herbs, with the leaves more or less lobed, and the small flowers in close axillary verticillasters, forming long leafy spikes. The calyx has five prominent ribs and five equal spreading almost prickly teeth; the corolla has a shortish tube, a concave entire upper lip, and a spreading three-lobed lower one; the stamens form two pairs; and the nuts are flat, angular at top. *L. Cardiaca*, or Motherwort, is found in wastes, hedges, &c., in Europe and Russian Asia, and has pinkish flowers with a very hairy upper lip. The genus is allied to *Stachys*, differing chiefly in the shape of the nuts.   [T. M.]

LEOPARD'S BANE. *Doronicum*; also *Senecio Doronicum*, *Aronicum Clusii*, and *Paris quadrifolia*.

LEOPARD-WOOD. The wood of *Brosimum Aubletii*: also said to be applied to a fancy wood of the palm tribe.

LEOPOLDINIA. A small genus of Brazilian palms, comprising three or four species, existing in considerable numbers on the Amazon and Rio Negro, and forming trees of medium size bearing terminal unarmed pinnate leaves, and having the upper part of their stems covered with a copious network of fibres. Their flower-spikes are very much branched, with two small spathes, the male flowers being seated on the upper, and the female on the lower part of the spike.
L. Piassaba is one of the palms which yield the Piassaba or Piaçaba fibre, now so extensively employed in this country by brush-makers as a substitute for bristles, and also for making the stout street brooms used in most large cities. Two distinct varieties of this fibre are recognised in commerce, one a coarse kind obtained from *Attalea funifera* and imported from Bahia; and the other a finer kind brought from Para, the produce of the *Leopoldinia*, which is found growing in great abundance on the extensive plains between the Rio Negro and Orinoco rivers, forming entire forests. It attains a height of fifteen or twenty, or occasionally as much as forty feet, and the fibre or beard, as it is usually called, which is the envelope of the young leaves, hangs down all round and completely covers the trunk quite to the ground, except in very tall trees, the lower part of whose trunk is generally bare.   [A. S.]

LEOTIA. A genus of the helvellaceous order of pyrenomycetous *Fungi*, distinguished by its gelatinous substance, and the button-shaped head, the borders of which are rounded and confluent below with the stem. *L. lubrica* is a common inhabitant of our woods, and varies in tint from dull yellow to olive.   [M. J. B.]

LEPALS. Sterile stamens.

LEPANTHES. A genus of minute-flowered West Indian orchids, closely related to *Pleurothallis*.   [T. M.]

LEPICYSTIS. *Goniophlebium*.

LEPIDADENIA. A genus of *Lauraceæ*, represented by an Indian tree, with ribbed leaves, and hermaphrodite flowers in umbels surrounded by an involucre. The perianth has six nearly equal segments; stamens twelve in four rows, the two inner surrounded by scales, whence the name; anthers four-celled, four-valved.   [M. T. M.]

LEPIDANCHE. A proposed genus of *Cuscutaceæ*, but generally accepted as a section of *Cuscuta*, including those species which have five sepals in the calyx, a subtubulose urceolate corolla, a two-celled ovary always with two styles, and a two-celled capsule with no more than one seed in each cell.   [W. C.]

LEPIDANTHUS. A genus of *Restiaceæ* from the Cape of Good Hope, with simple leafless stems, and spicate terminal male flowers, which have three glumes, and three stamens.   [J. T. S.]

LEPIDES (adj. LEPIDOTE). Scurfs; minute peltate scales, such as cover the foliage of *Elæagnus*.

LEPIDIUM. The Cresses form a very extensive genus of *Brassicaceæ* (*Cruciferæ*) widely spread throughout the temperate regions of the earth, but abounding in the greatest number in the northern hemisphere. They are annual or perennial herbs, occasionally with woody stems, and have entire or variously cut leaves, and numerous small white flowers arranged in terminal racemes, which grow longer while fruiting. The genus is distinguished from its congeners by characters taken from its pods, which are egg-shaped or oblong, entire, notched or two-lobed at the apex, and compressed at right angles to the narrow partition dividing them into two boat-shaped valves.
L. oleraceum is confined to New Zealand, where it is found growing abundantly upon the sea-shores, and, being a good antiscorbutic, it was eagerly sought after by early voyagers as a remedy for the dreadful scurvy with which their crews were so frequently affected. The natives call it Eketera; and it is now cultivated as a pot-herb. It is a smooth erectish branching plant, with a short woody stem and narrow-oblong or wedgeshaped leaves, two or three inches long, the lower ones being sharply serrated, and the upper entire or toothed towards the tip. The natives of the Society and Sandwich Islands make use of *L. Piscidium* for catching fish. It, in common with several other plants, possessing the property of intoxicating them so that they float upon the surface in a helpless insensible state, and are then easily taken. The

whole plant possesses an extremely pungent taste.   [A. S.]

L. *sativum*, the Garden Cress, is a hardy annual whose native country is stated to be Persia. It has been cultivated in this country since 1548, and is a comparatively dwarf uninteresting plant, having oblong alternate deeply-divided leaves, smooth erect branching stems, and small white flowers producing an orbicular winged seed-pod. The chief purpose for which it is grown in gardens is for its leaves, which are cut and used in a young state with those of mustard for salads, to which it gives a peculiarly warm and grateful flavour. It is on this account very generally cultivated and esteemed as one of the most useful plants for small salads that we possess. The leaves when full grown are frequently employed for garnishing like those of parsley.   [W. B. B.]

LEPIDOCARYUM. A genus of palms containing two species found in moist places in forests on the banks of the Rio Negro in Brazil. Both have slender stems of ten or twelve feet high, the upper part being covered with remnants of the stalks of dead leaves, and bearing at the summit a tuft of fern-shaped irregularly-cleft leaves with bristly margins. They have perfect and imperfect flowers; and their flower-spike consists of numerous little catkins proceeding from sheathing spathes at short intervals along its branches; the male catkins being longer than those of the female, and having their flowers in pairs within cup-shaped bracts, while in the latter they are solitary. Their fruits are of a reddish-brown colour and vary from the size of a hazel-nut to that of a pigeon's egg, and, like those of other palms belonging to the same section (*Calameæ*), are covered with hard scales arranged like plates of mail in ancient armour. Neither of the species (*L. gracile* and *L. tenue*) possesses any special feature of interest.   [A. S.]

LEPIDONEURON. *Nephrolepis.*

LEPIDOSTACHYS. A name given by Wallich to a genus of East Indian *Euphorbiaceæ*, which proves to be the same as the *Scepa* of Lindley and the *Aporosa* of Blume.

LEPIDOSTEPHANUS. *Achyrochæna.*

LEPIDOTIS. *Lycopodium.*

LEPIGONUM. *Spergularia.*

LEPINGIA *germanorum* is a procumbent branching Californian annual, forming a genus of *Compositæ*, which has the aspect of an *Astereœ* with the style of one of the *Senecionidæ*. The lower leaves are pinnatifid, the upper ones entire, the flower-heads yellow, not showy, either terminal or lateral, without rays. The involucre is imbricated, the receptacle naked, the achenes silky, villous, with a pappus of rather stiff bristles.

LEPIOTA. The annulus of certain fungals.

LEPISANTHES. A genus proposed by Blume for two or three East Indian trees which may be better considered as forming a subgenus or section of *Cupania*.

LEPISMA. A cup-shaped disk.

LEPISMIUM. A small genus of *Cactaceæ* at one time regarded as a section of *Rhipsalis*, but now separated, and characterised by the petal-like leaves of its perianth standing almost erect, while those of *Rhipsalis* are widely expanded; and by its smooth pear-shaped fruits being somewhat buried in the fleshy substance of the branches. The three or four known species are natives of Brazil. They have weak, fleshy, jointed branches, occasionally emitting roots, the joints being sharply three or four-angled, waved along the edges, and bearing tufts of hairs seated upon little cushions in the depressions from out of which the small cream-coloured flowers are produced. *L. commune* and *L. Myosurus* are cultivated in European gardens.   [A. S.]

LEPISTEMON. A genus of *Convolvulaceæ*, containing two species, natives of India and the islands of the Indian Archipelago. They are twining hairy shrubs, with many-flowered axillary peduncles. The calyx consists of five equal sepals; the corolla is tubular and inflated at the base; the five stamens spring from the back of as many large arched hairy scales which are united to the base of the corolla; the ovary is two-celled with two ovules in each cell, and bears a stigma composed of two capitate lobes.   [W. C.]

LEPISTOMA *javanicum* is a twining shrub, with elliptical oblong leaves, and interpetiolar peduncles, growing in the island of Java, and representing a genus of *Asclepiadaceæ*. The calyx is turbinate and has five teeth; the corolla is rotate and five-cleft; whilst the fruit is unknown. Uses not recorded.   [B. S.]

LEPRA (adj. LEPROUS). A white mealy matter, which exudes or protrudes from the surface of some plants; leprosy.

LEPRARIA. An abnormal condition of certain lichens in which the crust is broken up into a dusty mass, occasionally mixed with a few threads. The yellow powdery and white patches which are so common on oak are examples, the one being a condition of some lichen like *Parmelia parietina*, and the latter of *Porina pertusa*. The genus is now, however, justly exploded.   [M. J. B.]

LEPROSE. Having a scurfy appearance.

LEPTADENIA. A genus of *Asclepiadaceæ*, inhabiting tropical and subtropical parts of Africa and Asia, and comprising erect leafless shrubs, or twiners furnished with leaves. There are about a dozen species described, all having a greyish tomentum covering stem and leaves. The flowers are white, small, and arranged in interpetiolar umbels. The calyx is short, the corolla rotate or bell-shaped, the fruit quite smooth on the surface. [B. S.]

LEPTANDRA. *Veronica.*

LEPTANTHUS. A small genus of aquatic herbs belonging to the *Pontederiaceæ*, natives of North America, differing from *Heteranthera* in having the three filaments all alike. *L. graminea* is common in streams in North America, and has much the habit of the narrow-leaved pond-weeds. The small yellow flowers with a salver-shaped perianth float on the surface of the water, and are produced from a one-flowered terminal spathe. [J. T. S.]

LEPTARRHENA. A genus of *Saxifragaceæ*, found on the north-west coast of America, and in Kamtschatka. It is allied to *Saxifraga*, from which it differs by the anthers being four-celled (the partition being incomplete), and by the two carpels adhering only by their bases: a herb with shining evergreen leathery undivided and serrate leaves, resembling those of *Pyrola secunda*; scape with a terminal panicle of small inconspicuous white flowers. [J. T. S.]

LEPTINELLA. A genus of *Compositæ* of the tribe *Anthemideæ*, consisting of four or five prostrate or procumbent herbs with the scent of *Artemisia* or of tansy, all natives of the southern extremity of South America, or of some of the Antarctic islands. They are remarkable for the shape of the minute ray-florets, of which the corolla appears to be formed by a double membrane connected at the summit and the base, with a cavity between them. One species, *L. scariosa*, though possessed of no beauty, is interesting as one of the flowering plants which extend the furthest into the Antarctic regions.

LEPTOCARPUS. A genus of Australian *Restiaceæ*, consisting of leafless herbs, with the stems simple, and the diœcious flowers fasciculate. [J. T. S.]

LEPTOCAULIS. A genus of umbellifers, characterised by each half of the fruit having five inconspicuous ribs, and one oil-vessel (vitta) in each furrow. The species are natives of North America, of no great interest, having umbels of few small white flowers. [G. D.]

LEPTOCERAS. A genus of terrestrial Australian orchids belonging to the *Arethuseæ*. They have solitary or geminate radical leaves, and one or many-flowered scapes, the flowers often fragrant. They have membranaceous sepals, the upper fornicate, the lateral deflexed; clavate erect petals; a lip articulated with the winged column; and four pollen-masses. [T. M.]

LEPTOCHILUS. *Gymnopteris.*

LEPTOCHLOA. A genus of grasses belonging to the tribe *Chlorideæ*. The spikes of inflorescence are disposed in racemes, and the spikelets mostly unilateral, two or more-flowered; glumes keeled; outer pale keeled, three-nerved, with a straight awn.

The species, of which about three dozen are described, are, for the most part, handsome grasses, and chiefly natives of South America and the West Indies. *L. arabica* is found growing near Naples. [D. M.]

LEPTODACTYLON. A genus of *Polemoniaceæ*, though often considered as only a section of *Gilia*. The three species grouped together under this name are distinguished from the other species of *Gilia* by the following characteristics: they are lowly branching perennial herbs, with alternate sessile palmatisect leaves, the segments subulate and needle-like; and the solitary sessile flowers are either terminal or axillary at the tops of the branches; the divisions of the calyx are subulate and prickly; the corolla is somewhat salver-shaped, with entire lobes; the anthers are ovate; and there are many ovules in each cell of the ovary. The species are natives of North America. [W. C.]

LEPTODAPHNE. A genus of Brazilian lauraceous trees, with net-veined leaves, and flowers in panicles. The perianth is funnel-shaped, with a limb of six deciduous segments; stamens nine, in three rows, the outer six fertile, some of them provided with an erect tooth-like appendage; the inner three sterile, sometimes absent, and when present having two glands at their base; the anthers are four-celled. The fruit is fleshy and enclosed within the fleshy base of the perianth. [M. T. M.]

LEPTOGLOSSIS. A genus of Peruvian herbaceous plants of the family *Scrophulariaceæ*. The leaves are hairy; the flowers grow at the extremity of the branches; the corolla is plaited and overlapping in the bud: its limb somewhat two-lipped and salver-shaped. The genus is intermediate between *Schwenkia* and *Browallia*. [M, T. M.]

LEPTOGRAMMA. *Grammitis.*

LEPTOLÆNA *multiflora* is the sole representative of a genus of *Chlænaceæ*, inhabiting Madagascar, and forming an elegant tree with undulate glabrous leaves, corymbose flowers, a small rather fleshy cylindrical involucre, three sepals longer than the involucre; five petals; ten stamens; and a three-celled capsule, with one or two seeds in each cell. [B. S.]

LEPTOLOBIUM. A genus of tropical leguminous trees and shrubs, almost entirely confined to the forests of Brazil, where some of the species form large timber trees. They have pinnate leaves; deciduous stipules; and flowers in racemes, with the corolla somewhat papilionaceous. The pods are narrow, flat, and of a thin membranous texture. About ten species are known. [A. S.]

LEPTOMERIA. An Australian genus of *Santalaceæ*, abounding in the neighbourhood of Swan River. About twenty species are known, two of them separated by some botanists under the name of *Omphacomeria*. They are broom-like shrubs, with angular or roundish twiggy branches, generally entirely destitute of leaves, or with very small ones only upon the young twigs, and bearing spikes of extremely minute flowers. The fruit is either fleshy and juicy or dry and juiceless, and has a scar at the top surrounded by the remains of the calyx. *L. Billardieri* is a pretty broom-like shrub, growing about six feet high, with erect very slender branches, and numerous spikes of small white flowers producing greenish-red berries, which are called Native Currants in New South Wales and Victoria; they have a pleasant acid taste, combined with a certain degree of astringency. Mixed with other fruits, they are used for making preserves, and in the preparation of cooling acid beverages. The fruit of another species, *L.* (*Omphacomeria*) *acerba*, is also called Currants in Australia, and is used for the same purposes. [A. S.]

LEPTONEMA. A low branching Madagascar shrub, with the habit of a *Vaccinium*, but constituting a genus of *Euphorbiaceæ*, of the tribe *Phyllantheæ*. Dr. Mueller has since referred to the same genus, as a second species, a shrub from tropical Australia.

LEPTOPETALUM. This name, signifying slender or narrow petal, is applied to a Mexican shrub constituting a genus of *Cinchonaceæ*. The flowers are in terminal corymbs, and have a somewhat globular calyx tube, with a four-toothed limb; the corolla is divided into four long very narrow segments; stamens four, equalling the corolla; capsule hemispherical, crowned by the teeth of the calyx, and opening by a chink at the top; seeds small, angular. [M. T. M.]

LEPTOPTERIS. A Sumatra plant, proposed by Blume as a distinct genus, but which appears to be the same as the *Medicia* of Gardner, a species of *Gelsemium*.

The name is also sometimes unnecessarily given to those species of *Todea* which have delicate membranaceous fronds and oligocarpous sori. [T. M.]

LEPTOPUS. An East Indian herb proposed by Decaisne as a genus of *Euphorbiaceæ*, but reduced by Baillon to *Andrachne*.

LEPTORHACHIS. A genus of *Euphorbiaceæ* of the tribe *Acalypheæ*, founded by Klotzsch on a Brazilian herbaceous twiner with hastate leaves, which is, however, as yet but little known.

LEPTORHYNCHUS. A genus of *Compositæ* allied to *Helichrysum*, but the florets are all hermaphrodite, and the achenes are narrowed into a slender beak bearing a pappus of simple bristles. There are several species, natives of Australia, all erect herbs with narrow leaves and terminal flower-heads of yellow florets, not so handsome as other everlastings, the involucres being smaller and less scarious.

LEPTOS. In Greek compounds=slender, graceful; as *leptophyllus*, slender-leaved.

LEPTOSEMA. A North Australian papilionaceous shrub, proposed by Bentham as a genus of *Leguminosæ*, which has since been reduced to *Brachysema*.

LEPTOSIPHON. A genus of annuals belonging to the *Polemoniaceæ*, introduced from California by Douglas in 1833. The genus is marked by having a campanulate calyx with very narrow pointed sepals, and a funnel-shaped corolla, the tube of which is very long and slender. All the species have finely-divided leaves and bear their flowers in dense corymbose heads, the colour being yellow, pale blue, white, pink, or various shades of these colours combined. Several species are commonly cultivated in English gardens, and when in bloom present a showy appearance from the abundance of their flowers. [C. A. J.]

LEPTOSPERMUM. A large genus of shrubs or small trees belonging to the *Myrtaceæ*, and nearly all confined to Australia and Tasmania. The leaves are alternate, small, leathery, and full of dots or cells containing oil; and their white flowers are borne on short stalks on the sides of the young branches, either solitary or in little clusters. They have a bell-shaped calyx with five lobes; a corolla of five roundish petals; numerous short free stamens; and a four or five-celled ovary. *L. lanigerum*, a native of Tasmania and South-eastern Australia, is commonly called Tea tree on account of its leaves having been used by the early settlers in those countries as a substitute for tea. It sometimes forms a tree thirty feet high, with a trunk four or five feet in circumference, but in mountainous situations is only a small shrub a few feet in height. Its straight stems were used by the Australian aborigines for making their spears, the points being sharpened with a flint and then hardened by means of fire. *L. scoparium*, the Kahi-Katoa or Manuka of the New Zealanders, a shrub of moderate height, with harsh prickly leaves, produces a very hard heavy wood, but its small size renders it of little value. [A. S.]

LEPTOSTACHYA. A genus of *Acanthaceæ*, containing seventeen species chiefly natives of America and India. They are herbs, rarely shrubs, with opposite leaves, and distant opposite flowers in slender terminal or axillary spikes, furnished with many small bracts and bracteoles. The small calyx is five-parted; the corolla ringent with a longish tube and a two-lipped limb, the upper lip arching and two-toothed, the lower convex and trifid; two stamens are inserted in the tube; and the ovary is two-celled surmounted by a simple style and trifid stigma. This genus is less distinct from its technical character than from its habit and inflorescence. [W. C.]

LEPTOSTEGIA. *Onychium*.

LEPTOSTELMA. The Mexican Daisy (*Erigeron maximum*) is sometimes cultivated under this name. It attains a height of five to seven feet, and is rather handsome when in flower. The whole plant is more or less clothed with short stiff hairs; the lower leaves, a foot long, lanceolate and coarsely toothed, the upper amplexicaul; the flower-heads more than an inch across, the ray-florets strap-shaped, purple, and very narrow. [A. A. B.]

LEPTOTICHUS. Thin-sided; a term applied only to tissue.

LEPTOTES. A small genus of Brazilian orchids of the tribe *Epidendreæ*, distinguished by having the sepals and petals linear spreading and nearly equal; the lip three-lobed, parallel with the short thick column, around which the lateral lobes are convolute; the six pollen-masses incumbent, the two upper ones pear-shaped, the four lower ones unequal and thinner. *L. bicolor*, a pretty epiphyte with thick rush-like leaves, and white flowers blotched on the lip with purple, bears fragrant fruit with the odour of the Tonquin bean or of the sweet vernal grass. This fruit infused in cream gives it, when iced, a mild agreeable flavour, sweeter than vanilla but less penetrating. *L. serrulata* is a second species with larger flowers. [T. M.]

LEPTURUS. A genus of grasses belonging to the tribe *Rottbœlleæ*. The inflorescence is mostly in close round solitary spikelets, imbedded alternately on opposite sides of the rachis; glumes one or two, thick, on the same side of the spikelet, which contains one perfect floret, and the rudiment only of a second floret. The species are mostly natives of the north-east of Europe and New Holland, *L. incurvatus* extends to the British Isles, and grows on most of the salt marshes along the seaboard, where it often furnishes the principal pasture grass. [D. M.]

LEPURANDRA. The Sack-tree of Western India, a tree of the *Artocarpaceæ*, now referred to *Antiaris* and called *A. saccidora*, has been so called. It is a gigantic tree, reaching a height of a hundred feet, with a trunk six feet in diameter, exuding a milky juice when wounded, and having a strong tough fibrous inner bark useful for the manufacture of cordage, and of which the natives, by an ingenious yet simple process, make capital sacks. For this purpose young trees of about a foot in diameter are selected, and cut into junks of the same length as the sack required. These are then soaked for a short time and afterwards beaten with clubs until the outer bark is removed and the inner loosened so that it can readily be separated by turning it inside out. Sometimes a small piece of the wood is left to form the bottom of the sack, but more frequently the bark is pulled entirely off and the bottom sewed up. These sacks are commonly used by the natives of Western India and of Ceylon for carrying rice, &c., and are very strong and elastic. A considerable quantity of milky viscid juice exudes from the fruit when wounded, and hardens into the appearance and consistence of bees' wax, but eventually becomes black and shining; the seeds have an intensely bitter taste. [A. S.]

LEPYRODIA. A genus of Australian *Restiaceæ* with simple leafless stems, and compound spikes of diœcious, or rarely simple spikes of perfect flowers. [J. T. S.]

LEQUÉE. (Fr.) *Lechea*.

LERENA. A species of *Rajania*, whose roots are used in St. Domingo like potatos, and are said to be extremely nutritive.

LERIA. A genus of *Compositæ* of the tribe *Mutisieæ*, consisting of South American perennials, with the leaves all radical and white cottony underneath, and solitary flower-heads on long simple cottony scapes. The inner disk florets are obscurely bilabiate, while the outer radiating ones pass into ligules without any inner lip. The pappus consists of numerous simple bristles. There are about half a dozen species known, none of them in cultivation.

LESCHENAULTIA. A genus of goodeniaceous heath-like shrubs, distinguished by having a tubular calyx with five linear sharp-pointed lobes and a partially two-lipped corolla, the tube of which is split on its upper side. The anthers cohere previous to the opening of the flowers, which are axillary or terminal, of a red, blue, or yellow colour. The leaves are linear and sharp-pointed. The plants are natives of the south and south-west parts of Australia, and are very ornamental. [R. H.]

LESKEA. A genus of pleurocarpous mosses, distinguished from *Hypnum* by its erect more or less symmetrical capsule, and the want in general of intermediate cilia. The limits are not, however, very acutely marked. Our commonest species, *L. sericea*, grows on almost every ash tree, forming silky yellowish-green patches, which are darker when dry, and add much to the picturesque effect of the bark. There are many exotic species. [M. J. B.]

LESSERTIA. A genus of *Leguminosæ* of the suborder *Papilionaceæ*, consisting of herbs or undershrubs with pinnate leaves, and red or purple flowers in axillary racemes. There are nearly twenty species described, all from the Cape Colony. They much resemble the Australian *Swainsona*, both in habit and character, differing chiefly in the pod, which, though membranous as in *Swainsona*, is perfectly flat, and never inflated. None of the species are in cultivation, and few are so showy as those of *Swainsona*.

LESSINGIA. A genus of Californian *Compositæ* consisting of procumbent branched herbs, with thickish leaves, the lower ones pinnatifid, and yellow solitary terminal flower-heads, with an imbricated involucre and naked receptacle; the florets all tubulose, those of the ray larger than the rest. The achenes are silky and compressed, with a pappus of one row, the hairs rigid and scabrous. [T. M.]

LESSONIA. A genus of seaweeds belonging to the natural order *Laminariaceæ*, with a tall thick stem, branched above and bearing at each tip a pair of lanceolate leaves which hang down for a foot or more in length. The species form large submarine forests, and the stems when thrown ashore look like wood; hence they are sometimes collected by seamen for firewood, to their great disappointment when they attempt to use them. They are employed more profitably for knife-handles, and other similar purposes. The blade is fixed in when the plant is moist, and is effectually fastened by its contraction when dry. The stems have a kind of false exogenous growth, of which a representation may be seen in *Berkeley's Introduction to Cryptogamic Botany*, p. 56. The new rings seem to depend upon the growth of the leaves, whereas in the large *Laminarieæ* where a similar structure occurs, it depends upon the development of new roots or holdfasts. *Lessoniæ* are principally at home in the southern hemisphere.　　[M. J. B.]

LETHARGIA. A name applied in vegetable pathology to those cases in which the buds of transplanted plants and grafts, or the embryos of seeds, though still possessed of vitality, are sluggish and either are not developed at all, or are expanded imperfectly. Close pruning is often necessary to overcome this evil in plants which are not removed till spring; and artificial means, as the application of hot water, weak solutions of acids, &c., are sometimes needful to overcome the suspended animation of seeds. Some roots, again, like those of orchids, occasionally lie dormant in the soil for years, where they are excluded from the light by an overgrowth of shrubs. *Ophrys muscifera* and some other species in certain districts appear only after the underwood has been cut down. Portions of the tubers of dahlias, again, if no part of the crown be left, will live for years without throwing out a single bud.　　[M. J. B.]

LETTERED. Marked with letter-like spots.

LETTER-LEAF or **LETTER-PLANT.** *Grammatophyllum.*

LETTER-WOOD. *Brosimum Aubletii,* sometimes called *Piratinera guianensis.*

LETTSOMIA. A name given by Ruiz and Pavon to a genus of *Ternströmiaceæ,* since united with *Freziera;* and by Roxburgh to a convolvulaceous genus which has proved to be identical with *Argyreia.*

LETTUCE. *Lactuca.* —, BLUE. *Mulgedium.* —, CABBAGE. Those varieties of garden lettuce which form low depressed cabbage-like hearts. —, COS. The erect-growing crisp-leaved varieties of garden lettuce. —, FALSE. *Mulgedium.* —, GARDEN. *Lactuca sativa.* —, LAMB'S. *Valerianella olitoria.* —, PRICKLY. *Lactuca Scariola.* —, SEA. *Fucus vesiculosus.* —, WILD. *Lactuca virosa.*

LEUCADENDRON. A genus of proteaceous plants, mostly shrubs or small trees, natives of the Cape of Good Hope and the south-eastern parts of Africa, distinguished by having the calyx either four-cleft or with four sepals, each of which bears a nearly sessile anther, and a filiform style with an oblique club-shaped stigma. The seed-vessel is one-celled, containing a single wingless seed. The involucre is generally imbricated; the diœcious flowers (white or yellow) are produced in small heads; and the leaves are generally sessile, simple, entire, occasionally covered with white silky hairs. *L. argenteum,* the Witteboom or Silver tree of the Cape colonists, was formerly of great importance for firewood, but it is now nearly extirpated.　　[R. H.]

LEUCÆNA. A genus of *Leguminosæ,* of the suborder *Mimoseæ,* characterised by having the ten stamens of a *Mimosa,* with the flat two-valved pod of an *Acacia.* It consists of half a dozen trees or shrubs, all natives of central or South America, or the Pacific Islands, with twice-pinnate leaves, and small white flowers in globular heads. One species, *L. glauca,* is much cultivated as an ornamental tree in most warm climates, and has become naturalised and apparently wild in several parts of Africa and Asia. In Europe it will bear the winter only in the warmer parts of the Mediterranean region, where it is occasionally planted.

LEUCANTHEMUM. A name given to the Ox-eye Daisy, *Chrysanthemum Leucanthemum,* and a few other species, which have been distinguished from other *Chrysanthemums* as a genus on account of some very slight differences in the achenes.

LEUCAS. A genus of *Labiatæ,* having the upper lip of the corolla concave, usually entire and hairy on the outside, the lower lip spreading, its middle lobe largest; having also the end of the style of two unequal pieces, the upper of which is shortest. They are herbs or shrubs, natives chiefly of tropical Asia and Africa. The flowers are white, rarely purple.　　[G. D.]

LEUCERIA. A genus of *Compositæ* of the suborder *Mutisiaceæ,* consisting of eight or nine Chilian herbs, with erect or ascending stems, more or less clothed with white cottony wool. The leaves are mostly pinnately divided, cottony underneath, the flower-heads small in terminal panicles. The involucre is hemispherical and imbricate, the outer florets radiating; the pappus consists of shortly plumose bristles. None of the species offer any particular interest either as useful or ornamental plants.

LEUCHTENBERGIA. A remarkable genus of *Cactaceæ,* of which the only species, *L. principis,* a native of Southern Mexico, has been introduced to European gardens. In this plant the *mammillæ,* as the variously-shaped projections seen in most *Cacti* are called, grow very long, and being of a succulent nature and three-sided shape, they somewhat resemble aloe leaves, but bear tufts of long chaffy or horny scales on their apex. The plant itself grows a foot or more high, the lower part of the stem being about as thick as a man's arm, hard and woody, and covered with the remains of decayed mammillæ, while the upper bears long perfect mammillæ, and looks very much like an artichoke. The flowers, which are produced at the top of the plant among the younger mammillæ, bear a great resemblance to those of *Cereus*, but are distinguished by the tube of their perianth being more cylindrical, and having the stamens growing to its inside as far as the bottom of the petals, after which they converge and meet in the centre, closing up the mouth of the tube. [A. S.]

LEUCO. In Greek compounds = white: thus *leucocarpus* is white-fruited; *hypoleuca*, white beneath, &c.

LEUCOBRYUM. A genus of acrocarpous mosses, having the white hue of *Sphagnum*, and agreeing with *Dicranum* in the capsule and peristome, but distinguished by the peculiar structure of the external leaf-cells. These are disposed in two or more strata, and are large and rectangular, void of chlorophyll, and communicating with each other by means of circular apertures. The chlorophyll cells are imbedded in the centre of the leaves. Our only species, *L. glaucum*, occurs in the same sort of situations as *Sphagnum*, forming large tufts, which, however, seldom fructify; it agrees in the general appearance of the foliage with *Leucophanes* and *Octoblepharum*, and occurs in America and in the southern hemisphere. There are several exotic species. [M. J. B.]

LEUCOCORYNE. A genus of Chilian herbs of the order *Liliaceæ*. They have fleshy roots, linear leaves, and umbels of white or blue flowers supported on scapes. These flowers have a hypocrateriform perianth; three fertile stamens inserted in the middle of the tube, and three sterile fleshy ones seated in the throat; and a terminal style articulated with a sessile ovary, and having a simple stigma. [T. M.]

LEUCOJUM. A genus of European *Amaryllidaceæ* comprising a few very pretty bulbous plants called Snowflakes. They bear considerable general resemblance to snowdrops, but are larger, and the six perianth segments are nearly equal. They have sheathing erect linear lorate leaves, and hollow angular scapes, the flowers being campanulate, and white tipped with green. The six stamens are inserted on an epigynous disk, and their anthers open by a terminal pore, and also by a lateral exterior slit, not extending to the base. *Erinosma* and *Acis*, represented by *L. vernum* and *L. autumnalis*, were formerly included. The common species is *L. æstivum*. [T. M.]

LEUCOLÆNA. A genus of umbellifers, having the border of the calyx five-lobed; and the fruit compressed, each half with seven to nine narrow ribs. The species are natives of New Holland, generally of small size, and usually covered with fine down. The name indicates the white appearance of the bracts. [G. D.]

LEUCOMERIS. A Himalayan shrub or thick-stemmed erect herb, with long leaves hoary underneath, and numerous flower-heads in a terminal corymb, forming a genus of *Compositæ*, scarcely differing from the American *Gochnatia*.

LEUCOPHÆE. A genus proposed by Webb for the shrubby species of *Sideritis* from the Canary Islands, but which have generally been maintained as a section only of *Sideritis*, under the older name of *Marrubiastrum* of Mœnch.

LEUCOPOGON. A large genus of *Epacridaceæ*, distinguished by having a five-lobed calyx, with two or three bracts at the base; a funnel-shaped corolla with five spreading lobes; five anthers on very short filaments which are included within the corolla; and a style thickened at the base, bearing a capitate stigma. The fruit is either a berry or a dry capsule. The flowers are white in terminal or axillary spikes, and the leaves are lanceolate slightly toothed or hairy at the margin. They are handsome shrubs found in most parts of Australia, Tasmania, and New Zealand. [R. H.]

LEUCOPSIDIUM. A genus of *Compositæ* established by De Candolle in the tribe *Anthemideæ*, for some North American plants since reduced to *Egletis*. *L. arkansanum* is sometimes met with in gardens.

LEUCORCHIS. A genus of Java orchids consisting of terrestrial, perhaps leafless, herbs, having scapes bearing racemes of whitish flowers. They belong to the *Arethuseæ*, and have the leaflets of the perianth connate at the base, the lateral sepals forming an emarginate lower and the dorsal sepal with the petals a trifid upper lip, while the labellum is roundish undivided and spreading, articulate with the column. [T. M.]

LEUCOSMIA. A genus of *Aquilariaceæ*, consisting of a shrub, native of the Friendly Isles. It has opposite entire leaves; and terminal heads of flowers, surrounded by a deciduous involucre. The perianth is tubular, coloured, with five petaloid scales in its throat; stamens ten, in two rows; ovary girt round at the base by a short sheath, with a solitary ovule in each of its two compartments; fruit fleshy. [M. T. M.]

LEUCOSPERMUM. A proteaceous genus consisting of shrubs or small trees, natives of South and South-eastern Africa, reaching to the tropic. They are known by having a four-cleft silky calyx, the concave segments of which occasionally cohere, and each bear a sessile anther; style filiform, with a smooth stigma. The seed-vessel is one-celled, and contains a single smooth wingless seed. The involucre is imbricated, and the yellow flowers are borne in terminal globose heads; leaves sessile, of a leathery texture, often toothed at the apex, and generally covered with silky hairs. [R. H.]

LEUCOSTEGIA. *Acrophorus*.

LEUCOSYKE. The name of a small tree, native of Java, forming a genus of *Moraceæ*. The leaves are stalked, ovate, sharply pointed, white and hoary on the lower surface, with large stipules; and the flowers are unisexual, grouped in axillary globular heads, the males stalked, and the females sessile. The ovary contains a single ovule. [M. T. M.]

LEUCOTHAMNUS: A name proposed by Lindley for two or three species of *Thomasia*, in which the cup formed by the united base of the filaments is more adnate to the calyx, thus rendering the insertion of the stamens more perigynous than in the other species.

LEUCOTHOË. One of the subgenera of *Andromeda*.

LEUZEA. A genus of unarmed perennial composite herbs related to thistles, found in Eastern Australia, and in the Mediterranean region, and in Siberia. Their unbranched stems are furnished with entire or pinnatifid leaves, and terminate in a single rather large ovate or globose flowerhead, which contains numerous purple tubular florets, enclosed by an involucre of many series of silvery scales extended into thin dry membranous tips. The nature of these scales serves to distinguish the genus from some of its allies, and the feathery pappus-hairs which crown the four-sided achenes from others. [A. A. B.]

LEVENHOOKIA. A small genus of *Stylidiaceæ* consisting of minute herbaceous plants natives of King George's Sound, South-west Australia, and distinguished by having a five-cleft calyx with two lips; the limb of the corolla five-parted and irregular, the fifth segment or lip being dissimilar to the others, arched and longer than the erect column; the lobes of the anthers lie one above the other; there are two hair-shaped stigmas, and a one-celled capsule. The leaves are alternate, crowded at the tops of the branches, and intermixed with fascicles of flowers. [R. H.]

LEVERWOOD. *Ostrya virginica.*

LEVISTICUM. A genus of umbellifers, distinguished by having each half of the fruit with five wings, the two lateral of which are broader than the others. The only species is an herb, native of the Pyrenees; it contains an abundant yellow juice, and is employed as a domestic remedy. [G. D.]

LEWISIA *rediviva*, the Bitter-root plant or *Racine amère* of the Canadians, the Spatlum or Spœt'lum of the Oregon Indians, is the only species of this singular genus of *Mesembryaceæ*. It is a somewhat succulent stemless perennial, with a fleshy tapering root, from the summit of which arise numerous clusters of narrow succulent green leaves; and in the centre a fleshy stalk, jointed above the middle, and bearing a solitary rose-coloured flower, surrounded by an involucre of five to seven narrow scales. As soon as the flower opens, the leaves begin to wither and dry up, usually lasting only a few days, the entire period of the plant's existence above ground not exceeding six weeks, viz. from early in May till the middle of June. The flower, which remains open only during sunshine, has a persistent calyx, a corolla of eight to ten spreading petals, numerous stamens, and a one-celled ovary, in which respect it differs from allied genera.

This extremely curious plant is a native of the Upper Oregon territory, and its roots, which are largely collected by the Indians, afford a wholesome though bitter-tasted food, being composed almost entirely of starch. When fresh, these roots are covered with a dark-brown skin, and are bright-red within, but when skinned and dried for preservation they are nearly white. The specific name, *rediviva*, was given to the plant in consequence of the growth of some dried and apparently dead roots taken from an herbarium specimen. [A. S.]

LEYCESTERIA. A genus of *Caprifoliaceæ*, having the border of the calyx five-parted, the pieces narrow and unequal; and the fruit a berry with five cells and numerous seeds. The only species is a shrub, chiefly confined to the higher parts of Nepal, and now well known as an ornament of our shrubbery gardens. The name was given in honour of the late Mr. Leycester, of the Indian civil service, and a patron of horticulture. [G. D.]

LEYSSERA. A genus of *Compositæ*, of the tribe *Senecioneæ*, distinguished by the ray-florets being ligulate, female or neuter, with a pappus of short simple bristles, whilst the tubular and hermaphrodite disk-florets have a pappus of long plumose bristles, alternating with chaffy scales. It consists of three or four African herbs or undershrubs, with slender branches terminating in a long peduncle with a single yellow flower-head. The leaves are linear, and usually irregularly clustered.

LÉZARDELLE. (Fr.) *Saururus.*

LHOTSKYA. A genus of *Myrtaceæ*, of the section *Chamælauciaceæ*, peculiar to Southwestern Australia, and consisting of trees and shrubs with acerose or tetragonous leaves, and yellow or violet flowers, arranged in terminal heads. The calyx, supported by two bracts, has ten ribs, and is five-cleft; the petals are five; the stamens indefinite; and the fruit an oblong ten-ribbed capsule, indehiscent, one-celled, and often only one-seeded. [B. S.]

LIABUM. A genus of *Compositæ*, differing from *Andromachia* in the pappus, which consists of a single series of filiform bristles; and like *Andromachia* usually referred to *Vernoniaceæ*, on account of the style, but the opposite leaves, yellow radiating flower-heads, and anthers with points at the base, are much more those of some *Senecionideæ*. There are several species, all South American, and not all sufficiently distinct from *Andromachia*.

LIANE. A woody twining or climbing plant like those which occur in tropical forests.

LIANE À BLESSURES. (Fr.) A West

Indian name for *Vanilla claviculata.* — A SIROP. A name given by the French colonists to *Columnea scandens.* — ROUGE. *Tetracera Tigarea.*

LIARD. (Fr.) *Populus balsamifera.*

LIARDIER. (Fr.) *Populus nigra.*

LIATRIS. A genus of North American herbaceous plants, belonging to the tribe *Cichoraceæ* of compound flowers, distinguished by having a naked receptacle, an oblong imbricated involucre, and a feathery pappus. Many of the species are pretty plants, well worthy of cultivation: among them *L. squarrosa,* a handsome species with very long narrow leaves, and large heads of beautiful purple flowers; *L. scariosa,* well marked by the involucral scales, which are margined with purple; *L. spicata,* which, as its name indicates, bears its flowers in a spike; and *L. odoratissima,* of which the leaves, when dry, give out a smell resembling vanilla. *L. scariosa* and *squarrosa* are called in North America Rattlesnake's Master, because the tubers bruised are considered a specific for the bite of that reptile. [O. A. J.]

LIBANOTIS. A genus of umbellifers, chiefly distinguished by having the border of the calyx in five slender awl-shaped and coloured divisions, which fall off before the fruit ripens. The species are herbs, natives of Europe and middle Asia; their leaves are pinnate, with ovate pinnæ, cut or deeply incised. The name is from the Greek word signifying incense, indicating the odour of some of the species. [G. D.]

LIBER (adj.). Free; as when there is no cohesion between parts in contact with each other.

LIBER (subst.). The inner lining of the bark of Exogens, where alone its woody matter resides.

LIBERTIA. A small genus of *Iridaceæ*, natives of Australia, Tasmania, New Zealand, and Chili, distinguished from *Sisyrinchium* by the stamens being distinct, or connate only at the very base, and having versatile anthers. The few species are herbs, with creeping rhizomes or fibrous roots, grassy leaves, and panicled inflorescence, with the flowers almost in umbels. The flowers are always white, except the sepals, which are occasionally greenish. [A. S.]

LIBOCEDRUS. Two Chilian and two New Zealand trees are all the known species of this genus belonging to the *Cupresseæ* section of conifers. They are closely related to the arbor-vitæ (*Thuja*), from which they differ by the scales of their cones being valvate, and having each only one seed at its base, and also by their seeds being unequally winged. One of the New Zealand species, *L. Doniana*, the Kawaka of the natives, is a fine timber tree growing 60 or 100 feet high, and yields an excellent fine-grained heavy, dark-coloured wood, useful for both planks and spars; while the wood of *L. Bidwillii*, the other New Zealand species, is so soft and porous that soap-bubbles may be blown through a piece a foot in length. Both the Chilian species, *L. tetragona* and *L. chilensis*, are timber trees of large size. The former is the Alerse of that country, and yields the South American timber of that name, which is largely used on the Southern Pacific coast, and forms an important article of trade to the Chilians. Spars eighty or ninety feet long are obtainable from it; and a single tree often yields 800 to 1,000 or even 1,500 boards. Its grain, too, is so straight and equal that it can be split into shingles, which look as though they had been dressed with a plane. [A. S.]

LIBIDIBI. A name given to the pods of *Cæsalpinia* or *Libidibia coriaria.*

LIBRA. The best kind of tobacco grown in the western part of Cuba.

LICANIA. A genus of *Chrysobalanaceæ*, containing about twenty species, mostly inhabitants of the forests of Guiana and Brazil. They are timber trees or large shrubs, and have large entire leathery leaves, and small flowers in terminal clusters. Several undetermined species of this genus afford the Pottery bark, the ashes of which are used by the natives of the Amazon for mixing with the clay employed in the manufacture of pottery-ware, in order to enable the vessels to withstand the action of fire. The Indians call these trees Caraipe, but botanists have adopted that name for a genus of *Ternstrœmiaceæ*, owing to the Pottery tree having at one time been supposed to belong to that order. Mr. Spruce describes them as exceedingly straight slender and lofty trees, having trunks not exceeding twelve or fifteen inches in diameter, growing to a height of a hundred feet before sending forth branches, the wood being so hard that ordinary tools will not cut it. The bark is likewise exceedingly hard, and very gritty from the large quantity of silex it contains, and to which it owes its property. The Indians burn the bark, reduce it to powder in a mortar, and then mix it with an equal quantity of the best clay they can procure, using it for all kinds of utensils required to stand fire-heat. [A. S.]

LICCA TREE. *Sapindus spinosus.*

LICE, BEGGAR'S. An American name for *Cynoglossum Morisoni.*

LICHENS. A large tribe of cryptogams belonging to the fungal alliance, and distinguished from *Fungi* by their not deriving nutriment in general from the substance on which they grow, but from the surrounding medium; by their slow development and long endurance: and, technically, by their producing within their substance granules distinct from the general tissue, called gonidia, which in certain conditions are reproductive. In fructification they agree with ascomycetous *Fungi*, and like them have either a second form of fruit (stylospores) contained in distinct cysts (pycnidia), or minute bodies variously borne, which are supposed to have the power of impregnation. On these points the memoirs of Tulasne and Lindsay must be consulted by all who wish to have a complete knowledge of the subject. Lichens, perhaps, reach higher latitudes and altitudes, and are capable of enduring greater degrees of cold, than any other vegetables except *Diatomaceæ.* On the contrary, they may be exposed to a burning sun without injury; and, though apparently dried up and withered, they recover their proper appearance with the first shower. Most of them are essentially air-plants, but a few are either constantly wet with spray, or totally immersed.

Lichens are divisible into two principal sections, according to the nature of the fruit, thus:—

1. ANGIOCARPEI; fruit contracted, like a *Sphæria.*
2. GYMNOCARPEI: fruit expanded, like a *Peziza.*

In each there is a distinct gelatinous or collemaceous group; and various natural orders arise in either division from modifications of the fruit.

Nylander, who is perhaps the best modern authority on Lichens, divides them into three families, the vegetative element in his arrangement prevailing, as the fructiferous does in that of Acharius—MYRIANGIACEI, COLLEMACEI, and LICHENACEI, of which the two first are gelatinous. The Lichens proper he divides as follows:—

1. EPICONOIDEI: spores ultimately dusting the shields, as *Calicium.*
2. CLADONIOIDEI: lichens with a stem-shaped thallus, as *Cenomyce.*
3. RAMALODEI: lichens with a shrubby thallus, as *Usnea.*
4. PHYLLODEI: lichens with a leafy thallus, as *Parmelia.*
5. PLACODEI: lichens with a crustaceous thallus, as *Lecidea.*
6. PYRENODEI: lichens with capsule-like fruit.

Lichens are in some cases useful as articles of food and medicine, but their principal economical value consists in their properties as dyes. [M. J. B.]

LICHEN, CUP. *Cenomyce pyxidata,* also called Cup-moss. —, HORSEHAIR. *Cornicularia jubata,* also called Tree-hair.

LICHEN COMESTIBLE. (Fr.) *Lecanora esculenta.* — DES RENNES. *Cenomyce rangiferina.* — D'ISLANDE. *Cetraria islandica.*

LICHENOLOGY. That part of Botany which treats of Lichens.

LICHINA. A small genus of gelatinous capsule-fruited lichens, remarkable for its species growing on rocks exposed to the spray or covered at high water. They were in consequence formerly referred to *Algæ,* but their fructification is now well-known, and agrees in essential points with that of collemals. They are short-branched tufted lichens, with terminal fruit, which opens merely by a terminal aperture without any exposed disk. [M. J. B.]

LICHWALE. *Lithospermum officinale.*

LICHWORT. *Parietaria officinalis.*

LICIET. (Fr.) *Lycium.*

LICUALA. A genus of palms comprising about a dozen species from India and the Indian Archipelago. With the exception of one New Guinea species, none exceed ten or fifteen feet in height, some scarcely having any stem at all, while others have slender stems marked with circular scars or rough with the hard bases of fallen leaves. Their leaves are terminal and fan-shaped, with prickly stalks, the prickles being conical or often hooked; and their branching flower-spikes, with numerous incomplete spathes, stand almost erect, or hang down from amongst the leaves. The flowers have a cup-shaped three-cut calyx, and a three-parted corolla, and are all perfect.

L. acutifida yields the walking-sticks known by the curious name of Penang Lawyers. It is a native of the island of Pulo-Peuang, where it grows generally to a height of about five feet, but occasionally higher, its stems averaging about an inch in diameter, except at the very base, where they are considerably thicker. In order to convert these stems into walking-sticks, they are carefully scraped so as to remove the rough outside portion, then straightened by means of fire-heat, and afterwards polished, but those brought to this country come in an unpolished state. [A. S.]

LID-FLOWER. *Calyptranthes.*

LIEBERKUHNIA. A genus of *Compositæ,* founded by Cassini on a Montevideo plant, with the habit of *Leria,* and scarcely sufficiently distinct from that genus.

LIEBIGIA. A genus of *Cyrtandraceæ* peculiar to Japan and the Moluccas, and consisting of erect or climbing shrubs, with opposite equal or unequal serrated leaves, and axillary peduncles bearing fine violet-coloured flowers. The calyx is tubular, four to five-cleft, the corolla funnel-shaped, the stamens four, two of them sterile, and the capsule elongated, pod-like, two-valved, and falsely four-celled. [B. S.]

LIÉGE. (Fr.) *Quercus Suber.*

LIERRE. (Fr.) *Hedera Helix.* — DE COPENHAGEN or D'ÉTÉ. *Senecio mikanioides,* sometimes called *Delairea scandens.* — GRIMPANT. *Hedera Helix.* — TERRESTRE. *Nepeta Glechoma.*

LIF, LIEF, LOOF. Names for the fibre by which the petioles of the date-palm are bound together.

LIFT, or LOUF. *Luffa acutangula* and *ægyptiaca.*

LIGEA. One of the genera of *Podostemaceæ,* consisting of aquatic herbs, natives of Guiana. According to M. Tulasne, the able investigator of these humble plants, the species have larger stems than is usual in this order, these stems being either single, or tufted and curiously wavy, and the leaves alternate in two rows, decurrent, and of various shapes. The flowers are placed on long stalks, which are grouped together in cymes, and are further distinguished by the number of stamens, and the smooth, not ribbed capsule, whose valves are of equal size. [M. T. M.]

LIGHTFOOTIA. A genus of bellworts, having the filaments of the anthers broad and ciliated at the lower part, and the style beardless, its summit short, and with narrow divisions. The species are mostly small shrubs, and natives of the Cape, with small stalkless leaves which are alternate or opposite. The name was given in honour of the Rev. J. Lightfoot, author of a Flora of Scotland. [G. D.]

LIGHTWOOD. *Acacia Melanoxylon;* also *Ceratopetalum apetalum.*

LIGN-ALOES. The fragrant wood of *Aloexylum Agallochum.*

LIGNEOUS, LIGNOSE. Having the texture of wood; of or belonging to wood.

LIGNUM. The wood; that central part of a stem which lies below the bark, or its equivalent, the cortical integument.

LIGNUM CAMPECHIANUM. Logwood – COLUBRINUM. A drug obtained from *Strychnos ligustrina,* and perhaps other species, – RHODIUM. The wood of *Amyris balsamifera.* – VITÆ. The wood of *Guaiacum officinale,* or perhaps of other species. – of New South Wales. *Acacia falcata.* – of New Zealand. *Metrosideros buxifolia.* – –, BASTARD. *Badiera diversifolia.*

LIGULE. A strap. The radiant florets of certain composites; also the membrane which occurs at the base of the lamina of a grass-leaf; also certain appendages found on the coronet of some asclepiads, alternating with the horns and spreading over the corolla.

LIGULARIA. A genus of *Compositæ,* closely allied in habit and character to *Senecio,* and scarcely differing from some of the large-flowered herbaceous species, except in a tendency of the ray-florets to assume a bilabiate form, and in the anthers to have points at the base. The species are all natives of the mountainous regions of Asia, and have been more generally known as species of *Cineraria* or of *Senecio.* One only, *L. sibirica,* extends into the mountains of central Europe. It is a showy marsh plant, with broadly cordate leaves, and large yellow radiating flower-heads, in a simple terminal spike.

LIGULATE. Strap-shaped; narrow, moderately long, with the two margins parallel.

LIGULIFLORÆ. A name applied to a suborder of *Compositæ,* in which all the florets in the head of flowers are ligulate, and each of the florets has stamens and pistil. This suborder corresponds to the *Cichoraceæ* of Jussieu. [J. H. B.]

LIGULIFLOROUS. Having a capitulum composed exclusively of ligulate florets.

LIGUSTICUM. A genus of umbellifers, having the fruit nearly round, each half of it with five sharp ribs, and numerous oil-vessels in the furrows. The species are perennial herbs, widely distributed, being found, some in North America, others in central Asia. *L. scoticum,* a native of many parts of the British coasts, is sometimes used as a potherb. [G. D.]

LIGUSTRUM. The common Privet of our hedges is the most familiar and only European representative of this genus of *Oleaceæ,* but there are about twenty other species, which belong principally to China, Japan, and Northern India. They are mostly large shrubs from six to ten feet high, but some form trees, which in India attain a considerable height. They have opposite entire leaves, usually oblong egg-shaped or lanceolate; and the flowers are small and white, disposed in thyrse-like panicles at the ends of the young branches; they have a cup-shaped deciduous four-toothed calyx, and a funnel-shaped four-lobed corolla; and the fruit is globular, and contains two one-seeded cells.

L. vulgare, the common Privet, a native of most parts of Europe, is otherwise called Prim or Prim-print, in consequence of one of its chief uses being for the formation of hedges in ornamental gardens, owing to its bearing clipping or being kept in prim order without injury; and its generic name is said to be derived from the Latin *ligo,* to tie, on account of the long straight shoots being used in many places instead of osiers for tying, &c. It seldom grows higher than eight or ten feet, and has a short crooked trunk; but its wood is only large enough for turnery purposes, for which its hardness and whiteness render it suitable. Its purplish-black berries, which during winter afford food for many kinds of birds, yield an oil by pressure, and their juice is used in Germany for painting playing-cards and similar articles, and in other countries for colouring inferior descriptions of port wine. A bitter extract called *ligustrine* is obtained from the bark; and in Belgium the dried and powdered twigs are used for tanning purposes. [A. S.]

LILAC. Pale dull violet, mixed a little with white.

LILAC. *Syringa vulgaris.* –, AFRICAN. *Melia Azedarach.* –, AUSTRALIAN. A name used by the settlers for *Hardenbergia monophylla;* also *Prostanthera violacea.* –, INDIAN. *Melia semperflorens.* –, PERSIAN. *Syringa persica.*

LILAS. (Fr.) *Syringa vulgaris.* – DE MARLY. *Syringa purpurea.* – DE ROUEN. *Syringa dubia.* – DES INDES. *Melia Azedarach.* – DE TERRE or TERRESTRE. *Muscari monstrosum.* – VARIN. *Syringa dubia.*

LILIACEÆ. (*Hemerocallideæ, Tulipaceæ, Coronariæ, Asphodeleæ, Asparagineæ, Convallariaceæ, Lilyworts,* &c.) A natural order of monocotyledonous plants belonging to the subclass *Petaloideæ*, and constituting the type of Lindley's lilial alliance of Endogens. Herbs, shrubs, or trees, with bulbs, corms, rhizomes, or fibrous roots, simple sheathing or clasping leaves, and regular flowers. Perianth coloured, of six leaves or six-cleft; stamens six, inserted on the perianth, the anthers introrse; ovary three-celled; style one; stigma simple or three-lobed. Fruit three-celled, capsular, or succulent; seeds in one or two rows, sometimes in pairs or solitary; albumen fleshy. They are natives both of temperate and tropical regions, and emetic, purgative, and diaphoretic in their qualities. Certain species of *Aloë* supply the aloes used in medicine. *Urginea Scilla* furnishes a bulb which is used medicinally under the name of squill. New Zealand flax is prepared from *Phormium tenax*. Onions, leeks, garlic, chives, shallot, rocambole, tulips, the resin called dragon's blood, &c., are all furnished by plants belonging to this extensive order, which comprises upwards of 150 genera and 1,200 species. *Tulipa, Agapanthus, Yucca, Hyacinthus, Asphodelus*, and *Dracœna*, are examples of the principal groups.   [J. H. B.]

LILIUM. The genus which gives its name to the order *Liliaceæ*. It embraces a considerable number of species, all of which belong to the northern hemisphere, and, with the exception of the few found in the mountains of sub-tropical Asia, to the temperate regions. Several are Japanese, and from that country our gardens have lately been enriched with certainly the finest species of the genus, *L. auratum*, the stem of which, two to five feet high, bears a dozen or more magnificent flowers, each as much as a foot across, studded with purple spots and blotches on an ivory-white ground, their sepals and petals being also marked with a conspicuous stripe of yellow down their middle. Other Japanese species, such as *L. lancifolium, L. speciosum*, and *L. japonicum*, are also in much request in our gardens on account of the beauty of their flowers. *L. candidum*, the White Lily and the *Krinon of the Greeks*, and *L. chalcedonicum*, are both found in Palestine, Syria, and other Eastern countries, and are sometimes pointed out as the Lilies of the Field; but as the true lilies do not form a very conspicuous feature in Eastern scenery, it has been suggested that the plant alluded to by our Saviour was *Anemone coronaria*, which is there extremely abundant, and would be more likely to attract attention. The bulbs of several species are eaten, such as those of *L. kamtschatkense* in Kamtschatka, of *L. Martagon* by the Cossacks, of *L. tigrinum*, the Tiger Lily, and others, in China and Japan. Some medicinal uses have also been ascribed to various species, but none have any very marked properties in that respect.

All Lilies are herbs with scaly bulbs, whence arise tall slender stems, furnished with alternate or somewhat whorled leaves, and bearing upon their summit a few large, showy, erect or drooping flowers. These flowers have a perianth of six distinct or very slightly cohering segments, which are narrow and erect at the bottom, but broader, and spread or curve outwards towards the top; and at the base of the perianth the six stamens are inserted. Their three-celled ovary terminates in an elongated style bearing a three-angled or three-lobed stigma; and ripens into a three-valved capsule containing numerous horizontal winged seeds.   [A. S.]

LILY. *Lilium.* —, AFRICAN. *Agapanthus umbellatus*. —, ATAMASCO. *Zephyranthes Atamasco*. —, BARBADOS. *Hippeastrum equestre*. —, BELLADONNA. *Amaryllis Belladonna*, the *Belladonna purpurascens* of some modern botanists. —, BLACKBERRY. An American name for *Pardanthus chinensis*. —, BOURBON. *Lilium candidum*. —, BRISBANE. *Eurycles australasica*. —, CAPE COAST. *Crinum spectabile*. —, CORFU. A local name for *Funkia subcordata*. —, CUBAN. *Scilla peruviana*. —, DAY. *Hemerocallis*. —, FIRE or FLAME. *Pyrolirion*. —, FLAX. *Phormium tenax*. —, GOLDEN. *Lycoris*. —, GUERNSEY. *Nerine sarniensis*. —, IXIA. *Ixiolirion*. —, JACOBEA. *Sprekelia* or *Amaryllis formosissima*. —, KNIGHT'S-STAR. *Hippeastrum*. —, LENT. *Narcissus Pseudo-Narcissus*. —, MEXICAN. *Hippeastrum reginæ*. — OF THE VALLEY. *Convallaria majalis*. —, PERSIAN. *Fritillaria persica*. —, POND. *Nuphar*. —, ROCK. *Selaginella convoluta*. —, ST. BRUNO'S. *Anthericum Liliastrum*.—, SCARBOROUGH. *Vallota purpurea*. —, SUPERB. *Methonica superba*. —, SWAMP. *Zephyranthes*. —, TRUMPET. *Richardia æthiopica*. —, TURK'S CAP. *Lilium Martagon*. —, WATER. *Nymphæa*. —, WHITE. *Lilium candidum*.

LILY-PINK. *Aphyllanthes*.

LILY-THORN. *Catesbæa*.

LILYWORTS. Lindley's name for the *Liliaceæ*.

LIMATODIS. A genus of *Orchidaceæ*, nearly allied to *Calanthe*, from which it differs in having the lip quite free from the column instead of being united with it. It contains a few terrestrial species, natives of India and Java, the most familiar of them being *L. rosea*, a Moulmein plant with fusiform pseudobulbs, oblong lanceolate plaited leaves, and a many-flowered scape of very handsome bright rose-coloured flowers, having a straight blunt spur, and an oblong flat lip.   [T. M.]

LIMA-WOOD. The finest description of Nicaragua wood (*Cæsalpinia echinata*) produced in South America.

LIMB. The flat expanded part of a petal.

LIMBATE. Having one colour, surrounded by an edging of another.

LIME. *Citrus acida*. —, OGECHEE. *Nyssa candicans*. —, SWEET. *Citrus Limetta*. —, WILD. *Atalantia monophylla*.

LIME TREE. *Tilia europæa*.

LIMETTE. (Fr.) *Citrus Limetta.*

LIMEUM. A genus of *Phytolaceaceæ*, differing from most of the order in having a membranous seed-coat, and by the presence of petals, which, however, are often suppressed. They are African annuals or undershrubs, with branched procumbent stems, alternate fleshy entire leaves, and flowers in compact cymes, having a five-parted calyx, often coloured within, five petals when present, usually seven stamens, two styles, and a subglobose indehiscent fruit.   [J. T. S.]

LIMNANTHEMUM. This name, Marsh-flower, is applied to a genus of *Gentianaceæ*, consisting of aquatic plants, with roundish floating leaves, and yellow flowers. The calyx is five-cleft; the corolla rotate, or funnel-shaped, fringed with hairs in the interior; and the capsule bursts irregularly when ripe, by which latter circumstance the genus is distinguished from *Villarsia*, to which otherwise it is very closely allied. *L. nymphæoides* is one of our most beautiful water plants, having leaves like those of a waterlily, but smaller, and large funnel-shaped yellow fringed flowers. It is found in the Thames near Oxford, and in various places near London, but is supposed to have been introduced.   [M. T. M.]

LIMNANTHES. A sweet-scented ornamental annual, introduced from California in 1833 by Mr. Douglas. It belongs to the *Tropæolaceæ*, and is distinguished from *Tropæolum* by having the flowers regular. The stems are prostrate; the leaves pinnated, with an odd three-cleft leaflet; the peduncles one-flowered, and the petals five, yellow and white, emarginate. The whole plant partakes of the pungent properties of the Indian cresses, or, as they are often popularly called, nasturtiums. [C. A. J.]

LIMNOBIUM. A genus of American *Hydrochnridaceæ*, of which *L. spongiosum*, the North American Frogbit, and *L. Sinclairii*, from Guatemala, are the only known species. They very closely resemble our English frogbit in appearance, so much so indeed that without flowers it is difficult to distinguish them; and like it, they are aquatic plants, floating in stagnant water and propagating themselves freely by means of runners. Generically they are distinguished by the spathes of the male plants being one-leaved, and producing about three long-stalked flowers, which have the stamens completely united into a central column, bearing from six to twelve narrow anthers at unequal heights. In the female plants the spathes are two-leaved, and produce a single short-stalked flower.   [A. S.]

LIMNOCHARIS. A perennial herbaceous aquatic, belonging to the *Hydrocharidaceæ*. The leaves are broadly heart-shaped, oblong; and the flowers on long stalks, with three sepals, and as many delicate yellow caducous petals, shaded with orange near the claw. Two species are cultivated, *L. Plumieri* and *L. Humboldtii*, both South American.   [C. A. J.]

LIMNONESIS. A genus of *Pistiaceæ*, consisting, as the name implies, of plants growing in wet marshy places, chiefly in tropical America. The genus is closely allied to *Pistia*, but is distinguished by the stalked leaves, and by the spadix, which does not extend beyond the attachment of the anthers, which latter are two or three in number. The fruits contain two seeds only.   [M. T. M.]

LIMODORUM *abortivum* is a leafless erect terrestrial orchid, forming a genus of the tribe *Neotteæ*. It is found in dry shrubby places and woods, in Central and especially Southern Europe, and is believed to be parasitical on the roots of shrubs. It grows to the height of one or even two feet, and assumes more or less of a purple colour; the stem bears a few sheathing scales or bracts; the flowers are rather large of a dingy purple in a simple loose spike; the sepals and petals are nearly alike and erect; the lip, also erect, is prolonged into a spur at the base; the column is elongated, with an oblong erect anther on the summit.

LIMON. (Fr.) *Citrus acida.* — DOUX. *Citrus Limetta.*

LIMONELLIER. (Fr.) *Limonia.*

LIMONIA. A small genus of *Aurantiaceæ*, two species of which are natives of India and Ceylon, one of Mauritius, and another of Madagascar. They are shrubs with trifoliate or pinnate leaves, and the flowers with a four or five-lobed calyx, a similar number of whitish petals, twice as many free stamens, and a four or five-celled ovary. The fruit is pulpy.

L. acidissima is a spiny shrub, native of the East Indies, growing eight or ten feet high, and having leaves with winged stalks, and racemes of white flowers, producing round fruits about the size of damson plums, and of a yellowish colour, changing to a reddish or purplish tint. The Javanese employ the extremely acid flesh-coloured pulp of these fruits as a substitute for soap; and on the coast of Malabar they are used medicinally. [A. S.]

LIMOO. A name used in some of the Pacific Islands for Seaweed.

LIMOSELLA. Mudwort, a genus of humble aquatic annuals belonging to the *Scrophulariaceæ*, among which they are distinguished by their campanulate regular corolla, and one-celled capsule. *L. aquatica*, the only British representative of the genus, is a minute plant, growing in muddy places and the banks of ponds, sending up from the creeping roots clusters of narrow smooth leaves, and inconspicuous pale pinkish flowers.   [C. A. J.]

LIN. (Fr.) *Linum usitatissimum.* — DE LA NOUVELLE ZÉLANDE. *Phormium tenax.* — VIVACE. *Linum sibiricum.*

LINACEÆ. (*Lineæ, Flaxworts.*) A natural order of dicotyledonous plants belonging to Lindley's geranial alliance of hypogynous Exogens. Herbs with entire, sessile, alternate opposite or verticillate leaves, which are exstipulate, or which have occasionally a pair of minute glands at the base. Flowers regular and symmetrical; sepals three to five, imbricate; petals three to five, contorted in æstivation; stamens united at the base, three to five, usually with intermediate abortive ones in the form of teeth opposite the petals; ovary three to five-celled; styles three to five. Fruit six to ten-celled; seeds one in each cell; embryo straight. Abundant in Europe and North Africa. The plants yield mucilage and fibre. Flax and linseed are procured from *Linum usitatissimum.*. There are four genera and about ninety species. [J. H. B.]

LINAIGRETTE. (Fr.) *Eriophorum.*

LINARIA. A genus of herbaceous plants belonging to the *Scrophulariaceæ*, among which they are well marked by their personate corolla (the mouth of which is closed by a prominent palate), spurred at the base, and by the capsule opening with teeth at the extremity. The most common English species is *L. vulgaris*, Yellow Toad-flax, characterised by erect stems one to two feet high, numerous glaucous linear leaves resembling those of flax, and terminal racemes of crowded yellow and orange flowers. A singular variety of this species, named *Peloria*, is sometimes found with five spurs and regular flowers. *L. Cymbalaria*, Ivy-leaved Toadflax or Mother-of-thousands, is frequent on ruins and old garden walls. Among the cultivated kinds *L. speciosa* is a popular border annual; and *L. triornithophora* is remarkable for the singular form of the flowers, which resemble, as its trivial name indicates, three birds seated in the spur. French, *Linaire*; German, *Flackskraut*. [C. A. J.]

LINCONIA. A genus of bruniads, having the border of the calyx in five smooth short divisions; the corolla of five lanceolate pieces, folded and concealing the five stamens, the anthers of which have the two halves separated at the base; and the seed-vessel with two cells, each of which is usually two-seeded. The species are natives of the Cape, with the habit of heaths, the branches numerous and erect, the leaves spirally arranged, and the flowers solitary in the axils of the upper leaves. [G. D.]

LINDACKERIA. *Mayna.*

LINDELOFIA. A genus of *Boraginaceæ* from Kashmir, consisting of biennial or perennial plants with the habit of *Anchusa*, but an ovary like that of *Cynoglossum* or *Omphalodes*. The corolla is blue or purplish, funnel-shaped, with a long tube and erecto-patent five-parted limb, the throat open, with five erect notched smooth scales. The nuts are depressed ovate-deltoid, rough or prickly margined, with a border of long hooked prickles. [J. T. S.]

LINDEN. The Lime tree, *Tilia europæa.*

LINDENBERGIA. A genus of *Scrophulariaceæ* of the tribe *Gratioleæ*, consisting of annual or perennial herbs, of a weedy aspect, usually more or less hairy, and allied in the shape of their flowers to *Mimulus*, with the stamens of *Stemodia*. The leaves, at least the lower ones, are opposite, the flowers yellow or purplish, either solitary in the axils of the leaves or forming terminal spikes; the calyx is five-cleft; the corolla is tubular, with an erect notched upper lip, and a large spreading lower lip with a convex palate; the stamens are didynamous, the cells of the anthers distinct from each other and stipitate. The capsule opens loculicidally in two valves. There are eight species known, natives of the warmer parts of Asia and Eastern Africa.

LINDENBLOOMS. Lindley's name for the *Tiliaceæ*.

LINDENIA. A genus of cinchonaceous plants, represented by a shrub, native of Guatemala. The flowers are arranged in terminal corymbs, with oblong bracts. The calyx tube is roundish, marked by five ribs, its limb divided into five narrow erect segments; the corolla is salver-shaped, with a very long tube, the limb with five oblong spreading lobes; anthers five, sessile; capsule two-celled, crowned by the limb of the calyx. The genus differs from *Augustea* in the long slender cylindrical tube of the corolla, and in its smooth style. *L. rivalis* is a stove evergreen with large handsome white flowers. The genus is dedicated to M. Linden, a horticulturist of Brussels. [M. T. M.]

LINDERA. *See* BENZOIN. The name *Lindera* is, however, preferred by Meisner, to whom we owe the most recent account of the *Lauraceæ*, and who includes under it about a dozen species.

LINDERNIA *pyxidaria* is a small European annual, forming a genus of *Scrophulariaceæ* of the tribe *Gratioleæ*, and the type of a subtribe distinguished by the valves of the capsule being entire and parallel to the dissepiment. It is much branched, quite glabrous, and seldom attains six inches in height. The leaves are small, opposite and entire; the flowers small, pale pink or white, on axillary peduncles: the stamens didynamous, with arched filaments; the two-celled anthers cohering in pairs. It is a marsh plant, not uncommon in some parts of the continent, but not extending to Britain. It is named after Lindern, a Swiss botanist.

LINDHEIMERA. A genus of *Compositæ* allied to *Melampodium, Berlandiera*, and *Engelmannia*, consisting of a single Texan species, an erect dichotomous herb, with showy yellow radiating flower-heads on long slender peduncles. The involucre has four or five outer leaflike bracts, and as many internal flat oblong ones. The achenes of the ray are winged, with a short two-toothed pappus, those of the disk shortive, enclosed in the scales of the receptacle.

LINDLEYA *mespiloides* is the sole representative of a genus named by Humboldt and Kunth in honour of one of the editors of the present work. It is a small evergreen tree or large shrub, found wild in the mountain regions of Mexico, and belongs to the *Quillajæ* group of *Rosaceæ*, separated from the other groups of the order by its follicular or capsular fruits, and winged seeds. Amongst these *Lindleya* is distinguished by its five ovaries being consolidated, but having the styles distinct; and by its fruit being a hard bony five-celled and five-angled capsule, which splits open when ripe down the centre of the cells, each of which contains a couple of thin-winged seeds. It has simple crenulate shining leaves of an oblong-acute form, and solitary large white sweet-scented flowers, borne on the tips of its branchlets.   [A. S.]

LINDSÆA. A rather extensive genus of polypodiaceous ferns, typical of the section *Lindsæeæ*, a group in which the transverse more or less elongated sori are indusiate, with the indusium attached along the inner, and opening along the outer margin, the reverse of what occurs in *Pteris*. Among these, *Lindsæa* is known by its veins being free. The fronds are very variable in character, some being simple, others pinnate, and others bipinnate, generally with a more or less adiantoid aspect. They are found in the tropics both of the Old and New World.   [T. M.]

LINE (adj. LINEALIS). The twelfth part of an inch.

LINEA TRANSVERSALIS. The ostiolum of certain fungals.

LINEAR. Narrow, short, with the two margins parallel; as the leaf of the yew-tree.

LINEATE. Lined; marked by fine parallel lines.

LING. *Calluna vulgaris*; also a Chinese name for *Trapa bicornis*.

LINGUA CERVINA. *Scolopendrium.* DE FIN. *Casearia lingua.*

LINGUIFORM. Having the form of a tongue.

LINNÆA. This genus was so named by Gronovius in honour of the great Swedish naturalist Linnæus, who himself selected it as the most appropriate plant to bear his name, he having first pointed out its true character, besides which it was also an especial favourite with him, and common in his own native country. There is only one species, *L. borealis*, an extremely elegant little creeping evergreen plant, with slender branches a foot or more in length trailing along the ground, bearing small opposite broadly ovate or obovate leaves slightly toothed at the top, and sending up erect thread-like flower-stalks, which fork near the top and bear two gracefully

drooping highly fragrant bell-like flowers, of a pale pink colour or nearly white, and almost half an inch in length. These very beautiful little flowers have a calyx with a border of five teeth; a bell-shaped corolla narrow at its base but spreading upwards and dividing into five nearly equal lobes; four stamens, two of which are shorter than the other two; and a globular hairy three-celled ovary, which ripens into a dry one-seeded fruit. It grows almost exclusively in woods, and is widely dispersed over Northern Europe and Asia, and North America, occurring also in the mountains of Central Europe. In Britain it is found only in the east of Scotland, and in one place in Northumberland. According to Dr. Clarke, its scent is so powerful, especially at night, that it may be discovered at a considerable distance. The Laplanders use a decoction of its flowers as a remedy in rheumatic complaints, and the Norwegians consider a decoction of the entire plant good against the itch. It belongs to the *Caprifoliaceæ*.   [A. S.]

LINOSTIGMA. A genus proposed by Klotzsch for a species of *Viviania*, in which the parts of the flower are reduced to four, those of the pistil to two, and the styles are united nearly to the middle. Like the other species of *Viviania*, it is a native of extra-tropical South America.

LINOSTOMA. A genus of Indian shrubs belonging to the *Thymelaceæ*. The leaves are opposite, closely feather-veined, leathery, and shining; the flowers perfect, in terminal contracted racemes, the stalks of which are jointed in the middle. The perianth is tubular, coloured, and has ten petaloid scales placed in pairs opposite the five segments of its limb. The fruit is dry, not surrounded by any disk, nor, as happens in some adjacent genera, by the base of the perianth.   [M. T. M.]

LINOSYRIS. A genus of *Compositæ* of the tribe *Asteroideæ*, consisting of erect herbs or undershrubs with alternate narrow crowded leaves and yellow flower-heads at the ends of the branches, forming a flat terminal corymb. The involucral bracts are not numerous, imbricated, the outer ones loose, passing into the leaves; the florets are all tubular and hermaphrodite, on a flat honeycombed receptacle without scales. The achenes are oblong, compressed, silky, with a pappus of simple bristles in a double row. There are about a dozen species, natives of Europe, temperate Asia, Northern Africa, or North America, among which *L. vulgaris* is not uncommon in hot exposed stony places in Central and Southern Europe.

LINSEED. The seed of Flax, *Linum usitatissimum*.

LINUM. A genus which gives its name to the *Linaceæ*, consisting of herbs and small shrubs, natives of all the temperate regions of the globe, but rare in the tropics. The leaves are alternate, opposite, or even whorled; and the flowers, which are variable in colour and very fugitive, grow in panicles or corymbs. The calyx consists of five sepals; the corolla of five petals; and the stamens, which are the same in number, are connected into a tube at the base, and between them are five barren filaments, which are rudiments of stamens. The ovary is from three to five-celled, with the same number of styles and capitate stigmas; the capsule globular, most commonly ten-celled, from each cell being partially or completely divided in two by a spurious dissepiment, and each cell thus formed contains a single pendulous seed.

The species are numerous, but very few of them are of any importance except *L. usitatissimum*, the common annual Flax, which has been an object of cultivation from the earliest times. This plant has, for the most part, solitary quite erect stems, alternate smooth linear-lanceolate leaves, and a corymbose inflorescence; the sepals are ovate-acute with a membranous margin; and the petals are blue, three times longer than the calyx. The finer kinds of the linen of commerce are manufactured from the ligneous fibre of the stems of this plant; and the seed, called Linseed, is scarcely less valuable on account of the large quantity of oil contained in the embryo. The seeds contain a mucilage which dissolved in water is demulcent and emollient, and the meal of the seed is used for poultices. The cake remaining after the oil is expressed is extensively used in fattening cattle. *L. catharticum*, remarkable for its erect much-branched stem, its opposite smooth obovate-lanceolate leaves, and small white flowers, is occasionally used in medicine, being bitter and purgative.   [B. G.]

Flax (*L. usitatissimum*) is only known at the present day as a cultivated plant, or as occurring in a semi-wild state in places where it has escaped from cultivation. History tells us that it has been grown for its fibre from the earliest times of which we have any record, it being one of those plants which the wants of civilised man early taught him the use of; and the long period during which it has been an object of culture has doubtless, as in other known instances, so altered the appearance of the plant that it is not recognisable in its original form, if such exists at the present day. The Bible affords ample proof of the antiquity of the use of flax as a material for weaving cloth. We read (Gen. xli. 42) that Pharaoh clothed Joseph in fine linen, and in the account of the plagues with which the Egyptians were visited (Ex. ix. 31), we are told that the flax was smitten; from which passages it would appear not only that the art of weaving had reached a high state of perfection, but also that flax was one of the agricultural plants of Egypt at that early period; and this is confirmed by the representations of its culture which occur in ancient Egyptian pictures which have descended to us. Moreover, microscopists have proved that the cloth used for wrapping round mummies, the antiquity of which is undeniable, was made of flax. Flax and linen formed an article of commerce between the ancient Egyptians and Greeks. The plant was also cultivated by the early Romans; but as their clothing was chiefly made of wool, it did not find much favour.

In modern times the culture of Flax is widely spread in the northern hemisphere, extending from the tropics in India and Egypt to the northern parts of Europe. The principal producing country, and that from which we obtain the greater portion of our supply, is Russia, flax being an important crop in the northern districts of that country; but large importations are likewise received from Belgium, Holland, Prussia, and other countries, our total imports in 1860 amounting to 1,464,810 cwts., in addition to which a considerable quantity is annually produced in our own country, mainly, however, in the north of Ireland.

The processes which flax undergoes before it reaches the hands of the spinner, vary in different places, but the general principle is the same in all, and although numerous new processes have been invented for shortening the time occupied by the various stages, none has yet entirely superseded the old modes. They may be said to consist of six operations:—*Rippling*, which consists in the removal of the seed-capsules by drawing the stem through a kind of comb. *Steeping* or *watering*, the object of which is to facilitate the separation of the fibre from the wood, and to get rid of the mucilage. To accomplish this, the flax-straw is tied in bundles and placed in ponds or rivers, where it is allowed to remain for a period of eight to twelve days, when it is taken out, and then undergoes *Grassing*, the bundles being untied and the straw spread out evenly and regularly on pasture land, and frequently turned so as to expose both sides to be washed and bleached by exposure to the rain and sun. Then follows *Breaking*, by which operation the woody part of the stem is broken previous to *Scutching*, which removes all the broken fragments left adhering after the last process. These two operations are generally effected by machinery, but were formerly performed by hand labour. After scutching, flax finds its way into the market, but before being used by the spinner it undergoes a sixth operation called *Heckling*, which removes all extraneous matter and completely separates and arranges the filaments in parallel order. It consists in drawing the flax over sharp iron spikes arranged in a quincunx manner and inserted into oblong pieces of wood.

Besides the fibre of the Flax plant, its oily seeds, known as Linseed, are a commercial article of considerable importance, no less than 1,830,623 quarters having been imported in 1860, principally from Russia and India, for the supply of our oil-mills. The finest kind of linseed oil is the product of simple pressure, and is called 'cold-drawn;' but the ordinary kind is obtained by breaking up, beating, and re-pressing the marc or cake left after the last process. It is a non-drying oil, but by boiling with sugar of lead, red-lead, or white vitriol, it is converted into a drying oil fit for the use of painters, by whom it is most extensively employed. The cake is greatly valued by agriculturists for feeding purposes, and in addition to that made in this country, large importations are received from abroad, mainly from the United States. [A. S.]

LIONDENT. (Fr.) *Leontodon.*

LION'S-EAR. A common name in the Andes for some species of *Culcitium*; also *Espeletia*, and *Leonotis.*

LION'S-FOOT. *Leontopodium*; also *Hymenomena Tournefortii, Alchemilla vulgaris, Nabalus Fraseri*, and *N. serpentarius.*

LION'S-LEAF. *Leontice*, especially *L. Leontopetalon.*

LION'S-PAW. *Alchemilla vulgaris.*

LION'S-TAIL. *Leonotis Leonurus.*

LION'S-TOOTH. *Leontodon.*

LIPARIA. A genus of *Leguminosæ* of the suborder *Papilionaceæ* and tribe *Liparieæ*, consisting of South African shrubs, with undivided alternate lanceolate rigid and pungent leaves, and bright yellow flowers in terminal heads. The genus differs from *Priestleya* chiefly in the lowest division of the calyx, which is much larger than the others, being coloured and petal-like. There are three or four species, amongst which *L. sphærica* is remarkable for the dense nodding flower-heads, fully three or four inches in diameter.

LIPARIS. This genus of small-flowered orchids consists of about an equal number of terrestrial and epiphytal herbs, and is distinguished among the malaxideous genera by their four collateral pollen-masses, and by their free lateral sepals, entire lip plane at the base, and elongated semiterete column. One or two are European, or North American, but the majority are Indian or Javanese. [T. M.]

LIPOCHÆTA. A genus of *Compositæ*, of the tribe *Heliantheæ*, and very nearly allied to the opposite-leaved *Verbesina*, distinguished chiefly by the achenes, which are scarcely winged, those of the ray having usually three angles and short awns, whilst those of the disk have only two and are often abortive. There are about ten species, natives of the Sandwich Islands, and an eleventh from the Galapagos, which has been published under the name of *Macræa*. They are all rough or hoary herbs or undershrubs of little interest or beauty.

LIPPIA. A large genus of *Verbenaceæ*, containing nearly a hundred species, natives of America. They are herbs or shrubs, generally with glands containing an aromatic volatile oil, simple opposite or verticillate leaves, and small flowers in heads or spikes. The calyx is two or four-

toothed or two-lipped; the corolla strongly two-lipped, with the upper lip notched and the lower much larger and three-lobed; the stamens included; the ovary two-celled surmounted by a capitate stigma. The small capsular fruit is two-celled and two-seeded. [W. C.]

LIQUIDAMBAR. A genus of *Altingiaceæ*, consisting of trees, with alternate petiolate stipuled leaves, and unisexual flowers in catkins. The flowers are monœcious, surrounded by a four-leaved deciduous involucre; the male catkins conical or subglobular with numerous anthers; the female subglobular, surrounded by scales; ovary two-celled, with numerous ovules, the fruit forming a sort of strobilus. They are natives of North America, Java, and Asia Minor. [J. H. B.]

LIQUIDAMBAR COPAL. (Fr.) *Liquidambar styraciflua.* — A FEUILLES DE CÉTÉRACH. *Comptonia asplenifolia.* — DU LEVANT. *Liquidambar orientale.*

LIQUIRITIA. *Glycyrrhiza.*

LIQUOR AMNIOS. The fluid that is contained in the sac within which the embryo is engendered.

LIQUORICE. *Glycyrrhiza glabra.* — WILD. *Abrus*; also an American name for *Galium circæzans.*

LIRELLA. A linear shield with a furrow along its middle, in such lichens as *Opegrapha.*

LIRICONFANCY. *Convallaria majalis.*

LIRIODENDRON. A name derived from the Greek words signifying Lily-tree, and applied to a genus of *Magnoliaceæ*, the only representative of which is the well-known Tulip-tree of North America. This tree attains a height of 140 feet in America,

Liriodendron tulipiferum.

and of 50 to 100 feet in this country. The bark is smooth, the leaves large, bright green, truncate at the point, four-lobed and somewhat like a saddle in shape; hence the tree is sometimes spoken of as the

Saddle-tree. The stipules are large, opposite, flat, and serve the function of scales to the young buds, which are bent downwards, becoming subsequently erect, when the stipules fall off. The flowers are large, somewhat like a tulip in appearance; they have a calyx of three deciduous segments which are turned down, and a corolla of six erect petals forming a kind of cup or bell, and both sepals and petals are greenish variegated with yellow and orange. The fruits of the Tulip-tree do not split when ripe, as those of *Magnolia* do.

The noble appearance of this tree renders it a great favourite in English pleasure grounds, but the flowers are not produced until it has attained an age of from twenty to thirty years. In America the wood, which is yellow or whitish according to age, is employed by the Indians in the construction of their canoes, for which purpose its lightness renders it available. It is likewise used by cabinet-makers, and by coach-builders for the panels of coaches, &c. The tree shares in the bitter tonic principle common to most of the trees of the *Magnolia* family. The foliage of the Tulip-tree assumes in autumn an intensely bright golden yellow hue. [M. T. M.]

LIRIOSMA. A genus of *Olacaceæ*, consisting of a Brazilian tree with soft yellow odoriferous wood, alternate elliptical glabrous leaves, and axillary flower-panicles shorter than the leaves. The flowers have a calyx adherent to the ovary, with a truncate limb, and nine stamens, of which six are sterile, petaloid, and bifid. [J. T. S.]

LIS. (Fr.) *Lilium candidum.* — ASPHO-DÈLE. *Hemerocallis flava.* — D'ANGLE-TERRE. *Iris xiphioides.* — DE GUERNE-SEY. *Nerine sarniensis.* — DE MAI. *Convallaria majalis.* — DE PORTUGAL. *Iris xiphioides.* — DE SAINT BRUNO. *Anthericum Liliastrum.* — DE SAINT JACQUES. *Amaryllis* or *Sprekelia formosissima.* — DES ALLOBROGES. *Anthericum Liliastrum.* — DES INCAS. *Alstrœmeria Pelegrina.* — D'ESPAGNE. *Iris xiphioides.* — D'ÉTANG. *Nymphæa alba.* — DES VALLÉES. *Convallaria majalis.* — ISABELLE. *Lilium testaceum.* — JACINTHE. *Scilla italica.* — JAUNE. *Hemerocallis flava.* — JAUNE DORÉ. *Lycoris aurea.* — MA-THIOLE. *Pancratium maritimum.* — NARCISSE. *Pancratium maritimum;* also *Sternbergia lutea.* — TURBAN. *Lilium pomponium.*

LISERÉ. (Fr.) *Convolvulus arvensis.*

LISERON. (Fr.) *Convolvulus.* — DE MICHAUX. *Pharbitis hederacea.* — DE PORTUGAL. *Convolvulus tricolor.* — DES HAIES. *Calystegia sepium.* — ÉPINEUX. *Smilax aspera.* — GRAND. *Calystegia sepium.* — NOIR. *Polygonum Convolvulus.* — PETIT. *Convolvulus arvensis.* — SATINÉ. *Convolvulus Cneorum.*

LISET. (Fr.) *Convolvulus arvensis.* — PIQUANT. *Smilax aspera.*

LISIANTHUS. A genus of *Gentianaceæ*, consisting of tropical American herbs or undershrubs, with decussate sessile or stalked ribbed leaves. The flowers are more or less clustered, axillary or terminal; the calyx bell-shaped, with five erect segments, membranous at their edges; the corolla funnel-shaped, purple red blue or yellowish-green in colour, withering on the plant, its tube slightly irregular; the stamens five, within the corolla, the anthers ultimately rolled back; the capsule two-celled.

The flowers of *L. Russellianus* are very handsome; while those of *L. princeps* are described as constituting the plant one of the noblest in existence. It is a greenhouse shrub with long hanging flowers of a rich scarlet melting into yellow at either end, and having an emerald green five-lobed limb. [M. T. M.]

LISSANTHE. A genus of *Epacridaceæ*, entirely confined to Australia and Tasmania. They are small rigid shrubs, sometimes not more than three or four inches high, and seldom exceeding five or six feet, having small scattered sharp-pointed often needle-shaped leaves, and very small usually white flowers, borne either singly or in short spikes from the sides of the branches. The corolla is funnel-shaped, destitute of the hairs upon the limb possessed by its congeners, whence the generic name from *lissos*, smooth, and *anthos*, a flower. The fruit is a small fleshy berry containing a hard stone. That of several species is eatable. *L. sapida*, a native of South-eastern Australia, is called the Australian Cranberry on account of its resemblance both in size and colour to our European cranberry, but its flesh is thin, and more like that of the Siberian crab. *L. strigosa* and *L. montana* are eaten in Tasmania, the latter being a very dwarf mountain species bearing large white transparent fleshy fruits. [A. S.]

LISSOCHILUS. A genus of vandeous African orchids, of terrestrial habit, with striated or plicate leaves, and racemes of rather showy flowers springing from the base of the pseudobulbs. It comes near *Eulophia*, but is distinguished by the great disproportion between sepals and petals. The sepals are small, reflexed or spreading; the petals large, spreading, wing-like; the lip saccate; the column short, erect; and the pollen-masses two in number, bilobed behind, with a short linear caudicle, and a triangular gland. The species are not very numerous. [T. M.]

LISTERA. A genus of terrestrial orchids, consisting of slender herbs with a rootstock bearing a mass of thickish fibres, and two leaves at some distance from the ground, and so near together as to appear opposite. The flowers are small, green, in a slender raceme; the sepals and petals nearly alike, short and spreading; the lip longer, linear, and two-cleft; there is no spur; and the anther is fixed by its base in a cavity at the top of the short column. There are but few species, natives of Europe, Northern Asia, or North America

Two are British : *L. ovata*, the common Tway-blade, which has a stem often above a foot high, and broadly ovate leaves two to four inches long ; and *L. cordata*, a more northern mountain plant, seldom above six inches high, with the leaves small, and usually slightly cordate.

LITANTHES. A genus of *Liliaceæ*, from the Cape of Good Hope. An extremely small herb, with a bulb almost the size of a pea, a bristle-like scape appearing before the leaves, and a single small drooping flower, with a greenish-white tubular cylindrical perianth, having a six-cleft limb, and six included stamens.   [J. T. S.]

LITCHI. The fruit of *Nephelium Litchi*, a plant sometimes referred to *Euphoria* or *Dimocarpus*.

LITHOCARPUS. A genus of *Cupuliferæ*, consisting of lofty trees with alternate entire leaves, and monœcious flowers in catkins. The male catkins are filiform, with a cup-shaped six-cleft perianth, and twelve to twenty stamens inserted at its base ; while the female flowers are sessile on a common rachis, surrounded by scales. The fruit is a hard nut, enclosed in scales. *L. javensis* is the only species. [J. H. B.]

LITHOSPERMUM. The Gromwell genus, a large group of *Boraginaceæ*, known by having the corolla regular, funnel-shaped or salver-shaped, without scales at the throat, where are often five plaits; and by the nuts not being contracted at the base, and having a flat surface of adhesion to the receptacle. The species are generally distributed, but most humerous in the warmer parts of the temperate zone. They are rough strigosely hairy herbs or undershrubs, with bracteated racemes of purple, blue, white, or yellow flowers.   [J. T. S.]

LITHOXYLON. A genus of *Euphorbiaceæ*, established by Endlicher for the *Securinega nitida*, an Otaheitan plant, differing in some slight particulars from the rest of that genus.

LITHY-TREE. *Viburnum Lantana.*

LITMUS. A blue dye prepared from *Roccella tinctoria* and some other lichens, by maceration and occasional agitation in a mixture of urine, lime, and potash. A kind of fermentation takes place, and the lichen becomes first reddish, and then blue. When dried it has, if rubbed with the nail, a coppery tint like indigo. Litmus is of great importance to chemists, as it affords a delicate test for acids and alkalies, since blue litmus acquires from acids a red tint, which is restored by alkalies. For this purpose paper is steeped in a solution of litmus, and then dried and bound up in packets ; when so prepared, it is sold under the name of test-paper.   [M. J. B.]

LITOBROCHIA. A genus of pteroid ferns, closely allied indeed to *Pteris* itself, from which it is separated by the reticulation of the veins of the fronds. From *Amphiblestra*, another reticulated genus of *Pterideæ*, it is known by the absence of free veinlets from the areoles ; while *Lonchitis*, which also agrees with it in this particular, is known by its sori being for the most part confined to the sinuses of the segments, whence it takes a lunate form, those of *Litobrochia* being continuous along the whole margin of the segments. The group *Doryopteris*, with simple or palmate fronds, which is sometimes separated as a distinct genus, has the veins hidden in the substance of the fronds ; while in true *Litobrochia* the fronds are once, twice, or thrice pinnate, and the veins are more distinctly visible. They are nearly all of them natives of tropical climates, and are found in considerable numbers in both hemispheres. [T. M.]

LITSÆA. A genus of Indian trees of the laurel family, with reticulated leaves and flowers in axillary tufts, protected by numerous overlapping scales which fall off after a time. The flowers are unisexual, both males and females having a four to six-parted deciduous perianth : the former with six stamens having four-celled anthers, and some of the stamens glandular at the base ; the latter with four or six sterile stamens, and a number of glands surrounding the ovary. The fruit is fleshy, and placed upon the thickened top of the flower-stalk.   [M. T. M.]

LITTÆA. Under this name Tagliabue, an Italian botanist, described a South American *Agave*, which flowered for the first time in Europe in the garden of the Duke of Litta, near Milan, in 1815; but which now bears the name of *Agave geminiflora*. It has a short stout trunk, bearing on its summit a dense crowd of narrow whip-like dull-green leaves, from the midst of which, once in the lifetime of the plant, rises a straight spear-like stem, twenty or more feet high, bearing an immense number of yellowish-green flowers, with long protruding stamens furnished with versatile anthers.   [A. S.]

LITTLEGOOD. *Euphorbia helioscopia.*

LITTORAL. Growing on the sea-shore.

LITTORELLA. An herbaceous perennial belonging to the *Plantaginaceæ*, common on the margins of the English and Scottish lakes, where it forms a turf. The leaves, all of which proceed directly from the roots, are grass-like but fleshy ; and the flowers are some barren and some fertile, the latter sessile among the leaves, the former elevated in scapes two or three inches high, and remarkable for their four long slender filaments and tremulous anthers. *L. lacustris*, commonly called Shore-weed, is the only species.   [C. A. J.]

LITUATE. Forked, with the points a little turned outwards.

LITURATE. When spots are formed by the abrasion of the surface.

LIVÈCHE. (Fr.) *Levisticum.*

LIVELONG, or LIVE-FOR-EVER. *Sedum Telephium.*

LIVER-LEAF. *Hepatica.*

LIVERWORT. *Marchantia polymorpha.* —, GROUND. The herbalists' name for *Peltidea canina*, Dr. Mead's once celebrated remedy for hydrophobia. —, NOBLE. *Hepatica triloba.*

LIVERWORTS. Lindley's name for the *Marchantiaceæ.*

LIVID. Clouded with intermingled greyish brownish and bluish tints.

LIVISTONA. The geographical range of this genus of palms extends from Upper Assam and Southern China, through Malacca and the islands of the Indian Archipelago, to the continent of Australia, reaching as far south as the colony of Victoria. Of the eight or ten known species, two are noble trees attaining the height of eighty or a hundred feet, while the others seldom exceed twenty or thirty feet. Their leaves are terminal and fan-shaped, divided into numerous segments, which are split at the apex, and frequently have threads hanging between them, while the footstalks are sheathed at the base in a mass of netted fibres, and are often prickly along the edges. Their branching flower-spikes grow out from amongst the leaves, and have several incomplete leathery spathes surrounding their stalks. The flowers have a three-cut calyx, and a three-parted corolla, and are all perfect. The fruits are dry and one-seeded.

L. australis, also called *Corypha australis*, is one of the few palms belonging to the Australian continent, and is principally found, along the east coast to as far as latitude 37° S. It is the tallest of the species, occasionally attaining upwards of a hundred feet in height, with a trunk about a foot in diameter. Its unexpanded leaves, prepared by being scalded and then dried in the shade, are used for making hats; while the still younger and more tender leaves are eaten like cabbages. In Assam the leaves of *L. Jenkinsiana*, the Toko Pat of the natives, are used for making the peculiar umbrella hats worn in that country, and also for thatching roofs, &c. [A. S.]

LIZARD'S HERB. *Goniophlebium triloburn.*

LIZARD'S TAIL. *Saururus.*

LIZARD'S TONGUE. *Sauroglossum.*

LLAVEA. A very interesting genus of polypodiaceous ferns, belonging to the section *Platylomeæ*, and sometimes known by the name *Ceratodactylis*. The only species, *L. cordifolia*, has tripinnate glaucescent fronds, the lower parts of which have broadly cordate-ovate sterile pinnules, and the upper parts long linear siliquiform fertile ones, forming a marked contrast to each other. The sori are in simple or forked contiguous lines near the ends of the free veins, the frond-margin being somewhat revolute and attenuated, so as to become a spurious indusium. The plant is Mexican, and is found at considerable elevations. [T. M.]

LLITHI, or LITHRI. *Lithræa caustica.*

LLOYDIA. A liliaceous plant, from five to six inches high, with flowers composed of six nearly equal spreading persistent petals, or rather sepals, which are white, veined with red or green; stamens not bearded, the anthers and style erect. 'The flower-stalk is invested with its own sheath, and separated by an elongation of the root from the leaves, of which the most distant encloses within its fleshy base the rudiment of the plant of the following season. The plant is increased by offsets or creeping shoots with a bulb at the extremity, the point of the bulb being directed towards the parent root.' *L. serotina* was named in honour of Mr. Edward Lloyd, who first discovered the plant on the higher mountains of North Wales. [C. A. J.]

LOASACEÆ. (*Loaseæ, Loasads.*) A natural order of dicotyledonous plants belonging to Lindley's cactal alliance of epigynous Exogens. Herbs with rigid or stinging hairs, opposite or alternate exstipulate leaves, and showy flowers. Calyx adherent; limb four to five-parted; petals five or ten, often hooded; stamens numerous, distinct or united in bundles; ovary one-celled, with several parietal placentas; style single. Fruit capsular or succulent; seeds albuminous. American plants, some of which from their stinging qualities are called Chili Nettles. There are about a score of genera, of which *Loasa* is the best known. [J. H. B.]

LOASA. The typical genus of *Loasaceæ*, and one of those having ten petals in a double series, the five inner or smaller of which in this case are furnished with three bristles on their backs. It is best distinguished from the allied ten-petaled genera by its trifid stigma, with acute conniving lobes; and by its capsules opening by three valves at their shortly exserted summits. All the species belong to the cool regions of Peru and Chili, and thrive in the open air during summer in this country, several being grown in our gardens on account of their conspicuous yellow or orange flowers. Many are furnished with bristly hairs secreting an acrid fluid, and inflict a sharp sting when incautiously handled. [A. S.]

LOBBIA. A genus of *Aristolochiaceæ*, named after Mr. Lobb, a botanical traveller and comprising a climbing pepper-like shrub, with wavy knotted branches, stalked leaves without stipules, and pendulous spikes of flowers placed on a thread-like four-sided receptacle. The perianth is brownish-red, bell-shaped, with a three-lobed limb, the tube having a prominent rim running round the interior; stamens sixteen to eighteen, inserted on a disk surmounting the ovary, and united with the base of the style, the filaments free; ovary inferior, linear, four-celled. The shrub is a native of Singapore. [M. T. M.]

LOBEBERRY. A common name for *Coccoloba.*

LOBELIACEÆ. (*Lobeliads.*) A natural order of dicotyledonous plants, belonging to Lindley's campanal alliance of epigynous Exogens. Milky herbs or shrubs with alternate exstipulate leaves; calyx superior, its limb often five-lobed; corolla irregularly five-lobed, often deeply cleft; stamens epigynous, the anthers united; stigma fringed. Fruit capsular, one or more celled, opening at the top; seeds numerous, with albumen. Found chiefly in tropical and subtropical climates. Acrid and narcotic qualities prevail in the order, which contains about twenty-nine genera, and nearly four hundred species. Examples: *Lobelia, Siphocampylos,* [J. H. B.]

LOBELIA. This genus commemorates Matthew Lobel, a physician and botanist of the seventeenth century, who was attached to the court of James I. It also forms the typical family of *Lobeliaceæ*, and consists of a large number of herbaceous plants, widely distributed over the tropical and subtropical regions of the globe, especially in America, less abundantly found in Northern Europe and Asia. In general habit the species vary much, but are more constant in the characters presented by the flowers, which have a five-lobed calyx with a variously-shaped tube; a corolla whose tube is slit along the upper side, and whose limb is divided into two lips, the upper of two, the lower of three divisions; anthers united into a tube round the style, two, or sometimes all of them, hairy at the top; and an ovary more or less adherent to the calyx.

As is very frequently the case with milky-juiced plants, some of the species of this genus have acrid properties. Such are *L. cardinalis, L. syphilitica,* and especially *L. inflata,* a North American plant, sometimes called Indian Tobacco, the symptoms to which it gives rise, as well as its flavour, being not unlike those of tobacco. Given in small doses it operates as a diaphoretic and expectorant, in larger ones as an emetic, while in excessive doses it acts as a powerful acrid narcotic poison, causing great prostration, convulsions, and death. Serious results have followed the injudicious administration of this drug by so-called 'medical botanists,' who deny that the plant is a poison. In medicinal doses, the drug has been, and still is, occasionally used in spasmodic asthma with advantage.

Numerous species of this genus are cultivated in English gardens for the splendour of their flowers, among which *L. cardinalis, L. splendens,* and *L. fulgens* are especially conspicuous. Several varieties of these species are now cultivated, the flowers of which present every shade of scarlet, purple, and blue. *L. Erinus* is a low-growing trailing plant, with small pale blue flowers, much used as a bedding plant. Two species are British: *L. Dortmanna,* found in shallow lakes, and *L. urens,* which grows in heathy places. [M. T. M.]

LOBESTENS. The fruits of *Cordia Myxa* and *latifolia.*

LOBIOLE. One of the small lobes into which the thallus of some lichens is divided.

LOBULE. A small lobe. Thus *lobulate,* means divided into small lobes.

LOBLOLLY WOOD. The wood of *Cupania glabra*; also of *Pisonia cordata.*

LOBLOLLY SWEETWOOD. A West Indian name for *Sciadophyllum Jacquinii.*

LOBOCARPUS. A little-known genus of *Anonaceæ,* having the fruit described as enclosed within a persistent tubular leathery three-cleft calyx, and as consisting of five carpels combined into a five-lobed and five-celled fruit, with two seeds in each cell. [M. T. M.]

LOCELLI, LOCULI. The peridia of certain fungals.

LOCELLUS. A secondary cell; a small cell within a larger.

LOCHERIA. One of the subgenera of *Achimenes,* consisting of erect herbs with axillary or subpaniculate flowers, the peculiar features of which are an oblique funnel-shaped corolla much larger than the calyx, a nearly entire five-angled fleshy ring round the ovary, and a two-cleft stigma. *A. hirsuta* and *pedunculata* are illustrations. [T. M.]

LOCULATE, LOCULAR. Divided into cells.

LOCULUS, LOCULAMENTUM. A cell or cavity. Usually the cell of a fruit or ovary; that is to say, the cavity of one or more carpels. Also the perithecium of certain fungals.

LOCULICIDAL. That mode of dehiscence which consists in ripened carpels splitting or dehiscing through their backs.

LOCULOSE. Divided by internal partitions into cells, as the pith of the walnut-tree. This is never applied to fruits.

LOCUSTA. A spikelet of grasses: that is to say, one of the collections of florets formed in such plants.

LOCUST-BERRY. *Malpighia coriacea.*

LOCUST-TREE. *Ceratonia Siliqua*; also *Robinia Pseud-Acacia.* —, BASTARD. *Clethra tinifolia.* —, HONEY. *Gleditschia triacanthos.* —, SWAMP or WATER. *Gleditschia monosperma.* —, WEST INDIAN. *Hymenæa Courbaril*; also *Byrsonima coriacea* and *cinerea.*

LODDIGESIA. A small glabrous undershrub with trifoliolate leaves, and small purple and white flowers in short terminal racemes. It is a native of the Cape, and forms of itself a genus of *Leguminosæ* in the section *Papilionaceæ,* nearly allied to *Hypocalyptus,* but differing chiefly in the very short vexillum or upper petal and in the very flat ovate acute pod. It is a rather pretty species, and has been in cultivation, though now apparently abandoned.

LODICULE. The hypogynous scale of a grass.

LODOICEA. Prior to the discovery in 1743 of the Seychelles Islands, the existence of the palm, *L. sechellarum*, upon which this genus is founded, was unknown, but its immense woody nuts were frequently found floating upon the sea, or were thrown up on the shores of the Maldive Islands, and gave rise to many absurd fabulous tales. It was called the Double Cocoa-nut Palm, Cóço de Mer, or Coco des Maldives. The tree has a nearly cylindrical trunk, scarcely exceeding a foot in diameter, and bearing a crown of large fan-shaped leaves, some of which are upwards of twenty feet long, and twelve feet wide. They are of two sexes, both of which have three sepals and three petals to the flowers, those of the females being large, thick, and fleshy. The fruits externally are covered with a thick fibrous husk, and contain usually one, but sometimes two or even three immense stones or nuts with excessively hard and thick black shells, each being divided half-way down into two lobes, whence the popular name.

In olden times important medicinal virtues were attributed to these nuts, water drunk out of vessels made of them being supposed to preserve people from all complaints, and extravagant prices were consequently paid for them. At the present day they are converted into various domestic utensils, while the wood serves many useful purposes, and the leaves are made into hats and beautiful baskets, cigar-cases, &c., besides being used for thatching.   [A. S.]

This magnificent palm, which is found only in two small islands, Praslin and Curieuse, belonging to the Seychelles group, requires a great length of time to arrive at maturity. The shortest period before it puts forth its flower-buds is thirty years, and a hundred years elapse before it attains its full growth. From the age of fifteen to twenty-five years it is in its greatest beauty, the leaves at this period being much larger than they are subsequently. The stem grows quite upright, straight as an iron pillar, and in the male trees frequently attains a hundred feet in height, the females being shorter. At the age of thirty it first puts forth its blossoms, the males forming enormous catkins about three feet in length and three inches in diameter, while the females are set on a strong zigzag stalk, from which hang four or five, or sometimes as many as eleven nuts, averaging about 40 lbs. weight each. From the time of flowering to the maturation of the fruit, a period of nearly ten years elapses, the full size, however, being attained in about four years, at which time it is soft and full of a semi-transparent jelly-like substance. The arrangements provided by nature for the roots of this tree, are of a most peculiar kind. The base of the stem is rounded, and fits into a natural bowl or socket about two and a half feet in diameter and eighteen inches in depth; this bowl is pierced with hundreds of small oval holes about the size of a thimble, with hollow tubes corresponding on the outside, through which the roots penetrate the ground on all sides, never however becoming attached to the bowl, their partial elasticity affording an almost imperceptible but very necessary 'play' to the parent stem when struggling against the force of violent gales. This bowl is of the same substance as the shell of the nut, only much thicker; it rots very slowly, for it has been found quite perfect and entire in every respect sixty years after the tree has been cut down. The reprehensible practice of destroying the trees for the sake of their nuts will, it is to be feared, lead to the extinction of the Coco de Mer, which will become in reality as rare as it was supposed to be by the voyagers who picked up the first known specimens of its nuts floating on the sea.   [T. M.]

LŒFLINGIA. A small genus of *Illecebraceæ*, consisting of small annuals from the Mediterranean region and California. They have awl-shaped opposite leaves, bristle-like half-adhering stipules, and very small sessile flowers in pairs or threes in the axils of the leaves and the forks of the dichotomous branches, forming small dense fasciculate cymes.   [J. T. S.]

LOGANIACEÆ. (*Spigeliaceæ, Strychneæ, Potaliaceæ, Cœlostyleæ, Loganiads.*) A natural order of dicotyledonous plants, belonging to Lindley's gentianal alliance of perigynous Exogens. Herbs, shrubs, or trees, furnished with opposite entire stipulate leaves; calyx inferior, four to five-parted; corolla four, five, or ten-cleft, with convolute or valvate æstivation; stamens varying in number, not always equal to the parts of the corolla. Fruit a two-celled capsule with loose placentas, or a berry, or succulent with one or two nucules; seeds usually peltate, with albumen. They inhabit chiefly tropical and warm countries. The plants are bitter and highly poisonous. The poison-nut, *Strychnos nux vomica*, belongs to the order. There are upwards of thirty genera and nearly two hundred species. Examples: *Logania, Spigelia*, and *Strychnos*.   [J. H. B.]

LOGANIA. A genus of *Monopetals* which has given its name to the order *Loganiaceæ*. It consists of fifteen or sixteen Australian species, and one from New Zealand, all herbs or small shrubs, with opposite entire leaves, and small flowers in axillary or terminal cymes or panicles. In botanical characters they differ chiefly from *Buddleia* (by some referred to *Scrophulariaceæ*) in the parts of the flower being usually in fives instead of in fours, in foliage and habit, and in the absence of that stellate down or tomentum so universal in *Buddleia*. None of the species are of any particular interest either as useful or ornamental plants.

LOGGERHEADS. *Centaurea nigra.*

LOGWOOD. The wood of *Hæmatoxylon*

campechianum. —, BASTARD. *Acacia Berteriana.* —, WEST INDIAN. *Ceanothus Chloroxylon.*

LOISELEURIA. A genus of *Ericaceæ,* the only species of which, *L. procumbens,* is sometimes called *Azalea procumbens.* It is a low trailing evergreen shrub, with small opposite ovate or oblong leaves, and small rose-coloured flowers in terminal clusters, these having a calyx of five sepals, a campanulate five-lobed corolla, and a capsule with two or three cells containing several seeds. It is found on mountain moors in the northern parts of Europe, Asia, and America, and in our own country on the Scottish Highlands.　　[T. M.]

LOLIUM. A genus of grasses belonging to the tribe *Hordeæ,* distinguished chiefly by the inflorescence being in close spikes, with the solitary spikelets placed edgeways along the rachis; glumes solitary, or with that next the rachis very minute, having three or more flowers. The Ray or Rye Grasses are among the most valuable species cultivated in Britain, alike useful as parts of a mixture of grass seeds for sowing on land intended for permanent pasture, and for growing singly as crops in alternate husbandry cultivation. *L. perenne* and the variety called *L. italicum* are the best kinds, especially the latter, which is now extensively grown in all districts where good farming is carried on. By proper management the first crop may be ready for cutting in April, and three more cuttings of after-grass during the season. One of the few deleterious grasses is *L. temulentum,* or Darnel, which sometimes

Lolium temulentum.

prevails to a dangerous extent among white crops, particularly wheat. When ground up with the corn and made into bread, it is said to produce poisonous effects on the system, such as headache, drowsiness, vertigo, &c.　　[D. M.]

LOLO. The name in some parts of the Pacific for cocoa-nut oil.

LOMAGRAMMA. A genus of ferns of the section *Tænitideæ,* found in the Philippine Islands. They have pinnate fronds, with the pinnæ articulated, and the fertile ones contracted, the venation uniformly reticulated, and the fructification forming non-indusiate linear continuous marginal lines of spore-cases. There is only one species described.　　[T. M.]

LOMANDRA. *Xerotes.*

LOMARIA. An extensive genus of polypodiaceous ferns typical of the section *Lomarieæ.* They are various in size and character, but agree in having free veins, with linear continuous sori, on a broadish linear receptacle occupying nearly the whole under surface of the contracted fertile fronds. The indusium is marginal, opening on the inner side, while from the contraction of the parts the sorus is costal, that is, close to the midrib. They are closely allied to *Blechnum,* with which indeed some botanists propose to unite them, the most marked distinction being the marginal sori of *Lomaria* as opposed to the evidently intramarginal sori of *Blechnum. Lomaria* always has contracted fertile fronds, while those of *Blechnum* are generally not at all contracted, but this is not an absolute distinction. The species occur in most parts of the world, and comprise examples with simple pinnatifid and pinnate fronds, while one species, *L. Fraseri,* has a slender tree-like caudex and bipinnatifid fronds, but it is quite exceptional in the genus. The close affinity between *Lomaria* and *Blechnum* is indicated by the fact that our native *Blechnum Spicant* is frequently included in the former genus.　　[T. M.]

LOMARIOPSIS. A genus of acrostichoid ferns having altogether the aspect of *Lomaria,* that is to say, bearing coarse pinnate fronds, the fertile ones contracted; but differing in the spore-cases occupying the whole under surface of the fronds instead of being confined to the margin, and in the absence of a true indusium. They are mostly scandent ferns, climbing up the trees of tropical forests, both in the Old and New World.　　[T. M.]

LOMATIA. A genus of *Proteaceæ,* consisting of shrubs or small trees, natives of extra-tropical Australia, Tasmania, and South-west America. They have simple pinnate or bipinnate leaves, generally toothed, and of a leathery texture; and flowers of a brownish-yellow colour, occasionally red, and having an irregular spreading calyx of four sepals, four sessile anthers, and a filiform style with an oblique dilated stigma. The seed-vessel is an ovate two-valved leathery follicle, containing several partially winged seeds.　　[R. H.]

LOMATOPHYLLUM. A genus of *Liliaceæ* from the Isle of Bourbon, allied to *Aloë* and *Yucca,* having a tubular corolla like the former, but differing in the fruit, which is not membranous, but soft and leathery; also in the seeds, which have a thick black seed-coat. From *Yucca* it is known by the perianth not having the leaves all separate. It has an arborescent stem or caudex, with the leaves collected at the top, elongate-lanceolate, with cartilaginous spiny-serrate margins, and axillary peduncles bearing paniculate flowers.			[J. T. S.]

LOMENTACEÆ. A suborder of *Cruciferæ* characterised by the siliqua or pod being lomentaceous, that is, having complete transverse partitions separating each seed from those next to it. Sometimes the true siliqua is barren, and the seeds are placed in the partitioned beak of the pod. Among British plants this suborder is represented by *Cakile maritima, Crambe maritima, Raphanus Raphanistrum,* and *R. maritimus.*			[J. H. B.]

LOMENTUM (adj. LOMENTACEOUS). An indehiscent legume, which separates spontaneously by a transverse articulation between each seed.

LONCHITIS. A pteroid genus of ferns, having large herbaceous twice or thrice pinnate fronds, and a thick short rhizome, the fructification forming marginal indusiate lines as in *Pteris,* but differing in being of a lunate figure from their occupying the rounded sinuses between the segments rather than the margins of the segments themselves. This is the prevailing character, but occasionally the sori are extended up the sides of the segments. They occur in the Mauritius, Madagascar, the Cape, and South America.			[T. M.]

LONCHOCARPUS. An extensive genus of leguminous plants, of which the greater number belong to tropical America, and seven to tropical Africa. Some are small trees, seldom exceeding thirty or forty feet in height, and others tall climbing shrubs with woody stems. They have alternate pinnate leaves, except in a solitary species from Southern Mexico, in which they are reduced to a single leaflet; and their pea-like flowers are in racemes and either purple reddish or white, but never yellow. The genus is solely distinguished from its congeners by its pods, the structure of its flowers not differing from that of *Piscidia* and other allied genera. The pod is flat, much longer than broad, varying from a thin paper-like to a hard woody consistency, and without wings along the edges, the seed-bearing edge being merely thickened or flattened.

The leaves and young branches of several species of this genus are employed by the Indians of South America for poisoning fish, or rather for intoxicating them, so that they float upon the surface of the water in an insensible state, and are thus captured, but afterwards recover and are good food. One species used for this purpose by the Indians of Guiana was called *Nicou*—its Indian name, but it now bears the name of *L. rufescens.*			[A. S.]

LONCHOSTOMA. A genus of the hy-drophyllaceous order, having the border of the corolla in five lanceolate divisions; and the styles two, and shorter than the tube of the corolla. The species are Cape shrubs, with alternate entire ovate leaves; the flowers solitary in the axils of the upper leaves.			[G. D.]

LONDESIA. A genus of *Chenopodiaceæ* from the eastern shore of the Caspian Sea. *L. eriantha* is a branched annual covered with white wool; the leaves alternate, oblong or lanceolate, entire; and the flowers on short axillary branches, in involucrate bracteated small globose heads: they are polygamous, the females more abundant than the perfect ones.			[J. T. S.]

LONDON PRIDE. *Saxifraga umbrosa.*

LONGAN, or LONG-YEN. The fruit of *Nephelium Longanum.*

LONG-BEARD. *Tillandsia usneoides.*

LONG-GLAND. *Macradenia.*

LONGITUDO. In the direction of growth.

LONG-PURPLE. Shakspeare's name for *Orchis mascula.*

LONICERA. An extensive genus of climbing or upright shrubs inhabiting both eastern and western hemispheres, and much cultivated for the sake of ornament and the fragrance of their flowers. The genus is by some botanists divided into two subgenera, *Caprifolium* and *Xylosteum.* In its widest extent it includes all plants belonging to the order *Caprifoliaceæ* marked by the following characters: Calyx small, five-toothed; corolla tubular, five-cleft, generally irregular; stamens five; style filiform; stigma capitate; ovary one to three-celled, few-seeded. *L. Periclymenum,* the common Honeysuckle, the Woodbine of Shakspeare, the twisted Eglantine of Milton, is too well known to need any description, though it may be noticed in passing that the varieties with red and yellow buds are both of the same species. *L. Caprifolium* is distinguished from the preceding by having the upper pairs of leaves united at the base so as to form a cup. These two species have red berries which are glutinous and sweet, but unpalatable. The latter is sometimes found apparently wild, but is not considered to be a true native. *L. Xylosteum* bears its flowers in pairs, and has an upright mode of growth. It is indigenous to Britain, but of unusual occurrence. Besides these, many foreign species are described by botanists, of which *L. sempervirens,* Trumpet Honeysuckle, a handsome climbing species with evergreen foliage and scarlet flowers, is a native of North America; *L. etrusca* has orange-coloured flowers; and *L. japonica,* so often figured in Chinese drawings, has evergreen foliage and orange-coloured flowers in terminal pairs. By some botanists the genus *Lonicera* is limited to those Honeysuckles which have upright stems, the climbers being placed in the genus *Caprifolium.* Fr. *Chevrefeuille;* Ger. *Geisblatt.* [C. A. J.]

LONTAR. The Palmyra Palm, *Borassus flabelliformis.*

LOODH. An Indian name for *Symplocos racemosa* or *laurina,* the bark of which forms a mordant for red dyes.

LOOF. *Luffa ægyptiaca,* the interior netted fibres of which are used in Turkish baths as flesh-rubbers.

LOOKING-GLASS TREE. *Heritiera.*

LOOSESTRIFE. *Lysimachia.* —, COMMON. *Lythrum Salicaria.* —, FALSE. *Ludwigia.* —, SWAMP. *Decodon.* —, TUFTED. *Naumburgia.* —, WEST-INDIAN. *Jussiæa suffruticosa.*

LOPEZIA. A genus of annuals belonging to the *Onagraceæ,* and distinguished by having two filaments, of which one bears an anther, the other is petal-like and abortive; the seed-vessel is four-valved, four-celled, many-seeded. There are several species, all natives of Mexico, bearing alternate rarely opposite toothed leaves, and terminal racemes of small purple or red flowers. [C. A. J.]

LOPHANTHERA. The name of a Brazilian tree, constituting a genus of *Malpighiaceæ.* The leaves are opposite, with two stipules combined into one long axillary scale. The stamens are double the number of the petals, their anthers surmounted by a crestlike appendage; and the fruit is stalked, smooth, not winged, and divided into three lobes, each of which divides into two pieces. [M. T. M.]

LOPHANTHUS. A genus of the labiate order, distinguished by having the tube of the corolla as long as the calyx, its upper lip slightly notched, the lower having its middle lobe broad, with prominent convex divisions on its edge. The species are herbaceous, natives of North America and Eastern Siberia. The name is from the Greek words signifying crest and flower, to indicate the peculiar character of the corolla. [G. D.]

LOPHIOLA. A genus of the group *Wachendorfeæ,* which is sometimes referred to the *Liliaceæ,* but more usually to *Hæmodoraceæ.* It is a slender perennial, found in the warmer parts of the United States, with creeping rootstocks, narrow equitant root-leaves, and flowers in a crowded cyme at the top of a leafless scape, the upper part of which and the exterior of the yellowish perianth are densely woolly. The perianth is deeply six-cleft, with spreading divisions. [J. T. S.]

LOPHIRACEÆ, LOPHIRA. A natural order and genus of dicotyledonous plants belonging to Lindley's guttiferal alliance of hypogynous Exogens. Branching trees with alternate entire stipulate leaves, jointed petioles, and panicled regular yellow flowers with jointed pedicels. Sepals five, the three inner smaller, the two outer becoming expanded like wings; petals five, twisted in æstivation; stamens numerous, the filaments short, and the anthers

adnate; disk none; ovary conical, onecelled; ovules numerous on a free basal placenta; stigmas two. Fruit a coriaceous nut, spindle-shaped, one-celled, one-seeded. Trees from tropical Africa. There is only one known genus, viz. *Lophira.* [J. H. B.]

LOPHODIUM. *Lastrea.*

LOPHOGYNE. The name of a genus of Brazilian *Podostemaceæ,* having the appearance of liverworts or mosses. It would seem as though they had no true stem or leaves, but in their place a frond or thallus variously divided, on which are placed at irregular intervals the flowers, supported by little nerves or bundles of cells hidden in the substance of the frond. The flowers have a small number of free stamens, and a striated ovary, the stigmas of which are dilated and membranous, forming a sort of crest. [M. T. M.]

†LOPHOLÆNA. A South African glabrous undershrub with entire leaves, forming a genus of *Compositæ* closely allied to the discoid species of *Senecio,* but differing chiefly in the involucre, which has only five broad leafy scales, and in the long subulate appendages to the branches of the style.

LOPHOLEPIS. *Goniophlebium.*

LOPHOPETALUM. A genus of *Celastraceæ,* consisting of three or four shrubs from tropical Asia, allied to *Euonymus,* but differing chiefly in the cells of the ovary always containing more than two ovules.

LOPHOPHYTUM. A genus of *Balanophoraceæ,* consisting of fleshy species with a thick rootstock attached to the roots of trees, and clothed in its upper part with overlapping scales. From this rises the flower-stalk, which at its upper end is divided into pimple-like branches provided with deciduous bracts; along these branches the flowers are arranged, the males having free stamens, and the females two styles. The inflorescence and flowers are stated by Dr. Hooker to resemble those of *Gunnera scabra.* One species is said to be eaten in Bolivia. [M. T. M.]

LOPHOSORIA. *Alsophila.*

LOPHOSPERMUM. A genus of *Scrophulariaceæ,* of the tribe *Antirrhineæ,* distinguished by a five-cleft herbaceous calyx; by a large tubular corolla, without any spur or pouch, and not closed at the throat as in *Antirrhinum,* but marked with two longitudinal hairy lines; by the globular capsule, each cell opening in an irregular pore below the apex; and by the seeds surrounded by a fringed wing. There are two species, *L. erubescens* and *L. scandens,* both natives of Mexico, and both introduced into our gardens, where they are highly ornamental as herbaceous climbers with showy pink or red flowers. They support themselves by the petioles of their softly hairy triangular or cordate coarsely toothed leaves, and by their long often twisted axillary peduncles.

LOPHOSTEMON. A genus of *Myrtaceæ*, consisting of Australian shrubs, with alternate entire leaves, and white flowers in corymbs. The calyx has a roundish tube, and a limb divided into five reflexed deciduous segments provided with appendages at their base; petals five; stamens numerous, aggregated into five parcels, opposite the petals; fruit capsular, inferior, three-celled, many-seeded.　　[M. T. M.]

LOPHOSTYLIS. A name given by Hochstetter to the African species of *Securidaca*, in which the style is more dilated at the top than in the American ones.

LOPSEED. *Phryma*.

LOQUAT. *Eriobotrya japonica*.

LOQUE. (Fr.) *Solanum Dulcamara*.

LORANTHACEÆ. (*Viscoideæ, Myzodendreæ, Loranths*.) A natural order of dicotyledonous plants belonging to Lindley's asaral alliance of epigynous Exogens. Parasitic shrubs, with articulated branches, opposite exstipulate fleshy leaves, and hermaphrodite or unisexual flowers. Calyx tube adherent to the ovary, with bracts; petals four to eight, or confounded with the calyx; stamens four to eight, opposite the petals; ovary one-celled, with a solitary pendulous ovule. Fruit superior, succulent. Natives chiefly of the equinoctial regions of Asia and America, but a few are European and African. The mistleto is *Viscum album*. There are 30 genera and above 400 species. Examples: *Loranthus, Viscum*.　　[J. H. B.]

LORANTHUS. A genus of dicotyledonous plants belonging to the *Loranthaceæ*, consisting of dichotomous branching shrubs, usually parasitic, with opposite or alternate entire leaves, and flowers in spikes, corymbs, or panicles, sometimes unisexual. The calyx tube is ovate or top-shaped; the petals four to eight or five to six, free or united; the stamens equal in number to the petals and opposite to them, with introrse anthers dehiscing lengthwise. The berry is ovate or top-shaped, with one seed. They are natives of tropical and subtropical regions, and comprise nearly 300 species.　　[J. H. B.]

LORATE. Strap-shaped; the same as Ligulate.

LORDS-AND-LADIES. *Arum maculatum*.

LORD-WOOD. *Liquidambar orientale*.

LORICA. The skin of a seed.

LOROPETALUM. A genus of the witch-hazel order, having the petals long narrow and three-nerved; the lobes of the anther deciduous. *L. chinense* is a native of China, with ovate entire leaves, unequal at the base, and covered with fine down. The plant is placed by some in the genus *Hamamelis*.　　[G. D.]

LORULUM. The filamentary branched thallus of some lichens.

LOTIER ARBORESCENT (Fr) *Carmichælia australis*. — ODORANT *Melilotus cœrulea*. — ROUGE. *Tetragonolobus purpureus*.

LOTOS. *Zizyphus Lotus*.

LOT-TREE. *Pyrus Aria*.

LOTUS. A genus of *Leguminosæ*, of the suborder *Papilionaceæ*, easily known by its leaves consisting of five leaflets, of which two are close to the stem, and assume the appearance of stipules. There are about twenty species known, all herbaceous, the flowers on axillary peduncles, either solitary or in little umbels, yellow, red, or of a deep purple almost black; the calyx five-toothed, the corolla remarkable for its very pointed keel, the stamens diadelphous, and the pod cylindrical or somewhat flattened, with several seeds. The species are most of them European or North African, but a few are spread over Asia and Australia.

L. corniculatus, a decumbent perennial, with umbellate yellow flowers and a cylindrical pod, is the most common British species, and is found in the greater part of Europe, in Northern Africa, Northern and Central Asia, and in Australia. The larger varieties form a very good ingredient in our meadows and pastures. *L. purpureus*, formerly cultivated in our gardens for its dark red flowers, *L. biflorus*, and some allied species, constitute a considerable portion of the meadows of Sicily and other parts of Southern Europe; they, with *L. siliquosus*, a more common European maritime species, are often separated as a distinct genus under the name of *Tetragonolobus*, on account of the ripe pod having four longitudinal ribs or wings. *L. Dorycnium*, and some allied species from Southern Europe, constitute the genus *Dorycnium* of some botanists. *L. hirsutus*, with a few others, also South European, have been detached under the name of *Bonjeania*; and *L. glaucus*, with some other Canary Island species, under that of *Pedrosia*; but all these genera are founded on characters too trifling for general adoption.

LOTUS. A mythic name for the flower of *Nelumbium speciosum*. —, EGYPTIAN. *Nymphæa Lotus*. —, HUNGARIAN. *Nymphæa thermalis*. —, INDIAN. *Nymphæa pubescens*.

LOTUS-BERRY. *Byrsonima coriacea*.

LOTUS-TREE, or LOTE-TREE. *Zizyphus Lotus*; also reputed to be *Celtis australis*. The true Lotus-tree of the ancients is, however, more probably referred to *Nitraria tridentata*. —, EUROPEAN. *Diospyros Lotus*.

LOUDONIA. A genus of *Haloragaceæ* from Australia, comprising two or three herbs or undershrubs. *L. aurea* has the stem leafy at the base; the leaves alternate, leathery, linear, entire; the panicles terminal, corymbose; the flowers yellow, with the calyx tube four-winged, and its limb foor-parted; four petals, and eight stamens; and a fleshy clavate-tetragonous fruit. [J. T. S.]

LOUFF. *Luffa œgyptiaca.*

LOUREA. A genus of *Leguminosæ*, of the tribe *Hedysareæ*, and nearly allied to *Desmodium*, but with a broadly campanulate calyx, enlarged after flowering, and a pod consisting of two or more joints folded upon each other, as in *Uraria*. It comprises three or four species, natives of tropical Asia, herbs or undershrubs, with the habit of some *Desmodiums*. The leaves have one or three leaflets; the flowers are small, in terminal racemes or panicles. *L. vespertilionis*, from the Indian Archipelago, is remarkable for the form of its leaflets, transversely oblong, and three or four times as broad as long, such as to have been compared to bat's wings.

LOUREIRA. A name applied to a shrub or small tree, native of Cochin China, in honour of a Portuguese missionary who published a Flora of Cochin China in the latter part of the last century. It is included among *Amyridaceæ*, and has ovate entire lemon-scented leaves, and axillary or terminal stalked flowers. The calyx is bell-shaped, five-toothed; petals five, oblong, the lowest one the largest; stamens ten. The fruit is succulent, with a resinous juice, and one or two seeds. *L. glandulosa* is grown in hothouses in this country; it has ovate-acute leaves, thickly beset with glands. [M. T. M.]

LOUSEBERRY-TREE. *Euonymus europæus.*

LOUSE-BURR. *Xanthium Strumarium.*

LOUSEWORT. *Pedicularis.*

LOVAGE. *Levisticum officinale*; also *Achillea ligustica*, and a common name for *Ligusticum.*

LOVE. *Clematis Vitalba.*

LOVE-FLOWER. *Agapanthus.*

LOVE-IN-A-MIST. *Nigella damascena.* —, WEST INDIAN. *Passiflora fœtida.*

LOVE-IN-A-PUZZLE. *Nigella damascena.*

LOVE-IN-IDLENESS. *Viola tricolor.*

LOVE-LIES-BLEEDING. *Amaranthus caudatus.*

LOVEMAN. *Galium Aparine.*

LOVE-TREE. *Cercis Siliquastrum.*

LOWEA *berberidifolia* is a very singular and rare rosaceous plant, native of Northern Persia, and the Soongari desert, first described by Pallas, and by him referred to *Rosa*, in which genus it is now replaced. It is a little shrub, with yellow rose-like flowers, and simple obovate-cuneate serrated glaucous foliage. It agrees perfectly in the characters of its flowers with *Rosa*, but differs strikingly in its foliage. All true roses have pinnate leaves and stipules, whereas *Lowea* has either no leaves or no

stipules, according to the view taken of the nature of its leafy organs: for it is a matter of doubt whether these are true leaves without stipules, or stipules of suppressed leaves become confluent and putting on the appearance of leaves. In either case it is a remarkable plant. [A. S.]

LOWRY. *Daphne Laureola.*

LOXOGRAMMA. One of the genera of gymnogrammoid ferns, consisting of a few species with simple coriaceous fronds; uniformly reticulated venation, with free included veinlets in the areoles; and non-indusiate oblong or linear sori, the oblique receptacles occurring at intervals on each side the midrib. It comes near *Selliguea*, but has not the pinnate venation found in that genus. [T. M.]

LOXOSCAPHE. A group proposed to be separated from *Davallia*, in consequence of the oblique and sublateral position of the sori, which gives to them something of a daraoid character. The ultimate segments of the fronds are narrow, single-veined and soriferous obliquely at the apex, so that the indusium forms with the margin of the segment a short oblique boat-shaped cavity, instead of the usual straight terminal cyst of *Davallia*, with which in other respects these plants agree. The species are found in South America, South Africa, and the Pacific Islands. *L. gibberosa* is the type. [T. M.]

LOXSOMA. A genus of Australian ferns, closely related to *Trichomanes*, though having none of the pellucid character which belongs to that genus. It has, in fact, creeping rhizomes, with subcoriaceous decompound fronds, dark above and paler beneath, the general aspect much more nearly resembling that of *Davallia*. The sori, however, are involucrate in extrorse marginal cysts, the veins run out into free filiform receptacles, and the sessile oblique-ringed spore-cases indicate that it should be placed with the *Trichomaninæ*. It has free veins. [T. M.]

LOZANIA. A tree from New Grenada, published as constituting a genus of *Vochyaceæ*, but as yet very imperfectly known.

LUBINIA. A genus of primworts, having the corolla almost salver-shaped, the border in five deep divisions, the two posterior of which are shorter than the others; the seed ovate, acute at the end, one-celled, and opening by two valves. *L. atropurpurea*, the only species, is an annual, a native of Mauritius, with fleshy, smooth, and obovate leaves. [G. D.]

LUCEE. Some myrtaceous tree whose leaves are used in Guiana for dyeing black.

LUCERNE. *Medicago sativa.*

LUCHE. A Chilian name for *Ulva latissima.*

LUCID. Shining.

LUCRABAN SEED. An unrecognised oil-seed exported from Siam.

LUCULIA. The name given by the Nepalese to a tree of the *Cinchona* family, and latinised to form the generic title of a tree highly esteemed for the exceeding beauty and fragrance of its rose-coloured, somewhat fleshy flowers, which are borne in terminal corymbs. The linear segments of the limb of the calyx are deciduous; the corolla is salver-shaped, its limb five-cleft, with ovate-obtuse lobes; the anthers five, almost sessile on the throat of the corolla; stigmas two, fleshy, surmounting a thread-like style; capsule two-celled, two-valved, with many winged seeds. *L. gratissima* is the best known species. [M. T. M.]

LUCUMA. A genus of *Sapotaceæ*, containing between thirty and forty species, all natives of the American continent and the West Indian Islands, extending from Buenos Ayres to Mexico. Some are shrubs, others large trees, sixty to eighty feet high, or more, and, like most plants of the order, possessing a milky juice, and leathery entire leaves. Their flowers grow in clusters upon the sides of the branches, and are succeeded by large roundish fleshy eatable fruits. *L. mammosum*, one of these large trees, is a native of the West Indies and tropical America, where it is cultivated for the sake of its fruit, which is called Marmalade, or Natural Marmalade, on account of its containing a thick, agreeably flavoured pulp bearing some resemblance in appearance and taste to quince marmalade. This fruit is somewhat egg-shaped, three to five inches long, covered with a rusty-coloured skin, and contains usually a single hard seed. *L. Caimito*, whose fruit is called Caimito in Peru, is smaller than the foregoing, being only about three inches long, but its pulp is softer and superior in point of flavour. [A. S.]

LÜDDEMANNIA. A genus of orchids proposed to be separated from *Cycnoches*, and distinguished by its sessile pollen-masses and minute caudicle, as well as by the form of the lip. It is allied to *Lacæna*, from which the sessile depressed spherical pollen-masses and minute caudicle also distinguish it. *L. Pescatorei* is a Venezuelan species with the habit of *Acineta*, producing long pendent spikes of buff-yellow flowers, brown inside, with the petals and lip bright yellow. The lip is concave, wedge-shaped at the base, quadrate above, with the sides erect, and with a triangular lobe or tooth in front. [T. M.]

LUDWIGIA. A genus of onagrads, distinguished from its allies by having the stamens four, equal to the number of petals; and the seed-vessel long and cone-shaped at the end. The species are Indian herbs, growing in marshes; the leaves alternate, narrow, entire, and shortly stalked; the flowers yellow, solitary, in the axils of the leaves. The name was given by Linnæus in honour of Ludwig, Professor of Medicine at Leipsic. [G. D.]

LUFFA. A genus of *Cucurbitaceæ*, consisting of monœcious or diœcious herbs, with alternate petiolate rough leaves, simple tendrils, racemose male flowers, and solitary female flowers. The males have a bell-shaped five-toothed calyx, a five-parted corolla, and five stamens inserted in the calyx distinct or in bundles, with one-celled wavy anthers. The females have the calyx tube club-shaped and five-cleft, five petals, abortive stamens, and an inferior three-celled ovary with numerous ovules. The pepo is ovate or oblong, fibrous within, containing many compressed seeds. The species are natives of tropical Asia and Africa. [J. H. B.]

LUGAR. An unrecognised tanning bark imported from Singapore.

LÜHEA. A genus of *Tiliaceæ*, consisting of South American or Mexican trees or shrubs, clothed more or less with stellate down, alternate leaves usually toothed, and showy white or pink flowers either in axillary cymes or terminal panicles. Each flower is enclosed in an involucre of several linear bracts, often longer than the calyx; the petals are thickened at the base, but without any pit or scale; the stamens very numerous, the outer ones barren; the capsule hard and woody, opening at the top in five valves, and containing several winged seeds in each cell. There are about sixteen species known, most of them very handsome when in flower. The wood of *L. divaricata*, which is white and light, but very close-grained, is used in Brazil for musket-stocks, wooden shoes, &c., and the bark of *L. grandiflora* for tanning leather.

LUISIA. A genus of inconspicuous epiphytal caulescent erect orchids of tropical Asia and America, with terete rigid rush-like leaves, and small dingy green or purplish or yellowish flowers of very little interest. [T. M.]

LULUP. A vegetable touchwood or tinder, exported in large quantities from Labuan.

LUMBANG. The nuts of *Aleurites triloba* and *moluccensis*, from which an oil is expressed. They are called Candle Nuts.

LUMBRICAL. Worm-shaped; a term applied to the worm-like lobes of the frond of certain seaweeds.

LUNAIRE. (Fr.) *Lunaria.* — GRANDE. *Lunaria biennis.*

LUNANIA. A genus of woody plants inhabiting the West Indies and South America, and belonging to the *Samydaceæ*, though hitherto erroneously placed in *Flacourtiaceæ*. In habit and inflorescence it resembles *Osmelia*. The leaves are ovate, the flowers racemose and often emitting a disagreeable odour. The calyx is from four to five-cleft, the corolla wanting, the number of stamens is from six to ten, and there are scales or staminodia abortive stamens) interspersed among them. The fruit is an ovate capsule. According to

Bentham's recent revision, there are four species of this genus. [B. S.]

LUNARIA. A genus of *Cruciferæ* natives of Central and Southern Europe, and consisting of tall biennials or perennials with erect stems, large alternate or opposite cordate-acuminate leaves, and terminal racemes of large purple flowers having the two outer calyx segments bulging at the base. The pouch is very large, stalked, oval or oblong, flattened in the direction of the back, the partition silvery. *L. biennis* is the Honesty of gardens. [J. T. S.]

LUNARIE. *Botrychium Lunaria.*

LUNATE (dim. LUNULATE). Crescent-shaped.

LUNETIÈRE. (Fr.) *Biscutella.*

LUNG-FLOWER. *Gentiana Pneumonanthe.*

LUNGS-OF-THE-OAK. *Sticta pulmonacea.*

LUNGWORT. A name given to *Sticta pulmonacea*, a lichen which in moist subalpine countries grows abundantly on the trunks of trees. It is occasionally used, like Iceland moss, in diseases of the lungs, and for other medical purposes. It is also said to be employed in Siberia as a substitute for hops. The name is also given to *Pulmonaria officinalis* and *Hieracium pulmonarium*. —, BULLOCK'S. *Verbascum Thapsus*. —, SMOOTH. *Mertensia*. —, TREE. *Sticta pulmonacea.*

LUNULARIA. A remarkable genus of *Marchantiaceæ*, belonging to the natural order *Lunularieæ*, with crescent-shaped involucres to the gemmæ, and a pedunculate capitate fruit, which consists of four capsules, each of them surrounded by a proper involucre, and opening, like that of a *Jungermannia*, with four valves. *L. vulgaris* has been found both in England and Ireland, but is more common southward. It occurs also in Chili. [M. J. B.]

LUPINASTER. A section of *Trifolium*, characterised by having large red white or yellow flowers in heads, with coriaceous persistent petals, and subulate erect calyx segments. The leaves are composed of from three to seven coriaceous leaflets, with numerous veins.

LUPINE. *Lupinus*. —, BASTARD. *Trifolium Lupinaster*. —, SMALL. *Psoralea Lupinella.*

LUPINUS. A genus of *Leguminosæ* of the suborder *Papilionaceæ*, tribe *Genisteæ*, characterised chiefly by the two-lipped calyx, monadelphous stamens, and the keel-petal ending in a point or beak as in *Crotalaria*, but differing from that genus in the flattened pod. The species are very numerous in America, especially towards the western side, extending from Oregon to South Chili, but more rare within the tropics excepting in the mountainous districts. In the Old World the genus is confined to a few annual species in the countries bordering on the Mediterranean. The species are all herbs or undershrubs. The leaves consist of five or more digitate leaflets, or in some species are simple and entire; the flowers are blue, white, purple, or yellow, in terminal racemes or spikes, and often very handsome.

The genus is one of the most puzzling to botanists, who would distinguish its numerous species by positive characters, and cultivation appears in many instances to obliterate those distinctions which may be observed in the wild state. The following are the most remarkable among those found in gardens:—*L. albus*, an annual attaining two three or even four feet in height, with five or seven leaflets to its leaves, and rather large white or pale-coloured flowers. It is probably of Egyptian or East Mediterranean origin, and has been cultivated since the days of the ancient Egyptians. It is now very extensively sown in Italy, Sicily, and other Mediterranean countries for forage, for ploughing in to enrich the land, and for its round flat seeds, white outside but yellow internally, which when boiled, so as to remove the bitter somewhat deleterious principle, form a great article of food in some districts. It used also to be much grown in flower gardens, together with *L. luteus* with sweet-scented yellow flowers, and *L. varius* with differently coloured flowers, but usually of a rich blue, both of them annuals of Mediterranean origin. These have now been mostly superseded by some of the American and especially Californian kinds. Above a hundred of these are known, and most of them are ornamental. More than thirty have been at different times introduced. *L. arboreus*, from California and Oregon, will, when well trained, produce a branching stem several feet in height that will live through four or five years, forming a trunk of light soft wood of the thickness of a man's arm. *L. polyphyllus*, and a few allied species from the same country, are tall erect herbaceous perennials with very handsome richly coloured spikes of flowers, which have become permanent inmates of our gardens. *L. versicolor* (or *L. Cruikshanksii*), a tall annual from Peru, *L. affinis*, *L. nanus*, &c., Californian annuals, are also now common with us, and scarcely one of the genus can be considered as worthless in a flower garden.

LUPIS. The fine inner fibre of *Musa textilis.*

LUPULINE. Waxy globules, resembling pollen, found on the bracts of the female flowers of the hop.

LUPULINE. (Fr.) *Medicago lupulina.*

LUPULINOUS. Resembling a head of hops.

LURID. Dirty brown, a little clouded.

LUS-A-CHRASIS. The plant of gluttony, *Cornus suecica.*

LUSTRE D'EAU. (Fr.) *Chara.*

LUSTWORT. *Drosera.*

LUTEOFUSCUS. Between yellow and fuscous.

LUTEOLUS. Pale yellow, The same as Flavescens.

LUTESCENS. Yellowish.

LUTEUS. Such yellow as gamboge.

LUVUNGA. A genus of Indian aurantiaceous shrubs of climbing habit, often spiny, having ternate leaves, and flowers in axillary clusters or tufts. The calyx is cup-like; the petals four or five, oblong; the stamens eight to ten, free or combined into a tube, with linear anthers; the ovary two to four-celled, with two ovules in each cell. *L. scandens* has clusters of flowers whose appearance and fragrance resemble those of the orange.   [M. T. M.]

LUXEMBURGIA. A genus of *Ochnaceæ*, consisting of showy branching smooth shining trees or shrubs, with alternate leathery serrulate stipulate leaves, and terminal racemes of yellow flowers, having five unequal deciduous sepals; five imbricate-convolute petals; and hypogynous stamens, eight of indefinite, with linear anthers biporose at the apex. The capsule is leathery, one-celled, with numerous seeds. They are natives of Brazil.   [J. H. B.]

LUXURIA, LUXURIES. Rankness; an unnaturally exuberant growth.

LUZERNE. (Fr.) *Medicago sativa.* — DE SUÈDE, FAUCILLE, JAUNE, or SAUVAGE. *Medicago falcata.*

LUZULA. A genus of perennial herbaceous plants allied to the rushes, from which they may be distinguished by their seed-vessels each containing three seeds only, and by their flat leaves which are generally furnished with sparse long hairs. Several species are British. One of them, *L. campestris*, is popularly called a grass, but may at once be detected by its pilose leaves. *L. sylvatica* is a large species, bearing on leafy stalks, two feet high, its spreading panicles of rush-like flowers collected into small tufts. *L. spicata* is a subalpine species a few inches high, having its flowers in a nodding spike, which is somewhat compound at the base. There are many foreign species.   [C. A. J.]

LUZURIAGA. A genus of *Liliaceæ* from Chili and Peru, consisting of branched undershrubs, creeping on the stems of trees, and adhering to them by rootlets, having alternate leaves, and solitary axillary peduncles bearing umbels of yellowish-white flowers with purple dots; the perianth six-leaved, spreading and deciduous; the stamens six; and the berry three-celled, with two seeds in each cell.   [J. T. S.]

LYALLIA. A genus of *Portulacaceæ*, consisting of a small undershrub from Kerguelen Land, with somewhat the habit of *Lycopodium Selago*, the stem, however, being much branched, with imbricated adpressed leaves, small solitary terminal flowers with a four-parted calyx, and a one-celled subglobular utricular fruit with three seeds, two of which are abortive.   [J. T. S.]

LYCASTE. The orchids now associated in this genus were formerly referred to *Maxillaria*, from which they are well distinguished by the two pairs of pollen-masses being seated on a long caudicle attached to a small roundish gland; while from the other allied genera they are distinguished by the middle of the lip being furnished with a transverse fleshy entire or notched appendage. They number a score or more of species, exclusively tropical American; but some, being found in the cool mountain regions, are suited for growing in greenhouses or even in dwelling-rooms, and of these *L. Skinneri*, decidedly the finest of the genus, is the best example. The *Lycastes* have short unjointed pseudobulbs, and plicate leaves. Their flowers, borne singly upon the top of stalks rising from the base of the pseudobulbs, are showy and often of large size, with their sepals and petals frequently dissimilar, and with two of the former combined at the base and protruded in front like a chin.   [A. S.]

LYCHNIDE DES JARDINS. (Fr.) *Lychnis coronaria.* — LACINIÉE. *Lychnis Flos-cuculi.* — ROSE DU CIEL. *Viscaria Cæli-rosa.*

LYCHNIS. The Campion, a genus of *Caryophyllaceæ*, distinguished by having five styles. As this character is artificial, various attempts have been made to divide the genus into others, but in many instances the proposed divisions are founded on characters as artificial as those which are assigned to the group as a whole. The following may be taken as genera or subgenera:—1. Those in which the capsule opens by as many teeth as there are styles:—*Eulychnis*, calyx membranous in front; capsule septicidal; seeds stalked, rough with small tubercles. The Scarlet Lychnis (*L. chalcedonica*) and the Ragged Robin (*L. Flos-cuculi*) with pink flowers are examples of this. *Petrocoptis* differs from the last only in having the seeds sessile and quite smooth, as in *L. pyrenaica*, a white-flowered species. *Viscaria*, distinguished from the two preceding by the capsule splitting loculicidally; to this belong two British species, *L. Viscaria* and *L. alpina*, both having rose-coloured flowers. *Coronaria*, in which the calyx is thickened in fruit; the Rose Campion (*L. coronaria*) is a good example. *Agrostemma*, same as in the last, but without the scale-like appendages which occur at the base of the limb of the petals, forming the so-called crown; the Corn Cockle (*L. Githago*), and a closely allied species *L. gracilis*, are the only species which answer to this character. 2. Those in which the capsule opens by twice as many teeth as there are styles; nearly allied to *Silene* :—*Melandrium*, calyx teeth regular; calyx ovoid, with the veins not prominent in fruit, as in *L. vespertina* and *L. dioica*, the common wild Campions. *Wahlbergella*, like the last, but the calyx teeth are combined in pairs, and the petals are small or absent; they are all arctic plants. *Eudianthe*, calyx clavate, with the veins prominent in fruit, and often roughened, as in *Viscaria Cœli-rosa*.   [J. T. S.]

LYCHNIS, ROCK. *Viscaria.*

LYCIOPLESIUM. A few South American shrubs constituting a genus of *Solanaceæ*. They have spiny stems, rather thick leaves somewhat closely packed together in tufts, and solitary or axillary flowers, with a bell-shaped five-toothed calyx, and a tubular reddish-coloured corolla, whose limb is divided into five acute lobes. The fruit is succulent, enclosed within the persistent calyx, and of a red or orange colour. The generic name is expressive of its close affinity to the genus *Lycium*. [M. T. M.]

LYCIUM. A name applied to some thorny shrub by Dioscorides, and now adopted for one of the genera of *Solanaceæ*. The species are shrubs, natives of the Mediterranean region, and of some parts of tropical America. Their inflorescence is various. The calyx is cup-shaped, five-toothed, sometimes irregular; the corolla funnel-shaped or tubular, with a five-cleft limb; stamens five, the anthers opening lengthwise; ovary two-celled; fruit succulent in the cup-like calyx.

The species are numerous. Some are grown in greenhouses, whilst others are hardy. Among the latter is *L. barbarum*, a plant which, from its rapid growth, green foliage, and small lilac flowers, which are succeeded by scarlet or orange fruits, is often met with in gardens. It is well adapted to cover trellises, walls, &c., and is commonly known as the Tea plant, as its leaves have been recommended for use in place of tea—a piece of advice not generally acted upon, it would seem. The plant may sometimes be found in a semi-wild state in hedges, having escaped from cultivation. *L. europæum* is made use of as a hedge plant in Tuscany and Spain, and the young shoots are employed as a vegetable. *L. afrum*, a spiny species with violet flowers, forms a handsome plant on a sheltered wall.   [M. T. M.]

LYCOGALA. A genus of myxogastrous *Fungi*, familiar to many from one of its species giving out in its young state, when divided, a rich blood-like pulp. When dry, *L. epidendron* forms globose somewhat furfuraceous bodies about the size of a nut, filled with dull pinkish-grey cinereous dirty white or yellowish spores, and a few threads which are attached to the walls. It occurs on sticks in woods, and has a wide geographical range. The variability in the colour of the spores is singular, though a parallel example occurs in the genus *Æthalium*.   [M. J. B.]

LYCOPERDE DES BOUVIERS. (Fr.) *Lycoperdon Bovista.*

LYCOPERDON. One of the principal genera of the natural order *Trichogastres*, among the gasteromycetous *Fungi*. The peridium is double, but the outer coat, which breaks up into warts, spines, scales,

&c., is intimately connected with the inner coat, and the spores are mostly sessile, though occasionally stipitate as in *Bovista*, from which it is distinguished by its less persistent inner peridium, and more adnate outer coat. The species are produced abundantly in almost every country, but are so variable that it is often very difficult to distinguish them. *L. Bovista*, when quite young, in which state even it attains a large size, is one of the best of fungi if cut in slices and fried, but we cannot say much in favour of other large species. The dry mass of threads and spores is used as a styptic, and its fumes answer the purpose of chloroform. The spores are generally more or less olivaceous, but occasionally they assume a purple tint.   [M. J. B.]

LYCOPERDON NUTS. The name under which the herbalists sell our common species of *Elaphomyces*.   [M. J. B.]

LYCOPERSICUM. A genus of *Solanaceæ* established by Tournefort, but afterwards combined with *Solanum* by Linnæus, although now generally recognised by modern botanists as distinct. Ten species, all natives of South America, chiefly of the Peruvian side, are described. They are either annual or perennial herbaceous plants, generally with weak stems trailing upon the ground or supporting themselves on other plants; they have irregularly pinnate leaves, and stalks bearing many flowers growing from the sides of the stems. The flowers are easily distinguishable from those of the allied *Solanum*, by their stamens having the anthers connected together by a thin membrane which is prolonged upwards, and by their cells opening by means of a long slit down the inside, instead of by two pores or holes at the top. The fruits are fleshy, usually red or yellow, and very glossy, and are divided into two, three, or many cells, containing numerous seeds imbedded in pulp.

L. esculentum is the Tomato or Love Apple. It is an annual plant, native of the warmer parts of America, but long ago introduced into most other warm or temperate countries, where it is cultivated for the sake of its wholesome fruit. It was brought to Europe in the early part of the sixteenth century, soon after the discovery of America, and is now extensively grown in many parts; but in this country, owing to the shortness of our summers, its fruit does not always come to perfection. Several varieties are cultivated, differing only in the size and shape and red or yellow colour of their fruits. Two, however, are considered by some botanists as distinct species, and are named *L. cerasiforme* and *L. pyriforme*—the sole distinction between them being that the first-mentioned has a round two-celled fruit rather larger than a cherry, and the other a pear-shaped two-celled fruit about an inch and a half long; while the more common *L. esculentum* has a large irregularly shaped furrowed fruit, divided into several cells, the irregularity and multiplicity of cells, however, being frequently owing to two or more flowers having joined together so as to produce only one fruit.

Tomatos are much more commonly used for food in the south of Europe and other parts of the continent than they are in this country. Near Rome and Naples whole fields are covered with it, the fruit being one of the most common articles used in Italian cookery. Now that their agreeable qualities are better known, they are beginning to be more generally appreciated with us, and, in addition to those grown in this country, considerable quantities are imported from the continent. Although they belong to a family usually looked upon with suspicion, on account of the narcotic poisonous properties of so many plants belonging to it, they, in common with the fruits of many *Solanums*, are perfectly wholesome, and may be freely eaten. In a green state, Tomatos form an excellent pickle, and when ripe, various delicious sauces and ketchups are made of them ; besides which they are largely eaten either raw, or when cooked in various ways. Used as an article of diet, they are considered beneficial in affections of the liver, indigestion, diarrhœa, and other complaints. The word Tomato is derived from the Spanish-American name Tamate ; and the other common English name, Love Apple, has arisen from their supposed power of exciting tender feelings. [A. S.]

LYCOPODE. Vegetable brimstone, the highly inflammable powder contained in the spore-cases of *Lycopodium clavatum* and *L. Selago.*

LYCOPODIACEÆ. A natural order of Acrogens, consisting of two very distinct groups, one of which contains numerous species with the habit of the larger mosses or conifers, and the other of aquatics which have a more or less herbaceous aspect. *Phylloglossum*, consisting of a single species, is, however, nearly intermediate. They are distinguished from ferns by the absence of a ring to the capsules, which are either bi-tri-valved or altogether anomalous (see ISOÊTES) ; by their different mode of germination ; and, as far as is known, by the very different character of their antheridia. In *Selaginella* there are two distinct kinds of capsules, the one producing large four-sided (globoso-tetrahedric) spores, and the other smaller antheridia. The spores germinate by cell-division on one side, a quantity of archegonia being produced in the cellular stratum formed during the process of germination ; the antheridia, which at first have quite the appearance of spores or pollen grains, after several weeks produce spiral spermatozoids from their cavity, by means of which the embryo cell in each archegonium is fertilized. This in due time becomes further organised, acquires a distinct root and axis, and finally produces a dicotyledonous embryo strongly resembling that of phænogams. In the other genera whose fruit has been examined, the process of reproduction is essentially the same.

In *Lycopodium* there is no distinct second fruit, and the details of germination are at present unknown. It is conjectured that the cellular stratum produced during germination, or in other words the prothallus, produces antheridia together with the archegonia as in ferns. This is, however, very uncertain. The stem, when well developed, consists of a mass of thick-walled often dotted cells, enclosing one or many bundles of scalariform tissue, which send off branches to every leaf and bud. This is occasionally accompanied by distinctly reticulated cells. There is, however, no crossing of bundles as in Endogens, and there are no medullary rays. In many respects the structure is that of ferns.

a.   Selaginella spinulosa.
b.   Lycopodium clavatum.

Lycopodiaceæ occur in all parts of the world, but far the finest species and the most abundant occur in the tropics or in countries where there are no very striking distinctions of temperature. The finest modern lycopods, however, cannot bear comparison with the *Sigillariæ* and *Lepidodendra* of ancient strata, which vie with tree-ferns in their stem, and with conifers in their fruit. In essentials their stems agree in structure with modern lycopods, that of *Lepidodendron* consisting of a central mass made up principally of large scalariform vessels which send off branches to the leaves through the surrounding thick-walled cells. *Sigillaria*, however, takes a step towards phænogams, having, instead of a nearly uniform central mass, wedges of vessels interrupted by rays from the surrounding cellular tissue.   [M. J. B.]

LYCOPODIUM. One of the two great genera of lycopods, known more especially by the name of Clubmosses. They are distinguished from *Selaginella* by the coniferous habit, and single form of capsules. The species vary greatly in size, and while some are quite prostrate, others are erect, and some again attain such dimensions that they might at first sight be really taken for conifers. The leaves vary from mere threads to broad imbricated scales. The heads of fruit are mostly distinct and cylindrical, and sometimes branched. The same species may assume such various forms under different circumstances as to be recognised with difficulty. Dr. Hooker has given a remarkable instance of this in *L. densum*, a common New Zealand species. Species of *Lycopodium* occur in cold, temperate, and tropical countries, and six occur in our own islands. *L. cernuum*, one of the most widely diffused species, ascends as far north as the Azores, where it is found in the neighbourhood of warm springs; and it is found again as far south as St. Paul's.

Some of the species are cathartic when fresh, but they seem to lose their virtue when dry. One is commonly used as a medicine in Madeira, and *L. catharticum* has, as the name implies, a medical reputation in South America. A blue dye is prepared from some species, and the spores of our common Clubmoss are used on the stage to produce artificial lightning, from their highly inflammable nature. They are also employed by apothecaries to keep pills from sticking together. They have such a strong repulsive power, that if the hand is powdered with them, it can be dipped in water without be coming wet. *L. alpinum* is the badge of the McRaes, *L. clavatum* that of the Sinclairs.   [M. J. B.]

LYCOPSIS. A genus of *Boraginaceæ* now united to *Anchusa*, from which it differs only in the tube of the corolla being slightly curved. *L. arvensis*, a hispid annual with small blue flowers, is a common weed in cultivated ground.   [J. T. S.]

LYCOPUS. A genus of labiates, having the corolla scarcely longer than the calyx, bell-shaped and four-cleft; the two lower stamens alone perfect, the upper wanting or imperfect; and the ripe fruit with thick margins. The species are herbs usually inhabiting marshes, in Europe, Asia, North America, and Australia.   [G. D.]

LYCORIS. The plants separated under this name by Herbert are now regarded as forming a section of *Amaryllis*, technically distinguished by the undulated divisions of the spreading perianth being curved upwards, and by the style having likewise a curve upwards and bearing a simple fringed stigma. They are natives of Eastern Asia and Africa; and the two most conspicuous species are to be met with in our gardens.   [A. S.]

LYCOTROPAL. An orthotropal ovule curved downwards like a horse-shoe.

LYGEUM. A genus of grasses belonging to the tribe *Phalarideæ*. The inflorescence is contained in large sheath-like bracts, which have two or three florets, without glumes, with the base of the pales hardening into a two-celled seed-vessel. *L. Spartum* is the only species, and a rather handsome grass, which has extensive underground stems or soboles, and is only cultivated in botanical collections. [D. M.]

LYGODICTYON. *Hydroglossum.*

LYGODIUM. A genus of scandent ferns of the group *Schizæineæ*. The species are rather numerous, and widely dispersed over the warmer parts of the world, extending to New Holland, Japan, and North America. The fronds are branched, with a scandent rachis, and they usually bear conjugate branches, which are variously divided in a digitate or palmate manner, or else they are pinnatifid, or sometimes pinnate. The fructifications form compressed distichous spikelets, somewhat resembling in aspect those of *Selaginella*, but exserted on marginal teeth of the fronds. These spikes consist of bract-like indusia, each covering a single spore-case which is resupinate, and furnished with a many-rayed apical ring. The veins are free, which distinguishes this genus from *Hydroglossum*. They are plentiful in our hothouse collections of ferns.   [T. M.]

LYGODYSODEA. This harshly sounding name seems to be derived from the Greek words *lugos*, a slender branch or twig, and *dusodos*, pathless, in allusion probably to the obstruction caused by the climbing habit of the plants to which it is applied by botanists. The genus consists of Mexican and Peruvian shrubs of the *Cinchonaceæ*, characterised by an ovate calyx tube, having a five-toothed limb; a funnel-shaped corolla, with five revolute limb segments; five sessile anthers; and an inferior two-celled ovary, surmounted by a disk. The fruit consists of two carpels, crowned by the teeth of the calyx, and separating when ripe.   [M. T. M.]

LYMPH. Sap; the crude unelaborated fluid of vegetation. *Lymphæducts* are sap-vessels.

LYONIA. A genus of heathworts, having the corolla ovate or tubular, the mouth narrow and five-toothed, and the filaments of the stamens short broad and downy, the cells of the anthers opening lengthwise. The species are North American shrubs with alternate leaves, in some deciduous, in others evergreen; the flowers are sometimes hairy. The genus commemorates the services of Mr. Lyon, a well-known collector of North American plants.   [G. D.]

LYONSIA. A genus of the dogbane order, distinguished by having the stigma of a conical form, and the fruit a cylindrical capsule with two cells. *L. straminea*, a native of Australia, the only species, is a twining shrub with opposite leaves, named in honour of Mr. Lyons, who published a Flora of Cambridge.   [G. D.]

LYPERIA. A genus of *Scrophulariaceæ* of the tribe *Gratioleæ*, and nearly allied to *Manulea*, but distinguished chiefly by the slender tube of the corolla, which is more or less curved or gibbous at the back near the top. There are about thirty species, natives of the Cape Colony in Southern Africa. They are all herbs or low branching undershrubs, the leaves opposite or the upper ones alternate, usually small, entire toothed or divided, and often clustered in the axils. The flowers are axillary or in terminal spikes or racemes, usually more or less viscous, and always turn black in drying; when fresh, they are usually yellow or purple, or in some species of that peculiar greenish-yellow, with a brown tinge outside, which is usually accompanied by a tendency to exhale a sweet scent at the close of the day. Two species, *L. fragrans* and *L. violacea*, have been occasionally introduced to our gardens.

LYRATE, LYRESHAPED. Pinnatifid, with the upper lobes much larger than the lower.

LYROCARPA. A genus of *Cruciferæ* from California, distinguished by its fiddle-shaped two-lobed pouch. [J. T. S.]

LYSILOMA. A genus of *Leguminosæ* of the tribe *Mimoseæ*, formerly combined with *Acacia*, from which, however, it is distinguished by the stamens, which seldom exceed thirty in number, being united at the base into a tube unconnected with the corolla, and also by the thin flat pods having, as in *Mimosa*, *Entada*, &c., a thickened margin, which remains entire, while the thin inner portion breaks away in the centre, so as to allow of the escape of the seeds. The eight or ten species are inhabitants of tropical America, and are either shrubs or large trees, destitute of prickles, and resembling in general appearance the acacias of the same regions, having twice pinnated leaves, and round or cylindrical heads of small flowers. The genus is of considerable importance in an economic point of view, on account of one of its species yielding the valuable hard timber known as Sabicú, Savacú, or Sávicú wood, the origin of which was long unknown, but which has now been ascertained to be the produce of a species of this genus to which the name *Sabicu* has been given. Sabicú timber is imported in considerable quantities from Cuba, where only the tree is known to exist. It is a dark-coloured wood, very heavy, excessively hard, and extremely durable, the two latter qualities rendering it of great value to the shipbuilder, by whom it is much esteemed. On account of its hardness it was selected for the stairs of the building for the Great Exhibition in 1851, and, notwithstanding the immense number of people who passed up and down, the stairs were found, at the close of the Exhibition, to be scarcely at all the worse for wear. [A. S.]

LYSIMACHIA. A genus of herbaceous mostly perennial plants belonging to the *Primulaceæ*, and allied to *Anagallis*, from which they are distinguished by having glabrous, not hairy, filaments, and a capsule which opens at the summit with five or ten valves. *L. nemorum*, the commonest British species, approaches in size and habit the scarlet pimpernel, but has bright yellow flowers; from this resemblance it is often called Wood Pimpernel. *L. Nummularia*, Moneywort or Herb Twopence, is a trailing plant common on the margins of rivers, the banks of which it often fringes with pendent stems, thickly set with roundish glossy leaves, and large bright yellow flowers. It is often cultivated in gardens as a decoration to rockwork, especially where water is introduced, or is grown as a window plant and allowed to droop over the sides of the pot. There are many foreign species, most of which bear yellow flowers and affect moist situations. French, *Lysimaque*; German, *Gelbe weiderich*. [C. A. J.]

LYSINEMA. A small genus of *Epacrideæ*, natives of New South Wales and Southwest Australia, and having a coloured calyx surrounded with bracts of the same texture as the calyx; a salver-shaped corolla, the tube of which is often divisible into five parts, the segments of the limb smooth and inclined to the right; and the stamens attached below the ovary, and having peltate anthers. They are handsome shrubs, with white or rose-coloured flowers in sessile axillary spikes; the leaves smooth and sharp-pointed. [R. H.]

LYSIONOTUS *ternifolia* is an erect glabrous herb inhabiting Nepal, and the sole representative of a genus of *Cyrtandraceæ*. The leaves are ovate-lanceolate and arranged in whorls; the flowers are of a fine rose-colour, and arranged in terminal umbels. The calyx is five-cleft, the corolla bell-shaped, and the stamens five, two of which are fertile. The fruit is capsular, bivalved, and encloses an indefinite number of seeds. [B. S.]

LYSIOSTYLES. A genus of *Convolvulaceæ*, containing a single species, a native of British Guiana. It is a climbing shrub, with alternate petiolate oblong leaves, and flowers in axillary panicles. The calyx is five-cleft, with imbricated lobes; the corolla tube short, and the limb rotate and five-parted; there are five stamens; and the ovary is one-celled, with four erect ovules, surmounted by two styles, completely separate, and each with a capitate stigma. The genus is nearly related to the one hand to *Maripa*, on the other to *Erycibe*, yet abundantly distinct from either. It belongs to the group which Decandolle has raised to the rank of a natural order under the title of *Erycibeæ*. [W. C.]

LYSIPOMA. The name of a genus of small herbaceous plants of the *Lobeliaceæ*, natives of the Andes. The genus is known by the calyx, which has a five-nerved tube and a five-parted somewhat two-lipped limb; by the funnel-shaped corolla, with an entire distended tube and two-lipped limb, the upper lip of two, the lower of three divisions; by the five stamens united into a tube, the two lowermost anthers hairy; and by the inferior one-celled ovary. The capsule opens by a little lid at the top. [M. T. M.]

LYSURUS. A genus of phalloid *Fungi*, in which the receptacle of the fruit is split into a few free laciniæ. In other respects it resembles *Phallus*. The ashes of *L. Mokusin* are applied in China as a remedy to ulcerous sores. It is also sometimes eaten, but often proves poisonous.   [M. J. B.]

LYTHRACEÆ. (*Salicariæ, Calycantheæ mæ, Lythrads, Loosestrifes.*) A natural order of dicotyledonous plants, belonging to Lindley's saxifragal alliance of perigynous Exogens. Herbs, rarely shrubs, often with square branches, and usually opposite entire exstipulate leaves. Among the allied perigynous exalbuminous orders, it is distinguished by its tubular calyx, enclosing a two- to six-celled ovary which is free from it; its united styles; its membranous capsular fruit; and its stamens inserted in the calycine tube below the petals. The plants are chiefly tropical, but some are found in Europe and North America. They have astringent qualities. Examples: *Lythrum, Cuphea, Lagerströmia. Lawsonia alba* yields the henna of the Arabs. There are forty genera, and upwards of three hundred species.   [J. H. B.]

LYTHRUM. A genus of herbaceous plants, mostly perennials, giving name to the *Lythraceæ*. In these plants the tubular calyx has eight to twelve teeth, the alternate ones awl-shaped; the petals are four to six, and the capsule is two-celled. The genus is well represented in Britain by *L. Salicaria*, the Purple Loosestrife, a tall and very handsome plant, three to four feet high, with opposite lanceolate leaves, and long terminal leafy spikes of densely whorled purple flowers, common in most parts of Britain, often occupying a large space in marshy meadows, or lining a watercourse for a considerable extent, and thus to be classed among the few plants which, by breadth of colour, tend to characterise a landscape. There are many foreign species, of which *L. virgatum*, a native of Austria, sometimes cultivated, resembles *L. Salicaria* in habit, but is more branched above, and bears its flowers, which are large, in whorls of three or four. French, *Salicaire*; German, *Braunes weiderich*.   [C. A. J.]

MABA. A genus of *Ebenaceæ*, differing from *Diospyros* in the calyx and corolla having each only three lobes, instead of four or more. It consists of nearly twenty species, dispersed over tropical Africa and Asia, the Pacific islands, and North Australia, all shrubs or trees with alternate entire leaves, and small flowers, almost sessile, in their axils. The Ebony wood of Cochin China is believed to be the produce of a tree of this genus.

MABEA. A genus of *Euphorbiaceæ* of the tribe *Crotoneæ*, consisting of tropical American shrubs, sometimes climbing, with alternate usually oblong entire or toothed leaves, and flowers in terminal racemes or panicles, the majority usually males, with a few females at the base. The perianth is valvate, without petals;

the males have numerous stamens, and the females a long three-cleft style with one ovule in each cell of the ovary. There are nine or ten species known, all of which yield a copious acrid milky juice. The bark of one of them is, according to Martius, considered in the diamond district of Brazil as a febrifuge, and the straight hollow young shoots of several species are used for tobacco-pipes in Guiana and North Brazil under the name of Tacuari.

MACAHUBA. A Brazilian name for *Acrocomia sclerocarpa.*

MACARTHURIA. A genus of Southwest Australian herbs or undershrubs with erect rush-like stems, few small alternate leaves either linear or reduced to minute scales, and small flowers in lateral or terminal compact cymes. Its precise affinities are not very clear, but it is probably most nearly allied to the *Molluginæ*, next to which it has been recently proposed to place it. There are only three species known, and none are deserving of cultivation.

MACARY-BITTER. A West Indian name for *Picrámnia Antidesma.*

MACAW-BUSH. *Solanum mammosum.*

MACAW-FAT. A West Indian name for the Oil Palm, *Elæis guineensis.*

MACAW-TREE. *Acrocomia fusiformis* and *sclerocarpa.* —, GREAT. *Acrocomia lasiospatha.*

MACE. The aril of the nutmeg, *Myristica moschata*; also an Indian name for the gall-nuts formed on *Tamarix indica.* —, RED. The aril of *Pyrrhosa tingens.* —, WHITE. The aril of *Myristica Otoba.*

MACERON. (Fr.) *Smyrnium.*

MACFADYENA. A genus of *Bignoniaceæ*, named after Dr. Macfadyen, author of a Flora of Jamaica. The genus has a spathaceous calyx, funnel-shaped corolla, four fertile stamens of unequal length with glabrous divergent anthers, an elongated flat and smooth capsule, divided into two cells by a partition running parallel with the direction of the valves, and numerous winged seeds arranged in single rows. There are about a dozen species, all inhabitants of the West Indies and the tropical parts of South America. They are climbing shrubs, with trifoliate and conjugate leaves, in the latter instance furnished with tendrils, and large bright yellow or more or less purplish flowers, appearing in the axils of the leaves, or in corymbs at the end of the branches. *M. uncata* has for many years been an inmate of our hot-houses. Many of the species, from being imperfectly known, had until lately been classed with *Spathodea.* [B. S.]

MACHÆRANTHERA. A generic name proposed by Nees for the *Aster. tanacetifolius*, described from specimens grown in the Botanic Garden of Mexico, and differing in some slight points from the majority of the species of the great genus *Aster.*

MACHÆRINA. A genus of cyperaceous plants, belonging to the tribe *Rhynchosporeæ*. The inflorescence is in panicles; scales of the flowers two-rowed, keeled; stamens three; styles three, cleft, thickened conically at the base; seeds or nuts pear-shaped. There are two species, one of which belongs to the West Indies, the other to New Holland.   [D. M.]

MACHÆRIUM. An extensive genus of leguminous plants belonging to Central and South America, some forming large timber trees, others shrubs of moderate height, while others again are tall creepers, often armed with prickles. Their leaves are pinnate, and their flowers small, and purple violet or white. Their most obvious generic character resides in the fruit, which is compressed, but more or less thickened at the base where the solitary seed is situated, while the upper part is drawn out into a thin tapering wing terminated by the remains of the style.

Some of these trees are supposed to yield a portion of the Rose-wood of commerce. Notwithstanding the length of time Rose-wood has been known to our cabinet-makers, and the large quantities of it annually imported, its botanical history is very obscure, and it has been at various times referred to trees of widely different natural orders. The best description of true Rose-wood comes from Rio Janeiro, and is now said to be chiefly the produce of *Dalbergia nigra*, a tree belonging to the same section of leguminous plants as the present genus; but there are also several inferior sorts derived from the same country, and these are probably produced by different species of *Machærium*, three of which, viz. *M. firmum, M. incorruptibile*, and *M. legale* are large trees, and, moreover, bear the same Brazilian name (Jacaranda) as the true Rose-wood. *M. Schomburgkii*, a British Guiana species, produces the beautifully mottled wood called Itaka, Itiki, or Tiger-wood, used for furniture in that country.   [A. S.]

MÂCHE. (Fr.) The salad plants, *Valerianella olitoria* and *coronata*.

MACHOOTI. An Indian name for *Polygonum aviculare*.

MACKAYA. A genus of Indian *Olacaceæ*, with a short broadly campanulate calyx having a five-toothed limb; a rotate five-parted deciduous corolla; five stamens, with basal glands and sessile anthers; and a one-celled ovary with three pendulous ovules, and a three-lobed stigma. The fruit is indehiscent, with one pendulous seed. This plant, which is a smooth climbing shrub, with alternate leaves, and small flowers on long pedicels, is now referred to *Erythropalum*, of which two species are known, natives of tropical Asia. [J. H. B.]

MACLEANIA. A genus of Peruvian shrubs, referred to the *Vacciniaceæ*. They have alternate leaves, and axillary flower-stalks terminated by a single flower, which has a five-winged calyx tube, a tubular corolla with ten monadelphous stamens attached to its base, and whose anthers are prolonged into a tube, and an ovary adherent to the calyx tube, and with five many-seeded compartments. The flowers are reddish or yellow, and possess great beauty. The genus commemorates Mr. Maclean, a patron of Botany. [M. T. M.]

MACLEAYA. A genus of *Papaveraceæ*, closely allied to *Bocconia*, but differing from it in the fruit, which is sessile and one-celled, with four to six seeds. The cotyledons of the embryo are three in number and equal, or two or four and then unequal, in size; in germination they are stalked. *M. cordata*, better known perhaps under its old name of *Bocconia*, is a handsome herbaceous plant frequently grown in English gardens, but native of China. The leaves are stalked, somewhat cordate, irregularly toothed at the margin, and glaucous. The flowers are borne in terminal panicles. The genus is named in honour of Mr. Macleay, colonial secretary in New South Wales.   [M. T. M.]

MACLURA. This genus, which is peculiar to the western hemisphere—one species being found in the United States, one in Mexico, and five in Brazil and the West Indies—belongs to the *Moraceæ*, and consists of middle-sized, sometimes spiny, deciduous trees, with smoothish entire or coarsely serrated leaves, and unisexual flowers upon distinct trees; the males being in cylindrical or globular spikes or in racemes, and the females forming dense globular heads. The fruits are numerous small seed-like achenes, enveloped in the enlarged calyxes, which are packed closely together upon the globose somewhat fleshy receptacle, so that the fruits of a single flower-head form a round aggregate fruit.

M. aurantiaca, the Osage Orange, is a native of the Southern United States, and forms a spreading tree from thirty to sixty feet high, but it is frequently kept dwarf and used as a hedge plant, for which purpose its strong spines render it suitable. It has large entire egg-shaped leaves, and inconspicuous yellowish-green flowers, producing large round fruits from three to five inches in diameter and of a fine golden colour, very beautiful to the eye, but scarcely eatable. Its elastic yellow wood is called Bow-wood, from its being used by the Indians for making bows.

M. tinctoria, the Fustic-tree, is a large usually unarmed tree, with nearly entire oblong taper-pointed leaves, a native of the West Indies and tropical America, from whence large quantities of its bright yellow wood are exported for the use of dyers, who obtain from it shades of yellow, brown, olive, and green. There are two kinds of Fustic, technically termed the Young and the Old, the former being the wood of *Rhus Cotinus*, and the latter that of the present plant.   [A. S.]

MACNABIA. A genus of heathworts, distinguished by having the calyx four-cleft, two of the divisions keeled, the others plain ; eight stamens, with beardless anthers ; and nearly circular flat winged seeds. The genus was named in honour of the late Mr. McNab, of the Edinburgh Botanic Garden. There is but a single species, a Cape shrub, with the habit of a heath, having leaves in whorls of three, and flowers solitary or in pairs, borne by the shorter branches.   [G. D.]

MACODES *Petola* is a beautiful little orchid from Java, belonging to the group *Physurideæ*. Its oval leaves are clouded on the upper surface, and elegantly marked with netted golden veins ; but its flowers are small and inconspicuous, having free conniving green sepals and thread-like petals. As a genus, it is distinguished from *Myoda*, one of its closest allies, by its free lip ; and from another, *Hæmaria*, by its column having a two-lobed appendage at its base.   [A. S.]

MACOYA. A Guiana name for *Acrocomia sclerocarpa*.

MACRADENIA *lutescens* is a little Trinidad orchid, forming a genus allied to *Oncidium*, from which it differs by its cucullate-concave undivided taper-pointed lip, by its free perianth divisions, by its column having the two lobes at its top converging into a hood, and by its two furrowless or unindented pollen-masses. The plant is only about four inches high, and has one-leaved pseudobulbs, from the base of which arises a stalk bearing a raceme of four or five dingy yellow flowers spotted with brownish purple.   [A. S.]

MACRÆA. This name was given first to a Chilian genus of *Vivianiaceæ*, which proved to be identical with *Viviania* ; and afterwards to a composite plant from the Galapagos Islands, which has since been reduced to *Lipochæta*. The former is now included by Bentham and Hooker in the *Geraniaceæ*, under which they place the *Vivianieæ*, as a minor group.

MACRE. (Fr) *Trapa natans*.

MACROCEPHALOUS. Big-headed ; the term is sometimes applied to dicotyledonous embryos whose cotyledons are consolidated.

MACROPODAL. Big-footed ; applied by Richard to the embryo of grasses, whose cotyledon was mistaken by that author for a radicle.

MACROS. In Greek compounds long ; sometimes, large.

MACROCHILUS. The name of a small tree of the Sandwich Islands, forming a genus of *Lobeliaceæ*, and described as having a straight trunk of ten to twelve feet in height, terminated by a crown of leaves and flower stalks, the former sharp-pointed and wavy, the latter longer than the leaves, drooping, and bearing the flowers in terminal globose heads, surrounded by densely overlapping bracts. The calyx tube is inversely conical, the limb five-cleft ; the corolla has an elongated curved tube, cleft

on the upper side, and with a limb divided into five equal linear pendulous segments, whence the name of the genus, from *makros*, long, and *cheilos*, a lip.   [M. T. M.]

MACROCHLOA. A genus of grasses, belonging to the tribe *Stipeæ*, and included by Steudel in the genus *Stipa*, of which it forms a subsection. *M. tenuissima* and *M. arenaria* are natives of the North of Africa, Spain, and Portugal.   [D. M.]

MACROCYSTIS. A remarkable genus of dark-spored *Algæ*, belonging to the natural order *Laminariaceæ*. From a much-branched root springs, in the first instance, a small forked frond which alone bears the fruit in clouded patches, the endochrome of whose spore-cases ultimately breaks up into four spores, as in many other laminarioid *Algæ*. Besides this, however, arise one or more tall slender stems, several feet in length, with a vertical terminal lanceolate frond, which is repeatedly split, from the base upwards in such a way as to form new leaves, the attenuated base of which gradually passes into a short petiole, which becomes inflated above into a bladder. The original frond is thus repeatedly divided in a second manner, till the plant becomes hundreds of feet long. As, however, the stem does not increase in strength as the plant elongates, the strain is at length so great, notwithstanding the numerous bladders, that it at last gives way, and the plant floats. Many species have been proposed by authors, but all are reducible to one, *M. pyrifera*, which girds the

Macrocystis pyrifera, var. luxurians.

southern temperate zone, and stretches up from thence along the Pacific to the Arctic regions, through 120 degrees of latitude. This plant, like the *Sargassum*, has been celebrated by all voyagers, to whom it is of great service in indicating the presence of rocks, acting, as it does, like a great buoy. Vast masses are thrown up on exposed coasts, where it is rolled by the waves till it forms cables as thick as a man's body. Single plants have been estimated on reasonable grounds as attaining a length of 700 feet. It is apparently indifferent to cold, if not extreme, but inasmuch as like its near allies it is a deep-sea *Alga*, it requires a depth of at least six fathoms for its growth.	[M. J. B.]

MACROMERIA. A genus of *Boraginaceæ*, allied to *Lithospermum*, from which it differs by the exserted stamens, and by having the corolla with a long tube, dilated at the throat. They are Mexican strigose herbs, with simple stems, lanceolate serrated leaves, and terminal few-flowered bracteated racemes.	[J. T. S.]

MACROPIPER. This word, signifying large pepper, is applied to a genus of *Piperaceæ*, consisting of shrubs, natives of the islands of the Pacific, and having erect wavy knotted stems, alternate leaves on stalks that are dilated at the base, and provided with stipules, the blades of the leaves roundish or cordate with radiating venation. The male flowers are arranged in solitary catkins, the females in numerous catkins, placed in the axil of a leaf. *M. methysticum*, formerly called *Piper me-*

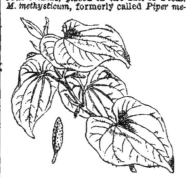

Macropiper methysticum.

thysticum, furnishes the root called by the Polynesians Ava or Kava, which has narcotic properties, and is employed medicinally in rheumatism and other complaints, but is chiefly remarkable for the value attached to it as a narcotic and stimulant beverage, of which the natives partake before they undertake any important business or religious rites. The approved method of preparing the Kava is to chew the root, and thus extract the juice.. Dr. Seemann, in some letters from the Feejee Islands, printed in the *Athenæum* (1861), gives some amusing information concerning this plant and its uses. It appears that Kava has, like tobacco, a calming effect, rather than an intoxicating one, unless indeed the juice be fermented, as is done by the European residents in some of the islands of the South Sea. Dr. Seemann, however, tells us that the Feejeans pride themselves on the non-intoxicating properties of Kava, that it does not make the partakers quarrelsome, and that drunk in moderation it does not appear to have any ill effect upon the system, but when used in excess it produces numerous skin

diseases. All the lower classes of whites in Feejee are Kava drinkers, and most of them prefer the drink prepared in regular Polynesian fashion. The more respectable of the population refrain from touching the filthy preparation. Another species of this, or some allied genus, is used similarly in the formation of a beverage, differing from Kava, and having, according to Dr. Seemann, a flavour of soap-suds combined with jalap and magnesia.	[M. T. M.]

MACROPODIUM. A genus of *Cruciferæ*, allied to *Cardamine* and *Parrya*, from both of which it differs in the pod, which is oblong-linear with plane one-nerved valves, being stipitate. A perennial Alpine plant from the Altai, with a terminal raceme of white flowers.	[J.T.S.]

MACRORHYNCHUS. A genus including about a dozen annual or perennial stemless herbs of the composite family, found in Oregon, California, and Chili. They have much resemblance to and affinity with *Taraxacum*, differing chiefly in the cylindrical ribbed achenes being destitute of any roughness, and being produced into a long beak, terminating in a pappus of numerous soft white hairs.	[A. A. B.]

MACROSTYLIS. A genus of rutaceous shrubs, natives of the Cape of Good Hope, and nearly allied to *Barosma*. The distinctive characters reside in the presence of five stamens only, and in the three carpels, terminated at their points by a single style, longer than the stamens. The reddish flowers are arranged in a kind of umbel on the ends of the branches. The orchidaceous genus of this name is synonymous with *Corymbis*.	[M. T. M.]

MACROZAMIA. A genus of *Cycadaceæ*, consisting of Australian trees, living in swampy places near the sea. The genus is described as intermediate between *Cycas* and *Encephalartos*. The rachis of the leaves is twisted in the young condition, the leaflets themselves being flat. The male flowers are borne on spoon-shaped pointed spikes, the pollen being collected in two spaces on the under surface of the anthers, and not diffused over the whole surface as in *Encephalartos*. The female spikes bear only two flowers.	[M. T. M.]

MACULA (adj. MACULATE). A broad irregular spot or blotch.

MACUSON. (Fr.) *Lathyrus tuberosus*.

MADAR, or MUDAR. The produce of *Calotropis gigantea*.

MADARIA. A genus of *Compositæ*, comprising two Californian annuals, closely allied to *Madia*, distinguished chiefly by the longer and more expanded ray florets, and by the florets of the disk being constantly sterile. The flower-heads form a loose terminal corymb with yellow florets.

MADAROGLOSSA. *Layia*.

MADDER. The root of *Rubia tinctoria*, which is sometimes called Dyer's Madder. —, BENGAL. *Rubia cordifolia*. —, CHILI.

Rubia Relbun. —, FIELD. *Sherardia arvensis.* —, INDIAN, *Oldenlandia umbellata.* —, WILD. *Galium Mollugo.*

MADDERWORTS. A name for the *Galiaceæ.*

MADHUCA, or **MADOOKA.** *Bassia butyracea* and *latifolia.*

MADIA. A coarse hairy more or less viscous erect annual, forming a genus of *Compositæ* of the tribe *Heliantheæ.* The lower leaves are opposite and entire, the upper ones alternate ; and the flower-heads nearly globular, in a terminal raceme, with yellow florets. The involucral bracts are in a single series, each one folded so as to enclose one of the ray florets, which are ligulate or irregularly enlarged ; between these and the disk is a single row of scales, but the centre of the receptacle, bearing the tubular disk florets, is entirely without scales. The achenes are flattened, without any pappus. *M. sativa,* the only species known, is a native of Chili and of North California, and is there cultivated for the oil extracted from its seeds.

MADOORKATI. An Indian name for *Cyperus Pangorei,* from which Indian matting is made.

MADOTHECA. A genus of *Jungermanniaceæ,* belonging to the division *Platyphyllæ,* which has incubous leaves with the lower lobe simply folded upon the upper, an involucre of the same shape as the leaves, and a perianth neither winged nor angular as in *Frullania.* The lobes do not throw out roots from their under surface, as in *Radula complanata.* *M. platyphylla* forms elegant tufts upon old wall-tops, and is very common. [M. J. B.]

MADWORT. *Alyssum* ; also *Asperugo procumbens.* —, GERMAN. *Asperugo procumbens.*

MÆRUA. The name of a genus of *Capparidaceæ,* consisting of small shrubs, natives of tropical Africa. The flowers have a funnel-shaped calyx, the tube of which is persistent, while the limb is divided into four equal deciduous segments. There is no corolla, but standing up from the throat of the calyx is a short crown deeply and irregularly divided. The stamens are very numerous, on an elongated receptacle ; and the pod is one-celled. [M. T. M.]

MÆSA. A genus of *Myrsinaceæ,* consisting of trees or shrubs with alternate entire or toothed leaves, and small flowers in simple or compound racemes, either axillary or very rarely terminal. It is distinguished from all others of the order by the ovary, which is wholly or partially inferior. There are several species, natives of the tropical regions of Africa, Asia, and Australia, but none of them present any special interest.

MAFUNA. A vegetable wax, suitable for making candles, obtained in Mozambique from a tree whose native name is Mutiana.

MAGHET. *Pyrethrum Parthenium.*

MAGALLANA *porrifolia* is the sole representative of a genus of *Tropæolaceæ* inhabiting Antarctic America. It is an annual climbing herb, with alternate tri-parted leaves furnished with pellucid dots, and having cirrhose petioles ; axillary flowers ; a five-lobed calcarate calyx, three of the lobes being united into one, two deeply divided. There are five unequal petals, eight stamens, and a three-winged fruit. [B. S.]

MAGNOLIACEÆ. (*Magnolia, Wintereæ, Illicieæ.*) A natural order of dicotyledonous plants belonging to Lindley's ranal alliance of hypogynous Exogens. Trees or shrubs with alternate leathery sometimes dotted leaves, and convolute stipules which cover the buds and are deciduous. Flowers fragrant ; sepals usually three to six, deciduous ; petals three or more, imbricated ; stamens numerous, distinct, with adnate anthers ; carpels one-celled, numerous, on an elevated receptacle. Fruit of numerous dry or succulent dehiscent or indehiscent carpels ; seeds often arillate, and suspended from the fruit by a long funiculus ; albumen fleshy homogeneous ; embryo minute. Magnolias abound in North America. They possess bitter, tonic, and aromatic qualities. *Drimys Winteri* yields Winter's bark. *Illicium anisatum* is called star-anise, from its flavour, and the star-like arrangement of its carpels. *Liriodendron tulipifera,* the tulip-tree, is remarkable for its truncate leaves. There are about a dozen genera, and upwards of seventy species. Examples : *Magnolia, Drimys, Liriodendron.* [J. H. B.]

MAGNOLIA. Few botanists have their name and fame commemorated by so splendid a genus of plants as that which derives its title from Pierre Magnol, Professor of Medicine and Botany, at Montpellier, in the latter part of the seventeenth and beginning of the eighteenth century. The genus gives its name to the order *Magnoliaceæ,* and consists for the most part of large trees with fine foliage, and handsome fragrant flowers. They are natives of the southern states of North America, of Northern India, China, Japan, and other parts of Asia. The leaves are alternate, entire, deciduous or evergreen, rolled round in the bud, in which state they are protected by the stipules, which originally adhere to the sides of the leafstalks, but ultimately fall off. The flowers are large, terminal, protected in the young state by scales that seem to be of a stipulary nature, as the writer has not unfrequently seen a leaf developed from them in the same manner and in the same situation as with the scales of the leaf-bud, which are acknowledged to be stipules. Moreover, Drs. Hooker and Thomson describe one species, *M. Campbellii,* as having constantly these leaf-bearing scales surrounding the flower. The calyx consists of three deciduous sepals ; the corolla of six to twelve petals like the sepals ; stamens and ovaries numerous, on a prolonged receptacle. The fruit consists of a number of follicles, in a compact spike, and opening along their outer edge to allow of the escape of the scarlet or brown seeds, which are suspended from the carpels by long slender threads.

Most of the species have aromatic tonic properties, which has led to their employment in fevers, rheumatism, and other complaints. The beauty of the foliage and flowers of these trees gives them yet greater claims to our regard than their medicinal properties, which, although not slight, are excelled by those of other plants. The noblest of all is perhaps *M. grandiflora*, a native of North Carolina, where it forms a tree sixty to one hundred feet high. In this country it is commonly grown against a wall, and has generally proved hardy in the south of England, in such a situation, with little or no other protection. But the severe winter of 1860-61 proved fatal in many cases to this, as to so many other reputedly-hardy plants. The leaves of this species are evergreen, nine to ten inches long, much like those of a cherry-laurel, but rusty-brown on the under surface. The flowers are large, cup-shaped, white or pale lemon-coloured, and having an exquisite fragrance; they bloom in the latter part of the summer, and occasionally produce their rich brown spikes of fruit in October. There are several varieties of this tree in cultivation, differing in the shape of the leaves, the period of flowering, &c.

M. glauca is a low-growing deciduous tree, called in America Swamp Sassafras, from the nature of the localities in which it grows, and from the resemblance in its properties to *Laurus Sassafras*. It is also known by the name of Beaver-tree, because the root is eaten by beavers, which animals also make use of the wood in constructing their nests. *M. tripetala* has very large leaves and flowers, the latter with so potent a perfume as to produce sickness; fever and gout even have been attributed, doubtless erroneously, to the strong smell of the flowers. The young wood is of a dark brown colour. *M. acuminata* and *M. Fraseri* are called Cucumber-trees in America, on account of the appearance of the unripe fruit. *M. conspicua*, or *M. Yulan*, is a tree attaining a height of forty to fifty feet in China, but not more than half that height in this country. It is remarkable for-producing its white flowers in spring, before the leaves are developed. *M. purpurea*, a Japanese species, has deciduous leaves and fragrant flowers, the outer segments of which are purple, the inner white. It forms a splendid bush in the south of England. *M. Campbellii*, a native of Sikkim, is described by Dr. Hooker as a superb species, flowering before the leaves appear, and attaining a height of 150 feet.

There are a few species and varieties that need the protection of a greenhouse in this country; that most frequently met with is *M. fuscata*, a low-growing shrub with evergreen leaves, and dull purple flowers of exquisite fragrance.   [M. T. M.]

MAGONIA. A genus of *Sapindaceæ*, consisting of two trees, natives of Brazil, occupying extensive tracts of land to the exclusion of other trees, and forming what the Brazilians term Catingas, i.e. woods consisting entirely of deciduous trees. They are middle-sized trees, with abruptly pinnate leaves, and large panicles of perfect and imperfect flowers mixed together, appearing before the leaves. The fruit is a large woody three-sided three-celled capsule, containing six or eight broad flat winged seeds in each cell, and opening longitudinally through the middle of the cells when ripe.

M. glabrata, which usually attains the height of thirty or forty feet, covers tracts of land some miles in extent in the province of Ceara. It is called Tingi by the Brazilians, who employ an infusion of the bark of its root for poisoning or stupefying fish, while that of the bark of the stem they use for curing old ulcers, or the sores in horses caused by the stings of venomous insects. From the broad flat seeds they manufacture a kind of soap, which answers very well for washing clothes; it is prepared by soaking the seeds in water until they are soft, and then boiling them with a small quantity of tallow, till a homogeneous mass is formed.   [A. S.]

MAGUAY, or MAGUAY DE COCUYZA. *Agave americana*, — DE COCAY. *Agave cubensis*. — METL. *Agave americana*, and *A. mexicana*.

MAGYDARIS. An umbelliferous genus of about three species, found in Spain, Sicily, and North Africa, technically distinguished from *Conium* by its seeds being covered on both sides with numerous very thin vittæ. They are hoary plants, with pinnately cut leaves, the segments of which are lobed and toothed.   [A. S.]

MAHALEB. (Fr.) *Cerasus Mahaleb*.

MAHARANGA. The three species forming this genus of *Boraginaceæ*, at one time included in *Onosma*, are small hairy or bristly herbaceous plants, natives of Northern India, with entire leaves and terminal racemes of clustered flowers. These latter have a five-parted calyx, and a corolla with a short cylindrical tube widened out suddenly, and having five deep longitudinal furrows, and as many clefts round the closed mouth, the inside of the tube above its insertion being furnished with a plaited coronet, which distinguishes the genus from its congeners.

The Nepalese apply the name Maharanga to *M. Emodi* only, but botanists have adopted it as a generic name. The word is said to signify 'a strong or intense colour,' in allusion to the dyeing properties of the roots. These are thick, and of a tapering form, of a deep purple colour outside, and yield a brilliant red to oil, but only a dirty brown to water; they are the same as the Rutton root of the Indian bazaars, used for colouring oils for staining wood of a mahogany colour.   [A. S.]

MAHERNIA. A genus of *Sterculiaceæ* only differing from *Hermannia* in the filaments of the stamens being dilated in the middle; also very slightly in the inflorescence, the peduncles being usually two-flowered and terminal or opposite to the leaves. There are above thirty species, all, like the majority of *Hermanniæ*, natives of the Cape Colony.

MAHLIB. The fragrant kernels of *Cerasus Mahaleb*, which are strung as necklaces, and much valued by the women of Scinde and other parts of India.

MAHOE. *Paritium tiliaceum*; also *Sterculia caribæa.* —, BLUE or COMMON. *Paritium elatum.* —, BOMBAST. *Ochroma Lagopus.* —, CONGO. *Hibiscus clypeatus.* —, GREY or MOUNTAIN. *Paritium elatum.* —, NEW ZEALAND. *Melicytus ramiflorus.* —, SEASIDE. *Thespesia populnea.*

MAHOE-PIMENT. *Daphnopsis caribæa.*

MAHOGANY. *Swietenia Mahagoni.* —, AFRICAN. *Khaya senegalensis.* —, BASTARD. *Ratonia apetala.* —, BAYWOOD. A Honduras name for *Swietenia Mahagoni.* —, EAST INDIAN. *Soymida febrifuga.* —, INDIAN. *Cedrela Toona.* —, MOUNTAIN. *Betula lenta.* —, MADEIRA. *Persea indica.* —, SENEGAL. *Khaya senegalensis.* —, SPANISH. *Swietenia Mahagoni.* —, QUEENSLAND SWAMP. *Angophora.* —, WHITE or WILD. *Stenostomum bifurcatum.*

MAHONILLE. (Fr.) *Malcolmia maritima.*

MAHOREE. A Bengal name for Aniseed.

MAHVA-TREE. *Bassia butyracea* and *atifolia.*

MAI-DENG. A hard heavy red wood of Siam, well adapted for furniture.

MAIDENHAIR-TREE. *Salisburia adiantifolia.*

MAIDEN-LIP. *Echinospermum Lappula.*

MAID'S-HAIR. *Galium verum.*

MAIMUNNA. A fruit-bearing rhamnad of Affghanistan.

MAIS. (Fr.) *Zea Mays.* — DE GUINÉE. *Milium nigricans.*

MAI-TAKLOU. A heavy timber of Siam, supposed to be that of *Nauclea orientalis*, considered to be incorruptible, and bearing a sacred character from being much used in the construction of temples.

MAI-TIKIEN. A valuable timber of Siam, obtained from *Metrosideros vera.*

MAITHES. *Pyrethrum Parthenium.* —, RED. *Adonis autumnalis.*

MAIZ DEL AGUA. *Victoria regia.*

MAIZE. *Zea Mays.* —, WATER. *Victoria regia.*

MAIZENA. A fine flour prepared from the Maize or Indian corn, *Zea Mays.*

MAJOE-BITTER. *Picramnia Antidesmia.*

MAJOON. A confection of Hemp, being a compound of butter, sugar, flour, milk, and bhang.

MAJORANA. *Origanum Majorana*, the Sweet Marjoram.

MAKANA. An Indian name for *Euryale ferox.*

MAKEBATE. *Polemonium cæruleum.*

MAKKER, or **MAKER.** An Abyssinian name for *Boswellia papyrifera.*

MALABAR LEAF. *Cinnamomum malabathrum.*

MALACH. A Turkish name for Hemp, *Cannabis sativa.*

MALACHADENIA *clavata.* An orchid from Rio de Janeiro, of which Mr. Bateman remarks: 'It is the only epiphytal orchideous plant I know which emits a positive stench, and that too at all hours by night and day. In the stove it resembles the foulest carrion.' It is the only species of the genus, and has a creeping rhizome bearing one-leaved pseudobulbs, and slender scapes with five or six small greenish brown-spotted flowers turned upside down. These latter have the side sepals joined, except at their reflexed apices, and the other one large, heart-shaped, and pointed; extremely minute petals; a fleshy ovate reflexed lip, articulated with the column, which has a prolonged foot and two cirri in front; and two waxy pollen-masses sessile on a large soft cubical gland. [A. S.]

MALACHIUM. A genus of *Caryophyllaceæ*, founded on *Cerastium aquaticum.* It differs from *Cerastium* in having the capsule ovoid, and the teeth joined in pairs; and from *Stellaria*, of which it has the habit, by the latter character, and by having five styles. *M. aquaticum* is a common English plant, resembling chickweed, but larger; and also *Stellaria nemorum*, but the flowers are not so large, and the ovate leaves have shorter stalks. [J. T. S.]

MALACHODENDRON. *Stuartia Malachodendron.*

MALACHRA. A genus of malvaceous plants, consisting of herbs or undershrubs, natives usually of marshy places in tropical regions. The stems have lines of hairs running down them, and the leaves are likewise covered with pungent hairs, while the yellowish flowers are grouped in heads, surrounded by an involucre. The calyx is five-cleft, the corolla five-petaled, the staminal tube divided into about twenty filaments, the ovary five-lobed and five-celled, and the fruit of five carpels. [M. T. M.]

MALACOID. Having a mucilaginous texture.

MALAPOO. The dried flowers of *Cedrela Toona.*

MALAQUIE. (Fr.) *Malachium.*

MALAXIS *paludosa* is a small delicate terrestrial orchid, forming of itself a genus, distinguished from *Liparis* by the proportion of the petals, and by the pollen-masses, which are club-shaped, in two pairs, both suspended from a gland which terminates the column. It grows to three or four inches in height, the rootstock producing a small solid bulb out of the ground, and three or four ovate or oblong leaves. The flowers are very small, of a greenish-yellow, in a loose slender raceme. It grows in spongy bogs in Northern Europe and Asia, and is sparingly dispersed over a great part of Britain.

MALCOLMIA. A genus of herbaceous plants, mostly annuals, belonging to the cruciferous order, and distinguished by having a roundish pod, and a simple pointed stigma. The species are mostly natives of the south of Europe, and agree in having roughish toothed or sinuated leaves, and purplish or white flowers disposed in racemes, and destitute of bracts. [C. A. J.]

MALESHERBIACEÆ. (*Crownworts*.) A natural order of dicotyledonous plants, belonging to Lindley's violal alliance of hypogynous Exogens. Herbs or half-shrubby plants, with alternate exstipulate leaves, and solitary yellow or blue flowers. Calyx tubular, five-lobed, inflated; petals five, convolute in æstivation, persistent, arising outside a short membranous rim or coronet; stamens five to ten, perigynous, with versatile anthers, the filaments often connected with the stalk of the ovary; ovary superior, stalked, one-celled, with parietal placentas; ovules numerous, pendulous, anatropal; styles three, the stigmas club-shaped; fruit a one-celled three-valved capsule; albumen fleshy. These plants, found in Chili and Peru, are allied to the passion-flowers. The two genera, *Malesherbia* and *Gynopleura*, contain about half a dozen species.   [J. H. B.]

MALESHERBIA. One of the two genera of *Malesherbiaceæ*, and consisting of a single species, a small pubescent shrub, native of Peru, with long narrow deeply sinuate-toothed leaves, and yellow sessile flowers, solitary in the leaf-axils, but forming a long raceme or thyrse. It is distinguished from its ally by its long cylindrical tubular calyx, and by the corona at the mouth of the calyx being deeply ten-lobed, with truncate denticulate lobes.   [A. S.]

MALE SYSTEM. All that part of a flower which belongs to the stamens.

MALHERBE. (Fr.) *Plumbago europæa*; also *Thapsia villosa*.

MALICORIUM. An old name for the woody rind of the pomegranate fruit, used medicinally.

MALKUNGUNEE. An Indian name for *Celastrus paniculatus*.

MALLEA *Rothii* is the sole representative of a genus of *Meliaceæ* peculiar to the East Indies. It is a shrub with impari-pinnate leaves, axillary paniculate or racemose flowers, a cup-shaped five-toothed calyx, five lanceolate petals, ten stamens, and a fleshy drupe containing five stony kernels. Uses unknown.   [B. S.]

MALLEE. The native name of *Eucalyptus dumosa*, which forms the dreary Mallee scrub of South Australia. — of Victoria. *Eucalyptus oleosa*.

MALLEOLUS. A layer; a shoot bent into the ground and half divided at the bend, whence it emits roots.

MALLETTE. (Fr.) *Capsella Bursa-pastoris*.

MALLOW. *Malva*; also *Malvastrum*. —, GLADE. *Napæa*. —, GLOBE. *Sphæralcea*. —, INDIAN. *Sida*; also *Urena*, and an American name for *Abutilon*. —, JEW'S. *Corchorus olitorius*, and *C. capsularis*. —, MARSH. *Althæa officinalis*. —, TREE *Lavatera arborea*. —, VENICE. *Hibiscus Trionum*.

MALLOWWORTS. Lindley's name for the *Malvaceæ*.

MALOO CREEPER. An Indian name for *Bauhinia racemosa*.

MALOPE. A genus of herbaceous plants belonging to the *Malvaceæ*, and closely allied to *Malva*, from which it may be distinguished by the broadly cordate leaflets of the calyx. *M. trifida* is an annual from North Africa, growing about two feet high, bearing during the whole of summer large deep rose-coloured or white flowers. *M. grandiflora* is taller and more robust, with larger flowers.   [C. A. J.]

MALORTIEA. There are three species of this genus of palms, all natives of Central America. They have slender reed-like

Malortiea simplex.

stems, long-stalked irregularly pinnate or sometimes simple jagged leaves, and simply branched spikes of unisexual flowers springing from the axils of the lowermost leaves, and producing small roundish or egg-shaped one-seeded fruits. Two Guatemala species, *M. gracilis* and *M. simplex*, are cultivated in our hothouses.   [A. S.]

MALPIGHIACEÆ. (*Nitrariaceæ, Malpighiads.*) A natural order of dicotyledonous plants belonging to Lindley's sapindal alliance of hypogynous Exogens. Trees or shrubs, sometimes climbing, with simple opposite or very rarely alternate stipulate leaves, without dots; hairs, when present, peltate. Flowers either perfect or unisexual; sepals five, slightly united, persistent, often glandular at the base; æstivation imbricated; petals five, unguiculate, with convolute æstivation; stamens usually ten, often monadelphous, the anthers roundish, with a projecting process from the connective; ovary formed by three (rarely two or four) carpels, more or less combined; ovules solitary, with a long pendulous cord; styles three, distinct or united. Fruit dry or fleshy, sometimes winged; seeds solitary, orthotropal, suspended, exalbuminous; embryo straight or curved in various ways; cotyledons foliaceous or thickish. They are inhabitants of tropical countries chiefly, and a great number of them are found in South America. *Malpighia, Banisteria, Hiptage, Hiræa,* and *Gaudichaudia,* offer examples of the forty-five genera, which contain nearly 600 species.   [J. H. B.]

MALPIGHIA. A genus of tropical American shrubs, with opposite leaves, either entire or slightly toothed, not infrequently having peltate, and sometimes stinging hairs. The flowers are of a reddish-yellow or white colour, usually grouped in axillary or terminal tufts, the stalks themselves jointed and bracteate. The calyx is five-cleft, some of the segments having two glands at their base; petals five, longer than the sepals, stalked; stamens ten, all fertile, united into a tube at the base; ovary three-celled, each cell with a single pendulous ovule; styles three, distinct. Fruit fleshy, with three crested stones. The genus derives its name from Malpighi, a celebrated Italian anatomist, one of the first to employ the microscope in physiological researches. He was Professor of Medicine at Bologna in the latter part of the seventeenth century. The order *Malpighiaceæ* takes its name from this genus. The fruits of *M. glabra* and *M. urens* are eaten in the West Indies, those of the latter being called Barbados Cherry. Some of them are of twining habit, and the singularity of their flowers renders them desirable in our hothouses.   [M. T. M.]

MALT. Barley which has been steeped in water so as to excite germination, and then kiln-dried.

MALVACEÆ. (*Mallowworts.*) A natural order of dicotyledons belonging to Lindley's malval alliance of hypogynous Exogens. Herbaceous plants, trees, or shrubs, with alternate stipulate leaves more or less divided, and often with stellate hairs. Sepals five, rarely three or four, more or less cohering at the base, with a valvate æstivation, often bearing, an external calyx (epicalyx) or involucre; petals equal in number to the sepals, with twisted æstivation; stamens indefinite, hypogynous, all perfect, their filaments monadelphous or polyadelphous, and the anthers monothecal, reniform, with transverse dehiscence; ovary formed by the union of several carpels round a common axis, either distinct or cohering; styles as many as the carpels, united or free. Fruit capsular or baccate; carpels one or many-seeded, sometimes closely united, at other times separate or separable, their dehiscence loculicidal or septicidal; albumen none, or in very small quantity; embryo curved; cotyledons twisted or doubled. Found in tropical countries and in the warm parts of temperate regions. They are mucilaginous and demulcent, and yield fibres. *Althæa officinalis* (marsh mallow) yields mucilage. *Gossypium* furnishes various kinds of cotton. *Hibiscus cannabinus* supplies Indian hemp. *Paritium elatum* gives Cuba bast. There are nearly fifty genera, including *Malva, Lavatera, Hibiscus,* and *Sida,* and upwards of one thousand species.   [J. H. B.]

MALVA. The typical genus of *Malvaceæ,* embracing a large number of species widely spread through the northern hemisphere, being found in most European countries, in Northern and Central Asia, and in North America, while the few species belonging to the southern hemisphere are confined to South Africa. These numerous species differ greatly in appearance, some being small annual or perennial herbaceous plants, others shrubs of variable height, but they all agree in possessing tough fibre, and an abundance of mucilage. Their flowers, which are frequently very showy, but of short duration; have an outer calyx or involucre, consisting of three distinct leaves attached to the lower part of the true calyx, which is more or less deeply cut into five broad lobes; and the numerous single-seeded carpels are disposed in a circle round a central axis, but become detached when ripe.

M. moschata, the Musk Mallow, derives its name from the peculiar musky odour given off by all parts of the plant when kept in a confined situation, particularly in warm dry weather, but it is seldom powerful enough to be smelt in the open air. The plant is a perennial, and has large rose-coloured flowers clustered together at the ends of the erect slightly branched stems. It is found along hedges, roadsides, and borders of fields in the British Isles. *M. rotundifolia* is an annual, with tough downy stems lying upon the ground, and has roundish lobed leaves, and small pale-bluish flowers clustered in their axils. It is common in waste places in most parts of Europe, including Britain, and in Western Asia. In Egypt, especially upon the banks of the Nile, it is extensively cultivated, and used by the natives as a pot-herb. *M. sylvestris,* the Common

Mallow, or *Mauve* of the French, is employed medicinally on account of its highly mucilaginous properties, a decoction of it being used as an outward *application* to bruises, and internally in dysentery. It is in great repute amongst herb-doctors and rustic practitioners generally, particularly in France, where its dried flowers are largely used in the preparation of a drink called Tisane, or Ptisan, held to be a cure for headache, feverish colds, and many other complaints ; its leaves are also made into poultices. It is a biennial, spread through Europe and Russian Asia, having erect somewhat hairy stems, roundish long-stalked leaves, and reddish-purple flowers. [A. S.]

MALVASTRUM. A genus of *Malvaceæ*, consisting of American herbs with axillary scarlet or orange flowers, usually solitary, but rarely clustered. Calyx usually unprovided with any involucel, but sometimes with a few deciduous hairy bracts, or three persistent leafy bracts ; tube of the stamens simple ; stigmas button-shaped, small ; carpels with or without a beak. [M. T. M.]

MALVAVISCUS. A genus of *Malvaceæ*, consisting of shrubs, with entire or slightly lobed leaves, and crimson flowers. The calyx is surrounded by a many-leaved involucre ; petals erect ; stigmas ten ; carpels five, berry-like, one-seeded, slightly separated one from the other, or more generally combined into a five-celled fruit. The species are natives of tropical America and Mexico. [M. T. M.]

MALVO DO CAMPO. The Brazilian name of *Kielmeyera speciosa*.

MAME. The seeds of *Soja hispida*.

MAMILLA. The apex of the nucleus of an ovule.

MAMILLARIA. Mexico may be looked upon as the head-quarters of this genus of *Cactaceæ*, the great majority of the species being confined to that country, comparatively few belonging to Southern California, Guatemala, Texas, Louisiana, and Missouri ; some, however, are indigenous to South America, and are found as far south as Buenos Ayres and Chili. The genus is, in most instances, readily distinguished from its allies by the fleshy stem, of which the plants solely consist, being entirely covered with tubercles of a teat-like form, giving rise to the generic name, from *mamilla*, a little teat. These are disposed in a series of spirals, each teat being furnished at the top with a tuft of radiating spines proceeding from a kind of cushion. The entire plants assume various forms, some species being more or less cylindrical, others nearly round, some pear-shaped, and others club-shaped, but the majority seldom exceed six or eight inches in height. The flowers are produced towards the summit of the plants, and usually in a transverse zone, each flower growing from the axil of one of the teats ; they are white, yellow, or of different shades of red or rose-colour, and remain open only during the day, closing at night and opening again

the following morning. They have the tube prolonged beyond the ovary, smooth and contracted below ; the numerous segments in several series, the outer or calycine ones being smaller than the inner or petaline ; and the stamens, which are also in several series, grow to the inside of the tube, being shorter than the thick style, which is terminated by a three to seven-rayed stigma. The fruit is an oblong or club-shaped smooth berry, containing numerous small seeds.

M. Clava is a native of Mexico, and is columnar or club-shaped, attaining a foot or more in height, with the mamillæ large, projecting, and of a pyramidal form, with bluntly-angled sides, and having tufts of white wool between them, and likewise upon their summit. The straw-coloured flowers are very large and showy. *M. coronaria* is the tallest species of the genus, growing, it is said, as high as five feet. In our gardens, however, it is seldom more than a foot high and three inches thick, of a cylindrical form, with large conical mamillæ bearing from thirteen to sixteen pellucid white spines radiating from a little tuft of white wool, and four inner brown ones. The flowers are of a fine crimson colour. *M. pusilla* is a very pretty little species, growing in crowded tufts usually of a hemispherical shape. The mamillæ, which are about the size of grains of wheat, have little tufts of white hairs between them, and bear bundles of spines, consisting of from four to six straight stiff inner ones, and from twelve to twenty outer ones like white hairs ; the flowers are yellow tinged with rose-colour, and are succeeded by beautiful bright crimson berries about the size of the mamillæ. [A. S.]

MAMMÆFORM, MAMMILLARIS. Teat-shaped ; conical, with a rounded apex.

MAMMEA. A genus of *Clusiaceæ*, characterised by the globular calyx, which opens in two valvate sepals ; by the ovary, which contains four ovules, distributed into two or four cells ; and by the fruit, which is an indehiscent drupe, containing one to four large seeds with very thick almost consolidated cotyledons and a very short radicle. The principal species, and the only American one, is the *M. americana*, a large tree, with opposite coriaceous leaves marked with very numerous transverse but reticulated veins, and with pellucid dots, and bearing white sweet-scented showy flowers on short peduncles, solitary or clustered in the lower axils of the young shoots. The fruit, known under the name of Mammee Apple, or South American Apricot, is very much esteemed in tropical countries. It often attains the size of a child's head, and is of a yellow colour. The outer rind and the pulp which immediately surrounds the seeds are very bitter, but the intermediate flesh is sweet and aromatic, and is eaten cut into slices and steeped in wine, or made into preserves of various kinds. The seeds, often as large as hen's eggs, are used as anthelmintics ; an aromatic liqueur called *eau de créole* is distilled from its flowers; and the acrid resinous gum distilled from its bark is used to destroy the chiggers, little insects that attack the naked feet of the negroes. The tree is a native of the West Indies and of continental tropical America, but is cultivated for its fruit and almost naturalised in some parts of tropical Africa and Asia. The genus is now sometimes made to include two or three tropical Asiatic species, with smaller flowers and fruits, but similar in structure, which had previously been published under the name of CALYSACCION: which see.

MAMMEE. *Lucuma mammosum.*

MAMMEE-TREE. *Mammea americana.*

MAMMOTH-TREE. *Wellingtonia gigantea.*

MANA. An Indian name for *Paspalum scrobiculatum.*

MANACA. A Brazilian name for *Franciscea uniflora.*

MANAWA. A New Zealand name for an aromatic resin reputed to be obtained from *Avicennia tomentosa.*

MANCHINEEL. The virulently poisonous *Hippomane Mancinella.* —, BASTARD. *Cameraria latifolia.*

MANCIENNE. (Fr.) *Viburnum Lantana.*

MANCUS. Deficient in something; wanting.

MANDAVALLI. An Indian name for the purgative *Convolvulus reptans.*

MANDEVILLA. A genus belonging to the order of dogbanes, distinguished by its calyx having internally a pectinate ring; by the five stamens enclosed in the corolla, their anthers lanceolate, membranaceous at the top, and forming a cone round the stigma; and by the single style, its stigma conical, five-lobed below. The only species is a climbing shrub, a native of Buenos Ayres, whence it was first introduced, under the name of Chili Jasmine; its large pure white and sweetly scented flowers render it an acquisition to collections. Named after H. J. Mandeville, H.B.M. minister at Buenos Ayres. [G. D.]

MANDIOC. *Manihot utilissima,* from which cassava is prepared.

MANDIROLA. A Brazilian gesnerad, related to *Achimenes,* the typical species being the plant known as *Achimenes multiflora.* It is characterised by its scaly stolones, by its subcampanulate corolla with a spreading fringed limb and narrow base, by its crenated membranaceous perigynous ring, and by its two-lobed stigma. *M. lanata* is now called *Eucodonia.* [T. M.]

MANDOBI, MUNDUBI, Portuguese names for *Arachis hypogœa.*

MANDRAGORA. This name, derived from two Greek words implying hurtful to cattle, is applied to a genus of Solanaceæ or Atropaceæ. The species are natives of Southern Europe and the East, and have very short stems, with a thick fleshy often forked root, from the summit of which the entire ovate lance-shaped leaves appear to proceed in compact tufts. The flower-stalks spring from among the leaves, and bear a solitary flower with a top-shaped calyx, a bell-shaped corolla, to the base of which are attached five stamens, whose filaments are dilated above their base. The fruit is fleshy, one-celled, from the breaking up of the partition between the two original cells of the ovary, and supported by the slightly enlarged and persistent calyx.

The Mandrakes, like their near ally *Belladonna,* have poisonous properties. They act as emetics, purgatives, and narcotics, and would seem to have been much used as sedatives in olden times, though now disused. Shakspeare is supposed to allude to this plant when he makes Banquo, in *Macbeth,* say: 'Or have we eaten of the insane root that takes the reason prisoner?' And also in *Antony and Cleopatra*: 'Give me to drink Mandragora.' Dr. Silvester has shown that Mandrake was employed in olden times as an anæsthetic, in the same way that chloroform now is.

In the days when the doctrine of signatures was an article of faith among the ignorant at least, the Mandrake root, from its occasional similarity to the lower part of the human figure, was considered to possess great virtues, and was in constant use for amorous incantations and love philtres. Its use in this manner is alluded to in Genesis, chap. xxx. (the Dudaim being identified with the Mandrake); and the superstition, kept alive by the craft and ingenuity of the charlatan, has not entirely died out even at present, although the root of *Bryonia dioica* is now employed under the erroneous name of mandrake. Nor was this the only superstitious notion connected with this plant, for Josephus mentions that its chief use is to dispel demons, who cannot bear either its smell or its presence. Shakspeare also alludes to the fanciful belief entertained as to this plant, in the following passage from *Romeo and Juliet*:—

And shrieks like mandrakes torn out of the earth,
That living mortals, hearing them, run mad.

Josephus even relates that it was certain death to touch this plant, except under certain circumstances, which he details (*Wars of the Jews,* book vii. cap. vi.). The same writer mentions that it was taken without danger, in the following manner: 'They dig a trench quite round about it, till the hidden part of the root be very small; they then tie a dog to it, and when the dog tries hard to follow him that tied him, this root is easily plucked up, but the dog dies immediately, as if it were instead of the man that would take the plant away; nor after this need any one be afraid of taking it into their hands.' Dioscorides mentions a male and female kind of Mandrake, which apparently correspond with the spring and autumnal species of modern botanists. In Professor Daubeny's interesting lectures on Roman husbandry, is a plate copied from the most ancient MSS. of Dioscorides, now at Vienna, 'representing Euresis, the goddess of discovery, presenting in triumph to Dioscorides the root of this mandrake, which she has just had pulled up, whilst the unfortunate dog which had been employed for that purpose is depicted in the agonies of death;' and in some other MSS. of this author, which the writer has had the opportunity of inspecting, representations are given of the mode of extracting male and female mandrakes from the

Mandragóra Autumnàlis.

ground, in the manner before related from Josephus. Indeed, in old herbals similar illustrations are not uncommon. Of the two species previously mentioned, *M. officinarum* or *M. autumnalis* is a very handsome autumn flowering plant, with wavy leaves, and deep blue flowers. [M. T. M.]

MANDRAKE. *Mandragora*; also an American name for *Podophyllum.*

MANETTIA. A genus of *Cinchonaceæ*, so called in honour of Xavier Manetti, Professor of Botany in Florence in the middle of the eighteenth century. The species are undershrubs of climbing habit, natives of tropical America. They have opposite leaves and wide stipules; axillary one or many flowered flower-stalks; a turbinate calyx, with the limb divided into four or five linear lance-shaped lobes, with an equal number of teeth between them in some cases; and a funnel-shaped corolla dilated and hairy at the throat, the limb divided into four or five obtuse segments. There are four or five stamens inserted into the throat of the corolla, and slightly protruding; and a thread-like style. The rind of the root of *M. cordifolia* has emetic properties, and is used by the Brazilians in dropsy and dysentery. Two or three species with scarlet or pink flowers are grown in hothouses in this country. [M. T. M.]

MAN FUNGUS. *Geaster.*

MANGABA, or MANGAVA. A Brazilian name for the fruit of *Hancornia speciosa.*

MANGEL-WURZEL. *Beta vulgaris macrorhiza.* According to Dr. Prior, this was originally Mangold-wurzel.

MANGIER. (Fr.) *Mangifera.*

MANGIFERA. A genus of tropical Asiatic trees, whose fruit is well known by the native name Mango, whence the technical name has been framed. The genus is included among the *Anacardiaceæ*, and consists of trees with alternate stalked entire leaves, and numerous small pinkish or yellowish flowers in much-branched panicles. The calyx is five-parted, and the petals and stamens five each, one or two only of the latter being fertile. The fruit is externally fleshy, and more or less fibrous, internally hard and bony.

The Mango, *M. indica*, grows abundantly in India, where numerous varieties are cultivated, as also in Brazil, the Mauritius, &c. The fruit of some varieties is esteemed as the most delicious of Indian fruits; but there are very numerous kinds, differing not only in flavour, but also in the size and shape of their fruit. Most of them have more or less of a turpentine flavour; the best varieties are most free from it, while the inferior kinds are stated to be little better in texture and flavour than a mixture of tow and turpentine. The unripe fruits are much used in India in conserves, tarts, and pickles, in which latter state they are frequently imported into this country. The ripe fruits, too, are constantly eaten, and are said in general to be wholesome, but frequently to produce boils in new-comers unaccustomed to their use. When cut with a knife, a blue stain is produced on the blade, from the presence of gallic acid in the pulp, which likewise contains gum and citric acid. The seeds are boiled and eaten in times of scarcity by the natives; they are said to possess anthelmintic properties.

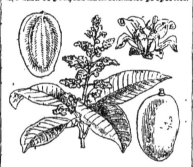

Mangifera indica.

The wood is soft and porous, of a grey colour when young, but brownish and harder in old trees; it is burnt together with sandal-wood by the Hindoos in the burning of their dead. The bark is employed medicinally to restrain discharges from the mucous membranes, and has been likewise well spoken of in the treatment of fevers in St. Domingo.

A soft reddish-brown gum-resin exudes from the bark when wounded, and is used externally in certain skin diseases, and internally for the cure of diarrhœa and dysentery. The leaves and leaf-stalks are used by the natives as tooth-brushes and to harden the gums; the leaves are likewise employed in chest affections and derangements of the liver; while calcined and powdered, they are employed as an application to burns to dry up the discharges, and for the removal of warts. The seeds of the Mango not unfrequently possess more than one embryo; and for an account of some curious deviations from the ordinary condition of a germinating seed, the reader is referred to a paper in the *Journal of the Linnean Society*, 1861. The Mango is cultivated as an object of curiosity in hothouses in this country, and has occasionally ripened its fruit.

An edible cake is prepared from the fruit of *M. gabonensis*, which is much used as an article of food by the natives of Sierra Leone. It resembles chocolate in appearance, and contains a large quantity of fatty material. [M. T. M.]

MANGKUDU. The red dye root of *Morinda umbellata*.

MANGLESIA. A genus of some authors, but considered by Meissner, in his monograph of the *Proteaceæ*, to form a section of the large genus *Grevillea*. It contains about eight species, all from South-west Australia; and is distinguished chiefly by its flowers having a thickened style, much swollen on one side, and about as long and thick as the one-sided ovary, from which it is separated by a constriction; and by its terminal conical stigma. [A. S.]

MANGLIETIA. An Asiatic genus of *Magnoliaceæ*, consisting of only three species, two of which are found in Nepal and Khasya, and the third in Java. All three are handsome tall trees with large entire leaves, and showy flowers borne singly at the ends of the branches, and scarcely distinguishable from those of *Magnolia*. *M. insignis*, one of the Indian species, attains a height of fifty or sixty feet, its trunk yielding an even-grained wood of a light colour. It has thickish oblong lance-shaped smooth and shining leaves, and large sweet-smelling whitish flowers tinged with rose-colour. The Javanese species, *M. glauca*, likewise has fragrant flowers, but they are of a pale yellow colour. This also produces a light-coloured solid wood of even grain, which is very much employed by the natives for making coffins, owing to its being supposed to prevent the decay of the bodies put into them. [A. S.]

MANGO. The fruit of *Mangifera indica*. —, MOUNTAIN or WILD. *Clusia flava*. —, WILD. The fruits of some species of *Irvingia*.

MANGOLD WURZEL. *Beta vulgaris macrorhiza.*

MANGOSTEEN. A delicious Eastern fruit, produced by *Garcinia Mangostana*. —, WILD. *Embryopteris glutinifera*.

MANGROVE. *Rhizophora*: hence Lindley's name of Mangroves for the *Rhizophoraceæ*. —, BLACK or OLIVE. *Avicennia tomentosa*. —, WHITE. *Laguncularia racemosa*. —, ZARAGOZA. *Conocarpus erectus*.

MANGUAI. *Agave mexicana*. —, DIVINUM. *Agave Theometl*.

MANGUIER DE L'INDE. (Fr.) *Mangifera indica*.

MAN-GUHL. An Indian name for *Arum indicum*.

MANI. *Moronobea coccinea*; also a Spanish name of the Ground Nut, *Arachis hypogæa*.

MANICARIA. In nearly all the genera of palms the leaves are either more or less pinnated or fan-shaped; but in the present genus, which consists of a solitary species inhabiting the tidal swamps of the Lower Amazon River, they are entire, or occasionally when old irregularly split. Individual leaves frequently measure as much as thirty feet in length, and four or five in width, having coarsely serrated edges, and transverse furrows; and being of a stiff habit they stand erect upon the summit of the stout crooked stem, which usually attains the height of fifteen or twenty feet, and is deeply ringed with the scars of fallen leaves, or covered with the remains of the fibrous sheaths of the leaf-stalks. The simply branched flower-spikes, measuring three or four feet long, hang down from among the leaves, and are enclosed in an entire brown spathe of a tough fibrous or cloth-like texture, which is ultimately torn open in an irregular manner by the expansion of the confined flower-spike. The flowers are of separate sexes, borne upon the same spike. The fruit is generally three-lobed, and covered with blunt angular tubercles of a dry corky nature.

The Indians call this palm Bussu, and its immense entire leaves are invaluable to them for thatching their huts, each leaf being for that purpose split lengthwise through the midrib, and the halves arranged so that the natural furrows act as gutters for conveying away the water. The fibrous spathes also are converted into capital bags and caps by simply cutting round them near the bottom and pulling them off entire, and afterwards stretching them open as wide as possible without tearing; or, when cut longitudinally down one side, they supply a coarse but strong kind of cloth. [A.S.]

MANICATE. Said of surfaces covered with hairs, so entangled that they can be stripped off like a skin.

MANIHOT. To this genus of *Euphorbiaceæ* belongs the celebrated Cassava or Mandioc plant, the fleshy root of which yields the greatest portion of the daily food of the natives of tropical America, and one of the products of which is well-known in this country under the name of Tapioca. A large number of species, all

American, are described. They are woody or shrubby plants growing from fleshy tuberous roots, their stems being without prickles or glands, their leaves generally long-stalked, palmately divided, and their flowers, which are of separate sexes, disposed in panicles in the axils of the leaves or at the ends of the branches.

Cassava or Mandiocca meal is yielded by two so-called species, which, however, bear such great resemblance to each other that most botanists combine them. These are: *M. utilissima,* the Bitter Cassava, a shrubby

Manihot utilissima.

plant growing from six to eight feet high or more, with erect somewhat twisted knotty stems rising from long thick fleshy cylindrical roots of a yellowish colour, containing a poisonous milky juice, and bearing deeply seven-parted leaves on very long slender stalks, crowded together at the tops of the branches ; and *M. Aipi,* the Sweet Cassava, which differs principally in having sweet wholesome roots of a reddish colour, and usually only five-parted leaves ; but these differences are not of specific value, and the plants must be regarded as varieties of one species. It is quite clear, however, that while the root of one is bitter and a most virulent poison, that of the other is sweet and wholesome, and is commonly eaten cooked as a vegetable. Both of them, especially the bitter, are most extensively cultivated over the greater part of tropical America, and yield an abundance of wholesome and nutritious food, the poison of the bitter kind being got rid of during the process of preparation it undergoes. This consists in first reducing the large fleshy roots to a pulp by grating them, the poisonous juice being then expelled by pressure, and the residual mass pounded into a coarse meal resembling bread-crumbs, which is made into thin cakes, or cooked in various ways, the heat dissipating any remaining poison. The poisonous expressed juice, if allowed to settle, deposits a large quantity of starch, known as Brazilian Arrowroot or Tapioca meal, from which the tapioca of the shops is prepared by simply torrefying the moist starch upon hot plates, the heat causing the starch grains to swell and burst and become agglutinated together. A sauce called Cassareep, used for flavouring soups and other dishes, particularly the West Indian dish known as pepper-pot, is also prepared from this juice by concentrating, and rendering it harmless by boiling.

Another of the products of Cassava is an intoxicating beverage called Piwarrie, but the manner of brewing it is not calculated to render it tempting to Europeans. It is made by the women, who chew Cassava cakes and throw the masticated material into a wooden bowl, where it is allowed to ferment for some days, and then boiled. It is said to have an agreeable taste. [A. S.]

MANIOC. (Fr.) *Manihot utilissima.*

MANINE. (Fr.) *Clavaria digitata.*

MANJACK. *Cordia macrophylla.*

MANISAN. A thick syrup obtained by boiling the saccharine sap of *Nipa fruticans.*

MANISURIS. A genus of grasses belonging to the tribe *Rottboelleæ,* and containing two species, both of which are annuals, natives of the warmest parts of Africa and the West Indies. [D. M.]

MANITA. *Cheirostemon platanoides.*

MANJIRIKA. An Indian name for *Ocymum Basilicum.*

MANKUCHOO. An Indian name for *Arum indicum.*

MANNA. A saccharine purgative product discharged from the bark of various species of ash, chiefly *Ornus rotundifolia* and *europæa.* Similar substances are also produced by the cedar, the oak, the cistus, and by *Eucalyptus mannifera.* — of Erianchon. A turpentiny saccharine exudation from the larch. — of Mount Sinai. A product of *Tamarix mannifera.* —, HEBREW or PERSIAN. A product of *Alhagi Maurorum,* or, according to others, of *Tamarix mannifera:* see GEN. —, POLAND. *Glyceria fluitans.*

MANNA CROUP. The prepared seeds of *Glyceria fluitans.*

MANNE DE PRUSSE. (Fr.) *Glyceria fluitans.*

MANONIM. A name in Minnesota for *Zizania aquatica,* or Wild Rice.

MANSIENNE. (Fr.) *Viburnum Lantana.*

MANSOA. A genus of *Bignoniaceæ,* named in honour of A. P. da Silva Manso, a Brazilian botanist, and consisting of only two species, both of which are climbing shrubs with conjugate leaves furnished with tendrils, and handsome white or violet flowers arranged in panicles, having a bilabiate calyx, the segments of which are divided into five long lobes, a funnel-shaped corolla, and four stamens, with the rudiment of a fifth. The fruit and uses of these plants, both natives of Brazil, are unknown. [B. S.]

MANTELET DES DAMES. (Fr.) *Alchemilla.*

MANTISIA. A genus of *Zingiberaceæ*, deriving its name from the resemblance of the flowers to the insect *Mantis.* It is nearly allied to *Globba*, but is distinguished from it by the lateral inner segments of the corolla being narrow and linear, and adherent to the filament of the stamen above the labellum; the anther, moreover, is dilated on each side into a membranous wing. One of the species has long been grown in hothouses in this country, from the singularity and beauty of its flowers, which

Mantisia saltatoria.

present some resemblance to a balletdancer : hence the popular name, Dancing Girls, applied to the plant. The filament and anther with its wing-like margins, represent the head and neck of the lady, the long inner segments of the corolla represent the arms, while the labellum corresponds to the dress. The flowers are purple and yellow. The name, *Mantisia saltatoria*, expresses the resemblance both to an insect and to a dancer. [M. T. M.]

MANULEA. A genus of *Scrophulariaceæ*, of the tribe *Gratioleæ*, distinguished by a five-cleft calyx with narrow lobes ; by a corolla with a slender straight tube, and a spreading limb nearly equally divided into five lobes which are often notched or cleft ; and by didynamous stamens enclosed in the tube, with one-celled anthers. There are nearly thirty species, natives of Southern Africa, all herbs or rarely low undershrubs, with the leaves usually radical on the lower part of the stem only. The flowers are terminal in racemes, or more frequently clustered in narrow irregularly compound panicles. They are usually yellow, orange, or red, small, but sometimes very numerous.

MANYROOT. A West Indian name for the emetic *Ruellia tuberosa.*

MAOOSA. The fibre of a species of *Urtica* used in Ceylon.

MAPLE. *Acer.* —, BIRD'S-EYE. *Acer saccharinum.* —, ITALIAN. *Acer Opalus.* —, NORWAY. *Acer platanoides.* —, SUGAR. *Acer saccharinum.* —, SWAMP, *Acer rubrum.*

MAPPA. A genus of *Euphorbiaceæ*, of the tribe *Crotoneæ*, consisting of trees with large usually peltate leaves, and small flowers in axillary or lateral panicles. The calyx is small without petals; the male flowers in clusters with three to ten stamens bearing small globular four-lobed anthers; the females solitary, usually with a two-celled ovary, growing into a capsule usually bearing soft prickles or subulate processes. There are several species in the tropical regions of Asia and Eastern Africa. Among them *M. Tanaria* is said to yield a good tan in the Indian Archipelago.

MAPROUNEA. A genus of *Euphorbiaceæ*, of the tribe *Crotoneæ*, consisting of trees with small glabrous alternate ovate entire leaves, and small flowers, the males growing in little oval cone-like heads, at the base of which are some long-stalked female ones. There are only two species known, both from tropical America.

MAQUI. (Fr.) *Aristotelia.*

MARA. A Guiana wood furnished by *Icica altissima.*

MARAQAUBA. A Brazilian furniture wood, intermediate in appearance between mahogany and tulip-wood.

MARAM or **MARRAM.** *Ammophila arenaria.*

MARANTACEÆ. (*Cannaceæ.*) A natural order of epigynous monocotyledons, belonging to Lindley's anomal alliance of Endogens. Herbaceous plants, with tuberous rhizomes, and leaves and flowers similar to those of the ginger family. Perianth superior, in two whorls : the outer (calyx) three-lobed short, the inner (corolla) tubular elongated three-parted, the segments nearly equal ; stamens in two whorls : the outer sterile petaloid irregular, resembling a tubular trifid corolla with one of the lateral segments different, the inner petaloid, two being sterile, and one lateral fertile, the filament of the latter petaloid ; anther on the margin of the filament, one-celled; ovary three-celled, rarely one-celled, the ovules solitary and erect, or numerous and attached to the axis; style petaloid; stigma either the naked apex of the style, or hollow hooded and incurved. Fruit a three-celled capsule, or baccate one-celled and one-seeded ; seeds round, without arillus; embryo straight, in hard albumen. They are natives of tropical America and Africa; several are found in India ; none are known in a wild state beyond the tropics. The plants contain much starch in the rhizomes and roots, but are destitute of aroma. Arrowroot is the produce of the tuberous rhizomes of *Maranta* ; while *Canna coccinea*,

C. Achiras, C. edulis, &c., yield Tous-les-mois. There are nine genera, including *Canna, Maranta,* and *Phrynium,* and upwards of 150 species.　　　[J. H. B.]

MARANTA. Maranti, after whom this genus was named, was a Venetian botanist and physician of the middle of the sixteenth century. The genus, which gives its name to the *Marantaceæ,* consists of herbaceous plants with fleshy tubers, and terminal panicled jointed inflorescence with deciduous scale-like bracts. The flowers have a calyx of three sepals; a corolla of six segments, the central one or lip of the inner series larger than the lateral ones, and cleft; a petaloid stamen with half an anther on one side of it, and a hooded style adhering to a barren petal-like filament.

The species are natives of tropical America, but are cultivated for the sake of the starch in their tubers in both East and West Indies, Sierra Leone, &c. *M. Allouya, M. nobilis,* and especially *M. arundinacea,* are cultivated in the West Indies, and, in addition to the above-named species, *M. ramosissima* is cultivated for like purposes in the East Indies. The term Arrow-root is said to be derived from the fact that the native Indians used the roots of these plants as an application to wounds inflicted by poisoned arrows. The tubers whence the Arrow-root is procured are whitish, jointed, and horizontal, and give origin to numerous offshoots, that are covered with rudimentary leaves or scales; these ultimately appear above ground and throw up new stems. The starch is extracted from the tubers, when these are ten or twelve months old, by reducing them to a pulp with water, straining, allowing the fecula to subside, again washing it, and ultimately allowing it to dry.

Arrow-root is a very pure kind of starch, and is very nutritious. It is frequently adulterated with other cheaper starches, which fact may readily be detected by the microscope. Other descriptions of Arrow-root are furnished by plants belonging to the following genera: *Arum, Canna, Curcuma, Jatropha, Tacca*—to which articles the reader is referred for further information. Mats used for shading in India are frequently made of the split stems of *M. dichotoma.*　　　[M. T. M.]

MARASCHINO. A liqueur prepared from the Cherry.

MARASMIUS. A genus separated from *Agaricus* on account of the leathery texture of the species, which revive on the application of water, and other less obvious characters. Two distinct sections occur, in the first of which the spawn is floccose, and in the second resembles fibrous roots. The former group contains the more fleshy species, of which *M. Oreades* or Champignon is one of our very best esculent fungi, while *M. scorodonius* is an excellent condiment. The latter comprises a multitude of thin often splendidly coloured fungi, which abound in tropical countries, and vie with each other in elegance. *M. hæmatocepha-*

lus has occurred in one of the stoves at Kew, and if some of the more showy species could be cultivated successfully, it would be difficult to conceive anything more attractive. Some of our own species, though more modest in point of colouring, are delightful objects; and the little *M. Hudsoni,* with its long tawny bristles radiating in every direction from the pileus, which is common on holly leaves, is a plant of surprising beauty when closely examined.　　　[M. J. B.]

MARATTIACEÆ, MARATTIA. An order and genus of ferns, separated on the one hand from *Polypodiaceæ* by the absence of a jointed ring to the spore-case; and on the other from *Ophioglossaceæ,* which agree

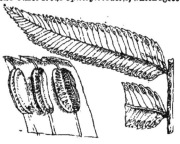

Marattia fraxinea.

in having ringless spore-cases, by having the sori dorsal, and the vernation circinate. The order includes the genera *Marattia, Gymnotheca, Eupodium,* and *Angiopteris,* which have distinct oblong sori consisting of free or concrete longitudinally bivalved spore-cases; *Kaulfussia,* which has distinct circular sori made up of an annular series of concrete spore-cases; and *Danæa,* in which the sori are connate over the whole dorsal surface of the fronds.

Marattia differs from the other genera of the order in having oblong sessile sori made up of concrete spore-cases, and seated on a fimbriate persistent involucre. It consists of a few coarse-habited plants, with large globose scaly rhizomes, and ample twice or thrice pinnate fronds, with fleshy stipes, and large oblong lance-shaped pinnules, bearing the sori in lines near their margins. They occur in South America, the Eastern and Pacific Islands, in South Africa, the Mascaren Islands, and the Island of Ascension.　　　[T. M.]

MARC. The cake or refuse after expressing the oil or juice from fruits or seeds, as of apples, olives, grapes, &c.; it is mostly used for manure.

MARCASSON. (Fr.) *Lathyrus tuberosus.*

MARCEAU. (Fr.) *Salix Caprea.* —, PETIT. *Salix aurita.*

MARCELLA. A Brazilian name for *Grangea maderaspatana.*

MARCESCENT, MARCID. Not falling

off until the part which bears it is perfected, but withering long before that time, as the flowers of *Orobanche.*

MARCETIA. Little rigid mostly hairy undershrubs, generally with small heath-like leaves, and small white or reddish flowers in the upper leaf-axils. The genus belongs to *Melastomaceæ,* and numbers about a dozen species, all Brazilian. It has tetramerous flowers, with a campanulate subulate-toothed calyx; mostly acuminate petals; eight stamens with subulate somewhat curved anthers opening by a single pore, and the connective scarcely prolonged at the base; and a four or rarely three-celled ovary bearing a filiform style and punctiform stigma. [A, S.]

MARCGRAVIACEÆ. (*Marcgraviads.*) A natural family of dicotyledons belonging to Lindley's guttiferal alliance of hypogynous Exogens. Trees or shrubs, with alternate entire simple leathery and exstipulate leaves. Flowers often furnished with pitcher-like bracts; sepals two to seven, coriaceous and persistent; corolla hypogynous of five petals, or gamopetalous calyptriform; stamens usually indefinite, very rarely five, hypogynous, the filaments dilated at the base, the anthers long, erect, introrse; ovary single, one-celled; style one; stigma often capitate. Fruit coriaceous, indehiscent, or dehiscing by valves in a loculicidal manner, the placentas being parietal and forming spurious dissepiments; seeds indefinite, minute. They occur chiefly in the warmer parts of America. There are four genera, and about two dozen species. Examples: *Marcgravia, Norantea.* [J. H. B.]

MARCGRAVIA. One of the few genera of *Marcgraviaceæ,* an order now reduced by some botanists to a section of *Ternströmiaceæ.* There are but few species, all belonging to tropical America, and all large climbing or almost epiphytal shrubs, with thick leathery quite entire leaves on short stalks, and long-stalked flowers in terminal umbels or corymb-formed racemes. It is distinguished from its allies by its petals being united into a cap-like corolla, which becomes detached round its base and falls off in a single piece; also by its stamens being indefinite, or never less than twelve; and by its incompletely four to twelve-celled ovary. In the West Indies, *M. umbellata* was formerly considered to possess medicinal properties. [A. S.]

MARCH. An old name of Parsley.

MARCHANTIACEÆ. An important section of liverworts, distinguished from other members by very striking characters. The frond is never leafy, frequently forked, with the surface divided into little areæ and porous. The male fruit is immersed in sessile or stalked discoid or peltate receptacles. The capsules are disposed symmetrically on the under side of stalked wheel-shaped receptacles, and are either valvate or bursting irregularly, or very rarely solitary and sessile, or merely grouped together. The stalk is often sheathed; and the spores are mixed with elaters. They are divided into three natural orders:—

1. TARGIONIEÆ: with single sessile capsules, sometimes grouped together.
2. JECORARIÆ: with capsules on the under side of a common stalked receptacle.
3. LUNULARIEÆ: with capsules on a common peduncle.

They grow in moist places, spreading over the ground, stones, &c., and attached by delicate rooting fibres. Besides the regular fruit, there are often separate organs which contain gemmæ, by means of which the plants are multiplied. The archegones are produced on the frond itself, and give rise to the fruit, not to a new plant, and the spermatozoids are like those of *Chara,* but have fewer volutions in the spiral, which is in many cases at length completely expanded. *Marchantia polymorpha,* which occurs everywhere on shady walks and on the soil of garden-pots, is the most familiar example, and will amply reward a close inspection. It is a popular remedy, along with some other allied species, for jaundice and consumption; but its virtues are in all probability imaginary. [M. J. B.]

MARCKEA. A genus named in honour of the famous French naturalist Lamarck, and belonging to the order *Atropaceæ.* The species is a climbing shrub, native of Guiana, with axillary clusters of scarlet flowers, having a tubular calyx; a funnel-shaped corolla, divided into five obtuse segments; five stamens, concealed within the tube of the corolla, to which they are adherent, the anthers opening longitudinally; and a two-celled ovary with numerous ovules in each compartment, and a simple style. Fruit capsular, two-valved, many-seeded. [M. T. M.]

MAREBLOBS. *Caltha palustris.*

MARE'S-TAIL. *Hippuris.*

MARGINAL. Belonging to the margin or edge of anything.

MARGINARIA. *Goniophlebium.*

MARGINATE. Furnished with an edge of a different texture from the remainder of the body.

MARGOSA-TREE. *Melia Azadirachta.*

MARGOTIA. A genus of campylospermous *Umbelliferæ,* characterised by the inner face of the seed being furrowed instead of flat. Its nearest ally is *Elæoselinum,* from which it differs in the white deeply bilobed petals with long incurved tongue-like apices. The only known species, *M. laserpitioides,* found in Spain, Portugal, and North Africa, is a smooth perennial herb with a tall erect naked stem, bearing many-rayed umbels of small white flowers which, as well as the leaves, are like those of the carrot. The carpels have the five primary ribs obsolete, and the four secondary produced into thin wings, the outer two of which are the broadest. They secrete an abundance of aromatic oil, which also occurs in the form of tears on the rays of the umbels. [A. A. B.]

MARGOUSIER. (Fr.) *Melia sempervirens.*

MARGUERITE. (Fr.) *Bellis perennis.* — BÂTARDE. *Silphium.* — BLEUE. *Globularia.* — DE LA ST. MICHEL. *Aster Amellus.* — DORÉE. *Chrysanthemum segetum.* —, GRANDE. *Chrysanthemum Leucanthemum.* —, PETITE. *Bellis annua.* —, REINE. *Callistephus chinensis.*

MARGYRICARPUS. A much-branched prostrate undershrub, with small pinnate linear-subulate leaves, and small insignificant flowers sessile in their axils, forming a genus of *Rosaceæ*, allied to *Acæna*, but without any hooked bristles on the calyx, and the fruit consisting of a small drupe. It is common on arid hills in Chili and Peru.

MARI. A Brazilian name for the fruits of *Geoffroya superba.*

MARIANTHUS. A small genus of Western Australian *Pittosporaceæ*, consisting of climbing shrubs. One species, *M. candidus*, has alternate elliptical attenuate leaves, with revolute margins, and white flowers in terminal heads. These latter have a small five-parted calyx, five spathulate petals slightly cohering at the base, five stamens with ovate anthers, a slightly curved filiform style, and a two-celled ovary containing numerous seeds. *M. cæruleopunctatus* has pretty pale blue spotted flowers, and is sometimes cultivated. [R. H.]

MARICA. This name was first improperly substituted by Schreber for Aublet's name *Cipura*, given to an iridaceous plant found in Guiana; and was afterwards applied by Ker to a closely allied plant of the same order, which now constitutes the type of a small genus. All the species belong to tropical America, and are herbaceous plants with short rhizomes, flat leaves placed edgeways, and a flat winged flower-stalk ending in a leaf-like spathe. Their perianth has three large spreading outer and three smaller inner segments; the stamens are distinct; the style slender below and triangularly enlarged upwards into three lobes, each with three sharp rigid crests; and the stigma is short and transverse like that of *Iris.* [A. S.]

MARICHU. A Sanscrit name for Pepper.

MARIET. *Campanula urticifolia.*

MARIETTE. (Fr.) *Campanula Medium.*

MARIGOLD. *Calendula officinalis.* —, AFRICAN. *Tagetes erecta.* —, BURR. *Bidens tripartita.* —, CORN. *Chrysanthemum segetum.* —, FIG. *Mesembryanthemum.* —, FRENCH. *Tagetes patula.* — — of the West Indies. *Pectis punctata.* —, MARSH. *Caltha.* —, POT. *Calendula officinalis;* also *Mesembryanthemum calendulaceum.* —, WATER. *Bidens Beckii.* —, WEST INDIAN. *Wedelia carnosa.*

MARILA. A genus of *Ternströmiaceæ*, differing from almost all others in its opposite leaves, and on that account placed by some in *Clusiaceæ*, and by others in *Hypericaceæ*, but the inflorescence and flowers are much more those of *Ternströmiaceæ*. There are four species, South American or West Indian trees, the evergreen leaves elegantly marked with transverse veins between the principal ones. The flowers are in axillary racemes, with four or five sepals and petals, numerous stamens, and an oblong ovary of four or five cells. The capsule contains numerous seeds, with fringed wings at each end.

MARINE SAUCE. A name sometimes given to the common Laver, *Porphyra vulgaris.*

MARISCUS. A genus of cyperaceous plants belonging to the tribe *Cypereæ*. The spikes of inflorescence are one to two-flowered, rarely three to five-flowered; scales two-rowed, imbricated; stamens three; styles three-cleft; nuts triangular. This extensive genus contains nearly a hundred species, the greater part of which are tropical, or bordering on the tropics. [D. M.]

MARJOLAINE. (Fr.) *Origanum Majorana.* — À COQUILLE. *Origanum nervosum.*

MARJOLIN. An early variety of Potato.

MARJORAM. *Origanum.* —, KNOTTED. *Origanum Majorana.* —, POT. *Origanum Onites.* —, SWEET. *Origanum Majorana.* —, WINTER SWEET. *Origanum heracleoticum.*

MARKING FRUIT. *Semecarpus Anacardium.*

MARMALADE-TREE. *Lucuma mammosum.*

MARMALADE-BOX. *Genipa americana.*

MARMALA-WATER. A fragrant liquid distilled in Ceylon from the flowers of the Bengal Quince, *Ægle Marmelos.*

MARMALEIRO DO MATO. *Casearia ulmifolia.* — DO CAMPO. *Maprounea brasiliensis.*

MARMELOS. *Ægle Marmelos.*

MARMORATE. Marbled; traversed by irregular veins of colour, as a block of marble often is.

MAROOL. The long fine fibre of *Sanseviera zeylanica.*

MAROUCHIN. (Fr.) An inferior sort of Woad.

MAROUTE. (Fr.) *Anthemis Cotula.*

MARRAM, or MARRUM. *Ammophila arenaria.*

MARROCHEMIN. *Marrubium vulgare.*

MARRON. (Fr.) The fruit of *Castanea vesca.* — D'EAU. *Trapa natans.*

MARRONETO. An Italian name for an orchard of chestnut trees.

MARRONNIER D'INDE COMMUN. (Fr.) *Æsculus Hippocastanum.*

MARROW, VEGETABLE. *Cucurbita ovifera.*

MARRUBE. (Fr.) *Marrubium vulgare.* — AQUATIQUE. *Lycopus europæus.* — BLANC. *Marrubium vulgare.* — NOIR. *Ballota nigra.*

MARRUBIUM. This name is said to be derived from the Hebrew word Marrob, signifying a bitter juice, and is applied to a genus of *Labiatæ*, of which the White Horehound is the most familiar example. The genus comprises several herbaceous species, natives of Southern Europe and Western Asia. The calyx is five to ten-nerved, and has an equal number of teeth; the corolla has the upper lip flat, entire or slightly notched, and the lower three-cleft; the stamens are concealed within the tube of the corolla; and the style is cleft.

M. vulgare, the Common or White Horehound, has an erect branched stem densely covered with cottony white hair; the leaves are roundish, crenated wrinkled and soft; the flowers whitish, crowded in the axils of the leaves. This plant is occasionally met with in a wild state in this country, and is widely distributed throughout Europe and Northern Asia, and has moreover become naturalised in America. It has bitter tonic properties, and was once employed in many diseases, but has fallen into disuse except as a domestic remedy in chest complaints.   [M. T. M.]

MARSDENIA. A large genus of *Asclepiadaceæ,* spread over the East Indies, Moluccas, New Holland, and tropical America. Only one species, *M. erecta,* inhabits the south-eastern parts of Europe. There are about thirty species, either erect shrubs or twiners, with opposite leaves, and interpetiolar bunches of whitish or greenish flowers. The calyx is five-cleft, the corolla bell-shaped, rotate or urn-shaped, and the fruit quite smooth. *M. tenacissima* yields a fibre which is employed for bowstrings by the mountaineers of Rajmahl. The leaves of *M. tinctoria* and *parviflora* yield by decoction a blue dye resembling indigo. The leaves of *M. erecta* were formerly used by chemists under the name of *Herba Apocyni folio subrotundo,* and are still sometimes employed. The milky juice of the plant raises blisters on the skin, and taken internally it causes violent trembling and convulsions, and ultimately death.   [B. S.]

MARSHALLIA. A genus of *Compositæ* of the tribe *Heliantheæ,* consisting of four North American species, perennial herbs, with alternate entire and glabrous three-nerved leaves, and solitary flower-heads of a pale purple or rose colour, resembling those of a scabious. The involucral scales are linear-lanceolate, leaflike, in one or two rows, the receptacle convex or conical and chaffy; the florets are all tubular, and the achenes hairy, with a pappus of five or six ovate or lanceolate scales.

MARSH-BEETLE, or MARSH-PESTLE. *Typha latifolia.*

MARSH-FLOWER. *Limnanthemum.*

MARSHWORT. *Oxycoccus palustris.*

MARSILEACEÆ. A natural order of pseudoferns, consisting of two distinct groups, to the first of which belong *Marsilea* and *Pilularia,* to the second *Azolla* and *Salvinia.* The æstivation is either straight or circinate, formed of a metamorphosed leaf; the receptacles one or many-celled; the antheridia in the same secondary receptacle with the mostly monosporous sporangia, or in a distinct sac; and the prothallus confluent with the spore itself. All the genera are aquatic, though, after the water is dried up, some of the species are still capable of maintaining life. *Azolla* is extra-European; the three other genera occur in Europe, but have representatives in other parts of the world. The fossil *Sphenophyllum* probably belonged to the same natural order.   [M. J. B.]

MARSILEA. A genus of pseudoferns, with a creeping rhizome and erect leaves consisting of a long stalk and two pairs of leaflets, which are circinate when young, disposed in a cross, nerved somewhat after the fashion of those of *Adiantum,* and which at night fold up like the leaflets of many *Leguminosæ.* The fruit consists of hard thick receptacles, divided into several cells arranged on the two sides of the principal septum parallel to the flattened surfaces of the receptacle. Each of these contains two kinds of organs, fixed to a sort of placenta, those at the base containing a single spore, those above granules which at length yield spermatozoids like the small spores of *Selaginella.* The receptacles sometimes spring from the rhizome, but are sometimes attached to the base of the petioles. Species occur in temperate and hot climates, as the South of Europe, Africa, Oregon, Madras, Australia, Brazil, &c. *M. macropus* is the Nardoo of Australia.   [M. J. B.]

MARSYPIANTHES. A genus of labiates, distinguished by its bell-shaped calyx having five equal erect teeth; by the upper lip of the corolla being bifid, the lower three-lobed, the lateral lobes nearly equal in size and ovate, the middle concave with an acute point; and by each piece of the fruit being concave on the inner surface, the border fringed. *M. hyptoides* of tropical America, the only species, is a procumbent annual with heads of blue-purple flowers.   [G. D.]

MARTINEZIA. A genus of tropical American palms consisting of six species, all of them small trees with cylindrical trunks seldom more than twenty or thirty feet high, and often armed with spines, as also are the leaf-stalks. The leaves are pinnate, with the segments of a wedge-shaped, or three-sided form, the broad upper end being very much jagged or torn. The simply-branched flower-spikes are enclosed in a double spathe, the outer of which is incomplete, the spathes and the lower part of the spike being frequently covered with black spines; both sexes of flowers have a three-parted or three-sepaled calyx, and a three-petaled corolla. The fruits are globular and fleshy, and contain a hard smooth pitted stone.	[A. S.]

MARTYNIA. A genus of *Pedaliaceæ*, mostly confined to Mexico. It consists of branching herbaceous plants covered with clammy hairs, and having roundish somewhat heart-shaped leaves, and spikes of flowers of which the calyx is divided into five nearly equal pieces, and the irregular bell-shaped corolla is unequally five-lobed and puffed out below. The fruit is a hard woody wrinkled capsule terminating in two curved beaks or hooks, and is divided into four cells containing several large seeds. *M. fragrans* is an annual, two or three feet high, occasionally seen in our gardens, where it thrives in the open air during the summer months, producing spikes of large rich purplish-red flowers streaked with yellow, and exhaling a most delicious odour. Its singular fruits are prolonged upwards into two curved sharp hooked horns three or four inches long, which cause great annoyance to travellers in Mexico by catching hold of their clothes. Another species, *M. proboscidea*, is called Testa di Quaglia by the Italians; while the Mexicans give the name of Unguis Diaboli to the short hooked fruit of *M. triloba*.	[A. S.]

MARUM. (Fr.) *Teucrium Marum.*

MARUTA. A genus proposed by Cassini, and adopted by De Candolle, for the *Anthemis Cotula*, and one or two other species, which have the ray florets neuter and barren. *M. Cotula* is a common cornfield weed with a very disagreeable smell, closely resembling in all other respects several other species of *Anthemis*, with which genus many botanists reunite it.

MARVEL OF PERU. *Mirabilis.*

MARY-BUD. *Calendula officinalis.*

MARY'S FLOWER. *Anastatica hierochuntina*; also *Marianthus.*

MARZUOLO. A kind of spring corn grown in Tuscany, the straw of which is used for plaiting.

MASCULAR, MASCULINE. Whatever belongs to the stamens.

MASDEVALLIA. A considerable genus of South American orchids, of the tribe *Malaxeæ*, consisting of little epiphytes, with creeping rootstocks, and broad leaves narrowed downwards into stalks. It is well distinguished by its flowers, which are borne singly on radical stalks, having the sepals joined into a tube, except at their apices, where they are free and drawn out into long narrow tails. The petals are free, very small, and concealed in the tube of the sepals, as also is the lip, which is sessile and articulated with the incurved half-rounded column. They are more remarkable for the singularity of their flowers than for their beauty.	[A. S.]

MASER-TREE. *Acer campestre.*

MASH. An Indian name for *Phaseolus radiatus*, a kind of pulse.

MASKED. The same as Personate. A body is also said to be masked when its true nature is concealed or disguised.

MASK-FLOWER. *Alonsoa.*

MASSE AU BÉDEAU. (Fr.) *Bunias Erucago.* — D'EAU. *Typha latifolia.*

MASSES. Collections of anything in unusual quantity; as, for example, *pollen-masses*, which are unusual collections of pollen.

MASSETTE. (Fr.) *Typha.*

MASSONIA. A genus of Cape bulbs, belonging to the *Liliaceæ*. The leaves are commonly two in number, and lie flat on the ground; and the flowers are in an umbel-like head nearly sessile between the leaves and surrounded by a many-leaved scarious involucre. The perianth is salver-shaped, usually white, with a six-parted spreading or reflexed limb. These plants have but little beauty, but their appearance is very singular.	[J. T. S.]

MASTACANTHUS. A genus established by Endlicher to receive a verbenaceous plant which has been since referred to *Caryopteris.*	[W. C.]

MASTER-WORT. *Imperatoria*; also *Astrantia.* —, ENGLISH. *Ægopodium.* —, GREAT. *Imperatoria Ostruthium.*

MASTIC DES INDES. (Fr.) *Schinus.* — DE SYRIE. *Teucrium Marum.*

MASTICH. The resiniferous *Pistacia Lentiscus.* —. BARBARY. *Pistacia atlantica.* —, WEST INDIAN. *Bursera gummifera.*

MASTWOOD, YELLOW. *Tobinia coriacea.*

MASTWORTS. Lindley's name for the *Corylaceæ.*

MASUR. An Indian name for *Ervum Lens.*

MATAR. An Indian name for Peas.

MATAYBA. A Guiana tree described as a genus of *Sapindaceæ*, as yet imperfectly known, but supposed to be a species of *Cupania.*

MATÉ. A South American name for *Ilex paraguayensis.*

MATFELLON. *Centaurea nigra.*

MATHEE. An Indian name for *Trigonella fœnum græcum.*

MATHER. *Anthemis* or *Maruta Cotula.*

MATHEWSIA. A genus of *Cruciferæ*, forming a branched Chilian shrub, having somewhat fasciculate linear-lanceolate pinnatifid leaves clothed with fine stellate hairs, and bearing elongated terminal racemes of rather large flowers. The pouch is two-valved, elliptical or lanceolate, surmounted by the sessile stigma, compressed, parallel to the partition, with flat reticulate one-nerved valves.　　[J.T.S.]

MATICO. A drug obtained from *Artanthe elongata* and *adunca*; also from *Eupatorium glutinosum*, and *Walteria glomerata*; and, according to Martius, from a species of *Phlomis*.

MATONIA *pectinata* is the only species of a genus of *Polypodiaceæ*, distinct in aspect and character from all other known ferns. From a creeping rhizome rises a tall slender erect ebony stalk, on the top of which is a conjugate fan-shaped frond, each half a counterpart of the other, and consisting of several long rigid linear pinnatifid branches. The fronds have something the aspect of the *Mertensia* group of *Gleichenia*, but the suboblique ring of the spore-case indicates relationship with the *Cyatheineæ*, in the neighbourhood of which it is now classed as a distinct tribe, the *Matonineæ*. The sori are globose on compital receptacles, and covered by umbonato-hemispherical indusia with a central stalk, and incurved margins. The veins are free, except where they anastomose to form the receptacles.　　[T. M.]

MATRICAIRE, or M. COMMUNE. (Fr.) *Pyrethrum Parthenium*. — MANBIANE. *Anthemis parthenioides*.

MATRICARIA. A genus of herbaceous plants belonging to the tribe *Corymbiferæ* of compound flowers, of which the characters are: fruit angular, crowned with a large disk; pappus, when present, a membranaceous border; receptacle naked; florets of two colours. The genus is represented by the Corn Mayweed, *M. inodora*, and the Wild Chamomile, *M. Chamomilla*, common weeds with daisy-like flowers, and deeply cut capillary leaves, the latter with a slightly bitter taste, and a smell approaching that of the true Chamomile. French, *Matricaire*; Germ. *Mutterkraut*. [C. A. J.]

MATRIMONY-VINE. *Lycium barbarum*.

MATTHIOLA. A genus of cruciferous plants, of which the characteristic features are: silique nearly cylindrical; stigmas connivent, thickened or horned on the back; seeds thin and flat, one-rowed, numerous. Two species are indigenous to Britain: *M. incana*, which grows on cliffs in the Isle of Wight, and is the origin of all the garden varieties of Brompton Stock; and *M. sinuata*, the Great Sea Stock, an herbaceous plant with rugged pods, rare on the shores of Cornwall and Wales. *M. tristis*, a humble plant with narrow hoary leaves and dingy brown flowers, a native of the south of Europe, is best known as the Night-scented Stock. *M. annua* is the original of all the varieties of Ten-week Stock, and *M. græca* of the smooth-leaved annual Stocks. French, *Giroflée*. [C. A. J.]

MATTIA. A genus of *Boraginaceæ*, found in South-eastern Europe and Asia Minor, consisting of white pubescent herbs, with linear-oblong leaves, and umbellate-corymbose blue or yellow flowers.　　[J. T. S.]

MATUTINAL. Happening early in the morning.

MATWEED. *Ammophila arenaria*, also called Sea Matweed. —, HOODED. *Lygeum Spartum*. —, SMALL. *Nardus stricta*.

MAUDLIN, SWEET. *Achillea Ageratum*.

MAUDLINWORT. *Chrysanthemum Leucanthemum*.

MAULE. *Malva sylvestris*.

MAURANDIA. A genus of *Scrophulariaceæ*, nearly allied to *Antirrhinum*, and like that genus comprising annuals and perennials, either erect, or more frequently climbing and supporting themselves by their twisted peduncles and petioles. They differ from *Antirrhinum* in the tube of the corolla not being swollen into a pouch at the base, in the less prominent palate at the mouth of the tube, and in the capsule, of which each cell opens in several valve-like teeth. Three handsome climbing species, *M. antirrhiniflora*, *M. semperflorens*, and *M. Barclayana*, all natives of Mexico, with cordate or hastate leaves and showy flowers, are frequently cultivated in our gardens. The two remaining erect species are Californian.

MAURITIA. A genus of palms peculiar to tropical South America. They grow to an immense size, some species attaining the height of a hundred or a hundred and fifty feet, and bearing a crown of enormous fan-shaped leaves, from amongst which the pendulous flower-spikes are produced. These spikes, which are often very large and much branched, bear the flowers in numerous catkins, which, as well as the branches, have their bases sheathed in incomplete tubular spathes. The different sexes are on distinct trees, but they are intermingled with perfect flowers. The fruits are covered with hard shiny scales, which give them a tesselated appearance. *M. flexuosa*, the Moriche or Ita Palm, is very abundant on the banks of the Amazon, Rio Negro, and Orinoco rivers. In the delta of the latter it occupies swampy tracts of ground, which are at times completely inundated, and present the appearance of forests rising out of the water. These swamps are likewise frequented by an independent tribe of Indians, called 'Guaranes,' who subsist almost entirely upon the produce of the Moriche Palm, and during the period of the inundations suspend their dwellings from the tops of its tall stems. Various parts are applied to useful purposes. The outer skin of the young leaves is made into string and cord for the manufacture of hammocks. The fermented sap yields palm-wine, and another beverage is prepared from the young fruits, while the soft inner part of the stem yields a farinaceous substance like sago.　　[A. S.]

MAURITIUS-WEED. *Roccella fuciformis*.

MAUVE. (Fr.) *Malva sylvestris.* — BÂTARDE. *Malope.* — EN ARBRE. *Lavatera.* — DES INDES. *Sida.* — FLEURIE. *Lavatera trimestris.* —, GRANDE. *Malva sylvestris.* —, PETITE. *Malva rotundifolia.*

MAUVISQUE. (Fr.) *Malvaviscus.*

MAWSEED. *Papaver somniferum.*

MAXILLARIA. Formerly this genus comprised a heterogeneous mass of orchids which are now separated into some half-dozen or more genera. It is now restricted to those possessing the following characters:—Flowers more or less ringent; lateral sepals adhering to the column at their oblique base; lip hooded, joined with the prolonged claw-like foot of the column, which is narrow, ascending; pollen-masses four, incumbent, or the two hind ones adhering to the two front ones; caudicle short, attached to a semicircular gland.   [A. S.]

MAXIMILIANA. The celebrated Humboldt, in his *Aspects of Nature*, speaks in glowing terms of the great beauty of the Jagua, an undetermined species of the present genus of palms, of which three or four are known, natives of the forests of Northern Brazil and the West Indies. All these are tall-growing trees, with slender smooth trunks, bearing at the summit gigantic pinnate leaves, having the narrow leaflets arranged in clusters along the leaf-stalks. The flower-spikes are each completely enclosed in a thick woody spathe, which tapers to a long point, is marked outside with deep longitudinal furrows, and eventually splits open down one side. The flowers are of separate sexes, either mixed together on the same or on distinct spikes.

M. regia, the Inajá Palm of the Amazon, has a trunk a hundred or more feet high, crowned with leaves from thirty to fifty feet long, and its woody spathes when open frequently measure as much as five or six feet in length by about two feet in breadth, tapering to a long point or beak. These spathes are so hard that when filled with water they will stand the fire, and are sometimes used by the Indians as cooking utensils, but more frequently as baskets for carrying mandiocca flour, &c. The Indians who prepare the kind of india-rubber called bottle-rubber, make use of the hard stones of the fruit as fuel for smoking and drying the successive layers of milky juice as it is applied to the mould upon which the bottles are formed. The outer husk, also, yields a kind of saline flour used for seasoning their food. [A. S.]

MAY. A popular name for the flowers of *Cratægus Oxyacantha.* —, ITALIAN. *Spiræa Filipendula.*

MAY-BUSH. *Cratægus Oxyacantha.*

MAYACEÆ, MAYACA. A natural order and solitary genus of hypogynous monocotyledons, belonging to the xyridal alliance, comprising three or four little moss-like marsh or semi-aquatic plants allied to *Xyridaceæ* and *Commelynaceæ*, but well distinguished by their one-celled anthers. Their inconspicuous little white, pink, or violet flowers have three sepals alternate with the carpels, three distinct petals, three stamens inserted into the base of the sepals, and three carpels combined into a one-celled pistil, which has a thread-like style and simple stigma. The species are all American, extending on the one hand to Virginia, and on the other to Brazil. Physiologically they are remarkable for their deficiency of spiral vessels. [A. S.]

MAYDEWEED. *Pyrethrum Parthenium.* —, RED. *Adonis autumnalis.*

MAY-DUKE. A kind of cherry.

MAYENNE. (Fr.) *Solanum esculentum.*

MAYFLOWER. *Epigæa repens.* —, WEST INDIAN. *Dalbergia Brownei*, and *Ecastaphyllum Brownei.*

MAY-LILY. *Convallaria majalis.*

MAYNA (including *Lindackeria*). A genus of *Flacourtiaceæ*, distributed over Mexico, New Grenada, Guiana, and Brazil, and represented by middle-sized trees, with ovate or oblong coriaceous leaves, polygamous flowers arranged in racemes, and a round fruit, covered with numerous prickles and resembling very much our common horse-chestnut in outward appearance. The sepals and petals are imbricated; the anthers linear, and opening by two slits; the styles completely united; and in the female flowers there appear to be never more than three placentas. From being imperfectly known, and on account of its stipules, the genus had been placed near *Magnoliaceæ* until united with *Lindackeria*, and placed amongst *Bixeæ* by Bentham.   [B. S.]

MAYPOLE of Jamaica. *Spathelia simplex.*

MAYS DEL MONTE. The Peruvian name of *Ombrophytum.*

MAYTENUS. A genus of *Celastraceæ*, consisting of South American evergreen shrubs or small trees, with alternate coriaceous serrate leaves, and small flowers solitary or clustered in their axils. The fruit contains but a single seed, as in *Myginda*, from which this genus differs chiefly in its alternate, not opposite leaves. There have been near fifty species described, but probably not so many are really distinct. The arborescent species have a very hard wood, and the leaves of the commonest Peruvian species, although astringent, are said to be greedily devoured by cattle.

MAY-WEED. *Anthemis* or *Maruta Cotula*; also *Pyrethrum Parthenium.* —, STINKING. *Matricaria Chamomilla.*

MAYWORT. *Galium cruciatum.*

MAZI. The Turkish name for Galls.

MAZUS. A genus of *Scrophulariaceæ*

nearly allied to *Mimulus*, of which it has the corolla stamens and capsule; but the calyx is broadly campanulate and deeply five-lobed. It consists of three or four South Asiatic or Australian herbs, either low branching annuals or perennial through their creeping runners. They are uninteresting weeds, the most common of them, *M. rugosus*, very widely spread over tropical Asia.

MAZZARD. The wild *Cerasus avium*.

MEADOW BEAUTY. An American name for *Rhexia*.

MEAD-SWEET, MEADWORT, or MEADOW-SWEET. *Spiræa Ulmaria*.

MEAL-BERRY. *Arctostaphylos uva ursi*.

MEALY-TREE. *Viburnum Lantana*.

MECHOACAN ROOT. *Batatas Jalapa*.

MECONELLA. A curious little papaveraceous genus, standing between *Platystemon* and *Hypecoum*, agreeing with the former in its foliage, floral envelopes, and dilated filaments, and with the latter in having definite stamens. Its characteristic marks are three sepals, five or six petals, four to six stamens with membranaceous filaments dilated upwards, and short anthers, three rarely four linear sessile stigmas, and a slender pod-shaped three rarely four-celled capsule, containing numerous smooth shining seeds. *M. oregana* is a dwarf smooth annual, with a rosulate tuft of spathulate root leaves, dichotomously forked slender stems bearing linear leaves, and very small ochroleucous flowers on filiform axillary peduncles. As its name implies, it is a native of North-west America. [T. M.]

MECONOPSIS. An herbaceous perennial belonging to the *Papaveraceæ*, distinguished from *Papaver* by having a short style and five to six free stigmas. *M. cambrica*, the Welsh Poppy, a native of Wales, Devonshire, North Britain, and the North of Ireland, is a pretty plant about a foot high, with bright green pinnate hairy leaves, slender stems, and large terminal remarkably fugacious flowers which droop while in bud, and are of a delicate sulphur-yellow colour. [C. A. J.]

MÉDAILLE DE JUDAS. (Fr.) *Lunaria biennis*.

MEDEOLA. A genus of *Trilliaceæ*, containing a North American herb, *M. virginica*, which has a white rhizome tasting like cucumber, from which the plant derives its local name of Indian Cucumber-root. It has an erect simple stem with a whorl of obovate-lanceolate sessile leaves, and a second whorl of smaller ones near the top, subtending a sessile umbel of small greenish-yellow flowers. [J. T. S.]

MEDER-DEUR. *Kigelia abyssinica*.

MEDICAGO. The Medick genus : one of the *Papilionaceæ*, and distinguished by its more or less spirally twisted legume. The more important species are the following :—

M. sativa, the Purple Medick, or Lucerne. This, though found apparently wild on the borders of fields, has doubtless escaped from cultivation; it is distinguished by its purple flowers and upright growth. Its herbage is green and succulent, and has the advantage of being early, on which account it has been highly extolled as an agricultural plant. It yields two rather abundant crops of green food in the year, of a quality highly relished by horses and cattle. *M. lupulina*, the Black Medick, or Nonsuch, is at first sight so much like the yellow trefoils as to be generally known by farmers as the Hop trefoil, or Hop; it is, however, distinguished by its naked black legume. It is used in farming to mix with grasses and clovers for artificial or shifting pastures, in which it often assumes a luxuriance of growth well befitting it for this purpose. *M. maculata*, remarkable for its spirally-coiled prickly legumes, has, from the quantity of herbage which it grows, been recommended for cultivation as a green fodder plant; but it is scarcely equal to the former, while in hay the long prickles to its seed-vessels render it very objectionable. [J. B.]

MEDIOIA *elegans* is a name given by Gardner to a very handsome Hongkong twiner, which has since proved to be a species of *Gelsemium*.

MÉDICINIER. (Fr.) *Jatropha*.

MEDICK. *Medicago*.

MEDINILLA. Between two and three dozen species of this genus of *Melastomaceæ* have been described, all from the islands of the Indian Ocean. They are shrubby plants, generally quite smooth, with opposite or whorled entire fleshy leaves, the primary nerves of which are strongly marked and often coloured, and having panicles of rose or white flowers, the calices and stalks of which are nearly always reddish. The principal characters of the genus reside in the limb of the calyx being entire or at most obsoletely lobed, and in the stamens, of which there are eight or ten (double the number of the floral envelopes), having basal-fixed generally incurved anthers with two lobes or spurs at the bottom in front and one behind. *M. magnifica* is a truly magnificent plant. [A. S.]

MEDIOCRE. Intermediate between large and small.

MEDLAR. *Mespilus germanica*. The Medlar of Surinam is said to be a sapotaceous plant. —, JAPAN. *Eriobotrya japonica*.

MEDORA. A genus of *Liliaceæ*, of the tribe *Asparagineæ*, founded on the *Smilacina fusca* of Nepal. It has a creeping rhizome, an erect simple stem, stalked cordate-ovate acuminate leaves, and terminal dichotomous many-flowered peduncles of long-stalked flowers, nearly racemose on the ultimate divisions. The perianth is deciduous, of six violet leaves with a green spot above the middle. [J. T. S.]

MEDRINAQUE. A coarse fibre from the Philippines, obtained from the Sago palm, and used chiefly for stiffening dress linings, &c.

MEDULLA (adj. **MEDULLARY**). The pith; that central column of cellular matter over which the wood is formed in Exogens.

MEDULLARY RAYS. The cellular plates or processes which connect the pith of Exogens with the bark, constituting the 'silver grain' of their wood.

MEDULLARY SHEATH. A thin stratum of spiral vessels formed immediately over the pith.

MEDULLOSE. Having the texture of pith.

MEDUSA'S HEAD. *Euphorbia Caput Medusæ*; also *Cirrhopetalum Medusæ*.

MEGACARPÆA. A genus of *Cruciferæ* of the tribe *Thlaspideæ*, containing one or two perennial herbs from the deserts of Central Asia. They have deeply pinnatifid and cut leaves covered with white woolly hairs, and terminal racemes of small purplish flowers. The pouch is very large and flat, compressed contrary to the partition, the valves orbicular, each with one seed. *M. polyandra*, the Roogee of Kunaon, is remarkable in the cruciferous order for its numerous stamens, from ten to sixteen in number. [J. T. S.]

MEGACLINIUM. A small genus of orchids of tropical Western Africa, remarkable for the curious flattened sword-shaped leafy rachis or flower-stalk upon which the no less curious little flowers are seated in a straight row along the middle on both sides. It is closely related to *Bolbophyllum*, with which, indeed, some orchidologists unite it, the chief distinctions being that in *Megaclinium* the posterior sepal is much larger than the other two, and united to them at the base, the lip is loosely articulated with the base of the column, and the four pollen-masses are all of the same size. The flowers are of a greenish or yellowish brown, spotted more or less with purple, and have a fancied resemblance to little frogs or toads, whence one species has been named *M. Bufo*. The four or five known species are all epiphytes, and have creeping rhizomes, bearing pseudobulbs furnished with leathery veinless leaves, and radical flower-racemes. [A. S.]

MEGALOS. In Greek compounds=large.

MEGASEA. *Saxifraga crassifolia, S. cordifolia*, and their allies.

MEIA. A Tahiti name for *Musa paradisiaca*.

MEION. Less; prefixed to the name of an organ, indicates that it is something less than some other organ understood. Thus *meiogyrus* means but little rolled inwards; and *meiostemonous* is said of a plant whose stamens are fewer in number than the petals.

MEISSNERIA. A Brazilian genus of *Melastomaceæ*, comprising about half a dozen species of small erect hairy herbs, with nearly simple or but slightly branched stems, small mostly sessile leaves, and small axillary bunches of reddish or purplish flowers. These latter have a calyx with a free campanulate tube and four lobes about as long as the tube itself; four petals; eight stamens, of which only four are fertile and have beaked anthers opening by a broad pore at their ends; and a filiform style ending in a punctiform stigma. [A. S.]

MELALEUCA. This name, derived from the Greek *melas*, black, and *leukos*, white, is stated to have been applied to a genus of *Myrtaceæ*, in consequence of the trunk of one of the species being black, and the branches white. The genus consists of trees or shrubs, natives of Australia and the islands of the Indian Ocean, with alternate or opposite flat or cylindrical leaves, and yellowish purplish or crimson flowers, sessile in spikes or heads. The calyx tube is hemispherical; there are five sepals and petals; alternate with the latter are five parcels of stamens; and the capsule is three-celled, united with and enclosed in the thickened tube of the calyx, which also adheres to the branch supporting it.

These plants are all of them aromatic from the presence of a volatile oil. The best known among them on this account is *M. minor* or *M. Cajuputi*, the leaves of which, after fermentation, are distilled for the purpose of yielding the oil known as Cajuput or Cajeput oil, which is green, and has a powerful aromatic odour. It is valuable as an antispasmodic and stimulant, and in 1831 was recommended as a remedy for cholera, in consequence of which the price of the oil was enormously increased, and its quality proportionately deteriorated. It is more than doubtful if, even in the pure state, it possesses any advantage over any oil of a similar nature. The leaves of this tree are used in China as a tonic in the form of decoction, where also the bark is made use of in the construction of boats and roofs for houses. Numerous species are grown as evergreen greenhouse plants in this country, on account of the simplicity of their foliage and the splendour of their clustered flowers. [M. T. M.]

MELAMPODIUM. A genus of *Compositæ* of the tribe *Heliantheæ*, consisting of coarse dichotomous annual or perennial herbs, with opposite leaves, and rather small flower-heads growing singly from the forks of the stem. The involucre has five outer spreading herbaceous bracts, and five to ten inner ones enclosing as many florets of the ray, which are ligulate, female, and usually yellow. The receptacle is convex or conical, scaly, with numerous small tubular male florets. The achenes of the ray are entirely enclosed in the persistent and usually hardened inner bracts of the involucre, and are usually crowned by a small cup-shaped pappus, often bearing one to three bristles. There are nearly twenty species, natives of tropical America, one of them found also in the Philippine Islands, but probably introduced with other American weeds.

MELAMPYRUM. The Cow-wheat, a genus of annuals belonging to the *Scrophulariaceæ*, having erect slender stems, narrow opposite leaves, and axillary or spiked flowers which are two-lipped, the upper lip being compressed and turned back at the margin, the lower three-cleft. The meaning of the systematic name, 'black wheat,' bears reference to an ancient belief that the seeds, when mixed with grains of wheat and ground into flour, tended to make the bread black. There are four British species : *M. pratense*, the most frequent, which inhabits dry woods ; *M. sylvaticum*, a much less common species, found in the north ; *M. cristatum*, which grows principally in the eastern counties ; and *M. arvense*, not unfrequent in the Isle of Wight, where it is a conspicuous object in the corn fields, with its large oblong spikes of flowers variegated with yellow, green, and crimson. French, *Mélampyre* ; German, *Wachtelweizen*.   [C. A. J.]

MELANCHOLY GENTLEMAN. *Hesperis tristis*.

MELANDRIUM. By a few authors the genus *Lychnis* is divided into several, and one of these is named *Melandrium*, and embraces all those species which have inflated calices, and capsules opening by ten instead of five teeth. There are about a dozen species having these characters, all of them Alpine or northern, and three natives of Britain : these are, *L. vespertina*, *diurna*, and *alpina*.   [A. A. B.]

MELANISM. A disease producing blackness.

MELANOGASTER. A genus of underground *Fungi*, belonging to the natural order *Hypogæi*, distinguished by a tough skin more or less overrun externally with branched fibres, and within containing sinuous moist cavities, whose walls support smooth naked spores. Most of the species have a disagreeable smell, but *M. variegatus*, which is less offensive, is used in the west of England as a substitute for truffles, under the name of Red Truffle. It has, however, none of the delicate aroma of the real truffle, and probably has little merit beyond giving a dark colour to the sauce of which it forms a part. We are not aware that the genus has been found out of Europe.   [M. J. B.]

MELANORRHŒA. Two very large East Indian trees constitute this genus of *Anacardiaceæ*, which derives its name from the Greek words *melanos*, black, and *rheo*, to flow, in consequence of the juice which flows from their trunks turning black upon exposure to the air. They grow upwards of a hundred feet high, and have broad spreading heads bearing large simple entire leaves of a thick texture, and axillary panicles of perfect flowers. These have five sepals cohering so as to form a kind of cap, five overlapping petals, and numerous stamens. The fruit is surrounded by the enlarged petals spread out in a star-like manner.

M. usitatissima is common in forests from Tenasserim and Pegu to Manipur in Sylhet. It is called Theet-see in the former, and Kheu in the latter country ; and its dark-coloured wood, on account of its excessive hardness and great weight, is known as the Lignum Vitæ of Pegu—so heavy, indeed, is it, that anchors for native boats are made of it. The most valuable and extensively used product of the tree, however, is the black varnish which it yields. This is obtained by the process of tapping, short joints of bamboo, closed at the bottom end, being thrust into holes made in the trunk and left for about two days, when they become full of a whitish thick juice which turns black when exposed to the air, and requires to be kept under water in order to preserve it. All kinds of domestic utensils and furniture are lacquered with this juice, which is laid on thin and slowly dried, the change from white to black being, according to Sir D. Brewster, attributable to its losing its organised structure and becoming homogenous, and then transmitting the sun's rays, which, in its previously organised state, it dispersed. Like other varnishes derived from the same natural order, it is apt to cause erysipelatous swellings if applied to the skin.   [A. S.]

MELANOSELINUM. A genus of umbellifers, distinguished by each half of the fruit having five narrow primary ribs and three secondary, the two outermost of the latter in the form of broad wings with a saw-like edge. The only species is *M. decipiens*, a shrub with a round simple stem, bare below, the leaves in three principal divisions, the flowers white.   [G. D.]

MELANOSINAPIS. One of the sections of *Sinapis* sometimes separated, and characterised by its small short not beaked style, and terete or sub-tetragonous pods. It embraces the black mustard, *Sinapis nigra*, and a few allied species.   [A. S.]

MELANOSPERMEÆ. One of the three great divisions of *Algæ*, characterised by their dark olivaceous spores. The plants themselves are of a light or dark olive, and the fruit is either external in diffuse or definite patches, or contained in distinct cysts sunk in the frond. The endochrome of the spore-cases is, for the most part, ultimately divided into several spores multiples of two. Impregnation is effected by means of minute spermatozoids moving by means of cilia, and produced in distinct antheridia. Occasionally there are two kinds of spores, both reproductive. The frond is either compact and cellular, or formed of jointed filaments. This division contains many of the largest and most important *Algæ*, especially the large brown seaweeds which seem in all countries to form the extreme limit of seaweed growth. The peculiarities of most of the natural orders, as *Fucaceæ*, *Laminariaceæ*, *Chordarieæ*, and *Ectocarpeæ*, have already been particularised, as well as the several uses to which the species have been applied. In the latter order we have minute filamentous *Algæ*, which form a strange contrast to the gigantic *Lessonia*, *D'Urvillæa*, &c., or even to our own *Laminaria*. In some of the lower species there is a departure from the main type, and the spores are replaced by zoospores. [M. J. B.]

MELANOXYLON. A large timber tree called Braúna by the Brazilians and *M. Braúna* by botanists, is the sole representative of this genus of leguminous plants. It has large pinnate leaves, covered with rust-coloured down underneath, and bears branched racemes of yellow flowers which are likewise clothed with rusty down. The pods are flat and sickle-shaped, and contain several seeds. Braúna timber is of a very dark reddish-brown colour, and of excellent quality, being both hard and durable. It is employed in Brazil in the construction of sugar-mills, particularly for making the heavy rollers for crushing the canes. A reddish-brown colouring matter is also obtained from both the wood and the bark, and is used by the Brazilians for dyeing cotton cloth of various shades from light-brown to nearly black. [A. S.]

MELANTHACEÆ. (*Colchicaceæ*, *Veratreæ*, *Melanths.*) A natural order of hypogynous monocotyledons, belonging to Lindley's lilial alliance of Endogens. Herbs with bulbs, corms, or fasciculated roots, and white green or purple flowers. Perianth petaloid, in six pieces, which are sometimes slightly coherent, usually involute in æstivation; stamens six, with the anthers extrorse; ovary three-celled, the ovules numerous, the style three-parted, and the stigmas three, undivided. Fruit a three-celled capsule, with septicidal or loculicidal dehiscence; seeds with a membranous spermoderm; albumen dense, fleshy; embryo very minute. Natives of various parts of the globe, but most abundant in northern countries. They are acrid, purgative, emetic, and sometimes narcotic in their qualities. *Asagræa officinalis* yields sabadilla seeds, used in neuralgia. *Colchicum autumnale*, the meadow saffron, is prescribed in gout and rheumatism, its corms and ripe seeds being used. There are upwards of thirty genera, and above a hundred and thirty species. Examples: *Colchicum*, *Melanthium*, *Uvularia*, *Veratrum*. [J. H. B.]

MELANTHERA. A genus of rough, branching, somewhat shrubby weeds of the composite family, found in the Southern United States, and southwards to Equador. They belong to the *Heliantheæ*, and differ from their near allies in the absence of strap-shaped ray florets, all the florets being tubular and perfect, and in the pappus, which consists of a few rigid bristles. The florets are white, and the anthers black: whence the generic name. [A. A. B.]

MELANTHIUM. A genus of Cape *Melanthaceæ*, consisting of bulbous herbs, with linear or lanceolate leaves sheathing at the base, and spicate flowers, which have a white yellow or pinkish perianth of six deciduous leaves, which are narrowed into claws and either hooded or bisaccate at the base. They have six stamens inserted on the perianth. [J. T. S.]

MÉLANZANE. (Fr.) *Solanum esculentum.*

MELARANCIO. An Italian name for the Orange-tree.

MELA-ROSA, or MELLA-ROSA. A variety of *Citrus Limetta.*

MELAS. In Greek compounds = black without the mixture of any other colour.

MELASTOMACEÆ. (*Melastomæ*, *Memecylaceæ*, *Mouririaceæ*, *Melastomads*.) A natural order of calycifloral dicotyledons belonging to Lindley's myrtal alliance of epigynous Exogens. Trees, herbs, or shrubs, with opposite ribbed leaves, and showy flowers. Calyx with four five or six divisions, sometimes united and separating from the tube like a lid; petals equal to the calyx, perigynous, the æstivation twisted; stamens alternate with the petals, usually with intermediate sterile ones; the anthers long, often beaked, two-celled, dehiscing by two terminal pores or longitudinally; ovary more or less adherent to the calyx; ovules usually indefinite; style one; stigma simple, either capitate or minute. Fruit many-celled, either capsular with loculicidal dehiscence, or succulent combined with the calyx and indehiscent. Seeds minute. They are found chiefly in warm climates. Many are natives of America and India. There are no unwholesome plants in the order, and the succulent fruit of several is edible. There are 165 genera, and about 2,000 species. Examples: *Melastoma*, *Lasiandra*, *Rhexia*, *Miconia*, *Charianthus*, *Memecylon.* [J. H. B.]

MELASTOMA. This genus gives its name to the order *Melastomaceæ*. It contains a considerable number of species, distributed over tropical Asia and the islands of the Indian and Pacific Oceans, extending to as far south as Moreton Bay. The plants are small shrubs covered with close-pressed hairs; and have three, five, or seven-nerved leaves, and large violet purple pale rose or white flowers, mostly in fascicles at the summit of the branches. Their floral envelopes are generally in fives: the calyx with a campanulate tube and acute deciduous teeth nearly as long as itself, and smaller teeth between them; the petals unequal-sided; the stamens ten in number, dissimilar in size, shape, and colour, five being large and violet, and five small and yellow, the anthers of the former having a downward arcuate prolongation of the connective generally ending in two spurs, while those of the latter have the cells seated immediately upon the filament. The ovary is usually five-celled. [A. S.]

MÉLÈXE. (Fr.) *Larix europæa.*

MELHANIA. A genus of *Sterculiaceæ* of the tribe *Dombeyeæ*, characterised by having three bracteoles persistent at the base of the calyx, and by the anthers being always solitary between each two barren lobes of the staminal cup. It consists of about sixteen species, natives of Africa or of tropical or subtropical Asia and Australia. They are all softly tomentose herbs or undershrubs, with entire or toothed alternate leaves, and axillary peduncles bearing one or very few flowers. The bracteoles, either broadly cordate lanceolate or linear, are often longer than the calyx, and the petals scarcely spread open. These plants, therefore, with the aspect of some *Malvaceæ*, or almost that of *Hermannia*, are of little interest except to the systematic botanist.

MELIACEÆ. (*Meliæ, Meliads.*) A natural order of dicotyledons, belonging to Lindley's violal alliance of hypogynous Exogens, Trees or shrubs with alternate exstipulate simple or compound leaves. Sepals four to five, imbricated; petals four to five, hypogynous, with a valvate or imbricated æstivation; stamens equalling the petals, or two, three, or four times as many; the filaments combined in a long tube; the anthers sessile within the orifice of the tube; disk often large and cup-shaped; ovary single, one-celled, the cells often equal in number to the petals; ovules one to two in each cell; style one; stigmas distinct or united. Fruit baccate, drupaceous, or capsular, many-celled or by abortion one-celled; seeds not winged. They are chiefly found in the tropical parts of America and Asia, and possess bitter, tonic, and astringent qualities. *Melia Azadirachta* is used in India as a febrifuge, and its fruit yields an oil which is employed for domestic purposes, and as an antispasmodic. The root of *Melia Azedarach* is bitter, and used as a vermifuge. Oils are procured also from species of *Trichilia* and *Carapa*. There are upwards of forty genera, including *Melia, Turræa, Trichilia,* and *Carapa*, and a hundred and eighty species. [J. H. B.]

MELIA. A genus of *Meliaceæ*, conferring its name upon the order to which it belongs, and consisting of trees and shrubs inhabiting the tropics. They have alternate pinnate or bipinnate leaves, and paniculate flowers. The calyx is five-cleft; the corolla has five linear petals; there are ten stamens; and an almost fleshy five-celled drupe, each cell containing one, seldom two seeds. *M. Azedarach*, vulgarly known as the Pride of India, False Sycamore, Holy-tree, Arbre à Chapelet, Bead-tree, or Hill Margosa, is widely diffused over the globe, having been carried to America, Africa, and different parts of Southern Europe. It is from thirty to fifty feet high, with bipinnate leaves, and large bunches of lilac flowers emitting an agreeable perfume. In Southern France and Spain the tree thrives well in the open air, and is planted in avenues. The Arabic name, Azedarach, implies a poisonous plant, and the fruit is generally considered so. The root is bitter and nauseous, and used in North America as an anthelmintic. The tree is supposed to possess febrifugal properties, and a decoction of the leaves is used as a remedy for hysterics. From another Indian species, *M. Azadirachta*, the Neem-tree or Margosa, a kind of toddy, which the Hindoos consider a stomachic, is obtained by tapping; and from the fruit an oil is extracted fit for burning and other domestic purposes. [B. S.]

MELIANTHUS. A singular genus of *Zygophyllaceæ*, consisting of small trees, natives of Nepal and of the Cape of Good Hope, the leaves of which are glaucous, unequally pinnate, the leaflets unequal and extended at the base along the side of the common stalk, and the stipules usually combined within the axil of the leaf. The flowers are in axillary or terminal clusters, the lower ones sometimes imperfect. The structure of the upper flowers, too, is very curious. The calyx is large and generally of a purple colour, its five segments unequal in size and form; the lowest very short, bulging below, hooded above, concealing a gland, which is itself girt round by a separate membrane; the others lance-shaped and flat, the two upper ones largest. The five petals are shorter than the sepals, strap-shaped; the four lower ones bent downwards, hairy in the middle, where they are united one to another, but elsewhere detached; the uppermost one when present very small, separate from the rest, placed between the two upper sepals, but usually absent. Stamens four, the two upper detached, the two lower united together at the base; ovary and stigma four-lobed; fruit bladder-like, four-celled, and winged. Two or three species from the Cape are grown in greenhouses in this country, and will even grow out of doors if protected in winter. They are singular in appearance, even when the flowers are not produced. The flowers, which rarely appear in this country, are full of honey, whence the name of the genus. [M. T. M.]

MELICA. A genus of grasses belonging to the tribe *Festuceæ*. The inflorescence of the different species consists either of open panicles or dense racemes. The glumes are nearly equal, larger than the pales, one to two-flowered, with the rudiments of one to two additional imperfect flowers. The pales become hardened on the seed. The species have a wide range over the globe, but are mostly natives of temperate climates. Two are British, namely, *M. uniflora* and *M. nutans*. They are handsome grasses, but of no agricultural value, though the latter is one which grows well under trees, and consequently is of some importance in that respect. [D. M.]

MELICOCCA. A genus of *Sapindaceæ*, now restricted to two American species, trees of considerable size, and natives of the northern part of South America. Their leaves are abruptly pinnate and without stipules, and their small whitish flowers are produced in divided racemes at the ends of the branches. *M. bijuga*, the Genip tree, though originally a native of Guiana and New Grenada, is now plentifully found in several of the West India Islands, especially in Jamaica, where it has become naturalised and grows commonly in the lowlands, attaining the height of forty or fifty feet, with a trunk four or five feet in circumference, yielding a hard and heavy timber. It produces numerous green egg-shaped fruits an inch or more in length, possessing an agreeable vinous and somewhat aromatic flavour: the generic name being derived from the Greek words *meli*, honey, and *coccos*, a berry, in allusion to the qualities of the fruit.   [λ. S.]

MELICOPE. A genus of New Zealand shrubs, belonging to the family *Rutaceæ*. The leaves are ternate; the flowers greenish-white; calyx four-parted, persistent; petals four, spreading; stamens eight, with awl-shaped filaments; ovary four-lobed, inserted on a glandular disk, each lobe with two ovules. Fruit divided into four carpels, each containing a single seed suspended by a thread.   [M. T. M.]

MELICYTUS. A New Zealand genus of *Violaceæ*, belonging to the equal-petaled division of the order. The four species all form large woody shrubs or small trees, with long smooth serrated short-stalked leaves, and little bundles of small flowers on the branches, each flower-stalk having one or more bracts. The flowers are usually of separate sexes, and borne on distinct plants. *M. ramiflorus* is the Mahoe of the New Zealanders, which must not be confounded with the Mahoe of the West Indies. It is a tree growing sometimes as high as forty or fifty feet, with a trunk about four feet in circumference covered with white bark, producing a heavy wood of inferior quality. The berries are eaten by the natives.   [A. S.]

MÉLIER À TROIS NERVURES. (Fr.) *Blakea trinervia*.

MELIGA. An Italian name for Millet or Dhurra.

MELILOT. *Melilotus officinalis*.

MÉLILOT DE SIBÉRIE. (Fr.) *Melilotus alba*.

MELILOTUS. A genus of leguminous plants containing about thirty species, the majority belonging to Southern and Central Europe and Western Asia. They are herbaceous plants with trifoliate leaves, having the stipules adhering to their footstalks, and each of the three leaflets on a separate stalk; and their small yellow or white flowers are disposed in long-stalked loose racemes growing from the bases of the leaves. The flowers are characterised by the calyx being five-toothed, by the corolla having a blunt keel, and falling away after fading, and by the upper one of the ten stamens being free. The pods, which are straight, thick, and short, contain one or few seeds.

M. officinalis, the Common or Yellow Melilot, is widely spread through Europe and Russian Asia. It is an annual or biennial of erect habit, from two to four feet high, having spreading branches and distant long-stalked leaves with bristle-like stipules. The long loose racemes of yellow flowers produce small oval pods, marked with irregularly netted veins. When dried the Melilot acquires a peculiar odour, due to the presence of *coumarine*, a principle which exists likewise in the Tonka bean and the vernal grass, the latter when mixed with hay contributing largely to its fragrance. Its flowers are sold by the herbalists as Balsam flowers. In Switzerland, *M. cæruleus* is called Zieger Kraut, i.e. curd herb, and is employed for giving the odour and flavour to the peculiar cheese called Schabzieger or Chapziger, the dried flowers being reduced to powder and worked up into a paste with the curd.   [A. S.]

M. officinalis is an annual under ordinary circumstances, but ' if cut continually and not allowed to flower, it will last several years.' *M. alba* has been grown under the names of Cabul and Bokhara or Buchara Clover. As a forage plant 'it has been found too watery when young, and too sticky when old.' But besides this, we have found that the aromatic flavouring principle is too powerful to make it advisable to use this plant by itself. There is, however, one use to which it may be well applied—that of putting an occasional layer of it sandwichwise with less highly-flavoured fodder, or with hay that has lost some of its savour by wet; here its aroma, which is so much like that of the sweet vernal grass, to which the flavour of meadow hay is mainly due, might be productive of benefit in rendering what would otherwise be insipid, more spicy and palatable. This White Melilot is also an excellent bee plant.   [J. B.]

MÉLINET. (Fr.) *Cerinthe aspera*.

MELIOLA. A genus of *Fungi* allied to *Sphæria*, and analogous to *Erysiphe*, which it replaces in tropical or subtropical countries. The species form black felt-like patches on leaves, and bear conspicuous perithecia filled with asci containing a few large articulated dark sporidia. [M. J. B.]

MELIOSMA. A genus considered as the type of a small order or suborder allied to *Terebinthaceæ*. It consists of tropical trees or shrubs, usually hairy, with alternate simple or pinnate leaves without stipules, and very small flowers in large terminal racemes or panicles. In the structure of the flowers the genus is remarkable for its stamens being opposite the petals. The ovary is three-celled, with two ovules in each; and the fruit is a small one-seeded drupe. The seeds have a curved or twisted radicle, and folded cotyledons. There are about twenty species, natives of America or tropical Asia, chiefly in mountain districts, supplying timber used for various purposes. The genus was described by

Roxburgh under the name of *Millingtonia*, and probably includes also the *Ophiocaryon* or Snake-nut of Guiana, so called from the very much twisted embryo, compared to a snake coiled up within the nut.

MELISSA. A genus of labiate plants, having the calyx two-lipped, the upper three-toothed and spreading, the lower bifid; the tube of the corolla is somewhat inflated; and the two upper stamens are at times imperfect. The different species are widely diffused, having representatives in Europe, middle Asia, and North America. The name is from the Greek word signifying bee, indicative of the attraction the flowers have for the insects, on account of the honey they produce. [G. D.]

MÉLISSE DE MOLDAVIE. (Fr.) *Dracocephalum Moldavica.* — DES BOIS. *Melittis Melissophyllum.*

MELITTIS. A genus of labiates, characterised by its membranous bell-shaped calyx, the lower lip of which is bifid, with round lobes; the tube of corolla wide, its upper lip round, entire, slightly concave, the lower three-lobed; the divisions of the style ovate. *M. Melissophyllum*, the only species, widely diffused in Europe, is a native of the southern parts of England; it is a handsome plant, with ovate serrated leaves, and large showy flowers. [G. D.]

MELKHOUT. The hard durable wood of the South African *Sideroxylon inerme.*

MELLAGHOO. An Indian name for Pepper.

MELLA-ROSA. *Citrus Bergamia;* also a variety of *Citrus Limetta.*

MELLEOUS. Having the taste or smell of honey.

MELLIGO. Honey-dew; a disease of plants in which an unnatural secretion of sweet matter appears on their surface.

MELLINUS. The colour of new honey.

MELLOCA. The *Melluco* or *Ulluco*, extensively cultivated throughout the elevated regions of Bolivia, Peru, and New Grenada on account of its esculent roots, which resemble little yellow potatos, forms the present genus of *Basellaceæ*. This plant, *M. tuberosa*, also called *Ullucus tuberosus*, has weak fleshy stems from one to two feet long, lying upon the ground or twining round neighbouring bushes, furnished with fleshy entire somewhat heart-shaped roundish leaves, and bearing short spikes of inconspicuous yellow flowers, all the parts being smooth. The flowers have an outer calyx of two roundish lobes, and an inner deeply five-parted one with taper-pointed segments; five stamens having very short filaments, and uniting at the base into a ring which combines with the inner calyx; and a roundish ovary which bears a short style and undivided stigma, and ultimately becomes a berry-like fruit surrounded by the unchanged calyx.

The tuberous roots of the *Melloca*, called Oca quina, in Bolivia, to distinguish them from other Ocas belonging to the genus *Oxalis*, are largely used as food in the elevated regions of the Peruvian Andes, principally in the vicinity of Potosi and La Paz in Bolivia, but extending as far north as Popayan in New Grenada; and during the famine caused by the failure of the potato crops, they were, in common with many other roots, recommended as a substitute for that esculent, but upon trial were found to be unpalatable on account of the quantity of earthy slime contained in them. In the elevated regions of the Andes, where the boiling point of water is scarcely high enough to allow of the roots being cooked in the ordinary way, the inhabitants prepare them by alternately freezing and steeping them, by which process they are rendered amylaceous. [A. S.]

MELOBESIA. A genus of coralline seaweeds, in which the mineral element abounds so much, and the resemblance to corals is so great, that the species at first sight resemble anything rather than vegetables. They either consist of a few thick branches or nodules, or of an expanded simple or variously imbricated crust. Several species occur in deep water on our coast, one has been found as high as 74° north latitude, and nine are figured by Dr. Harvey in the *Phycologia Britannica*. Dr. Johnson believed them to be mere states of *Corallina officinalis*, but there is no reason to think this correct. Their medical qualities are those of common chalk. [M. J. B.]

MELOCACTIDÆ. A suborder of *Cactaceæ*, characterised by the globose melon-like form of the stem of the plants, which bear sessile flowers. It includes the genus *Melocactus*, *Discocactus*, *Anhalonium*, and *Mamillaria*. [J. H. B.]

MELOCACTUS. The principal characteristic of this genus of *Cactaceæ* resides in the flowers being produced in a hemispherical or cylindrical head at the top of the plant, consisting of a dense mass of bristly wool and slender spines, from amongst which the small ephemeral flowers scarcely emerge. The plants themselves consist of simple fleshy stems of a somewhat globular or conical form, with numerous prominent ribs armed with fascicles of stiff spines placed at regular distances. The flowers closely resemble those of *Mamillaria*, but the divisions of the perianth are fewer, and nearly all petal-like, and the thread-like style has a five-rayed stigma. The oblong smooth berries crowned with the withered flower, contain numerous small seeds with minute globose cotyledons. There are numerous species, principally natives of the West Indies and tropical America; the best known, however, and the one usually found in our gardens, is *M. communis*, the Turk's-cap Cactus, so called from the flowering portion on the top of the plant being of a cylindrical form and red colour like a fez cap, but sometimes called Englishmen's Head, or Pope's Head. It is common in South America and also in many of the West Indian Islands, where it grows in great quantities, covering large tracts of barren soils. The plants are usually globose when young, but ultimately increase more in length than in diameter, seldom, however, growing much more than a foot and a half high, with from twelve to twenty ridges. Notwithstanding the arid places in which they grow, they contain a considerable quantity of moisture, and the mules, being aware of this fact, resort to them when hard pressed for water, carefully removing the prickles with their fore feet previous to quenching their thirst in the juice. [A. S.]

MELOCHIA. A genus of *Sterculiaceæ*, of the tribe *Hermanniæ*, distinguished from *Hermannia* and *Mahernia* by the ovules, which are only two in each cell of the ovary, and by the straight seeds and embryo; and from *Waltheria* by the cells of the ovary being always five. There are about fifty species, dispersed over the tropical regions of the globe, the majority herbs or undershrubs, clothed with more or less of a stellate tomentum often intermixed with simple hairs. The leaves are alternate, toothed, narrow ovate or cordate; the flowers small, in axillary panicles, in terminal compound spikes, or in loose cymes or panicles. Some species are, however, shrubby, or even grow into small trees. The genus is sometimes restricted to a small number of herbs with very angular pyramidal capsules; and the majority of species with globular capsules are separated under the name of *Riedlea*; and a few of the taller shrubby ones with winged seeds take the name of *Visenia*. Several of the species are common tropical weeds.

MELODINUS. A genus of *Apocynaceæ*, containing about a dozen species of woody-stemmed climbing shrubs with milky juice, natives of Silhet, Hong-Kong, the islands of the Indian Archipelago, New Caledonia, and Norfolk Island. They have opposite entire leaves, and white sweet-smelling flowers disposed in short terminal cymes. The five-parted calyx is destitute of glands, and the corolla has a cylindrical tube and five oblique or sickle-shaped spreading lobes, the mouth of the tube being furnished with a coronet composed of five or ten small erect scales sometimes united together. The fruit is a large globular or egg-shaped fleshy berry containing numerous seeds lying in pulp.

M. monogynus is a tall woody climber, found in the forests of Northern and Eastern India, bearing round or somewhat four-cornered smooth deep yellow fruits about the size and appearance of small oranges, and containing numerous seeds imbedded in a firm sweet-tasted pulp, which the natives eat. [A. S.]

MELON. *Cucumis Melo.* —, MUSK. *Cucumis Melo.* —, QUEEN ANNE'S POCKET. *Cucumis Dudaim.* —, WATER. *Citrullus vulgaris.*

MELON D'EAU. (Fr.) *Citrullus vulgaris.*

MÉLONGÈNE. (Fr.) *Solanum esculentum.*

MELONIDIUM. An inferior fleshy many-celled fruit; such as an Apple.

MELON-SHAPED, MELONIFORM. Irregularly spherical, with projecting ribs; as the stem of *Melocactus communis.*

MELON-THICK. A West Indian name for *Melocactus communis.*

MELON-WOOD. A yellow Mexican wood, which resembles Sander's wood, used for furniture.

MELOPEPO. *Cucurbita Melopepo.*

MELUB. The fragrant kernels of *Cerasus Mahaleb*, which are strung as necklaces, and valued by the women of Scinde.

MEMBRANOUS, MEMBRANACEOUS. Thin and semi-transparent, like a fine membrane; as the leaves of mosses.

MEMECYLON. This genus was formerly regarded as typical of a natural order to which the name *Memecyleæ* was given, but it is now placed in *Melastomaceæ*. It contains upwards of fifty species, all of which inhabit the tropical regions of the Old World, and are small trees or shrubs with entire thickish leaves having a prominent midrib and pinnate often scarcely perceptible veins, their small bluish flowers being borne in clusters upon the sides of the branches. *M. capitellatum* (alias *M. tinctorium*) is a small tree of Ceylon and the Carnatic, where its leaves, which turn yellow in drying, are used for dyeing, but the colour obtained from them is fugitive. Those of *M. umbellatum* are used by the Cingalese for mixing with the wood of *Morinda citrifolia* and Sappan wood (*Cæsalpinia*), for producing a permanent red dye; while the ripe berries of *M. edule* are eatable, but rather astringent. [A. S.]

MEMNONIUS. A brown black colour; pitch black.

MENAIS. A genus of *Ehretiaceæ*, found in South America, forming a shrub with a woolly stem, alternate ovate entire rough leaves, and flowers with a three-parted persistent calyx, a salver-shaped five-parted corolla with a flat limb, five sessile anthers, and a globose four-celled berry with one seed in each cell. [J. T. S.]

MENDEE. An Indian name for Henna.

MENDO. A wild Sweet Potato of North America.

MENIOCUS. A few annual weeds belonging to the *Cruciferæ*, found in South Europe and West Asia, have been associated under this name, but are now placed in the large genus *Alyssum*. They are much branched herbs, with linear leaves clothed with white starry hairs, and small white flowers disposed in racemes at the ends of the twigs. Each of the six stamens —four of which are long, and two short— has a small scale in front, and the elliptical compressed silicules contain numerous immarginate seeds. [A. A. B.]

MENISCATE. A cylinder bent into half a circle.

MENISCIUM. A genus of coarse-habited polypodiaceous ferns, with simple or pinnate fronds, having the venules angularly or arcuately anastomosing between the pinnate veins, and throwing out an excurrent free veinlet from the apex of the arc or angle. The sori are naked, linear-oblong, and curved, placed on the transverse venules. Sometimes the fronds are contracted, and the fructifications then become crowded and almost acrostichoid. The genus inhabits the tropics of both the Old and the New World, and is not very numerous in species. [T. M.]

MENISCOID. Thin, concavo-convex, and hemispherical, resembling a watch-glass.

MENISPERMACEÆ. (Menispermads.) A natural order of dicotyledons belonging to Lindley's menispermal alliance of diclinous Exogens. Trailing shrubs with alternate simple usually entire leaves, and incomplete usually unisexual (often diœcious) flowers. Sepals and petals similar, in one or several rows, hypogynous, deciduous; stamens monadelphous, or occasionally free, the anthers adnate, extrorse; carpels solitary or numerous, distinct or partially coherent, one-celled; ovule solitary. Fruit a succulent one-seeded drupe. They occur in the tropical woods of Asia and America, and have bitter and narcotic properties, some being very poisonous. Anamirta paniculata yields cocculus indicus, illegally used to impart bitterness to malt liquor; Jateorhiza palmata supplies bitter Calumba root; and Cissampelos Pareira is the tonic Pareira brava. There are about 60 genera and 350 species. [J. H. B.]

MENISPERMUM. A genus of Menispermaceæ, the species of which have broad, palmately lobed or angled leaves, and panicled flowers with four to eight sepals in two rows, six to eight petals, the males with twelve to twenty-four free stamens, the females with six sterile stamens and two to four capsules. The fruit is a compressed drupe. There are two species, one in North America, and the other in the temperate parts of Eastern Asia. The name Moon-seed is derived from the lunate form of the seed. [J. H. B.]

MENODORA. A small genus of Jasminaceæ inhabiting Mexico, having a shrubby habit, erect or creeping quadrangular branches, simple leaves, axillary or terminal but always isolated flowers, a bell-shaped persistent and many-toothed calyx, a funnel-shaped corolla with a long tube and five lobes, and a bivalved capsule. The two known species grow on dry and sterile hills. [B. S.]

MENONVILLEA. A genus of Cruciferæ, of the tribe Cremolobidæ, from Peru. The species have smooth, linear leaves, the radical ones crowded and toothed at the apex, and terminal racemes of dull reddish flowers. The pouch is somewhat stipitate, crowned by the furrowed style, with the

valves convex on the back, and the margin of each expanded into a wing. The seeds are solitary. [J. T. S.]

MENOW WEED. Ruellia tuberosa.

MENSTRUAL, MENSTRUOUS. Lasting for a month. Bimestris is said of things that exist for two months; trimestris, for three months, &c.

MENTHA. The Latin version of the Greek name Mintha borne by the daughter of Cocytus, who, according to the poets, was metamorphosed into a mint plant by Proserpine from motives of jealousy. The name is applied to a genus of Labiatæ, whose species are widely distributed over the world, but are not met with in the hotter regions. They are herbaceous plants with flowers in dense whorls, arranged in terminal or axillary heads or spikes. The calyx is five-toothed, usually regular; the corolla bell-shaped with a short tube and a nearly regular four-lobed limb; and the stamens are four, erect, of equal size. Great difficulty exists in discriminating the species, owing to the capacity for variation possessed by these plants.

M. Piperita, a plant occasionally found wild in this country, is the well-known Peppermint. It is extensively cultivated for the sake of its volatile oil, which is procured by distilling the leaves. The oil and the preparations made from it, are largely used as aromatics, carminatives, and stimulants, and are especially useful in the alleviation of nausea, griping pains, and flatulence. Owing to its powerful taste, Peppermint in some shape or other is frequently used to conceal the nauseous taste of medicine. A kind of liqueur is also prepared from it. M. viridis, or Spearmint, is the plant that is used for culinary purposes under the name of Mint. It possesses the same properties as Peppermint, but in a less degree; its flavour, however, is preferred by many people. M. Pulegium, like the two preceding a native of Britain, is best known under its common name of Pennyroyal. Its taste is very peculiar, and to most people not a little objectionable; its properties are similar to those of the other mints, but in former times, and still by the vulgar, this plant had special virtues assigned to it, hence it is still employed as a domestic remedy in female complaints. M. citrata furnishes a sweet-smelling oil, in odour like oil of Bergamot. The species are abundantly propagated by suckers, and but rarely produce perfect seed, hence the constancy of the variations. [M. T. M.]

MENTHASTRE. (Fr.) Mentha rotundifolia.

MENTHE. (Fr.) Mentha. — À COQ, or DES JARDINS. Pyrethrum Tanacetum. — DES MONTAGNES. Calamintha officinalis. — POIVRÉE. Mentha Piperita. — ROMAINE. Mentha viridis.

MENTOOLOO. An Indian name for Trigonella fœnum græcum.

MENTUM. A projection in front of the

flowers of some orchids, caused by the extension of the foot of the column.

MENTZELIA. A genus of *Loasaceæ*, found principally in Mexico, California, and the southern United States, one species, however, extending as far as Panama and the West Indies, while two others belong to South America. All are annual or perennial herbaceous plants, with the leaves alternate upon the stem, but often opposite upon the flowering branches. The flowers are of an orange or yellow colour and open only during sunshine; they have a long cylindrical calyx tube divided into five lobes; five petals; an indefinite number of stamens, often collected into five or more bundles; and a one-celled ovary cohering with the tube of the calyx. *M. albicaulis*, a low branching plant from six to ten inches high, with white polished stems, and deeply-cut lance-shaped rough leaves, is found abundantly on the arid sandy plains of Oregon and California, where the oily somewhat cubical seeds, from twenty to forty of which are contained in each of its narrow cylindrical fruits, are pounded by the Indians and used as an ingredient in a kind of cake, called Piñole mantica, forming part of their food. [A. S.]

MENYA. An Indian name for *Paspalum scrobiculatum.*

MENYANTHES. The beautiful Buckbean or Marsh Trefoil, is the only species of this genus of *Gentianaceæ*, which is distinguished by its capsule bursting by two valves, and by its ternately divided leaves. *M. trifoliata* is a water plant, extensively diffused over the northern hemisphere, having a creeping rootstock, whence proceed densely matted roots and tufts of long stalked leaves, whose limbs are divided completely into three oblong segments. The flowers are borne on a long-stalked raceme, and have a five-parted calyx, and a bell-shaped five-lobed corolla, pinkish externally, white internally, and delicately fringed. Like the other members of this family, this plant possesses bitter tonic properties, and in large doses is cathartic and emetic. It is little used at present, but was formerly in request in cases of fever, gout, and rheumatism. Linnæus mentions that the leaves were used in Sweden as a substitute for hops, and a like use is made of them in Silesia and other parts of Germany. In Lapland, in times of scarcity, the roots are dried and mixed with meal for making bread. The elegance of the flowers, and the ease with which it may be cultivated, render the plant a most desirable acquisition to ornamental ponds or lakes. [M. T. M.]

MENZIESIA. A genus of heathworts, having the calyx four or five-lobed; the corolla somewhat bell-shaped, with the border four or five-lobed and reflexed; the stamens eight, enclosed in the corolla; and the stigma blunt. The species are handsome shrubs, natives of North America, with alternate narrow or ovate leaves, and

terminal flowers, solitary or several together. The name was given in honour of the late Mr. Menzies, surgeon and naturalist to Vancouver's expedition. [G. D.]

MÉRANGÈNE. (Fr.) *Solanum esculentum.*

MERCURIALE. (Fr.) *Mercurialis annua.* — DES BOIS. *Mercurialis perennis.*

MERCURIALIS. Herbaceous plants belonging to the *Euphorbiaceæ*, distinguished by having the barren and fertile flowers separate, the former containing nine to twelve stamens, the latter two simple styles and a two-celled two-seeded capsule. *M. perennis*, the Dog's Mercury, is a common woodland plant, eight to twelve inches high, with extensively creeping roots, simple stems, and large ovate serrated rough leaves. The barren flowers grow in long lateral spikes near the summit of the stem, and are conspicuous in early spring by their greenish yellow stamens; the fertile flowers, on separate plants, also grow in spikes but are less evident owing to their being concealed among the upper leaves. The whole plant is poisonous, and being consequently rejected by cattle, may often be seen forming dense patches of a dark green hue in places where most other herbage has been consumed. It turns dull bluish green in drying, and may be made to furnish a deep blue dye—of a fugitive nature, however. *M. annua* is taller and more branched, with the barren and fertile flowers on the same plant. French, *Mercuriale*; German, *Bingelkraut.* [C. A. J.]

MERCURIO DO CAMPO. A Brazilian name for *Erythroxylum suberosum.* — VEGETAL. A Portuguese name for *Franciscea uniflora.*

MERCURY. *Mercurialis.* —, DOG. *Mercurialis perennis* —, ENGLISH. *Blitum* or *Chenopodium Bonus Henricus.* —, THREE-SEEDED. *Acalypha.* —, VEGETABLE. *Franciscea uniflora.*

MÉRÉDICK. (Fr.) *Cochlearia Armoracia.*

MERENCHYMA. Spherical cellular tissue.

MERENDERA. A genus of *Melanthaceæ*, containing about a dozen species of pretty bulbous crocus-like plants, spread over the Mediterranean region and Abyssinia. The pink flowers like those of a crocus, appear above the ground in the autumn, and the grassy leaves with the ovary (which is hidden under ground when the plant is in flower) grow after the flowers wither, and are mature in spring, when the ripe ovary is elevated upon a stalk. The limb or flattened portion of each of the six perianth-segments is contracted abruptly into a long narrow claw, and at the point of contraction furnished on each side with a small tooth. These teeth do not exist in *Colchicum*, which is nearly allied. The clawed portions of the petals unite by their edges and form a long slender tube, which bears at its apex six stamens. The three styles are free not united into one as in *Bulbocodium.* The name is given by Spaniards to *Colchicum.* [A. A. B.]

MÉRIANE. (Fr.) *Watsonia.*

MERICARP. One of the half fruits of an umbellifer; it is a carpel ripened and separated from a common axis or growing point.

MÉRINGEANNE. (Fr.) *Solanum esculentum.*

MÉRISIER. (Fr.) *Cerasus avium.* — À GRAPPES. *Cerasus Padus.*

MERISMATIC. Separating by the formation of internal partitions. Cellular tissue is often thus multiplied.

MERMAID-WEED. An American name for *Proserpinaca.* —, FALSE. *Florkea.*

MERMAN'S SHAVING BRUSHES. A name given in North America to different species of *Chamædoris* and *Penicillus.* The root is much branched, with matted fibres, and generally penetrates deeply into the sand on which the plant grows, while the stem is more or less coated with carbonate of lime, and is either annulated or composed of a multitude of closely placed and densely interwoven longitudinal one-celled threads, which send off laterally throughout their length short level-topped branchlets. [M. J. B.]

MEROS. In Greek compounds the parts of a flower. Thus, *pentamerous* means composed of parts arranged in fives, *trimerous* in threes, &c.

MERRY. The small wild black fruit of *Cerasus avium.*

MERTENSIA. The name of that section of *Gleichenia,* in which the segments are elongated, and the sori are medial or axillary, consisting of several (five to twelve) spore-cases. They have a different aspect from the species with orbicular segments, and terminal sori of two to four spore-cases, and are by some authors regarded as distinct, but the difference is hardly to be regarded as of generic value. [T. M.] This name has also been applied to two other genera. One is a genus of *Ulmaceæ* from tropical America, now called *Momisia* or included in *Celtis,* and consisting of spiny trees with alternate leaves; and axillary panicles of polygamous flowers, with a five-parted perianth, five stamens, and a one-celled ovary becoming a drupe. The other is a genus of *Boraginaceæ* sometimes called *Steenhammera.* [J. T. S.]

MERULIUS. A genus of *Fungi* belonging to the pore-bearing *Hymenomycetes,* distinguished by the waxy soft hymenium which forms porous reticulate or sinuous toothed depressions. It borders, in fact, very closely on the gill-bearing fungi, and more especially on *Cantharellus.* One species, *M. lacrymans,* is unfortunately too well known, being the grand agent of the decomposition of domestic and naval timber when composed of the wood of coni-

fers, and known by the name of Dry Rot. It is not, however, confined to such wood, but attacks other timber when it comes in its way, and, when once established, penetrates even thick walls to the destruction of the mortar. In wine-cellars it not only destroys the shelves and laths, but creeps amongst the sawdust, and ultimately attacks the corks, and spoils the wine. Sawdust should never be used in cellars subject to rot, and if laths are used, they should be injected with a solution of some metallic salt. Creosote, which is the most effectual agent in the prevention of Dry Rot, might not be admissible from its powerful smell. [M. J. B.]

MERYTA (including *Botryodendrum*). A genus of *Araliaceæ,* comprising six species inhabiting Tahiti, Samoa, Norfolk Island, New Zealand, and the New Hebrides, and somewhat resembling *Gustavia* in habit. Their stem is arboreous, twelve to twenty-four feet high, generally simple, and crowded on the top with simple entire more or less oblong leaves, of a thick leathery consistence, shining, and from two to four feet long. Their fine foliage has procured for two species, *M. Denhami* and *M. macrophylla,* a place in our conservatories, for their polygamous flowers are green and insignificant; these are collected into heads, and arranged in panicles. The calyx is divided into three to nine segments, the corolla is entirely wanting, and the number of stamens and cells of the ovary corresponds with that of the calyx-lobes. The oldest species is *M. lanceolata,* also called *Botryodendrum taitense,* discovered by Forster at Tahiti in 1771, and, like all the other species of the genus, extremely local in its geographical range. [B. S.]

MESEMBRYACEÆ. (*Ficoideæ, Lewisieæ, Ficoids.*) A natural order of calycifloral dicotyledons belonging to Lindley's ficoidal alliance of perigynous Exogens. Succulent shrubs or herbs with opposite simple leaves and often showy flowers. Sepals definite, four to eight, more or less combined, with valvate or imbricate æstivation; petals indefinite, sometimes wanting; stamens perigynous, distinct, the anthers oblong, incumbent; ovary usually many-celled; stigmas several, distinct; ovules anatropal or amphitropal; placenta central or parietal. Fruit a many-celled capsule, opening in a stellate or circumscissile manner at the apex, or an indehiscent nut; seeds numerous, rarely definite or even solitary. They are found in warm regions chiefly, the greater part of them at the Cape of Good Hope. Some are used as articles of diet, as the leaves of the Hottentot's fig (*Mesembryanthemum edule*) and the New Zealand spinach (*Tetragonia expansa*). Others yield soda, and have been employed in the manufacture of glass. The flowers of many of them exhibit the phenomenon of opening only under the influence of sunshine, and closing in dull weather. There are sixteen genera, and upwards of 400 species. [J. H. B.]

MESEMBRYANTHEMUM. A most extensive genus of *Mesembryaceæ*, the name of which, derived from the Greek words *mesembria*, mid-day, and *anthos*, flower, is applied to these plants because many of them open their flowers only for a short time in the middle of the day. Between three and four hundred species are described, and upwards of one hundred and fifty

Mesembryanthemum deltoideum.

are cultivated in our gardens, where some of them are favourites on account of their showy flowers. They are very succulent and grow in hot sandy plains, the genus being almost entirely confined to the Cape of Good Hope. Their leaves are very variable in form, but almost always of a thick fleshy texture; and their flowers have four or five sepals united by their base and cohering with the ovary, and numerous narrow petals generally in several series. The ovary is one or many-celled, and bears numerous stigmas; and the one or many-celled fruit opens by means of slits disposed in a star-like manner upon the top, each cell containing numerous seeds.

M. crystallinum, a native of the Canary Islands and Greece, as well as of the Cape of Good Hope, is the common Ice Plant of our gardens, so called in consequence of every part of the plant being covered with small watery pustules, which glisten in the sun like fragments of ice. Large quantities

Mesembryanthemum tigrinum (leaf).

of the plant are collected in the Canaries and burnt, the ashes being sent to Spain for the use of glassmakers. *M. edule* is called the Hottentot's Fig, its fruit being about the size of a small fig, and having a pleasant acid taste when ripe. The leaves, also, of several species are eatable, those of *M. papulosiforme* being a good substitute for spinach; but some, such as *M. tortuosum*, possess narcotic properties, and are chewed by the Hottentots for the purpose of producing intoxication. The fruits possess hygrometric properties, the dried shrivelled capsules swelling out and opening so as to allow of the escape of the seeds when moistened by rain, which at the same time fits the soil for their germination. [A. S.]

MESENTERICA. The mycelium of certain fungals.

MESOCARP. That part of a pericarp which lies between the outer and inner skins or integuments.

MESOCHIL, MESOCHILIUM. The intermediate part of the lip of such orchids as have this organ separated into three distinct portions.

MESOCHLÆNA. A small genus of eastern tropical ferns, of the affinities of which different opinions are held. The plants have the aspect of the larger species of *Nephrodium*, and their oblong or hippocrepiform indusia have a longitudinal attachment along the middle of the sorus, after the manner of *Didymochlæna*, with which the genus is therefore associated by some. Others regard the attachment as merely an exaggeration of the normal condition of *Nephrodium*, and class *Mesochlæna* as an aberrant form of that genus. [T. M.]

MESODERM. The middle layer of tissue in the shell of the spore-case of an urn-moss.

MESOGLŒA. A genus of dark-spored *Algæ*, consisting of extremely gelatinous marine seaweeds, with a solid centre and radiating slimy branched threads producing obovate spore-cases at their base. It resembles *Chordaria*, but is still more gelatinous. Several species are common on our coasts; most of them are found also in the United States, and one species is met with in the Philippine Islands. They grow on other *Algæ*, on plants like *Zostera*, and occasionally on stones. The purple species belong to the genus *Nemalion* amongst rhodosperms. [M. J. B.]

MESOPHLŒUM. The cellular integument of bark, overlying the liber, and underlying the epiphlœum.

MESOPHYLL. All the interior parenchyma of a leaf, lying between the two skins.

MESOPHYTUM. The line of demarcation between the internode and petiole.

MESOSPERM. The same as Sarcoderm.

MESPILODAPHNE. A genus of Brazilian trees of the laurel family. The leaves are net-veined, the flowers disposed in axillary panicles, each with a funnel-shaped perianth, enclosing nine to twelve stamens, the three innermost sterile, and sometimes altogether wanting; some of the fertile stamens have glands attached to them, and all have four-celled anthers. The fruit is included within the thickened persistent base of the perianth, the upper part of which ultimately falls off. *M. pretiosa* yields a bark whose properties are similar to those of cinnamon. [M. T. M]

MESPILUS. A genus of *Rosaceæ* of the tribe *Pomaceæ*, originally intended to include all the *Cratægi* with five styles, but now generally restricted to the Medlar, *M. germanica*, which has the calyx-lobes more leafy, and leaving between them a broader and more open disk than in other species. The wild Medlar, the origin of our cultivated varieties, is common as a shrub in the hedges of a great part of Continental Europe. The Medlar has been found wild in various parts of England, especially in hedges about Minshull in Cheshire, and Ashburnham in Sussex; but as it is not found commonly in the woods of this country, it is supposed that the seeds have been those of introduced plants, and disseminated chiefly in hedgerows by birds.

There are several varieties of Medlar cultivated for their fruit. Some of them grow tolerably upright, but generally they are of spreading habit, forming low deciduous trees, the branches of which are elbowed, turning at nearly right angles in any direction (especially those of the large Dutch Medlar) so that the tree has a very rustic appearance. Indeed, on this account it may be very properly introduced where rustic scenery is an object. The leaves are oval-lanceolate, but in the variety just mentioned they are large, and broader than those of the other kinds. It blossoms late, not before June or the beginning of July, the flowers being solitary and produced at the ends of the shoots or of short side spurs; the petals are roundish and white; the calyx is green and leafy, but as the fruit approaches maturity it withers and dies back till at last only the fleshy stubs at the base remain. The skin of the fruit is brown, and the flesh firm and austere, not at all fit to eat when first gathered, and requiring to be kept till it begins to decay, but when it becomes completely disorganised, and its green colour has entirely gone, the pulp, in its incipient state of decay, has, to many tastes, an agreeable acidity. The change which takes place is called bletting. Some persons, again, have the fruit prepared and glazed with sugar. Tastes are different, and persons who are very fond of Medlars, prefer them, in their naturally mollified state, to the finest melting pears. In this state they will keep fit for use for several weeks, if in a dry airy situation; and there is a stoneless variety, *Néflier à fruit sans noyeau,* which keeps longer than the other kinds. The best as regards quality is the common small-fruited or Nottingham Medlar, which has, to medlar fanciers, a rich brisk subacid fla-

vour; but from the large size of the fruit and the rustic appearance of the tree, the large Dutch is the one generally preferred. The Medlar has been successfully grafted on the pear, and even on the common hawthorn, notwithstanding their external dissimilarity. [R. T.]

MESQUITE. A French name for American Oak; also a kind of gum.

MESUA. A genus of *Guttiferæ* of the tribe *Calophylleæ*, characterised by having four imbricate sepals, four petals, numerous stamens with oblong anthers, a long style with a peltate stigma, and a two-celled ovary with two ovules in each cell; and by the seeds having thick fleshy cotyledons and a small radicle. There are three species, all trees from tropical Asia, with narrow coriaceous leaves, elegantly marked with numerous parallel veins diverging from the midrib, and large axillary flowers. *M. ferrea*, common in East India, is a very handsome hard-wooded tree. Its highly fragrant flowers are sold in the Indian bazaars, both for *sachets* and for their supposed medical properties, under the name of Naghas or Nagkesur, and the wood is said to be one of those known under the name of Iron-wood.

METABASIS. A genus of *Compositæ*, of the tribe *Cichoraceæ*, proposed for *Seriola ætnensis* and *cretensis*, two Mediterranean species, in which the outer achenes have a shorter beak than the inner ones, and a pappus of short scales only, instead of all the achenes having a plumose pappus as in other *Seriola*. They are herbs, with the aspect of hawkweeds.

METAXYA. *Amphidesmium.*

METHER-SEED. An Indian name for *Trigonella fænum græcum.*

METHONICA. A genus usually placed among *Liliaceæ*, but referred to *Melanthaceæ* by Dr. Wight, from its affinity with *Uvlariæ*, forming another example of the difficulty of separating the orders in a satisfactory manner. It consists of climbing tuberous herbs from India and tropical Africa, with branched stems and scattered leaves, which, however, are opposite or verticillate by threes under the branches; in shape they are lanceolate acuminate or terminating in a tendril. The flowers are solitary on axillary or terminal peduncles, and have a coloured withering perianth of six nearly equal crimped reflexed segments, and six stamens with anthers fixed by the middle. The ovary is three-celled, and the style obliquely bent, with a three-cleft stigma. The capsule is roundish, splitting into three segments, thus showing the relation to *Melanthaceæ*; seeds roundish, with a spongy red seed-coat. The flowers are mostly yellow or crimson. The species, which are better known under Linnæus's name of *Gloriosa*, are of very ornamental character; they are, however, extremely poisonous. *M. superba, grandiflora,* and *virescens* are all favourite plants amongst cultivators. [J. T. S.]

METL. A Mexican name for *Agave americana*.

METRODOREA. A Brazilian shrub, constituting a genus of *Rutaceæ*. The leaves are opposite, entire, dotted, stalked, the stalks dilated and confluent at their bases, enclosing the terminal bud. The flowers are small, glandular, purplish, and borne on panicles; calyx five-cleft; petals five, larger than the calyx; stamens five, inserted into the disk which surrounds the five-lobed ovary, each compartment of which contains two ovules. [M. T. M.]

METROSIDEROS. Several species of this genus of *Myrtaceæ* are remarkable on account of their climbing habit, all the other plants of the order being erect trees or shrubs. In some instances, however, they are climbers only while young, their stems sending out numerous strong woody roots which clasp round the trunk of a tree and compress it so tightly that it ultimately dies, by which time, however, the climber is sufficiently strong to support its own weight. Other species are large timber trees or shrubs. All have opposite entire thick leaves, marked with pellucid dots; and heads of showy red or white flowers, having the calyx either wholly or only half-way adherent to the ovary, the rim being thickened and bearing five rounded lobes, and as many rounded petals, the numerous long coloured stamens, which are the most conspicuous part of the flower, forming a crown round the mouth. The fruits are three-celled, opening by three slits at the top or bursting irregularly, and containing a great number of narrow seeds. *M. robusta*, the Rata of the New Zealanders, is a tall tree, sixty or eighty feet high, with a stout erect trunk, never climbing, a branching head of myrtle-like foliage, and showy bright red flowers. The hard close-grained timber of the Rata is used in New Zealand for ship-building and other purposes, and by the natives for making their war-clubs, paddles, &c. Other species likewise produce timber suitable for ship-building, such as *M. tomentosa*, the Pohutu Kawa of the New Zealanders, called Fire-tree by the colonists on account of the brilliancy of its flowers; while the wood of the Aka, *M. scandens*, is called New Zealand Lignum Vitæ on account of its hardness. [A. S.]

METROXYLON. *Sagus.*

METTERNICHIA. The name of a Brazilian tree forming a genus of *Solanaceæ*. The flowers are handsome, white or pink, with a bell-shaped calyx irregularly five-cleft, and a funnel-shaped corolla, with a limb of five equal segments. There are five stamens, with anthers opening lengthwise; and a two-valved capsule with numerous seeds. [M. T. M.]

METZGERIA. A genus of *Jungermanniaceæ* belonging to the frondose section. The fruit springs from the midrib on the under side, with a one-leaved involucre, and the fronds are forked. *M. furcata*, which is found in all parts of the world, is one of our commonest liverworts, and occurs of various breadths on trees, rocks, &c., though always retaining its essential characters. [M. J. B.]

MEUM. A genus of umbellifers, having the fruit almost round, each half of it with five prominent equal ridges, and vittæ in the furrows and on the line of junction. The species are natives of the upland parts of Europe, having deeply divided leaves, and white or purple flowers. The name is given in allusion to the narrow divisions of the leaves. [G. D.]

MEW. *Meum athamanticum.*

MEXICAL. An intoxicating spirit obtained from pulque, the fermented juice of *Agave americana* and allied species. It is also called Aguardiente de Maguey.

MEXOCOTL. *Bromelia Acanga.*

MEYENIA. A genus of *Acanthaceæ*, containing one Indian species, *M. Hawtayneana*, a climbing plant, with opposite entire leaves, and axillary pedunculate flowers; and *M. erecta* and *Vogeliana*, beautiful tropical African shrubs. The calyx is small, five-lobed, and included within two large bracteoles; the corolla funnel-shaped, with a very short tube; there are four didynamous stamens, with two-celled anthers hairy at the apex; the stigma is dilated and has two bilobed lips; and the capsule is enlarged below, where it is two-celled and four-seeded. [W. C.]

MEYERIA. A genus of *Compositæ*, closely allied to the radiate species of *Calea*, and chiefly distinguished by the branches of the styles terminating in a short cone, and by the scales of the pappus being oblong obtuse, not acuminate. Four Brazilian undershrubs, with opposite leaves, and rather showy yellow flower-heads, have been referred to it.

MEZEREON. *Daphne Mezereum.*

MEZEREUM. This has sometimes been separated from *Daphne*, by reason of its deciduous perianth, and the small quantity of albumen present in the seed. See DAPHNE. [M. T. M.]

MEZQUIT-TREE. *Prosopis* or *Algarobia glandulosa.*

MIBORA. *Knappia agrostidea*, sometimes called *Sturmia verna*.

MICHAUXIA. A genus of bellworts, having the border of the calyx eight-cleft; the corolla with eight divisions which are reflexed; the style short with rows of hairs ending in eight short divisions; and the ripe capsule with eight ribs and eight cells. The species are biennials, chiefly found in the Levant. *M. campanuloides* is sometimes seen in gardens. The genus was named in honour of Michaux, a French botanist. [G. D.]

MICHELIA. A Florentine botanist of the early part of the eighteenth century is commemorated by this genus of *Magnolia-*

ceæ, which consists of lofty trees, natives of India and the islands of the Eastern Archipelago, and is nearly allied to *Magnolia*, but distinguished by the axillary flowers, the looser arrangement of the carpels, and the more numerous ovules.

M. Champaca, the Chumpaka of the Hindoos, is cultivated commonly in India for the powerful fragrance of its flowers, which, indeed, according to Sir W. Jones, is so strong that bees seldom if ever alight on them. The tree is sacred to Vishnu, and is therefore an object of superstitious regard on the part of the Hindoos, who adorn their dark hair with the rich orange-coloured flowers. The root, like all parts of the tree, has bitter properties, and is used medicinally. There appears to be some difficulty in defining the species; or probably that just mentioned, having been long cultivated, has originated numerous varieties which are mistaken for species: thus, *M. Rheedii* is referred to *M. Champaca* by Hooker and Thomson. The timber of *M. Rheedii* is employed in Bombay for cabinet-work, and has been tried in ship-building, while various parts of the tree are used medicinally as stimulants, &c. *M. Doltsopa*, another variety of the *Champaca*, is mentioned as furnishing a fragrant wood used in house-building in Nepal. Lindley mentions the bark of *M. montana* as having properties like those of cascarilla, but milder, and that of *M. gracilis* as having the odour of camphor. *M. Champaca* is cultivated as a hothouse plant in this country, where, however, it does not appear to be as great a favourite as its Indian reputation would lead us to infer. [M. T. M.]

MICO, MIJO. A solid oil, made in Japan from *Soja hispida*.

MICOCOULIER. (Fr.) *Celtis.*

MICONIA. A very considerable genus of exclusively tropical American melastomads, mostly shrubs or even small trees, very variable in their foliage, and with terminal panicles (sometimes spikes) of small generally white flowers. The floral envelopes are mostly in fives (rarely four, six, or eight); the calyx more or less campanulate, with a short limb having the teeth obsolete in some and evident in others, and the little external teeth either altogether absent or punctiform; the petals obovate, rounded or retuse; and the stamens nearly always double as many as the petals, and mostly curved, their anthers variable in shape, opening by pores or slits, the connective either without any downward prolongation, or shortly and variously prolonged. The ovary is two to five-celled, the style slender; and the stigma punctiform, capitellate or peltate. Fruit a globose berry. [A. S.]

MICRANDRA. This generic name was originally applied to a large Brazilian tree which has since been found to belong to *Siphonia*. It has now been given to two other closely allied trees belonging to the same order, *Euphorbiaceæ*, but easily distinguished by their leaves being simple,

instead of consisting of three leaflets as in *Siphonia*. The flowers are of separate sexes, borne in panicles from the axils of the leaves, the males being much more numerous than the females, and distinguished from those of allied genera by having five free stamens, the females having a conical ovary terminated by a very short style bearing three notched stigmas. Both the species, *M. siphonioides* and *M. minor*, inhabit the banks of the Rio-Negro and its tributaries, forming large trees, often having as many as ten trunks rising in a cluster from one root, and growing from fifty to sixty feet high. They abound in milky juice, which, when inspissated, yields pure caoutchouc; and the natives who collect the caoutchouc sent to this country from Pará, commonly known as 'bottle-rubber,' obtain it indiscriminately from these trees and the various species of *Siphonia*, and apply to them the same name (Xeringue or Seringue) as that by which the latter trees are known. [A. S.]

MICROCODON. A genus of bellworts, distinguished by having the border of the calyx in five pieces; the corolla nearly cylindrical, five-lobed, and persistent; the style slender, short, five-lobed at the summit; and the seed-vessel spherical and very hairy. The species are Cape annuals of lowly habit, with small stalkless narrow leaves, and terminal short-stalked flowers. The name alludes to the small size of the bell-formed flowers. [G. D.]

MICRODON. A small genus of *Selaginaceæ*, containing five species of undershrubs, natives of the Cape of Good Hope. They have alternate entire leaves, and terminal flower-spikes with broad bracts. The calyx is tubular, shortly five-toothed, adnate for nearly half its length to the bracts; the corolla has a funnel-shaped tube and a five-lobed limb; there are four didynamous stamens, of which the longer pair are exserted, the filaments slender, and the anthers one-celled. The ovary is two-celled, each with one ovule depending from the apex. The fruit consists of two achenes which separate spontaneously. [W. C.]

MICROGONIUM. *Trichomanes.*

MICROLÆNA. A genus of grasses belonging to the tribe *Oryzeæ*. The spikes of inflorescence are three-flowered, the two lower flowers neuter and one-valved, the terminal one two-valved and hermaphrodite. There is only one species, *M. stipoides*, a native of New Holland. [D. M.]

MICROLEPIA. One of the principal of the groups into which the old genus *Davallia* is separated by modern pteridologists. It differs in this: that, whereas *Davallia* has the indusium of the sorus tubulose or cup-shaped and marginal, *Microlepia* has the sorus intra-marginal, and the indusium semiorbicular or short and half cup-shaped. The species are mostly large-growing herbaceous plants, with variously divided fronds, and are widely scattered over the tropical or subtropical parts of the world, some few extending to China and Japan. [T. M.]

MICROLICIA. A considerable genus of Brazilian melastomaceous plants, consisting of stiff erect branching undershrubs usually not more than a foot or two high, with twiggy branches, very small leaves, usually dotted with resinous glands, and solitary deep rose purple or white (rarely yellow) flowers in the leaf-axils towards the tips of the branches. The latter have a calyx of five acute teeth; five obovate petals; ten stamens, five alternate with the petals larger than the rest, their anthers terminated by an oblique one-pored beak, and having a more or less arcuate prolongation of the connective below the cells, which, in the larger stamens, is continued beyond the junction with the filament. The ovary is three-celled. [A. S.]

MICROLOMA. A genus of *Asclepiadaceæ* peculiar to South Africa, and consisting of twining or erect shrubs, with opposite smooth sagittate or oval leaves, small flowers in umbels, a five-cleft calyx, an urn-shaped five-lobed corolla, and a smooth fruit. Uses unknown. [B. S.]

MICROLONCHUS. A small genus of *Compositæ*, distributed over the Mediterranean region and North-west India. They are erect or prostrate branching herbs one to two feet high, with toothed or pinnatifid leaves, the upper ones linear entire, and solitary terminal flower-heads, containing many tubular rose-coloured florets, enclosed in a cone-shaped involucre, consisting of many series of overlapping scales, which in some species terminate in a slender spine. The genus is near to *Centaurea*, but differs in the nature of the pappus, which is double, the inner row of pales broader than the others and sometimes represented by a single scale, the outer of rough hairs. [A. A. B.]

MICROMELUM. A genus of small trees of the *Aurantiaceæ*. The species are natives of India and of the Indian Archipelago; they have pinnate leaves, terminal corymbose inflorescence; a five-toothed or entire calyx; a five-petaled valvate corolla; ten stamens, with disunited filaments; and an ovary with several cells, which are separated one from the other by curiously twisted dissepiments, or partitions. The cotyledons of the embryo are also described by Professor Oliver, the most recent investigator of this family, as remarkably twisted. [M. T. M.]

MICROMERIA. A genus of the *Labiatæ*, numbering about sixty species, which are spread over nearly all the temperate and warmer parts of the globe, but occur in greatest abundance in the Mediterranean region. They are erect or prostrate branching perennial herbs, with opposite leaves, and axillary whorls of small purple or white two-lipped flowers, or the flowers are gathered in spikes at the ends of the twigs. Some of the species have an odour like common thyme; others smell like mint.

They are chiefly recognised by the tubular thirteen to fifteen-ribbed and five-toothed calyx, which is not distinctly two-lipped as in *Thymus*. [A. A. B.]

MICROPERA *pallida*. The East Indian orchid to which this generic name was first applied, having turned out to be a species of *Camarotis*, Dr. Lindley has suggested that the name *Micropera* should be retained for another East Indian plant of the same family, not referable to any before known genus, described by Dalzell under the name of *Micropera maculata*. This is a little stemless epiphyte, with flat oblong leaves notched at their one-sided top, and a simple raceme of small flowers, having nearly equal free obovate sepals and petals of a yellow colour with a purple spot in their centre. The lip is white marked with rose, saccate or pouched, and looks, as Dr. Lindley says, 'like a side-saddle with two horns instead of one—the pouch, into which there is an opening only between the horns, being almost concealed by the lamina, which hangs down in the manner of saddle-flaps.' [A. S.]

MICROPTERIS. *Xiphopteris.*

MICROPTERYX. A genus proposed by Walpers for the *Erythrina crista-galli* and some other species, which have the keel petals united. It has not, however, been adopted otherwise than as a section of *Erythrina.*

MICROPYLE. The aperture in the skin of a seed which was once the foramen of the ovule; it indicates the position of the radicle.

MICROPYXIS. A genus of primworts, distinguished by having the calyx five-parted; the corolla funnel-shaped, shorter than the calyx, and remaining adherent till the fruit is ripe, its tube short, the border five-parted, the acute lobes approaching after flowering; stamens five, filaments broad at the base and slightly hairy; the seed-vessel globose, membranous, and opening across. The species are small annuals, natives of Bolivia, New Holland, and Madagascar; their upper leaves are alternate, and the flowers axillary and solitary. [G. D.]

MICROS. In Greek compounds = small; thus *microphylla* means small-leaved.

MICROSERIS. A genus of cichoraceous *Compositæ*. The two species, *M. Forsteri* and *pygmæa*—the former found in Australia, Tasmania, and New Zealand, the latter in Chili—are smooth stemless perennial herbs, with entire or deeply pinnatifid leaves, and simple flower-scapes bearing a solitary head of yellow florets like that of *Taraxacum*. The genus is most readily recognised by the many-striate terete beakless achenes crowned with a pappus of numerous tawny bristles which are rough above and dilated at the base. The fleshy fibres of the roots of *M. Forsteri* are eaten by the natives about Port Philip, according to Mr. Gunn. *Monermos* and *Phyllopappus* are synonyms. [A. A. B.]

MICROSORIUM. *Pleopeltis.*

MICROSPERMA. A genus of *Loasaceæ*, closely allied to *Mentzelia*, but differing in the tube of the calyx being short and top-shaped; in the numerous stamens collected into five bundles, each of which is attached to one of the five large spreading petals; and in the one-celled fruit opening by five slits at the top, and containing innumerable minute seeds arranged in five rows. Only two species are known, both natives of Mexico. *M. bartonioides*, occasionally seen in gardens, is an herbaceous annual with rough hairy stems, jagged leaves, and showy flowers with large sulphur-yellow petals and very long slender stamens of the same colour.   [A. S.]

MICROSTEGIA. *Callipteris.*

MIDA. A genus of sandalworts, having the stamens and pistils on different plants: the males having the border of the calyx four-cleft, eight glands at its throat, the four outer small, the four inner larger, ciliate and opposite the divisions of the calyx; the females with a four-cleft wheel-shaped deciduous calyx, and a short cylindrical style ending in three spreading and blunt lobes. The species are New Zealand trees, with alternate entire leaves, of dry texture.   [G. D.]

MIDNAPORE CREEPER. *Rivea bona nox.*

MIDSU. An oily pulp for cooking, used in Japan, and made from beans.

MIDSUMMER MEN. *Rhodiola rosea.*

MIEL DE PALMA. A syrup extracted from the trunk of *Jubæa spectabilis.*

MIELE. A Cingalese name for *Bassia longifolia.*

MIERSIA. A genus of *Gilliesiaceæ* from Chili, consisting of herbs with coated bulbs, grass-like leaves, and umbellate flowers from a kind of spathe. Each flower is surrounded by a double involucre, of which the exterior has six herbaceous bracts, three pointing upwards and three downwards, and the interior as many small petaloid bracts; perianth an urceolate six-toothed cup, within which are six fertile stamens.   [J. T. S.]

MIGNARDISE. (Fr.) *Dianthus plumarius.*

MIGNONETTE. *Reseda odorata.* —, JAMAICA. *Lawsonia alba.*

MIGNONETTE. (Fr.) *Dianthus chinensis.*

MIGNONNETTE. (Fr.) *Saxifraga umbrosa.*

MIKANIA. A genus of *Compositæ*, only differing from *Eupatorium* in the flower-heads containing constantly only four florets, and the involucre having as many nearly equal bracts, with the occasional addition of one or two small ones outside. The genus would indeed have been united with *Eupatorium*, were it not that the constancy in the number of florets gives it a peculiar habit easily recognised through a large number of species. Nearly a hundred and fifty have been published, but these ought probably to be reduced by nearly one-third. With the exception of three or four African or tropical Asiatic species, they are all natives of America, chiefly within the tropics. All of them have opposite leaves. A few are erect undershrubs; the remainder are herbaceous or half-woody twiners, with oblong ovate cordate or lobed leaves, and numerous small cylindrical flower-heads in racemes, corymbs or panicles. The most common species, *M. scandens*, a twiner with cordate leaves, extends over the greater part of North America, and is probably identical with some of the South American species described as distinct, as well as with the East Indian *M. volubilis*, and the African *M. capensis*. Some South American species, especially the *M. Guaco*, are supposed to supply a powerful antidote for the bite of venomous serpents, but this valuable property is perhaps not yet sufficiently tested by reliable experiments. The Guaco has, however, been supposed to be a species of *Aristolochia*: which see.

MIL. (Fr.) *Panicum miliaceum.*

MILDEW. A word properly applied to the white moulds which affect the leaves of plants, as the German derivation (Mehl Thau, flour dew) implies; but at the present day extended to such productions as the dark mildew of wheat, or even to cases in which no parasitic fungus is present. The hop mildew, the rose mildew, the mildew of peaches and of grapes, are examples of the first, all of which yield to one or more dustings of sublimed sulphur. The wheat mildew, which arises from the attack of a species of *Puccinia*, is at present without any known remedy. It is to be observed that in the former case the white mealy appearance represents merely the young state of the fungus, the perfect form being evidently some *Erysiphe* or closely allied genus. In the peach mildew the perfect form is seldom produced, and at present that of the vine is unknown, though the ravages of the young plant have been so disastrous.

The word mildew is also applied to the dark spots which are so common on linen when kept in damp places. We believe that this is due to one of the multitudinous forms of the common *Cladosporium herbarum*. On closely examining such mildewed spots, we have generally found minute fragments of the cuticle of the wheat from which the starch was made, used in the dressing of the goods. If there be any justice in this observation, care must be taken in the first place not to use any flour with the starch, and thus to have the starch as free as possible from impurities. There was a notion formerly that silk became mildewed from the use of potato starch, the grains being infested with the peculiar parasite of the potato murrain. The assertion, however, is totally without foundation, as the specimens on which the notion was originally built, most clearly proved. [M. J. B.]

MILFOIL. *Achillea Millefolium.* —,
HOODED. *Utricularia.* —, WATER. *Myriophyllum*; also *Hottonia palustris.*

MILHO. A Brazilian name for Maize.

MILIARY GLANDS. The same as Stomates.

MILIUM. A genus of grasses belonging to the tribe *Paniceæ.* The inflorescence is in large loose panicles; glumes herbaceous; pales thin and membranaceous, nearly equal, hardening on the seed. Steudel describes fourteen species, which have a considerable range over the globe, though mostly natives of the temperate parts of it. *M. effusum* is one of the handsomest grasses belonging to the British Flora, and is moreover a valuable species for growing under the dense shade of trees, where it forms a beautiful plant. The large seeds are useful for pheasants, which feed on them.　　　[D. M.]

MILK-TREE. *Tanghinia lactaria.*

MILK-VESSELS. Those tubes which contain the milky fluids. See CINENCHYMA and LATICIFEROUS VESSELS.

MILKWEED. *Asclepias.* —, GREEN. *Acerates.*

MILK-WOOD. *Pseudolmedia* (formerly *Brosimum*) *spurium*; also *Sideroxylon inerme.*

MILKWORT. *Polygala.* —, BITTER. *Polygala amara.* —, SEA. *Glaux maritima.*

MILLA. A genus of *Liliaceæ* from Mexico. The species have thickened fleshy fibrous roots, radical cylindrical hollow leaves, and white long-stalked terminal umbellate flowers: the perianth salver-shaped with an elongate bell-shaped tube, and a six-cleft flat limb, and the six stamens inserted in its throat. The capsule is three-celled, three-valved, containing numerous seeds with a black seed-coat.　　[J. T. S.]

MILLEFEUILLE. (Fr.) *Achillea Millefolium.*

MILLEPERTUIS. (Fr.) *Hypericum.* — DE MAHON. *Hypericum balearicum.*

MILLERIA. A branching pubescent or hairy annual, a native of Mexico and some parts of tropical South America, forming a genus of *Compositæ* of the tribe *Heliantheæ.* The leaves are opposite, the flower-heads small on terminal dichotomous peduncles. The involucre has only three to five bracts, and the head contains but few yellow florets, one ligulate and female, the others tubular and male. The receptacle has no scales, and the achene is without pappus.

MILLET. A common name for various species of small seed corn; more particularly *Panicum miliaceum* and *miliare.* —, GERMAN. A variety of *Setaria italica.* —, INDIAN. *Sorghum vulgare.* —, ITALIAN. *Setaria italica.*

MILLET. (Fr.) *Milium*; also *Panicum miliaceum.* — D'INDE. *Zea Mays.* — DES OISEAUX. *Setaria italica.* — GRAND. *Sorghum vulgare.* — LONG. *Phalaris canariensis.* — NOIR. *Sorghum.*

MILLETIA. A genus of *Leguminosæ* of the suborder *Papilionaceæ*, allied on the one hand to *Wistaria*, and on the other to *Lonchocarpus* and *Pongamia*, distinguished from the former chiefly by the want of any inflected appendages at the base of the upper petal or standard, and from the two latter by the pod opening in two rather thick hard valves. It comprises a considerable number of species from tropical Africa, Asia, and Australia, either tall woody climbers resembling in habit the well-known *Wistaria* of our gardens, or trees like *Robinia.* Their leaves are pinnate with opposite leaflets, almost always furnished with stipellæ, and the flowers in racemes in the upper axils or in panicles terminating the branches, and often very handsome. The arborescent ones have a hard wood, and one species is said to supply some of the Moulmein Rosewood. None are in cultivation, for they are mostly too large for our hothouses, and too tender for the open air in European climates.

MILLIGANIA. A genus of ivyworts, having stamens and pistils on distinct plants: the former single in the axils of bracts; the latter grouped in heads, each flower having the border of the calyx three-cleft, one of the divisions being larger than the others; styles usually two, rarely four. The only species is a small marsh shrub, a native of Van Diemen's Land.　　[G. D.]

MILLINGTONIACEÆ. A group of thalamifloral dicotyledons described by Wight and Arnott, but included by most botanists in *Sapindaceæ.*　　[J. H. B.]

MILLINGTONIA *hortensis* is the only representative of a bignoniaceous genus, peculiar on account of its combining an arboreous habit with a fruit divided into two cells by means of a partition running parallel with the direction of the valves. *Millingtonia* is a middle-sized tree, with impari-bipinnate leaves, quite entire leaflets, and large panicles of white flowers, emitting a delicious odour, on account of which the plant is cultivated in many parts of India and the Indian Archipelago. The calyx is bell-shaped, and with five equal and short lobes; the corolla has a very long tube, and is divided into five lobes, the two uppermost of which are more or less grown together; the stamens are four in number, and the anthers not divergent as in most *Bignoniaceæ*, but parallel; both stamens and style are longer than the corolla, whilst the fruit is a smooth flat capsule, enclosing broadly winged seeds. Several other species formerly classed under *Millingtonia*, have now more properly been referred to other genera of *Bignoniaceæ.*　　[B. S.]

MILL-MOUNTAIN. *Linum catharticum.*

MILNEA. A genus of *Meliaceæ*, confined to tropical Asia, and consisting of trees and shrubs, the young branches of which are covered with scurfy hair. The leaves are alternate, imparipinnate; the flowers arranged in axillary panicles, the calyx five-cleft, the corolla five-petaled, the five anthers placed on an urn-like cup, and the fruit a dry berry, generally with one seed, the arillus of which is edible. · [B. S.]

MILTONIA. A genus ranking amongst the most beautiful of garden orchids. Nine species are known, and, with the exception of the Mexican *M. Karwinskii*, they are exclusively Brazilian. They belong to the vandeous *Brassideæ*, and are readily distinguished by the peculiar habit of the species. They are epiphytes, generally with an unhealthy yellowish hue, the pseudo-bulbs furnished with narrow flat leaves, and simple radical scapes bearing a raceme of a few (sometimes one) large showy flowers, the predominant colours of which are yellow and purple. Their flowers have the sepals and petals alike; an undivided sessile lip continuous with the column, marked with interrupted lines near its base; a short column with two auricles, which in a few species, constituting a separate section, are confluent with a raised edge of the anther-bed; and a membranous naked anther, containing two waxy pollen-masses, furrowed behind, and having an obovate caudicle and oblong gland. [A.S.]

· **MILTWASTE.** *Ceterach officinarum.*

MIMETES. A proteaceous genus of shrubby plants, natives of the Cape of Good Hope, distinguished by having a four-parted calyx, the concave segments of which bear each a nearly sessile anther, and a straight filiform style with an acute stigma. The flowers are red or purple, in axillary or terminal heads; and the fruit, a nut, contains a single smooth seed. The leaves are oval or linear, entire or slightly dentate, generally imbricate, and clothed with scattered silky hairs. [R. H.]

MIMEUSE. (Fr.) *Mimosa.*

MIMOSA. A genus of *Leguminosæ*, which, if maintained as originally established by Linnæus, would comprise nearly the whole of the present suborder *Mimoseæ*, that is, about a thousand species. It has, however, been much subdivided, and the name retained only for about two hundred species which have definite stamens not more than twice the number of petals, anthers not tipped by a gland, and a pod of which when ripe the valves are detached either entire or breaking into transverse joints, leaving the rim persistent on the peduncle. These species are mostly herbs, undershrubs, or climbers; a few are erect much-branched shrubs; and scarcely any grow into trees. A large number are prickly. The leaves are twice pinnate, usually with a large number of very small leaflets, but in a few species the leaflets are much larger and reduced to eight in the whole leaf. In many species the leaves are sensitive; that is, when touched they close downwards (as do all the species when night comes on), and only recover their position

after a lapse of time greater or less according to climate, season, weather, or the vigour of the individual.

The true *Mimosas* are almost all tropical. The greater number are American, a few of them extending southwards beyond the tropics; a few species are natives of tropical Africa and East India, but none are yet known from Australia, where the largest genus of *Mimoseæ* (*Acacia*) is so abundant. Very few species also are in cultivation. Of these *M. sensitiva* is an herbaceous twiner, with only one pair of pinnæ to the leaves, each pinna bearing two pairs of ovate leaflets, the inner one of the lower pair always very small. This species as originally defined is now divided into five or six, all South American, of which one, *M. albida*, has been frequently grown in hot-houses, especially on the Continent, for its sensitive leaves, and elegant flower-heads of a pale pink. *M. pudica* is, however, the common Sensitive Plant of our hot-houses. It is a branching annual of one or two feet, assuming sometimes a somewhat woody appearance, of tropical American origin, but now naturalised over a great part of tropical Asia and some parts of Africa. The common leafstalk bears at its extremity two, sometimes three pairs of pinnæ, each with many small leaflets, all highly sensitive wherever they are touched; but if a point be applied to the gland at the base of the pinnæ, the leaflets may be seen to be gradually cast down, beginning at the last pair of each pinna, and as soon as the movement has extended to the basal pair the whole pinna will be bodily dejected. *M. marginata*, from extratropical South America, is a very elegant half-herbaceous climber, occasionally grown in our conservatories. It is scarcely sensitive in our climate. *M. asperata*, a small shrub with numerous pinnæ and leaflets, is perhaps the widest spread species over South America and Africa. *M. myriadenia* in tropical America, a woody climber, is remarkable for the great height it attains, ascending like the *Entadas* to the tops of the tallest trees. Several other South American prickly species are very tall woody climbers, as are also *M. rubifolia* and a few others in India. No species appears to have been applied to any special purpose, and few are as worthy of cultivation for ornament as the majority of the species of *Acacia* and *Calliandra*.

MIMULUS. A genus of herbaceous plants, belonging to the order *Scrophulariaceæ*, with opposite mostly toothed leaves, quadrangular stems, and showy flowers which are generally solitary and axillary. The distinctive characters are: calyx five-angled, five-cleft; corolla ringent, the upper lip reflexed; stigma compressed, two-cleft; seed-vessel two-celled, many-seeded. None of the species are indigenous, but *M. luteus*, the yellow Monkey-flower, is not unfrequently found, apparently in a wild state, on the banks of rivers and in other wet places. Owing to the creeping habit of this plant, its readiness to throw out roots, and its adaptation to the climate of the British Isles, it soon establishes itself in any moist ground on which it may be thrown, to the exclusion of other plants of less robust habit; so that it may be said to have become naturalised. Many varieties of this species are cultivated, the corollas of which are large and showy, bright yellow blotched with rich brown. *M. moschatus* is commonly cultivated as a cottage-window plant, under the name of Musk-plant. It is a native of North America, about the Columbia River, but does not adapt itself so readily to our climate as the preceding species. French, *Mimule*; German, *Gaukler*. [C. A. J.]

MIMUSOPS. A genus of *Sapotaceæ*, containing thirty or more described species, about one third of which are imperfectly known. The better known species are found in the East Indies, tropical Australia, Mauritius, and the Cape of Good Hope, Brazil, and Guiana; and are generally large milky-juiced trees, frequently eighty or a hundred feet high, with thick entire smooth leaves, and clusters of small white often sweet-smelling flowers. These latter are characterised by having a six or eight-parted calyx with the segments in a double series; and a corolla divided into three times as many parts, also in a double series. Their fruits are globose or somewhat ellipsoid, and one or two-celled by abortion, containing one or two hard smooth seeds marked with a small egg-shaped scar.

Several species yield hard, durable, and very heavy timber, such, for instance, as *M. Elengi* and *M. indica* in Ceylon, where the wood is used for ordinary house-building purposes, and *M. hexandra* in the peninsula of India. A species called the Bully-tree or Bullet-tree in British Guiana, grows from a hundred to a hundred and twenty feet high, with a trunk six feet in diameter and destitute of branches for the first sixty or seventy feet, affording a very close-grained timber of an exceedingly durable nature, being but little influenced by the weather. Its small fruits, about the size of coffee-berries, are delicious when ripe. The fruits of other species, also, are commonly eaten in their native countries, such as those of *M. Elengi*, the seeds of which likewise afford an abundance of oil, while its highly fragrant flowers yield their perfume to water by distillation. [A. S.]

MINA. A genus of *Convolvulaceæ*, containing a single species from México. It is a beautiful twining herbaceous plant, with flowers in scorpioidal racemes, and having five sepals, a salver-shaped corolla with a swollen tube, five exserted stamens, and a four-celled ovary with a single ovule in each cell. The form of the corolla separates this genus from *Quamoclit*, but the difference is very slight. [W. C.]

MINDI DES INDES. (Fr.) *Lawsonia.*

MINDOUBI. A Brazilian name for the Ground Nut, *Arachis hypogæa.*

MINETTE. (Fr.) *Medicago lupulina.* — DORÉE. *Trifolium agrarium.*

MINIATUS. Scarlet, with a decided mixture of yellow.

MINOOMOOLOO. An Indian name for *Phaseolus Mungo.*

MINT. *Mentha.* —, BERGAMOT. *Mentha citrata.* —, BROOK. *Mentha sylvestris.* —, CAT. *Nepeta Cataria.* —, FLEA. *Mentha Pulegium.* —, GARDEN. *Mentha viridis.* —, HORSE. *Mentha sylvestris*; also *Monarda punctata.* —, MOUNTAIN. *Pycnanthemum.* —, PEPPER. *Mentha Piperita.* —, SPEAR. *Mentha viridis.* —, WATER. *Mentha sylvestris.*

MINT TREE. *Prostanthera violacea.*

MINUARTIA. A section of *Alsine*, distinguished by having the calyx indurated at the base when in fruit, and marked with dark ribs. Some authors exclude the species with evident petals, and raise the others to the rank of a genus. [J. T. S.]

MIQUELIA. A genus of *Olacaceæ*, of the tribe *Phytocreneæ*, consisting of two or three woody climbers from tropical Asia, remarkable for the open porous structure of their wood. The leaves are alternate, oblong, and entire or scarcely toothed; the flowers small, diœcious, in little globular heads, the female heads very compact, but the males, owing to the corollas being contracted at the base into a long slender stalk, appear to be umbellate. In both sexes the heads are clustered or in short racemes, above the axils of the leaves. The genus is allied to *Phytocrene* and *Sarcostigma*, but readily distinguished by the male flowers, as well as by the seeds, which have a fleshy albumen, and a rather large embryo with flat but thickish cotyledons.

MIRABELLE. (Fr.) A name applied to candied Plums. — DE CORSE. *Physalis tomentosa.*

MIRABILIS. Handsome herbaceous plants with tuberous roots, belonging to the *Nyctaginaceæ*, and distinguished by a tubular corolla bearing beneath its base a single farinaceous seed invested with the hardened tube of the corolla, and simulating a nut. *M. dichotoma* is called in the West Indies, Four-o'clock Flower, from the fact of its flowers expanding about that time in the evening. *M. Jalapa*, which was supposed at one time to furnish the jalap of commerce, is a showy herbaceous perennial, with large smooth leaves, and handsome flowers collected in clusters at the summit of the stem; it is commonly cultivated under the name of Marvel of Peru. The flowers, which are red white yellow or variegated, are fragrant; they expand as in the rest of the genus, in the evening, and wither on the following morning. *M. longiflora* bears long viscid-tubed white flowers which have the scent of those of the orange tree. French, *Belle de nuit*; German, *Wunderblume.* [C. A. J.]

MIRBELIA. A genus of *Leguminosæ* of the tribe *Podalyrieæ*, remarkable among the *Papilionaceæ* with free stamens, in having the pod divided longitudinally into two cells, as in *Astragalus*. It consists of eight or nine species. Australian shrubs with opposite whorled or rarely alternate leaves, either entire or broadly lobed at the top, and often prickly. The flowers are usually purple or bluish, and often handsome. Three or four species have been introduced into our greenhouses.

MIRLIROT. (Fr.) *Medicago lupulina.*

MIROIR DE VÉNUS. (Fr.) *Specularia Speculum.*

MIRZA. An Indian *Amaranthus.*

MISHMISH. An Arabic name for the Apricot.

MISO. A fatty substance obtained from *Soja hispida.*

MISSEBRŒD. A kind of bread made from the rhizomes of *Calla palustris.*

MIST-FLOWER. *Conoclinium.*

MISTLETO, or MISSELTO. *Viscum album.* —, WEST INDIAN. *Loranthus, Phoradendron,* and *Arceuthobium.*

MITCHAMITOHO. The Abyssinian *Oxalis anthelmintica,* used for the same purposes as *Brayera.*

MITCHELLA. A genus of North American creeping herbs of the *Cinchonaceæ.* The flowers are sessile, sometimes in pairs, and, when this is the case, united by their calyces, as happens in some species of *Lonicera.* The corolla is funnel-shaped, the limb four-lobed, the throat and lobes hairy; stamens four; ovary four-celled. The fruit is succulent, surmounted by the limb of the calyx, with four stones, or, when two fruits are united, as is usually the case, with eight one-seeded stones. *M. repens* is widely distributed in North America. [M. T. M.]

MITELLA. A genus of *Saxifragaceæ,* consisting of perennial herbs, with stalked roundish cordate lobed and crenate radical leaves, and small flowers in a simple spicate raceme, with the bracts mostly suppressed. The calyx is short, bell-shaped, five-cleft; the petals five, pinnatifid; the stamens ten (or five), and the capsule one-celled. A single species, *M. nuda,* occurs in Siberia, and this and the other species occur in North America. [J. T. S.]

MITELLOPSIS. A genus of *Saxifragaceæ,* differing from *Mitella* in having only five stamens, and in the ovules being produced from the sides of the ovary, not merely from the basal portion; so that there seems little doubt that Torrey and Gray are right in merging it in *Mitella.* The character given by some authors, taken from the styles, is incorrect, as they are not united in *Mitella.* [J. T. S.]

MITRÆFORM, or MITRIFORM. Having the form of a mitre, that is to say, conical and not slit on one side; applied to the calyptra of urn-mosses, in opposition to dimidiate.

MITRARIA *coccinea* is the sole representative of a genus of *Gesneraceæ* confined to the island of Chiloe. It is a trailing sub-shrubby plant, with small opposite or sometimes trifoliate leaves, and solitary flowers of a bright scarlet colour. The calyx seems to be double in consequence of two bracts, by which it is supported. The corolla is ventricosely tubular, and the ovary surrounded by a glandular disk. [B. S.]

MITRASACME. A genus of *Loganiaceæ,* consisting of small slender herbs, mostly annuals, some of them not half an inch high. They have opposite leaves, and small flowers, usually terminal, in loose panicles or on long peduncles. As a genus, they are remarkable in the styles, which separate at the base, at least after flowering, whilst they remain united at the top, even till the ripening of the capsule. In this they resemble *Mitreola,* from which they differ chiefly in the parts of the flower being in fours, not in fives. There are about twenty species known from Australia, and three more from tropical Asia.

MITREMYCES. A genus of puff-balls, distinguished by their cartilaginous peridium, which opens by a sinuous thickened mostly bright red orifice, and is capped with a hard deciduous outer coat. There is, moreover, a thin inner sac, which fills only a portion of the peridium, containing the spores mixed with a few threads. The peridium is supported beneath by cartilaginous intricate bodies, which together form a sort of stem, or by fragmentary flakes somewhat like those of shell lac. When fresh, the species sometimes exhibit brilliant tints of vermilion, but sometimes they are yellowish, greenish, or dark brown. The genus was formerly supposed to be peculiar to North America, but it has since occurred in the Sikkim Himalayas, Australia, and Java. The habit is much like that of *Husseia.* [M. J. B.]

MITREOLA. A genus of *Loganiaceæ,* consisting of annual or perennial herbs, with opposite leaves, and small flowers in axillary cymes, the upper ones forming a terminal panicle like *Mitrasacme;* the styles, especially after flowering, are widely spread at the base, and meet at the stigmas; but the parts of the flowers are in fives, not in fours. There are four species, of which two are American, and two East Indian, all weedy-looking plants of no special interest.

MITREWORT. *Mitella.* —, FALSE. *Tiarella.*

MNIARUM. A genus of *Scleranthaceæ,* consisting of small herbs, with opposite exstipulate leaves, resembling *Scleranthus,* from which they are distinguished by having only a single stamen, and by the calyx being always only four-cleft. They are found in Australia, New Zealand, and at the Straits of Magelhaens. [J. T. S.]

MNIOPSIS. A name applied to a genus of *Podostemaceæ,* the species of which are very small, with a stem, or sometimes a lichen-like frond, provided with numerous variously shaped leaves, and with terminal flowers. The fruit, by which it is known, is a smooth cartilaginous capsule, bursting into two unequal valves. [M. T. M.]

MNIUM. A fine genus of mosses, separated from *Bryum* on account of the habit, rather than any essential differences in the fruit. They are perennial, and conspicuous for their large size and broad leaves, occurring in shady situations on the ground, or on rocks. The innovations do not spring generally, as in *Bryum*, from beneath the fruit, but from the base. *M. punctatum* is one of our finest mosses, and is very striking, with its roundish entire thick-margined leaves and handsome fruit. It is dioecious, and by this character distinguished readily from *M. stobglobosum*, which it closely resembles, though a stouter and stronger plant. *M. undulatum*, with long strap-shaped leaves, is common, the ornament of almost every wood; when in fruit, which grows in tufts, but is rare, it is extremely handsome. *Mnium* has its headquarters in Europe; it is rare elsewhere. Two species occur in New Zealand. [M. J. B.]

MO'ACHIBO. A name for the Cotton plant in some of the Pacific islands.

MOACURRA. A name given by Roxburgh to an East Indian tree which proves to be a species of *Chailletia*.

MOC-MAIN. A Chinese name for *Bombax Ceiba*.

MODECCA. A genus of climbing shrubs belonging to the *Papayaceæ*, natives of tropical Asia and Africa, and having entire or palmately lobed leaves, whose stalks are glandular; and axillary branched flowerstalks, some of the branches being tendrils, while others bear small greenish flowers. Altogether the general appearance is not unlike that of bryony. The genus is characterised by the flowers, which are unisexual: the males have four or five stamens inserted into the base of the calyx, the filaments united below into a membrane; and the females have four or five sterile stamens united together so as to form a stalk supporting the ovary, which is one-celled and contains numerous ovules; stigmas three, petallike; capsule three-valved. *M. palmata* and *M. integrifolia* are both said to be used medicinally in tropical Asia. [M. T. M.]

MODEL-WOOD. *Nauclea cordifolia.*

MODIOLA. A genus of *Malvaceæ*, closely allied to *Malva*. The chief difference consists in the column of stamens, which divides above into five separate parcels, each parcel consisting of about five filaments; and in the ovules, of which there are two, attached to the inner angle of each carpel, one above the other, and separated by a transverse partition. The species are lowgrowing herbs, with solitary or twin flowerstalks, bearing violet or red flowers, and are natives of the southern and warmer regions of America. [M. T. M.]

MODIOLIFORM. Shaped like the nave of a wheel, round, depressed, with a very narrow orifice; as the ripe fruit of *Gaultheria*, or the carpels in *Modiola*.

MODUGA. An Indian name for the red dye flowers of *Butea frondosa*.

MOENCHIA. Described as a genus by Ehrenberg, but now reduced to a section of *Cerastium*, distinguished by the divisions of its flowers being nearly always in fours, and by their petals being entire. The name *Moenchia* is also a synonym of *Berteroa*, a genus of cruciferous plants; and has, besides, been applied to the moly section of the genus *Allium*. [A. S.]

MOGORI SAMBAC. (Fr.) *Jasminum Sambac.*

MOHA (or **MOHA DE HONGRIE,** Fr.) *Setaria italica.*

MOHAUT, or **MOHOE.** *Paritium tiliaceum.*

MOHO MOHO. A Peruvian name for *Artanthe elongata.*

MOHRIA. A genus of polypodiaceous ferns of the tribe *Schizæineæ*. It occurs in South Africa and the Mascaren Islands, and consists of a single species, *M. thurifragra*, an elegant bipinnate plant, with a good deal the aspect of *Woodsia obtusa*, but essentially different in the fructification. The sori are oligocarpous, and situate near the revolute margins of the pinnules, while the spore-cases have the manyrayed apical ring characteristic of the schizæineous group. [T. M.]

MÖHRINGIA. A genus of *Caryophyllaceæ*, allied to *Arenaria*, from which it differs in the seeds, which have a strophiole at the hilum. The flowers are pentamerous or tetramerous, with the stamens twice as many as the petals; the styles two or three (rarely four); and the capsule with twice as many teeth as the styles. The common British *M. trinervis*, and a few allied species, agree only in respect to the strophiole of the seed. [J. T. S.]

MOINSON. (Fr.) *Bunium Bulbocastanum.*

MOISISSURE. (Fr.) *Mucor.*

MOKA, or **MOKKA.** An Indian name for Maize.

MOKMOKO. *Rumex abyssinicus.*

MOLÈNE. (Fr.) *Verbascum.*

MOLINIA. A genus of grasses belonging to the tribe *Festuceæ*, the inflorescence of which forms branching panicles; spikelets two to five-flowered; pales acute, entire, membranaceous, and hardening on the seed. Of the three described species, one is a native of Britain, *M. cærulea*, the blue Moor-grass; and this, though of little importance, in an agricultural point of view, where the superior grasses grow freely, becomes valuable in many instances, in consequence of its thriving on bleak wet moors, where the better sorts of grasses refuse to flourish. [D. M.]

MOLLÉ. (Fr.) *Schinus.*

MOLLINEDIA. A genus of *Monimiaceæ*, distinguished from *Citrosma*, chiefly by the perianth falling off from the fruit as it ripens. About twenty South American species or varieties, and an Australian one, have been referred to it. They are trees or shrubs, with coarse usually downy or hairy opposite leaves, and insignificant green flowers in their axils. Several species are highly aromatic like the nutmegs, with which the genus has several points of affinity. It has been described by some botanists under the name of *Tetratome.*

MOLLUGINE. (Fr.) *Mollugo.*

MOLLUGINEÆ. A suborder of *Caryophyllaceæ*, in which the sepals are distinct or nearly so, and alternate with the stamens, when the flowers are isostemonous. In the suborders *Alsineæ* and *Sileneæ*, the stamens are opposite the sepals, when the flowers are isostemonous. By some botanists the *Mollugineæ* are placed as a section of *Portulacaceæ.* [J. H. B.]

MOLLUGO. A genus of *Caryophyllaceæ*, comprising inconspicuous annuals found in the warmer regions of both hemispheres, and having dichotomously branched stems, with verticillate (rarely opposite) leaves, obsolete stipules, and small inconspicuous flowers in axillary dichotomous cymes, or axillary sessile umbels. The species have somewhat the habit of *Galium.* [J. T. S.]

MOLOPOSPERMUM. A genus of the umbellifer order, having the border of the calyx in five leafy divisions; each half of the fruit with five wing-like ribs, the three middle of which are broadest; and in each furrow a single brown vitta. *M. cicutarium*, the only species, is a native of Southern Europe. The name, from the Greek signifying 'stripe' and 'seed,' is given in allusion to the yellow colour of the ripe fruit, contrasted with the brown oil-cells. [G. D.]

MOLUCCELLA. A genus of *Verbenaceæ*, having the calyx somewhat bell-shaped, its border broad with sharp teeth; the corolla with the upper lip entire or bifid, the lower having its middle lobe broad and inversely heart-shaped; and each piece of the fruit with three sharp edges and blunt at the top. The species are annuals, natives of the Eastern Mediterranean zone. The name was given by Linnæus in the belief that the one known to him was a native of the Moluccas. [G. D.]

MOLY. *Allium Moly.* —, DWARF. *Allium Chamæmoly.* —, HOMER'S. *Allium magicum.*

MOLYBDÓS. In Greek compounds = lead-coloured.

MOMEEA. A Nepalese name for Churrus, the resinous exudation of the hemp plant.

MOMORDICA. A small genus of cucur-bitaceous annual or perennial climbing herbaceous plants, with lobed or compound leaves, and solitary white or yellow flowers of separate sexes. They are natives of the tropical and subtropical regions of both hemispheres. The two kinds of flowers are borne on the same or on different plants. Both kinds have a campanulate five-lobed calyx, and five distinct largish petals. The males contain three stamens with short free filaments and zigzag anthers, two of which are two-celled, and the third one-celled; and the females an ovary contracted at the top and bearing a short style with three two-lobed stigmas. Its fruits are fleshy, prickly or warted externally, and burst when ripe, generally with elastic force, into irregular valves. The genus gets its name from *mordeo*, to bite, in reference to the singular jagged or bitten appearance of its seeds. Several species are commonly grown in hothouses, and are very ornamental when in fruit, particularly when the ripe fruits burst and show the seeds covered with their fleshy generally red aril. Of these the handsomest is *M. Charantia*, a widely-spread East Indian species, which has bright orange-yellow oblong fruits, from four to six inches long, tapering to both ends and covered all over with little wart-like protuberances, some irregular and others in lines along which they split when ripe. *M. mixta*, another Indian species, has large creamy flowers, and red fruits shaped like a bullock's heart, and covered with little triangular prickles; and *M. Balsamina*, pretty little orange-coloured warted fruits about as large as walnuts. [A. S.]

MOMORDIQUE. (Fr.) *Ecbalium agresta.*

MONACHANTHUS. The name formerly given to certain orchids, now very properly regarded as forming a section of *Catasetum*, from the type of which they are distinguished by their column having no cirrhi at the top. The untenableness of the genus is abundantly proved by the occasional occurrence of plants which bear upon the same spike the flowers of a species of *Catasetum*, those of a so-called species of *Monachanthus*, and those of a species of another spurious genus named *Myanthus* —three genera upon one plant! Well indeed might it be said, that 'such cases shake to the foundation all our ideas of the stability of genera and species.' [A. S.]

MONADELPHOUS. Having all the stamens united by their filaments into a tube.

MONARDA. A genus of herbaceous plants belonging to the labiate order, and distinguished by their ringent corolla, the upper lip of which is very narrow and conceals the two anthers. The leaves are downy and variously notched, and the flowers, which grow in whorls and heads, are made conspicuous by their coloured calyces and bracts. *M. didyma*, called Oswego Tea from the use sometimes made of its leaves in America, bears bright scarlet flowers and bracts, and the leaves emit a grateful refreshing odour resembling that of mint or sage. —, SMALL, *Pycnanthemum Monardella.* [Ö. A. J.]

MONESES. The *Pyrola uniflora* of authors, a subalpine woodland plant belonging to the *Ericaceæ*, and separated from *Pyrola* on account of the different structure of the stamens and stigma: the cells of the former being furnished each with a tubular horn opening at the end, the stigma radiated, and the capsule opening from the summit. *M. grandiflora* has creeping roots, short reclining leafy stems, roundish much-veined evergreen leaves, and an erect stalk three inches long usually bearing one concave bract and a solitary drooping large elegant white or slightly reddish flower, nearly an inch broad, with the sweet and powerful scent of the lily of the valley. It is rare in Britain, but has a wide geographical range both in the eastern and western hemispheres. [C. A. J.]

MONETIA. A Cape of Good Hope shrub, named in compliment to Monet de laMarck, an eminent French naturalist. It constitutes a genus of *Aquifoliaceæ*, with the branches four-cornered, the leaves opposite, undivided and leathery like those of the holly, but with two spines proceeding from the axils; and the small flowers greenish, with a bell-shaped three or four-cleft calyx, a corolla of four linear reflexed petals, four stamens inserted on to the receptacle, and a fleshy one or two-seeded fruit of the size of a pear. [M. T. M.]

MONEY-FLOWER. *Linaria biennis.*

MONEYWORT. *Lysimachia Nummularia*; also *Anagallis tenella, Thymus Nummularius, Taverniera Nummularia,* and *Dioscorea Nummularia.* —, CORNISH. *Sibthorpia europæa.*

MONGÊTTE. (Fr.) *Dolichos melanophthalmus.*

MONILIFORM. Necklace-shaped; cylindrical or terete, and contracted at regular intervals.

MONIMIACEÆ. (*Monimiads.*) A natural order of monochlamydeous dicotyledons belonging to Lindley's menispermal alliance of diclinous Exogens. Trees or shrubs, with opposite exstipulate leaves, and unisexual flowers. Perianth somewhat globose, in one or more rows, divided at the border. Male flowers with indefinite stamens, covering the whole interior of the perianth, the filaments often with two scales at the base; females with several superior ovaries, enclosed within the perianth tube, each with one style and one stigma, and a solitary pendulous anatropal ovule. Fruit consisting of several achenes enclosed within the enlarged perianth. They are natives chiefly of South America and Australia. The bark and leaves are aromatic and fragrant; and the succulent fruit of some is eaten. There are eight genera, and about forty species. Examples: *Monimia, Boldoa.* [J. H. B.]

MONIMIA. A genus w ch gives its name to the order *Monimiaceæ*, and is distinguished in the order, by the carpels containing each one pendulous ovule, and being enclosed as they ripen in the enlarged succulent berry-like tube of the perianth. The genus consists of three species natives of the Mauritius, trees or shrubs, with opposite entire leaves, more or less hairy or downy, and inconspicuous yellowish fragrant flowers, in axillary racemes or panicles.

MONIZIA. The generic name of a curious somewhat arborescent plant of the order *Umbelliferæ*, found in the island called Deserta Grande, one of three uninhabited islands lying south-east of Madeira. *M. edulis,* the Carrot-tree, has a crooked woody stem one to four feet high, gouty at the base, and terminating in a tuft of decompound, broadly triangular, fern-like leaves, which, including their stalks, are from one to three feet in length; the flowers are small, white, and disposed in compound many-rayed umbels furnished with partial and universal involucres of entire leaflets. Mr. Lowe, who described the plant—dedicating it to M. Moniz, a botanist of Madeira—saw it growing far down in fissures of perpendicular cliffs 1,200 to 1,500 feet high, and remarks that it can only be gathered by expert cragsmen let down by ropes for the purpose. The orchil-gatherers and fishermen who resort to the island, eat the roots when prevented by weather from getting better food from Madeira: therefore the plant is becoming scarce. The roots have long curved horn-like divisions, black outwardly, farinaceous and white within, and much more fibrous than those of a carrot. They are eaten raw or boiled—when raw tasting like earth-nuts, and stringy and insipid when boiled. The Portuguese call it Rock Carrot, Cenoula da Rocha.

The nearest relationship of the genus is with *Melanoselinum,* from which it differs at first sight in the finely divided foliage, but more especially in the fruits, which are dorsally compressed, with fourteen ribs—the ribs of a corky consistence and entire, whereas in *Melanoselinum* they are thin and toothed. Under the four dorsal secondary ribs of each carpel (not under all) are vittæ, and two broader than the others on the inner face of the carpel. The plant is cultivated at Kew. [A. A. B.]

MONJOLI. *Cordia.*

MONKEY BREAD. The fruit of *Adansonia digitata.*

MONKEY-FLOWER. *Mimulus.*

MONKEY-POT. The woody pericarp of *Lecythis Ollaria.*

MONKEY-PUZZLE. *Araucaria imbricata.*

MONK-FLOWER. *Monachanthus.*

MONKSHOOD. *Aconitum Napellus*; also *Dielytra Cucullaria.*

MONNAIE DU PAPE, or MONNAYÈRE. (Fr.) *Lunaria annua.*

MONNIERIA, sometimes written *Moniera*, in honour of William le Monnier, Professor of Botany in the Jardin du Roi at Paris, is the name of a genus of *Rutaceæ*, represented by a single species, *M. trifoliata*, a native of the sea-shore of tropical America. The calyx consists of five unequal sepals; corolla two-lipped, the upper entire, the lower four-lobed; stamens five, two fertile and three sterile joined together; ovaries five; fruit capsular five-valved, each carpel with one seed. [M. T. M.]

MONNINA. A genus of *Polygaleæ*, consisting of herbs mostly erect, shrubs, or even small trees, with alternate or scattered entire leaves, and flowers usually rather small, in terminal or rarely axillary racemes or spikes. The calyx has the two large wing-like sepals of *Polygala*, and the stamens are nearly the same; but the corolla is very different, having, besides the large petal called the keel, only two small ones adhering to it on the inner side, not overlapping it; and the fruit is indehiscent, either a fleshy drupe, or surrounded by a winged border. There are about fifty species, all natives of South America, and chiefly from the Andes, extending from South Chili almost to Mexico. The bark of the root of some of the Peruvian species, especially *M. polystachya* and *salicifolia*, is moulded into balls and used both medicinally and as a substitute for soap, and also by the silversmiths of Huanaco for cleaning and polishing wrought silver.

MONNOYÈRE. (Fr.) *Lysimachia Nummularia*; also *Thlaspi arvense.*

MONO. In Greek compounds = one; as *monanthos*, one-flowered.

MONOCARPOUS. Producing fruit but once in its life, as an annual, or such perennials as the American aloe, which always perishes after flowering.

MONOCHÆTUM. Shrubs or undershrubs of the order *Melastomaceæ*, natives mostly of mountainous regions from Mexico to Columbia and Peru, and numbering about twenty species. They have three to seven-nerved leaves, with the nerves impressed so as to give the upper surface a channelled appearance, and purple or violet flowers. Their floral envelopes are in fours, and their stamens double as many and alternately unequal, with the filaments complanate, and those of the small or sterile anthered ones longer than the others. The anthers are subulate and one-pored at their acute apices, and have the connective extended into a tail behind them. *M. ensiferum* is a beautiful greenhouse plant. [A. S.]

MONOCHILUS. A small East Indian genus of orchids, belonging to the *Physurideæ*, and having the habit of *Goodyera.* Its principal characteristics consist in the side sepals being free beneath the lip, and the hind one agglutinated to the petals; in the lip adhering to the column, being without a spur at its base, and having a membranous split limb much larger than the sepals; and in its short terete column having a glandular swelling on each side, but no finger-like processes as in the allied genus *Cheirostylis.* [A. S.]

MONOCHLAMYDEÆ. A subclass of dicotyledons, containing plants having either a single floral envelope (a calyx) or none. It includes many natural orders of dicotyledons in which the parts of the flower are incomplete, and in which the flowers are unisexual, and corresponds nearly to the *Apetalæ* of Jussieu. [J. H. B.]

MONOCHLAMYDEOUS. Having but one floral envelope.

MONOCHORIA. A genus of *Pontederaceæ*, differing from *Pontederia* in the three-celled and many-seeded capsule, and from *Eichornia* in the stamens being inserted at the bottom of the tube of the perianth, the anterior one longer than the others. They are aquatic tropical herbs. *M. vaginalis*, an Indian plant with oblong-lanceolate cordate leaves and hollow leafstalks, is eaten when young as a potherb. It is also used as a native remedy in liver complaints and disorders of the stomach; when chewed it is considered as a remedy for toothache, and it is used internally and externally for other complaints. [J. T. S.]

MONOCLINOUS. Having the two sexes in the same flower; hermaphrodite.

MONOCOTYLEDONS. (*Endogenæ, Endogens, Amphibrya.*) One of the primary classes in the natural system. The plants which it comprises have a cellular and vascular system, the latter consisting partly of elastic spiral vessels. The woody stem, as in palms, is usually more or less cylindrical, simple, and unbranched; there is no true separable bark, no concentric zones, and no true pith. The wood is endogenous, i.e. it increases by additions which first tend towards the centre and then curve outwards in an interlacing manner towards the circumference, where much hard ligneous matter is deposited, so as to make the exterior the hardest part. The development of the stem usually takes place by a single central and terminal bud, but occasionally lateral buds are produced, and at times the stem is hollow. The leaves are parallel-veined, except in the subclass Dictyogens, where a kind of reticulation is visible. The parts of the flower are arranged in a ternary manner, and they are in some cases petaloid, sometimes scaly or glumaceous. The ovules are contained in an ovary, and are fertilised by the application of the pollen to the stigma. The embryo has one cotyledon, and the germination is endorhizal. The subclasses are: *Dictyogenæ, Petaloideæ* or *Floridæ*, and *Glumiferæ* or *Glumaceæ.* [J. H. B.]

MONOCOTYLEDONOUS. Having only one cotyledon, or if two are present, then having one much smaller than the other, and on a different level.

MONOCYSTIS. A genus of *Zingibera-ceæ*, represented by a Chinese herbaceous plant, with lance-shaped leaves, and flowers in a terminal cluster. The latter have a tubular calyx contracted at the throat, the limb short, three-lobed; a corolla with a short tube, and the outer limb-segments linear and hooded at the point, the inner lateral ones very small, and the central one or lip large roundish and crisped at the margin; a linear filament; and an inferior one-celled ovary, with one erect ovule. The style passes between the lobes of the anther, and terminates in a fleshy concave stigma. —[M. T. M.]

MONODICHLAMYDEOUS. Having indifferently either a calyx only, or both calyx and corolla.

MONODORA. Until recently only a single species belonging to this genus of *Anonaceæ* was known, but a second has been found in western tropical Africa. The original species, *M. Myristica*, was described from specimens obtained from Jamaica, where it was supposed to have been introduced from South America, but there is more reason to believe that it was taken there by the negroes from Western Africa. The genus has hitherto been regarded as anomalous among its congeners, on account of its ovary being supposed to consist of a single carpel, with the numerous ovules distributed over the whole of its inner surface; but it has lately been shown that it does not essentially differ from the rest of the order, the ovary being in reality compound, consisting of numerous carpels united together, the placentas becoming confluent, and giving the appearance of the ovules being irregularly dispersed over the whole surface. The Jamaica species is a small tree about fifteen feet high, and the African a shrub seven feet high. Their flowers are solitary, large, and sweet-scented, and are characterised by their three outer petals being large and spreading with crisped or waved edges, and the three inner ones heart-shaped and erect, meeting together at their apices. The fruit is perfectly smooth, nearly globular, and about the size of an orange, containing a number of seeds packed close together with great regularity in the midst of a quantity of pulp.

The outer petals of the flowers of *M. Myristica* are of a bright yellow colour, variegated with purple spots, and the inner whitish on the outside and downy, but shining and pale yellow with crimson spots inside. Its seeds contain a quantity of aromatic oil which imparts to them the odour and flavour of nutmegs; and as they likewise possess the same kind of interior structure, they are commonly called Jamaica or American Nutmegs, or Calabash Nutmegs from the entire fruit resembling a small calabash. [A. S.]

MONŒCIOUS. Having male and female organs in different flowers on the same plant—thus: expressed by signs. ♂ → ♀.

MONOGAMIA (adj. MONOGAMIC). Having flowers distinct from each other, and not collected in a capitulum.

MONOGRAMMA. A small group of minute graminiform or rachiform ferns, with simple or forked fronds, and having a non-indusiate line of spore-cases near the apex of the frond, the receptacle consisting of a portion of the costa. In one set the sori lie in a longitudinal depression of the graminiform fronds; while in another they occupy a vaginiform expansion of the rachiform fronds. They occur in the tropics of the old and new worlds. [T. M.]

MONOGYNOUS. Having but one style, even although many carpels be present.

MONOICOUS. The same as Monœcious.

MONOLEPIS. A genus of *Chenopodiaceæ* from North America and Arctic Siberia, with polygamous monandrous flowers, and two styles united at the base, destitute of perianth but furnished with an herbaceous scale. The utricle is compressed with a vertical seed, having a subcrustaceous integument. It is a branched annual, with scattered stalked lanceolate, often trifid leaves, and axillary glomerules of small green dry flowers. [J. T. S.]

MONOLOPHUS. A genus of *Zingiberaceæ*, represented by an Indian herbaceous plant, with fibrous roots, oblong leaves, flowers in a terminal spike, enclosed at the base within a bract. The calyx is tubular, the tube of the corolla elongated, its outer segments narrow equal, the inner ones wider, two equal, and a third, the lip, larger and cleft; filament prolonged beyond the anther into a reflexed strap-like body; ovary three-celled. [M. T. M.]

MONOLOPIA. A genus of *Compositæ* of the tribe *Anthemideæ*, consisting of two Californian woolly annuals, with narrow entire or scarcely toothed leaves, and solitary terminal flower-heads yellow and radiating. The involucral scales are in a single row and united below, the receptacle convex and naked, and the achenes without pappus, the inner ones apparently abortive. One species, *M. major*, is rather showy.

MONOPETALOUS. Having all the petals united by their edges.

MONOPHYLLOUS. Having only one leaf, or several leaves united by their edges into one.

MONOPLOCA. A genus of *Cruciferæ* from South-west Australia, with narrowly linear leaves, and a compressed suborbicular deeply bifid pouch, two-valved, with the valves winged on the back, and each cell containing one seed. [J. T. S.]

MONOPSIS. A genus of *Lobeliaceæ*, consisting of perennial herbaceous plants, natives of the Cape of Good Hope and of Australia, having weak prostrate stems, and perfect or occasionally diœcious flowers, borne on long axillary stalks or in terminal tufts. The tube of the corolla is slit along its upper edge, its limb divided into five nearly regular segments : hence the name of the genus, implying uniformity, as irregular flowers are most common in this order. *M. Speculum* is a pretty little plant with blue flowers. [M. T. M.]

MONOPTEROUS. Having one wing.

MONOPYRENOUS. Containing one stone.

MONOS. A Spanish name for *Melicocca bijuga*.

MONOSEPALOUS. Having the sepals all united into one body by their edges.

MONOSTICHOUS. Arranged in one row.

MONOTAXIS. A genus of *Euphorbiaceæ* of the tribe *Crotoneæ*, allied in structure to *Jatropha*, but very different in appearance. It consists of two or three small Australian shrubs or undershrubs with narrow almost heath-like leaves, and small flowers in little terminal or axillary cymes, the central flower usually female, the others males. The latter have small white petals, the females have none.

MONOTOCA. A genus of *Epacridaceæ*, having a five-lobed calyx with two bracts at the base, a funnel-shaped corolla with five smooth lobes, stamens shorter than the corolla, and a lobed cup-shaped disk. The seed-vessel is a nearly globose berry containing a single seed. They are small trees or shrubs, natives of New South Wales and Tasmania, and have oblong or lanceolate striated entire leaves, generally grey on the under side, and small white often diœcious flowers borne on axillary or terminal spikes. [R. H.]

MONOTROPACEÆ. (*Fir-rapes.*) A natural order of corollifloral dicotyledons belonging to Lindley's erical alliance of hypogynous Exogens. Parasitic plants of a brown colour, allied to *Pyrolaceæ*, but differing in the scaly stems, in the longitudinal dehiscence of their anthers, and in their minute embryo being at the *apex* of the albumen. They are considered by many as a suborder of *Ericaceæ*, from which their habit, their antherine dehiscence, loose testa, and minute embryo separate them. Chiefly parasitic on firs in Europe, Asia, and North America. The six genera comprise about ten species. [J. H. B.]

MONOTROPA. The typical genus of *Monotropaceæ*, distinguished by the covering of the flower being single and deeply five-cleft ; and the stamens ten, emitting their pollen by transverse openings near the middle of the anther. The species are parasitical on the roots of trees. [G. D.]

MONSONIA. A genus of *Geraniaceæ* from the Cape of Good Hope, distinguished by having five equal sepals, five equal petals, and fifteen stamens disposed in five bundles or all united. The genus is divided into three sections. *Odontopetalum*, consisting of herbs, with alternate lobed or multifid leaves, and one-flowered peduncles with an involucre in the middle of each ; petals oblong, toothed at the apex; stamens in five bundles. *Holopetalum*, herbs with alternate oval toothed leaves, and one-flowered peduncles with two or two-flowered with four bracts ; petals obovate crenulate ; stamens in five bundles, *Sarcocaulon*, plants with shrubby fleshy spiny stems, alternate entire or toothed leaves, one-flowered peduncles with two bracts in the middle ; petals entire ; stamens monadelphous. *M. spinosa* or *Burmanni*, which belongs to the last section, has a stem which burns like a torch, and emits an agreeable odour. [J. T. S.]

MONSTERA. A curious genus of tropical American herbs belonging to the *Araceæ*. They are climbing plants, with stalked leaves, the stalks invested at the base by a sheath, the blades entire or perforated with holes, and ultimately divided at the margin. The leaf-buds are placed at some distance above the axils of the leaves. The spathe is deciduous, the spadix sessile, with female flowers below, hermaphrodite ones above ; stamens of the upper flowers with flattened filaments, and two-celled anthers, opening by a short lateral slit ; ovary two-celled, each cell with two inverted ovules; style short, conical. The fruits are succulent, fused together, and ultimately casting off their outer skin ; and the seeds are compressed, imbedded in pulp.

M. Adansonii, more generally known by the old name of *Dracontium pertusum*, is frequently cultivated in hothouses for the singularity of its leaves, which appear as if holes had been cut through them at irregular intervals. The plant is reputed to possess caustic properties. M. Trécul, who has examined the mode of formation of the holes in the leaves, says that they are the result of changes that take place in the tissue of the leaf whereby ultimately the outer skin or epidermis becomes torn, and a hole is produced, the size of which depends on the age of the leaf at the time of its formation, and that they have nothing to do with the imperfect development of lobes as might at first sight be supposed. *M. deliciosa*, a Mexican species, has a succulent fruit, with a luscious pine-apple flavour. [M. T. M.]

MONSTROSITY. Any unusual kind of development, or absence of development.

MONTAGNITES. A genus of *Fungi* bearing affinities on the one side to *Agaricus*, and on the other to the higher *Gasteromycetes*, from which it differs in having regular gills. There is a universal veil continuous with the cuticle of the pileus, which as it bursts exposes a large portion of the dry gills, much in the same way as the gills on a smaller scale are exposed in *Agaricus pusillus*. The genus occurs in the south of Europe, in North Africa, in the steppes of Asia, and in Texas. [M. J. B.]

MONT-ETNA. (Fr.) *Tulipa turcica*.

MONT-JOLI DE CAYENNE. (Fr.) *Lantana involucrata*.

MONTE-AU-CIEL. (Fr.) *Polygonum orientale.*

MONTEZUMA. A Mexican sterculiaceous tree, said to be very handsome, but only known by descriptions made from Mocino and Sesse's Mexican drawings. It appears to form a distinct genus of the tribe *Bombaceæ.*

MONTIA. A minute aquatic belonging to the order *Portulaceæ.* The whole plant, which rarely exceeds five or six inches in length, is succulent, and furnished with opposite spathulate leaves, in the axils of which, near the summit of the stem, are a few very small flowers, having five petals united into a tube which is split on one side. *M. fontana,* Water Blinks, or Water Chickweed, is common on the banks of streams, especially on a gravelly soil, and has, like many other aquatic plants, a wide geographical range.　　[C. A. J.]

MONTINIA. A genus of onagrads, distinguished by having stamens and pistils on separate plants, the flowers of each having the border of the calyx four-toothed; the corolla in four divisions; the style two-cleft at the apex; and the seed-vessel two-valved, two-celled, and crowned by the teeth of the calyx. *M. acris,* the only species, is a Cape shrub, with acute fleshy and alternate leaves. It was named in honour of Montin, a Swedish botanist.　　[G. D.]

MOOCHERUS. A gum-resin obtained in India from *Bombax malabaricum.*

MOOJANEE. An Indian name for *Phaseolus trilobus*

MOON-FLOWER. *Chrysanthemum segetum*; also *Ipomœa bona-nox.*

MOONG. Indian varieties of Gram.

MOON-PENNY. *Chrysanthemum Leucanthemum.*

MOON-SEED. *Menispermum.*

MOONWORT. *Rumex Lunaria*; also *Botrychium Lunaria.*

MOONYAH. An Indian name for the fibre of *Arundo Karka.*

MOOQL. An Arab name for Gum Bdellium.

MOORBALLS. The common name of *Conferva ægagropila,* an *Alga* which forms compact sponge-like balls at the bottom of freshwater lakes. The whole plant consists of a mass of branched articulated green threads constricted at the joints somewhat resembling the hair balls found in the stomachs of ruminants. The moorballs exhibit the normal growth of a particular *Alga,* but similar substances are found occasionally on the sea-coast, which derive their origin from the action of the waves, exactly as masses of human hair are sometimes rolled by the waves into compact rounded masses. Moorballs are sometimes used as pen-wipers.　　[M. J. B.]

MOOR-BERRY. *Oxycoccus palustris.*

MOORCROFTIA. A little-known genus of *Convolvulaceæ,* containing two species from Penang. They are twining undershrubs, with opposite petiolate leaves, and axillary peduncles bearing several flowers; the calyx consists of five sepals; the corolla, which has been seen only in the unopened flower, is then densely hairy; the berry is one-celled, very rarely two-celled, and one-seeded.　　[W. C.]

MOORWORT. *Andromeda polifolia.*

MOOSE-WOOD. *Dirca.*

MOOSKDANA. An Indian name for *Abelmoschus moschatus.*

MOOTCHIE-WOOD. A light soft Indian wood, the produce of *Erythrina indica.*

MOOTHA. An Indian name for *Cyperus rotundus* or *hexastachyus.*

MOOTHE, or METHA. Indian names for Fenugreek seed.

MOPHA. *Bassia latifolia.*

MOQUILEA. A genus of *Chrysobalaneæ,* now limited to two or three tropical American trees, distinguished from *Coupia* by their short campanulate calyx; and from *Chrysobalanus* by the stamens inserted all round the ovary, by the racemose inflorescence, and probably also by the fruit, which is, however, insufficiently known. Several species with a tubular base to the calyx, referred to *Moquilea* by some botanists, belong to *Coupia.*

MOQUINIA. A genus of *Compositæ,* of the tribe *Mutisieæ,* differing from *Gochnatia* chiefly in its diœcious flower-heads. It consists of three or four Brazilian shrubs, the underside of whose leaves is white cottony, and whose inflorescence consists of small racemose or paniculate flowerheads.

MOR. The Malay name for Myrrh.

MORACEÆ. (*Sycoideæ, Morads.*) A natural order of monochlamydeous dicotyledons, belonging to Lindley's urtical alliance of dielinous Exogens. By many botanists it is considered a suborder of *Artocarpaceæ.* Trees or shrubs with a milky juice; leaves commonly rough and lobed; flowers small unisexual, collected in heads spikes or catkins. The calyx of the male flowers is either wanting, or three to four-parted, with three to four stamens, opposite its segments, the anthers opening lengthwise. The female flowers have three four or sometimes five sepals, and a one-celled ovary, with solitary pendulous ovules. Fruit a succulent sorosis or syconus. Natives of temperate and tropical climates. The plants abound in milky juice yielding caoutchouc; their fruit is often bland and nutritious, while their bark yields fibres. The mulberries, *Morus nigra* and *alba,* belong to the order; as does *Ficus Carica* the common fig, *Sycomorus antiquorum* the Sycomore fig, and *Broussonetia papyrifera* the paper mulberry. Various species of *Ficus* and *Urostigma* supply india-rubber. There are twenty-two genera, and about 200 species. [J. H. B.]

MORA. The Mora of Guiana, *M. excelsa*, a gigantic timber tree, forms a genus of *Leguminosæ*, of the tribe *Cæsalpinieæ*. Extensive forests of it exist in British Guiana and the island of Trinidad, it being one of those trees which grow together in large masses to the exclusion of every other kind. It grows from a hundred and thirty to a hundred and fifty feet high; and as the trunks are branchless to near the top, logs three or four feet square and nearly a hundred feet long are obtainable exclusive of sap-wood. Its wood is exceedingly tough and close-grained, and, under the name of Mora timber, is now imported into this country in considerable quantities for the use of our ship-builders, it being one of the few timbers admitted into Lloyd's list of ship-building woods. One of its most valuable properties is its non-liability to splinter, even rivalling oak in this respect, being, in fact, one of the toughest woods known. The Mora tree has large pinnate leaves, and small flowers in dense compound spikes about eight or ten inches long. These have a bell-shaped calyx, five or six equal petals, and ten or twelve long stamens, every alternate one of which is sterile; these are followed by hard woody pods, containing a solitary large kidney-shaped seed. The bark of the Mora is astringent and useful for tanning, although it does not contain sufficient tannin to enable it to be substituted for oak bark; and the seeds are used by the Indians as food in seasons of scarcity. [A. S.]

MORÆA. A numerous South African genus of *Iridaceæ*, closely related to *Iris* itself, and containing many species with very brilliant sweet-scented flowers. All its species have two-ranked sword-shaped leaves, and their flower-stalks have long slightly overlapping spathes. The perianth has three broad spreading or reflexed outer segments, and three narrower inner ones. The three stamens are distinct; the style slender, and bearing three petal-like bifid or rarely multifid stigmas opposite the stamens. [A. S.]

MORASS-WEED. *Ceratophyllum demersum.*

MORCHELLA. A genus of ascomycetous *Fungi*, distinguished by a deeply pitted naked head supported on a peduncle. The depressions are sometimes regular, but occasionally they assume the appearance of mere furrows with wrinkle-like interstices. The common Morel is a familiar example. The genus occurs both in the north and south hemispheres, but does not seem to like a very hot climate. The fructification is very like that of *Helvella.* [M. J. B.]

MORÉE DEMI-DEUIL. (Fr.) *Moræa lugens.* — ENGAINÉE. *Moræa Northiana.*

MOREL. The common name of *Morchella esculenta*, which, under a variety of forms, occurs in various parts of the world.

It is occasionally plentiful in this country, but the greater part of what is sold by the oilmen comes from Germany. A large quantity is collected in Kashmir. As it dries very readily, and may be kept for some time, it is much used by cooks to flavour gravies. It is also dressed in various ways when fresh, and makes an excellent dish if stuffed with finely minced white meat. When plentiful it may be advantageously employed instead of mushrooms to make ketchup. Morels are particularly fond of

Morchella esculenta.

burnt soil, and the collection of them is so profitable to the peasants in Germany, that they were formerly in the habit of setting fire to the woods to encourage their growth, till the practice was made punishable by a special law. *M. semilibera* may be known from the common Morel by the border being quite free for some distance. It has a bad reputation, and requires, therefore, some caution in its use. [M. J. B.]

MOREL, GREAT. *Atropa Belladonna.* —, PETTY. *Solanum nigrum.*

MORELLA. A variety of cherry.

MORELLE. (Fr.) *Solanum.* — À GRAPPES, or GRANDE DES INDES. *Phytolacca.*

MORÈNE. (Fr.) *Hydrocharis.*

MORENIA. A genus of palms confined to the mountains of Peru, allied to *Hyophorbe* and *Kunthia*, and composed of two species, *M. fragrans* and *M. Pöppigiana*, both of which have a thin unarmed reed-like trunk, terminal pinnatisect leaves, diœcious white or yellow flowers and a one-seeded berry. [B. S.]

MORETTIA. A genus of *Cruciferæ*, containing an Egyptian herb, with grey stellately pubescent obovate leaves, and erect racemes, the pedicels with leaf-like bracts at the base exceeding the flowers; pouch dehiscent, oblong, slightly compressed, with an oblong partition and short style; valves concave, produced within into a small partition separating the seeds, which are round. [J. T. S.]

MORGALLE. African hemp, the fibre of *Sanseviera guineensis.*

MORGELINE. *Veronica hederacea.*

MORGINATE. (Fr.) *Elatine.*

MORIA. The parts of a flower in general; as *pentamorius*, which signifies all the parts being arranged in fives.

MORICANDIA. A genus of *Cruciferæ*, containing about half a dozen species, natives of Southern Europe, Northern Africa, and Western Asia. These are glaucous smooth herbs, sometimes shrubby at the base, with entire stem-clasping or pinnately cut leaves, and large purple or rose flowers, succeeded by long narrow siliquiform pods with flat or keeled valves, and either beakless or with a compressed sometimes one-seeded beak, ending in a short style, the stigmas united into an erect cone. [A. S.]

MORILLE COMESTIBLE. (Fr.) *Morchella esculenta.*

MORINA. A genus of *Dipsaceæ*, distinguished by the tubular irregular corolla and four stamens either didynamous or united in two pairs. It consists of four or five species natives of the Levant and Central Asia. They are erect thistle-like herbs with oblong prickly-toothed leaves, and pink flowers in dense whorls in the axils of the upper short floral leaves. *M. longifolia*, from the Himalaya, has been introduced into European gardens.

MORINDA. A genus of *Cinchonaceæ*, containing between thirty and forty species almost confined to the tropics of Asia and Africa. A few of them are climbing plants, but the greater portion are small trees or shrubs, usually having opposite but occasionally whorled leaves, with thin entire stipules united at the base within the leafstalks; and flowers in dense heads on stalks produced either singly or several together in the axils of the leaves or at the ends of the branches. The fruit is fleshy, and consists of the berries of the several flowers in a head united into one compound berry.

The roots and bark of several species of *Morinda* are useful in their native countries on account of their dyeing properties, but their colours are not very permanent. Amongst those most commonly used, the following are all small trees common in India and very closely allied to each other: *M. citrifolia*, used in Madras for dyeing red turbans; *M. tinctoria*, the Ach root; and *M. bracteata*, the bark of which contains two colours, a red and a yellow changing to crimson upon the application of alkalies, but though commonly used in India, the colours obtained from it are very dull. *M. umbellata*, also used for dyeing, has climbing stems which the Cingalese employ instead of ropes for tying fences. The fruits of several species are eatable, but insipid. [A. S.]

MORINGACEÆ. (*Moringads.*) A natural order of calyciﬂoral dicotyledons, belonging to Lindley's violal alliance of hypogynous Exogens. Trees with bipinnate or tripinnate stipuled leaves, allied to leguminous plants; calyx five-parted; petals five

rather unequal, the upper one ascending; stamens eight or ten, perigynous, the filaments slightly petaloid, callous, and hairy at the base, the anthers simple, one-celled disk lining the tube of the calyx; ovary superior, stipitate, one-celled, the ovules attached to parietal placentas; style filiform; stigma simple. Fruit a pod-like three-valved capsule; seeds numerous, half buried in the spongy substance of the valves, sometimes winged. Natives of the East Indies and Arabia, with pungent and aromatic properties. [J. H. B.]

MORINGA. The only genus of *Moringaceæ*, and having, therefore, the characters of the order. It is a peculiar genus, having the general appearance of *Leguminosæ*, from which it differs in the odd petal being inferior, the anthers one-celled, the ovary tricarpellary, and the ovules anatropal. There are three species, natives of North Africa, the warm parts of Western Asia, and the East Indies. The seeds of *M. pterygosperma*, the Horse-radish tree, are winged, and are called Ben-nuts; from them is procured a fluid oil used by watchmakers, and called oil of Ben; the root is pungent and stimulant, and resembles horse-radish in its taste. [J. H. B.]

MORISONIA. The name of a West Indian tree belonging to the *Capparidaceæ*, and so called in memory of Robert Morison, Professor of Botany at Oxford in 1683. The flowers are white, axillary, somewhat tufted, with a distended calyx, corolla of four blunt petals, numerous stamens combined into a tube below, and a long-stalked ovary. Fruit succulent. [M. T. M.]

MORITA. A Spanish name for *Maclura tinctoria.*

MORITZIA. A genus of *Boraginaceæ* allied to *Anchusa*, but differing in its exserted stamens, and in the scales which close the throat of the corolla being fringed. It is a Brazilian herb, with the habit of a *Myosotis*, the radical leaves very large, those of the stem much smaller ciliated; flowers in scorpioid racemes, small, with a funnel-shaped corolla; nuts shining, often by abortion reduced to one. [J. T. S.]

MORMODES. The species of *Mormodes* when not in flower are undistinguishable from *Catasetum*, having the same fusiform stems clothed to the base with the remnants of fallen leaves, and the same plicate sheathing-based leaves. The chief technical points by which it is distinguished are the want of cirrhi upon the column; the lip being membranous, turned upwards, and often shaped something like a saddle; and the pollen-masses being four in number, connate in pairs, fixed to a thick caudicle which adheres to a fleshy gland. About a dozen or fifteen species are known, all of them natives of America from Mexico to Caraccas. Most of them have at one time or other been cultivated in the orchid houses of this country, where they are grown more for their singularity than for their beauty. [A. S.]

MORNA. A genus of *Compositæ*, allied to *Helichrysum*, and characterised chiefly by the long beak of its achenes, crowned by a pappus of simple scabrous bristles. It has since been included, with *Leptorhynchus*, in the older genus *Waitzia*. Some of these beautiful everlastings have been introduced into our gardens from Swan River, e. g. *M. nitida* with golden involucral scales, and *M. nivea* with white ones.

MORNING GLORY. A name applied to certain species of *Ipomœa* and *Pharbitis*, e. g. *P. hispidus*, the Convolvulus major of gardens.

MOROCARPUS. A name given by Siebold and Zuccarini to a genus of *Urticaceæ* consisting of a few Japanese and East Asiatic shrubs or undershrubs which have been since referred to the older genus *Villebrunea*.

MORONOBEA. A small genus of *Clusiaceæ*, confined to the West Indies, Guiana, and Brazil. Three or four species have been described, but they are probably not all distinct. They are large slender-stemmed trees, with branching heads of dense foliage, the leaves being of a lance-shaped or elliptical form and feather-veined, and the scarlet flowers borne in umbel-like heads. Each flower has two outer bracts, a calyx of five sepals, a corolla of five petals twisted partly round each other, fifteen or twenty stamens united into a three or five-cleft tube, and a five-celled ovary with two or several ovules in each cell.

M. coccinea, the Hog Gum tree, is a lofty straight-stemmed tree attaining ninety or a hundred feet in height, with horizontally spreading smooth branches, and thick entire glossy leaves. A fluid pellucid juice exudes from incisions in the trunk, and after a short exposure hardens into a yellow resin resembling Burgundy pitch in appearance. It is said that in Jamaica hogs, when wounded, rub the injured part against the tree, so as to smear themselves with the resin, which possesses vulnerary properties, and hence it is called Hog Gum. The resin has been employed medicinally as a substitute for balsam of copaiba, and in Jamaica pitch plaisters are made of it. In Guiana and Brazil, where it is called Mani or Oanani, the natives make torches with it, and use it to pitch their boats. [A. S.]

MORPHOLOGY. That part of botany which treats of the transformations of organs.

MORPHOSIS. The manner of development; the order or mode in which organs form themselves, from their earliest condition till their final state.

MORPHUS. In Greek compounds=shape or appearance; whence *rhizomorphous*, having the appearance of a root.

MORRENE. *Hydrocharis.*

MORRENIA *odorata* is a hoary twining asclepiadaceous plant with hastate leaves, from Buenos Ayres and Paraguay. It has greenish sweet-smelling flowers, with five erect sepals; a five-parted corolla with the segments spreading and eventually reflexed; a tubular five-angled crown with five obtuse lobes conniving over the gynostegium; and a convex stigma with a central obscurely two-lobed apiculus. [A. S.]

MORS DU DIABLE. (Fr.) *Scabiosa succisa.* — DE GRENOUILLE. (Fr.) *Hydrocharis Morsus-ranæ.*

MORSGELINE. (Fr.) *Stellaria media.*

MORSUS DIABOLI. *Scabiosa.* — GALINÆ. *Lamium amplexicaule.* — RANÆ. *Hydrocharis.*

MORT-AU-CHIEN. (Fr.) *Colchicum autumnale.* — AUX-RATS. *Hamelia patens.* —AU-CHANVRE. *Orobanche ramosa.*

MORUNG-SAUL. The ship-building timber of *Shorea robusta.*

MORUS. The Mulberry genus, belonging to the order *Moraceæ*, has representatives in the tropics and temperate regions of Asia and America, but none in Europe or Africa. It consists of milky juiced trees or shrubs, with large often rough entire or lobed deciduous leaves, and unisexual greenish-white inconspicuous flowers, the two kinds being usually in separate axillary catkin-like spikes, and the whole of the female spike ultimately ripening into an oblong juicy aggregate fruit, composed of numerous egg-shaped compressed achenes (or true fruits) covered by the enlarged succulent calyces. Black Mulberries are eaten as a dessert fruit ; besides which preserves and a kind of wine are made from them, and their juice is used in pharmacy for colouring and flavouring. [A. S.]

M. nigra, the Black Mulberry, is the species chiefly cultivated for its fruit. The tree grows to the height of twenty to thirty feet, and forms a large round head, with dense foliage affording a complete shade. The leaves are bluntly heart-shaped, or slightly lobed, thick, with a rough surface. The fruit is roundish-oval, dark red or black, the surface uneven. The tree is late in leafing, which takes place in May, when usually all danger of frost is over.

The name *Morus*, according to some authors, is derived from the Celtic *mor*, black ; but M. de la Bretonnerie says that the tree does not push forth its leaves till the frosts are over, and hence it has been designated 'the wisest of trees,' and that from this peculiarity it derives its Latin name of *Morus* from the word *mora*, 'a delay. Dr. Butler (*Sketch of Modern and Ancient Geography*, p. 188) says : 'The modern name of Peloponnese is Morea, from the Mulberry trees which grow there, having been introduced for supplying silkworms.' Botanists are not decided as to its native country. It has certainly been found wild in the chains of the Caucasus and adjoining mountains, but it is probably also indigenous to Persia and Asia Minor. It appears to have been well known to the ancients. We read in the Bible that 'He destroyed their vines with hailstones, and their mulberry-trees with frost.' Also that

'David came upon the Philistines, and smote them over against the mulberry-trees.' It is therefore evident that the mulberry must have been well known to the Jews at that time, otherwise it would not have been mentioned by the sacred historian for the purpose of indicating the particular locality of a battle.

Mulberries are mentioned by the early Greek writers, Theophrastus, Dioscorides, and Galen ; and among the Romans by Virgil, Horace, Pliny, &c. All these writers are supposed to refer to the Black Mulberry, *M. nigra*, which must have been the species first employed for feeding the silkworm after its introduction to Western Asia and the South of Europe. Dr. Tozzetti states that the introduction of the White Mulberry into Italy is of a date long posterior to that of the silkworm. These were imported into Sicily in 1148, by King Ruggieri, after he had conquered Thebes, Athens, and Corinth. The Lucchese are said to have learned the art of rearing them from the Sicilians, and introduced it into Florence, when in 1315 they took refuge there from the sack of their own city. Pognial has, however, proved that silk was produced in Florence in and previous to the year 1225, and from Italian histories and chronicles it appears that there were silk factories there before 1266. From Sicily Mulberry-trees were brought to France, about 1494. The Black Mulberry is mentioned by Tusser in 1557 ; and it is stated that the first trees were planted at Syon House in 1548, but the first Duke of Northumberland said, previous to 1824, that he could trace these trees back three centuries. Indeed there is every reason to suppose that as very old Mulberry-trees were found near monasteries, they had been introduced by the monks whilst they were in possession of these establishments. Bacon enjoyed in London the shade of a mulberry tree ; and Shakspeare, as is well known, had a favourite one at Stratford-on-Avon. We have seen two others that were raised from this celebrated tree and planted by Garrick at his villa near Hampton Court, where they are, or were very lately, still alive. They had been planted in line with hollies, apparently of the same age, and were the common Black Mulberry. The trees had been reared with taller stems than usual, but had been blown down and were prostrate when we saw them ; nevertheless, as the Mulberry is very tenacious of life, vigorous shoots were rising perpendicularly from their stems, and these with care might form large trees. The planting of mulberry-trees was much encouraged by King James I., not so much for the fruit as for the rearing of silkworms ; but that has never been successfully carried on in this country on a large scale.

M. alba, the White Mulberry, is a native of China, and the north of India according to some authors ; but in the latter, Dr. Royle states (*Botany of the Himalayan Mountains*, p. 337) that it is not found wild. It is said to have been unknown to the ancients, although some allusion is made to its fruit in their writings. In the *Journal of the Horticultural Society* (ix. 170), is mentioned that 'a variety of the White Mulberry, said to be delicious eating, &c. unknown in Europe, is now abundant in Beloochistan, Affghanistan, and probably in Persia, and apparently of very ancient cultivation there. It is therefore by no means impossible that some knowledge of it may have reached such of the ancient writers as may have been in the East or had communication with it.' It is commonly supposed that cuttings of the White Mulberry were first brought into Tuscany from the Levant, by Francesco Buonvicini, in 1434. In the following year a law for encouraging its cultivation was made in Italy ; and in the course of the fifteenth century the White Mulberry had gradually, but entirely, superseded the Black as far as regards its cultivation for the feeding of silkworms, although for about two hundred years previously the Black Mulberry had supplied the food of the silkworms which produced the silk spun in Europe. The tree grows to the height of twenty or thirty feet, and has heart-shaped or ovate undivided or lobed serrated and rather glossy leaves. The fruit is white or pale red. The tree is of more rapid growth than the *M. nigra*, and its leaves contain more of the glutinous milky substance resembling caoutchouc which gives tenacity to silk produced by the worms which feed on them, and is found in all plants on which they exist. The White Mulberry and its varieties are more tender than the Black, which, as above stated, has withstood for more than three hundred years our severest winters ; but not so the White, for in most winters its shoots are killed back more or less, and in less than thirty years the tree becomes very stunted. Hence without due precautions it could not be grown in this climate to supply food for silkworms. If cut down, however, like raspberry canes, the White Mulberry pushes again very rapidly, and if not constantly nipped almost in the bud, a profusion of leaves would soon be produced.

Herein, we suppose, must have lain the error by which a British Irish and Colonial Silk Company, formed in 1825, must have failed, independent of other adverse causes which may have existed. This company imported 26,000 White Mulberry trees from the south of France into Ireland, and soon afterwards 200,000 more. The speculation however, proved unsuccessful ; though we know from experience that fine silk has been abundantly produced in Britain, the silkworms being fed on leaves of the Black Mulberry, those of the White Mulberry and its varieties, and of the Osage orange, being used as occasional substitutes. The deaths of the worms under such conditions have not been above three per cent. In such a company the question of success would resolve itself into two heads :—1st, the proper management of the Mulberry plantations, which would be very easy ; and 2ndly, the price of labour. The labour might be performed by otherwise unem-

ployed persons, at a rate, we suppose, remunerative to both employers and employed. Mulberry trees will grow almost
anywhere, but their growth and the crops
of leaves may be limited by injudicious
gathering on their first pushing out. What
then is to be done? The worms being
hatched must be fed; but it is in our
power to accelerate or retard the hatching.
In our northern climate the eggs should be
kept cool, so that they may not be hatched
till the vegetation of the trees is sufficiently
advanced to afford without injury a plentiful supply of food for the young worms.
This observation may prove useful even
to amateurs, who may have only a single
mulberry tree on which to feed silkworms
for amusement. A pound of silk is worth
its weight in silver, and this pound may
be produced from thirty pounds of mulberry leaves. This quantity may be obtained from a single tree, which might
yield annually the essential material for
sixteen yards of gros de Naples.

There are many varieties of *M. alba*, all
of which may be utilised for feeding the
silkworm; but that called *M. alba multicau-
lis* is, both in France and Italy, considered
the best.

M. rubra is a native of America, and
grows from forty to seventy feet in height.
M. tatarica, a tree resembling the White
Mulberry, bears reddish or pale fruit, which
is not of good flavour, though made into
a sweetmeat in Tartary. There are some
other species, but those we have noticed
are the most important : the Black more
especially for its fruit, and for its leaves;
and the White for its leaves chiefly, its
fruit being of little estimation, although
it also may be turned to account for feeding
poultry. [R. T.]

MORVEN. (Fr.) *Juniperus phœnicea.*

MOSCHARIA. An erect annual from
Chili, with the aspect of a *Sonchus*, but
with a strong smell of musk, forming a
genus of *Compositæ* of the tribe *Nassau-
vieæ*. It is characterised chiefly by the
involucre of five or six spreading leafy
bracts, and by the pappus consisting of
very short lanceolate ciliate chaffy scales.

MOSCHATEL. *Adoxa.*

MOSCHATOUS. Having the smell of
musk.

MOSCHOSMA. A genus of labiates,
having the calyx ovate, its upper tooth
largest, the others smaller and nearly
equal; and the style club-shaped, slightly
two-lobed at the end. The species are
herbs, natives of the East Indies, of Holland, or of Africa, and bear small flowers.
The name bears allusion to the odour possessed by certain of them. [G. D.]

MOSSES. A large alliance of cryptogams,
consisting on the one hand of the Liverworts or *Hepaticæ*, and on the other of the
true Mosses or *Musci*. Their grand technical distinction, however they may differ in
habit, rests upon the fact that the archegonia and antheridia are produced upon

the perfect plant, and not upon some previous growth or prothallus; and that the
act of impregnation produces a capsule,
and not a new plant as in ferns and pseu-
do-ferns. The word Moss is applied popularly to many low tufted plants, whether
phænogams or cryptogams. Small species
of *Sedum*, for instance *S. anglicum*, are
sometimes termed Mosses—of course merely on account of their habit. [M. J. B.]

MOSS, BLACK. *Tillandsia usneoides*,
also called Spanish Moss, and Long Moss.
—, BOG. *Sphagnum*. —, CANARY, *Parmelia perlata*, a lichen used for dyeing.
—, CEYLON. The common name for *Plo-
caria candida*, which is imported from
Ceylon with some other species. Its qualities are like those of Carageen. *Sphærococcus lichenoides*, which is found on the
southern coast of England as well as in the
tropics, has much the same qualities, and
has been prepared as a pickle and preserve,
or an ingredient in soup, the requisites for
such a use being delicacy of texture as well
as other qualities. —, CORSICAN. A supposed vermifuge, once in some repute, but
now almost exploded. If genuine, it should
consist of *Gracilaria Helminthochorton*,
one of the rose-spored *Algæ*, but for this
the common *Laurencia obtusa* is frequently
substituted, and probably with no diminution of the real value of the sample. Many
other species are mixed up with the true
Corsican Moss, when that is really present.
The notion of its virtues probably arose
from the old doctrine of signatures, the
cylindrical stems and branches bearing a
fancied resemblance to a worm. —, CUP.
The common name of *Cenomyce* (*Scypho-
phorus*) *pyxidata*, a lichen which grows
abundantly on gravelly banks, rotten wood,
&c., deriving its name from the cup-shaped
processes to the margin of which the fruit
is attached. It is still kept by the herbalists
as a remedy for hooping-cough, though its
virtues are probably quite imaginary. —,
FILM. *Hymenostomum*. —, ICELAND.
Cetraria islandica, a nutritious article of
food : see CETRARIA. —, IDLE. An old
name for various tree lichens, especially
those which are pendulous. The epithet
'idle' seems to imply that they are barren
and useless. —, IRISH. *Chondrus crispus* : see CARAGEEN. —, JAFFNA. *Alectoria sarmentosa*, a dye lichen collected in
Ceylon. —, LONG. *Tillandsia usneoides*.
—, NECKLACE. A name especially applied
to the form of *Usnea* in which the stem
is cracked transversely so as to look like
a strung necklace; but it is extended
to other conditions. —, NEW OR-
LEANS. *Tillandsia usneoides*, or Black
Moss. —, PEARL. *Chondrus crispus*.
—, REIN-DEER. *Cenomyce rangiferina*.
—, SCALE. *Jungermannia*. Scale Mosses
is a term applied to the order *Jungermanniaceæ*. —, SPANISH. The commercial
name of *Tillandsia usneoides*. —, SPLIT.
Andræa.

MOSS-BERRY. *Oxycoccus palustris.*

MOSS-CROPS. *Eriophorum vaginatum.*

MOSTAHIBA. A hard Brazilian wood.

MOTE. The nut of the West African *Carapa guineensis.*

MOTHER-CELLS. Cells in which other cells are generated.

MOTHER-CLOVES. A name in the East for the fully expanded flower-buds of *Caryophyllus aromaticus.*

MOTHER-OF-THOUSANDS. *Linaria Cymbalaria.*

MOTHER-OF-THYME, or MOTHER-OF-TIME. *Thymus Serpyllum.*

MOTHER-OF-VINEGAR. The flocculent mycelium of various moulds (*Mucor, Penicillium*, &c.) which forms on the surface of vinegar.

MOTHERWORT. *Leonurus;* also *Artemisia vulgaris.*

MOUCERON. (Fr.) *Agaricus oreades.*

MOUCOU-MOUCOU. A Guiana name for the seeds of *Caladium arborescens.*

MOULDS. A name given popularly to the thread-like *Fungi* which prey upon our provisions, and which attack other substances, as gum, glue, ink, &c., living at their expense, and destroying their valuable properties. These, however, belong to two very different series, *Hyphomycetes* and *Physomycetes*, which we must treat separately. Many of the Moulds are capable of sustaining life when immersed in fluids, contrary to the habit of most *Fungi;* and from their capability of appropriating what is nutritious, and rejecting what is hurtful, they are often developed in solutions of poisonous metallic salts, which would be fatal to *Fungi* in general. In a solution of sulphate of copper, for example, they become as it were electrotyped by the copper, while they appropriate the other elements. In such situations, moreover, they are often propagated by cells separated from the threads, which in their turn produce new cells; and therefore they are described as *Algæ*, under various names. As their spores are often able to sustain a considerable degree of heat without destruction, they occur in situations where they would otherwise not be expected, as in preserved fruits which have been subjected to heat, and when there was no possibility of the access of fresh spores. Where there is any possibility of communication, there are few kinds of vegetable tissues which they cannot penetrate; and in animals, they occur in situations where they must, like intestinal worms, have worked their way through the tissues to the cavities in which they grow. They are amongst the most destructive agents in the production of disease, as is proved by the potato murrain. In the human frame they are the fruitful source of cutaneous disorders. [M. J. B.]

MOUNTAIN LAVER. A reddish gelatinous *Alga*, belonging to the genus *Palmella*, consisting of a roundish slightly lobed frond, growing on the sides of mountains, after the fashion of the common *Nostoc.* It is used occasionally to cure calves. It was formerly called *Ulva marina*, though it has little affinity with *Ulva.* [M. J. B.]

MOUNTAIN-PRIDE, or MOUNTAIN-GREEN. A West Indian name for *Spathelia simplex.*

MOUNTAIN-SWEET. A Canadian name for *Ceanothus americanus.*

MOUREAU, MOURESIOLE, or MOURETTE. (Fr.) A kind of olive.

MOUREILLER. (Fr.) *Malpighia.*

MOURIRIACEÆ. A natural group of perigynous Exogens, now included in *Melastomaceæ. Mouriria* wants the marked ribs of *Melastoma*, and its leaves are very distinctly dotted.

MOURNING WIDOW. *Geranium phæum.*

MOURON. (Fr.) *Anagallis,* especially *A. arvensis* and *cærulea*, also *Veronica Anagallis.* — BLANC. *Stellaria media.* — D'EAU. *Samolus Valerandi.* — DES OISEAUX. *Stellaria media.*

MOUSE-BANE. *Aconitum myoctonum.*

MOUSE CHOP *Mesembryanthemum murinum.*

MOUSE-EAR. *Hieracium Pilosella;* also *Cerastium vulgatum.* —. BASTARD. *Hieracium Pseudo-Pilosella.*

MOUSETAIL. *Mygalurus;* also *Myosurus minimus*, and *Dendrobium Myosurus.*

MOUSE-THORN. *Centaurea myacantha.*

MOUSSACHE. (Fr.) Cassava starch.

MOUSSE DE CORSE. (Fr.) *Gracilaria Helminthochorton.* — PERLÉE. *Chondrus crispus.* — TERRESTRE. *Lycopodium clavatum.*

MOUSSELET. (Fr.) *Thlaspi perfoliatum.*

MOUSSONIA. A genus of *Gesneraceæ*, separated from *Gesnera*, and represented by *G. elongata.* It is known by its subshrubby habit, by the short-limbed tubular corolla, whose tube is very slightly inflated, and by the presence of a thick sinuous ring at the base of the ovary, consisting of five nearly equal glands. The species are very ornamental and of free flowering habit. [T. M.]

MOUTAN. A name given to that section of *Pæonia* which contains the Tree Pæony (*Pæonia Moutan*). This plant, which is sometimes separated as a distinct genus, differs from the other species in having the disk enormously developed, forming an irregular cup which envelopes the five carpels. The shrubby habit, so very rare among *Ranunculaceæ*, also separates it from the herbaceous pæonies destitute of the cup-like disk. *Moutan* (derived from Meu-tang, king of flowers) is the name by which the Tree Pæony is known in China and Japan, where it is a favourite garden flower. Its native place is said to be the north of China, on Mount Ho-an. In English gardens it seldom attains a greater height than from three to five feet; but in China it is reported to be sometimes ten feet high. The leaves resemble those of the herbaceous pæonies, but are less leathery; the flower in the wild state is purple, but in cultivation white, pink, pale purple, and pale with purple or red spots occur. [J. T. S.]

MOUTARDE. (Fr.) *Sinapis.* — BATARDE. *Arabis.* — BÂTARDE DE MI-THRIDATE. *Biscutella.* — DES CAPUCINS. *Cochlearia Armoracia.* — DES INDES, or ÉTRANGÈRE. *Cleome.* — DE HAIE. *Erysimum officinale.*

MOVING PLANT. *Desmodium gyrans.*

MOWHA. *Bassia latifolia.*

MOWLOO. An Indian name for *Dioscorea aculeata.*

MOWRA. A kind of arrack obtained from *Bassia latifolia.*

MOXA. A name applied to different substances used in surgery to produce a sore by means of slow combustion. The practice in some countries almost supersedes every other kind of medical treatment. One of the best substances for this purpose is amadou (*Polyporus fomentarius*). The Japan and China Moxa, however, is prepared from certain species of *Artemisia* (*A. Moxa, chinensis, &c.*). In England, cotton-wool, and the pith of the sunflower, which contains nitrate of potash, are more frequently employed. Moxa is not, however, much used in this country, on account of the great pain it produces, and it does not appear that it has any compensating advantages over more speedy methods of producing the same effect on the skin and the underlying tissues. [M. J. B.]

MOXO-MOXO. A Bolivian name for *Eupatorium glutinosum.*

MUCEDINES. A natural order of hyphomycetous *Fungi*, containing those naked-spored moulds whose threads are never coated by a distinct membrane, and are mostly white or coloured. The common species of *Aspergillus* and *Penicillium* are well-known examples. It has been supposed that different species occur on bodies according as they are acid and alkaline, but this does not appear to be confirmed by the latest experiments. Their agency in fermentation will be mentioned under the article YEAST. It is very probable that more perfect observation will reduce many of the objects recognised at present as species to the condition of mere mycelia-bearing conidia. Such observations, however, require repetition, and are so liable to error that they must at first be received with considerable caution. [M. J. B.]

MUCIDOUS. Musty; smelling of mouldiness.

MUCOR. The typical genus of the mucorinous Moulds, characterised by a globose sporangium, into which the tip of the stem enters in the guise of a clavate columella, and indefinite sporidia produced irregularly in the cavity. These spores are mostly elliptic; but sometimes, as in *M. fusiger*, a species with brownish threads produced not uncommonly on decaying agarics, the spores are much elongated and spindle-shaped. *M. Mucedo* is extremely common on fruit, and is believed to expedite its decay, which is true only when the surface is broken, or the cellular substance communicates with the outer air. *M. Phycomyces* is noticed in the article MUCORINI. The common species of *Mucor* have their part in the production of yeast. [M. J. B.]

MUCORINI. A natural order of physomycetous *Fungi*, analogous to *Mucedines*, which they resemble in habit, but producing their fruit within vesicles, and not externally. The sporidia arise sometimes indifferently in the sacs, without any especial point of attachment; but in *Acrostalagmus* they rise from the tips of the branches which penetrate the crust. The bread mould is one of the most familiar examples, but the finest of all is that which grows in prodigious masses on grease, the walls of oil mills, and other unctuous situations. The threads when dry have a peculiar shining aspect, and a dark green colour; and the species, which is a true *Mucor*, was formerly assigned to *Algæ*, under the name of *Phycomyces*. Several of the species bear two kinds of fruit on the same stem, both the sporidia and the sacs which contain them being different in size and character. Some, again, as *Acrostalagmus*, appear to assume two forms—an ascomycetous and a gymnomycetous. The latter must be considered either as bearing stylospores or male fruit. In one genus the cyst is formed after the combination of two branches, as in the conjugate *Algæ*; and in *Endodromia* there is an active motion within the vesicles whose nature has not yet been ascertained. [M. J. B.]

MUCOUS, MUCOSE. Covered with a slimy secretion, or with a coat that is readily soluble in water, and becomes slimy.

MUCRO. A sharp terminal point.

MUCRONATE. Abruptly terminated by a hard short point; thus *mucronato-serrate* is when the serratures terminate in a hard short point.

MUCUNA. The plants of this genus are well known to travellers in tropical countries from the exceedingly annoying character of their seed-pods, which are thickly covered with stinging hairs easily detached by the slightest shake, and causing great irritation if they happen to fall upon exposed parts of the body. It belongs to the leguminous order, and consists of a considerable number of species, mostly found in tropical Asia and America, only two or three occurring in Africa, and one in the Feejee Islands. All are twiners or tall climbers, with trifoliate leaves, and long-stalked often pendulous racemes of large purple white or yellow flowers, rising singly or in clusters from gland-like swellings; they have a bell-shaped four-toothed calyx, papilionaceous corolla with the upper petal shorter than the rest and the keel curved upwards, and the stamens all united except the upper one. The pods are thick and leathery. *M. pruriens*, the pods of which afford the Cowage, or Cow-itch of the Materia Medica, a celebrated remedy for intestinal worms, is a native of the West Indian Islands. These pods are four or five inches long, shaped like the letter *f*, and clothed with a thick coating of short stiff brittle hairs of a bright brown colour, the points of which are notched or finely serrated, and cause intolerable itching, or even an eruption on the skin, which is allayed by the application of oil. Their beneficial effects when taken internally are due, it is said, to their mechanical or stinging action upon the worms; they are administered in treacle, syrup, or honey. [A. S.]

MUCUS. Gummy matter soluble in water.

MUDAR. *Calotropis gigantea*, and *C. procera.*

MUDWEED. *Helosciadium inundatum.*

MUDWORT. *Limosella.*

MUFLE DE VEAU. (Fr.) *Antirrhinum majus.*

MUFLIER. (Fr.) *Antirrhinum.* — DE VEAU, or DES JARDINS. *Antirrhinum majus.*

MUGGET. *Convallaria majalis.* —, PETTY. *Galium verum.*

MUGHO. (Fr.) *Pinus Pumilio.*

MUGUET, or M. DE MAI. (Fr.) *Convallaria majalis.* — DES BOIS, or PETITE. *Asperula odorata.*

MUGWEED, GOLDEN. *Galium cruciatum.*

MUGWORT. *Artemisia vulgaris.* —, INDIAN. *Artemisia hirsuta.* —, WEST INDIAN. *Parthenium Hysterophorus.*

MÜHLENBECKIA. A genus of *Polygonaceæ* from South America and Australia, consisting of twining shrubs or small trees, with the leaves often cordate or hastate at the base; and bearing axillary or terminal often paniculately branched spikes of polygamous flowers. The five lobes of the perianth are often unequal; stamens eight; styles three; nut three-edged. There are two subgenera—*Eumühlenbeckia*, from South America, with simple stigmas; and *Sarcogonum*, from Australia, with plumose stigmas. [J. T. S.]

MÜHLENBERGIA. A genus of grasses

belonging to the tribe *Agrostideæ*, the inflorescence of which is generally in the form of light elegant panicles, which give the plants a handsome appearance. Steudel describes fifty species, a large portion of which are natives of South America and the Southern States. *M. Spica-venti*, better known as *Agrostis Spica-venti*, and sometimes referred to *Apera*, is a native of Britain, and a very beautiful grass. [D. M.]

MUHOOA, or MUOHWA. An Indian name for *Bassia latifolia.*

MUKKA, or MUKUEE. Hindustani names for Indian Corn or Maize.

MUKKI. An Indian name for Gamboge.

MULBERRY. *Morus.* —, AUSTRALIAN. *Hedycarya Pseudo-Morus.* —, COMMON. *Morus nigra.* —, DANDOLO'S. *Morus alba Morettiana.* —, INDIAN. *Morinda citrifolia.* —, NEW ZEALAND. *Entelea arborescens.* —, PAPER. *Broussonetia papyrifera.* —, WHITE. *Morus alba.*

MULDERA. A genus of Javanese shrubs belonging to the *Piperaceæ*, and named in honour of the celebrated Dutch chemist Mulder. They are either erect or climbing in habit, with stalked leathery ribbed leaves, and diœcious flowers on a slender spike, which ultimately becomes thickened. Each flower emerges from a fleshy cup, which is at first closed, but afterwards cleft transversely, and formed from a number of confluent bracts. The berries are large scattered reddish and very aromatic. [M. T. M.]

MULES. Plants obtained from the seeds of one plant fertilised by the pollen of some other species.

MULGEDIUM. A genus proposed by Cassini, and adopted by several modern botanists, for the blue-flowered species of *Sonchus*, which differ slightly from the yellow-flowered ones in the achenes tapering into a very short beak, and sometimes in the pappus not being so white. These differences, however, slight as they are, are not quite constant, and one of the pale blue American species has occasionally pale yellow flowers. Besides the *S. alpinus* and *S. Plumieri*, both very handsome species, common in several mountainous districts of continental Europe, six or seven species from North America or Northern Asia are referred to *Mulgedium*. The *S. alpinus* has been found in some of the Scotch Highlands, but is now become very rare there, or almost extinct.

MULINUM. A genus of umbellifers, distinguished by each half of the fruit being five-ribbed, the two intermediate ribs broad and wing-like. The species are natives of the Chilian Andes, and have entire or three to five-cleft leaves, and simple umbels of yellow flowers. [G. D.]

MULLEIN. *Verbascum.* —, GREAT TORCH. *Verbascum Thapsus.* —, MOTH. *Verbascum Blattaria.* —, PETTY. *Pri-*

mula veris. —, WHITE, *Verbascum Lych-nitis.*

MÜLLERA. A genus of *Leguminosæ* of the tribe *Dalbergieæ*, founded on a tall woody climber from tropical America, with the pinnate leaves and racemose flowers of a *Lonchocarpus*, from which genus it only differs in the pod, which is thick, of a dry fleshy consistence, and either contracted between each seed so as to resemble a succession of large globular beads, or if reduced to a single seed the whole pod is nearly globular. The *Cyanobotrys* of Zuccarini, from Mexico, appears to be a second species of the same genus.

MULSARI. An Indian name for *Mimusops Elengi.*

MULT, MULTUS. In Latin compounds = many. Thus, *multifarious* or *multiserial* means in many rows; *multiflorous*, bearing many flowers; *multifoliate*, bearing many leaves, &c.

MULTICEPS. Having many crowns, as some roots.

MULTIFEROUS. Producing several times in one season.

MULTIFID. Cut halfway into many segments.

MULTIJUGOUS. Bearing a very considerable number of pairs of leaflets.

MULTIPLE. Composed of several distinct parts.

MULTISEPTATE. Divided by many stages into many chambers, as the pith of the walnut.

MULTISILIQUÆ. A natural order of plants, proposed by Linnæus, and the same as the order *Ranunculaceæ.*

MUNDIA. A genus of *Polygalaceæ*, consisting of two species, one from the Cape, the other from South Brazil, both of them little low prickly much-branched shrubs, with small leaves and flowers. It is nearly allied to *Muraltia*, but the two inner sepals are large and wing-like as in *Polygala*, and the fruit is a small drupe containing one or two seeds; that of the Cape species is said to be eatable.

MUNDIKEI. The Malay name for the Water-Melon.

MUNDULI. An African name for *Arachis hypogæa.*

-MUNGPALLI. An Indian name for *Arachis hypogæa.*

MUNJEET, or MUNJEETH. The commercial name for the Madder root, furnished by *Rubia cordifolia.*

MUNRONIA. A genus of *Meliaceæ*, inhabiting the East Indies, and consisting of erect shrubs, with imparipinnate glabrous leaves, and isolated axillary white flowers, emitting a delicious scent. The calyx is four or five-cleft; the corolla four or five-petaled; the stamens united into a tube or ten in number; and the capsule five-

valved and five-celled, containing two or often only one seed in each cell. [B. S.]

MUNTINGIA. A tree from tropical America, constituting a genus of *Tiliaceæ*, remarkable for the broad sessile stigma, and for the fruit, which is a globular berry containing a large number of small seeds immersed in pulp. In St. Domingo the wood is used for staves, and cords are made from its bast.

MURALTIA. A genus of *Polygalaceæ* consisting of about fifty species, all from South Africa. They are all small low much-branched shrubs or undershrubs, often rigid and scrubby, with alternate often stiff and needle-like leaves, and small flowers solitary in their axils. As a genus this is distinguished from *Polygala*, by the inner sepals being scarcely larger than the others, and by the capsule, which almost always terminates in four short points, horns, or protuberances. None of them are known to have useful properties.

MURUMURÚ. *Astrocaryum Murumuru.*

MURDANNIA. A genus of *Commelynaceæ*, founded on *Commelyna scapiflora*, an Indian herb, with ensiform root-leaves, and a branched scape bearing blue flowers. The perianth has the three outer leaves herbaceous, and the three inner larger and petaloid; there are six stamens with bearded filaments; the parallel anther-cells separated by a bicrural connective, the alternate ones sterile. [J. T. S.]

MURET. (Fr.) *Cheiranthus Cheiri.*

MURICARIA. A genus of *Cruciferæ*; forming a procumbent herb, growing in sandy places in Northern Africa, and having pinnatifid leaves, and terminal or lateral racemes of white flowers. The pouch is indehiscent, globose, with a short style, feathery and rough on the surface; the seed solitary, globose. [J. T. S.]

MURICATED. Furnished with numerous short hard excrescences.

MURICI. A Brazilian name for the bark of *Byrsonima.*

MÛRIER. (Fr.) *Morus.* — À PAPIER. *Broussonetia papyrifera.* — DE RENARD. *Rubus fruticosus.* — NAIN. *Rubus Chamæmorus.*

MURINUS. Mouse-coloured; grey, with a touch of red.

MURLINS. The Badderlocks, *Alaria esculenta.*

MURRAYA. A genus of *Aurantiaceæ*, consisting of trees or shrubs, without spines, having pinnate leaves, and a terminal many-flowered cymose inflorescence. The flowers have a five-cleft calyx, oblong petals, ten free stamens, and one or two ovules. The fruit is succulent. With this genus Professor Oliver associates *Bergera*, there being too many transitional characters between the two to allow them to remain separate. The species are natives of India, Java, China, &c.; two of them with white fragrant flowers, *M. exotica* and *M. paniculata*, are cultivated as stove plants in this country. The genus derives its name from John Adam Murray, Professor of Botany at Göttingen.   [M. T. M.]

MURRAYA WOOD. Another name for Box-wood.

MURUCUJA. A genus of West Indian climbing shrubs, belonging to the *Passifloraceæ*, and very closely related to *Passiflora*, but distinguished from it by the coronet or ray, which, in place of consisting of distinct thread-like segments, as in true passion-flowers, has them combined into a tube surrounding the stalked ovary. *M. ocellata*, the old *Passiflora Murucuja*, whose handsome scarlet flowers render it very attractive, is said to possess anthelmintic and diaphoretic qualities, and to be used in Jamaica as a narcotic.   [M. T. M.]

MURTILLA. A Spanish name for *Eugenia Ugni*.

MURURA. *Victoria regia*.

MURUTE. A Cingalese name for *Lagerströmia regina*.

MUSACEÆ. (*Musœ, Musads*.) A natural order of petaloid monocotyledons, belonging to Lindley's anomal alliance of Endogens. The plants have shoots proceeding from subterranean rootstocks, which form spurious stems, composed of the sheathing leafstalks; veins in the limb of the leaf parallel, and proceeding in a curved manner from the midrib to the margin; flowers bursting through spathes. Perianth six-cleft, adherent, in two whorls, more or less irregular; stamens six, some usually abortive, the anthers linear, introrse, often with a membranous petaloid crest; ovary inferior, three-celled, the ovules numerous; style simple; stigma usually three-lobed. Fruit either a three-celled capsule with loculicidal dehiscence, or succulent and indehiscent; seeds sometimes surrounded by hairs. They are natives of warm and tropical regions, and furnish a large supply of nutritious fruit, while their leaves afford valuable fibres. Spiral vessels abound in them. There are five genera, including *Musa* and *Strelitzia*, and a score or more of species. [J. H. B.]

MUSA. The typical genus of *Musaceæ*, consisting of a small number of noble herbaceous species, now found growing in the tropical and subtropical zones of both hemispheres. The true stem is small, but the sheaths of the leaves are very long, and closely compacted so as to form a kind of false stem, rising in some cases from twenty to thirty feet high. The blade of the leaf is large, oblong, with a very prominent midrib, from which smaller ones pass off at right angles. The flowers are borne on a long nodding spike, and are clustered together in groups, protected by large sometimes highly coloured bracts. The perianth is two-lipped, the lower lip consisting of five segments separated above, but partly united below, the upper lip consisting of a single concave segment; there are six stamens, one of which is abortive, and the ovary is inferior, three-celled, the ovules numerous, attached in two rows the inner angle of each compartment; the ovary. The fruit is berry-like, the seeds imbedded in pulp.

M. paradisiaca and *M. sapientum* are the botanical names by which the Plantain and Banana are respectively known. The latter has its stems marked with purple spots, and its fruits are shorter and rounder than those of the Plantain, but otherwise the two plants are little different one from the other. They have been cultivated from the most remote times in tropical climates, in subtropical Asia, America, Africa, and the islands of the Atlantic and Pacific Oceans, for the sake of their fruits, which they produce in enormous quantities with very little attention. There are several varieties, the fruits of which differ in flavour, but all are more or less mawkish and viscid, at least in the ripe state, for the starch that abounds in the unripe fruit becomes converted, as it ripens, into mucilage and sugar. They are highly nutritious, and serve as the staple food of a large number of the human race. Though less nutritious than wheat or potatoes, yet the space occupied by their culture, and the care required, are so very much less, that Humboldt has calculated the produce of Bananas compared to that of wheat as 133 to 1, and to that of potatoes as 44 to 1.

Plantain meal is obtained by powdering the dried fruit; it is very nutritious, as it contains not only starch, but protein or flesh-forming material. The fruits of the Plantain are stated by chemists to be most nearly allied in composition and nutritive value to the potato, and the Plantain meal to rice. The natives of many parts of India live almost entirely on Plantains, and the stems, laden with fruit, are made use of at wedding festivities, in token of plenty. Plantations of Bananas or Plantains are made by settlers to support their families, and the fruits are eaten raw, or cooked in various ways. The expressed juice is in some countries made into a fermented liquor, and the young shoots eaten as a vegetable.

The specific name, *paradisiaca*, was given under the supposition that the fruits of the Plantain were the Forbidden Fruit of Scripture, or the fruits called Grapes that the spies brought to Moses from the Promised Land as evidence of its fertility; but it is hardly necessary to say that there is no foundation for such opinions.

When the stems are cut down, or decay after the formation of the fruit, new suckers are sent up from below, and these in the course of a few months produce fruit in their turn. Each bunch of fruit weighs from sixty to eighty pounds and upwards, even when ripened in hothouses in this country. The abundance and nutritive properties of the fruit are not the only qualities which give these plants their value. Their leaves serve as thatch for houses, and for other domestic purposes; and some parts are used medicinally in cases of dropsy, and as an external application to burns and ulcers.

The *Musas* are likewise remarkable for the quantity of fibrous tissue pervading their leafstalks, and which is capable of being employed for weaving purposes, for making paper, &c. One species, *M. textilis*, is especially valuable on this account. It furnishes what is known as Manilla Hemp, the plant being cultivated in the Philippine Islands for the sake of its fibre, the finer kinds of which are woven into beautiful shawls, and the coarser employed in the manufacture of cordage for ships, &c. A very large supply of fibre, adapted for paper-making and other purposes, could be obtained at comparatively little cost from this and various species of Plantain.

Several species are cultivated in hot-houses in this country for their foliage or for their fruit. *M. chinensis*, also called *Cavendishii*, a dwarf species from China, produces fruit abundantly in our hothouses. *M. Ensete* is a native of Abyssinia, where it was discovered by the traveller Bruce. Its fruit is dry and inedible, containing a few large stony seeds; but the base of the flower-stalk is cooked and eaten by the natives. A plant of this species was for many years one of the chief ornaments in the palm-house at Kew, its leaves being upwards of twenty feet long, and traversed by a stout vivid red rib, while the trunk attained a circumference of nine feet in three years. It was remarked by Bruce, that on ancient Egyptian sculptures representations of Isis with ears of corn, and the foliage of the Banana occur, and sometimes carvings are met with showing the hippopotamus destroying the Banana. Now the true Banana is not a native of Egypt; hence Bruce surmised that the Abyssinian *Ensete* was intended. The hippopotamus typifies the Nile, the inundations of which have gone so far as to destroy not only the wheat, but also the *Ensete* which was to supply its place. [M. T. M.]

MUSADA. An Indian name for *Strychnos nux-vomica*.

MUSANGA. The name applied to a tree of western tropical Africa, which constitutes a genus of *Artocarpaceæ*. It is nearly allied in habit and other characters to *Cecropia*, but its male flowers have each only one stamen, in place of two. The fruit is covered by the hardened perianth, and contains a single seed, which is eaten by the natives of Guinea. [M. T. M.]

MUSCADIER. (Fr.) *Myristica*.

MUSCAIRE. (Fr.) *Moscharia*.

MUSCALES. The group or alliance of Acrogens, comprising the MOSSES: which see; see also MUSCI.

MUSCARDINE. A disease to which silkworms are subject, which derives its name from a little pastille to which the dead silkworms bear some resemblance. The malady is due to the agency of a mould, *Botrytis Bassiana*, which commences its growth in the intestines, and gradually penetrates every part of the insect till life is destroyed. It is not confined to the larva, the pupa sometimes being affected after the cocoon is spun. Where a silkworm establishment is attacked by this formidable parasite, nothing except the greatest care and cleanliness will remove it. Every particle of dung, every withered leaf, every dead insect, must be carefully removed, and the walls washed with a solution of quicklime, or some other substance which may destroy the spores. It is of consequence, also, to avoid as much as possible all intercourse with other establishments in which disease exists. A few spores scattered over the leaves, and consumed by the caterpillars, will be sufficient to keep up the evil. [M. J. B.]

MUSCARI. Bulbous plants, with narrow leaves, and flowers in racemes at the end of a simple stalk, belonging to the hyacinth tribe of *Liliaceæ*, and natives of middle Europe and the Mediterranean region. The genus is known by the flowers having a tubular almost globose perianth, constricted at its very shortly six-toothed mouth; six stamens with very short slender filaments inserted into the perianth tube; and a short straight style, bearing a three-cornered papillose stigma. Its membranous, acutely triquetrous three-celled capsules contain about two black seeds in each cell. [A. S.]

MUSCARIFORM. Formed like a brush or broom; that is to say, furnished with long hairs towards one end of a slender body, as the style and stigma of many composites.

MUSCARIUM. A collection of corymbose branches, such as are found in many *Asters*.

MUSCATEL. A choice kind of grape, dried on the vine, for fine table raisins.

MUSCI. An important tribe of cryptogams, comprising the Mosses proper, which stand apart from other cryptogams by their peculiar habit and fruit, with a very few exceptions only. Whether the axis is elongated or reduced to a mere point, the more or less pointed and lanceolate imbricated or distichous leaves, and ovate fruit opening horizontally by the separation of a terminal lid, and bearing one or more whorls of tooth-like processes at the orifice, in far the greater number, are at once distinctive. In a few exceptional cases the leaves are obtuse, the lid does not separate, the capsule opens by vertical valvular lobes, and the orifice is naked; yet even in these, the general habit and the nature of the fruit preclude all possibility of mistake.

The leaves of Mosses are destitute of stomates, but these organs are found not unfrequently upon the capsules. Their colour is mostly green, though occasionally nearly white from the absence of endochrome in the outer cells. In a few instances the walls of the cells communicate with each other by means of apertures, or contain a spiral thread. The cell walls of the stem occasionally exhibit scalariform marks or a spiral structure. The spores are generally numerous, and produce on germination a green conferva-like mass of threads, forming a thin felt. From this the plant springs immediately, and either on the same or on different individuals produces bundles of antheridia and archegonia. The antheridia produce spiral spermatozoids, which impregnate the embryo cell at the base of the archegonia. This by cell-division gives rise to a capsule, which swells, and in most cases is lifted up by a stem bursting the archegonium, which remains as a kind of hood or veil at the top of the capsule. The capsule in the space between the outer wall and the axis, which often forms a permanent columella, produces by cell-division the spores; and at the same time provision is made in most cases for the separation of a lid, and the gradual dispersion of the spores by the formation of one or more whorls of hygroscopic often brightly coloured teeth, which arise from a modification of the different layers of cells in the walls of the capsule. These teeth, when present, are either only four in number or multiples of four, and both in colour and structure afford beautiful microscopic objects.

The fruit in Mosses is either terminal (ACROCARPOUS) or lateral (PLEUROCARPOUS); and in the latter division a few produce fruit on short lateral branchlets (CLADOCARPOUS). The main sections are founded on these differences in the position of the fruit, but in a few instances the same genus has acrocarpous and pleurocarpous species.

Mosses are either annual or perennial. In the latter instance new branches are thrown out, which are called innovations. When dried, the leaves recover their original appearance completely if immersed in water. They require, however, in general, a good deal of moisture when in active growth. They are found in all parts of the world, and occur on mountains at heights where all phænogamic vegetation ceases. A few species occur in amber. They perhaps yield fewer objects of utility to man than any other division of plants, except those of the same alliance. In agriculture and in the garden, though of small size, they are often noxious weeds. [M. J. B.]

MUSCOLOGY. That part of botany which treats of Mosses.

MUSHROOM. A term applied sometimes collectively to certain of the larger *Fungi*, but more usually restricted to *Agaricus campestris*, and the species confounded with it. If the use of mushrooms as food were, however, restricted to that species as it occurs in our pastures, a very small quantity would be consumed comparatively, our market being largely supplied with coarser species. A vast quantity, moreover, are raised artificially, and may he had at almost any season of the year, though their price is necessarily high.

The common Mushroom appears to depend greatly upon the prevalence of the horse. Mushrooms, at least, can be raised with a great degree of certainty from horse droppings, properly prepared, without the admixture of any artificially raised spawn. The manure of the riding school at Belvoir, where the straw is pounded down into minute fragments, gives a constant supply. There is no doubt that *A. campestris* is preferable to any of the allied species, but it is not to be supposed that it is the only one that is wholesome. Indeed it is rejected from many Italian markets, where species of more suspicious character are allowed to pass muster. Further information will be found under HORSE MUSHROOM, KETCHUP, &c. —, HEDGE. The common name of a large form of *Agaricus arvensis*, which is finely figured at tab. 77 of Mrs. Hussey's *Illustrations of British Mycology*. The pileus is sometimes as much as fourteen inches across, and of a tawny yellow, with rich brown closely pressed concentric scales. The flesh turns yellow when salted. The gills are at first white, then pallid red without admixture of grey, and at length purple-brown. The stem is more or less bulbous, and stuffed with shining fibres, scaly below, with a thin broad ring above. It grows under trees, or on banks near water, always more or less tufted, and never occurring in rings. The Hedge Mushroom is recommended by Mrs. Hussey for ketchup, but eaten in substance, she says, it produces violent sickness. Cases of mischief from eating Mushrooms are generally traceable to this peculiar form. —, MITRE. *Helvella crispa*. —, OX. A name given to a large variety of the true Mushroom, *Agaricus campestris*, which measures sometimes fifteen inches across, with a proportionately stout stem. The pileus is rough with scales, which are at first white, and then tawny or reddish-brown. The gills are quite free, leaving a groove round the top of the stem, which takes a vinous hue when bruised. The smell is powerful, but agreeable. No part of the plant turns yellow. We have seen this variety in enormous rings many yards in diameter. It is perfectly wholesome, and has a fine flavour.　　　[M. J. B.]

MUSHROOMS, POISONOUS. As so many accidents occur from the use of *Fungi*, we are often asked for some general characters by which the bad may be distinguished from the good. It is impossible, however, to give any satisfactory answer, and we must therefore trust to experience, without which, we should be subject every day to trouble in respect to other objects of use. The Field Mushroom assumes so many forms that it is impossible to assign any characters which shall embrace all, and the hotbed Mushroom is different from these. The bright rosy tint of the gills, and the absence of any yellow stain when bruised, are the surest indications. The test of a silver spoon is fallacious. As a general rule, no one would eat *Fungi* which have a revolting smell, and if they leave, when tasted, a hot sensation in the mouth and throat, they should be used with caution. *Hydnum repandum*, however, and *Cantharellus cibarius* are both acrid, and yet are excellent articles of food. It is a good practice with such species to slice them into hot water, and press the slices in a cloth before stewing.

In general, we would suggest as to the use of *Fungi*, that they should be eaten with moderation, and with plenty of bread to secure sufficient maceration. In case of accident, a strong mustard emetic should be taken immediately, and medical advice called in. The narcotic symptoms, and attendant inflammation of the intestines, are too grave to be trifled with by domestic medicine. If, however, medical aid is not at hand, the system must be kept up with chloric ether, brandy, or other stimulants; and if diarrhœa and painful colic, as often happens, are urgent symptoms, opium must be given freely. The narcotic symptoms, except from the use of such *Fungi* as the Fly Agaric, are seldom predominant. [M.J.B.]

MUSK. *Mimulus moschatus*; also *Erodium moschatum.*

MUSKROOT. The Sumbul root, supposed to be derived from a species of *Angelica*; also the Spikenard, *Nardostachys Jatamansi*; and *Adoxa Moschatellina.*

MUSK-SEED. The seeds of *Abelmoschus moschatus.*

MUSK-TREE. *Eurybia argophylla.*

MUSK-WOOD of Jamaica. *Moschoxylum Swartzii*; also *Guarea Swartzii.* — of New South Wales and Tasmania. *Eurybia argophylla.*

MUSOOR, or MUSSOOR. Indian names for *Ervum Lens* and *E. hirsutum.*

MUSQUAMEENA. A native American name for *Cornus circinata.*

MUSQUASH-ROOT. An American name for *Cicuta maculata*; also *Claytonia acutiflora.*

MUSSÆNDA. A genus of *Cinchonaceæ*, deriving its name from the word applied by the Cingalese to some of the species. It consists of shrubs, natives of tropical countries, but not of common occurrence in America. The flowers are arranged in terminal corymbs, and have a five-parted calyx, one of the segments of which is occasionally extended into a large white leaf; a funnel-shaped corolla, with a five-parted limb and hairy throat; and five sessile anthers concealed within the tube of the corolla. The fruit is succulent and two-celled, with the placentas stalked and curved, so as to resemble a Burgundian cross.

Several species are in cultivation, the best known being *M. frondosa*, whose yellow flowers, contrasted with the white calycine leaf, give it a singular and pretty appearance. All the flowers do not produce this leaf-like sepal, but two or three in each corymb, and occasionally two sepals

are thus developed. The venation differs in these from that of the stem leaves, for while the latter have a midrib and a network of smaller veins, the dilated sepals have several veins of about equal size, proceeding from the base towards the apex, where they converge. This might be cited in support of Dr. Dresser's notion, that the sepals, &c., should, in many cases at least, be considered as modifications rather of the leafstalk than of the leaf itself. The bark and leaves of some of the species are esteemed as tonics and febrifuges in the Mauritius, where they are known as Wild Cinchona. Elsewhere the leaves and flowers are used as diuretics and expectorants, while in India the juice of the leaves and fruit is said to be used as an eyewash. [M. T. M.]

MUSSCHIA. A genus of bellworts, distinguished by its corolla being deeply five-cleft; by the filaments of the stamens being broad below and smooth; and by the capsule being five-celled, opening by several transverse fissures. *M. aurea* is the only species. It is a small glabrous shrub, a native of Madeira and Teneriffe, and has large handsome yellow flowers. The genus was named in honour of M. Mussche, a French botanist. [G. D.]

MUSTARD. *Sinapis.* —, BASTARD. *Cleome.* —, BLACK. *Sinapis nigra.* —, BOWYER'S. *Lepidium ruderale.* —, BUCKLER. The common name for *Biscutella*; also applied to *Clypeola Jonthlaspi.* —, GARLIC. *Erysimum Alliaria.* —, HEDGE. *Erysimum.* —, MITHRIDATE. *Thlaspi arvense.* —, TREACLE. *Clypeola.* —, TOWER. *Turritis*; also *Arabis Turrita.* —, WHITE. *Sinapis alba.* —, WILD. *Sinapis arvensis.*

MUSTARD-TREE of Scripture. *Salvadora persica*; or by some regarded as a species of *Sinapis.*

MUTABILIS. Changeable in colour or in form.

MUTHAR, MUTTER, or MUTTIR. Indian names for Peas, *Pisum sativum.*

MUTIANA. The Mozambique name of a tree which produces Vegetable wax.

MUTICOUS. Pointless. A word employed in contradistinction to some other term indicating being pointed: thus, if, in contrasting two things, one is said to be mucronate, the other, if it had not a mucro, would be called muticous; and the same term would be equally employed in contrast with cuspidate or aristate, or any such. It is also used absolutely.

MUTISIACEÆ. A division of the *Compositæ*, included in the two-lipped suborder *Labiatifloræ*, and further distinguished by its cylindrical or somewhat tumid style, the arms of which are usually blunt or truncate, convex on the outside. [J. H. B.]

MUTISIA. A genus of *Compositæ* which gives its name to the tribe *Mutisieæ*, characterised by their irregular florets, most of them more or less two-lipped. The genus consists of undershrubs or climbers, with alternate entire or pinnately divided leaves, often terminating in a tendril, and solitary terminal pedunculate flower-heads. The involucre, usually cylindrical, has broad imbricated scales, the receptacle naked, the florets of the disk slightly irregular, with long exserted anthers furnished at the base with long points, or tails, those of the ray female and more distinctly labiate. The pappus consists of long feathery bristles. There are above thirty species, natives of South America, and the greater number confined to the Andes of the West and especially of Chili. Many of the species with purple pink or yellow flowers, are highly ornamental.

MUTTY-PAL. A resinous exudation from *Ailantus malabaricus.*

MYAGRUM. A genus of *Cruciferæ*, consisting of erect glabrous annuals, growing in sandy fields in South-eastern Europe. The stem leaves are arrow-shaped and embracing ; and the racemes elongate, spikelike, with small pale yellowish flowers. The pouch is indehiscent, of a corky texture, compressed at the apex and attenuated at the base, one-seeded. [J. T. S.]

MYALL-WOOD. The hard violet-scented wood of *Acacia homalophylla.*

MYANTHUS. A spurious genus of orchids, now reduced to *Catasetum*, plants having been found, as already mentioned under MONACHANTHUS, bearing flowers of the three supposed genera on one spike. As a section it is distinguished by having the two cirrhi at the base of the column, instead of its apex as in *Catasetum.* [A. S.]

MYCELIUM. A word equivalent to spawn, denoting the vegetative part of *Fungi*, the greater portion of what most readily attracts notice being frequently merely the fructification. The vegetative part of a mushroom, for instance, is represented by the delicate white down and strings which traverse the soil ; the fruit is the stem, pileus, and gills, which we call the mushroom. The mycelium of *Fungi* is sometimes filamentous, sometimes cellular, and has received different names in different families. The mould-like web of *Sphæria aquila* has not, however, more title to notice than the indistinct apparently scarcely organised stain of which the spawn of *Sphæria pulvis pyrius* consists. In those cases, however, which are apparently so obscure, if a thin slice of the matrix be submitted to the microscope, delicate threads will be found penetrating the tissues in every direction.

As the spawn of *Fungi* assumes various forms, and may be dry or moist, fleshy or filamentous, friable or gelatinous, and as it frequently remains for a long time dormant without producing fruit, a number of spurious genera, as *Himantia, Rhizomorpha*, &c., have been introduced into systems, which it has taken the labour of years to eradicate. Occasionally the spawn

bears a kind of fruit, which has tended to make a correct estimation of its nature more difficult. The spawn of *Sphæria maxierii*, for instance, in the absence of capsules, might be taken for a true moth. Spawn may be either annual or perennial. In the latter case it may ' run ' for years without bearing fruit, till a favourable season occurs, a fact which will account for the apparently capricious growth of many species.

The spawn of our common mushroom is raised artificially for sale by nurserymen. Many attempts have been made to prepare the spawn of truffles, but they have as yet been unsuccessful. The introduction of the spawn of valuable varieties of mushroom will, we have no doubt, some day cause a considerable change in the produce of the mushroom bed. [M. J. B.]

MYCETALES. An important alliance of cryptogams, consisting of *Fungi* and lichens, which are so closely allied, and so distinct from other cryptogams, that in any natural arrangement they must be placed in one section. They derive nutriment either from the matrix on which they grow, as *Fungi*, or from the surrounding air, as lichens. *Algæ* are distinguished by their deriving nourishment by their whole surface from the water in which they are submerged. There are, however, exceptions in either case, and though there is seldom the slightest difficulty in determining the alliance to which each particular object belongs, it is almost impossible to draw up satisfactory general characters from fruit or structure. Both lichens and *Fungi* produce a distinct spawn or mycelium, whereas in *Algæ* the new plant arises at once from the spore. [M. J. B.]

MYCINA. Such a shield as occurs in the genus *Bæomyces* among lichens.

MYCODERMA. A spurious genus, assigned sometimes to *Fungi*, sometimes to *Algæ*, consisting of a peculiar condition of certain moulds when developed in liquids. Common yeast is an example. [M. J. B.]

MYCOLOGY. A name derived from two Greek words importing a knowledge of *Fungi*. It is equivalent to the barbarous word Fungology, which, like Muscology, has been retained sometimes as a good selling title, with a full sense of its incorrectness. Though Mycology in the first instance regards simply the classification of *Fungi*, no truly scientific man will be content without ascertaining in some measure the properties of the subjects of his investigation. We consider ourselves bound, therefore, in the present volume, to bring forward more particularly those species into notice which have some economical value, or which are to be avoided as dangerous. [M. J. B.]

MYGALURUS. A genus of grasses belonging to the tribe *Festuceæ*, now included in the section *Vulpia* of *Festuca* itself. *F. uniglumis*, or *Mygalurus uniglumis*, is a small annual grass, which generally grows among sandhills near the sea, and flowers early in the season, before most other kinds of grasses. It is scarcely of any agricultural value, though rather interesting botanically. [D. M.]

MYGINDA. A genus of *Celastraceæ*, differing from *Maytenus* chiefly in its leaves being usually opposite, and in its inflorescence; and from *Elæodendron* and its allies in the ovules being always solitary in each cell of the ovary. It consists of about eight species, from various parts of South America: shrubs with usually small leaves, and minute flowers either solitary or in cymes on axillary peduncles, which are often very short.

MYLITTA. A curious genus of underground *Fungi* supposed to be allied to the real truffles, but whose affinities are uncertain, as the fruit has not yet been found in a perfect state. *M. australis*, the Native Bread of Australia, is a large subglobose fungus, sometimes many inches in diameter, with a black skin which chips off in little fragments, enclosing a veined white mass, which at first is soft, and has a peculiar acid smell, but when dry becomes extremely hard and horny. It is eaten by the natives, and is probably very nutritious. The other species are either spurious or belong to different genera. [M. J. B.]

MYOGALUM. A genus of *Liliaceæ*, of which *Ornithogalum nutans* is the type. It differs from *Ornithogalum* by having the leaves of the perianth connivent in the shape of a bell; in the stamens having broader filaments, almost resembling petals, and having two lobes at the apex, between which is the anther; and in the capsule being more fleshy than in *Ornithogalum* proper. *M. nutans* is a European plant which occurs but rarely in England; it has a loose raceme of large green and white flowers. [J. T. S.]

MYOPORACEÆ. (*Myoporineæ, Avicennieæ, Myoporads.*) A natural order of corollifloral dicotyledons, belonging to Lindley's echial alliance of perigynous Exogens. Smoothish shrubs, with simple exstipulate leaves often covered with transparent glands, and bractless flowers. Calyx five-parted, persistent; corolla gamopetalous, hypogynous, more or less two-lipped: stamens four, didynamous; ovary two to four-celled, the cells one to two-seeded; ovules pendulous; style one. Fruit a drupe, or dry and two to four-celled. Natives chiefly of Australia, some occurring in the warm parts of South America. Some botanists consider the order as a division of *Verbenaceæ*. *Myoporum* and *Avicennia* are examples of the few genera, which contain about fifty species. [J. H. B.]

MYOPORUM. The typical genus of *Myoporaceæ*, containing upwards of thirty species of shrubs, chiefly from Australia. They have alternate rarely opposite entire or serrated leaves, and white or rarely purple flowers on axillary peduncles, which are either solitary, in pairs, or in fascicles. The branches and young leaves are viscid. The calyx is five-parted, sometimes a little enlarged around the fruit, the corolla campanulate, with a short tube and unequally five-lobed limb; the four stamens are scarcely didynamous; and the ovary is two-celled, or frequently, by the reduplication of the margins of the carpels, four-celled, with a single ovule in each cell. The fruit is a baccate drupe. [W. C.]

MYOSOTIDIUM. A genus of *Boragineæ*, from the Chatham Islands off New Zealand, with the habit of *Myosotis*, but the ovary is like that of *Cynoglossum*, and the mature nuts are winged like those of *Omphalodes*; the wing, however, is not introflexed, and the nuts adhere to the receptacle and are not attached to the style. The root-leaves are ovate, stalked, about as large as those of a small cabbage, the upper ones much smaller and sessile, and all glabrous and shining. The flowers are large, purplish-blue, in scorpioid racemes, arranged in a corymb, and having a five-parted calyx, and a silver-shaped corolla with a very short tube, the throat of which is closed by five scales. Nuts smooth, with undulated wings. [J. T. S.]

MYOSOTIS. The Forget-me-not or Scorpion-grass genus, belonging to the *Boragineæ*, and comprising numerous European and Northern Asiatic, a few North American, and three or four Australian species. It is distinguished by its five-parted or five-cleft calyx; by its straight-tubed corolla with five spreading flat or concave contorted lobes, and the throat closed by five short conniving scales; and by its smooth and shining compressed nucules, which are not perforated at their narrow base. They are more or less erect herbs, of small size, with rather rigid spreading of appressed hairs: stalked root-leaves, shorter and broader than those of the stem; and scorpioid racemes of smallish blue rose or white flowers, sometimes with yellow eyes. The name of the genus is derived from two Greek words signifying mouse-ear, in allusion to the shape and hairiness of the leaves of some species, five of which are natives of this country. Of these *M. palustris* is the true and well-known Forget-me-not. [A. S.]

MYOSURUS. A minute plant belonging to the *Ranunculaceæ*, and well marked by having its seeds arranged on a long columnar receptacle, so as to produce no very fanciful resemblance to a mouse's tail, whence its name. *M. minimus*, or Mouse-tail, the only species, rarely attains more than three or four inches in height, and bears a few linear spathulate leaves and leafless stalks terminating in a small greenish flower. It grows most frequently among corn, in a chalky or gravelly soil, but is often overlooked in consequence of its small size. French, *Queue de Souris*; German, *Mäuseschwänzchen*. [C. A. J.]

MYPE. *Brassica Rapa*.

MYRIACTIS. A genus of erect branching herbs of little beauty, belonging to the composite family. They have ovate or lance-shaped coarsely-toothed leaves, and daisy-like flower-heads, disposed in a panicled manner at the end of the stem. The achenes are compressed and naked, or tipped with a coroniform pappus. There are five species, all found in India, and one common also to Persia. [A. A. B.]

MYRIANGIUM. A genus of gelatinous lichens, which was found about the same time in Australia and Algeria, and has since been met with in the Channel Islands and the United States. The asci are broad and packed irregularly, and not parallel to each other as in most lichens, on which account principally Nylander considers it as belonging to a distinct tribe. They appear to grow constantly on the living bark of trees, especially ash. In the two original species the fructification is capsular, or closed with a veil; but in *M. Curtisii* the disk is exposed. [M. J. B.]

MYRIANTHUS. The name of a tree of tropical Africa, constituting a genus of *Artocarpaceæ*. The leaves are digitate; the male flowers borne on thick branching receptacles, somewhat like those of *Hovenia*; and the perianth four-parted, containing four stamens united at their base. The fruit is fleshy, and consists of several ovaries fused together. [M. T. M.]

MYRICA. By some botanists *Myrica*, *Comptonia*, and *Clarisia*, or in fact the whole of the plants of the order *Myricaceæ*, are combined into a single genus. The first of these, the Linnæan genus *Myrica*, is technically distinguished from the two latter by its stamens being four to eight in number, as well as by the hypogynous scales of its female flowers, regarded by some as a perianth, being sessile and having no glands inside. Representatives of the genus are found widely scattered over the temperate regions of both hemispheres, in North America, at the Cape of Good Hope, in Northern India, China, and Japan; and in Europe we have *M. Gale*, the Sweet Gale or Bog Myrtle, and the badge of the Campbells. They also occur within the tropics in South America, but are there confined to the cool mountainous regions. Most of the species are shrubs, but some grow into small trees; and they are mostly abundantly furnished with glands and dots filled with aromatic secretions, whence arises the fragrance for which they are noted. Their leaves are simple, and their flowers, of separate sexes, in catkins, borne generally on distinct plants. The fruits are nuts or drupes, often of small size, covered all over with a thickish coating of a waxy resinous secretion. Hence arises the chief economic value of the genus; for in the countries where the plants abound the fruits are largely collected, and when properly treated yield an abundance of excellent wax, from which very tolerable candles are manufactured. [A. S.]

MYRICACEÆ. (*Galeworts*.) A natural order of monochlamydeous dicotyledons, belonging to Lindley's amental alliance of diclinous Exogens. Shrubs or small trees with resinous glands, alternate leaves, and unisexual flowers. They have no perianth: stamens two to eight, the anthers two to four-celled; ovary one-celled, with hypogynous scales, the ovules solitary, and orthotropal. Fruit drupaceous, often covered with wax, and with adherent fleshy scales. They inhabit temperate and tropical countries, and have aromatic, tonic, and astringent properties. [J. H. B.]

MYRIOARIA. A genus separated from *Tamarix*, and containing those plants of the order *Tamaricaceæ* which have ten stamens, and feathery seeds inserted in the middle of the valves of the capsule. *M. germanica* is a shrub from six to eight feet high, with very narrow flat leaves, and spikes of pink flowers, indigenous throughout most parts of Europe and the Caucasus. There are several other species, some shrubby, some herbaceous, but none possess any particular interest. [O. A. J.]

MYRIOCARPA. A genus of *Urticaceæ*, consisting of half a dozen trees or shrubs, from the hotter regions of the Andes of America, remarkable for their exceedingly long and slender pendulous racemes or spikes, along which are arranged hundreds of minute green flowers.

MYRIOMELES. A name given by Lindley to an East Indian evergreen shrub, more generally considered as forming a section of *Photinia*.

MYRIOPHYLLUM. A genus of submersed aquatics belonging to the *Haloragaceæ*, among which they are distinguished by having flowers with four or eight stamens, and four stigmas and seeds. There are two British species, *M. verticillatum* and *M. spicatum*, slender plants, with long stems, pinnatifid capillary leaves, and small inconspicuous flowers, which rise above the water to expand. Both species are common throughout Britain in stagnant water, and allied species are to be found in most parts of the world. They are called Water Milfoil. French, *Volant d'eau*; German, *Federball.* [C. A. J.]

MYRIOPTERIS. *Cheilanthes.*

MYRIOTHECA. *Marattia.*

MYRISTICACEÆ. (*Myristiceæ, Nutmegs.*) A natural order of monochlamydeous dicotyledons, belonging to Lindley's menispermal alliance of diclinous Exogens. They are trees with alternate exstipulate entire not dotted leaves. Flowers unisexual; perianth trifid, rarely quadrifid, in the females deciduous; stamens three to twelve, the filaments combined into a cylinder; ovary free, composed of one or more carpels, one-celled, the ovule solitary erect, the stigma somewhat lobed. Fruit succulent, one-celled, two-valved: seed solitary, usually covered by a laciniated arillus; embryo small, at the base of ruminated albumen; cotyledons foliaceous. Natives of the tropical regions of Asia and America. Acridity and aromatic fragrance are the properties of the order.   [J. H. B.]

MYRISTICA. A genus of plants remarkable as furnishing the Nutmeg and Mace of commerce. It belongs to the *Myristicaceæ*, and consists of lofty trees or shrubs, natives of tropical countries, and especially of India. They are most of them aromatic, and abound in a reddish acrid juice. The leaves are entire; the flowers diœcious, very small, clustered in the axils of the leaves, or sometimes in panicles. The perianth consists of three or four segments, more or less united together, and enclosing a variable number of stamens, which are united into one parcel below. The ovary is free, with a single inverted ovule. The fruit is fleshy, but divides when ripe into two pieces, disclosing the seed covered by the arillode or mace.

M. moschata, or *M. officinalis*, is largely cultivated in the Molucca Islands, Java, Sumatra, Bengal, &c. It is a tree of twenty to twenty-five feet in height, with oblong aromatic leaves, and fruit very much like a peach, having a longitudinal groove on one side, and bursting into two pieces, when the enclosed seed, covered by the false aril or arillode, which constitutes the substance known as Mace, is exposed. The seed itself has a thick hard outer shell, which may be removed when dry, and which encloses the nucleus of the seed, the Nutmeg of the shops. The nutmeg consists of the albumen or perisperm, with the embryo at one end, and is covered by a thin membrane, which adheres closely to its surface, and projects into the substance of the albumen, thereby giving it the mottled appearance for which it is so remarkable.

In the Banda isles, the principal seat of the cultivation of the Nutmeg, the fruits are gathered at three seasons, July, November, and March or April. The mace, which at first is of a beautiful crimson colour, is dried in the sun, or by artificial heat if the weather be unfavourable, when it speedily assumes a golden-yellow colour. The nutmegs are dried, and then the outer shell of the seed is removed. Occasionally they are imported in the shell, a procedure which prevents the ravages of the nutmeg insect, but on the other hand adds considerably to the weight and to the waste. The nuts are sometimes washed over with lime to protect them from the attacks of the insect just mentioned. Several kinds of nutmegs are met with in commerce, perhaps the produce of as many different species. The most esteemed are those of Penang, which are about an inch in length, of the shape of a damson, pale-brown and furrowed on the exterior, internally grey with red veins, the odour and taste aromatic. Penang mace is also considered better than that from Java or Singapore, and is of a pale cinnamon colour when dry. Maces and nutmegs are in large use as spices, and medicinally as stimulants and carminatives; in large doses they have narcotic properties.

At one time the culture of nutmegs was almost entirely in the hands of the Dutch, who took every means to monopolise the growth of the plants, in which they were in a measure defeated by a kind of pigeon, which, extracting the nutmeg from its pulpy covering, digests the mace, and voids the nutmeg uninjured. It is related that the Dutch used to burn nutmegs when the crops were too abundant, in order to keep up high prices. Old ladies in the country, to this day, keep a nutmeg in their pocket, as was customary in their younger days, when the effects of the war with France, and of the Dutch monopoly, rendered all spices very expensive. *M. fatua, Otoba, tomentosa, spuria, acuminata*, and other species, yield nutmegs in Brazil, in the Philippine islands, and in Madagascar. The produce of some of these, especially of *M. fatua*, finds its way into the English market under the name of Long or Wild Nutmegs; they are longer and more pointed and of inferior quality to the true Penang nutmeg. Nutmegs contain both a fixed and a volatile oil; the former is extracted by pressure, and forms what is called butter of mace; the latter is obtained by distillation. Nutmegs are occasionally sent into the market

Myristica moschata.

after the oil has been distilled from them, and in a comparatively valueless condition. The French are said to have various ingenious methods of dressing up inferior nutmegs to resemble good ones, and even to fabricate artificial nutmegs of bran, clay, and the powder of nutmegs.   [M. T. M.]

MYRMECODIA. A genus of cinchonaceous shrubs, natives of the Molucca Islands. They are epiphytes with a tuberous stock, whence issue a few short fleshy branches. The leaves are stalked; the stipules peltate, ciliated; the flowers axillary fessile, with an undivided calyx, and a funnel-shaped corolla; the latter has a four-lobed limb, and hairy throat, into which the four very short stamens are inserted. The fruit is succulent, surmounted by the calyx, four-celled, four-seeded.   [M. T. M.]

MYROBALANEÆ. A natural group of dicotyledonous plants, now included in the Combretaceæ.

MYROBALAN. *Terminalia.* —, BASTARD, or BELLERIC. The fruit of *Terminalia Bellerica.* —, CHEBULIC. *Terminalia Chebula.* —, CITRINE. *Terminalia citrina.* —, EMBLIC. The fruit of *Emblica officinalis.* —, INDIAN. The small unripe fruit of *Terminalia citrina.*

MYRODIA. A genus of *Sterculiaceæ* of the tribe *Helictereæ*, consisting of South American trees or shrubs often aromatic, with alternate entire or scarcely toothed leaves, and white flowers, not large for the order, usually solitary on short peduncles opposite the leaves. They have an obconical three to five-toothed calyx, five petals, ten to fifteen two-celled anthers sessile at the top of the column on the outside, and a two or three-celled ovary sessile within the base of the column. The fruit is dry and indehiscent, containing one or two seeds. There are about seven species, of which no particular properties are recorded, except that, in common with others of the family, the mucilaginous roots may be used medicinally. Some botanists have united the genus with *Quararibea*, which, however, has very different anthers and belongs to the tribe *Bombaceæ*.

MYROSPERMUM. This name, given in consequence of the myrrh-likeodour of the seeds, is applied to a genus of tropical American trees or shrubs, of the family *Leguminosæ*. The leaves are unequally pinnate, and marked with pellucid dots. The flowers are white or rose-coloured in axillary or terminal clusters; they have a bell-shaped five-toothed calyx, a papilionaceous corolla, ten distinct stamens, a stalked ovary, and a thread-like lateral style. The fruit is indehiscent, with one or two seeds, and is borne on a stalk, the upper part of which is winged.

M. peruiferum, a native of Peru and other parts of Central and Southern America, yields the drug known as Balsam of Peru. This is procured by making incisions into the bark, thrusting cotton rags into the

Myrospermum peruiferum.

wound, and lighting a fire round the tree to liquefy the balsam. When the rags are saturated, they are boiled in water, and as the water cools, the balsam collects below. (*Pereira*,)

Balsam of Peru is a thick treacly-looking liquid, with a fragrant aromatic smell and taste. It has been used in chronic coughs, and as an application to ulcers, but is now rarely employed. Balsam of Tolu is a product of a similar character, derived from *M. toluiferum*. It is at first soft, but becomes hard and brittle by exposure. It is used for like purposes as the Balsam of Peru, and in the manufacture of pastilles, &c. [M. T. M.]

MYRRH. An aromatic medicinal gum-resin yielded by *Balsamodendron Myrrha*; also the common name of *Myrrhis.* —, FALSE. *Amyris commiphora*, also called *Balsamodendron Roxburghii.*

MYRRHIS. A genus of umbellifers, having each half of the fruit with five equal sharp ribs, and no oil-vessels. The species are hairy odoriferous herbs. One of them, *M. odorata*, is a well-known plant, often cultivated and used in various ways. The name is from the Greek word for perfume. [G. D.]

MYRRH-SEED. *Myrospermum pubescens.*

MYRSINACEÆ. (*Myrsineæ, Ardisineæ, Ardisiads.*) A natural order of corollifloral dicotyledons belonging to Lindley's cortusal alliance of perigynous Exogens. Trees, shrubs, or undershrubs, with alternate or opposite coriaceous exstipulate leaves, and hermaphrodite or occasionally unisexual flowers; calyx four to five-cleft, persistent; corolla monopetalous, equal; stamens four to five, inserted into the corolla, opposite its segments, the filaments distinct, the anthers sagittate, erect; ovary one-celled, the ovules definite or indefinite, campylotropal, immersed in a free central placenta. Fruit fleshy, one or many-seeded. They are found in Africa, Asia, and America, and are said to abound chiefly in islands with an equable temperature. Little is known of their properties. There are thirty-three genera, and above three hundred species. *Myrsine, Ardisia, Theophrasta*, and *Clavija* are some of them. [J. H. B.]

MYRSINE. A genus of *Myrsinaceæ*, consisting of shrubs or small trees, mostly evergreen, and glabrous or nearly so, with alternate coriaceous entire or rarely toothed leaves, and small flowers on very short pedicels in dense axillary clusters. This inflorescence distinguishes them from all other genera of the order except *Samara*, which has the petals quite free, and *Reptonia*, which has scales alternating with the corolla lobes, whilst in *Myrsine* the corolla is lobed only, without scales. There are a considerable number of species, all tropical, or nearly so, but dispersed over both the New and the Old World. Their properties are little known. The berries of *M. africana*, a species widely dispersed over Africa from Abyssinia and the Azores to the Cape, and occasionally to be seen in European greenhouses, are said to be mixed with barley by the Abyssinians as food for their asses and mules.

MYRSIPHYLLUM. A genus of *Liliaceæ* from the Cape of Good Hope, consisting of branched twining plants, with ovate-lanceolate or lanceolate leaves obliquely heart-shaped at the base, and white flowers on nodding pedicels two or three together at the base of the leaves, from the axils of small white scales, which are in fact the true leaves, the organs generally so called being metamorphosed branches as in *Asparagus*. The perianth is persistent, bell-shaped, six-parted, and there are six stamens with subulate filaments. The berry is globose, three-celled.   [J. T. S.]

MYRTACEÆ. (*Myrti, Granateæ, Myrtleblooms.*) A natural order of calycifloral dicotyledons belonging to Lindley's myrtal alliance of epigynous Exogens. Trees or shrubs with entire exstipulate usually opposite and dotted leaves, often having an intramarginal vein. Calyx limb sometimes cohering at the apex; petals attached to the calyx, alternating with its segments; stamens inserted with the petals, twice as many or indefinite, the filaments distinct, or united in one or more parcels; ovary adherent to the tube of the calyx, one to six-celled; style and stigma simple. Fruit dry or fleshy, dehiscent or indehiscent. They are natives chiefly of warm countries, as South America and the East Indies; many, however, are found in more temperate regions, and some of the genera are peculiar to Australia. Many yield an aromatic volatile oil. This is particularly the case with those having pellucid dots in their leaves. Some yield edible fruits; others furnish astringent and saccharine substances. The leaves of certain species of *Leptospermum* and *Melaleuca* are used as tea in Australia. The leaves of *Melaleuca minor* (*Cajuputi* of some), a native of the Moluccas, yield the volatile oil of cajeput. Pimento or allspice is the berried fruit of *Eugenia Pimenta*, a tree of the West Indies and Mexico. The flower-buds of *Caryophyllus aromaticus*, a tree which was originally a native of the Moluccas, but is now cultivated in the East and West Indies, constitute the cloves of commerce. The species of *Eucalyptus* are the gigantic gum-trees of Australia, some of which attain a height of two hundred feet. Guavas are produced by species of *Psidium*. *Punica Granatum* yields the pomegranate. There are about 100 genera and 1,500 species. An illustration of a myrtaceous tree is given in Plate 7.   [J. H. B.]

MYRTE. (Fr.) *Myrtus.*

MYRTILLE. (Fr.) *Vaccinium Myrtillus.*

MYRTLE. *Myrtus communis.* —, CANDLEBERRY. *Myrica cerifera.* —, DUTCH. *Myrica*; also a broad-leaved variety of *Myrtus communis.* —, JEW'S. A three-leaved variety of *Myrtus communis.* —, OTAHEITE. *Securinega.* —, ROMAN. A

common broad-leaved variety of *Myrtus communis.* —, SAND. An American name for *Leiophyllum.* —, TASMANIAN. *Fagus Cunninghami.* —, WAX. *Myrica cerifera.* —, WEST INDIAN. *Eugenia.*

MYRTLEBLOOMS. Lindley's name for the *Myrtaceæ.*

MYRTUS. The typical genus of *Myrtaceæ*, the species of which are widely scattered, the greater number, however, being found in the mountains of tropical South America, extending into the temperate parts of Chili, and even as far south as the Falkland Islands; others occur in Central Asia and New Zealand, while about a dozen species, which some botanists distinguish as a separate genus under the name *Jossinia*, are confined to the Mauritius, Bourbon, and the neighbouring islands. They vary greatly in stature. *M. Nummularia*, a native of the Falkland Islands, spreads over the ground like our European thyme, while the Common Myrtle generally forms a large bush, and others are small trees. Their leaves are opposite, entire, and marked with transparent dots; and their white or yellowish-white flowers are borne singly in the axils of the leaves. The genus is principally distinguished from its congeners by its seeds, which are contained in a globular two or three-celled fruit, crowned with the calyx lobes, few or many in each cell, and of a kidney or horse-shoe shape with a bony shell.

M. communis, the Common Myrtle, is well known by its shining evergreen leaves, and white sweet-scented flowers. Though extremely abundant in Italy, Southern France, Spain, &c., it is not indigenous to Europe, but only naturalised, having originally been brought from Western Asia, where, at the present day, it is found in a wild state as far east as Affghanistan. In England it is not sufficiently hardy to withstand the frost of very severe winters, except in the extreme southern parts, although it frequently survives long enough to attain its full growth. Several varieties exist, differing principally in the size and form of the leaves, in the shape and colour of the fruits, and in the flowers being single or double. Amongst the ancients the Myrtle was held sacred to Venus, and was a plant of considerable importance, wreaths of it being worn by the Athenian magistrates, by the victors in the Olympic games, and by others; besides which various parts were used in medicine, in cookery, and by the Tuscans in the preparation of myrtle wine, called Myrtidanum, for which purpose it is still employed. In modern times its chief use is in perfumery, particularly in the preparation of sachet powders, pot-pourris, &c.; and a highly perfumed astringent water, known as *Eau d'ange*, is distilled from its flowers. The fruits, which have a sweetish powerfully aromatic taste, are eaten in a fresh state, or dried and used as a condiment. The wood is of great hardness and beautifully mottled or veined, but from its small size it is only fit for turnery purposes.

M. orbiculata is one of the species placed by some botanists in the genus *Jossinia*, on account of the calyx and corolla having four parts instead of five, but the distinction does not hold good, and they are consequently referred to *Myrtus*. It is a large shrub, with thick dark green leathery elliptical or nearly round leaves, and an abundance of yellowish-white fragrant flowers, with small petals and numerous conspicuous stamens. In the Mauritius and adjacent islands, where this and the allied species are natives, their wood, on account of its hardness, is called Bois de Clous, or Bois de Nèfle (Medlar wood). The fruits are eatable.   [A. S.]

MYSORE-THORN. *Cæsalpinia sepiaria.*

MYSTROPETALINÆ, MYSTROPETALON. An order and genus of monœcious root-parasites allied to *Balanophoraceæ*. The genus is considered by Dr. Hooker as the type of a distinct natural order. It has a sheathing stem, covered by imbricated scales, and terminated by dense heads of flowers which present three villous bracts. The male flowers at the top of the spike are one to three-valved, the sepals united at base, the two extrorse stamens inserted on the petals and opposite to them. The female flowers have a superior tubular three-toothed perianth, and a one-celled ovary on a disk, with pendulous ovule, filiform style, and three-lobed stigma. The fruit is a rounded achene. The two known species are natives of South Africa.   [J. H. B.]

MYXA. The same as *Cordia*, from which some authors have separated it.

MYXOGASTRES. A natural order of gasteromycetous *Fungi*, characterised by their semigelatinous state when young, and by their thin brittle peridia, containing a mass of dust-like spores, with or without the admixture of a few threads. In consequence of their peculiar condition when forming their spores, it is often impossible to see their mode of attachment or origin; when this, however, has been possible, they have been found attached to threads either naked or contained in a distinct hyaline sac or ascus. Some doubts have been lately raised as to the title of these productions to a place in the vegetable kingdom, because the matter of which they are composed resembles a substance called sarcode, known only to animals, and because the spores in some instances, when germinating, produce a soft body resembling some Infusoria. Another peculiarity is that the peridium often contains carbonate of lime, a substance, however, which abounds in many *Algæ*. There are, however, so many arguments in favour of their vegetable character, and especially the fact that they do not all germinate in the same way, that there is a true filamentous mycelium in *Lycogala terrestre*, added to the spiral threads in *Trichia*, that the mere circumstance of motion in the young state, or peculiarity of substance, is not sufficient to overthrow it. The occurrence of starch in animals, or the infusorioid character of the spores

in many *Algæ*, might as well be taken as proofs that animals which contain starch in their tissues are vegetables, or that the *Algæ* which bear zoospores are animals. Indeed doubts have been raised, on the other hand, whether the infusoria containing sarcode should not be arranged with vegetables, though we do not subscribe to such hasty opinions.

Myxogastrous *Fungi* seem more than all others to be independent of the nature of the matrix on which they are produced. We have seen them growing on lead, and there are well-authenticated examples of their being produced on iron which a few hours before was red-hot. Indeed we possess a portion of such a specimen from the herbarium of Schweinitz. Most of them are microscopical, but *Æthalium*, which is the pest of hothouses, attains a considerable size, while both *Reticularia* and *Licea* afford specimens of similar habits. Few orders, however, of *Fungi* present so many elegant objects for the microscope, both in respect of form and colour. They are found in all parts of the world, but prefer temperate to hot climates; but neither extreme heat nor moisture is favourable to their growth, though they require a damp atmosphere.   [M. J. B.]

MYZODENDRON. A genus of *Loranthaceæ*, found growing parasitic upon the beeches of Tierra del Fuego and Antarctic America, to as far north as Valdivia, and characterised by its almost membranous one-seeded fruits being furnished with three long generally feathery bristles. These bristles are of a viscid nature, and serve the same purpose as the glutinous matter of our well-known mistleto berries, viz. that of attaching the fruit to a tree until the seed germinates and takes root in the bark. They also serve to effect the transport of the fruits from the parent plant to other trees by attaching them to the plumage of birds.   [A. S.]

NABEE. The Bish or Bikh, a powerful Indian poison obtained from *Aconitum ferox.*

NABK. The berries of *Zizyphus Lotus.*

NÆGELIA. A genus of *Gesneraceæ*, of which the type is the well-known *Gesnera zebrina*. It consists of perennial herbs with catkin-like scaly stolones, broad richly-shaded velvety-surfaced leaves, and erect racemes of large showy flowers, the ample campanulate cylindrical tube of which is somewhat ventricose beneath, and has a short and slightly two-lipped limb. The flowers are furnished with a five-lobed glandular ring, and a stomatomorphous stigma. *N. cinnabarina*, like *N. zebrina*, has scarlet blossoms, and there are many garden varieties remarkable for the pile of richly-coloured hairs which clothe the surface of their leaves.   [T. M.]

NAGEESA. A strong durable Indian timber, obtained from *Mesua ferrea.*

NAGEIA. A genus formerly proposed by Gærtner for the *Myrica Nagi* of Thunberg, a Japanese tree which has since been shown to be a species of *Podocarpus*.

NÄGELIA. A genus of the pome-bearing division of *Rosaceæ* (*Pomaceæ* of Lindley) allied to *Cotoneaster*, with which it agrees in the structure of its flowers and in its general appearance ; but the fruit, which is of a pale pink colour, about as large as a pistol-ball, has a brittle semitransparent flesh, and the thin putamen of *Pyrus*, instead of the hard bony stone of *Cotoneaster*. It is founded on the *Cotoneaster denticulata*, a Mexican shrub, and is further marked by having a semimembranaceous calyx, small spreading petals, ten to fifteen stamens, and a spheroidal pome, crowned by the calyx. The same name has been given to a rhamnaceous shrub from Java, now referred to *Gouania*. [T. M.]

NAGKUSHUR, NAGKESUR. Indian names for the fragrant flowers of *Mesua ferrea*.

NAGLA-RAGEE. An Indian name for *Eleusine coracana*.

NAGUR-MOOTHA. *Cyperus pertenuis*.

NAHLEH. An Arabic name of the Date Palm, *Phœnix dactylifera*.

NAIADACEÆ. (*Fluviales, Potameæ, Naiads*.) A natural order of monocotyledonous plants belonging to Lindley's hydral alliance of Endogens, consisting of plants living in fresh or salt water, and having cellular leaves with parallel veins, and inconspicuous flowers. The latter are hermaphrodite or unisexual. Perianth of two or four pieces, often deciduous, sometimes wanting ; stamens definite, hypogynous ; ovary free, of one or more carpels, with a solitary ovule. Fruit dry, one-celled, usually indehiscent ; seed erect or pendulous, exalbuminous. The few species are found in various parts of the world, and have no properties of importance. [J. H. B.]

NAÏADE. (Fr.) *Najas marina*.

NAIL. Half an inch, or the length of the nail of the little finger.

NAILWORT. *Draba verna*; also *Saxifraga tridactylites*.

NAIN D'AMÉRIQUE, or NAIN FLAGEOLET. (Fr.) *Phaseolus tumidus*.

NAJAS. A genus giving its name to the order *Naiadaceæ*, and consisting of about eight widely distributed species. It is distinguished by its mostly diœcious axillary naked flowers, the males with a single nearly sessile anther enclosed in a membranous spathe, and the females with a single ovary tapering into a short style bearing two to four awl-shaped stigmas. All the species are little branching herbs, growing under water, with narrow opposite or whorled, usually toothed, broad-based leaves, and insignificant flowers which produce little seed-like nuts. *N. flexilis*, a common North American species, has of late years been found in Connemara. [A. S.]

NAKED LADIES. *Colchicum autumnale*.

NAKED SEEDS. Seeds having no pericarpal covering, as in conifers and cycads.

NAMA. A genus of *Hydroleaceæ*, containing half a dozen diffuse herbs or shrubs, natives of America, with entire leaves, and blue or white axillary or terminal flowers. The calyx consists of five persistent sepals; the corolla is tubular and funnel-shaped ; there are five included stamens inserted in the tube of the corolla ; the ovary is two-celled, containing numerous ovules, and bearing two distinct styles with obtuse stigmas ; the capsule is two-celled, dehiscing loculicidally, and containing numerous small seeds. [W. C.]

NAMEDOU. *Alangium hexapetalum*.

NANA, or NANON. A South American name of the Pineapple, *Ananassa sativa*.

NANANTHEA. A genus of *Compositæ* peculiar to Corsica, and represented by a single species, *N. perpusilla*, which is a smooth branching herb, seldom above an inch high, with very minute white-rayed flower-heads placed singly on the end of a slender stalk longer than the leaves. Its chief characteristics are the oval compressed achenes without pappus, thick style branches, narrow naked receptacle, and involucre of eight to nine distinct scales, placed in a single series. [A. A. B.]

NANCY-PRETTY. *Saxifraga umbrosa*.

NANDHIROBEÆ. A suborder of the *Cucurbitaceæ*, characterised by its anthers not being sinuous, the placenta adhering to the axis of the fruit, and the seeds being numerous. The plants are climbing herbs, natives of hot climates, as India and South America. *Telfairia* and *Feuillœa* are examples. [J. H. B.]

NANDINA. A genus of *Berberidaceæ*, differing from *Berberis* in having several rows of scales on the outside of the six sepals, six white petals without glands, and red globose berries, with two plano-convex seeds. *N. domestica* is a handsome evergreen shrub, with ternately compound leaves, and terminal panicles of flowers. It is a native of China and Japan, where it is extensively cultivated in gardens, and is known by the names of Nandsookf, Nattam, or Nandto. [J. T. S.]

NANEEL. An Indian name for *Bassia latifolia*.

NANGKA. A Bornean name for the Jack-fruit.

NANKAH. The Persian name for Ajowains.

NANODEA. A genus of sandalworts, distinguished by the calyx having a four-cleft border ; four stamens with very short filaments and two-celled anthers ; and a short style ending in two lobes. The only species is a small fleshy plant, a native of Magelhaens' Straits. [G. D.]

NANODES *discolor* is a curious little Brazilian and West Indian orchid, with leaves and flowers very much alike in appearance. The plant, which is only an inch or two high, has small rather fleshy greenish-purple leaves, banded with purple, set closely together on opposite sides of a short stem, which is concealed by their sheathing bases; and its little purple flowers are borne solitary upon the summits of the branches, and almost hidden amongst the leaves. The genus belongs to the *Vandeæ*, and is distinguished by its lip being adnate to the column, and cohering with the lateral sepals above which it is placed, and by its four compressed pollen-masses being sessile side by side on an ovate gland. [A. S.]

NAPÆA. *Sida.*

NAPATAIN. An Indian name for the Physic-nut.

NAP-AT-NOON. *Tragopogon porrifolius.*

NAPEANTHUS *brasiliensis* is the sole representative of a genus of *Cyrtandraceæ*, peculiar to Brazil, where it inhabits the dense virgin forests of the Organ Mountains. It is a small shrub, with opposite unequal sessile, and towards the apex crenated, leaves; pink flowers arranged in axillary umbels; a tubular calyx, and a funnel-shaped corolla; four stamens, the anthers of which are coherent; an oblong ovary not surrounded by any glandular disk; and a one-celled two-valved capsule with an indefinite number of seeds. [B. S.]

NAPELLUS. *Aconitum Napellus.*

NAPHA-WATER. A delicious perfume distilled from orange-flowers.

NAPIFORM. Turnip-shaped; having the figure of a depressed sphere, as the root of the turnip-radish.

NAPOLEONA. A very singular genus of shrubs, natives of Western tropical Africa, whose place in the natural system is a contested point among botanists. Dr. Lindley places it in a separate order, *Belvisiaceæ*. They are shrubs of the size of a pomegranate, with alternate leathery leaves, and sessile axillary flowers in groups of three. The calyx is adherent, leathery, five-cleft; and the corolla of three rows, the outer largest, concave, strongly plaited, and many-toothed, bent backwards so as to conceal the calyx when fully expanded, the next row divided like the crown of the passion-flower into a number of thread-like spreading segments, and the innermost division erect cup-shaped, with the margin bent inwards and divided into numerous small tooth-like segments: ten to twenty stamens are inserted into the base of the corolla in a single row, the filaments being united together below. Within these is a cup-shaped disk, surrounding the adherent ovary, which latter has five compartments, with two ovules suspended in each, a five-cornered style, and a disk-shaped five-angled stigma. The fruit is soft, much like a pomegranate, the rind very astringent, and containing so much tannin that the natives make a kind of ink from it. *N. imperialis* has produced its cream-coloured flowers in this country. [M. T. M.]

NARANJITAS DE QUITO. The berries of *Solanum quitöense*, called Quito Oranges.

NARASCALO. A hard Mexican wood, probably Ironwood.

NARAVELIA. A genus of *Ranunculaceæ*, distinguished from *Clematis* by the presence of petals; from *Atragene* by the petals being longer than the calyx; and from both by the carpels being each seated on a thick hollow stalk. The only species is *N. zeylanica*, the Narawael of Ceylon, a climbing shrub resembling a *Clematis*, but having the leaves with only a single pair of ovate acuminate leaflets, beyond which the leaf-stalk takes the form of a tendril. The flowers are yellow, with four sepals and six to twelve linear petals. [J. T. S.]

NARCISSE. (Fr.) *Narcissus.* — À BOUQUETS. *Narcissus Tazetta.* — AIAULT. *Narcissus Pseudo-narcissus.* — D'AUTOMNE. *Sternbergia lutea.* — DE PÉROU. *Ismene Amancaes.* — DES PRÉS, or SAUVAGE. *Narcissus Pseudo-narcissus.*

NARCISSUS. An extensive genus of bulbous plants belonging to the *Amaryllidaceæ*. Their distinguishing features are a hypocrateriform perianth having a straight cylindrical tube, a six-parted equal spreading or reflexed limb, and a funnel-shaped bell-shaped or wheel-shaped cup or coronet; six included stamens inserted below the coronet; a three-celled ovary, the ovules in many series; a simple style and obtuse stigma; and a membranaceous capsule. The numerous species of *Narcissus* are amongst the most beautiful of spring-flowering bulbs. They have linear-lorate leaves, and radical scapes bearing one or many flowers, which are usually yellow but sometimes white, not unfrequently nodding, and generally imbued with a powerful, and when confined rather overpowering, odour. They have been thrown into several groups or subgenera, of which the principal are:—

Ajax: the Daffodils, distinguished by having the cylindrical cup longer than the funnel-shaped tube, the filaments adnate to the lower part of the tube, and the style subulate and three-furrowed. The Common Daffodil, *N. Pseudo-narcissus*, is an illustration of this group.

Ganymedes: the Rush Daffodils, distinguished by the slender drooping tube, reflex limb, and short cup, the filaments very unequally adnate to the upper part of the tube, and the style slender. Example: *N. triandrus.*

Hermione: the Polyanthus Narcissus, distinguished by the slender cylindrical tube and shallow cup, the filaments unequally adnate near the mouth, and the style slender, as in *N. Tazetta.*

Queltia: the Meek Narcissus, distinguished by the subcylindrical tube and short crown, the filaments unequally adnate to the upper part of the tube, and the style attenuated upwards, as in *N. montanus* and *odorus*.

The true forms of *Narcissus*, represented by *N. poeticus*, are distinguished by their slender cylindrical tube widened at the mouth, their very short cup, their filaments very unequally adnate near the mouth, and their slender style. [T. M.]

NARCISSUS of Japan. *Nerine sarniensis*.

NARD. The Spikenard, or Nard of the ancients, *Nardostachys Jatamansi*. —, COMMON. *Nardus stricta*.

NARD. (Fr.) *Nardus*. — ASPIC. *Lavandula Spica*. — CELTIQUE. *Valeriana celtica*. — SAUVAGE. *Asarum europæum*.

NARDOO. An Australian name for *Marsilea macropus*, sometimes called *M. hirsuta*, and *M. salvatrix*, the spores and spore-cases of which are used by the aborigines for food. They are pounded up, and baked into bread, and also made into porridge; and according to Dr. Beckler both preparations furnish a nutritious food, by no means unwholesome, and free from unpleasant taste, but affording sorry fare for civilised man. Some of the survivors of the Australian exploring expedition, under Mr. Burke, prolonged their lives by the sole use of this food. The plant has been not inaptly described, in the newspapers, as 'a quatrefoil something like trefoil.' It must be very abundant and prolific, as Nardoo fields, probably swampy places in which it abounds, are mentioned; and the survivor of Burke's exploring party found, left in a hut by the natives, a bag of the Nardoo containing sufficient to last him for a fortnight. [T. M.]

NARDOPHYLLUM. A genus of *Compositæ* of the tribe *Asteroideæ*, consisting of about half-a-dozen species from extratropical South America, especially Chili, including *Dolichogyne* of De Candolle. They are all closely allied to *Lepidophyllum* from the same country, to *Chrysothamnus* and *Ericameria* from North-west America, and to *Pteronia* from the Cape.

NARDOSMIA. A name under which the Winter Heliotrope (*Tussilago fragrans*), and some allied Northern species of *Tussilago*, have been separated generically, on account of trifling differences in the female florets. Together with *Petasites*, of which they have the habit, they are much more appropriately considered as a section only of the well-marked and natural genus *Tussilago*.

NARDOSTACHYS. A genus of Nepalese herbaceous plants belonging to the *Valerianaceæ*. The flowers are in corymbs, protected by an involucre; the calyx limb is divided into five persistent leafy segments; the corolla is regular, spurless, its tube enclosing four stamens; the ovary is inferior, three-celled, two of the compartments being empty, and the third containing a single ovule. The roots of these

plants are very fragrant. According to Dr. Royle, those of *N. Jatamansi* constituted the Spikenard of the ancients. [M. T. M.]

Nardostachys Jatamansi.

NARDUS. A genus of grasses belonging to the tribe *Agrostideæ*. The inflorescence is in simple unilateral two-rowed spikes; glumes none; pales two, terminating in a bristle. The common Nard, or Matgrass, is the only species described. It is a worthless grass for agricultural purposes, but, growing on dry bare moory places, is valuable for sheep pasture. [D. M.]

NARGIL, NARIKEL, NARIYUL. Indian names for the Cocoa-nut.

NARTHECIUM. A genus of marsh herbaceous perennials belonging to the *Juncaceæ*, and of which the characters are:—Sepals coloured; filaments hairy; stigma one; capsule three-celled at the base, many-seeded. The genus, which is a small one, is represented in Britain by the Lancashire Asphodel, *N. ossifragum*, a plant with creeping roots, ensiform leaves all in the same plane, and scapes terminating in a spiked cluster of pretty yellow flowers. It is common on wet moors and the boggy sides of mountains. Since sheep pasturing in such localities are liable to the rot, it was formerly thought that this disease was attributable to the herbage on which they fed; and hence this innoxious plant received the ill-omened name ossifragum, or 'bone-breaker.' An American species, *N. americanum*, is similar in all respects. French *Brise-os*; Germ. *Beinbrechgras*. [C. A. J.]

NARTHEX. A genus of *Umbelliferæ* closely allied to *Ferula*, but the umbels have no involucre, the limb of the calyx is suppressed, the stylopods are depressed and cup-shaped, the styles recurved, and the fruit compressed at the back with a dilated margin, each half traversed by three central ridges and two lateral ones, which are very minute. There is one vitta in each channel on the back of the fruit, and a variable number on the commissure. *N. asafœtida*, a tall-growing plant much like a *Ferula*, grows in Western Tibet, &c. The plant has recently produced its flowers in the Edinburgh Botanic Garden.

It seems certain, from the researches of Falconer and others, that this plant produces some of the asafœtida of commerce, while *Scorodosma fœtida*, a gigantic umbelliferous plant found in the sandy steppes east of the Caspian, as well as some other allied plants, also furnish the drug. On cutting into the upper part of the root, a juice exudes which hardens by exposure, and is collected and sent to this country from Bombay. The drug is well known

Narthex asafœtida.

for its disgusting odour, which it seems has charms for some people, as the Persians and other Asiatics use it as a condiment. It has even been called the 'food of the gods,' a strange contrast to its popular name in this country, namely, 'Devil's dung.' In medicine this drug is used as a stimulant in hysteria with excellent effect; also in cases of flatulence and chronic catarrh. Its smell is a very serious impediment to its use. [M. T. M.]

NARUNGEE. An Indian name for the Sweet Orange.

NASEBERRY. *Achras Sapota*, sometimes called Neesberry or Nisberry.

NASEBERRY-BULLY TREE. *Achras Sideroxylon.* —, BROAD-LEAVED. *Lucuma multiflorum.*

NASITORT. (Fr.) *Lepidium sativum.*

NASSAUVIACEÆ, or NASSAVIACEÆ. A tribe of composite plants included in the suborder *Labiatiflorœ.* In this suborder the hermaphrodite florets, or at least the unisexual ones, are two-lipped. The tribe is distinguished by its style not being tumid, and its arms being long linear truncate, fringed only at the point. [J. H. B.]

NASSAUVIA. A genus of *Composita*, the type of a tribe of *Labiatiflorœ.* It consists of low much-branched perennial herbs or undershrubs, with crowded stem-clasping entire or toothed leaves, almost always prickly, and solitary or clustered heads of yellow or white flowers. Each head contains five bilabiate florets in an oblong cylindrical involucre; the receptacle is naked, the achenes glabrous, with a pappus of linear or capillary bristles. There are about twenty species known, all natives of extratropical South America.

NASTANTHUS. A genus of *Calyceraceœ*, comprising nine species from elevated dry rocky and exposed situations in the Andes of Chili, all stemless glabrous herbs, with spreading radical leaves mostly cut or toothed, and short succulent scapes bearing numerous flower-heads closely collected into one large terminal globular head.

NASTURTIUM. A genus of *Cruciferœ*, or *Brassicaceœ* consisting of dwarf uninteresting weedy-looking plants whose stems and leaves partake more or less of the acrid flavour peculiar to crucifers. The genus is said to have derived its name from the effect its acrimony produces on the muscles of the nose—*nasus tortus* signifying a convulsed nose.'

N. officinale, the Common Watercress, is a well-known hardy perennial, indigenous to Britain, and usually found in abundance near springs or open running watercourses. It is of a creeping habit, with smooth shining brownish-green pinnatifid leaves, and ovate somewhat heart-shaped leaflets, the terminal one being much larger than the rest. The flowers are small and white, produced towards the extremity of the branches in a sort of terminal panicle.

As a spring salad the young shoots and leaves of Watercresses have been used from time immemorial. They are stated to have been eaten by the ancients along with lettuces, to counteract the coldness of the latter by their warm and stimulating qualities; and at the present day they are to be found almost on every table, the popular belief being that, when eaten fasting, they possess the property of exciting the appetite, and acting as a powerful antiscorbutic. The first attempt to cultivate watercresses by artificial means in Europe was made by Nicholas Meissner at Erfurt, the capital of Upper Thuringia, about the middle of the sixteenth century. The soil and other circumstances being highly favourable for their growth, the experiment proved successful, and the watercresses of Erfurt soon acquired that celebrity for their superior quality which they still maintain, most of the cities on the Rhine as well as the markets of Berlin, 120 miles distant, being constantly supplied with them. In the neighbourhood of London the mode of cultivating watercresses was first introduced by Mr. Bradbury at Northfleet, Springhead, near Gravesend, and has continued to spread, particularly in localities favourably situated with regard to springs of water. Near Rickmansworth in Hertfordshire, Waltham Abbey in Essex, Uxbridge in Middlesex, and various other places, there are plantations many acres in extent, which are scarcely sufficient to supply the great demand for this popular salad herb during the season. [W. B. B.]

NASTURTIUM. The garden name of *Tropæolum*.

NATA. The Bengalee name of the Bonduc nut tree, *Guilandina Bonduc.*

NATANS. Floating *under water* like a *Conferva.*

NATCHNEE. An Indian name for *Eleusine coracana.*

NATIVE BREAD. *Mylitta.*

NATJI. A name in Natal for a small variety of *Citrus nobilis.*

NATSIATUM. The name of a genus of *Phytocrenaceæ*, represented by a climbing shrub native of tropical Asia, with alternate leaves, and small greenish diœcious flowers, arranged in long hairy pendent clusters. The calyx and corolla are five-parted, and the disk five-lobed, each lobe having two linear teeth. In the male flower there are five stamens alternating with the lobes of the corolla, with anthers opening longitudinally; and in the female the ovary is free, one-celled, with two pendulous ovules.   [M. T. M.]

NAUCLEA. An extensive genus of *Cinchonaceæ*, principally natives of tropical Asia. Of the several sections, one frequently described as a distinct genus under the name of *Uncaria*, is composed of climbing shrubs having the old or sterile flower-stalks converted into hooked spines; the others consist of middle-sized trees or shrubs. The leaves are opposite or in whorls of three or four, and the flowers crowded together upon receptacles forming dense globose heads.

N. Gambir, or *Uncaria Gambir*, a native of the Malayan islands, yields the Gambir or Terra Japonica of commerce. In a wild state it is a rambling climber, but under cultivation it forms when trimmed a bushy shrub, seven or eight feet high, with smooth oblong or ovate leaves, and globular heads of green and pink flowers upon the upper flower-stalks, the lower ones being barren and converted into hooked spines. Gambir, or Terra Japonica, is prepared by boiling the leaves for several hours in large cauldrons of water, after which they are taken out and allowed to drain into the cauldron. The decoction is kept boiling until it thickens, when it is left to cool; and is afterwards poured into oblong moulds, where it remains until it acquires the consistency of clay, and is then cut into small cubes, which are thoroughly dried and hardened in the sun. Among the Malays the chief use of Gambir is as a masticatory, in combination with the areca-nut and the betel-leaf; but considerable quantities are annually exported to China for tanning purposes, and likewise to this country, where it is used for tanning 'kips' for the upper leather of shoes, and also by dyers and curriers.   [A. S.]

NAVÆA. A genus of *Malvaceæ*, allied to *Lavatera*, comprising a single species, native of the Canary Isles. The flower-stalks are axillary or terminal, racemose, each of them so twisted that what was the lower part of the flower becomes the upper. The involucel or outer calyx is three to four-leaved, ultimately deciduous; the true calyx bell-shaped with four to six segments; petals bluntish, with membranous convolute stalks forming little hollow pouches; column bent downwards; ovary rounded, depressed, of numerous crested lobes, attached to a central prolonged axis, each containing a single seed. Fruit indehiscent. *N. phœnicea* has beautiful pink flowers, and is a rare plant in the Canary Isles. The generic name is given in honour of J. de Nava, the founder of the Botanic Garden at Orotava.   [M. T. M.]

NAVARRETIA. A genus of *Polemoniaceæ*, containing nine species, natives of America. They are annual herbs, generally glutinous, often fœtid, with pinnatisect alternate leaves, the lower ones sometimes entire, and flowers in dense heads furnished with spiny bracts. The calyx is obconical or tubular, campanulate, with five very sharp lobes; the corolla tube slender and the limb spreading, cut into oblong laciniæ; the stamens usually exserted; the disk minute; and the capsule ovoid and obtuse, with ovoid wingless seeds. This genus can scarcely be separated from *Collomia* or *Gilia*, except by its habit.   [W. C.]

NAVELWORT. *Cotyledon.* —, VENUS'S. *Omphalodes linifolia.*

NAVE-SHAPED. The same as Modioliform.

NAVET. (Fr.) *Brassica Napus.* — D'ÉTÉ. *Brassica campestris.* — D'HIVER. *Brassica Napus oleifera.* — DU DIABLE. *Bryonia alba.* — SAUVAGE. *Brassica Napus.*

NAVETTE. (Fr.) *Brassica Napus sylvestris.*

NAVEW. *Brassica campestris.*

NAVIA. A genus of Brazilian herbs belonging to the *Bromeliaceæ*, having tufted leaves and downy flower-stalks, bearing tufts of flowers in the axils of the bracts. The perianth is divided into three outer and three inner segments, two of the former larger and more acutely keeled than the third, the three inner petaloid segments conjoined below into a tube; stamens six, hypogynous; ovary free, three-celled; stigmas three, thread-like; capsule membranous, three-valved.   [M. T. M.]

NAVICULARIA. A genus of grasses now included in *Panicum.*

NAVICULAR. Boat-shaped. The same as Cymbiform.

NAW. A kind of Ironwood met with in Ceylon.

NEBBEK. An Arabian name for the fruit of the Jujube.

NEB-NEB, or NIB-NIB. The pods of *Acacia vera*, which are used for tanning in Egypt.

NEBOO. An Indian name for the Lemon.

NEBULOSE. Clouded.

NECKERA. A beautiful genus of mosses, the type of the *Neckerei*, which are distinguished from *Hookeriei* by the pinnate branching, and the cuculliform frequently pilose veil. The peristome is double or single, and the branches almost always flattened. The foliage is peculiarly elegant, and is frequently beautifully undulated, as in *N. crispa*, which is one of our finest mosses. *Neckera*, however, obtains its maximum in hotter countries, though *N. pennata*, which is almost cosmopolitan, occurs as far north as Scotland. [M. J. B.]

NECKLACE-SHAPED. The same as Moniliform.

NECKLACE-TREE. *Ormosia.*

NECKWEED. *Cannabis sativa.*

NECROSIS. Canker. A drying and dying of the branch of a tree, beginning with the bark and eating gradually inwards.

NECTANDRA. A considerable genus of *Lauraceæ*, abounding in Peru, Guiana, and the West Indian Islands. The species all form large forest trees, with alternate leaves, and loose axillary panicles or corymbs of perfect flowers, having a six-parted wheel-shaped calyx, the segments of which fall away, while the tubular part increases in size and ultimately forms a cup, surrounding the lower part of the one-seeded fruit; the twelve stamens are arranged in four series, the nine outer fertile, and the three inner sterile. The Greenheart or Bibiri tree of British Guiana, named *Nectandra Rodiœi* by Sir R. Schomburgk, but by some botanists considered a variety of *N. leucantha*, is a large tree sixty or seventy feet high, frequently without branches for the first fifty feet, the trunk being between two and three feet in diameter and covered with an ash-coloured bark, which, under the name of Bibiru bark, is used medicinally as a tonic and febrifuge, its properties being due to the presence of an uncrystallisable alkaloid, found likewise in the seeds. These latter, however, are more remarkable for containing upwards of fifty per cent. of starch, which the Indians mix with rotten wood, and make into a bitter disagreeable kind of bread. The most valuable part of the tree is its timber, large quantities of which are regularly imported for ship-building purposes, its great strength and durability, together with the long lengths in which it is obtainable, rendering it well suited for beams, planking, and similar purposes; and its reputation is so high that it is placed in the first or twelve-year class in Lloyd's list of shipbuilding woods, though it is by no means free from the attacks of the ship-worm, or of the fungi which are such a fertile cause of decay in ships' timbers. [A. S.]

NECTAR. The honey of a flower; the superfluous saccharine matter remaining after the stamens and pistil have consumed all that they require.

NECTARILYMA. A collection of long hairs found on the inner surface of some flowers, as *Menyanthes*.

NECTARINE. A smooth-skinned variety of the Peach, *Amygdalus persica.*

NECTARIUM, NECTARY. A place or thing in which honey is secreted. Sometimes also applied to any supplementary or anomalous organ in a flower.

NECTAROSCORDUM. A genus of bulbous *Liliaceæ* founded on *Allium siculum*, which differs not only from *Allium*, but from the great majority of the order, in having the ovary adhering to the perianth at the base so as to be partly inferior; the perianth also differs from that of *Allium* in being somewhat bell-shaped, with a short pear-shaped tube, and a six-parted limb. In its habit, odour, and umbellate flowers, it quite agrees with *Allium*. The leaves are linear-lanceolate, channelled; and the scape two or three feet high, with a loose umbel of green and purplish flowers on drooping pedicels. [J. T. S.]

NECTAROSTIGMA. A gland secreting honey in certain flowers, as in *Ranunculus.*

NECTAROTHECA. Literally, a honey or nectar case; the spur of certain flowers.

NECTRIA. A genus of ascomycetous *Fungi* closely allied to *Sphæria*, and comprising all the species which have naked bright-coloured perithecia. Several exhibit the most brilliant tints. *N. cinnabarina* occurs in every garden on dead currant twigs, always succeeding the common *Tubercularia*, which is supposed to be merely a young state of the *Nectria*. The species are numerous, and abound in temperate regions in either hemisphere, though not confined to them. [M. J. B.]

NEEA. A genus of tropical American trees and shrubs belonging to the *Nyctaginaceæ*. The flowers are panicled, without involucre, but having a tubular perianth, within which are included five to eight stamens of unequal length; the ovary contains a single erect ovule. The fruit is contained within the hardened persistent base of the perianth, but is not united with it. [M. T. M.]

NEEDLES, SPANISH. An American name for *Bidens bipinnata.*

NEEDLE-SHAPED. Linear, rigid, tapering to a fine point from a narrow base, as the leaves of juniper.

NEELA. An Indian name for Indigo.

NEELE. *Lolium temulentum.*

NEEM, or NIM. *Melia Azadirachta.*

NEEMOOKA. An Indian name for *Clypea hernandifolia.*

NEESIA. A genus of *Sterculiaceæ*, of the tribe *Bombaceæ*, very nearly allied to *Durio*; but the numerous filaments are almost free, and each bears only one or two ring-shaped anthers. There are two species, one from Java, the other from the Malayan peninsula : both very large trees, with alternate leaves scaly-white underneath, and rather large reddish flowers in short racemes or clusters along the branches. The fruit is hard and woody, covered with asperities, and much resembling the durian in outer aspect, but without its edible pulp.

NÉFLIER. (Fr) *Mespilus.* → COTONIER. *Cotoneaster, vulgaris.* — DU JAPON. *Eriobotrya japonica.*

NÉGRETTE. (Fr.) A kind of olive.

NEGRO-CORN. A West Indian name for the Turkish Millet or Dhurra.

NEGRO'S HEAD. *Phytelephas macrocarpa.*

NEGUNDO. A North American tree belonging to the *Aceraceæ,* and distinguished from the true maples by having pinnate leaves. *N. fraxinifolium,* the Box Elder or Ash-leaved Maple, a tree of forty feet high, growing on the banks of rivers from Pennsylvania to Carolina, is sometimes introduced into English shrubberies. The leaflets are opposite, deeply toothed, the terminal one usually three-lobed. [C. A. J.]

NEILLIA. A genus of *Rosaceæ* of the group *Spiræidæ,* and closely allied to *Spiræa* itself, from which, however, it is distinguished by its seeds having copious fleshy albumen. Two species are known, both natives of the Himalayas, and both shrubs with simple doubly-serrated leaves, and racemes of white flowers. [A. S.]

NEIPPERGIA chrysantha is a species of *Acineta,* erected into a genus by Morren. The points relied upon for its separation were the erect instead of pendulous flower-racemes, and the presence of a long blunt papillose horn arising from the lower part of the lip; but the racemes are not always erect, and other species of *Acineta* have analogous horns of different forms. It is a native of Mexico, and has long racemes of large golden-yellow flowers, which have an aromatic odour at night but are odourless during the day. [A. S.]

NEJA. A genus of *Compositæ,* consisting of half a dozen South Brazilian perennials or low undershrubs, generally hispid with long spreading hairs, and bearing scattered narrow linear finely pointed leaves, and yellow flower-heads. In essential characters they only differ in their rather narrower achenes from *Chrysopsis,* with which they ought probably to be united. The *N. gracilis,* occasionally met with in our gardens, is a rather neat and pretty greenhouse plant.

NELSONIA. A small genus of *Acanthaceæ,* widely distributed over tropical and subtropical regions in both the Old and the New Worlds. The species consist of diffuse often tomentose herbs, growing in low moist localities, furnished with smallish leaves, and small solitary flowers covered by a single large bract, the lateral ones being either deficient or very small. These flowers are arranged in terminal or axillary spikes like those of *Origanum.* The calyx is unequally five-parted, and the corolla two-lipped, with only two stamens, one cell of the anther placed above the other. The capsule has eight small seeds in each cell. [W. C.]

NELUMBIACEÆ, NELUMBIUM. A natural order and genus of beautiful thalamifloral water-plants, belonging to Lindley's nymphal alliance of hypogynous Exogens. They have an elongated horizontal rootstock, from which are sent up long cylindrical leafstalks, bearing the plate-like leaves in a peltate manner on their summit. These leaves are circular in outline, with radiating venation, and covered on the upper surface with a glaucous bloom. The flowers are also borne on long stalks, traversed like those of the leaves by a number of air-canals, regularly disposed. The calyx consists of four to five deciduous sepals ; the corolla of numerous deciduous petals, arranged in several rows ; the stamens are numerous, in several rows, attached with the petals to the base of the receptacle ; the stigma is sessile ; the receptacle or torus is in form like a funnel ; and the ovaries, which are numerous, are placed in sockets on the upper surface ; the ovule solitary, or sometimes two placed side by side. The seeds contain an embryo without albumen, but with thick cotyledons, and a much-developed plumule.

N. speciosum, the Sacred Lotus, is interesting for its associations, as well as for the beauty of its rose-coloured flowers. It is found throughout India, China, Japan, Australia, the Malay and Philippine Islands, Persia, and even the Caspian Sea, but is no longer to be met with in the Nile. Herodotus, however, describes the plant with tolerable accuracy, comparing the receptacle of the flower to a wasp's nest. Strabo and Theophrastus, likewise, mention the plant as a native of Egypt. Sculptured representations of it abound among the ruins of Egyptian temples, and many other circumstances prove the veneration paid to this plant by the votaries of Isis. In a manuscript of Dioscorides supposed to be of the twelfth century, formerly in the Ripuccini library at Florence, there is a figure of the *Nelumbium,* under the name *kuamos,* while under the name *lotos* a tolerably good representation of *Celtis australis* is given. But the worship of the Lotus was by no means confined to the ancient Egyptians, for in India, Tibet, China, and Japan, the plant was deemed sacred, and indeed it is still employed in religious invocations and ceremonies. The leaves are covered with a fine microscopic down, which, by retaining a film of air over the upper surface, prevents it from being wetted when water is poured on it, the water rolling off in drops; this has a very pretty appearance, the drops of water looking like drops of molten silver. The Hindoos have a proverb founded on this peculiarity of the leaves, to the effect that the good and virtuous man is not enslaved by passion nor polluted by vice; for though he may be immersed in the waters of temptation, yet like a lotus leaf he will rise uninjured by them. The leafstalks abound in spiral fibres, which are carefully extracted and used as wicks to burn in the temples of India, before the idols. The rootstock and seeds are eaten as food in China, India, and Australia, and medicinal properties are assigned to the viscid juice of the leafstalks.

The young leaves of these plants float on the surface of the water, but as the stalk supporting them lengthens they are carried upwards. The fact of the contact of the lower surface of the leaf with the water, together with the structure of the upper surface of the leaf as before described, accounts for the peculiar position of the breathing pores or stomates, which are only to be found within a small space in the centre of the upper surface of the leaf opposite to its junction with the stalk. This space is of a lighter colour than the rest of the upper surface, and is devoid of the covering of microscopic hairs, &c. The breathing pores are in communication with the air-canals in the stalk.　　[M. T. M.]

NEMA. In Greek compounds = the filament.

NEMATANTHERA. The name of a Surinam shrub which constitutes a genus of *Piperaceæ*. The leaves are alternate, oblique at the base, ribbed; the stipules small, opposite the leaves, deciduous; the spikes stalked, with fleshy peltate bracts, in the axils of which the flowers are placed; the stamens two in number, with very long slender anthers which separate from the filament at a joint. The ovary, which is in the same flowers with the stamens, is sessile, with three lanceolate stigmas.　　[M. T. M.]

NEMATODES. Filamentous, threadlike; a term applied to *Confervæ*.

NEMATANTHUS. A genus of *Gesneraceæ* inhabiting humid places in South American forests, and consisting of fleshy shrubs, with lengthened scandent, often rooting branches; opposite oblong leaves; solitary axillary flowers rather large in size, and of a purplish colour; a five-cleft calyx having linear segments; a corolla with obconical tube gradually merging into a funnel or bell-shaped expansion; and a one-celled two-valved capsule, containing an indefinite number of seeds.　　[B. S.]

NEMATHECIA. Warty excrescences of the fronds of certain rose-spored *Algæ*, producing tetraspores, as in *Phyllophora*.

NEMATOCERAS. The five species of New Zealand orchids described under this generic name have now been combined with *Corysanthes*. They are curious little terrestrial plants, with solitary broad membranous leaves, and solitary dirty purple flowers. In technical characters

they differ from the original species of *Corysanthes* by having very long filiform lateral sepals projecting horizontally from beneath the lip, and similar long filiform erect petals.　　[A. S.]

NEMEÆ. A word used by Fries for cryptogams, to indicate that they germinate by means of the protrusion of a thread, and do not possess true cotyledons. It is, however, to be remarked that many *Algæ* cannot be said to germinate at all, and in *Selaginella* and some other allied Acrogens germination consists in cell-division without the slightest appearance of a thread.　　[M. J. B.]

NEMESIA. A family of herbaceous annual plants belonging to the *Scrophulariaceæ*, distinguished from *Linaria* by the compressed capsule which opens lengthwise in the middle. The species are natives of the Cape of Good Hope, and grow from a few inches to a foot high or more, with opposite or whorled leaves, and terminal racemes of unpretending flowers usually of a purplish hue.　　[C. A. J.]

NEMOCHLOA. A genus of cyperaceous plants belonging to the *Rhynchosporeæ*, and described by Steudel under *Pleurostachys*. They are all Brazilian.　　[D. M.]

NEMOPHILA. A genus of herbaceous annual plants, with diffuse brittle stems, pinnatifid leaves, and conspicuous flowers, belonging to the *Hydrophyllaceæ*, and well marked by the reflexed teeth between the lobes of the calyx. Several species are in common cultivation, of which *N. insignis*, introduced by Mr. Douglas from California, is by far the most beautiful, and is much prized as a border plant for its showy large flowers of a clear brilliant blue with a white centre. *N. atomaria* bears white flowers singularly dotted with purple-black. *N. maculata* has whitish flowers with one large purple spot at the tip of each petal.　　[C. A. J.]

NEMOROSE. Growing in groves?

NE M'OUBLIEZ PAS. (Fr.) *Myosotis palustris.*

NÉNUPHAR. (Fr.) *Nymphæa.* — **JAUNE.** *Nuphar.*

NEODRYAS. An inconspicuous little orchid from Bolivia, with the habit of a *Polystachia. N. rhodoneura* has flowers with a concave broadly oblong cordate lip, upon a long claw, through which runs an obtuse crest ending, just beyond the junction of the claw with the lamina, in a callosity composed of two four-lobed plates, one on the top of the other. Their column is semiterete, channelled in front, and prolonged upwards into two ears which are notched at the tips. The two pyriform pollen-masses are attached to a reniform gland by a ligulate caudicle.　　[A. S.]

NEOGYNE. Proposed as a genus by the younger Reichenbach, but since reduced by Lindley to a section of *Cælogyne*, characterised by its flowers being closed and having carinate sepals with saccate bases and a bisaccate lip. Only one species is known *Cœlogyne* (§ *Neogyne*) *Gardneriana*, a very fine plant of Nepal and Khasya, with long flask-like pseudobulbs, very large five-nerved lanceolate leaves, and dense nodding terminal or radical racemes of large pure white flowers, with a yellowish stain on the lip, each flower having beneath it a conspicuous petal-like bract.   [A. S.]

NEOTINEA *intacta* is the *Aceras intacta* or *Aceras secundiflora* of most botanists, a common South European orchid, which has recently been found wild in Ireland. It was first separated as a distinct genus by an Italian botanist, and named *Tinea*, which name has been changed to *Neottinea* by Reichenbach.   [A. S.]

NEOTTIA. With the exception of the longer column and the generally cucullate anther-bed, there are no technical characters for separating this genus of orchids from *Listera*; but it is well marked and easily distinguishable by the habit of its species, all of which are leafless brown-stemmed plants with sheathing scales in place of leaves. Only about four species are known, one of which, a peculiar withered-looking plant, *N. Nidus-avis*, is the Bird's-nest Orchis of this country, while the others belong to Northern Asia. Owing to confusion in nomenclature, a large number of species of *Spiranthes* erroneously bear the name of *Neottia* in many works.   [A. S.]

NEOTTOPTERIS. *Thamnopteris.*

NEOWIEDIA. *Apostasia.*

NEOZA. An Indian name for certain edible Pine seeds.

NEP. *Nepeta Cataria.* —, WILD. *Bryonia dioica.*

NEPENTHACEÆ. A natural order of monochlamydeous dicotyledons, belonging to Lindley's euphorbial alliance of diclinous Exogens. They consist of herbs, or half-shrubby plants, with alternate leaves, slightly sheathing at the base, and forming an ascidium at the extremity. Flowers dioecious, the perianth four-parted, inferior; males: stamens united in a solid central column, anthers about sixteen, forming a spherical head, extrorse; females: ovary free, four-cornered, four-celled, stigma sessile; capsule four-celled, four-valved, with loculicidal dehiscence, and indefinite ascending seeds. They are natives of swampy ground in the East Indies and China, and have no known properties. The pitchers have been found to contain a solution of binoxalate of potash, and some chemists have detected muriate of soda, malic, and other acids in them. Spiral vessels abound in all parts of pitcher plants, and the woody bundles are without concentric zones.   [J. H. B.]

NEPENTHES. The sole genus of *Nepenthaceæ*. About twenty species are known, by far the greater part of which are natives of Borneo, Sumatra, and the adjacent islands of the Indian Archipelago; but a few extend to Continental Asia, and one to as far north as the Khasya mountains, and another to China. One is confined to Ceylon, and two to Madagascar. The oddity of the foliaceous organs in this genus, with their remarkable terminal pitcher-like appendages, has given rise to some difference of opinion amongst botanists as to which part of the leaf is the petiole or stalk, and which the lamina or blade. It has been commonly stated that the broad part at the base is a leafy stalk, and that the lid of the so-called pitcher is the true lamina. The recent investigations of Dr. Hooker, however, have confirmed the statement long ago made by Griffith, that the basal portion, that which appears like an ordinary leaf, is the true lamina, tapering downwards into a more or less evident stalk; and that the pitcher-like appendage is a modification of the prolonged midrib of the leaf, or, rather, of a gland situated at the apex of the midrib.

The size and shape of the pitchers differ considerably in the different kinds. Dr. Hooker has described one species from Borneo, and named it after Rajah Brooke (*N. Rajah*), in which the blade of the leaf is eighteen inches long by seven or eight broad, the excurrent midrib or tendril twenty inches long and as thick as the finger, and the pitcher twelve inches long by six inches in diameter, of a broad ampulla form, with two fringed wings in front.

One of the species sometimes seen in hot-houses in this country is *N. Rafflesiana*, a native of Singapore, Malacca, Sumatra, and Borneo. This, like many others, has two kinds of pitchers. Those on the lower leaves are of an ampulla form, with two fringed wings in front, about four inches long by two wide, and beautifully spotted with rich brown; while those on the upper leaves are less beautifully coloured, a good deal longer, and funnel-shaped, narrowing gradually to the base, where they gracefully curve upwards. *N. distillatoria*, the Cingalese species, is so called because its pitchers are partly filled with water before they open; but that is also the case with the other species. The Cingalese use the tough flexible stems as withes.   [A. S.]

NEPETA. A genus of the labiate order, distinguished by the calyx having about fifteen ribs, and an oblique five-toothed mouth; and the corolla with the upper lip straight and notched, and the lower usually three-cleft. The species are natives of Europe and the temperate parts of Asia; they are numerous, and owing to differences in character have been divided into several subgenera.   [G. D.]

NEPHELAPHYLLUM. A small genus of terrestrial orchids belonging to the tribe *Epidendreæ*, and mostly natives of the islands of the Indian Archipelago. The plants belonging to it have creeping sheathed stems, stalked ovate or cordate leaves, usually purplish beneath and spotted or clouded above, and flowers in racemes on terminal scapes.   [A. S.]

NEPHELIUM. Three celebrated Chinese and Malayan fruits, the Litchi, the Longan, and the Rambutan, are produced by different trees belonging to this genus of *Sapindaceæ*, which contains in all about twenty-five species, and is confined to Southern Asia and the Indian Archipelago, except a single species found in the Feejee and neighbouring Islands. They are mostly trees of small size, with alternate pinnate (rarely simple) leaves, and panicles of small flowers at the ends of the branches, producing bunches of globular or egg-shaped warted or rough prickly fruits, which do not open in a regular manner when ripe; each fruit contains a single seed covered with a fleshy arillus. Their flowers have from four to six sepals, sometimes united into a cup-shaped calyx, as many petals or none, twice as many stamens inserted inside the ring-like disk, and a short-stalked, two-lobed, two-celled ovary occupying the centre of the flower.

N. *Litchi*, the Litchi, or, as it is variously written, Litschi, Li'tchi, Lichi, Leechee, or La'tji, is the most celebrated of the indigenous fruits of China, and is now frequently imported to this country, and sold in the

Nephelium Litchi.

fruit shops. There are several varieties, but the most common is nearly round, about an inch and a half in diameter, with a thin brittle shell of a red colour covered all over with rough wart-like protuberances; others are larger and heart-shaped. When fresh, they are filled with a white, almost transparent, sweet jelly-like pulp, surrounding a rather large shining brown seed; after they have been gathered some time the pulp shrivels and turns black, and then bears some resemblance to prunes. The Chinese are very fond of these fruits, and consume large quantities of them, both in a fresh state and when dried and preserved in various ways. The tree, which grows about twenty feet high, is a native of Southern China, but is only known in a cultivated state. It has abruptly pinnate leaves composed of from two to four pairs of oblong or lance-shaped, pointed, shining leaflets about three inches long and of a thick leathery texture, and bears panicles of small flowers which are without petals, having only a small cup-shaped slightly four or five-toothed calyx.

N. *Longanum*, the Longan tree, is likewise a native of Southern China, where, like the last, it is much cultivated for the sake of its fruit. Its leaves have generally five pairs of leaflets much resembling those of the Litchi, but it is readily distinguished by its flowers having a deeply five-parted calyx and five narrow hairy petals about the same length as the calyx. The Longan is a smaller fruit than the Litchi, varying from half an inch to an inch in diameter, and quite round, with a nearly smooth brittle skin of a yellowish-brown colour. It contains a similar semitransparent pulp, of an agreeable sweet or subacid flavour, and is largely sold in the Chinese markets.

N. *lappaceum* yields the Rambutan or Ramboostan, a well-known and favourite fruit in the Malayan Archipelago. It is a small tree, with leaves composed of from five to seven pairs of oblong leaflets; and its flowers have a five or six-cleft calyx and no petals. The fruit is of a bright red colour, about two inches long, of an oval form and slightly flattened, and covered with long soft fleshy spines or thick hairs, from which circumstance it takes its name, *rambut* signifying hair in the Malayan language. Like the two above mentioned, the Rambutan contains a pleasant acidulous pulp very grateful in tropical countries. [A. S.]

NEPHRODIUM. A genus of aspidioid ferns, distinguished among their near allies by their reniform indusia, and their connivently anastomosing veins. In the former peculiarity they agree with *Lastrea*, which has free veins; and some botanists unite both these groups under the present name, distinguishing *Aspidium* (including *Polystichum*) by its peltate indusia. As limited by the characteristics of reniform indusia and connivently anastomosing venation, *Nephrodium* is still an extensive genus, distributed freely over the warmer parts of the Old and New Worlds, and consisting mostly of species which have more or less the aspect of the common male fern. The most familiar species is N. *molle*, which is everywhere met with in collections of cultivated plants, as well as among dried ferns from nearly all parts of the world. [T. M.]

NEPHROID. Kidney-shaped.

NEPHROLEPIS. A genus of polypodiaceous ferns belonging to the tribe *Aspidieæ*, and to that section of it with free veins and reniform indusia. They are pinnate ferns, with narrow elongate fronds, and articulated pinnæ; and produce from their crown long slender stolones, which, at intervals bear other fasciculate crowns, and sometimes also develope fleshy tubers. One tuber-bearing species, N. *undulata*, has annual fronds; but the majority are evergreen, and are very easily recognised by the features we have indicated. [T. M.]

NEPHROPHYLLUM. A genus of *Convolvulaceæ* founded on a single species from Abyssinia, a small humifuse plant, with a slender creeping stem, rooting at the joints, reniform entire leaves, and solitary axillary flowers on very short peduncles. In habit and structure it is very near to *Dichondra repens*, from which, however, it differs in having a one-celled ovary with two ovules, a single style, and a fruit composed of a single utricle. [W. C.]

NEPHROSTA. The spore-case of lycopods.

NEPTUNIA. A genus of *Leguminosæ* of the suborder *Mimoseæ*, consisting of undershrubs or stiff but slender herbs with bipinnate leaves, flowers in globular heads, the lower ones barren with elongated petals, the upper ones fertile with definite stamens as in *Desmanthus*, but differing from that genus chiefly in its broad flat short pods. There are not many species, all natives of hot climates in America or in the Old World. *N. oleracea*, which is common in many parts of tropical Asia, Africa, and America, is remarkable for its short stems frequently floating by means of hollow swellings, and branching and rooting so as to cover shallow waters or liquid swamps to a considerable extent. *N. plena*, a terrestrial species without these inflations, is also common to America, Asia, and Africa.

NERAUDIA. A genus of *Urticaceæ*, consisting of two Sandwich Island shrubs remarkable for their milky juice, as in *Artocarpeæ*, whilst the floral characters are those of the true *Urticaceæ*. The leaves are entire, the flowers diœcious, small and green, clustered in the axils of the leaves.

NEREOCYSTIS. One of the most extraordinary seaweeds among the *Laminariaceæ*, which occurs on the north-east coast of America, and the opposite shores of Asia. The stem is filiform and many fathoms in length, attached below by branched rootlike processes. This swells above into a swollen hollow turnip-shaped or retortlike cylinder a fathom in length, and containing a quantity of fluid, which gives off from the centre a bunch of leaf-like processes many feet in length. The stems become entangled below, and then the plants form large floating islands, which are the favourite seat of the sea-otter, who rocks with the waves and sleeps on the bladders. The plant, though so enormous, appears to be only of annual growth. The stem is employed by the Aleutians for fishing-lines, of whom Mertens informs us that he purchased one, and that they sometimes attain a length of forty-five fathoms. He also saw the bladders used, like the stems of *Ecklonia* (*Fucus*) *buccinalis*, as a siphon. [M. J. B.]

NERIANDRA. A genus of dogbanes, having the calyx five-parted and without glands; the corolla nearly salver-shaped, hairy internally, and somewhat inflated above; five hairy glands between the stamens; and two spindle-shaped smooth ovaries. The species are shrubs, natives of Central America, having entire leaves with glands at their base. The name is a

compound of that of the genus *Nerium* and the Greek for stamens, on account of the resemblance between them in the characters of these organs. [G. D.]

NERINE. A small genus of *Amaryllidaceæ*, consisting of bulbous plants from South Africa, distinguished by having a regular six-parted perianth without tube, six stamens having the filaments united by a gibbous junction at the base, and a suberect style with trifid stigma. The plants produce umbellate flower-scapes before the bifarious leaves appear, and their scarlet or rose-colour or pale pink blossoms are very ornamental. The Guernsey Lily, *N. sarniensis*, is one of the most popular species. [T. M.]

NÉRINE DE GUERNÉSEY. (Fr.) *Nerine sarniensis*.

NERIUM. A genus of dogbanes, characterised by having a salver-shaped corolla which has a crown of torn appendages in the throat, and a border of twisted unequal segments; five stamens attached to the middle of the tube of the corolla; and

Nerium Oleander.

cylindrical seed-vessels. The species are erect glabrous shrubs, natives of India, the leaves coriaceous with parallel veins. The name is from the Greek word signifying *humid*, to indicate the localities where some of the species grow. [G. D.]

NÉROLI. An essential oil obtained by distilling orange-blossoms.

NERPRUN. (Fr.) *Rhamnus catharticus*.

NERTERA. The name applied to a creeping herbaceous plant, constituting a genus of *Cinchonaceæ*, native of the southern part of South America. Its leaves are oval and fleshy; its flowers solitary, sessile, white, with a calyx whose limb is divided into four minute teeth, a funnel-shaped four-lobed corolla, and four stamens slightly projecting from the tube; the fruit is berry-like, red, containing two or four stones, each with a single seed. The plant is mentioned by Lindley as the most southern species of the extensive family of which it is a member. [M. T. M.]

NERVATE, NERVED, NERVOSE. Having several ribs.

NERVATION. The manner in which veins are arranged.

NERVES, NERVURES. The ribs or principal veins of a leaf.

NESÆA. A genus of *Lythraceæ*, consisting of perennial herbs, with opposite or whorled leaves, and axillary flowers. These have a short bell-shaped or cup-shaped calyx with four to seven erect teeth, and as many longer and spreading horn-like processes between them; five blue or purple petals, several exserted stamens, and a roundish three to five-celled capsule. There are two subgenera: *Nesæa*, from Senegambia and Morocco, with one-flowered peduncles and usually twelve to fourteen nearly equal stamens; and *Decodon* from North America, with many-flowered peduncles and ten stamens, the alternate ones much larger than the others. To this last section belongs *N. verticillata*, which is said to be injurious to cows about to calve. [J. T. S.]

NESODAPHNE. Two very large evergreen New Zealand trees, belonging to the *Lauraceæ*, have been formed into a genus under this name, which is derived from the Greek words *nesos*, an island, and *daphnos*, a laurel. They have axillary and terminal panicles of small greenish perfect flowers with a six-cleft calyx; twelve stamens arranged in a double series, the outer bursting inwards consisting of six fertile ones without glands, and the inner bursting outwards of alternating fertile and sterile ones; the former having two glands opposite the bases of their filaments, and a one-celled ovary with a short style and simple stigma. *N. Tarairi*, the Taraire of the New Zealanders, is a tree varying from fifty to eighty feet high, with a trunk about three feet thick, producing a light spongy white wood easily split but not durable, and consequently seldom used except by the natives for their fences. Its leaves are five or six inches long, smooth and shining upon the upper surface, but covered with a bloom on the under side, and with prominent nerves clothed with red or rusty-brown down, as also are the branches and panicles of flowers.
N. Tawa, called Tawa by the natives, is distinguished from the former by its shorter and narrower leaves having finely netted veins on both sides, and being covered with a dense bloom underneath, and by its panicles of flowers being more loosely branched, and not clothed with down. The fruits of both trees are ovoid and deep purple, those of the Taraire being the largest, and eagerly sought after by birds and by the aborigines; but as their seeds contain a poisonous principle, they require to be well boiled in order to deprive them of their injurious property. [A. S.]

NETTED. Covered with reticulated lines which project a little; any arrangement of veins which irregularly anastomose.

NETTLE. *Urtica.* —, BEE. *Galeopsis versicolor.* —, CHILI. *Loasa.* —, DEAD. *Lamium*; also *Galeobdolon.* —, FALSE. An American name for *Böhmeria cylindrica.* —, GREAT. *Urtica dioica.* —, HEDGE. *Stachys sylvatica.* —, HEMP. *Galeopsis.* —, HORSE. *Solanum carolinense.* —, ROMAN. *Urtica pilulifera.* —, SMALL. *Urtica urens.* —, STINGLESS. *Pilea.*

NETTLE-TREE. *Celtis.*

NETTLEWORTS. Lindley's name for the *Urticaceæ.*

NEUMANNIA. The name of a Mexican herbaceous plant, constituting a genus of *Bromeliaceæ.* The flowers are arranged in a cylindrical spike, and nearly concealed by the overlapping ovate pointed bracts. The perianth is six-parted, with the outer segments erect, convolute, and one of the three inner ones larger than the other two, and flat. There are six free stamens; and a three-celled ovary slightly adherent to the base of the perianth, and containing numerous ovules. The fruit is leathery, three-valved. The name is also synonymous with *Aphloia*, a genus of *Flacourtiaceæ.* [M. T. M.]

NEURACHNE. A genus of grasses belonging to the tribe *Paniceæ.* The inflorescence is in simple oval solitary spikes; glumes nearly equal, nerveless and acute; exterior smallest, hardening about the fruit; flowers two, the exterior neuter, and the interior hermaphrodite; stamens three; styles two, plumose. The species are natives of New Holland. [D. M.]

NEURADA *procumbens.* A prostrate annual with pinnatifid leaves, small axillary flowers, and a curious flattened circular capsule, surrounded by the prickly calyx, and divided into ten one-seeded cells. It has been referred to various natural orders, but is now usually associated with *Rosaceæ.*

NEUROCALLIS. A genus of acrostichaceous ferns, containing a few tropical species, of which the type is the pinnate-fronded *N. præstantissima* of the West Indies. Like other acrostichoid ferns, they are dimorphous, and their sori occupy the whole under-surface of the separate contracted fertile fronds. The veins, which are best seen in the sterile fronds, are reticulated in a regular manner, forming hexagonal meshes, which do not contain any free veinlets within the areoles. [T. M.]

NEUROLÆNA *lobata* is a West Indian tall herb or undershrub, forming a genus of *Compositæ*, with the aspect and chaffy receptacle of the *Heliantheæ*, but with the bristly pappus of *Senecioneæ.* The leaves are alternate, the lower ones three-lobed, the flower-heads without rays, in terminal corymbs.

NEUROPELTIS. A genus of *Convolvulaceæ*, containing two species, natives of India. They are spreading undershrubs, having the stem and branches whitish, and covered with numerous white elevated dots. The small flowers are in axillary racemes, and have a calyx consisting of five persistent sepals; a funnel-shaped corolla

Neuropeltis racemosa.

divided below the middle into five lanceolate acute lobes, which are valvate and not plicate in æstivation; and a two-celled ovary, with two ovules in each cell, and bearing two styles with fleshy reniform stigmas. The capsule is one-seeded, attached by a decurrent pedicel, considerably below the centre of the floral bract, which becomes enormously enlarged in fruiting, and is very delicate in texture. [W. C.]

NEUROSPERMA. *Momordica.*

NEWCASTELIA. A low shrub with crowded opposite entire leaves, thickly hirsute with coarse woolly hairs, and small flowers in terminal spikes remarkable for the long rigid hairs covering the calyx, and giving them the appearance of little hispid balls. It is a native of the deserts of the interior of South Australia, and has been described by F. Mueller as constituting a genus of *Verbenaceæ.*

NEZ-COUPÉ. (Fr.) *Staphylea pinnata.*

NHANDIROBA. *Feuillæa cordifolia.*

NIBONG. The Malay name for *Oncosperma filamentosa.*

NICANDRA. A genus of *Solanaceæ*, distinguished by its pentagonal calyx, which is persistent and finally closes and becomes inflated, with five compressed angles, and encloses a juiceless berry. The flower is broadly campanulate, indistinctly five-lobed, large, blue, white in the centre, where it is marked with five dark blue spots. *N. physaloides*, so called from the resemblance of its fruit to that of *Physalis*, is a stout annual plant about two feet high, with smooth deeply sinuated leaves, and a native of Peru. [C. A. J.]

NICARAGO, BASTARD. *Cæsalpinia bijuga.*

NICARAGUA WOOD, An inferior kind of Brazil-wood, the produce of *Cæsalpinia echinata.*

NICHOLSONIA. A genus of *Leguminosæ* of the tribe *Hedysareæ*, originally proposed by De Candolle, but since reduced to a section of *Desmodium.*

NICKER-TREE. *Guilandina Bonduc.*

NICOTIANA. A genus of *Solanaceæ* or *Atropaceæ*, consisting of sticky-leaved herbaceous plants, natives of tropical America and Eastern Asia, several of which are extensively grown to furnish Tobacco. The genus derives its name from Joan Nicot, a Portuguese, who was the means of introducing the tobacco plant into France. The generic characters are: calyx tubular, bell-shaped, five-cleft; corolla funnel-shaped or salver-shaped, the limb five-lobed; stamens five within the tube of the corolla; ovary two-celled, the style simple, and the stigma button-shaped. Fruit a two-valved capsule, with numerous seeds.

The best-known species, and that which furnishes the largest quantity of Tobacco, is *N. Tabacum*, the specific name, according to Humboldt, being derived from the Haytian word for the pipe in which the herb is smoked, and which has been transferred from the instrument to the plant. It is a handsome plant, attaining a height of three to six feet, with large oblong lance-shaped leaves, some of which are attached to the stem for some distance before they are given off (decurrent). These leaves are covered with minute hairs, on the summit of which a gland is placed, which secretes the viscid fluid that invests the surface of the plant. The flowers are in panicles on the end of the stem. The corolla is more than an inch in length, funnel-shaped, with a distended throat, and of a pretty rose or pink hue. This species is largely cultivated in the Southern States of America, especially Virginia—also in China, Holland, various parts of Germany, France, &c. With us tobacco cultivation is illegal, except on a very restricted scale. *N. rustica* is grown in all quarters of the globe. It is a smaller plant than the preceding, has ovate leaves, and a greenish corolla with a cylindrical tube. It grows more quickly, ripens earlier, and is more hardy than *N. Tabacum.* This species produces East Indian tobacco; also that furnished by the Manilla Isles, and the kinds called Latakia and Turkish. *N. persica*, a species not in cultivation in Great Britain, yields Persian tobacco. *N. repanda*, a native of the Havannah, is used in the manufacture of some of the most highly esteemed cigars. Its leaves clasp the stem, and the corolla is white with a slender tube. Other species, such as *N. multivalvis, N. quadrivalvis, N. latissima*, are also employed in the manufacture of various kinds of Tobacco; the last-mentioned yields the kind known as Orinoco. *N. multivalvis* and *N. quadrivalvis* have, as their names imply, several-valved or four-valved capsules.

Tobacco contains an extremely poisonous substance called *nicotine*. This, when extracted by the chemist, is a colourless liquid with alkaline properties and an acrid burning taste. This ingredient, as well as a concrete oily substance called *nicotianin*, exists, in the unpurified oil which is formed when tobacco is burned. Tobacco in poisonous doses, or when taken in any form by those unaccustomed to its use, produces (according to the quantity taken and the mode of taking) nausea, vomiting, purging, giddiness, remarkable languor and relaxation of the muscles, and in extreme cases cold

Nicotiana Tabacum.

sweats, fainting, convulsions, and death. Death has occurred from smoking even so small a quantity as two pipes, from the application of the drug to the raw skin, and from the incautious use of injections. Nevertheless, its moderate use is in many instances beneficial, from the sedative effects it produces. Its power of allaying hunger is also well attested. There can be no question, however, that the abuse of this substance does, at the present day, produce much serious impairment, first of the digestive organs, then of the nervous system, till at length the whole frame participates in the ill effects derived from what, under proper restraint, would be beneficial, or at all events harmless. In medical practice Tobacco is now rarely employed. At one time it was frequently used in cases of hernia, in order to relax the muscles and allow of the replacement of the displaced bowel; but for this purpose it has been superseded by the more safe and more efficacious chloroform.   [M. T. M.]

Smoking is a custom of very great antiquity in both hemispheres, although previous to the discovery of America it was not common among the inhabitants of the Old World, and the substances smoked were either hemp or such herbs as colts-foot. But when Columbus and his followers landed in Cuba in 1492, they discovered the now far-famed Tobacco in common use

among the natives; and subsequent explorers found that it was spread over the whole continent of America, where it had been cultivated from time immemorial. The pleasantly soothing effects of this new herb were so enticing that it soon found patrons among the adventurers, and in an almost incredibly short time after their return to Spain, tobacco-smoking began to be practised in Europe; but it did not gain much ground among the nations of the North until the famous Sir Walter Raleigh and his companions introduced the custom into England in 1586. At first it met with the most violent opposition: kings prohibited it; popes fulminated bulls against it; and sultans sentenced smokers to the most cruel kinds of death. Persecution, however, only helped to spread it. In spite of all penalties the custom rapidly progressed, until, at the present day, it may be said to be universally practised by both civilised and uncivilised man—Tobacco, of all the varied productions of the earth, being the substance most universally used by mankind.

Tobacco now forms one of the most important articles of commerce, and a large revenue is derived from it in this and other countries. In 1863 the total imports into the United Kingdom amounted to 55,122,048 lbs., of which 37,616,240 lbs. were retained for home consumption, the duty thereon amounting to 5,986,447*l*.

A great number of varieties are recognised, and mostly distinguished by the country from which they are derived. Thus, we have American tobacco, from the United States, Maryland, Ohio, Virginian, and Kentucky, which form the bulk of our imports, and come in hogsheads, the leaves being tied together in bundles called 'hands;' from Venezuela the kinds known as Varinas, Orinoco, and Cumana; from New Granada the Columbian; from Cuba, the Cuban and Havannah; and large imports from Buenos Ayres, Uruguay, Paraguay, Brazil, Peru, &c. Of European tobacco we receive large supplies from Holland, Germany, France, Turkey (Salonica), Italy, Greece, and other parts. Asiatic tobaccos come principally from India, the Philippine Islands (Manilla), Latakia, and occasionally from Persia (Shiraz).

The first process which the leaves undergo after gathering, is that of sweating for three or four days, after which the plants are hung in airy sheds to dry, and then placed in heaps and again sweated for one or two weeks, and while slightly moist packed for exportation. Before being used it is manufactured into cut and roll tobacco for smoking and chewing, into cigars and cheroots, and into snuff. For cutting, the tobacco is moistened and pressed into hard cakes, and then cut by machinery. The principal varieties are Bird's-eye, which contains portions of the stalk; Shag, prepared from dark-coloured Virginian or Kentucky leaves; Canaster or Kanaster (derived from the Spanish *canastra*, a basket, because it was imported in baskets), coarsely-cut Ohio, German, Varinas, or Havannah leaves; Returns, which consists of the refuse of the various processes of manufacture; and other kinds known by the name of the countries from which they are derived. Of roll tobaccos, the principal kinds are Pigtail, Negro-head, and Cavendish. Pigtail is the damp leaves spun into cord upon a wheel. The varieties of cigars and cheroots are too numerous for mention. Cigars are made by rolling fragments of leaves called fillings in a strip of leaf, and then winding a finer strip spirally round it. For all the above purposes, except for Bird's-eye, the leaves are stripped of their midribs, technically termed stalks, and these are used in snuff-making; but some snuffs are made from the entire leaves. Scotch, Irish, and Welsh high-dried snuffs are dried or roasted previous to grinding, but Rappees are ground moist.   [A. S.]

NICOTIANIN. A volatile oil containing the odorous principle of tobacco.

NICOTINE, or **NICOTINA.** A colourless liquid alkaloid, the poisonous principle of tobacco.

NICTAGE. (Fr.) *Mirabilis.*

NID D'OISEAU. (Fr.) *Neottia nidus avis.*

NIDOSE. Having a disgusting smell between that of burnt meat and rotten eggs.

NIDULANT, NIDULATE. Nestling. Lying free in a cup-shaped or nest-like body; as in the genus *Nidularia*, or the baskets of *Marchantia*. Also lying loose in pulp, like the seeds of true berries.

NIDULARIACEI. A natural order of gasteromycetous *Fungi* of a very singular structure. The peridium or common outer covering, which consists of one or more coats, sometimes separable from each other, contains one or many sporangia, which are free or attached to the walls by an elastic cord. These consist of a cellular dark coat enclosing hyaline cells, from which rise sporophores terminating in the centre and bearing naked spores. The structure is in fact that of one of the hypogæous *Fungi* reduced to single isolated cells, each surrounded by a separate coat and collected within a common envelope. In *Sphærobolus* the sporangia are reduced to one, which is exploded with violence in consequence of the eversion of the inner membrane of the peridium. The species are partly European and partly natives of hot climates, or of countries where there are no great extremes of temperature. *Atractobolus,* which should shoot out a spindle-shaped sporangium, appears to be nothing more than the eggs of a mite of the genus *Rhipignethus,* but highly curious as containing cellulose in the inner membrane, a very rare circumstance in animals, though not without example, as it occurs also in *Tunicata.*   [M. J. B.]

NIDULARIA. A genus of gasteromycetous *Fungi* closely allied to *Cyathus,* but distinguished by its simple peridium, which either bursts irregularly or opens by a circular mouth, and its sporangia, which are destitute of any umbilical cord. No species has yet occurred in Great Britain, though two or three are European, nor can they boast of the elegance of *Cyathus* and *Crucibulum,* however interesting they may be in connection with these genera. *N. dentata* is probably a *Sphærobolus.*   [M. J. B.]

NIDULARIUM. The mycelium of certain fungals.

NIELLE. (Fr.) *Agrostemma Githago;* also *Nigella arvensis.* — DES CHAMPS. *Agrostemma Githago.*

NIEREMBERGIA. A genus of *Atropaceæ* (*Solanaceæ*), consisting of decumbent herbaceous plants, natives of South America, with alternate leaves, and flowers on short stalks opposite to the leaves. The corolla, which is usually white or purple, is funnel-shaped with a slender tube, and a spreading five-lobed limb; stamens five, of unequal length, projecting more or less and somewhat united at the base; stigma kidney-shaped, concealing the anthers; fruit a two-valved capsule, concealed by the persistent calyx. Four or five elegant species are cultivated in this country. [M. T. M.]

NIESHOUT. The South African Sneezewood, *Pteroxylon utile.*

NIGELLA. The English name of Fennel-flower has been given to the plants of this genus of *Ranunculaceæ,* in consequence of their finely-cut leaves resembling those of fennel. About twenty species are known, all erect annuals bearing solitary terminal flowers, and chiefly natives of Asia Minor and the countries bordering the Mediterranean. Their flowers are sometimes surrounded by a leafy involucre, and have five coloured spreading deciduous sepals, from five to ten petals, numerous stamens, and from five to ten single-celled ovaries partly cohering by their bases and terminated by long simple styles, ultimately becoming dry seed-vessels more or less connected to-

Nigella sativa.

gether and opening along their inner edge. The seeds are numerous, black, acrid, and aromatic. *N. sativa,* or an allied species, is supposed by some to be the Fitches mentioned by the prophet Isaiah (xxviii. 25, 27).

It is a native of Southern Europe, Egypt, the Levant, &c., and has rather hairy stems, about a foot and a half high, with bluish flowers destitute of an involucre, and capsules connected almost to the top and covered with short hard points. French cooks employ the seeds of this plant under the name of *quatre épices* or *toute épice*, and they were formerly used as a substitute for pepper. They have a strong pungent fennel-like odour, and an aromatic somewhat acrid oily taste. In Eastern countries they are commonly used for seasoning curries and other dishes, and the Egyptians spread them over bread or put them on cakes like comfits, the ladies considering them to possess the property of augmenting the *embonpoint* so much admired by the Egyptian male sex. They are also used in India for putting among linen to keep away insects; and the native doctors employ them medicinally as a carminative in indigestion and bowel complaints. [A. S.]

NIGELLE AROMATIQUE. (Fr.) *Nigella sativa.*

NIGER. Black, or black a little tinged with grey. *Nigrescens,* or *nigricans,* signifies blackish; and *nigrittus,* blackened, as when a portion only is black—like the point of the glumes of a *Carex.*

NIGER-SEED. The small black seed of *Guizotia oleifera.*

NIGHTFLOWER. *Nyctanthes.*

NIGHTSHADE. *Solanum.* —, DEADLY. *Atropa Belladonna.* —, ENCHANTER'S. *Circœa.* —, MALABAR. *Basella.* —, THREE-LEAVED. *Trillium.* —, WOODY. *Solanum Dulcamara.*

NIGRITELLA. A genus of orchids proposed by Richard for the *Orchis* or *Habenaria nigra,* a small Alpine species with a dense head of remarkably dark-coloured almost black flowers. It has most of the characters of *Orchis,* but the glands of the pollen-masses are half-exposed, almost as in *Gymnadenia.*

NILOUFAR DES ÉGYPTIENS. (Fr.) *Nymphœa cœrulea.*

NIMA. *Picrasma.*

NIMBLE WILL. An American name for *Mühlenbergia diffusa.*

NIMBOOKA. An Indian name for the Lemon.

NIMMOIA *floribunda* was described as a genus of *Saxifragaceæ* by Dr. Wight, but is now referred to the meliaceous genus *Amoora.* It is a much-branched herb, native of Bombay, and has alternate sessile coriaceous cordate-lanceolate leaves, and panicled corymbs of small rose-coloured flowers. [A. S.]

NINE BARK. *Spiræa opulifolia.*

NINETY-KNOT. *Polygonum aviculare.*

NIN-TOO DES JAPONAIS. (Fr.) *Lonicera confusa.*

NINZIN. (Fr.) *Panax quinquefolium.*

NIOPO TREE. *Piptadenia peregrina.*

NIPA *fruticans,* the only representative of the genus to which it belongs, is a palm-like plant, with creeping often furcated trunk, feathery leaves, and large round bunches of fruits. It is commonly met with in the salt-marshes of the coasts and islands of the Indian seas, and is generally classed with *Pandanaceæ* or *Palmaceæ,* but does not quite agree with either of these natural orders. A similar plant abounds in the tertiary formations at the mouth of the Thames, where its fruit must at one time have floated about in as great profusion as those of *N. fruticans* do at the present day in Indian rivers. This plant is called Nipa and Susa in the Philippine Islands. The leaves are unarmed and pinnatisect, often more than twenty feet long. The flowers are monœcious, axillary, and enclosed in a spathe, like those of genuine palms; the fruit is a one-seeded drupe, aggregated in heads as large as those of a man. The foliage, called Nipah, is used as thatch, and when burnt yields a supply of salt. From the spadix toddy is extracted, convertible into syrup, sugar, vinegar, yeast, and a strong spirit. The kernel of the fruit is edible. [B. S.]

NIPHÆA. A genus of *Gesneraceæ* peculiar to Central America and Venezuela, comprising about half a dozen species of small herbs with decumbent stems, and more or less densely covered with hair. The leaves are often crowded together, forming rosettes; the corolla is rotate (by which *Niphœa* may easily be distinguished from all other *Gesneraceæ*), nearly symmetrical, five-lobed, and of a snow-white colour, sometimes marked towards the base with yellow; the stamens are four in number, and their anthers connected; the stigma is mouth-shaped (stomatomorphous), and the fruit a capsule. All the known species are favourites in our stoves. *N. oblonga* was the first introduced; *N. rubida, albo-lineata* and its varieties, *N. parviflora,* and *N. caripensis* are newer additions to our collections. [B. S.]

NIPHOBOLUS. A genus of polypodiaceous ferns, separated from *Polypodium* by their netted venation, and from other netted *Polypodieæ* by the ultimate areoles of the venation containing free divaricate veinlets, and by the surface of the fronds being clothed with a felt of minute stellate hair-scales of a brownish or whitish colour. The round dot-formed sori are generally numerous, and push out from amongst this stellate pubescence. In some cases the fertile fronds are contracted. One species, *N. angustatus,* to which the name *Niphopsis* has been sometimes given, bears only a single row, of very large size, on each side the costa; but it otherwise agrees entirely with the genuine species, which are well represented by the familiar *N. Lingua* and *N. pertusus.* The species are chiefly eastern and tropical, but a few extend to Japan, others to Australia, and one occurs in South Africa. [T. M.]

NIPHOPSIS. *Niphobolus.*

NIPPLEWORT. *Lapsana.* —, DWARF. *Arnoseris pusilla.*

NIRA. A Malay name for the saccharine juice obtained from *Nipa fruticans.*

NIR BIKHI, or NIR BISHI. The Bikh poison, *Aconitum ferox.*

NISA. A genus of shrubs natives of Madagascar, and belonging to the family *Homaliaceæ.* The leaves are alternate; the flowers in spikes occasionally concealed by large coloured bracts; the perianth top-shaped, its limb divided into ten or twelve segments, the inner of which are petaloid; the stamens five or six in number, alternate with as many glands; and the ovary partly adherent to the perianth, and having two or three styles. [M. T. M.]

NISSOLIA. A genus of *Leguminosæ* of the tribe *Hedysareæ,* distinguished by its five-toothed calyx, and its one-seeded pod ending in a ligulate wing. It comprises a few South American trees and shrubs of twining habit, with pinnate leaves, and axillary racemes of white or yellowish flowers. Also *Lathyrus Nissolia.* [T. M.]

NITELLA. A genus of *Characeæ,* distinguished from *Chara* by the component cells being simple and not coated with secondary cells, a circumstance which makes the species peculiarly adapted for observing the curious phenomena of the circulation. *Nitella* was supposed, moreover, to differ from *Chara* in having the antheridia separate from the spore-cases, on distinct plants, or at the tips of the branchlets, while in *Chara* they are placed immediately beneath the spore-cases; but these characters do not hold good. Ruprecht has made of those *Nitellæ* which agree in fruit with *Chara,* a genus *Chgropsis,* while in his *Lychnothamnus* the antheridia are placed by the side of the spore-cases. The simpler plan, perhaps, is to consider *Nitella* merely as a subgenus, since even in *Chara* parts of the fronds are uncoated. The species are not so common in this country as those of *Chara.* In Australia most of the *Characeæ* are *Nitellæ.* [M. J. B.]

NITID. Having a smooth even polished surface; as many seeds.

NITRARIA. A genus of *Malpighiaceæ,* by some considered to constitute a distinct order *Nitrariaceæ.* The species are natives of salt plains in Central Asia and Northern Africa. They are generally thorny shrubs, with fleshy leaves, and solitary or clustered white flowers. The calyx is five-cleft, small, persistent; the petals five, concave; the stamens fifteen, with anthers opening by an oblique cleft; and the ovary free, sessile, three to six-celled, with a single pendulous ovule in each compartment, and a short thick style, terminated by three to six stigmas. The fruit is fleshy externally, bony internally, one-celled, one-seeded by

abortion, and opening at the top by six valves of unequal size. The generic name was given to these plants from their having been first found in the vicinity of some Siberian nitre-works. The fruits are eaten in the Caspian desert, despite their salt taste. Camels also browse on the young shoots. *N. tridentata* has been supposed to be the true Lotus tree of the ancients. *N. Billardieri,* an Australian species, is said to produce fruit of the size of an olive, of a red colour, and with an agreeable flavour much relished by the natives. [M. T. M.]

NITTA-TREE. *Parkia africana.*

NIVALIS. Growing near snow, or appearing at a season when snow is on the ground.

NIVENIA. A genus of *Proteaceæ* having a regularly four-cleft calyx, the concave segments of which bear a nearly sessile anther and a filiform silky style with a club-shaped stigma. The fruit is a nut containing a single shining seed. They are large shrubs, natives of the Cape of Good Hope, with simple or much-divided leaves, the segments of which are filiform and sharp-pointed. Flowers in terminal or axillary spikes: florets in fours within a persistent hairy involucre of four leaves. [R. H.]

NIVÉOLE. (Fr.) *Leucojum.*

NIVETTE. (Fr.) A kind of Peach.

NIVEUS. Snow-white, the purest white.

NOBLE-ÉPINE. (Fr.) *Cratægus Oxyacantha.*

NODE. That part of a stem from which a leaf, whether complete or incomplete, arises.

NODOSE, NODULOSE. Knotted; an irregular form of necklace-shaped. These terms are chiefly applied to roots.

NODOSITAS. A knot; a woody swelling of any kind.

NOIRPRUN. (Fr.) *Rhamnus catharticus.*

NOISERAIE. (Fr.) A grove of Walnut trees.

NOISETIER. (Fr.) *Corylus Avellana.*

NOISETTIA. A genus of tropical American shrubs of the violet family. Some of the species are erect, others climbing. Their flowers are in clusters or rarely solitary, sometimes nodding, and with jointed stalks; the three anterior segments of the calyx are larger than the other two; the five petals are very unequal in size, the posterior one largest and prolonged at the base into a long spur: and the five stamens have the anthers adherent, crested, two of the filaments prolonged at the base, and concealed within the spur of the hindmost petal. The fruit is a three-valved capsule. [M. T. M.]

NOIX. (Fr.) A general term for Nut. — D'ACAJOU. The Cashew nut, *Anacardium occidentale.* — DE BANCOUL.

Aleurites Ambinux. — DÉ-BEN. The Ben nut, *Moringa pterygosperma.* — MUS-CADE. The Nutmeg, *Myristica moschata.* — VÓMIQUÉ. The Nux-vomica, *Strychnos nux vomica.*

NOLANACEÆ. (*Nolanads.*) A natural order of corolliflorsl dicotyledons belonging to Lindley's echial alliance of perigynous Exogens. Herbaceous or shrubby plants, with alternate exstipulate leaves, and having some features in common both with *Convolvulaceæ* and *Boraginaceæ.* Their distinguishing characteristics are their straight inflorescence, their valvate calyx, their plaited corolla, and their ovary of five or more separate carpels, variously combined with united styles and somewhat capitate stigma. They are natives of South America, and consist of half a dozen genera (e.g. *Nolana* and *Alona*), which comprise about three dozen species. [J. H. B.]

NOLANA. A genus of annual *Nolanaceæ*, well marked by the bell-shaped corolla, plaited while in bud. *N. atriplicifolia* is a pretty plant, with prostrate much-branched stems, ovate fleshy leaves, and large axillary flowers (resembling those of a convolvulus), of which the limb is bright blue, and the tube white and yellow. They are all natives of Peru or Chili. [C. A. J.]

NOLI-TANGERE. The Touch-me-not, *Impatiens Noli-tangere.*

NOMBRIL DE VÉNUS. (Fr.) *Cotyledon umbilicus*; also *Omphalodes linifolia.*

NOMOLOGY. That part of Botany which relates to the laws which govern the variations of organs.

NONDA. *Parinarium Nonda,* one of the few edible fruits of Australia.

NONDO. An American name for *Ligusticum actæifolium.*

NONE-SO-PRETTY. *Saxifraga umbrosa.*

NONI. Nine together.

NONNEA. A genus of *Boraginaceæ*, natives of the Mediterranean region and of Middle Asia. It consists of hispid plants, often of annual duration, with terminal leafy racemes of yellow purple or variegated flowers, having a five-cleft calyx swelling at the base as the fruit ripens, a funnel-shaped corolla with a straight tube bearded or with small pilose scales at the throat, and four nuts often reticulated and pubescent, excavated at the base where they are attached to the receptacle, quite free from the style. [J. T. S.]

NONSUCH. *Medicago lupulina*; also *Lychnis chalcedonica.*

NONUS. The ninth.

NOONFLOWER, or NOONTIDE. *Tragopogon pratensis.*

NOONGPOO. The Tamil name of the wine obtained from the Palmyra Palm.

NOOPS. The Cloudberry, *Rubus Chamæmorus.*

NOPAL. (Fr.) *Opuntia vulgaris.*

NOPALEA. The three species to which this generic name is applied have been separated from the old cactaceous genus *Opuntia*, and are characterised by their flowers having the petals erect and drawn together at the top instead of being expanded as in *Opuntia*, and by the stamens being longer than the corolla but shorter than the style. They have round stems, and fleshy jointed flat branches like *Opuntia*; but the tubercles upon the branches are usually unarmed with spines, and the flowers are crimson or reddish instead of yellow or orange. They are natives of Mexico and the West Indies.

N. coccinellifera grows about eight or ten feet high, and has a tree-like appearance. Its stem and older branches are nearly cylindrical and of an ash-grey colour, but the younger parts are flat and of a deep green, the joints being of an oblong or obovate form, and varying from five or six inches to a foot in length, usually unarmed with spines, but having when young several short awl-shaped fleshy leaves, which soon fall off, leaving a white scar and tuft of short wool and bristles. Plantations for rearing the cochineal insect (*Coccus Cacti*) are called *nopaleries*, and sometimes contain 50,000 plants, arranged in lines, and kept about four feet high. The female insects are placed on the plants in August, and in four months the first crop is gathered, two others being obtained in the course of the year. Mexico is the native country of the cochineal, but the greater part of our supply now comes from New Grenada and the Canary Islands; the annual imports being from 1,200 to 1,400 tons, worth about 400l. per ton. Although the name *coccinellifera* (i.e. cochineal-bearing) has been given to this species, it is not the only one upon which the insect feeds, *Opuntia Tuna* being most commonly cultivated for the purpose in Mexico. [A. S.]

NOPUGÈTE. (Fr.) A kind of Olive.

NORANTEA. A genus of *Marcgraviaceæ*, a group regarded by some authors as a suborder of *Ternstrœmiaceæ.* They are epiphytal or scandent shrubs, rarely trees, with coriaceous entire leaves, and terminal bracteated racemes of flowers. The five sepals are imbricated, as are the five petals; the stamens are numerous, with linear innate anthers; and the ovary is three to five-celled, with a sessile radiating stigma, and anatropal ovules. Fruit globose, indehiscent. There are eight species found in the tropical parts of America. [J. H. B.]

NORCA. The Portuguese name of the Port Moniz Yam, *Tamus edulis.*

NORDMANNIA. A genus of *Thymelaceæ*, referred by Endlicher to *Hargasseria.* One species, *H. cordifolia*, with flowers of a pale blue, a native of the West Indies, is in cultivation. [M. T. M.]

NORMAL. When the ordinary structure peculiar to the family or genus of a plant is in nowise departed from.

NORONHIA. A traveller in Madagascar has given his name to this genus of *Oleaceæ*, which comprises a few shrubs, natives of that island and of the Mauritius. The leaves are opposite, entire, with thick woody stalks; and the flowers yellowish, in axillary clusters. Calyx small, persistent; corolla globular thick, four-cleft; anthers two, sessile or nearly so within the tube of the corolla; ovary two-celled, with two pendulous ovules in each. Fruit drupe-like, one-seeded by abortion. [M. T. M.]

NORRISIA. A genus of *Loganiaceæ*, established by Gardner for a Malayan shrub, which Wight had referred to the Brazilian genus *Antonia*, but which differs in the want of any imbricated bracts under the calyx, in the slender tube of the corolla, and in the linear placenta to which the ovules and seeds are attached.

NOSEBLEED. The Yarrow, *Achillea Millefolium*.

NOSEBURN TREE. *Daphnopsis tenuifolia*.

NOSTOC. A genus of green-spored *Algæ*, consisting of gelatinous globose or lobed, rarely forked masses, filled with necklaces of globules, some of which, of a larger size than the rest, reproduce the plant by cell-division of the endochrome, or propagate it by zoospores. They resemble so closely young fruitless *Collemata* that they have been supposed to be merely barren lichens. Ascigerous fruit, indeed, has been figured by Bayrhoffer in the *Botanische Zeitung* for 1857, but the observation requires confirmation, to show that there has been no delusion about specimens. Many of the species grow on the naked soil on rocks, while others are as constantly immersed in water, whether fresh or brackish. Their colour is usually green, but sometimes is of a decided blue. A species which abounds in streams in China, *N. edule*, is dried, and forms a favourite ingredient in soup, for which its gelatinous substance, rich in bassorin, makes it appropriate. A closely allied alga, *Hormosiphon arcticus*, abounds in the Arctic regions, and affords a mass of wholesome food, which is far preferable to the Tripe de Roche, as it has none of its bitterness or purgative quality. The most singular species we have met with is *N. flagelliforme*, which grows on naked aluminous soil in Texas. This has a long forked frond, and at first would not be taken for a *Nostoc*, though its structure is precisely similar. See FALLING STARS. [M. J. B.]

NOSTOCHINEÆ. A natural order of green-spored *Algæ*, consisting of gelatinous fronds or masses made up of necklace-shaped threads, some of whose joints are larger than others. The gelatinous element is more or less predominant, and according to its firmness the forms assumed are more or less definite. *Anabaina*, and one or two other genera, remarkable for the different forms assumed by some of the component joints, are mere floating masses. *Sphærozyga spiralis* forms clouds in the water, tinging the whole body with a delicate green. *Monormia* is singular, as consisting of a single complicated thread of immense length. The threads, after a time, break up into their component joints, which have been observed by Thuret to have active motion—a fact which he finds especially in aquatic species, enabling them to contend against currents which would otherwise carry them away. The larger joints are often differently coloured from the others. Derbès records their transformation into zoospores. It is probable that in many cases the endochrome is resolved into minute active bodies, and that the cell-division which Thuret observed in *Nostoc* is not a true mode of fructification, but merely a case of multiplication. The large connecting cells are sometimes provided with cilia. Occasionally there is an external tube to the necklaces, in which case we have a close approximation to *Oscillarieæ*. A few species occur in warm springs, and these, possibly from the presence of iodine, are often used as an outward application in glandular affections. *Nostochineæ* grow in all parts of the world, and are capable of bearing a very low temperature, while their addiction to warm springs shows that they are not at all averse to considerable heat. Where the contrast of the component joints as to form, size, and colour is great, they are charming microscopical objects. [M. J. B.]

NOTCHWEED. *Chenopodium Vulvaria*.

NOTELÆA. A genus of *Oleaceæ*, consisting of six or seven species, which form shrubs or small trees, with opposite entire leathery leaves, and axillary racemes of small yellowish-green flowers. The generic name is derived from the Greek words *notos*, the south, and *elaia*, the olive, in reference to the genus being confined to Australia and Tasmania. Their flowers have a very small four-toothed calyx; four concave petals cohering in pairs with the two short stamens placed between them; a two-celled ovary, with two pendulous ovules in each cell; scarcely any style; and a notched, two-lobed, or undivided stigma. The fleshy drupe is one-seeded by abortion.

N. ligustrina, the Tasmanian Ironwood tree, is in general only a bush six or eight feet high, but occasionally forms a tree growing thirty feet or more, with a trunk twelve or fourteen inches or sometimes as much as a foot and a half in diameter, yielding an extremely hard dense wood to which the name of Ironwood has been given by the Australian colonists, who use it as a substitute for lignum-vitæ, for making sheaves for ships' blocks, and also for turnery and inlaid-work. It is common in Tasmania, and found also in Victoria and New South Wales. Other species yield hard heavy timber, such as *L. ovata*, the Dúnga-rúnga of New South Wales, a small crooked tree, growing from fifteen to twenty feet high, but as they are of small size the timber is of limited use. [A. S.]

NOTHOCHLÆNA. A genus of ferns closely related to *Polypodium*, from which it differs in its small, oligocarpous sori, which finally become confluent in narrow lines near the margin, as well as in its aspect, which more nearly resembles that of *Cheilanthes*; the latter, however, being distinguished by the presence of a marginal indusium, which is wanting in *Nothochlæna*. The veins are free. The small tufted fronds are either once, twice, or thrice pinnate, some of them, as *N. pulveracea*, having the under-surface farinoso-ceraceous, and others, as *N. lanuginosa* and *sinuata*, having the under-surface scaly, hairy, or woolly. They occur in North and South America, both Indies, Australia and the Eastern Islands, North and South Africa, and the South of Europe. [T. M.]

NOTHUS. False or bastard; usually applied to the false roots formed by parasites when they attack living plants.

NOTOBASIS. The Syrian Thistle, *N. syriaca*, is the only species of this genus of *Compositæ*, and is distinguished from other thistles by the central florets of the flower-head only being fertile. It has stems one to four feet high furnished with white-veined leaves, the lower of which are six to eight inches long, sinuately lobed and coarsely spine-toothed, and the upper pinnatifid, the lobes prolonged into rigid spines. The sessile flower-heads are solitary or two or three together, on short axillary branches, each head fenced in by a very rigid pinnatifid bract, whose spiny points are often two inches in length. The florets are purple. The plant is distributed throughout the Mediterranean region, and in the Canary Islands. [A. A. B.]

NOTOCERAS. A genus of *Cruciferæ* from Siberia, the Canary Islands, and the Mediterranean region, comprising small annuals, with the racemes of small yellowish flowers opposite the leaves. The pod is two-valved, four-sided, with two of the angles acute and two obtuse, the valves drawn out into two or four short horns. [J. T. S.]

NOTORHIZEÆ. A term derived from two Greek words signifying back and root, and applied to a suborder of cruciferous plants in which the radicle of the embryo lies on the back of the cotyledons. In this case the cotyledons are said to be incumbent, and the radicle dorsal. Among British plants examples are seen in *Hesperis, Brassica, Sinapis, Capsella*, &c. [J. H. B.]

NOTYLIA. A genus of tropical American epiphytal orchids, with one-leaved pseudobulbs, and radical racemes of inconspicuous flowers, which have the two side sepals cohering beneath the lip, the lip itself unguiculate, quite entire, and free or slightly adherent by its claw to the slender erect column, at the back of which is the anther, containing two solid pollen-masses attached to a wedge-shaped caudicle adhering by a minute gland. [A. S.]

NOUFAR. An Arabian name for *Nymphæa Lotus*.

NOVENI. Nine.

NOYAU. (Fr.) A liqueur flavoured with the kernel of *Cerasus occidentalis*; it is also said to be sometimes prepared from *Convolvulus dissectus*.

NOYER. (Fr.) *Juglans.* — À FEUILLES DE FRÊNE. *Pterocarya fraxinifolia.* — BLANC. *Carya alba.* — COMMUN. *Juglans regia.* — DE CEYLON, DES INDES, or DE MALABAR. *Adhatoda vasica.* — DES POURCEAUX. *Carya porcina.* — PACAVIER. *Carya olivæformis.*

NTABA. The Gaboon name for a blood-red wild grape.

NUCAMENTACEÆ. A suborder of *Proteaceæ*.

NUCAMENTACEOUS. Having the hardness of a nut.

NUCAMENTUM. An obsolete term for an amentum or catkin.

NUCLEUS. The word Nucleus is variously applied by botanists. Sometimes it is applied to cytoblasts, or to bodies resembling cytoblasts. It is also applied to the centre part of the ovule, in which the embryo is engendered. By mycologists it is applied to the gelatinous mass of asci or spores which is found in the perithecia of *Sphæriæ*, or the analogous fungi among the *Coniomycetes*; while in *Algæ* it is applied to the fructifying mass of the rhodosperms, whether contained in a single cell or in a compound cyst or conceptacle, the word *nucleoli* being used when there is a group of nuclei. — PROLIGERUS. A distinct cartilaginous body coming out entire from the apothecia of some lichens, and containing the spores. [M. J. B.]

NUCULANIUM. A pulpy thin-skinned superior fruit, having seeds lying loosely in the pulp; as a grape.

NUCULE. A small hard seed-like fruit; also the same as Glans; also a small stone or seed.

NUCUMENTACEÆ. A name derived from a Latin word meaning a nut, and applied to a suborder of cruciferous plants, in which there is a one-celled silicule from the absence of septum or partition, and often a single seed, the valves being indistinct and indehiscent. In British plants, this is seen in *Isatis*. [J. H. B.]

NUDE, NUDUS. Naked, that is to say, either bald from the total absence of hairs, or uncovered in consequence of the absence of any investing organs. *Nudiusculus* is nearly naked, having scarcely any hairs.

NULLIPORES. A synonym of *Corallines*, more especially applied to the different species of *Melobesia* and similar productions. [M. J. B.]

NUMMULAIRE. (Fr.) *Lysimachia Nummularia*.

NUPHAR. A genus of water-plants of the family *Nymphæaceæ*, acquiring its name from an Arabic word applied to *Nymphæa Lotus*. The species are few in number—some say only two: one European and Asiatic, the other American. They have a thick horizontal rootstock, whence proceed the leaf and flower-stalks, which are smooth cylindrical or somewhat triangular. The leaves are heart-shaped roundish or sagittate. The calyx consists of five or six concave yellow persistent sepals; there are ten to eighteen petals, much smaller than the sepals, secreting a honey-like fluid at their base; and numerous stamens in several rows, ultimately bent backwards. The ovary is many-celled on the top of the receptacle, not surrounded by it as in *Nymphæa*, and becomes a globular fruit, bursting irregularly to allow of the escape of the seeds, which are imbedded in pulp.

N. lutea is the well-known Yellow Water-lily, common in most parts of Britain, and frequently associated with the common white water-lily. The flowers have a perfume of brandy—hence the name Brandy-bottles, which is applied in some counties to this plant. The rootstocks bruised and infused in milk are stated to be destructive to cockroaches, and when burnt to be particularly obnoxious to crickets. The leaves and leafstalks have a somewhat bitter and astringent taste. The flowers are used by the Turks in the preparation of cooling drinks, like sherbet. The seeds too, as they contain a quantity of starch, are said to be used in some countries as food. The leaf-stalks and flower-stalks are traversed by a great number of minute air-canals, whose arrangement is the same in both organs. A small variety occurs in the North of Britain, also in Siberia, Canada, &c.: it is sometimes considered as a distinct species under the name of *N. minima*. *N. Kalmiana* does not differ materially from this.

The American species, *N. advena*, has larger flowers than *N. lutea*, with six sepals, and arrow-shaped leaves of thinner texture than those of the European species. The arrangement of the air-canals is the same. These several kinds are frequently grown in ornamental waters in this country.   [M. T. M.]

NUT. A hard indehiscent pericarp usually containing only one seed; the same as Glans and Achene. —, SPURIOUS. A nut which owes its hardness to some other cause than the induration of the pericarp; as in *Mirabilis*.

NUT. The fruit or kernel of the seed of various plants; more rarely applied to certain tubers. —; ACAJOU. The Cashew nut, *Anacardium occidentale*. —, AR. *Bunium flexuosum*. —, BAMBARRA GROUND. The seed of *Voandzeia subterranea*. —, BARBADOS. The seed of *Curcas purgans*. —, BEAZOR. The seed of *Guilandina Bonducella*. —, BEDDA. The fruit of *Terminalia Belerica*, called also Bastard Myrobalans. —, BEN. The winged seed of *Moringa pterygosperma*. —, BETEL. The seed of *Areca Catechu*. —; BITTER. *Carya amara*. —, BLADDER. *Staphylea*. —, —. AFRICAN. *Royéna*. —; BOMA. The fruit of some West African oil-palm. —, BONDUC. The seed of *Guilandina Bonduc*. —, BRAZIL. The seed of *Bertholletia excelsa*. —, BREAD. The fruit of *Brosinum Alicastrum*. —, —, MONKEY. The fruit of *Adansonia digitata*. —, BUFFALO. The fruit of *Pyrularia oleifera*. —, BUTTER. The seed of *Caryocar nuciferum*; also *Juglans cinerea*. —, CANDLE. The seed of *Aleurites triloba*. —, CASHEW. The seed of *Anacardium occidentale*; sometimes called Acajou Nut. —, CASTANHA. The seed of *Bertholletia excelsa*. —, CHEST. *Castanea vesca*. —, COB. *Corylus Avellana barcelonensis*. —, of Jamaica. *Omphalea*. —, COCOA. The fruit of *Cocos nucifera*. —, COLA. The seed of *Cola acuminata*. —, COQUILLA. The fruit of *Attalea funifera*. —, COROZO. The Vegetable Ivory, *Phytelephas macrocarpa*. —, DRINKER'S. *Strychnos potatorum*. —, EARTH. *Arachis hypogæa*; also *Bunium flexuosum*, and *Carum Bulbocastanum*; also *Geocaryum*. —, EBOE. The seed of *Dipteryx oleifera*. —, ELK. The fruit of *Pyrularia oleifera*. —, EUBŒAN. *Castanea vesca*. —, FRENCH. *Juglans regia*. —, GOORA. The seed of *Cola acuminata*. —, GROUND. *Arachis hypogæa*; also an American name for *Panax trifolium*. —, HARA. The drupe of *Terminalia citrina*. —, HAZEL. *Corylus Avellana*. —, HICKORY. *Carya amara*. —, HOG, or PIG. *Carya porcina*. —, —, of Jamaica. *Omphalea*. —, HOG PEA. An American name for *Amphicarpæa*. —, ILLINOIS. *Carya olivæformis*. —, IVORY. *Phytelephas macrocarpa*. —, JESUITS. *Trapa natans*. —, JUPITER'S. The Walnut, *Juglans regia*. —, KEENA. The fruit of *Calophyllum Calaba*. —, KISKY THOMAS. *Carya alba*. —, KOLA, or KOLLA. The seed of *Cola acuminata*. —, KUNDOO. The fruit of *Carapa Touloucouna*. —, LEVANT. The fruit of *Anamirta Cocculus*. —, LUMBANG. The seed of *Aleurites triloba*. —, MALABAR. *Adhatoda Vasica*. —, MANILLA. *Arachis hypogæa*. —, MARANY. A name under which the Marking Nut has been occasionally imported into Liverpool. —, MARKING. The nuts of *Semecarpus Anacardium*. —, MOCKER, or MOKER. The nut of *Carya tomentosa*. —, MOTE. The fruit of *Carapa Touloucouna*. —, OIL. The fruit of *Pyrularia (Hamiltonia) oleifera*; also a West Indian name for the seed of *Ricinus communis*. —, OLIVE. The fruit of *Elæocarpus*. —, PAGANE or PECCAN. *Carya olivæformis*. —, PARA. The same as Brazil Nut. —, PEA. An American name for *Arachis hypogæa*. —, PHYSIC. *Curcas purgans*. —, PIG. *Carya porcina*, and *C. glabra*; also *Carum Bulbocastanum* and *Bunium flexuosum*. —, PISTACIA, or PISTACHIO. The edible seed of *Pistacia vera*. —, POISON. The poisonous seed of *Strychnos nux vomica*. —, PURGING. The seed of *Curcas purgans*. —, QUANDANG. The fruit of *Fusanus acuminatus*.

—, RAVENSARA. The fruit of *Agathophyllum aromaticum*, used as a spice in Madagascar. —, RUSH. *Cyperus esculentus*. —, SAPUCAIA. The seed of *Lecythis Zabucajo*; also *L. Ollaria*, and *L. grandiflora*. —, SARDIAN. The Chestnut, *Castanea vesca*. —, SASSAFRAS. *Nectandra Pichury*. —, SINGHARA. The fruit of various species of *Trapa*, especially *T. bispinosa* and *bicornis*. —, SNAKE. The seed of *Ophiocaryon paradoxum*. —, SOAP. *Mimosa abstergens*. —, SOUARI, or SUWARROW. The seed of *Caryocar nuciferum*; also *C. butyrosum*. —, SPANISH. *Morœa Sisyrinchium*. —, TAQUA. *Phytelephas macrocarpa*. —, VEGETABLE IVORY. *Phytelephas macrocarpa*. —, VOMIT. *Strychnos nux vomica*. —, WATER. The fruit of various species of *Trapa*. —, WOOD. *Corylus Avellana*. —, YEA, YUR, or JUR. The fruit of *Arachis hypogœa* and *Bunium flexuosum*.

NUTANT, NUTANS. Nodding; inclining very much from the perpendicular, so that the apex is directed downwards, as the flower of the snowdrop.

NUTGALLS. The galls formed on *Quercus infectoria*.

NUTMEG. *Myristica moschata*; called also *M. fragrans* and *M. officinalis*. —, AMERICAN. *Monodora Myristica*. —, BRAZILIAN. *Cryptocarya moschata*. —, CALABASH. *Monodora Myristica*. —, CALIFORNIAN. *Torreya Myristica*. —, CLOVE. *Agathophyllum aromaticum*. —, JAMAICA. *Monodora Myristica*. —, LONG. *Myristica fatua*. —, MADAGASCAR. *Agathophyllum aromaticum*. —, MALE. *Myristica tomentosa*. —, PERUVIAN. The seed of *Laurelia sempervirens*. —, PLUME. *Atherosperma moschata*. —, SANTA FÉ. *Myristica Otoba*. —, STINKING. *Torreya Myristica*. —, WILD. *Myristica tomentosa*, and *M. fatua*.

NUTMEG-WOOD. The wood of the Palmyra palm, *Borassus flabelliformis*.

NUTTALLIA. A name given by Torrey and Gray to a North-west American shrub constituting a genus of *Rosaceæ*, remarkable as forming a transition from the *Amygdaleæ* to the *Spiræœ*. The flowers are diœcious, with only fifteen stamens. There are five distinct ovaries, the fruiting carpels usually fewer, coriaceous, and one-seeded. It is a small tree, with obovate entire leaves, and white flowers in axillary racemes.

NUX. The same as Nut. —, BACCATA. A nut enclosed in a pulpy covering formed by some external organ, as in the Yew.

NUX VOMICA. *Strychnos nux vomica*.

NUYTSIA. The Flame-tree or Fire-tree of South-western Australia is *N. floribunda*, a plant belonging to the *Loranthaceæ*, but differing from all the rest of the order by growing in the ground like ordinary trees, instead of being parasitic like the *Loranthus*, mistleto, &c. It attains the height of twenty-five or thirty feet, and, when covered with its long narrow orange-coloured flowers, is an extremely brilliant object, and is compared by the colonists to a tree on fire. Its flowers are abundantly produced in large terminal racemes, and are in threes, each three with an involucre of three separate bracts at the base. A large quantity of gum, somewhat like gum-arabic, exudes from its trunk. [A.S.]

NYCTAGE. (Fr.) *Mirabilis*.

NYCTAGINACEÆ. (*Nyctagines, Nyctagos*.) A natural order of monochlamydeous dicotyledons belonging to Lindley's chenopodal alliance of hypogynous Exogens, and consisting of herbs, shrubs, or trees with opposite often unequal leaves, and involucrate flowers. Perianth tubular, coloured, contracted in the middle, becoming indurated at the base, the limb deciduous; stamens definite, hypogynous; ovary superior, one-celled, with a solitary erect ovule. Fruit a caryopsis, enclosed within the enlarged persistent tube of the perianth. The plants of the order have in general purgative qualities. *Mirabilis Jalapa* was at one time considered the Jalap-plant. *M. dichotoma* is called in the West Indies 'four o'clock flower,' on account of opening its blossoms at that hour in the afternoon. They are natives principally of warm countries. The order comprises about a score of genera, and upwards of one hundred species. Examples: *Mirabilis* (*Nyctago*), and *Pisonia*. [J. H. B.]

NYCTAGINIA. Mexican herbs constituting a genus of *Nyctaginaceæ*. The principal characteristics are: leaves opposite; flowers aggregated within a many-leaved involucre; perianth tubular, dilated at the apex; stamens five, attached to the base of the perianth, and projecting beyond it; style as long as the stamens, terminated by a small button-like stigma; fruit surrounded by the hardened base of the perianth, and by the membranous base of the stamens. [M. T. M.]

NYCTALIS. A genus of gill-bearing *Fungi*, all the species of which are parasitic on *Russula adusta, elephantina*, and one or two allied fungi. They are, however, chiefly remarkable for the comparatively small development of the hymenium in some of the species, and the constant growth of a parasite with curious stellate spores (*Asterophora*) on the extremely thick pileus, or, according to the views of some, the conversion of its tissues into stylospores. *N. parasitica*, which has a different habit, is also described as producing stylospores on the hymenium instead of true fruit; but whether this is really the case, or whether the appearance is due to some parasite, is at present undecided. [M. J. B.]

NYCTANTHES. *Arbor tristis*, the Night Jasmine of India, is a shrub or small tree of the *Jasminaceæ*, with acutely four-angled branches, ovate-acuminate entire leaves, and highly fragrant flowers. These have salver-shaped corollas, the flat limb of which is white with an orange eye, and the long terete tube also bright-orange.

The genus is characterised by its tubular very minutely five or six-toothleted or quite entire calyx; and capsular fruit with a single seed in each of the two cells. Its brilliant flowers do not expand till evening, and fall off about sunrise; so that during the day it loses its brightness, whence its specific name *Arbor tristis* or Sad-tree. Its flowers are collected for use as a perfume, and also as a dye, but their colour is not permanent. [A. S.]

NYCTERINIA. A genus of *Scrophulariaceæ*, of the tribe *Gratioleæ*, and allied to *Manulea* in its one-celled anthers. The corolla, as in that genus also, has a long slender tube, and a spreading nearly equally five-lobed limb, with entire or bifid lobes; but the lower stamens, inserted much higher than the others, have small transverse and often abortive anthers. There are about sixteen species, all natives of the Cape Colony, chiefly annuals, with a few perennials or undershrubs, mostly villous and glutinous, drying black like the *Lyperias*, but with more entire leaves, and flowers in terminal spikes. Two or three species, especially *N. Lychnidea*, have been occasionally cultivated in our gardens.

NYMPHÆACEÆ. (*Water-lilies.*) A natural order of thalamifloral dicotyledons, belonging to Lindley's nymphal alliance of hypogynous Exogens, and consisting of aquatic plants, with peltate or cordate fleshy leaves, and a rootstock or stem which extends itself into the mud. Sepals usually four, sometimes confounded with the numerous petals, and these often passing gradually into stamens; stamens indefinite, inserted above the petals into the torus, with petaloid filaments, and adnate introrse anthers, opening by two longitudinal clefts; torus large, fleshy, surrounding the ovary, which is many-celled, many-seeded, with radiating stigmas. Fruit many-celled, indehiscent; seeds very numerous, attached to spongy dissepiments. The plants of this order are found throughout the northern hemisphere, and are generally rare in the southern. Little is known in regard to their properties. Some are astringent or bitter, while others are said to be sedative. They have showy flowers, and their petioles and peduncles contain numerous air-tubes. *Victoria regia* is one of the largest known aquatics. It is found in the waters of South America, and is said to range over thirty-five degrees of longitude. There are five genera (e.g. *Nymphæa, Victoria, Nuphar*), and about sixty species. [J. H. B.]

NYMPHÆA. The technical name of the genus to which the White Water-lily of our streams belongs. It constitutes the type of the *Nymphæaceæ*, and consists of water-plants, found in lakes or rivers almost all over the world. They have a fleshy or tuberous rootstock, sending down rootlets into the mud, and throwing up leaves and flowers. The leaves are usually somewhat circular in outline, entire or toothed, the veins on the under-surface either prominent or depressed; they float on the surface of the water, but after a time are partially raised from it; the leafstalks are cylindrical, traversed with air-canals, which are arranged in a regular manner. The flowerstalks are like the leafstalks in appearance, and like them are permeated by air-canals, which in some instances are arranged in the same manner as those in the leafstalk, in others are disposed differently. The leaf and flower-stalks vary in length according to the depth of the water in which the plant is growing. The flower is placed on the end of the stalk, and consists of a calyx with four sepals, green on the outside but petal-like on the inner surface, falling off as the fruit ripens; the petals are numerous, arranged in several rows upon the prolonged receptacle, the inner ones passing by insensible gradations into the stamens, which are likewise very numerous—the outer ones petaloid, the inner linear with their stalks not exceeding the anthers in breadth. The ovary is imbedded within the receptacle, on which the outer portions of the flower are inserted; internally it is divided into numerous many-seeded compartments, and surmounted by a plate-like stigma with several diverging rays, and a depressed centre, occupied by a small conical or ovate body. When ripe the fruit sinks towards the bottom of the water, and rots, and thus liberates the seeds.

The flowers vary in form and colour in the different species, as also do the leaves. The best-known, and by no means the least beautiful, of these eminently beautiful plants, is the common White Water-lily, *N. alba*, pretty generally distributed over Great Britain, but found also in other parts of Europe, and in Northern and Central Asia. No flowers show better the transition from petals to stamens than those of the White Water-lily, and they are also interesting from their power of collapsing their petals, and of drooping on to the surface of the water, or even sinking below its surface during the night, emerging and expanding again in the sunlight. This peculiarity is also noticed in several of the foreign kinds, as in the Egyptian *N. Lotus*, of which Moore, in 'Paradise and the Peri,' thus sings:—

> Those virgin lilies, all the night
> Bathing their beauties in the lake
> That they may rise more fresh and bright
> When their beloved sun 's awake.

The rootstocks of *N. alba* are said to be used for dyeing purposes, as they contain gallic acid, and also a large quantity of starch. In France they are used in the preparation of a kind of beer. Numerous species are cultivated in this country, some of which deserve notice, such as *N. odorata* and the small variety of it, *N. odorata minor*. These are North American, and resemble our European species. *N. scutifolia* and *N. cœrulea* have fragrant blue flowers; the latter is the Blue Lotus of the Nile, and is generally met with in English gardens under the erroneous name *N. cyanea*. One of its varieties, and also another species called *N. micrantha*, or *N. guineensis*, are remarkable for producing on their leaves, just at the junction of the blade with the stalk, little buds which in process of time become detached and form new plants. *N. gigantea*, a native of Moreton Bay, has very large blue flowers, in which the stamens are much shorter in proportion to the petals than in most of the other species. *N. blanda*, a South American species, and some others expand their flowers at night. *N. Lotus* has white flowers tinted with pink, and strongly toothed leaves, on the under side of which the veins are very prominent. This is the White Lotus of the Nile. Varieties of this species occur in Guinea, India, and elsewhere. Some of them are grown in this country, under the names of *N. dentata*, *N. edulis*, &c. Some of the Indian varieties have red or rose-coloured flowers, such as *N. rubra*, &c. All these are without doubt variations of one common form, of which the *N. Lotus* of the Nile may be taken as the type. The tubers and seeds of some of these are used by the Hindoos as articles of food. The species of this genus are so variable, that much diversity of opinion exists as to the actual number of species, and there is much difficulty in discriminating them.

In addition to the characters laid down in systematic treatises, the writer has derived much assistance in the determination of these beautiful plants by paying attention, amongst other things, to the form of the flower-buds, the arrangement of the air-canals, and the appearance of the seeds. The Botanic Garden at Oxford has for some years been noted for its numerous collection of these lovely flowers, which are cultivated with great success by the Curator, Mr. Baxter.　　　[M. T. M.]

NYSSA. A genus of doubtful affinity, made by some botanists the type of a natural order (*Nyssaceæ*), by others associated with *Alangiaceæ*. It comprises about eight species, all trees inhabiting the swamps and banks of rivers of North America. Their leaves are alternate, entire and without stipules, their flowers greenish, small, solitary, or in little pedunculate clusters, and polygamo-diœcious. The calyx tube (of the fertile flowers) is adherent to the ovary, five-cleft, and valvate in æstivation; the stamens are from four to ten in number, the corolla is wanting, and the fruit is a berry-like drupe with a single seed, and black bluish or orange-coloured. Several species ornament our arboretums. *N. villosa*, the Sour Gum, Black Gum, Pepperidge, or Tupelo tree, common from New England to the Carolinas, attains from forty to seventy feet in height, and has remarkably curled woody fibres, so as to render the timber very difficult to split, on which account it is much used for making naves or hubs for heavy carriage-wheels, and also hatters' blocks. *N. candicans* is the Ogeechee Lime.　　　[B. S.]

NYSSACEÆ. A group of calycifloral dicotyledons, now included in *Alangiaceæ*.

NYSSANTHES. A genus of Australian *Amaranthaceæ*, consisting of herbs or undershrubs with opposite leaves and terminal and axillary heads of flowers, having spiny bracts, a four-leaved perigone, the exterior pair of leaves spiny, and two to four stamens united at the base, the staminodes strap-shaped.　　　[J. T. S.]

N'Y TOUCHEZ PAS. (Fr.) *Impatiens Noli-tangere.*

OAK. *Quercus*; also the Australian name for *Casuarina*. —, AFRICAN. *Oldfieldia africana.* —, AMERICAN TURKEY. *Quercus obtusiloba.* —, AMERICAN WHITE. *Quercus alba.* —, BARREN. *Quercus nigra.* —, BEAR. *Quercus ilicifolia.* —, BELOTE. *Quercus Gramuntia.* —, BITTER. *Quercus Cerris.* —, BLACK. *Quercus tinctoria.* —, BLACK JACK. *Quercus nigra.* —, BOTANY BAY. *Casuarina torulosa.* —, BURR. *Quercus macrocarpa.* —, CAPPADOCIAN. *Ambrina ambrosioides.* —, CHAMPION. *Quercus rubra.* —, CHESTNUT. *Quercus sessiliflora*; also the varieties of *Quercus Prinus.* —, COMMON. *Quercus Robur* (including *pedunculata* and *sessiliflora*). —, CORK. *Quercus Suber.* —, CYPRESS. *Quercus pedunculata fastigiata.* —, DOMINICA. *Ilex sideroxyloides.* —, DURMAST. *Quercus sessiliflora pubescens.* —, DYER'S. *Quercus tinctoria.* —, EVERGREEN. *Quercus Ilex.* —, FEMALE. *Quercus pedunculata.* —, FRENCH. *Catalpa longissima*; also *Bucida Buceras.* —, GREEN. A condition of oak-wood caused by its being impregnated with the spawn of *Peziza æruginosa*, which communicates a beautiful green tint, of which the turners and cabinet-makers at Tunbridge Wells avail themselves for inlaying and making beads and other articles of ornament. A similar effect is produced in the Sikkim Himalaya by a closely allied species of *Peziza.* —, HE. *Casuarina stricta.* —, HOLLY, or HOLM. *Quercus Ilex.* —, INDIAN. *Tectona grandis*, the Teak tree. —, IRON. *Quercus Cerris* and *obtusiloba.* —, ITALIAN. *Quercus Æsculus.* —, JERUSALEM. *Chenopodium Botrys.* —, KERMES. *Quercus coccifera.* —, LAUREL. *Quercus imbricaria.* —, LIVE. *Quercus virens*, an important shipbuilding wood. —, MALE. *Quercus sessiliflora.* —, NEW ZEALAND. *Alectryon excelsum.* —, NUTGALL. *Quercus infectoria.* —, PIN. *Quercus palustris.* —, POISON. *Rhus Toxicodendron.* —, POST. *Quercus obtusiloba.* —, RED. *Quercus sessiliflora* and *rubra.* —, RIVER. *Casuarina leptoclada.* —, SCRUB. *Quercus Catesbæi* and *ilicifolia.* —, SCRUBBY. *Lophira africana.* —, SEA. *Fucus vesiculosus.* —, SHE. *Casuarina quadrivalvis.* —, SHINGLE. *Quercus imbricaria.* —, SILKY, or SILKBARK. *Grevillea robusta.* —, SPANISH. *Quercus falcata.* —, STONE. *Lithocarpus javensis.* —, SWAMP. *Quercus Prinus*; also *Viminaria denudata.* —, SWAMP POST. *Quercus lyrata.* —, VALONIA. *Quercus Ægilops.* —, WHITE. *Quercus pedunculata* and *alba.* —, —, of New South

Wales. *Casuarina leptoclada.* —, WILLOW. *Quercus Phellos.* —, YELLOW. *Quercus Castanea.* —, WAINSCOT. *Quercus Cerris.*

OAK-CURRANT. A kind of gall produced on the oak by *Cynips Quercus pedunculi.*

OAKESIA. A North American genus of *Empetraceæ*, consisting of a small depressed branched shrub, with narrowly linear leaves in whorls of three or four, and diœcious flowers in terminal heads, surrounded by awned bracts. The perianth is absent, but each flower is surrounded by five or six thin scarious bracteoles; male flowers with three stamens; females with a slender three-cleft style; drupe small dry, with three nuts. [J. T. S.]

OAK-LEATHER. The common name of a kind of spawn found in old oak, running down the fissures, and having when removed somewhat the appearance of white kid-leather. It is figured by Sowerby under the name of *Xylostroma giganteum.* It does not appear very clearly what is its perfect form, whether *Dædalea quercina* or some *Polyporus.* It is extremely common in the United States, where it is sometimes used as a material for receiving plaister, a purpose which it answers admirably from its pliable texture. A substance remarkably similar in appearance is woven by certain insects on walls of granaries in Brazil, the true nature of which may be easily ascertained by microscopical examination, or by burning. A mycelium resembling Oak-leather also occurs in Australia on different species of *Eucalyptus.* The Oak-leather of ships suffering from dry-rot arises from *Polyporus hybridus.* [M. J. B.]

OAK-LUNGS. *Sticta pulmonacea.*

OAK-SPANGLE. A kind of gall produced on the oak by *Diplolepis lenticularis.*

OAK-WEED. A name given to the large and best-known form of *Laminaria digitata,* called by some authors *L. Cloustoni.*

OAT. *Avena sativa.* —, ANIMAL. *Avena sterilis.* —, FALSE. *Arrhenatherum.* —, SEASIDE. *Uniola.* —, WATER. An American name for *Zizania aquatica.* —, WILD. *Avena fatua.* —, — of the West Indies. *Pharus latifolius.*

OB. A prefix signifying inversion. Thus *obovate* is inversely ovate; *obcordate,* inversely cordate; *obclavate,* inversely club-shaped, &c.

OBCOMPRESSED. Compressed, so that the two sutures of a fruit are brought into contact; flattened, back and front.

OBELISCARIA. A genus of *Compositæ,* proposed for the *Rudbeckia pinnata,* and two other North American species which have a much longer receptacle, and in which the achenes are considerably flattened laterally, and sometimes bordered by a wing on the inner edge. They would,

however, be much better considered as a section only of *Rudbeckia.*

OBERONIA. A genus of nearly fifty species of orchids, found principally in tropical Asia. All are epiphytal plants, with equitant leaves, and terminal spikes of minute flowers, having free sepals, of which the hind one is smaller than the two others, still smaller petals, a sessile immovable usually concave variously-divided lip, cushioned or keeled at its base and embracing the short column; and a two-celled anther containing four free waxy pollen-masses. [A. S.]

OBESIA. A name given by Haworth to a group of *Stapelia,* now generally included in that genus.

OBIER. (Fr.) *Viburnum Opulus.*

OBIONE. The name under which certain species of *Atriplex,* as *A. pedunculata* and *portulacoides,* are sometimes separated. The most obvious distinction resides in the perigone of the fruiting flowers, which consists of two parts, three-toothed, free only at the top, and wedge-shaped at the base. The pericarp is very thin, ultimately adhering to the perigone tube. [T. M.]

OBLIQUE. Unequal-sided; also slanting.

OBLONG. Elliptical, blunt at each end, as the leaves of *Hypericum perforatum.*

OBOLARIA. A small vernal plant belonging to the *Orobanchaceæ,* with a simple stem and opposite leaves, by which latter character, and the fact of its being terrestrial not parasitical, it differs from *Orobanche.* *O. Virginica,* the only species, is a native of North America, especially the shady woods about Lake Erie. It has a small branching root, a stem from three to four inches high, thick almost fleshy opposite leaves, round leaf-like bracts, and bell-shaped bluish-white or pale-red flowers, which are collected into pairs or threes near the summit of the stem. [C. A. J.]

OBOVATE, or OBOVAL. Inversely ovate.

OBOVOID. Approaching the obovate form.

OBROTUND. Somewhat round.

OBTECTO-VENOSE. Having the principal and longitudinal veins held together by simple cross-veins.

OBTEGENS. Covering over anything.

OBTUSE. Blunt, or rounded. Thus, *obtusely crenated* is when crenatures are quite round, and not at all pointed; *obtusely cut,* when incisions are blunt, &c.

OBTUSE-ANGLED. When angles are rounded, as in the stem of *Salvia pratensis.*

OBTUSIUSCULUS. Rather obtuse.

OBVERSE. The same as Ob.

OBVERSE-LUNATE. Inversely crescent-shaped; that is to say, with the horns of the crescent projecting forwards instead of backwards.

OBVOLUTE, OBVOLUTIVE. When the margins of one organ alternately overlap those of an opposite organ.

OCA. The Peruvian name for the tuber-bearing *Oxalis crenata* and *tuberosa*.

OCELLATED. When a broad round spot of some colour has another spot of a different colour within it.

OCHNA. A genus of trees or shrubs, natives of Asia and tropical Africa, and giving its name to the order *Ochnaceæ*. Their leaves are provided with two axillary deciduous stipules, and their flowers yellow, in racemes, with stalks jointed near the middle. Calyx of five deciduous coloured sepals; petals five to ten, much larger than the sepals; stamens numerous, the anthers opening lengthwise. The lobes of the ovary equal the petals in number, and are placed obliquely upon a thickened receptacle, each containing a single ascending ovule. The style is single, divided into five or ten branches. The fruits succulent, of five, ten or fewer carpels placed on the enlarged receptacle.　　[M. T. M.]

OCHNACEÆ. (*Ochnads*.) A natural order of thalamifloral dicotyledons belonging to Lindley's rutal alliance of hypogynous Exogens, consisting of undershrubs or trees, with alternate simple stipulate leaves and articulated pedicels; sepals five, persistent, imbricated; petals imbricated, as many or twice as many, deciduous; stamens five opposite the sepals, or ten, or indefinite, rising from an hypogynous disk; anthers bilocular, innate, opening by pores, or longitudinally; carpels as many as the petals, seated on an enlarged gynobase or torus. Fruit gynobasic, consisting of several succulent indehiscent monospermous carpels. They grow in tropical countries, and are remarkable for their large succulent torus; they are generally bitter, and some of them are used as tonics. There are six genera, including *Ochna* and *Gomphia*, and upwards of eighty species.　　[J. H. B.]

OCHRA, or **OCHRO.** *Abelmoschus esculentus*. —, AFRICAN, or AUTUMNAL. *Abelmoschus Bammia*, probably a variety of the preceding. —, BUN. *Urena lobata*. —, MUSK. *Abelmoschus moschatus*. —, WILD. *Malachra*.

OCHRACEUS. Ochre colour; yellow, imperceptibly changing to brown.

OCHRADENUS. A genus of *Resedaceæ*, distinguished by its fruit being a berry. A small Egyptian shrub, with numerous twiggy branches, linear obtuse leaves, and spicate yellow flowers, the peduncles at length becoming spinescent. Calyx rotate, five-toothed; petals absent; hypogynous disk urceolate, the anterior limb truncate, the posterior expanded into a lamina; stamens ten to twenty; berry ovate, three-sided, one-celled, closed, with numerous kidney-shaped seeds.　　[J. T. S.]

OCHRANTHACEÆ. The name under which it was formerly proposed to separate *Ochranthe*, a genus now included in *Cunoniaceæ*.

OCHRANTHE. A genus of *Cunoniaceæ*, consisting of a Chinese shrub, with the old branches grey, the leaves stalked opposite serrated, and furnished with ovate serrulate interpetiolar stipules, and a terminal panicle of white flowers, which turn yellowish. Calyx of five coloured sepals; the two exterior shorter; petals five, resembling the sepals; stamens five, hypogynous; disk fleshy, five-angled; ovary free, of three united carpels.　　[J. T. S.]

OCHREA. A tubular membranous stipule through which the stem passes, formed by the consolidation of two opposite stipules; as in *Polygonum*.

OCHROLEUCUS. Nearly the same as *Ochraceus*, but whiter.

OCHROMA. The well-known Corkwood tree of the New World, forms, with an allied species, a genus of *Sterculiaceæ*, characterised by their flowers having a shortly five-lobed calyx, surrounded by a three-leaved involucre which soon drops off; five petals larger than the calyx; the tubular staminal column covered in the upper part with narrow contiguous spiral one-celled anthers, and five or ten-lobed at the top; and the five narrow stigmas spirally twisted together. The five-celled fruit opens longitudinally through the cells, and contains numerous seeds enveloped in silky wool. Both species are trees, with leaves heart-shaped at the base and angular or somewhat five to seven-lobed, and bear their flowers at the ends of the branches.

O. Lagopus grows about forty feet high, and is very common, particularly along the seashores, in the West Indies and Central America, where its soft spongy and exceedingly light wood, called Corkwood in Jamaica, is commonly employed as a substitute for cork, both for stopping bottles and for the floats of fishing-nets. The very buoyant rafts or balsas, the unsinkable properties of which caused such surprise among the discoverers of America, are likewise made of it, whence the tree is called Balsa in some parts of America. Its specific name *Lagopus*, signifying hare's foot, alludes to the fruit, which is about a foot in length and when ripe splits open by five slits, out of which the silk-cotton of the seeds protrudes and spreads over the whole surface, giving it the appearance of a hare's foot. The cotton is used for stuffing pillows and cushions.　　[A. S.]

OCHROPTERIS. A genus of polypodiaceous ferns, referred to the *Pterideæ*, and distinguished amongst those with free veins, chiefly by the oblong transverse sori being placed at the apices of the lobes, the opposite condition from that which occurs in *Lonchitis*, one of the genera of net-veined *Pterideæ*, in which the sori are placed in the sinuses of the lobes. *Pteris*, which is technically very closely allied to *Ochropte-*

ris, differs in the more elongated lateral and marginal rather than short apical sori. The only species is *O. pallens*, a large decompound fern of the Mascaren Islands, with small glossy coriaceous ultimate divisions. *Cheilanthes* differs in its punctiform receptacles, as does *Hypolepis*. [T. M.]

OCHROS. In Greek compounds=pale-yellow; thus *ochroleucus* is pale-yellow blended with white; yellowish-white.

OCHROSIA. A genus of dogbanes, having the corolla funnel-shaped, with the tube swollen in the middle; five stamens inserted in the throat of the corolla; and a single style, ending in two points. The species are shrubs, natives of Mauritius and New Caledonia, having three or four leaves in a whorl, the flowers in terminal or lateral corymbs. [G. D.]

OCIMUM. An extensive genus of *Labiatæ* characterised by the large roundish upper tooth of the calyx having winged decurrent margins, the whole calyx being bent downwards after flowering; by the short corolla having the lower lip flat, with the four fertile stamens bent down and lying upon it; and by the style being divided at the apex into two short-pointed or flattish lobes. It is widely dispersed throughout the tropical and subtropical countries of Asia, Africa, and America, and consists of strong-scented annual or perennial herbs or small shrubby plants, with flowers disposed in whorls forming terminal interrupted racemes.

O. sanctum, a common Indian and Ceylon species, is frequently planted about Hindoo temples, whence the specific name. It is a hairy-stemmed plant, about a foot high, with small, long-stalked, oval, blunt, downy leaves, toothed along the edges, and small pale purplish flowers; the whole plant, indeed, generally having a purplish tinge. It is much used in medicine by the Cingalese. The leaves of *O. viride*, which is a native of Western Africa, possess febrifugal properties; and at Sierra Leone, where it bears the name of Fever-plant, a decoction of them, drank as tea, is used as a remedy for the fevers so prevalent at that place. It is a shrubby plant, with hairy somewhat four-sided branching stems, having oblong egg-shaped pointed leaves tapering to the base, and with round-toothed margins, smooth or with down on the ribs, and glandular dotted underneath. The leaves of *O. canum* and *gratissimum* in India, and of *O. crispum* in Japan, all very aromatic, are prescribed as a remedy for colds. *O. tenuiflorum* is regarded as an aromatic stimulant in Java; and *O. guineense* is much employed by the negroes as a medicine in cases of bilious fever. [A. S.]

These plants are in all cases destitute of any deleterious secretions: for the most part they are fragrant and aromatic, and hence they have not only been used as tonics, but are also valuable as kitchen herbs. The most important of them is *O. basilicum*, the Sweet or Common Basil,

a tender annual, native of India; which, as a culinary aromatic herb, has been celebrated from a very early period. This plant, which was well known to the ancient Greeks and Romans, though it does not appear to have been cultivated in this country until 1548, is of erect growth, about a foot high, much-branched, and furnished with small oval lanceolate deep-green leaves, and very small flowers arranged in clustered whorls at the extremity of the branches. It is chiefly valued for the leaves and leafy tops, which are the parts that are used, and have a flavour somewhat resembling that of cloves. On this account they are much employed for seasoning soups, stews, sauces, and various other dishes. Under the name of *O. hirsutum*, the seeds of this plant, which form a mucilaginous infusion, are used by the women of India to relieve after-pains.

O. minimum, the Bush or Lesser Basil, is a tender annual, and like *O. basilicum* a native of India, from whence it was introduced in 1573. It is much branched, seldom exceeding nine inches in height, the leaves small, oval, deep-green, and the flowers white. The leaves have a strong aromatic smell, and are employed for seasoning dishes in the same way as those of *O. basilicum*. To preserve the Basils, or indeed any other sweet herbs, the plants should be cut off close to the ground when the flowers are about to open, and hung up in a warm place, shaded from the sun, until they are perfectly dry. Each sort should then be put into a small box eight or ten inches long, five or six inches broad, and seven or eight inches deep; a board the size of the box inside is to be placed over the herbs, which by means of a screw-press are to be pressed into cakes. These are afterwards to be wrapt in clean paper until required for use; and if kept in a dry place, they will retain their aroma for two or three years, as perfect nearly as when they were first gathered. [W. B. B.]

OCTARILLUM. A genus of sandalworts, distinguished by having stamens and pistils in the same flower; the calyx with four sharp divisions; the stamens four; and the style top-shaped, longer than the stamens, and ending in a thick point. The only species known is a shrub found in Cochin China, having alternate entire lanceolate leaves, solitary flowers, and red berries. [G. D.]

OCTO. Eight.

OCTOBLEPHARUM. A genus of acrocarpous mosses forming the small natural order *Octoblepharei*, remarkable for the leaves being of a pale colour, with the chlorophyll cells situated beneath those on the surface, which have the contiguous walls perforated, but do not contain a spiral thread as in *Sphagnum*. It is further remarkable for having a peristome with eight undivided teeth. *O. albidum* is one of the commonest tropical mosses, and if imported in a Ward's case bears cultivation in the stove, where it makes a pretty contrast with *Hymenophylla* of a dark-green. [M. J. B.]

2 F

OCTOMERIA. A genus of orchids distinguished from all others of the *Pleurothallideæ* by having eight pollen-masses, which, moreover, are all arranged side by side in a single series, cohering together in two sets of four each. It is a small group, confined to the West Indies and South America, and consists of little plants with one-leaved terete-jointed stems, clothed with fibrous sheaths and bearing axillary fascicled or solitary flowers. [A. S.]

OCTONI. Growing eight together.

OCULUS. An eye, i.e. a leaf-bud.

ODES. A termination in Greek compounds = similar to; as *phyllodes*, like a leaf.

ODIALS. The young roots of the Palmyra which are eaten in Ceylon.

ODINA. A genus of *Anacardiaceæ*, consisting of trees, natives of India and tropical Africa. They have alternate pinnate leaves placed near the ends of the branches, and small polygamous flowers aggregated together in slender terminal drooping racemes; calyx with four persistent rounded lobes; petals four, concave, placed at the base of an eight-lobed disc, into which also the eight stamens are inserted. In the male flowers the ovary is sterile, divided into four compressed lobes; in the female it is free, sessile, one-celled with a single ovule, and terminated by four erect styles. The fruit is a drupe. *O. Wodier* is a common tree in India, its specific name being derived from the native appellation. The old wood is close-grained and mahogany-coloured, and is used for sheaths of swords; the bark is fibrous, and there exudes from it a gum which is used as an application to sprains and bruises. [M. T. M.]

ODONTARRHENA. A genus of *Cruciferæ* closely allied to *Alyssum*, from which it has small claims to be separated on account of the elliptical not suborbicular pouch, and the one-seeded cells, the seeds having the setaceous seed-stalks free from the partition. It is found in Europe and Middle Asia, has the habit of *Alyssum*, and bears small yellow flowers. [J. T. S.]

ODONTOGLOSSUM. An extensive genus of orchids, found principally in the cool mountain regions of Mexico, Peru, New Grenada, and Venezuela. A considerable number of its species have been introduced to this country, and are much prized by cultivators for their magnificent flowers, which are remarkable both for their size and the beauty of their colours. Some species are epiphytal and others terrestrial. Their flowers have spreading free sepals (or the lateral ones rarely united at the base), nearly equal-sized petals, the lip with its base parallel with the column and its limb deflexed and generally crested in various ways, a long column, narrow at the base and eared or winged at the summit, and two pollen-masses with a narrow caudicle attached to an oval gland. *O. grande*, a native of Guatemala, has been found to live and flower in the open air in this country during the summer season. Its scape bears from two to five large handsome flowers, each some six or more inches across, yellow, closely marked with cinnamon-brown bands and blotches. *O. tigrinum*, an allied species, has equally large yellowish flowers marked with chestnut-purple tiger-like spots, except on its lip, which is wholly yellow. Its flowers have a powerful odour of violets, and are used by the Mexicans for decorative purposes under the name of Flor de Muertos. *O. Pescatorei*, so named after an eminent

Odontoglossum grande.

French orchid-grower, is found in New Grenada. The flower panicle of this species is between two and three feet high and nearly as broad, and bears large but delicate semitransparent flowers, the sepals of which have a faint blush-coloured stain along their middle, and the lip a yellow stain at its base and a deep crimson crest. A plant somewhat like the last has been dedicated to the Princess of Wales under the name *O. Alexandræ*. [A. S.]

ODONTOLOMA. A South American shrub, constituting a genus of *Compositæ*, with the one-flowered heads of *Monosis*, but differing in the pappus being reduced to a small toothed ring. It is a native of the Valley of Caraccas. The name is also applied to a small group of davallioid ferns here referred to *Acrophorus*.

ODONTOPTERIS. *Lygodium*.

ŒCEOCLADES. With the exception of *Œ. maculata*, all the orchids formerly associated under this name are now referred to *Angræcum* and *Saccolabium*, from both of which the remaining species is distinguished by its three-lobed lip. It is a Brazilian pseudobulbous epiphyte, bearing single fleshy spotted leaves, and having a radicle scape bearing a few small ringent rose-and-white flowers.　　　[A. S.]

ŒDEMA. A swelling; the so-called tumid glands found on the woody tissue of conifers.

ŒDIPODIUM. A most interesting genus of mosses belonging to the natural order *Splachnei*, differing from the rest not only in its toothless peristome, but in the swelling at the base of the capsule (*apophysis*) being confluent with both capsule and stem. The columella, moreover, is strongly developed and dilated at the apex, and the spores do not radiate from it. *Œ. Griffithianum*, the only species, is not like the other *Splachnei* decidedly an inhabitant of dung, but grows in the crevices of Alpine rocks, where it attracts notice from its pale very obtuse leaves. It is found rarely in Europe, and occurs in several localities in Great Britain.　　　[M. J. B.]

ŒDOGONIUM. A curious genus of green-spored *Algæ* belonging to the natural order *Conjugatæ*, but producing fruit by the division of a cell and not by the junction of the cells of two contiguous threads. The propagation is very much like that described under *Bulbochæte*, except that the product of impregnation is a simple zoospore which throws out rootlike holdfasts at the base as soon as it becomes stationary, and is not resolved, as in *Bulbochæte*, into four distinct spores. The spores of *Œdogonium*, though at first green, often become of the most brilliant red. Multiplication sometimes takes place by the division of the threads, which is readily effected from the peculiar structure of the dissepiments. The species are numerous. Few foreign species have been observed at present, so that we know little or nothing of their geographical limits. *Vesiculifera* of Hassall is the same genus.　　　[M. J. B.]

ŒIL DE BŒUF. (Fr.) *Anthemis tinctoria*; also applied to *Chrysanthemum Leucanthemum*, the species of *Buphthalmum*, and *Adonis autumnalis.* — DE BOURIQUE. The seeds of *Mucuna urens.* — DE CHAT. The seeds of *Guilandina Bonduc.* — DE CHRIST. *Aster Amellus.* — DE OISEAU, or DE PERDRIX. *Adonis æstivalis.* — DE PAON. *Anemone Pavonina.* — DU SOLEIL. *Tulipa Oculis solis.*

ŒILLET. (Fr.) *Dianthus.* — À BOUQUET, or À RATAFIA. *Dianthus Caryophyllus.* — BADIN. *Dianthus hispanicus.* — DE DIEU. *Lychnis Flos Jovis*, and *L. coronaria*; also *Agrostemma Githago.* — D'INDE. *Tagetes erecta.* — D'INDE TACHETÉ. *Tagetes signata.* — DE POÈTE. *Dianthus barbatus.* — DES CHARTREUX. *Dianthus carthusianorum.* — DES FLEURISTES. *Dianthus Caryophyllus.* — DES PRÉS. *Lychnis Flos cuculi.* — GIROFLE. *Dianthus Caryophyllus.* — JANSÉNISTE. *Lychnis Viscaria.* — MARIN. *Statice Limonium.* — MIGNARDISE, or PLUME. *Dianthus plumarius.* — PETIT D'INDE. *Tagetes patula.* — VELU. *Dianthus Armeria.*

ŒILLETTE. (Fr.) *Papaver somniferum.*

ŒNANTHE. A genus of *Umbelliferæ*, consisting for the most part of plants frequenting wet or marshy places, or even growing in water. The leaves are much divided, and the umbels compound, generally without a common involucre, but with partial involucels of many narrow bracts. The outermost flowers are usually on long stalks, sterile and with large petals; the inner ones on shorter stalks. The fruit is cylindrical or ovate, surmounted by the teeth of the calyx, and by the long styles, which latter are dilated at the base; and the carpels marked by five convex ribs, between which, within the rind, run as many vittæ.

The species are distributed throughout the whole of the northern hemisphere, but are rare in America. Some of them are

Œnanthe crocata.

met with in this country, and certain of these are very poisonous. *Œ. crocata* is a stout branched species attaining a height of three to five feet; the root consists of a number of thick whitish parsnip-like tubers; the leaves are twice or thrice pinnate, with broad lozenge-shaped segments; the umbels are on long terminal stalks, the outer florets imperfect; and the fruits are somewhat cylindrical, densely packed. The juice of the stem and roots becomes yellow when exposed to the air. The roots act as a narcotic acrid poison, and from their resemblance to parsnips have been the cause of frequent and sometimes of fatal accidents. The difference between this plant and the parsnip is, however, sufficiently obvious in the foliage, inflorescence, &c.: thus the root of the parsnip is single, while there are several tubers in *Œ. crocata*. The locality in which the plant is found, and its wild not cultivated condition, should likewise induce caution. The plant has been used with beneficial result in certain skin-diseases; also in the form of poultices to ulcers, &c., as well as for the purpose of poisoning rats and moles.

Œ. Phellandrium, the Water Dropwort, is less poisonous than the preceding. It grows in wet places or even in the water, its rootstock varying in appearance, according to the locality. Thus if in deep or running water the rootstock and stem are long and slender; in other cases thicker and erect. The leaves are repeatedly pinnate, with very small segments, which when under water become long and hair-like. The umbels are smaller than in the foregoing, opposite to the leaves or in the forks of the branches. The variety that grows in deep running water is by some considered a distinct species under the name *Œ. fluviatilis.*

Œ. fistulosa has fibrous roots, some of which become swollen and tuberous. The stem is thick and hollow, slightly branched, the root-leaves twice pinnate, with small wedge-shaped segments, the stem-leaves with long hollow stalks and a few pinnate linear segments at the top. The umbel terminating the main stem has in general three rays, and all the flowers are fertile, while the umbels that occur on the branches have more than three rays; but the flowers are barren. This is perhaps the most common species. *Œ. pimpinelloides* has tuberous roots, leaves much more divided than in the last, stems nearly solid, all the umbels with many rays, and having fertile and barren flowers intermixed; the latter are on longer stalks than the former. The shape of the leaves and tubers is subject to much variation. Mr. Bentham combines with this species *Œ. Lachenalii.*

In spite of the dangerous qualities of some of these plants, others are innocuous, and their tuberous roots are eaten as food. Cultivation, and the locality in which the plants are grown, will go far towards explaining this seeming anomaly. The name, derived from two Greek words signifying wine-flower, is applied in allusion to the vinous odour of the blossoms. [M. T. M.]

ŒNOCARPUS. An exclusively South American genus of *Palmaceæ*, consisting of six or seven species, abounding principally on the banks of the Amazon and Orinoco and their tributaries, forming lofty trees with smooth straight stems, and bearing a terminal crown of large pinnate leaves, the segments of which are narrow and somewhat crisped. Their broom-like flower-spikes spring from beneath the leaves, and are enveloped in double woody spathes, the inner of which is entirely closed when young, but ultimately opens and falls off. The flowers, which have no bracts at their base, are of separate sexes on the same spike. The fruits are oval or nearly round, and have a granular fibrous oily flesh, enclosing a single seed of a nutmeg-like appearance inside.

Several species common on the Amazon, such as the Patawa *Œ. Batava*, the Bacaba *Œ. Bacaba*, as well as *Œ. distichus*, yield colourless sweet-tasted oil, used in Pará for adulterating olive-oil, and excellent both for cooking and for lamps. The Indians also prepare a palatable but slightly aperient beverage, by triturating the fruits in water and adding sugar and mandiocca-flour. The stiff slender nerves of the decayed base of the leafstalks of *Œ. Batava* are used by the Indians for making arrows for their blow-pipes. [A. S.]

ŒNOTHERA. A genus of onagrads, distinguished by having the border of the calyx four-cleft, reflexed, and fugacious; and the seeds numerous, without an appendage. The species are chiefly herbaceous, natives of North and South America, their lower leaves with triangular footstalks and usually crowded; and the upper leaves alternate, almost sessile, entire or slightly toothed, rarely pinnatifid. The flowers present considerable difference in colour, being in some yellow, in others white or purple, and they usually open at night. Many species of this well-known genus have been long in cultivation, occupying deservedly a very prominent place in collections. They are all handsome border flowers, and have the recommendation of being easily cultivated. *Œ. biennis*, one of the best known, has now become naturalised in some parts of England. [G. D.]

ŒONIA. A small genus of epiphytal orchids, with distichous coriaceous leaves, and showy flowers. They are found in Madagascar, Mauritius, and Bourbon; and are allied to *Angræcum*, from which they are distinguished by the three-lobed hooded lip, and the pollen-masses having two glands, and no caudicle. [A. S.]

OERSTEDELLA. *Epidendrum centropetalum*, a Central American orchid, was first described under that name by Reichenbach, who, however, soon afterwards raised it to the rank of a genus called *Oerstedella*, and split it into two so-called species; now, however, he reverts to his original view, and combines the two species under the original name. [A. S.]

OFBITEN. *Scabiosa succisa.*

OFFSET. A short lateral shoot, bearing clustered leaves at its extremity, and propagating a plant ; as in houseleek.

OIDES, OIDEUS. See *Odes.*

OIDIUM. A genus of naked-spored moulds, which has obtained considerable notoriety from its connection with the Vine Mildew, which arises from the attacks of *O. Tuckeri.* This fungus derived its name from a gardener at Margate, who was one of the first to use sulphur as a remedy. It is now pretty clear that the *Oidium* of the vine, like some other supposed species, is but an early stage of some *Erysiphe*, though the perfect plant has not yet been found. Another form of fruit, indeed, besides the necklace-like spores, has occurred, consisting of little cysts filled with minute bodies or stylospores, such as occur in undoubted species of *Erysiphe.* Though, however, several supposed species of *Oidium* are referable to *Erysiphe*, there still remain true species. Some, which grow on decayed wood and other substances, are remarkable for their tawny or golden-yellow spores ; but another species with large pallid spores, *O. fructigenum*, deserves notice, from its frequently forming patches of little concentric tufts on pears, apples, and other fruits. Whether it is itself productive of decay, or only contingent to it, is uncertain. In the white mealy species, the necklaces of spores are very short, seldom exceeding three joints, but in others they are often much longer.   [M. J. B.]

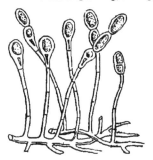

Oidium Tuckeri.

OIGNON (Fr.) *Allium Cepa.* — D'ESPAGNE, or D'HIVER. *Allium fistulosum.*

OIL. The general name for a variety of fatty matters, fixed or volatile : those of the former class more or less of a solid or fluid consistence, and those of the latter being known also as essential oils. We here mention only some of the more important of the oils of vegetable origin. —, ALLSPICE. An aromatic oil obtained by distillation from the fruits of *Eugenia Pimenta.* —, ALMOND. The fixed oil obtained by pressure from the kernels of *Amygdalus communis,* used both in manufactures and medicine. That of Bitter Almonds is very poisonous. —, ANDIROBA. The same as Carap Oil. —, ANISE. The volatile oil distilled from the fruits of *Pimpinella Anisum*; see also Oil of Star-anise. —, ASAFŒTIDA. The volatile oil obtained by distillation from the gum-resin of *Narthex Asafœtida.* —, ASPIC. The same as Oil of Spike. —, BACABA. A fixed oil obtained from *Œnocarpus Bacaba,* used in Pará both for lamps and cooking. —, BALM. The volatile oil distilled from *Melissa officinalis.* —, BALSAM OF PERU. An acrid oily fluid obtained from *Myrospermum peruiferum.* —, BANCOUL. The same as Lumbang Oil. —, BAY. A fixed oil obtained from the berries of *Laurus nobilis.* —, BEECH-NUT. The fixed oil obtained from the mast or nuts of *Fagus sylvatica.* —, BEN. A limpid fixed oil obtained from the seeds of *Moringa pterygosperma,* used in perfumery, and for lubricating delicate machinery. —, BERGAMOT. The volatile oil obtained from the rind of the fruit of *Citrus Bergamia*; a similarly fragrant oil is obtained from *Mentha citrata.* —, BIRCH-BARK. An empyreumatic volatile oil, distilled from the bark of *Betula alba,* employed in the preparation of Russia leather. —, CADE.

An empyreumatic oil obtained from the wood of *Juniperus Oxycedrus.* —, CAJEPUT, or CAJUPUTI. The stimulant antispasmodic oil distilled from the leaves of *Melaleuca minor.* —, CAMPHOR. A limpid oil obtained from *Dryobalanops aromatica,* employed in the preparation of scented soap ; also the volatile oil obtained from the branches of *Camphora officinarum.* —, CARAP. The solid fixed anthelmintic oil obtained from the seeds of *Carapa guianensis,* also called Crab Oil; in South America it is used for burning. —, CARAWAY. The volatile oil distilled from the fruits of *Carum Carui.* —, CARDAMOM. The volatile aromatic oil distilled from the seeds of *Elettaria Cardamomum*; also a fixed oil obtained from the same plant. —, CASHEW APPLE. A vesicatory oil obtained from the pericarp of *Anacardium occidentale.* —, CASHEW-NUT. The edible fixed oil of the kernels of *Anacardium occidentale.* —, CASSIA. The heavy volatile oil obtained from the bark of *Cinnamomum Cassia.* —, CASSIE. The volatile oil distilled from the flowers of *Acacia Farnesiana.* —, CASTANHA. The fixed oil expressed from the seeds of *Bertholletia excelsa.* —, CASTOR. The fixed oil obtained from the seeds of *Ricinus communis,* used medicinally ; the common jungle lamp-oil of India is an inferior kind of this. —, CEBADILLA. A fixed fatty oil obtained from *Asagræa officinalis.* —, CEDAR. The volatile oil distilled from the wood of *Abies Cedrus* and *Juniperus virginiana.* —, CEDRAT. The same as Citron Oil. —, CHAMOMILE. The volatile stimulant oil distilled from the flower-heads of *Anthemis nobilis.* —, CHEEROJEE, or CHEROONJEE. A fixed oil obtained from the fruit of *Buchanania latifolia.* —, CHERRY. A volatile oil obtained from the bark of *Cerasus serotina.* —, CHERRY-LAUREL. A volatile oil obtained from the leaves of *Cerasus Laurocerasus.* —, CINNAMON. The heavy volatile medicinal oil obtained from the bark and leaves of *Cinnamomum zeylanicum.* —, CITRON. The fragrant volatile oil obtained from the fruits, rind, and leaves of *Citrus medica.* —, CITRONELLE. The volatile oil of the Lemon Grass. —, CLOVE. The heavy volatile oil obtained from cloves, *Caryophyllus aromaticus* ; the name is also applied to the oil obtained from cinnamon leaves. —, COCOA-NUT. The fixed oil pressed from the fruit of *Cocos nucifera,* used in manufactures, and throughout Western India for illumination. —, COCUM, or KOKUM. A solid fixed oil obtained from the seeds of *Garcinia purpurea.* —, COHUNE. A fixed oil obtained from the kernels of *Attalea Cohune.* —, COLZA. The fixed oil expressed from the seeds of *Brassica campestris,* much used as a lamp-oil and for manufacturing purposes. —, COONDI. The same as Kundah Oil. —, COPAIVA. A volatile oil distilled from the balsam of *Copaifera multijuga,* and other species. —, COROOKO. An Indian medicinal oil obtained from *Argemone mexicana.* —, COTTON-SEED. The fixed oil expressed from the seeds of *Gossypium*. —, CRAB. The same as Carap Oil. —, CROTON. The fixed medicinal oil expressed from the seeds of *Croton Tiglium*; the same name is also used in India for an oil obtained from other species of *Croton*. —, CUBEB. A volatile medicinal oil obtained from the fruit of *Cubeba officinalis*. —, CUMARU. The same as Tonquin Oil. —, CUMIN. A volatile oil distilled from the fruits of *Cuminum Cyminum*. —, DILL. The volatile oil obtained from the fruits of *Anethum graveolens*. —, DOMBA. The same as Poonseed Oil. —, EPIE. A fixed oil obtained from the seeds of *Bassia latifolia*, resembling Ilpa Oil, and adapted for the same purposes. —, ERGOT. A volatile medicinal oil obtained from Ergot of Rye. —, EUPHORBIA. An acrid oil obtained from the seeds of *Euphorbia Lathyris*. —, EXILE. A fixed oil obtained from the kernels of *Thevetia nereifolia*. —, FENNEL. The volatile medicinal oil distilled from the fruits of *Fœniculum dulce* and *F. vulgare*. —, FLORENCE. A fine kind of Olive Oil. —, FUSEL. An essential oil distilled from wine. —, GARLIC. The stimulant volatile oil obtained from *Allium sativum*. —, GENTIAN. The oil obtained from the root of *Gentiana lutea*. —, GERANIUM. The volatile oil distilled from the leaves of *Pelargonium odoratissimum*; also a commercial name for Grass Oil. —, GINGELLY, or GINGILLE. A fixed oil of fine quality expressed from the seeds of *Sesamum indicum*. —, GINGER-GRASS. The same as Grass Oil. —, GRASS. The volatile oil obtained from *Andropogon Calamus aromaticus*, employed in medicine and perfumery. —, GROUND-NUT. The fixed oil expressed from the seeds of *Arachis hypogœa*, used as food, and for lamps. —, HEMP-SEED. The fixed drying oil pressed from the seeds of *Cannabis sativa*, used by painters, and for soap-making. —, HOP. An acrid oil obtained by pressure from the flower-heads of *Humulus Lupulus*. —, HUTS-YELLOW. The fixed oil of *Guizotia oleifera*. —, ILPA, ILLIPOO, or ILLUPIE. A fixed solid oil obtained from the seeds of *Bassia longifolia*, and useful for manufacturing purposes. —, JASMINE. The volatile perfumery oil obtained from *Jasminum officinale*, *grandiflorum*, *Sambac*, &c. —, JATROPHA. An oil obtained from the seeds of *Curcas purgans*, and *C. multifidus*. —, JUNIPER. The volatile oil obtained by the distillation of the green berries of *Juniperus communis*. —, KANARI. The fixed oil of *Canarium commune*, used in the East for culinary purposes. —, KATJANG. An Eastern name for an oil said to be obtained from the seeds of *Arachis hypogœa*. —, KEENA. An oil obtained from some species of *Calophyllum*. —, KEKUNE. The same as Lumbang Oil. —, KEORA. An Eastern volatile perfumery oil obtained from *Pandanus odoratissimus*. —, KHATZUM. A solid fixed oil obtained from the seeds of *Vernonia anthelmintica*. —, KHUS-KHUS. The fragrant attar prepared from *Andropogon*

muricatus. —, KIKUEL. An oil said to be obtained from the seeds of *Salvadora persica*. —, KOKUM. The same as Cocum Oil. —, KOSSUMBA. The fixed oil obtained from the seeds of *Carthamus tinctorius*. —, KRUIN, or KRUNE. A crude elastic gummy substance imported from Borneo. —, KUNDAH, or COONDI. The fixed oil obtained from *Carapa guineensis* (*C. Touloucouna*), also called Mote Grease; it is suited for lamps, and has anthelmintic properties. —, KURUNJ, KURRING, or POONGUM. A stimulant fixed oil obtained from the seeds of *Pongamia glabra*. —, KYAPOOTIE. The same as Cajeput Oil. —, LAUREL. The volatile oil obtained from the berries of *Laurus nobilis*; also a fixed solid oil from the same plant. —, LAVENDER. The fragrant volatile oil distilled from the flowers of *Lavandula vera*. —, LEMON. The volatile perfumery oil obtained by pressure from the rind of the fruit of *Citrus Limonum*. —, LEMON-GRASS. The volatile perfumery oil obtained from *Andropogon citratum*. —, LILY. An infusion of the flowers of *Lilium candidum* in oil. —, LIMBOLEE. The clear fixed oil obtained from the seeds of *Bergera Königii*. —, LINSEED. The fixed drying oil obtained by pressure from the seeds of *Linum usitatissimum*, much used in oil-painting and varnish-making. —, LUMBANG. The fixed oil expressed from the nuts of *Aleurites triloba*, a good substitute for rape oil. —, MACE. The volatile oil obtained from the arillode of *Myristica moschata*; also a fixed oil obtained by pressure from the same. —, MACUJA. A concrete yellow oil obtained from the fruit of *Acrocomia sclerocarpa*. —, MADIA. A fixed oil obtained from the seeds of *Madia sativa*. —, MAHOWA-SEED. The same as Epie Oil. —, MALE FERN. The anthelmintic oil obtained from the rhizomes of *Lastrea Filix-mas*. —, MARGOSA. The solid fixed oil expressed from the seeds of *Melia Azadirachta*. —, MARJORAM. The volatile Oil of Origanum, obtained by distillation from *Origanum vulgare*; Oil of Sweet Marjoram is obtained from *O. Majorana*. —, MARKING-NUT. The acrid vesicatory oil of the pericarps of *Semecarpus Anacardium*. —, MARMOTTES. A fixed oil obtained from the kernel of *Prunus Brigantiaca*, a substitute for oil of almonds. —, MEADOW-SWEET. A product of salicine. —, MEZEREON. The acrid volatile oil of the root of *Daphne Mezereum*. —, MOGREE. The same as Oil of Jasmine. —, MUSTARD. An excellent fixed oil obtained from *Sinapis nigra*, and in India from other species, as *S. glauca*, *dichotoma*, *juncea*, &c.; also a volatile or essential oil obtained from the marc of *S. nigra*. —, MYRRH. A volatile oil obtained from *Balsamodendron Myrrha*. —, NAHOR. An oil obtained from the seeds of *Mesua ferrea*. —, NAMUR, or NEMAUR. The fragrant deep yellow Grass Oil, obtained from *Andropogon Calamus aromaticus*. —, NAPALA. The fixed oil obtained from the seeds of *Curcas purgans*. —, NAPOOTA. An East African oil, obtained from the Agati, and used as a substitute for olive oil in India. —, NARCISSUS. A perfumery oil obtained by maceration from the flowers of *Narcissus odorus*. —, NARPAULAH. A fixed oil obtained from the seeds of a *Croton* allied to *C. Tiglium*. —, NEEM. The same as Margosa Oil. —, NEROLI. The volatile fragrant oil obtained by distilling the flowers of *Citrus Bigaradia* and *C. Aurantium*, much used in perfumery and for flavouring. —, NUT. The fixed drying oil pressed from the kernels of *Corylus Avellana* and *Juglans regia*; also a commercial name for the oil expressed from the seeds of *Arachis hypogœa*. —, NUTMEG. The volatile medicinal oil obtained from *Myristica moschata*; also a fixed solid oil from the same plant. —, OLIVE. The fixed oil expressed from the pericarps of *Olea europæa*, so much valued for its domestic, economical, and medicinal uses, and commonly known as Sweet Oil. —, ONION. An acrid medicinal volatile oil obtained from *Allium Cepa*. —, OONDEE. The same as Poonseed Oil. —, ORANGE. The volatile perfumery oil distilled from the rind of the fruit of *Citrus Aurantium* and *Bigaradia*; Orange-leaf Oil is a volatile oil distilled from the leaves of the same plants. —, ORIGANUM. The same as Oil of Marjoram. —, OUABE. An excellent lubricating fixed oil obtained from the seeds of *Omphalea diandra*. —, PALM. The dark yellow fixed oil obtained from the fruits of *Elæis guineensis* and *melanococca*, used in manufactures, and for lubrication. —, PAND. The volatile perfumery oil distilled from *Michelia Champaca*. —, PANDANG. The volatile fragrant oil distilled from *Pandanus odoratissimus*. —, PATAWA, or PATAUA. An excellent fixed oil, equal to that of olives, obtained from *Œnocarpus Bataya*, used in Pará both for cooking and for lamps. —, PATCHOULI. The volatile perfumery oil obtained by distilling the leafy tops of *Pogostemon Patchouli*. —, PENNYROYAL. The stimulant volatile oil distilled from *Mentha Pulegium*. —, PEPPERMINT. The volatile aromatic oil distilled from *Mentha piperita*. —, PHOOLWA. The fixed oil of the seeds of *Bassia butyracea*, also called Vegetable Butter, and commonly burnt in India. —, PHYSIC-NUT. The fixed oil expressed from the seeds of *Curcas purgans*. —, PIMENTO. The same as Oil of Allspice. —, PINHOËN. A purgative oil obtained from *Curcas multifidus*. —, PINNACOTTAY. The same as Poonseed Oil. —, PIQUIA. A concrete oil obtained in Brazil from the pulp of the fruit of *Caryocar brasiliense*. —, POONGA. The same as Kurunj Oil. —, POONGUM. The fixed oil obtained from *Sapindus emarginatus*. —, POONSEED, or POONAY. A fixed oil obtained from the seeds of *Calophyllum Inophyllum*, and used for lamps and medicinal purposes. —, POOTUNGEE. A fixed oil obtained in India from the fruits of *Calophyllum spurium*. —, POPPY. The fixed drying oil obtained from the seeds of *Papaver somniferum*, used for the same purposes as olive oil. —, PORTIA-NUT.

A fixed oil obtained in India from *Thespesia populnea*. —, POTATO. An acrid limpid liquid obtained from potato spirit. —, PROVENCE. An esteemed kind of Olive Oil, the produce of Aix. —, PURQUEIRA. A Portuguese name for Physic-nut Oil. —; RAM-TIL. The fixed oil of *Guizotia oleifera*, used exclusively for burning. —, RAPESEED. The fixed oil pressed from the seeds of *Brassica Napus*, &c. —, RHODIUM. A volatile balsamic oil distilled from the wood of the species of *Rhodorhiza*. —, ROSE. The same as Attar of Roses; an oil obtained by distillation from *Rosa damascena*, *centifolia*, and others. —, ROSEMARY. The volatile oil distilled from the branches of *Rosmarinus officinalis*. —, ROSIN. An oil obtained from the resin of the pine-tree, used by painters for lubricating machinery, and other purposes. —, RUE. A volatile stimulant oil obtained from the shoots of *Ruta graveolens*. —, SAFFLOWER. The same as Kossumba oil. —, SANDAL, or SANDER'S WOOD. The volatile oil obtained from *Santalum album*, much esteemed as a perfume. —, SAPUCAIA. The fixed oil expressed from the kernels of *Lecythis Zabucajo* and others. —, SARSAPARILLA. The volatile medicinal oil obtained from Sarsaparilla. —, SASSAFRAS. The volatile stimulant oil distilled from the wood of *Sassafras officinale*; also a volatile oil obtained from *Nectandra cymbarum*, an excellent solvent for resinous gums. —, SAVIN. The volatile oil distilled from the green tops of *Juniperus Sabina*. —, SEED. An indefinite name for several kinds of oil which enter into commerce, especially for those made from til, poppy, and other Indian seeds. —, SENNA. A volatile medicinal oil distilled from senna-leaves. —, SERINGA. An oil obtained in Brazil from the fruits of *Siphonia elastica*. —, SERPOLET. The essential oil distilled from *Thymus Serpyllum*. —, SESAMUM. The fixed oil obtained from the seeds of the black til, a variety of *Sesamum orientale*. —, SHANGHAE. The fixed oil of *Brassica chinensis*. —, SIRI. The same as Lemon-grass oil. —, SOAP-NUT. The same as Poongum Oil. —, SPEARMINT. The volatile aromatic oil distilled from *Mentha viridis*. —, SPIKE. The volatile oil obtained from *Lavandula Spica*, used by painters on porcelain, and in preparing varnish for artists; also, the oil of *L. Stœchas*. —, SPIKENARD. A druggist's name for Grass Oil. —, SPURRY. A lamp-oil obtained from *Spergula sativa*. —, STAR-ANISE. The volatile oil distilled from the fruits of *Illicium anisatum*. —, SUNFLOWER. The fixed oil expressed from the achenes of *Helianthus annuus*, scarcely inferior to olive oil. —, SWEET. The same as Olive Oil. —, SWEET BAY. The volatile form of Laurel Oil. —, TALLICOONAH. The same as Kundah Oil. —, TAR. The volatile oil obtained by distilling tar. —, TEUSS. A Chinese oil obtained from *Arachis*, and used both for food and burning in lamps. —, THYME. The volatile oil obtained from *Thymus vulgaris*, also applied in the shops to Marjoram Oil. —, TO-BACCO. A volatile poisonous oil distilled from *Nicotiana Tabacum*. —, TONQUIN. The expressed perfumery oil obtained from the seeds of *Dipterix odorata*. —, TUBEROSE. A perfumery oil obtained by maceration from the flowers of *Polianthes tuberosa*. —, TUMIKA. A concrete fixed oil obtained from the seeds of the wild mangosteen, *Diospyros Embryopteris*. —, TURPENTINE. The volatile oil obtained by distillation from the resinous juice of *Pinus sylvestris, maritima*, and other coniferous trees; it is much used in house-painting. —, UGGUR. An oil distilled from the wood of *Aquilaria Agallocha*, and esteemed for its perfume by the Orientals. —, VALISALOO. The same as Ram-til Oil. —, VERBENA. An essential oil distilled from *Aloysia citriodora*; also, the same as Lemon-grass Oil. —, VETIVER. The same as Khus-khus Oil. —, VIOLET. A perfumery oil obtained by maceration from the flowers of *Viola odorata*. —, WALNUT. The fixed drying oil obtained from the kernels of *Juglans regia*, valuable for domestic purposes. WINTERGREEN. The aromatic volatile oil obtained from the fruit of *Gaultheria procumbens*, used in medicine and by perfumers. —, WOOD. The balsam-like product of *Dipterocarpus turbinatus*; also a product of *Chloroxylon Swietenia*. — WORMSEED. The volatile anthelmintic oil obtained from *Ambrina anthelmintica*. —, YAMADOU. The fixed oil expressed from the seeds of *Myristica sebifera*. —, ZAKKOUM. An oil obtained in Palestine from *Elæagnus hortensis angustifolia*.

OILCAKE. The residuum after expressing the oil of various seeds, especially linseed and rape, which is used for cattle-feeding, and as a manure.

OIL-PLANT. *Sesamum orientale.*

OIL-SEED. *Guizotia oleifera;* also *Ricinus communis*. —, SIBERIAN. A Canadian name for *Camelina sativa*.

OILY-GRAIN. *Sesamum.*

OKENIA. A genus of *Nyctaginaceæ*, named in honour of the German philosopher Oken. The only species, *O. hypogæa*, a native of Vera Cruz, has a prostrate stem, viscid leaves, and solitary purple flowers, enclosed within a three-leaved involucre. The perianth has a regularly five-cleft limb with notched segments, and from fifteen to eighteen stamens, united at the base. The fruit is marked with ten ribs, and is enclosed within the hardened corky base of the perianth.   [M. T. M.]

OKRA, or OKRO. *Abelmoschus esculentus.* See also OCHRA.

OLACACEÆ. (*Olacineæ, Olacads*). A natural order of thalamifloral dicotyledons belonging to Lindley's herbaceal alliance of hypogynous Exogens. Tropical or subtropical trees or shrubs, with simple alternate exstipulate leaves, which are, however, sometimes abortive. Calyx small, gamosepalous; petals three to six, hypogynous,

free, or adhering in pairs by means of the stamens, valvate in æstivation; stamens hypogynous, the fertile three to ten, alternate with the petals, the sterile opposite to them, inserted either upon the external elevated margin, or outside the conspicuous disk; ovary one to three or four-celled; ovules one to three, pendulous from a central placenta; fruit fleshy, one-celled, one-seeded, indehiscent, often surrounded by the enlarged calyx.   [J. H. B.]

OLAX. The typical genus of *Olacaceæ*, containing about a dozen species, mostly Asiatic and Australian. A few are small trees, but the greater number are erect or climbing sometimes thorny shrubs, with entire smooth leaves, and small whitish flowers either solitary or in short axillary racemes. The calyx is cup-shaped and very small at first, but it increases in size and eventually entirely encloses the ripe fruit; the petals are either six, joined in pairs by the fertile stamens cohering between them, or five, four being in pairs, and the fifth free; three (rarely four or five) of the stamens are fertile and five or six sterile, the former being alternate with and the latter opposite the petals to which they all partly adhere; and the free one-celled ovary contains three ovules hanging from the apex of a free central column, and ripens into a dry one-seeded fruit.

O. zeylanica is a small tree about twenty feet high, abundant in the southern part of Ceylon, where it is called Malla. Its young branches are sharply angled and marked with fine transverse wrinkles; its leaves egg-shaped, pointed, and smooth, and its racemes consisting of a few short-stalked flowers. The Cingalese eat the leaves in their curries; and use the wood, which possesses a fœtid smell and saltish taste, in putrid fevers.   [A. S.]

OLDENLANDIA. Some botanists regard this as a section of *Hedyotis*, while others make it a separate genus, characterised by the fruit not separating into two carpels, but opening at the top in two valves, bearing the partition in their centre. It is a very extensive group of *Cinchonaceæ*, and is widely dispersed over tropical and subtropical Asia, Africa, Australia, and tropical and temperate America. The species are low spreading herbaceous or rarely erect somewhat shrubby plants, with opposite or whorled leaves, having their stipules united with the leafstalks and usually fringed with several bristles, and small flowers either solitary or in clusters in the axils of the leaves or rarely in terminal leafy panicles. The calyx and corolla are four-lobed, the anthers protruding out of the corolla tube, and the style entire or two-lobed.

O. umbellata, the Chayroot plant, is in its wild state a low widely-spreading almost stemless plant, but under cultivation it assumes a more erect habit and grows six or eight inches high. It is a biennial, with narrow somewhat whorled leaves, and small white flowers in short racemes, having one to three-flowered stalks. Its long slender twisted roots, commonly known as Chay-root, yield a red dye, and are largely employed by the dyers of Southern India, the plant being there extensively cultivated. Several shades varying from pale to very deep red are dyed with them, or by combination with other dyestuffs a fine chocolate is produced, while with an iron mordant they give a deep black. The celebrated red turbans of Madura are dyed with chayroot, as also are the chocolate-and-red handkerchiefs known as pulicats or bandanas, which are exported to the West Indies and slave States of America for the use of the negroes. [A. S.]

OLDFIELDIA. During the past half-century several kinds of hard timber have been brought into use by shipbuilders, and among these not the least important is that known as African Oak or African Teak, which however, botanically speaking, is neither an oak nor a teak; but, according to the most reliable information, is the produce of a large tree belonging to the *Euphorbiaceæ* to which the name of *Oldfieldia africana* has been given. All that is at present known of this tree is its leaves and its fruit. The former are digitate, having from five to nine short-stalked leaflets radiating from a common leafstalk; and the latter a roundish three-furrowed three-celled capsule nearly one inch in diameter, splitting through the middle of the cells into three valves bearing the partition in their centre but having no external mark indicating its position, each cell containing one or two seeds hanging from the central column. Though nearly one-third stronger than either English oak or Malabar teak, African Oak or Teak is not so generally useful as those woods, its ponderous weight detracting greatly from its value and rendering it unsuitable as an exclusive material for shipbuilding, the vessels built entirely of it being too heavy. It is, however, very useful in certain parts, such as for beams, keelsons, waterways, shelf-pieces, &c., and particularly in steamboats, as it will stand a great degree of heat in the wake of fires, where there is a free current of air, but when in confined situations it decays rapidly. The sapwood, like that of other timbers, is also very subject to decay; and even the solid heartwood does not escape the attacks of large larvæ, or from being perforated by teredos. [A. S.]

OLD-MAID. A West Indian name for *Vinca rosea.*

OLD-MAN. A name given by rustics to the Southernwood, *Artemisia Abrotanum.*

OLD-MAN'S BEARD. *Clematis Vitalba;* also *Geropogon,* and *Tillandsia usneoides.*

OLD-MAN'S EYEBROW. *Drosera binata.*

OLD-MAN'S HEAD. *Pilocereus senilis.*

OLD SOW. *Melilotus cœruleus,* or *Trigonella cærulea,* which gives its peculiar flavour to chapziger cheese.

OLD-WOMAN'S BITTER. *Picramnia Antidesma;* also *Citharexylum cinereum.*

OLD-WOMAN'S TREE. *Quiina jamaicensis.*

OLEACEÆ. (*Oleineæ, Lilaceæ, Fraxineæ, Oliveworts.*) A natural order of corolliflotal dicotyledons belonging to Lindley's solanal alliance of perigynous Exogens, and consisting of trees or shrubs, with opposite simple or compound leaves, and hermaphrodite or unisexual flowers. Calyx gamosepalous, persistent; corolla four-cleft, sometimes of four petals connected in pairs by means of the filaments, sometimes wanting; stamens free, two (rarely four), alternate with the corolline segments; ovary free, two-celled; ovules in pairs, collateral or pendulous. Fruit drupaceous, baccate or capsular, sometimes samaroid; seeds often by abortion solitary. The plants of the order are bitter, tonic, and astringent, and some yield fixed oil. *Olea europæa* is the olive-tree; and several species of *Ornus,* more particularly *O. rotundifolia* and *O. europæa,* yield manna. They are natives chiefly of temperate regions, and occur in North America, Asia, Europe, and New Holland. There are upwards of a score of genera, including *Olea, Fraxinus,* and *Syringa;* and nearly 150 species. [J. H. B.]

OLEA. The order *Oleaceæ* takes its name from this genus, of which, in addition to the Common Olive, about thirty species are known, mostly belonging to Asiatic and African countries, but some few occurring in Australia and New Zealand. Many are trees varying from twenty to fifty feet high, and producing hard useful timber, while others are large shrubs. All have

Olea europæa.

entire leathery evergreen leaves, and small whitish frequently fragrant flowers, either in axillary racemes or clusters or in axillary or terminal panicles. They have a four-lobed calyx and corolla, the latter wanting in the New Zealand species, two stamens placed opposite each other, with their anthers projecting, and a two-celled ovary with two pendulous ovules in each cell. The fruit has an oily flesh and a bony two-celled stone, one of the cells being frequently abortive, and the other ripening only one seed.

The Common Olive, *O. europœa*, was one of the plants brought into cultivation at a very early period of man's history, and considerable doubts now exist as to its native country; some authors supposing it to have originally belonged to Western Asia, from whence it migrated into Southern Europe and Northern Africa, while others regard it as indigenous to both Europe and Asia. The tree seldom exceeds twenty feet in height, and has oblong or lance-shaped leaves smooth upon the upper surface but hoary underneath, axillary erect racemes of flowers, and pendulous ellipsoidal fruits. It is a tree of slow growth, very tenacious of life and of great longevity—so great, indeed, that it is thought probable that the trees at present existing in the Vale of Gethsemane are those which existed at the commencement of the Christian era.

Two varieties of Olive are distinguished, namely: the Oleaster or Wild Olive, the branches of which are more or less four-sided and spiny, the leaves oblong or oval, and the fruit small and valueless; and the Cultivated Olive (var. *sativa*), which has roundish unarmed branches, lance-shaped leaves, and large oily fruits varying in form, size, and colour in each of the numerous subvarieties. The principal products of this tree are olive-oil and pickling olives, and for these it is extensively cultivated in Italy, Southern France, Spain, and other parts of Southern Europe, in Northern Africa, Western Asia, Australia, &c. The oil is derived from the flesh of the fruit, and is obtained by first passing the olives through a mill with crushing stones arranged so as to bruise the flesh without breaking the kernels, after which the mass is put into bags and subjected to pressure in a screw-press—the first product being termed virgin oil. A second quality is obtained by moistening the marc or cake with boiling water and re-pressing it; and a third by crushing the cake so as to break the stones, and then boiling and again pressing it. Olive-oil is imported from several Italian ports, and also from France, Spain, Portugal, Morocco, &c. That from Leghorn, called Florence oil, is the kind used in this country as salad oil, and comes in flasks surrounded by rushwork; but Gallipoli oil, which forms the bulk of that imported, comes in casks, and Lucca oil in jars holding nineteen gallons. In the olive countries, oil forms an important article of food, but with us it is only eaten as a condiment, the bulk of the large quantity imported being consumed in the arts and manufactures. The pickling olives are the unripe fruits deprived of a portion of their bitterness by soaking in water to which lime and wood ashes are sometimes added, and then bottled in salt-and-water flavoured with aromatics. The wood of the Olive-tree is beautifully clouded and veined, especially the root part.   [A. S.]

OLEAGINOUS. Fleshy in substance, but filled with oil.

OLEANDER. *Nerium Oleander.*

OLEANDRA. A genus of ferns belonging to the *Aspidieæ*, amongst which they are known by their simple fronds, combined with free veins, and sori placed near the base of the veins. They have globose sori and reniform indusia, and hence having also free veins, they are technically

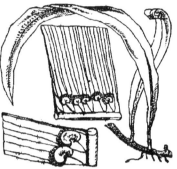

Oleandra Wallichii.

not far removed from *Lastrea*; but their aspect is altogether different, and they are generally regarded as distinct. The rhizomes are creeping in some, as *O. nodosa*, erect and frutescent in others as *O. nerii-formis*; but the stipites are nodosely articulate, and the fronds undivided and strap-shaped, the veins being simple or forked and parallel, and the sori placed very near the mid-rib of the fronds. They are tropical or sub-tropical plants of Asia, Africa, and America.   [T. M.]

OLEANDRE. (Fr.) *Nerium.*

OLEARIA. A genus of *Compositæ* of the tribe *Asteroideæ*, very nearly allied to *Aster* itself, and only distinguished from *Eurybia*, which generally represents *Aster* in Australia and New Zealand, by the pappus being more distinctly double, and the outer ring of setæ being shorter and often more chaff-like. It consists of about a dozen shrubs, natives of Australia or New Zealand, with small entire or toothed leaves, cottony underneath. The flower-heads are usually larger than in *Eurybia*, and either solitary or two or three together at the summit of the branches. One species, *O. dentata*, from New South Wales, has been occasionally cultivated in our greenhouses.

OLEASTERS. Lindley's name for the *Elæagnaceæ*.

OLERACEOUS. Having esculent properties, that is to say, fit for kitchen use, of the nature of a potherb. Also, growing in cultivated places.

OLFERSIA. A genus of acrostichaceous ferns with creeping rhizomes and dimorphous fronds, found chiefly in tropical America. The typical species is *O. cervina*, which has pinnate sterile fronds, the pinnæ traversed by parallel simple or forked veins, connected at the margin by a straight marginal vein. The fertile contracted fronds are pinnato-pinnatifid or bipinnate, and covered on both surfaces with spore-cases. With this are sometimes associated a few other species having the marginal vein arcuate, as in the South American *O. longifolia*; or having the marginal vein zig-zag with an excurrent veinlet from each exterior angle, as in the St. Helena *O. sub-diaphana*.   [T. M.]

OLIBANUM, AFRICAN. The fragrant gum-resin produced by *Boswellia papyrifera*. —, INDIAN. The gum-resin of *Boswellia thurifera*, also called *B. serrata*.

OLIETTE. (Fr.) *Papaver somniferum*.

OLIGOS. In Greek compounds=a small number. It is generally used in contrast with many (*poly*), when no specific number is employed, as in the definition of things the number of which is small, but variable; thus *oligocarpous* is applied to sort in which the spore-cases are few in number.

OLIO DI MARMOTTA. A Piedmontese name for the oil obtained from the buds of *Rhododendron ferrugineum*.

OLIVACEUS, OLIVE-GREEN. A mixture of green and brown.

OLIVE. *Olea europœa*. —, BARBADOS WILD. *Bontia daphnoides*. —, BLACK. *Bucida Buceras*. —, CALIFORNIAN. *Oreodaphne californica*. —, SPURIOUS, of Victoria. *Notelæa ligustrina*, —, WILD. *Elæagnus angustifolius*; also *Rhus Cotinus* and *Daphne Thymelæa*. — of India. *Olea dioica*; also *Putranjiva Roxburghii*. —, — of the West Indies. *Ximenia americana*; also *Bucida Buceras*, and *Bucida capitata*.

OLIVE-BARK TREE. *Bucida Buceras*.

OLIVETIER. (Fr.) *Elæodendron*.

OLIVE-WOOD. *Elæodendron*; also the yellowish fancy wood of the Olive-tree.

OLIVEWORTS. Lindley's name for the *Oleaceæ*.

OLIVIER. (Fr.) *Olea*; also applied to the West Indian wood of *Bucida Buceras*. — BÂTARD. *Bontia daphnoides*. — DE BOHÊME. *Elæagnus angustifolius*. —DES BARBADES. *Bontia daphnoides*. — ODORANT. *Osmanthus*.

OLLUCO. (Fr.) *Melloca tuberosa*.

OLMEDIA. A genus of Peruvian trees of the family *Artocarpaceæ*. The flowers are diœcious; the males attached to a globose receptacle, surrounded by an involucre of numerous bracts, and having a tubular perianth with two or four erect segments, opposite to which the stamens are placed; the females solitary, surrounded by numerous overlapping bracts, tubular, contracted at the throat, with a slightly four-toothed limb, an ovate one-celled ovary, with solitary pendulous ovules, and a style dividing into two long thread-like

branches. The fruit is enclosed within the thickened fleshy perianth, protected by the involucre.   [M. T. M.]

OMALANTHUS. A small genus of *Euphorbiaceæ*, confined to the tropics of Asia and New Holland. The plants have long-stalked entire leaves, and terminal spikes of inconspicuous unisexual flowers, the males in clusters of three or four on the upper part of the spike, and the females solitary at the base. Both have a calyx of two flat semicircular leaves notched and glandular at the base; the males containing six to ten stamens with short flat filaments partly adhering to each other, and the females a somewhat cylindrical two-celled ovary, terminated by a thick two-pronged style and two stigmas. The fruits are two-celled and two-valved, each cell containing a solitary seed.   [A. S.]

OMALOTHECA. A generic name adopted by some authors for the *Gnaphalium supinum*, which differs from other species in the outer row of female florets being in a single series, and in the flattened achenes. It is a small tufted perennial herb found in Alpine places in Europe and Western Asia, and not uncommon on some of our highland mountains. The narrow leaves are clothed with white down, and the small flower-heads at the end of the stalk have brown involucral scales. Sometimes very dwarf varieties about half an inch high are found, and in these the flower-heads are sessile in the midst of the leaves.   [A. A. B.]

OMANDER-WOOD. A variety of Calamander wood obtained in Ceylon from *Diospyros Ebenaster*.

OMBROPHYTUM. A genus of *Balanophoraceæ*, consisting of fleshy herbaceous plants, with shield-like rootstocks attached to the roots of trees. The flower-stalk is surrounded at the base by a leathery or woody sheath, the flowers themselves being crowded along the sides of the little stalks supporting the peltate bracts, unisexual and monœcious, the females having two styles. These plants, according to Pöppig, are boiled and eaten like fungi: they spring up suddenly in Peru after rain, whence the name from the Greek *ombros*, a shower, and *phuton*, a plant.   [M. T. M.]

OMIME-ROOT. *Plectranthus ternatus*.

OMLAH. A Bengal name for *Emblica officinalis*.

OMŒA. *Ceratochilus*.

OMPHALARIA. A small genus of gelatinous lichens, remarkable for its conidia being generated in the same manner as *Hæmatococcus* is multiplied.   [M. J. B.]

OMPHALEA. A genus of tropical *Euphorbiaceæ*, consisting of trees or tall woody climbers, remarkable for the structure of the male flowers, in which the staminal body is composed of a mushroom-shaped receptacle or disk, round the edge of which are two three or four sessile anthers. The leaves are alternate or nearly opposite, large broad and entire; the flowers in terminal panicles, intermixed with narrow leaf-like or coloured bracts, each bract having in its axil a small cyme of one central female flower and two or more lateral male ones, or sometimes all are males. There are five species known, two from Madagascar, and three from the West Indies and tropical South America. Amongst the latter *O. triandra* has a white juice, which turns black in drying, and is said to be used either for making ink or as glue; and the seeds both of that species and of *O. diandra* are eatable, after extracting the deleterious or poisonous embryo. The *O. diandra* especially, is cultivated in St. Domingo and Jamaica, under the name of Noisettier or Cobnut, from the resemblance of the flavour of the seeds to that of the European nut.

OMPHALOBIUM. The name of a genus of trees and shrubs of the family *Connaraceæ*, met with in the tropical parts of Asia, Africa, and America. The leaves are ternate or pinnate; and the flowers in axillary clusters, or crowded together in a panicle at the end of the branches. They have much the same structure as that of *Connarus*, but differ in that the fruit consists of five pods (fewer by abortion), which are slightly stalked, one-celled, one or two-seeded, and two-valved. Zebra-wood is stated by Schomburgk to be the produce of *O. Lambertii*, a native of Guiana. *Guettarda speciosa*, a cinchonaceous plant, is also stated to furnish this wood.   [M. T. M.]

OMPHALODES. A genus of herbaceous plants, belonging to the *Boraginaceæ*, distinguished by having the four nut-like seeds furnished with an indexed margin which renders them cup-shaped. They are natives of Southern Europe, Asia Minor, and the Caucasus; and several species are grown in English gardens, under the name of Venus's Navelwort. *O. linifolia* is a common border annual with linear leaves, and white flowers tinged with blue. *O.verna,* the Petite Consoude of the French, is a charming plant with creeping shoots, ovate heart-shaped leaves, and brilliant blue flowers like those of the forget-me-not. This is a perennial, and a common ornament of shrubberies and cottage gardens.   [O. A. J.]

OMPHALODIUM. The central part of the hilum, through which vessels pass into the raphe or chalaza.

ONAGRACEÆ, (*Onagrariæ, Epilobiaceæ, Circæaceæ, Onagrads.*) A natural order of calycifloral dicotyledons belonging to Lindley's myrtal alliance of epigynous Exogens, consisting of herbs or shrubs, with simple leaves, and the parts of the flower usually tetramerous. Calyx tubular, the limb usually four-cleft (sometimes two, three, or six) and cohering in various ways, the æstivation valvate; petals usually of the same number as the calycine segments; stamens usually four or eight, epigynous, the filaments distinct; ovary two to four-celled, usually with an epigynous disc; ovules anatropal. Fruit succulent or capsular, one to two or four-celled. They inhabit chiefly temperate regions of Europe, Asia, and America, and are found sparingly in Africa. Some yield edible fruits, as *Fuchsia*; others furnish edible roots, as *Œnothera biennis*; and both *Trapa natans* and *T. bicornis*, remarkable for their horned fruit, supply edible seeds. There are about thirty known genera, and upwards of 450 species.   [J. H. B.]

ONAGRAIRE. (Fr.) *Œnothera.*

ONAGRES. (Fr.) *Onagraceæ.*

ONCIDIUM. One of the largest of the genera of orchids, comprising upwards of 200 species, and exclusively confined to tropical America. As many of the species are found growing at great elevations in the mountain regions, they do not, in cultivation in this country, require such an elevated temperature as might at first be expected; indeed, *O. Warczewiczii*, which grows on oaks in the mountains of Costa Rica and Veraguas, at an elevation of 8,000 to 10,000 feet, where the thermometer stands at 40° Fahrenheit in November, actually perishes as soon as it descends into the warm zone. In its botanical features the genus comes extremely close to *Odontoglossum.* Its flowers have similar spreading sepals and equal-sized petals, with the two lateral sepals sometimes united beneath the lip, and the lip itself continuous with the column and tubercled or crested at its base. The chief distinction resides in the column being shorter, and not narrowed at the base like that of *Odontoglossum.*

O. Papilio is well known in the orchid-houses of this country by the name of the Butterfly-plant, a name applied to it on account of the appearance of its flowers, which are borne singly upon the ends of very long slender stalks, and have the petals and hind sepal long and narrow, and the lateral sepals shorter and much broader. It is a native of Trinidad and Venezuela. In some species the racemes or panicles of flowers are of very great length. This is especially the case in *O. altissimum,* a West Indian species, with bright-yellow and brown-spotted flowers, in which they are thirteen feet long; in *O. corynephorum,* a Peruvian species, which has twining scapes between fifteen and twenty feet long, bearing numerous flowers, which have dull-brown sepals, pale cinnamon-and-white petals, and a deep crimson-and-white lip; and in *O. falcipetalum,* a Venezuelan plant, which has great scrambling panicles twenty feet long, with large brown flowers as much as three inches in diameter. In a great number of them the prevailing colour of the flowers is yellow, usually variegated, however, with other tints, but in *O. concolor* the flowers are wholly yellow, and very large. One section of the genus consists of species with what are called terete (i. e. almost cylindrical) leaves. The most remarkable of these is *O. Sprucei*, found by Mr. Spruce on the Rio Negro in Brazil, where the natives call it Rabo de Satu or Armadillo's Tail, in allusion to these terete leaves, which are between two and three feet long and nearly an inch thick, like the tail of some animal.

O. Lanceanum of Surinam, is perhaps the most beautiful species known, having its sepals and petals richly mottled with brown upon a greenish ground, and its lip rose-coloured and deep violet. It is also

Oncidium bicallosum.

remarkable for the rich vanilla-like fragrance of its flowers. The tubercular development at the base of the lip is shown in the accompanying figure of *O. bicallosum*. [A. S.]

ONCOBA. A genus of *Flacourtiaceæ* confined to Nubia and tropical Africa, and consisting of spiny trees with alternate oblong and serrated leaves, white racemose flowers, and a leathery berry the pulp of which is sweet and eaten in Nubia. The flowers are hermaphrodite; the calyx five-cleft and deciduous; the corolla has five petals; the style is simple, and the fruit encloses numerous seeds. [B. S.]

ONCOSPERMA. The two species of *Oncosperma*, a genus of Palms, are placed by some botanists in *Areca*. They are lofty elegant palms, with slender spiny trunks marked with circular scars, terminal pinnate leaves with very spiny sheathing footstalks, and pendulous flowerspikes springing from below the leaves and enclosed in double spathes. The flowers are unisexual and usually in threes, one female between two males upon the lower part, and in pairs higher up; in structure they resemble those of *Areca*, except that the males uniformly have six stamens with short stout free filaments and arrow-shaped anthers; and the three stigmas of the females closely connive. The small round one-seeded fruits bearing the remains of the stigma on one side have a granular (not fibrous) flesh enveloping a thin shell, which closely adheres to the seed.

O. filamentosa, the Nibung or Nibong of the Malays, is a very elegant palm found growing in masses in swampy places upon the coasts of Malacca, Sumatra, Borneo, and the islands of the Indian Archipelago. It attains a height of forty or fifty feet, and has leaves ten or twelve feet in length, with very numerous narrow drooping leaflets about two feet long. In Borneo the delicate white heart of unexpanded leaves, called the cabbage, is highly esteemed as a vegetable. The unsplit trunks are used for house-building, for posts, &c., and the hardest part of the split trunks for rafters, flooring, &c. [A. S.]

ONCOSPORUM. A genus of South-west Australian *Pittosporaceæ*, having a calyx of five small leaves, a corolla with five petals, five stamens alternate with the petals, and a short filiform style with a simple stigma. These are succeeded by a membranaceous two-celled seed-vessel, each cell containing from six to ten seeds. It consists of climbing shrubs with alternate leaves, and white flowers occasionally striped with purple. [R. H.]

ONE-BERRY. *Paris quadrifolia.*

ONE-BLADE. *Convallaria bifolia.*

ONE-SIDED. Having all the parts turned one way, in consequence of a twist in their stalks.

ONION. *Allium Cepa.* —, BARBADOS. *Ornithogalum scilloides.* —, BOG. *Osmunda regalis.* —, POTATO. A variety of *Allium Cepa.* —, SEA. *Urginea Scilla.* —, TREE. *Allium proliferum.* —, WELSH. *Allium fistulosum.*

ONOBROMA. A name given by De Candolle to some Eastern species of *Carthamus* separated from the rest of the genus on account of the outer florets being neuter without a pappus, whilst the hermaphrodite central ones have a pappus of linear chaff-like bristles. They are thistle-like plants, with yellow flowers.

ONOBRYCHIS. A handsome genus of *Leguminosæ* of the tribe *Papilionaceæ*, which may be distinguished by its pinnate leaves without tendrils, its spicate flowers, and its wrinkled one-seeded legume or pod. Our only British species is *O. sativa*, the Common Sainfoin, which occurs not unfrequently on English downs where the substratum is calcareous; it is said, however, not to be met with in Scotland or Ireland.

Sainfoin has been much cultivated as a shifting fodder crop, especially on the oolite soils, in which its deeply-penetrating roots, by bringing up organic matter from below, act most beneficially in the formation of a thicker crust of soil. This crop was formerly capable of holding on to the soil for as long as eight years, but latterly it has become so mixed with burnet (*Poterium Sanguisorba*) as to be very materially injured as a crop, the burnet growing so much faster than the Sainfoin, that the land is taken possession of by the former to the prejudice of the latter. The mixture takes place in the seed, more especially in foreign samples ; for as the weed and the crop-plant are harvested together, and the two seeds are somewhat similar in colour, it has escaped detection by the careless and uneducated farmer, and consequently the seedsman has not been particular in their separation. They are, however, very different in shape. The best way to avoid errors of this kind is to buy the Sainfoin seed decorticated. The leaves of both plants are pinnate, but the leaflets of the Sainfoin are entire, whilst those of the burnet have deep saw-like teeth.   [J. B.]

ONOCLEA. A very distinct genus of ferns associated with the *Aspidieæ*. The principal and perhaps only species is *O. sensibilis*, sometimes called the Sensitive Fern, but having no other claim to this name beyond the fact of its speedily withering when cut. This has a creeping rhizome, and dimorphous fronds, the sterile ones pinnato-pinnatifid, bright-green, with closely reticulated veins, and the fertile bipinnate, with small incurved bacciform pinnules, in which lie a few large globose sori having a special cucullate indusium behind each. It is North American, and quite hardy in our ferneries.   [T. M.]

ONOMATOLOGY. That branch of knowledge which relates to the rules to be observed in the construction of names.

ONONIS. A numerous genus of *Leguminosæ*, abounding principally in the countries bordering on the Mediterranean. None of the species grow very tall, the majority being undershrubs about two feet high. They have trifoliate or rarely simple leaves, with the leaflets generally toothed, and the stipules adhering to the leafstalks ; and solitary yellow or purple flowers growing from the axils of the leaves, but sometimes forming terminal leafy racemes. The calyx is cut into five narrow segments ; the upper petal of the papilionaceous corolla is large and striated, while the two lower ones terminate in a pointed beak, and the stamens are all united into a sheath. The pods are few-seeded and usually inflated.

O. arvensis is indigenous to this country, where it occurs in barren pastures, on the borders of ill-cultivated fields and similar places. It is usually a low-spreading undershrub, often with creeping underground stems, but is sometimes more erect and one or two feet high, and has thorns when growing in dry situations. In England its most common name is Restharrow, but in Sussex, Hampshire, and some other counties it is also called Cammock ; and the country people, having the idea that it communicates its nauseous goat-like odour to the cheese made from the milk of cows who have eaten it, call the cheese so tainted cammocky. The name Restharrow has arisen from its tough underground roots causing stoppages when harrowing or ploughing fields where it abounds.   [A. S.]

ONOPORDON. A genus of spinous herbaceous plants belonging to the tribe *Cynarocephalæ*, of compound flowers, and distinguished among its congeners by having a pilose pappus, the hairs of which are at the base united into a ring, four-ribbed seeds, and a honeycombed receptacle. *O. Acanthium*, or Cotton-thistle, the only English species, is a common wayside plant, with dull-green woolly very spinous leaves, of which those seated on the stem are prolonged at the base so as to run down the stem, and give it the appearance of being armed with prickles on all sides. The stem is three to four feet high or more, branched above, and bears many large heads of dull purple flowers, of which the involucre is nearly globose and very spinous. It is less common in Scotland than in England, but according to Sir W. J. Hooker it is cultivated in the former country as the Scottish thistle. Some foreign species, and among them *O. arabicum*, are cultivated for the picturesque effect produced by their stately habit of growth, white leaves, and heads of purple flowers. French, *Chardon commun* ; German, *Zellblume*.   [C. A. J.]

ONOSMA. A genus of *Boraginaceæ*, consisting of scabrous undershrubs, covered with stiff white hairs, and having numerous linear or lanceolate leaves, and terminal scorpioid racemes of large yellow or purplish flowers, with a five-parted calyx, a tubular bell-shaped corolla without scales at the throat, exserted stamens, and ovate stony nuts, affixed to the receptacle by a flat base. The species are found in Middle Asia, and a few in Europe.   [J. T. S.]

ONOSMODIUM. A genus of *Boraginaceæ*, differing from *Onosma* in having a corolla with a ventricose five-parted limb of somewhat converging segments. They are North American hispid herbs, with oblong ribbed leaves, and white greenish or yellowish flowers, with included anthers. The nuts are ovoid, swollen, and affixed by the flat base to the receptacle.   [J. T. S.]

ONYCHACANTHUS (including *Bravaisia*.) A genus of *Acanthaceæ*, confined to Mexico and the northern parts of South America, and consisting of two species, *O. Cumingii* alias *Bravaisia floribunda*, and *O. Berlandierianus*, both large shrubs or small trees of considerable beauty. The leaves are ovate or oblong, glabrous, and petiolated. The panicle is axillary or terminal, and bears whitish or yellowish flowers, the calyx of which is five-cleft, and the corolla nearly funnel-shaped, and enclosing four stamens. The capsule is oblong, smooth, two-celled, and contains from four to eight seeds.   [B. S.]

ONYCHIUM. A genus of pteridoeous ferns with decompoundly divided fronds, often of a somewhat membranous texture, and with small narrow alternate segments. They are very elegant plants, and in some cases, such as *O. auratum*, have the fronds of a somewhat dimorphous character. The fertile segments are soriferous along their margins. The sori are linear or oblong, with continuous receptacles, and membranous indusia; and being usually opposite, the indusia in the early stages of growth nearly meet across the back of the little segments into which the frond is divided. It belongs to the free-veined *Pterideæ*, and contains but three or four species, found chiefly in subtropical and temperate India and Japan. One, however, is Abyssinian, and one West Indian.   [T. M.]

ONYGENA. A curious genus of ascomycetous *Fungi* growing for the most part on animal substances, as hoofs, horns, feathers, wool, bones, &c., one of which is intimated by the generic name. They look like minute mostly stipitate puffballs, but they differ materially in their fruit. The Tulasnes were the first to indicate the true structure in this genus. Whether the species which grow on wood are really closely allied must be determined by future observation; at present it would seem that they are more nearly allied to *Pilacre* than *Onygena*, unless the latter genus should prove to have species with both sporiferous and sporidiferous fruit. Three species at present have occurred in England, one of which, occurring on bones, is distinguished from all the others by the absence of a stem. No species has at present occurred out of the northern hemisphere.   [M. J. B.]

OOD-BEG. An Indian name for *Areca Catechu*.

OOKH. An Indian name for the Sugar Cane.

OOLUNDOO. An Indian name for the seed of *Phaseolus radiatus*.

OOLYSIS. Monstrous ovular development in plants.

OOMUGGI. The Japanese name for Barley.

OOPHORIDIUM. The larger form of spore-case in *Selaginella*.

OORD. An Indian name for a species of *Dolichos*.

OOSPORANGIA. In some of the dark-spored *Algæ*, as *Leathesia* and *Mesogloea*, two kinds of zoospores of different sizes are produced in separate organs. The organs which produce the larger are by Thuret called trichosporangia, and the others oosporangia. It is not to be imagined that either of these have the power of impregnation, as both are reproductive. In *Cutleria* there are organs answering to antheridia, which produce active bodies, which have neither male functions nor do they germinate. They seem, in fact, to form a transition between spermatozoida and minute zoospores.   [M. J. B.]

OOTRUM. The Indian name for the fibre of *Dæmia extensa*.

OOWA. A species of Barley grown on the banks of the Sutlej.

OPAQUE. The reverse of shining; dull. Not the reverse of transparent.

OPEGRAPHA. A genus of lichens belonging to the order *Graphidei*, distinguished by a linear or elliptic simple or forked disk, surrounded by a distinct perithecium. Taken in its wider sense, it includes the great mass of those lichens found growing on trees or on rocks, resembling *Hysterium* in their fruit. They are known at once by the strong resemblance they bear to the characters of some Oriental languages. These lichens are of little practical importance, except in so far as, in company with some other cortical species, they help to enable persons to distinguish different kinds of medicinal bark.   [M. J. B.]

OPERA-GIRLS. *Mantisia saltatoria*.

OPERCULUM (adj. OPERCULATE). The lid of anything, as in the pitcher of *Nepenthes* or the fruit of *Lecythis*; more especially the lid of the spore-case of urn-mosses.

OPHELIA. A genus of Indian herbs of the gentian family, distinguished from *Agathotes* by the glandular pits at the base of the segments of the corolla being unprovided with any scale, and by the stamens, which are slightly dilated at the base and even adherent one to the other. *O. elegans* is described as a very elegant species, with light-blue flowers streaked with veins of a darker hue. The stems are used as a bitter tonic, like those of its ally, the Chiretta: see AGATHOTES.   [M. T. M.]

OPHIOCARYON. The only species of this remarkable genus is *O. paradoxum*, a large tree peculiar to British Guiana, and chiefly found on the banks of the River Essequibo and its tributaries. The generic name signifies Snake-nut, and alludes to the curious form of the embryo of the seed, which is spirally twisted so as to closely resemble a coiled-up snake, the radicle or rudimentary root being long and gradually thickening towards its lower extremity, and the cotyledons thin and leafy. The tree has pinnate leaves, and panicles of minute flowers, producing roundish fruits rather larger than walnuts. Some of the flowers are perfect and others of one sex only; they have five sepals, five petals, ten stamens, two of them fertile and opposite the inner petals, and a two-celled ovary. The fruits are often sent to this country as curiosities, under the name of Snake-nuts or Snake-seeds. They are not known to possess any medicinal properties, but the singular snake-like form of the embryo has induced the Indians to employ them as an antidote to the poison of venomous snakes. The genus belongs to the order *Sapindaceæ*.   [A. S.]

OPHIODERMA. A name sometimes given to the *Ophioglossum pendulum*, which differs from typical *Ophioglossum* in having the sterile branches fasciæform and dichotomously forked.   [T. M.]

OPHIOGLOSSACEÆ. A natural order of ferns, separated from the *Polypodiaceæ* by wanting the elastic ring which girts the spore-cases of the latter; and from *Marattiaceæ*, the only other order of *Filices*, by having a straight instead of circinate vernation. They have, moreover, the fructifications marginal, on narrow rachiform fronds or branches of the frond. The order contains the three genera, *Botrychium, Helminthostachys*, and *Ophioglossum*, two of which are represented in our own country. [T. M.]

OPHIOGLOSSUM. The typical genus of *Ophioglossaceæ*, distinguished from all

Ophioglossum pendulum.

others of that order by having its fructification borne in the form of spikes, the spore-cases, which are merely globose recesses placed in a single line side by side along the two margins of the spike, being connate with the latter, and bursting horizontally into two equal hemispherical valves: hence the spike, after bursting, has the appearance of being notched at regular short intervals along its two edges. These spikes terminate either a separate frond, as in *O. Bergerianum*, or else a separate branch of the frond, as in *O. vulgatum*; or sometimes, as in *O. palmatum*, several fertile spikes branch out from the same frond. The leafy sterile fronds are everywhere reticulated. The species are spread over the whole world, from the torrid to the arctic zones, and being of simple structure are not readily discriminated. Indeed, some botanists go so far as to regard the greater part of them as forms of a single species, our common Adder's-tongue, *O. vulgatum*. [T. M.]

OPHIOMERIS. A small leafless plant found on decayed trunks of trees in the deep shady forests of Brazil, forming a genus of *Burmanniaceæ*. It appears to be seldom above two inches high, and is remarkable for its obliquely pear-shaped perianth tube with the three inner lobes long subulate and incurved, as in the allied Asiatic genus *Thismia*, from which it differs in its free stamens and the almost lateral orifice of the perianth.

OPHIOPOGON. A genus of *Liliaceæ* from China and Japan, consisting of herbs, with linear ensiform leaves, and racemes of subsecund flowers terminating the two-edged scape. The perianth is adherent to the ovary at the base, with a six-parted rotate limb; stamens six with dilated filaments; fruit a one-celled one-seeded berry, or with several seeds, at length exposed by the rupture of the ovary. [J. T. S.]

OPHIORHIZA. A genus of *Cinchonaceæ* deriving its name from the Greek words *ophis*, a snake, and *rhiza*, root; the roots of some species being reputed cures for snake-bites. It contains a considerable number of species, usually dwarf perennial herbaceous or shrubby plants, all of them limited to tropical and eastern subtropical Asia. The leaves are opposite and often unequal, and the flowers sessile in a single row along one side of the branches of terminal (rarely axillary) flower-stalks. The short top-shaped calyx has five persistent teeth, and the corolla a slender tube, five-lobed at the top, with the edges valvate in the bud. The capsules are broad, flat, and two-celled.

In most countries where venomous snakes abound, the natives highly extol the roots of some plant as a certain remedy for their bites; but these seldom prove efficacious in the hands of European practitioners, and are often found to have acquired their reputation from their snake-like form rather than from their physical properties. Amongst others the roots of *O. Mungos* are thus used by the Cingalese and the natives of India; they are most intensely bitter, and may possess some medicinal virtues. The plant is also a native of Java, Sumatra, Penang, &c., and is called Earth-gall by the Malays from its bitterness. [A. S.]

OPHIOXYLON. A genus of dogbanes,

Ophioxylon serpentinum.

distinguished by having a funnel-shaped corolla the border of which is five-cleft and oblique, short stamens inserted in the middle of the tube, and a short slender style ending in a round head. The only species is *O. serpentinum*, a native of the East Indies, a climbing shrub with leaves in whorls. The name is from the Greek words for 'serpent' and 'wood,' in allusion to the twisted root and stems. [G. D.]

OPHIRA, or OPHIRIA. A synonym of *Grubbia*, applied by recent authors to one of the sections of that genus.

OPHIURIS. A genus of grasses belonging to the tribe *Rottboelleæ*. The inflorescence is in solitary or compound spikes; spikelets one or two-flowered, the inferior sterile, the superior fertile; glumes two, the lowest thick and leathery, five to seven-nerved, the nerves often obsolete; the upper thin and paper-like, two to three-nerved; stamens three; styles two. Steudel describes nine species, which are either tropical or subtropical. [D. M.]

OPHRYS. A genus of terrestrial orchids, with the habit of *Orchis*, but the flowers have no spur, and the lip is usually very convex resembling more or less the body of a bee or other insect. Hence the names of Bee-orchis, Spider-orchis, &c., under which they are popularly known. There are a considerable number of species in the countries bordering on the Mediterranean, and they are often found there in great abundance in spring and the early part of summer. In Britain we have but few, of which the principal are the *O. apifera*, or Common Bee-orchis with a broad very convex lip of a rich velvety brown, and *O. muscifera* or Fly-orchis with an oblong purplish brown lip with pale marks in the centre. Both grow in dry pastures chiefly in the south-eastern counties.

OPIUM. The inspissated juice of *Papaver somniferum*. —, LETTUCE. Lactucarium, the juice of *Lactuca sativa* and *L. virosa*.

OPLISMENUS. A genus of grasses belonging to the tribe *Paniceæ*, now included in *Panicum*. Only one of the species is British, namely, *O. Crus galli*, better known as *Panicum* or *Echinochloa Crus galli*, which occurs sparingly on the southern coast of England. [D. M.]

OPOBALSAMUM. An oleo-resin obtained from *Balsamodendron gileadensis*, and *B. Opobalsamum*.

OPOCHALA. *Pentaclethra macrophylla*, an oil-yielding plant of W. Tropical Africa.

OPOIDIA. Dr. Lindley has described a Persian herbaceous plant under this name, and considers it to form a genus of *Umbelliferæ*. It has a tall stout erect stem, with decurrent pinnate leaves; the general umbels unsurrounded by bracts, the partial ones having an involucel of many bracts; the calyx obscurely five-toothed, and the petals yellowish. Fruit cylindrical or oval, with three ridges, and having a large oil-channel beneath each furrow, and a smaller one beneath each ridge. *O. galbanifera* was so named under the idea that it produced the fœtid gum-resin known as galbanum, but this seems open to doubt. [M. T. M.]

OPOPANAX. Dioscorides and other Greek writers mention a medicinal plant, under this name, which is used by botanists to designate a genus of *Umbelliferæ*, represented by a single species, *O. Chironium*, a plant six or seven feet in height, resembling the parsnip, and a native of the South of Europe. Its leaves are pinnate, with unequal heart-shaped segments and crenated margins; and the flowers are yellow, in compound umbels, with both partial and general involucres, an undeveloped calyx-limb, and roundish petals with the point bent inwards. The fruit is thin, flattened from back to front, each half with three thread-like ridges, and three oil-channels in each furrow, with six others on the surface that adjoins the other half-fruit. The plant yields a milky juice, which dries into a gum-resin, having similar properties to those possessed by ammoniacum, but is now scarcely used. The plant is to be met with here and there in botanic gardens, but is of no ornamental value. [M. T. M.]

OPORANTHUS. A genus of *Amaryllidaceæ*, founded on the *Amaryllis lutea*, a very pretty dwarf autumn-flowering bulbous plant of the South of Europe. It has roundish bulbs, hiemal lorate leaves, and one-flowered scapes, supporting the pure yellow flowers, which are crocus-like in shape but larger. It is distinguished by its solid scape, by the short funnel-shaped tube of its cupless regular perianth, and by its filaments being inserted equally within the mouth of the perianth tube. [T. M.]

OPORINIA. *Leontodon*.

OPPOSITE. Placed on opposite sides of some other body or thing and on the same plane. Thus, when leaves are opposite, they are on opposite sides of the stem; when petals are opposite, they are on opposite sides of the flower; and so on.

OPPOSITIFOLIUS. Opposite a leaf, that is to say, growing on the side of a stem opposite to that on which a leaf grows; also applied to leaves opposite each other.

OPUNTIACEÆ. The same as *Cactaceæ* (which see). One of the divisions of this order receives the name of *Opuntidæ*.

OPUNTIA. The Prickly Pears form a most extensive genus, consisting of upwards of a hundred and fifty species, confined to the American continent, and, like the rest of the order, inhabiting hot dry places. They abound chiefly in Mexico and California in the northern, and in Brazil, Chili, and Peru in the southern hemisphere. All the species are more or less fleshy, especially while young; but as they get old most of them form a short round woody trunk, and the older branches also become hardened. They are erect or decumbent, and seldom grow higher than eight or ten feet, nearly all being more or less armed with strong sharp spines. A few have jointless cylindrical stems and branches, but by far the greater number have both the stems and branches jointed, the joints being generally thick and flat and somewhat resembling leaves in form; but the true leaves are very small and fleshy, and soon drop off, being found only on the young branches, one being seated under each of the tufts of bristles and spines with which the branches are furnished, and from which also the flowers arise. These latter are usually of a yellow or reddish orange-colour, and remain open for several days. The sepals and petals are undistinguishable, the outer or sepal-like segments being narrow and often green, but passing gradually into the petal-like ones, which are broad, coloured, and widely expanded; the numerous free stamens are shorter than the petals, but almost as long as the cylindrical style, and the stigma has from five to seven thick erect rays. The fruits are pear or egg-shaped, with a broad scar at the top left by the falling-away of the flower, and more or less covered with tufts of small spines, their fleshy rind enclosing numerous somewhat kidney-shaped seeds nestling in pulp.

Opuntia vulgaris.

Tuna is a Spanish-American name given to several Opuntias, but botanists have adopted it as the scientific name of a single species, O. Tuna, a native of various parts of America, from Quito to Mexico and the West Indies, from some of which countries it has been introduced into, and now grows abundantly in Southern Europe, Northern Africa, the Canaries, Madeira, &c. It is one of the tallest growing species, having, when old, an erect woody stem sometimes as much as twenty feet high, and jointed branches from four to eight or more inches long, of an oval or oblong form, and having distant bundles of spines growing from bristly cushions, each bundle consisting of from four to six, or sometimes fewer, stiff unequal spreading yellowish spines. It has dull reddish-orange flowers, and produces pear-shaped fleshy fruits two or three inches long and of a rich carmine colour when ripe. The Tuna, on account of its prickly nature, is much used for hedges, and in Mexico it is cultivated for rearing the cochineal insect (see *Nopalea*), besides which several parts are turned to useful account. The sweet juicy fruits, called Prickly Pears, are extensively eaten and greatly esteemed for their cooling properties; they contain an abundance of saccharine matter, and sugar has been made from them in Sicily; at Naples their juice is used as a water-colour, and in the West Indies for colouring confectionery; while in Mexico a beverage called Colinche is prepared from them. The old branches and stems contain a network consisting of annual layers of hard woody fibres, of which the French in Algiers make various ornamental articles, such as vases, fancy baskets, flower-trays, &c., and even use it for veneering.

O. vulgaris has likewise been introduced from America, and become naturalised in Southern Europe, the Canaries, and Northern Africa. [A. S.]

ORACH, or **ORACHE.** An old-fashioned potherb, *Atriplex hortensis.*

ORANGE. *Citrus Aurantium*, which furnishes one of the most grateful of fruits, the Orange of commerce. —, BERGAMOT. *Citrus Bergamia.* —, HORNED. A monstrous form of *Citrus Aurantium*, having the carpels separated. —, MANDARIN. The Chinese name for a large-fruited deep-coloured variety of orange. —, JAMAICA. *Glycosmis citrifolia.* —, MOCK. *Philadelphus coronarius.* —, NATIVE, of Australia. *Citriobatus.* —, OSAGE. *Maclura aurantiaca.* —, QUITO. The berries of *Solanum quitoënse.* —, SEVILLE. *Citrus Bigaradia.* —, SWEET. *Citrus Aurantium.* —, WILD. *Drypetes glauca.*

ORANGE COLOUR. The same as apricot colour, but redder; as in a ripe orange.

ORANGER. (Fr.) *Citrus.* — DES OZAGES. *Maclura aurantiaca.* — DU SAVETIER. *Solanum Pseudo-capsicum.*

ORANGE-ROOT. *Hydrastis canadensis.*

ORANGE-THORN. A colonial name for *Citriobatus.*

ORANIA. A genus of palms containing only two species, one of which is a native of New Guinea and the other of the peninsula of Malacca. Both have tall unarmed closely-ringed stems, crowned with a dense head of large pinnate leaves, the leaflets of which are of oblique form and irregularly toothed or jagged at their tips. The flower-spikes are enclosed in double spathes, the inner of which is woody and completely closed, but ultimately bursts along one side, and the outer two-keeled and open at the top; the flowers are unisexual, the upper portion of the spike being occupied by male flowers in pairs, and the lower by solitary females between two males. The Malayan species, *O. macrocladus*, is called Ebool by the natives. Nothing is known of the uses of either it, or the New Guinea species, *O. regalis.* [A. S.]

ORBEA. A name given by Haworth to some of the species of *Stapelia*, but not generally adopted.

ORBICULAR. Perfectly circular; as the leaf of *Cotyledon orbiculare.*

ORBICULUS. The fleshy ring formed by the stamens of *Stapelia*. The circular bodies found in the cup of a *Nidularia.*

ORBIGNYA. Two Bolivian palms, one with a tall stem and the other dwarf, and perhaps a third little-known species from Brazil, are comprehended in this genus, which belongs to the same section of palms as the cocoanut. The leaves are pinnate, and the flower-spikes simply branched and enclosed in double spathes, the inner of which is completely closed while young. Some spikes bear male flowers only, and others both female and perfect ones. The fruit has a fibrous husk enclosing a hard bony stone. *O. phalerata*, the Cusi or Cusich palm of Bolivia, is a tall-stemmed plant with large rather erect pinnate leaves, which the Indians use for building and thatching their huts, and for weaving into hats and mats. They also obtain a fatty oil from the seeds, and use it for anointing their hair. Each fruit contains from three to seven seeds, but the stone in which they are enclosed is so hard that they are extracted with difficulty. [A. S.]

ORBILLA. Such a shield as is found in lichens of the genus *Usnea.*

ORCANETTE. (Fr.) *Alkanna tinctoria*: also *Onosma.* — JAUNE. *Onosma echioides.*

ORCHELLA-WEED. The name of several species of *Roccella*, a genus of lichens celebrated for their valuable properties as dye-weeds. These vary much in value according to their species, or rather varieties (for authors have most needlessly multiplied species), and the country in which they grow, that from Angola being the most valuable and at the same time most economical, a matter of much consequence when the high price is taken into consideration. Some specimens were exhibited from Ceylon in 1851 in the Great Exhibition, whose estimated value was 880*l.* per ton. Two kinds of orseilic acid and erythric acid are the chemical substances on which their dyeing properties depend. Orchella-weed is found on the maritime rocks of hot or warm temperate regions. In Great Britain it is confined to the south. In India it is found occasionally on the trunks of the Mango, and a similar habitat produces a species in Algiers. The flat and cylindrical forms run so much into each other that the distinction of species is a matter of some difficulty.   [M. J. B.]

ORCHIDIUM. *Calypso.*

ORCHIDOFUNKIA. *Cryptarrhena.*

ORCHIDACEÆ. (*Orchideæ, Orchids.*) A natural order of Endogens, the type of the orchidal alliance, in which they are distinguished by their irregular gynandrous flowers and parietal placentæ. They are perennial herbaceous plants or shrubs, in temperate countries assuming a terrestrial habit, in warmer latitudes growing on trees (epiphytes), or fixing themselves to stones. Their roots are fibrous and fasciculated, or fleshy, or tuber-like and filled with starch or horny nodules of bassorin. Their stems are sometimes annual, sometimes perennial and woody, and sometimes pseudo-bulbous; their leaves are flat, terete or equitant, generally sheathing; and their flowers are irregular, extremely variable in form, and often most gratefully fragrant. The flowers consist of three sepals, equal at the base, or variously extended there: three petals placed between the sepals, the lateral usually similar to the dorsal sepal; the third, called the lip or labellum, usually larger than the petals, and quite unlike them in form, horned or furnished with various appendages, occasionally moveable as if spontaneously, now and then contracted so as to form separate parts, of which the lowest is called the hypochil, the highest the epichil, and the middle one the mesochil. The stamens and style are consolidated into a central body called the column; and of the three stamens the central only is perfect, except in *Cypripedium*, where the central is abortive and the two lateral perfect. The pollen is powdery, or collected into grains, or adhering in wedges tied together by an elastic material, or consolidated into masses of a waxy texture and fixed number, the masses either free or adhering by a caudicle to a gland belonging to the apex (or rostellum) of the stigmas, which latter are usually confluent in a hollow mucous disk. The ovary is adherent, one-celled; the capsule very rarely fleshy, indehiscent and pod-shaped, usually breaking up into six dry woody rigid valves with horizontal cells, of which three only bear the innumerable very minute seeds which have a loose netted skin.

The order owes its chief peculiarities to the consolidation of stamens and pistil into one common mass, called the column; to the suppression of all the anthers, except one in the mass of the order, or two in *Cypripedeæ*; to the peculiar consistence of its pollen, and the anther which contains it; and to the very general development of one of the inner leaves of the perianth, or petals in an excessive degree, or in an unusual form. The irregularity of the labellum, however, disappears in such genera as *Thelymitra*, *Paxtonia*, *Hexisea*, and others; but irregularity is predominant, and the flowers assume such unusual figures that there is scarcely a common reptile or insect to which some of them have not been likened.

The irritability of the labellum is one of the curious peculiarities of these plants. This is seen in different species of *Pterostylis*, *Megaclinium*, and *Bolbophyllum.* In *Caleana nigrita* the column is a boat-shaped box resembling a lower lip; the labellum forms a lid that exactly fits it, and is hinged on a claw which reaches the middle of the column; when the flower opens, the labellum turns round within the column, and falls back, so that, the flower being inverted, it stands fairly over the latter. The moment a small insect touches its point, the labellum makes a sudden revolution, brings the point to the bottom of the column, passing the anther in its way, and thus makes prisoner any insect which the box will hold. When it catches an insect it remains shut while its prey continues to move about, but if no capture is made the lid soon recovers its position. *Drakæa elastica* and *Spiculæa ciliata* are other species with remarkable moveable appendages.

Orchids are found in almost all parts of the world, except upon the verge of the frozen zone, and in climates of excessive dryness. In Europe, Asia, and North America they grow everywhere, in groves, marshes, and meadows; at the Cape of Good Hope they abound in similar situations; but in the hot damp parts of the West and East Indies, in Madagascar and the neighbouring islands, in the damp and humid forests of Brazil, in the warm mild parts of Central America and Western Mexico, in the damp tropical parts of India, and on the lower mountains of Nepal, they flourish in the greatest variety and profusion, no longer seeking their nutriment from the soil, but clinging to the trunks and limbs of trees, to stones and bare rocks, where they vegetate among ferns and other shade-loving plants in countless thousands.

The *Orchidaceæ* are divided into seven tribes, upon characters derived from the staminal apparatus, thus:—

* Anther one only ; pollen masses waxy—
　　Malaxeæ : no caudicle or separable stigmatic gland.
　　Epidendreæ : a distinct caudicle, but no separable stigmatic gland.
　　Vandeæ : a distinct caudicle, united to a stigmatic gland.
** Anther one only; pollen powdery, granular, or sectile:—
　　Ophreæ ; anther terminal, erect.
　　Arethuseæ: anther terminal, opercular.
　　Neotteæ: anther dorsal.
*** Anthers two—*Cypripedeæ.*

The nutritive substance called salep has been prepared from the subterraneous succulent roots of *Orchis mascula* and various species of the ophreous division, and in India from the tubers of a species of *Eulophia* ; it is said to consist almost entirely of a chemical principle called *bassorin.* The viscidity of the tuber of *Aplectrum hyemale* is such that it is called putty-root in the United States, and it is used for cementing earthenware. The substance called vanilla in the shops, which is the dried fruit of *Vanilla planifolia* and other species, contains a great quantity of essential oil, and a good deal of benzoic acid, and is one of the most delightful aromatics known ; it is used in the manufacture of chocolate, of liqueurs, and of various articles of confectionery.

For various interesting particulars respecting the structure of the flowers of these plants, the reader is referred to Mr.

Darwin's book, *On the Fertilisation of Orchids.*　　　　　　[T. M.]

ORCHIDS. The popular name of the *Orchidaceæ,* or *Orchis* family.

ORCHIL, ARCHIL, ORCHAL, or ORCHILL. Various names for the dye prepared from Orchella-weed. Two varieties occur : the one blue, formed by steeping the weed in some ammoniacal liquor, as urine, in a covered wooden vessel: the other red, made in earthen jars in a room heated by steam. Both are sold in the liquid form, and, notwithstanding their name, are of a more or less decided red. —, BURMESE. A dye-stuff prepared in Burmah, from *Roccella phycopsis.*　　[M. J. B.]

ORCHIS. A genus of terrestrial orchids, which comprises the largest number and the commonest of the European species, and which has thus given its name to the whole order. The species are all perennials, although the whole plant dies down and is renewed in the course of each year, for the rootstock produces each year a fleshy tubercule by the side of the decaying one of the preceding year, the following year's stem shooting from the top of the new tubercule. The herbaceous erect stem is leafy at the base, with a terminal spike of flowers, usually red or purple, but occasionally white or greenish. The five sepals and petals are nearly equal, the upper sepal or all three often arching over the others; the lip, either dilated at the top or three-lobed, is always produced at the base underneath into a spur or pouch. The anther is on the face of the column, the two cells converging at the base, each cell containing one pollen-mass, contracted below into a short stalk, terminating in a gland. The species are most numerous in Europe and temperate Asia, with only a very few in North America ; the British ones are variously estimated at from ten to fifteen species, according to the extent attributed by different botanists to the genus itself, or to the individual species.

O. maculata and *O. latifolia,* two species very closely allied to each other, are amongst the commonest in our meadows, pastures, and open woods. The tubers are rather flat and divided into two or three finger-like lobes, the leaves often marked with dark spots or blotches, the flowers more or less pink, in a dense spike, with the lower bracts almost always longer than the ovary, and in *O. latifolia* exceeding the flowers; the lip is broad and spotted or variegated, and the spur nearly as long as the ovary. *O. mascula,* found in rich moist meadows and shady places, is a much handsomer plant, with entire tubers, and showy flowers in a loose spike, varying from a bright pinkish-purple to flesh-colour. *O. laxiflora,* more common on the Continent, but notfound nearer to us than the Channel Islands, is like it but still handsomer, with richly coloured flowers. *O. militaris,* with its two allied species or varieties, *O. fusca* and *O. tephrosanthos,* is another very handsome species, with a dense oblong spike of variegated flowers, and a rather short spur. It is scarce in Britain, being limited to the counties bordering on the Thames from Berkshire downwards; and on the continent is seldom found in large numbers, usually scattered over hilly pastures or the borders of woods. *O. ustulata* is a small species remarkable for the dense spike of small flowers, the deep purple of the unexpanded ones giving it a burnt or scorched appearance. *O. Morio*, one of the commonest continental ones in meadows and pastures, is only to be met with in some of the southern counties of England. *O. coriophora*, a continental species with green-and-brown variegated flowers, is remarkable for having three varieties, the common one with a strong smell of bugs, another quite inodorous, and the third sweet-scented. *O. hircina*, on account of the shortness of its spur, is often placed in the genus *Aceras*; it has a curious strap-like linear greenish labellum, spirally rolled inwards in the bud, and in the expanded flower hanging down to the length of above an inch. It grows usually in almost isolated specimens, and is scarce in Britain. *O. pyramidalis* and *O. conopsea*, with dense spikes of small pink flowers, have a very long slender spur; although in many respects very nearly allied to each other, they are now usually placed in distinct genera, the one in *Anacamptis*, the other in *Gymnadenia*. Both are natives of Britain as well as of the greater part of Europe. The tubers of Orchises abound in a nutritive starch, which is extensively prepared in some parts of Turkey, from some of our common species, and sent to Western Europe under the name of Salep.

ORCHIS, BEE. *Ophrys apifera.* —, BELL. *Codonorchis.* —, BOG. *Malaxis.* —, BUTTERFLY. *Habenaria.* —, CRANE-FLY. *Tipularia.* —, DOG. *Cynorchis.* —, DRONE. *Ophrys fucifera.* —, EARLY. *Orchis mascula.* —, FALSE. *Platanthera.* —, FLY. *Ophrys muscifera.* —, FROG. *Peristylus viridis.* —, GREEN-MAN. *Aceras anthropophora.* —, HAIR. *Trichosma.* —, HAND. *Orchis maculata.* —, LIZARD. *Orchis hircina.* —, MAN. *Aceras anthropophora.* —, MEADOW. *Orchis Morio.* —, MEDUSA'S-HEAD. *Cirrhopetalum Medusæ.* —, MONKEY. *Orchis tephrosanthos.* —, MUSK. *Herminium Monorchis.* —, SPIDER. *Ophrys aranifera* and *arachnites.*

ORCHIS BARBE-DE-BOUC. (Fr.) *Orchis hircina.* — BOUFFON. *Orchis Morio.* — BOURDON. *Ophrys arachnites.* — MILITAIRE GRANDE. *Orchis fusca.* — MILITAIRE PETITE. *Orchis ustulata.* — PALMÉ. *Orchis latifolia.*

ORDEAL ROOT. The root of a species of *Strychnos*, used in Western Africa by the natives.

ORDEAL TREE. *Erythrophlœum guineense.* — of Madagascar. *Cerbera venenifera.*

OREILLE D'ÂNE. (Fr.) *Symphytum officinale.* — D'HOMME. *Asarum europæum.* — DE JUDAS. *Hirneola Auricula Judæ.* — DE LIÈVRE. *Bupleurum falcatum.* — D'OURS. *Primula Auricula.* — DE RAT. *Hieracium Pilosella.* — DE SOURIS. *Cerastium tomentosum*, and *Myosotis arvensis.*

ORÉLIE. (Fr.) *Allamanda.*

OREODAPHNE. A considerable genus of *Lauraceæ*, principally inhabiting tropical America. Most of the species form large trees, occasionally upwards of a hundred feet in height, with alternate leaves, and panicles or racemes or sometimes small umbel-like heads of unisexual or perfect flowers, the sexes generally on different trees. The flowers have a calyx with a top-shaped tube and a six-parted limb, which falls away after flowering, and the tube then increases in size and ultimately surrounds the lower part of the fruit; they contain nine fertile stamens with short narrow filaments in three series, and sometimes three sterile ones forming a fourth inner series, and their short style bears a disk-like stigma. *O. californica* is a common tree in the mountainous parts of California, where it goes by a variety of names, such as Mountain Laurel, Spice-bush, Balm of Heaven, Sassafras Laurel, Cajeput-tree, Californian Olive, &c. In some parts it attains a height of fifty or seventy or even a hundred feet, but in the southern districts it is seldom more than fifteen or twenty feet high. When bruised it emits a strong spicy odour which is apt to excite sneezing, and the Spanish-Americans use the leaves as a condiment. *O. opifera*, a large tree found on the Orinoco, yields an abundance of volatile oil from incisions made into its trunk, and another kind is obtained from its fruits by distillation. The first is used as an application to tumours, and the other in contractions of the joints, pains in the limbs, &c. [A. S.]

OREODOXA. Some of the species of this genus are among the most graceful of palms, their slender ringed stems frequently attaining upwards of a hundred feet in height, and bearing large terminal pinnate leaves with long sheathing stalks forming a cylinder around the summit. Six species are described, all natives of the West Indies and tropical America. The flower-spikes are enclosed in double somewhat woody spathes, the flowers being of separate sexes, and surrounded by small bracts.

O. oleracea, the West Indian Cabbage Palm, a plant formerly included in the genus *Areca*, sometimes attains a hundred and seventy feet high, with a trunk perfectly straight and almost cylindrical; but like other palms it is quite useless as timber, having but a thin outside layer of hard wood, fit only for making ramrods or the walking-sticks called cabbage-sticks, or, when the soft inside is scooped out, for gutters. The semicylindrical portion of the leafstalks are formed into cradles for negro children, or made into splints for fractures; their inside skin, peeled off while green and dried, looks like vellum, and bears ink on one side. The heart of young leaves, or cabbage, is boiled as a vegetable or pickled, and the pith affords sago. Oil is obtained from the fruit. [A. S.]

OREORCHIS. A genus of terrestrial orchids founded on the *Corallorhiza foliosa* of Lindley, a plant inhabiting mountain meadows in the north of India. The species are tuberous plants with grass-like leaves, small red or red-and-white flowers, and with the appearance of small *Eulophias*, from which the genus differs especially in having four distinct globular pollen-masses. Four species are known : *O. foliosa* and *micrantha* from the Himalayan mountains, *O. patens* from Siberia, and *O. lancifolia* from Japan.

OREOSERIS. A name given by De Candolle to three Himalayan species of *Gerbera*, which have since been reunited with that genus.

ORGANOGENESIS. The gradual formation of an organ from its earliest appearance.

ORGANOGRAPHY. The study of the structure of the organs of plants.

ORGANY. *Origanum vulgare.*

ORGE. (Fr.) *Hordeum.* — CARRÉE, or D'HIVER. *Hordeum hexastichon.* — ÉLYME. *Hordeum sylvaticum.* — EN ÉVENTAIL, or PYRAMIDALE. *Hordeum Zeocriton.*

ORGIBAO. An American name for *Stachytarpha jamaicensis.*

ORGYA (adj. ORGYALIS). Six feet, or the ordinary height of a man.

ORIGAN. (Fr.) *Origanum vulgare.*

ORIGANUM. This name is derived from two Greek words, *oros* mountain, and *ganos* joy, in allusion to the gay appearance they give to the hillsides on which they grow. Botanically it is applied to a genus of *Labiatæ*, consisting of herbs or low shrubs, with their flowers aggregated into cylindrical or oblong spikes, and protected by coloured bracts as long as or longer than the calyx, which latter is tubular with ten to thirteen ribs, and has a nearly regularly five-toothed or sometimes two-lipped limb and hairy throat; the corolla is slightly irregular; and the stamens four, at a distance from each other. The species are natives of the Mediterranean region, also of Northern India, &c. *O. vulgare*, the Wild Marjoram, is a common plant in this country, especially in limestone or chalky districts. Its stem is one to two feet in height, with stalked ovate acute leaves, and purplish or white flowers, arranged in compact round heads at the ends of the branches. The corolla is longer than the calyx, and the stamens than the corolla. This plant yields an acrid stimulant oil, sold in the shops as Oil of Thyme. It is used as a caustic by farriers, and on similar grounds as an application to decayed teeth. The plant has also been used for dyeing purposes. The writer has on several occasions met with a variety of this plant, with elongated cylindrical spikes of flowers in place of the usual globular heads.

O. Onites and *O. Majorana* are included among seasoning herbs, under the name of Marjoram : one or the other is supposed to be the plant called Amaracus by Greek writers. In addition to the species just mentioned, others are cultivated in this country as ornamental plants, such as *O. Dictamnus*, the Dittany of Crete, which has roundish leaves thickly invested with white down, and flowers in drooping spikes; and *O. sipyleum*, which is similar but taller and less woolly. These last are popularly called Hop plants, and are often seen in cottage-windows. [M. T. M.]

ORITHYA. A genus of *Liliaceæ*, found in Eastern Europe and Middle Asia, closely allied to *Tulipa*, of which it has the habit, but differing in having the three inner perianth leaves narrowed into a claw at the base, and in possessing a distinct style. From *Ornithogalum*, in which it was included by Linnæus, it differs not only in habit, but by having the perianth deciduous. [J. T. S.]

ORME. (Fr.) *Ulmus.* — À TROIS FEUILLES. *Ptelea trifoliata.* — BLANC. *Ulmus effusa.* — À LIÈGE. *Ulmus suberosa.* — D'AMÉRIQUE. *Guazuma tomentosa.* — DE SAMARIE. *Ptelea trifoliata.* — DE SIBÉRIE. *Planera Richardi.*

ORMENIS *mixta*, or *Anthemis mixta*, a plant of South Europe, having a great resemblance to the chamomile, has along with the latter been placed by Grenier and Godron in *Chamomilla*, which they distinguish from *Anthemis* by the cylindrical (not compressed) corolla tube enlarged below, and the slightly compressed achenes rounded at the summit and having three slender ribs on their inner face. From the common chamomile this plant is chiefly distinguished by the remarkably oblique base of the corolla tube. [A. A. B.]

ORMOCARPUM. A genus of *Leguminosæ*, of the suborder *Papilionaceæ*, consisting of three or four shrubs from tropical Africa or the Indian Archipelago, very nearly allied to *Æschynomene*, and chiefly differing in the pod, of which the joints or articles are marked by deep longitudinal furrows, and usually covered with glandular warts. In two species the leaves are reduced to a single rather large terminal leaflet ; in the remaining one or two they are pinnate with numerous small leaflets, as in *Æschynomene*.

ORMOSIA. A genus of papilionaceous *Leguminosæ*, chiefly tropical American, with one or two species from Hong-Kong and India. It consists of timber trees, with pinnate leaves, and terminal panicles of flowers, which have a bell-shaped calyx, a pea-like corolla, ten distinct often unequal stamens, and a style curved inwards at top and bearing the stigma on one side. The pods, which are flat and woody, split into two valves when ripe, and contain from two to four shining scarlet and black or brownish-red seeds.

O. dasycarpa is the West Indian Bead-tree or Necklace-tree, the seeds of which, and of other species, such as O. coccinea, a native of Guiana and Brazil, are roundish, beautifully polished, and of a bright scarlet colour with a black spot at one end resembling beads, for which they are substituted, being made into necklaces, bracelets, &c., or mounted in silver for studs and buttons. The name is derived from the Greek ormos, signifying a necklace, in allusion to this use of the seeds. The timber of O. panamense, a tree of fifty feet high or upwards, native of Veraguas, is durable and used for building.   [A. S.]

ORNE. (Fr.) Fraxinus.

ORNITHIDIUM. A small genus of West Indian and tropical American orchids. Some species have ascending and others root-like branching stems, sheathed with imbricate scales, and bearing one-leaved pseudobulbs. Their flowers are axillary, and have erect slightly spreading free sepals and petals, and an ascending cucullate lip, which is almost always connate with the base of the column and parallel with it. The anther is two-celled, with four pollen-masses, oblong or linear caudicles, and a minute gland.   [A. S.]

ORNITHOGALUM. A rather large genus of lilyworts, the species of which are for the most part confined to the South European and West Asiatic regions and the Cape of Good Hope. Three are admitted into the British Flora, but it is questionable whether any of them be truly indigenous, though O. pyrenaicum is so abundant in the neighbourhood of Bath, that its young shoots are collected in the spring, and brought to the market for sale as a substitute for asparagus; and O. umbellatum is a common weed in many parts of England and Scotland. The last-named species is commonly known as the Star of Bethlehem, from its being abundant in Palestine, and having star-like flowers. It is also supposed to be the Dove's Dung of Scripture (2 Kings, ch. vi.); and its bulbs, which are wholesome and nutritious when cooked, are eaten to this day in Palestine. The genus is closely allied to Scilla, from which it is distinguished only by its flowers being persistent instead of deciduous, and white greenish or yellowish instead of blue. All the species are bulbous plants, with radical not stem-sheathing leaves, and terminal racemes of flowers, each flower with a withered bract beneath it. Their perianth has six distinct segments, spread out star-fashion; and their six stamens have flattened filaments, and are almost free from the perianth. [A. S.]

ORNITHOGLOSSUM. A genus of Melanthaceæ, the four species of which belong to the Cape Flora. They are bulbous plants, with simple or slightly branched leafy stems, and long-stalked somewhat racemose green and purple or white flowers, which have a perianth of six short-clawed spreading pieces, with the stamens inserted at their base, and a fleshy gland in the centre, and three styles somewhat united below.   [A. S.]

ORNITHOPUS. A genus of leguminous plants of which one species, O. perpusillus is a small prostrate herb well marked by its umbellate heads of minute cream-coloured flowers veined with crimson, which have a bract at the base; and its jointed curved pods, which bear a singular resemblance to the claws of a bird, whence the name Ornithopus, or Bird's-foot. It is not uncommon on gravelly commons in Great Britain, but owing to its small size is perhaps often overlooked. O. sativus, the Serradilla, by some considered a variety of O. perpusillus, a native of Portugal, is a valuable agricultural plant, introduced in 1818, and particularly worthy of attention from the fact of its producing an abundant crop of excellent fodder where nothing else will grow to perfection. All the species are annuals. French, Pied d'oiseau; German, Vogelfuss.   [C. A. J.]

ORNUS. The species of Ornus are by some regarded as forming merely a section of Fraxinus, but others recognise them as a distinct genus, and they are readily distinguished by their flowers having petals, for which reason they gain the name of Flowering Ash. About a dozen species are known, all belonging to the temperate regions of the northern hemisphere. They are middle-sized trees with pinnate leaves and terminal or axillary panicles of small flowers, which are either perfect or of distinct sexes, and have a small four-parted or four-toothed calyx, and four long narrow petals usually cohering in pairs, the perfect ones containing two long stamens and a pistil with a notched stigma. The fruit is flat and two-celled, with a thin wing at top.

O. europæa and O. rotundifolia, both natives of the South of Europe and Asia Minor, are known by the name of Manna Ash, from their yielding the saccharine substance commercially known as Manna. They form trees about twenty-five feet in height, and chiefly differ in the leaflets of the former being lance-shaped on short stalks and tapering to both ends, while those of the latter are egg-shaped or roundish, narrow at the base, and without stalks. Manna is chiefly collected in Calabria and Sicily, where the trees are cultivated in square plantations for the purpose, and is principally imported from Palermo, Messina, and Naples. It is obtained by making incisions about two inches long in the stem, with a hooked knife. The finest kind, called 'flake manna,' or 'manna canellata,' is obtained from incisions in the upper part of the stem, and the inferior, or 'manna in sorts,' from cuts near the ground. For collecting the latter kind, leaves of the ash are inserted into the incision so as to conduct the juice into receptacles formed of the flat joints of the Opuntia, or prickly-pear cactus.   [A. S.]

OROBANCHACEÆ. (Broomrapes.) A natural order of corollifloral dicotyledons belonging to Lindley's gentianal alliance of perigynous Exogens. They are herbaceous parasitical plants, having scales in place of leaves; and their didynamous flowers have a persistent inferior calyx, a monopetalous irregular usually bilabiate persistent corolla, four stamens, a fleshy disk, and a free one-celled ovary of two carpels, with two or more parietal placentas, the style manifest, with a two-lobed stigma. Fruit capsular, enclosed within the withered corolla, two-valved; seeds indefinite, minute. They are natives of Europe, more especially the southern parts, and of Asia, North America, and the Cape of Good Hope. Their general properties are astringency and bitterness; and some have been used as tonics, and as applications to indolent ulcers. They attach themselves to the roots of various plants, and are hence called root-parasites. The order contains about a dozen genera and upwards of a hundred species, of which those of *Orobanche* and *Lathræa* are the most familiar. 　　[J. H. B.]

OROBANCHE. A genus of singular-looking parasitic plants typical of the *Orobanchaceæ*, and represented in England by a variety of species which grow severally on the roots of furze, clover, flax, ivy, wild carrot, &c. All the species agree in having a dingy brownish-yellow stem, which is leafless throughout but furnished with numerous pointed scales, which take the place of leaves. The upper portion of the stem bears a spike of rather large flowers, of which the calyx is of the same russet hue as the stem; the corolla is two-lipped, of a yellowish colour tinged with pink or purple-blue and veined; there are four stamens in pairs of unequal length; and the capsule is one-celled, two-valved, many-seeded.

O. major, the largest British species, is parasitical on the roots of furze and other leguminous plants, and grows to the height of two feet or more. The others attain usually a height of from six to eighteen inches, varying little in habit and general characters, yet so far differing in minute points that botanists reckon up to ten or a dozen species. It may be a question, however, whether the dissimilarity ought not to be referred to the variety in the structure and habit of the plants on which they are parasitic, so that the number of distinct species may be much less than is commonly supposed. 　　[C. A. J.]

That *O. minor*, called the Lesser Broomrape, which we have occasionally observed nearly two feet high, may, after all, include some two or three other forms, is an opinion deriving some weight from Dr. Arnott's remark, that in all parasitical plants the appearance may be so altered by the structure of the tribe they prey upon, that many reputed species are probably different states of the same. Thus *O. minor* occurs on different clovers, whilst a great number of plants are affected by so-called

different species. It remains, however, to be determined what amount of difference may be brought about by the same seed electing to grow on different plants. The annexed woodcut shows the mode of attachment of the parasite to its foster-parent; and as this is yearly becoming a more formidable enemy to our crops, we recommend its further study to the farmer.

As regards the manner in which this parasitism takes place, we are as yet in the dark. It may be mentioned that perhaps few plants produce more seeds than the

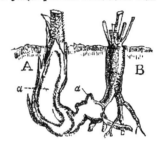

Orobanche minor.

A, the parasite attached to B, an old plant of Alsike Clover; *a, a*, section showing the mode of attachment.

Broomrapes, but they are very minute. It seems certain that seeding affected crops only ensures the spread of the plants where this seed is sown, so that farmers should if possible avoid seed grown where the Broomrape prevails. 　　[J. B.]

OROBE. (Fr.) *Orobus tuberosus*, now called *Lathyrus macrorrhizus*.

OROBUS. A genus of papilionaceous *Leguminosæ*, now generally united with *Lathyrus*, from which it cannot be distinguished by any marked character. There are a considerable number of species, chiefly found in mountainous or woody districts, and dispersed over Europe and Northern Asia.

ORONCE. (Fr.) *Orontium*.

ORONGE. The French name of *Agaricus cæsareus*, which is at the same time one of the best and handsomest of *Fungi*. The scarlet pileus, yellow gills, and white volva must make it at all times easy of recognition, and it is to be hoped that it will some day reward our researches in the south of England or Ireland. A form of it was found in the Sikkim Himalayas by Dr. Hooker. This is the species which was so celebrated among the Romans under the name of *Boletus*, and it was a favourite vehicle for poison in both imperial and papal Rome. It was with this fungus that Agrippina poisoned her husband Claudius, to which Juvenal and Martial allude. Martial, moreover, speaks of it some fifteen times, and places it as an object of luxury above the truffle. 　　[M. J. B.]

ORONTIACEÆ. (*Callaceæ, Acoraceæ, Acoroideæ, Orontiads.*) A natural order of monocotyledonous plants, belonging to Lindley's juncal alliance of Endogens. They are herbs with broad occasionally ensiform leaves, and spadiceous flowers enclosed by a spathe. They are usually associated with *Araceæ*, from which they differ in their hermaphrodite flowers, or in having frequently a perianth consisting of four to eight scales. Natives both of tropical and cold regions. Acridity is met with in the order. *Acorus Calamus*, the common sweet sedge or flag, has an agreeable odour, and has been used as a stimulant and antispasmodic. There are nearly a score of genera, and about eighty species : *Calla, Acorus,* and *Pothos* are examples.   [J. H. B.]

ORONTIUM. A name adapted from the Greek appellation of some unascertained plant, and applied to a genus of *Orontiaceæ* consisting of North American waterplants with elliptic leaves on long stalks, and a spathe reduced to a tubular sheath surrounding the middle of the very long stalk which supports the spadix, the latter being conical and covered with perfect flowers, the lowest of which have six, the uppermost four sepals ; the anthers open transversely, and the ovary is one-celled with one inverted ovule. *O. aquaticum,* a native of North American marshes, is cultivated in this country. The seeds and rootstock are stated to be edible after the acridity has been removed by boiling or drying.   [M. T. M.]

OROTHAMNUS. A genus of *Proteaceæ* proposed by Dr. Pappe, but now regarded as a section of *Mimetes*, characterised by the spheroidal sessile flower-heads being terminal, few together, and having a many-leaved coloured and persistent involucre. There is only one species, *O. Zeyheri,* a Cape shrub, with imbricate concave quite entire leaves rather more than an inch in length, and margined with purple, and large drooping flower-heads with beautiful rose-red villous involucral leaves. [A. S.]

ORPIN. (Fr.) *Sedum*, especially *S. Telephium.*

ORPINE. *Telephium Imperati*; also *Sedum Telephium.* —, BASTARD. *Andrachne telephioides.*

ORRIS-ROOT. The fragrant violet-scented rhizome of *Iris florentina* and *I. germanica.* It is also called Orrice-root.

ORSEILLE DES CANARIES. (Fr.) *Roccella tinctoria* and *R. fuciformis.* — DE TERRE. *Lecanora perella.*

ORTEGIA. A small genus of *Illecebraceæ* inhabiting the Mediterranean region, and consisting of erect branched annuals or perennials, with four-sided branches, opposite linear leaves, setaceous stipules enlarged into black glands at the base, and very small flowers in compact cymes, combined into panicles.   [J. T. S.]

ORTHOCERAS. Two species of this genus of orchids are known, one a native of

Australia, and the other of New Zealand. It belongs to the suborder *Neottieæ*, and is distinguished by its side sepals being very long and narrow, almost filiform, and quite erect, while the upper one is hooded, fleshy, and obtuse ; and by its minute sessile petals, which are two-toothed at the tips. They are erect glabrous terrestrial herbs, with narrow filiform leaves, and rather large flowers in racemes.   [A. S.]

ORTHOS. In Greek compounds = straight.

ORTHOSTEMON. A genus of *Gentianaceæ*, consisting of tropical Asiatic and Australian species of slender herbaceous habit, having broad leaves, and terminal flowers, with a tubular four-toothed calyx, a somewhat funnel-shaped corolla, which remains on the plant in a withered condition, four stamens projecting from the tube and having straight anthers : from which circumstance the name of the genus, signifying straight-stamen, is derived. [M. T. M.]

ORTHOTRICHUM. A large and important genus of acrocarpous mosses, the type of the order *Orthotrichei.* The capsule is erect and mostly striate ; the peristome double, the outer composed of thirty-two teeth, combined into sixteen or eight, rarely naked ; and the veil campanulate plaited and generally hairy. The species form tufts on the trunks of trees and stones, and are at once known by their peculiar habit and veil. The genus obtains its maximum in the northern hemisphere, numbering twenty-three species in our own islands. It is not, however, confined to cold latitudes, though in warm or equable climates it is replaced in great measure by *Macromitrium*, which has a narrow awl-shaped veil, a rostrate lid, and no apophysis. *Leucophanes,* a tropical genus, which has the pale leaves of *Leucobryum* and *Sphagnum*, belongs to the same natural order.   [M. J. B.]

ORTHOTROPAL. A straight nucleus, having the same direction as the seed to which it belongs, the foramen being at the end most remote from the hilum.

ORTHOTROPIS. A genus of *Leguminoseæ* proposed by Bentham for the *Chorozema pungens* and some other species, which differ from others of that genus in their narrow pungent leaves and straight keel. Meisner has, however, shown that these characters are not sufficiently marked to maintain the group otherwise than as a section of *Chorozema.* The species are all from South-western Australia.

ORTIE. (Fr.) *Urtica.* — BLANCHE. *Lamium album.* —, GRANDE. *Urtica dioica.* — GRIÈCHE. *Urtica urens.* — JAUNE. *Lamium Galeobdolon.* — MORTE DES MARAIS. *Stachys palustris.* — PUANTE. *Stachys sylvatica.* —, PETITE. *Urtica urens.* — ROMAINE. *Urtica pilulifera.* — ROUGE. *Galeopsis Ladanum,* or *Lamium purpureum.* — ROYALE. *Galeopsis Tetrahit.*

ORVALE. (Fr.) *Salvia Sclarea.*

ORYGIA *decumbens*, the only species of this genus of *Mesembryaceæ*, is a small decumbent much-branched spreading shrubby plant found in Arabia Felix, India, and the Cape of Good Hope. It has roundish and elliptical fleshy bluish leaves, and purplish flowers. These have a five-parted calyx, about twenty narrow entire petals, numerous stamens partly cohering in bundles, a five-celled ovary with numerous ovules, and five narrow at length recurved stigmas. The fruit is roundish, with five angles and corresponding furrows. [A.S.]

ORYZA. A genus of grasses belonging to the tribe *Oryzeæ*. The inflorescence is in panicles; glumes two, not exactly opposite; outer pale ribbed. The seeds grow on separate pedicels, which spring from the main stalk, and each grain is usually terminated by an awn or beard resembling that of some kinds of wheat. Steudel describes fourteen species, including *O. sativa*, the well-known Rice of commerce. This important grain, which supplies food for a greater number of human beings than are fed on the produce of any other known plant, is supposed to be of Asiatic origin, though recent travellers in South America mention finding the rice-plant apparently in a wild state on the banks of some rivers there. Throughout the Chinese Empire and the

Oryza sativa.

continent of India, as well as in all the great islands in the Indian Archipelago, Rice is the principal, and frequently the only, food of the great mass of the population. In the Southern States of America, whence it has formed a valuable article of exportation, its culture did not begin sooner than A.D. 1700, when it is said to have been accidental: 'A brigantine from the island of Madagascar happened to put in at Carolina, having a little seed-rice left, which the captain gave to a gentleman of the name of Woodward. From part of this he had a very good crop, but was ignorant for some years how to clean it. It was soon dispersed over the province, and by frequent experiments and observations, they found out ways of producing and manufacturing it to so great perfection, that it is thought to exceed any other in value.' (*Library of Entertaining Knowledge.*)

The Common Rice is a marsh-plant, and can only be cultivated successfully when the ground can be inundated during a certain period of its growth; besides, it requires a temperature of 60° to 80° Fahrenheit to ripen it; consequently, its cultivation in Europe is limited, being chiefly confined to Lombardy. [D.M.]

ORYZOPSIS. A genus of grasses belonging to the tribe *Stipeæ*, sometimes regarded as a section of *Urachne*. [D.M.]

OSBECKIA. A rather extensive genus of melastomaceous plants, confined to tropical Asia and Africa and the adjoining islands. The species are mostly herbs, rarely shrubs, and bear clusters or short racemes of usually small rose purple or violet flowers upon the ends of the branchlets. Generally they may be known by the four or five lobes or teeth of the calyx having bristle-like appendages between them ending in a tuft of hairs. The petals are obovate and equal in number with the calyx-lobes, while the stamens are twice as numerous, and have anthers opening by a single pore, without any or scarcely any appendage to the base of the connective; and the four or five-celled ovary is crowned with bristles, and ripens into a capsular fruit containing cochleate seeds. [A.S.]

OSCHNAH. *Alectoria arabum.*

OSCILLATING. Adhering slightly by the middle, so that the two halves are nearly equally balanced, and swing freely backwards and forwards.

OSCILLATORIÆ. A natural order of green-spored *Algæ*, with simple articulated threads, or branched by a peculiar change in one of the cells, which is diverted from its course, or more rarely by the protrusion on one side of the central cord, in consequence of the rupture of the outer coat. Articulations very narrow. Propagation by zoospores where the mode of fructification is known. The order contains a large mass of the confervoid *Algæ*. Some of them are mere strata of threads held together by a little jelly; others form dense gelatinous masses after the fashion of *Tremella*. In very many of the species the outer coat separates from the thread which it encloses; the end of it becoming lacerated, and the divisions reflected and curled; and as this process takes place repeatedly, we have occasionally very beautiful forms, either from the curious condition of the torn end, or from the complication of the several coats. In some species the outer coat is extremely thick; and if the articulation is continued through it from the central thread, we have the most elegantly striated frond as in *Petalonema*. Sometimes it is extremely gelatinous, and bears a very high proportion to the central thread, as in *Dasygloea*.

In some of the species, especially of the typical genus *Oscillaria*, a regular motion has been observed backwards and forwards like that of a pendulum, from whence the name. Such motion has in some cases undoubtedly not been independent, but in some species cilia have been observed in the terminal joints, by which it is in all probability effected.

In most of the genera multiplication takes place by the division of the central thread, which often protrudes and breaks up, each fragment forming a new plant. When the central thread protrudes at the sides, we have a peculiar mode of branching, the two branches growing in different directions, one directed downwards and the other upwards, as in *Scytonema*. Occasionally the outer coat is so tough, and at the same time so yielding, that a fascicle of parallel thread is formed within it, there being no room for the branches to expand. In this case we have such genera as *Coenocoleus*, one of whose species is amongst the commonest *Algae* on the tops of mud walls and on the naked ground. Under the microscope it looks like little sausages stuffed with threads. The curious genus *Trichodesmium*, to which we shall advert hereafter, owes its origin to a similar structure. In one genus, *Rhizonema*, the outer coat itself is cellular.

Oscillatoriae grow in various situations— in salt and fresh water, on damp ground, amongst grass on close-shaved lawns, like lichens on the trunks of trees, floating on the surface of lakes and seas, or suspended like a cloud, giving rise to variously coloured waters. One or two fine purple species form thick woolly fleeces in the hotter parts of India, while many inhabit hot springs. [M. J. B.]

OSEILLE COMMUNE. (Fr.) *Rumex Acetosa.* — DE BREBIS. *Rumex Acetosella.* — DE GUINÉE. *Hibiscus Sabdariffa.* — ÉPINARD. *Rumex Patientia.* —, GRANDE. *Rumex Acetosa.* —, PETITE. *Rumex Acetosella.* — SAUVAGE. *Rumex Acetosa.*

OSHAC, or **OOSHAK.** The Persian name for *Dorema ammoniacum.*

OSIER. *Salix viminalis.* —, BASKET. *Salix Forbyana.* —, GOLDEN. *Salix vitellina.* —, GREEN. *Salix rubra.* —, RED. *Salix rubra.* —, VELVET. *Salix viminalis.*

OSIER DES ÎLES, O. DE RIVIÈRE, or O. BLANC. (Fr.) *Salix viminalis.* — BRUN. *Salix triandra.* — FLEURI. *Epilobium angustifolium.* — JAUNE. *Salix vitellina.* — ROUGE. *Salix purpurea.* — VERT. *Salix viminalis.*

OSMANTHUS. A genus of *Oleaceae*, closely allied to *Olea* and *Phillyrea.* The corolla is four-parted, the anthers adnate, and the style two-cleft, its lobes thick and conical. Fruit unknown. The flowers of *O. fragrans*, better known as *Olea fragrans*, are used by the Chinese to perfume tea. The plant is in cultivation in this country. *O. ilicifolius* is a very elegant evergreen hardy Japanese shrub, with holly-like leaves. [M. T. M.]

OSMONDE. (Fr.) *Osmunda regalis.*

OSMUNDACEÆ, OSMUNDINEÆ. One of the principal subdivisions of the *Polypodiaceæ*, well distinguished by bearing spore-cases which are two-valved and burst vertically at the apex. In the other subdivisions of the order the spore-cases are not valvate. The *Osmundineæ* differ further in having on the spore-cases only a rudimentary ring. The group comprises *Osmunda* with paniculate, and *Todea* with dorsal fructification. [T. M.]

OSMUNDA. The principal genus of the *Osmundineæ*, and that of which our native Flowering Fern or Royal Fern, *O. regalis*, is the type. It comprises a few species of somewhat various aspect: some, like our own *O. regalis*, having the upper pinnæ of the fronds transformed into a sporangiferous panicle; others, like *O. Claytoniana*, having a few of the lateral pinnæ transformed and sporangiferous, the base and apex being leafy and sterile; and others again, like *O. cinnamonea*, having distinct sterile and fertile fronds. In all cases, however, the fertile parts are contracted, and generally rachiform. They have caudiciform or tufted stems, and pinnate or bipinnate fronds, the segments of which are often articulated, and are always traversed by free forking veins. The spore-cases are crowded on the margins or over the surface of the segments, and have an incomplete ring represented by a few parallel striæ near their apex. Our native species or forms, closely allied, are found widely distributed over the temperate regions of both hemispheres. One species, *O. javanica*, with pinnate coriaceous fronds, rather distinct in character, is found in the tropical Eastern Islands. [T. M.]

OSMUND ROYAL. *Osmunda regalis.*

OSSEOUS. Bony, hard, brittle, and very close in texture, not to be cut without difficulty; as the stone of a peach.

OSTÉOSPERME PORTE-COLLIER. (Fr.) *Osteospermum moniliferum.*

OSTEOSPERMUM. A genus of *Compositæ* of the subtribe *Calenduleæ*, consisting of South African shrubs and undershrubs or sometimes herbs, with entire or pinnatifid leaves, and yellow radiating flower-heads, remarkable for the achenes of the ray becoming hard nuts or drupes without any pappus, whilst those of the disk are constantly abortive. There are nearly fifty species known, among which *O. spinosum* and *O. moniliferum* used to be occasionally cultivated in continental flower-gardens.

OSTERICK. *Polygonum Bistorta.*

OSTIOLUM. The orifice through which spores are discharged, as in the perithecium of such fungals as *Sphæria*; also an opening over the disk of the shield of certain lichens.

OSTODES. A genus of *Euphorbiaceæ*, consisting of two Javanese trees very nearly allied to *Aleurites*; but the stamens of the male flowers are free, not monadelphous, and the ovary of the females has three instead of two cells.

OSTRYA. The Hop Hornbeam genus, composed of two species, one a native of the south of Europe, and the other of North America. It belongs to the *Corylaceæ*, and is closely allied to the Common Hornbeam. Both species form trees thirty or forty feet high, with deciduous feather-veined serrated leaves, and unisexual flowers borne in distinct catkins upon the same plant. The male catkins are long, cylindrical, and drooping, composed of a number of simple scale-like bracts, each with twelve or more irregularly united stamens inserted into its base; and the female ones short, with small deciduous bracts, each flower enclosed in a pair of thin involucral scales which become enlarged and grow together so as to form an inflated covering to the fruit, and these being imbricated give the ripe catkin a hop-like appearance. The fruit is a small one-seeded nut bearded at the top.

O. vulgaris, the Common Hop Hornbeam, is a native of the south of Europe, but is quite hardy in the climate of England. It forms a large spreading tree, and has a very handsome appearance, particularly in the autumn, when the pendent hop-like catkins are in perfection. *O. virginica* is extensively spread over North America, and is sometimes regarded as a variety of the last species, the chief difference being that the fruit catkins are upright instead of pendulous as in *O. vulgaris*. The wood of the Virginian kind is excessively hard and heavy, and is called Ironwood; levers are sometimes made of it, whence it is frequently called Lever-wood.   [A. S.]

OSTRYOCARPUS. A weak half-climbing shrub from tropical Africa, constituting a genus of *Leguminosæ*, closely allied to *Lonchocarpus* in foliage, in habit, and in most of the floral characters; but the tenth stamen is free, the wing-petals do not adhere to the keel, and the fruit is a broad round flat indehiscent pod, something of the shape of an oyster-shell, whence the generic name.

OSUS. A termination indicating augmentation, as *radiosus*, having a large root.

OSYRIS. A genus of some half-dozen species of *Santalaceæ*, inhabiting widely separated regions of the eastern hemisphere; two being found in the Mediterranean region, one in Abyssinia, two in India, and one at the Cape of Good Hope. They are shrubs or small trees, with angular branches, alternate or rarely opposite leaves, and usually unisexual flowers on different trees; one, however, always has perfect flowers. The flowers are deeply three or four-parted, with three or four

stamens, and a one-celled ovary containing usually three ovules. The fruit contains a single seed. In Kumaon the leaves of *O. arborea*, which is sometimes called *O. nepalensis*, are employed as a substitute for tea. This is a small tree, with somewhat elliptical leaves an inch and a half to two inches long, and is found all along the foot of the Himalayas.   [A. S.]

OTACHYRIUM. A genus of grasses belonging to the tribe *Paniceæ*. There are only two species, both Brazilian, and included by Steudel in *Panicum*.   [D. M.]

OTHONNA. A genus of *Compositæ* of the subtribe *Calenduleæ*, distinguished by the scales of the involucre being united in a single row and valvate at the top, by their female ligulate ray-florets with achenes bearing a dense pappus of simple bristles, and by their disk florets being all male with abortive achenes. There are above sixty species known, herbs or shrubs, with entire or divided leaves, often somewhat succulent, and solitary pedunc+ate flower-heads, usually yellow, rarely blue. The *O. cheirifolia* inhabits the African shores of the Mediterranean, and has been frequently grown in flower-gardens. All the other species are natives of the Cape Colony.

OTIDIA. Six species of *Pelargonium* with succulent knobby stems, fleshy pinnately or bipinnately compound leaves, nearly equal petals the upper ones eared at the base, and five stamens, have been separated as a genus with the name *Otidia*; but they are retained as a section of *Pelargonium* by Dr. Harvey in the *Flora Capensis*. They are all South African. The flowers are small, usually white, and disposed in few or many-flowered umbels.   {A. A. B.]

OTOCHILUS. A small genus of orchids, natives of the Himalaya mountains, where they are found creeping on trees. They have no rhizomes, but creep by means of their proliferous pseudobulbs, which are continuously produced one above the other, each successive one coming out just below the apex of the old one and there emitting a few fibrous roots. Each pseudobulb bears a couple of leaves, and from the base of some of the upper ones many-flowered racemes of smallish blossoms are produced. The genus belongs to the tribe *Cœlogynidæ*, and its flowers have equal free sepals and petals, a three-lobed lip with the side-lobes very small and embracing the column, and the middle one long and petal-like, and a very long club-shaped column, bearing a terminal anther, which contains four pollen-masses held together in twos by a granular substance.   [A. S.]

OTTELIA. A genus of *Hydrocharidaceæ*, consisting of perennial herbs inhabiting the mouth of the Nile, Ganges, and Australasian rivers, and eaten as potherbs in India. They are quite stemless, have cordate leaves, and hermaphrodite flowers placed on a scape, and surrounded by a spathe. The perigone is divided into six parts, the outer three of which resemble a calyx, the inner a corolla; there are from six to twelve stamens, six stigmas, and a six to eight-celled berry, with numerous seeds. The generic name is derived from the Malabar Ottel-ambel.   [B. S.]

OTTOA. A genus of umbellifers, distinguished by its calyx being destitute of border; by its entire petals, its spreading styles, and by each half of the fruit having five membranous ribs. The only species is *O. œnanthoides*, a native of Quito, which has a simple stem with fine leaves, which are round and hollow within, with transverse partitions; the flowers white, in dense umbels, a few with stamens and pistils and therefore perfect, the others with stamens only. The genus was named in honour of F. Otto, of Berlin.   [G. D.]

OTTO or OTTAR OF ROSES. A fragrant oil obtained from *Rosa centifolia* and *R. damascena*.

OURARI. The Wourali or Urari poison, the basis of which is the juice of *Strychnos toxifera*.

OUTLINE. The figure formed by the margin of a body.

OUVIRANDRA. The genus of *Juncaginaceæ*, to which belong the singular aquatic Lace-leaf or Lattice-leaf plants of Madagascar. It is closely allied to *Aponogeton*, from which it principally differs in its seeds having a thick leafy cotyledon embracing a two-leaved plumule, and in its sepals being deciduous. The habit of the two genera also is different. Only three species were originally referred to *Ouvirandra*, two from Madagascar and one from Senegambia; but four other Indian species possessing the technical characters of the genus, though previously referred to *Aponogeton*, are now included in it. All these plants are aquatic herbs, with tuberculate roots, radical submerged leaves, and a scape or flower-stalk long enough to reach the surface of the water, where it either bears a single spike or divides into from two to five little spikes of small flowers. These have two or three coloured deciduous sepals, six persistent stamens with wide-based filaments, and three or four one-celled ovaries ending in short styles.

The two most remarkable species are those of Madagascar, *O. fenestralis* and *O. Bernieriana*, both of which have within the last ten years been introduced into our hothouses by the Rev. H. Ellis, well known through his missionary labours in that island. The former is best known as the Lattice-leaf plant, from its singular leaves resembling open lattice-work, or apparently consisting of only a skeleton of nerves. These leaves grow in radiating clusters from the rhizome, and float just beneath the surface of the water, presenting a flat side to the light. They have rather long stalks, and are of an oblong form, rounded at both extremities, very variable in size, but usually nine inches to a foot long by two or three inches broad. When super-ficially inspected they seem to be composed simply of a stout midrib and several slender longitudinal nerves parallel with it all connected by numerous short cross-nerves,

Ouvirandra fenestralis.

and to be wholly destitute of the parenchyma or cellular tissue with which the spaces between the nerves in ordinary leaves are closed up; but the microscope shows that this cellular tissue is really present, surrounding the nerves, and in the very young state of the leaf the spaces are nearly, if not quite, filled up by it. The flower-stalks rise from the centre of the tuft of leaves, and fork into a couple of spikes at the top. The plant, however, is not only curious, but is a valuable one to the natives of Madagascar, who collect its fleshy farinaceous roots as an article of food, calling the plant, on this account, Ouvirandram, which means literally Water-Yam, and this is the source of the generic name. It grows on the margins of running streams in shallow water.   [A. S.]

OVAL. The same as Elliptic.

OVARY. That part of the pistil which contains the ovules.

OVATE. Oblong or elliptical, broadest at the lower end, so as to resemble the longitudinal section of an egg.

OVENCHYMA. Oval cellular tissue.

OVERLOOK. A name given by the West Indian negroes to *Canavalia gladiata*.

OVIEDA. *Lapeyrousia.*

OVOIDAL. A solid with an ovate figure, or resembling an egg.

OVULE, OVUM. The young seed.

OVULE TUBE. A thread-like extension of the apex of the nucleus, or of the sac of the amnios, rising up beyond the foramen.

OWALA. *Pentaclethra macrophylla*, the seeds of which furnish a useful oil, and are also eaten by the natives of West Tropical Africa.

OWLER. The Alder, *Alnus glutinosa.*

OXALIDACEÆ. (*Ledocarpeæ, Rhynchotheceæ, Hugoniacceæ, Oxalids.*) A natural order of thalamifloral dicotyledons, belonging to Lindley's geranial alliance of hypogynous Exogens. They are herbs, undershrubs, or trees, with alternate, rarely opposite, compound (occasionally simple) leaves, generally without stipules, and are found in hot as well as temperate climates, abundantly in North America, and at the Cape of Good Hope, the shrubby species being confined to the hotter parts of the world. Their symmetrical flowers consist of five persistent imbricate sepals; five unguiculate petals, with a twisted æstivation; ten stamens, more or less monadelphous, in two rows; and a five-celled ovary, with filiform distinct styles. Fruit capsular, membranous or fleshy, usually five-celled; seeds few, albuminous, attached to a central placenta, sometimes with a peculiar elastic integument. In some cases phyllodia or winged petioles occupy the place of leaves. They are often acid in their properties, and some of them yield esculent roots. There are upwards of 300 species, distributed in about ten genera, of which *Oxalis, Averrhoa,* and *Hugonia* are examples.   [J. H. B.]

OXALIDE OSEILLE. (Fr.) *Oxalis Acetosella.*

OXALIS. A very large genus of *Oxalideæ,* of which the greater number of species occur in tropical America and at the Cape of Good Hope. They are herbs or more rarely shrubs, and one, *O. scandens,* from Mount Quindiu in South America, is a climber; but by far the greater number have the stem reduced to a rhizome, sometimes subterranean, sometimes above ground, often taking the shape of a bulb or forming a tuber. In these the leaves are all produced in a tuft. In some of the bulbous species, as *O. cernua,* bulbs are also produced in the axils of the leaves. The leaves of most of the species consist of three entire leaflets which are usually inversely heartshaped, and occasionally slightly sensitive, as in *O. stricta.* Sometimes the leaflets are reduced to two, or even to one, when the leaf appears to be simple; and finally a few have even this solitary portion deficient, which occurs in such species as *O. fruticosa* and *O. leptopodes,* which have flat dilated leaf-like petioles. The leaves contain an acid juice. One section of the genus (*Biophytum*) has pinnate leaves, with many pairs of pinnæ, but no terminal leaflet. In one of these, from India, *O. sensitiva,* these compound leaves are nearly as sensitive as in the sensitive plant, for they contract on the slightest touch. The peduncles (scapes in the acaulescent species) are generally terminated by an umbel of brightly coloured flowers, the pedicels of which are bracteated. The flowers consist of five sepals, free or combined at the base; five petals; ten stamens, the five outer ones smaller, the filaments combined at the base (except in *Biophytum*); five styles; the capsule ovoid or oblong, often five-sided; the seeds covered by an elastic coat, which ruptures when they are ripe, and by its contraction expels them with considerable force.

Three species occur in Britain. One of these, the common Wood Sorrel, *O. Acetosella,* has a scaly rhizome with a tuft of leaves at the top, and solitary white flowers more or less veined with purple. This plant has a pleasant acid taste from containing binoxalate of potass; and hence it was once used in medical practice as a refrigerant in fever, and an antiscorbutic in scurvy, and still remains in the London Pharmacopœia, though fallen into disuse. The other British species, *O. corniculata* and *O. stricta,* are caulescent. *O. Acetosella* is said to be the Shamrock of Ireland, though some prefer *Trifolium,* and other plants have been suggested.

O. crenata has an erect leafy stem and umbellate flowers, which are yellow streaked with purple. It is a native of Peru, and is largely cultivated about Lima for its very acid leafstalks; it also produces yellowish tubers of the size and shape of small potatos, and having a slightly acid flavour, which disappears on boiling. When introduced into this country it was expected that it would have proved a valuable substitute for the potato, but this, however, has not been realised, the tubers being insipid and the produce small, not exceeding half a pound from a plant.

O. Deppei, from Mexico, a stemless species, with four leaflets, red flowers, and a

Oxalis Deppei.

large scaly bulb, produces fleshy edible fusiform roots of moderate size. *O. tuberosa,* from Bolivia, where it is called Oca, is cultivated in its native place for its potatolike tubers.   [J. T. S.]

OXERA. A genus of *Verbenaceæ,* containing a single species from New Caledonia. It is a branching glabrous shrub, with opposite shortly petiolate leaves, and large flowers in axillary cymes. The calyx is four-parted, and the corolla funnel-shaped, ventricose, and slightly bent, with a four-cleft limb; of the four didynamous stamens the two posterior are short and fertile, the others are exserted and barren. The ovary, placed on a fleshy disk, is four-celled and four-lobed, with a single ovule in each cell. The genus is nearly related to *Clerodendron* and *Cyclonema*.   [W. C.]

OXHOOF. A Brazilian name for *Caulotretus microstachyus*, and various species of *Bauhinia*.

OX-EYE. *Buphthalmum*: also *Chrysanthemum Leucanthemum*, and *Anthemis arvensis*. —, CREEPING. *Wedelia carnosa*. —, SEASIDE. *Borrichia arborescens*.

OXLIP. *Primula elatior*.

OX-HEEL, or OX-HEAL. *Helleborus fœtidus*.

OX-HORN. *Bucida Buceras*.

OX-TONGUE. *Helminthia*; also *Anchusa officinalis*.

OXLEYA. A genus of *Cedrelaceæ*, represented by *O. xanthoxyla*, a tree forty-five to fifty feet high, and six feet in circumference, producing the Yellow Wood of Queensland. The foliage is of dark green and sombre aspect, the leaves imparipinnate; while the flowers appear in racemes, and are small, white, and inconspicuous, according to Bennett. The fruit is a woody capsule, with spiny tubercles on the surface, five-celled, each cell enclosing three winged seeds. The first discoverer of the tree was Allan Cunningham, Colonial Botanist in New South Wales.   [B. S.]

OXYACANTHA. *Cratægus Oxyacantha*.

OXYANTHUS. A genus of tropical African *Cinchonaceæ*, consisting of shrubs, with elliptic pointed leaves and axillary corymb-like racemes of large flowers; these have a sharply five-toothed calyx-limb, and a salver-shaped corolla, with a very long slender tube, from which the five anthers project. The ovary is adherent to the tube of the calyx, two-celled, and surmounted by an epigynous disk. The genus is closely allied to *Gardenia*, but is distinguished by its large corolla, its inflorescence, &c. The name, signifying ' sharp-flower,' is applied in allusion to the acute pointed segments of the limb of the corolla. *O. speciosus* and others are highly ornamental stove plants.   [M. T. M.]

OXYBAPHUS. One of the genera of *Nyctaginaceæ*. The species are herbaceous plants, natives of tropical America, and have opposite leaves, and flowers arranged in corymbs at the end of the branches, surrounded by a bell-shaped five-cleft persistent involucre. The perianth is pink-coloured and has a short dilated tube, which is persistent, while the plaited five-lobed limb is deciduous; stamens three, united at the base into a very short tube. Fruit surrounded by the hardened base of the perianth, and by the enlarged membranaceous involucre. *Calymenia* and *Calyxhymenia* are synonyms. [M. T. M.]

OXYCARYUM. A genus of cyperaceous plants belonging to the tribe *Scirpeæ*. The inflorescence is in dense heads of crowded spikelets, umbellately disposed; spikelets many-flowered; scales membranaceous at the base; styles cleft, persistent, decurrent at the base; stamens two. *O. Schomburgkianum*, a native of Guiana, is the only species described.   [D. M.]

OXYCOCCOS. The Cranberry genus, a group of the *Vacciniaceæ*, comprising three species—*O. palustris*, *macrocarpus*, and *erectus*. The name is derived from *oxys*, sharp, and *kokkos*, a berry, the fruit having a sharp acid taste; that of Cranberry, according to some, comes from the crooked peduncle together with the unexpanded flower resembling the head and neck of a crane, but according to others, and with greater probability, because the berries are eaten by cranes; just as the fruit of the *Empetrum nigrum* is called the Crowberry, because where this is plentiful the crows, and more especially the rooks, leave the fields and resort to the hills, where they live on the berries till harvest-time.

O. palustris, the Common Cranberry, is a native of Britain; and is indigenous also to the mountainous parts of Europe, Siberia, and North America. It grows in turfy bogs, the stems creeping and slender, with small ovate leaves revolute at the edges, and terminal pink or rose-coloured pedicels bearing each a single flower. The berries are roundish pear-shaped, and of a crimson colour.

In the form of tarts, preserves, &c., the fruit is grateful to most people, and many in this country prefer the flavour of the native species to that of the imported American fruit produced by *O. macrocarpus*. Before the bogs in Lincolnshire were drained, the common Cranberry was sold in Norwich by cartloads. According to Lightfoot, as much as twenty to thirty pounds' worth of the fruit was sold by the poor people each market-day, for five or six weeks, in the town of Langton, on the borders of Cumberland—a considerable sum to be picked up from otherwise barren wastes, in a thinly inhabited district. Large quantities, for use in tarts, are imported from Russia. According to Don's *Miller*, the berries are used in Sweden to boil silver plate in, in order to render it white by the action of the acid which they contain. This plant is the badge of the Grants.

The Large-fruited or American Cranberry, *O. macrocarpus*, which is also of slender creeping habit, and has elliptic obtuse nearly flat leaves, bears spherical berries, larger and of a brighter red than those of the common sort; they ripen in October and successionally, often remaining on the plant throughout the winter. It is found from Canada to Virginia, in bogs, principally on a sandy soil. The berries are collected in large quantities, and form an article of export to Britain and other parts of Europe. The American Cranberry can be cultivated in England, and was so very successfully by Sir Joseph Banks and others. Downing, in his *Fruits and Fruit Trees of America*, states that 'in some parts of New England, low and coarse meadows of no value have been drained and turned to very profitable account by planting them with this fruit. The average produce is from eighty to one hundred bushels of Cranberries [per acre], worth at least one dollar a bushel.' As a large quantity can be obtained from a small space, and at little expense, the American Cranberry might be advantageously cultivated, for private use at least, in this country, where, by picking the berries only as they became perfectly ripe, and carefully rejecting such as were but partially so, a produce of more uniform and better quality would be insured. [R. T.]

OXYDENDRON. A genus of heathworts, having the corolla ovate and five-toothed, the filaments of the stamens hairy, and the style thick and five-angled. The only species is a native of North America, a shrub with alternate acute and serrate leaves. The name is from the Greek words signifying 'sharp' or 'acid,' and 'tree,' to indicate the taste of the plant. [G. D.]

OXYGONIUM. A genus of polypodiaceous ferns of the tribe *Asplenieæ*, and belonging to the diplazioid division, with double sori, set back to back. Among these it is known by its reticulated venation, which is of this form : the veins and venules are parallel below, and on this elongated parallel portion bear the sori, exterior to which they become joined so as to form near the margin one or two series of small areoles, from which short free veinlets point outwards. The few species are tropical Eastern ferns, with somewhat coarse simple or pinnate coriaceous fronds. [T. M.]

OXYGONUM. A genus of *Polygonaceæ* from the Cape of Good Hope, comprising an annual plant with lanceolate leaves, and pedunculated spikes of monœcious flowers, the males with a four-cleft coloured perianth, and eight stamens. The fruit is oblong and trigonous, with membranous wings at the angles. [J. T. S.]

OXYLOBIUM. A genus of papilionaceous *Leguminosæ* of the tribe *Podalyrieæ*, characterised chiefly by the calyx, which has the two upper lobes larger and more united than the others, forming a kind of upper lip, by the ovary having always more than two ovules, and by the pod, which is more or less turgid, being usually coriaceous and not divided between the seeds. There are nearly thirty species, including *Callistachys*, which has no sufficient characters to distinguish it. They are all Australian shrubs or undershrubs with opposite whorled or sometimes scattered, simple and entire leaves, usually silky underneath. The flowers are yellow, in axillary clusters heads or short racemes, or in terminal racemes or spikes. Several species have been occasionally introduced into our collections amongst ornamental Australian shrubs, but they are generally less showy than the *Chorozemas*, which some of them much resemble.

OXYPETALUM. A genus of *Asclepiadaceæ* composed of South American twiners or erect herbs, with opposite generally pubescent cordate leaves, and interpetiolar rather large, and often scented white, yellow, blue, or greenish flowers. The calyx is five-cleft, the tube of the corolla bell-shaped, and the fruit smooth or covered with soft prickles. *O. cœruleum* (*Tweedia cœrulea* of authors) is a favourite in our gardens on account of its fine blue flowers. The genus is a large one, nearly fifty species being enumerated in systematic works, but nothing seems known about their uses. [B. S.]

OXYRAMPHIS. A name given by Wallich to those species of *Lespideza* which have a very pointed keel-petal, and which now form a section of the latter genus.

OXYRIA. A genus of *Polygonaceæ*, distinguished from *Rumex* by having the perianth with four segments only, the inner pair enlarged over the lens-shaped winged nut. They are small alpine acid plants, found in Europe, Asia, and the Arctic regions, and have stalked cordate-reniform root-leaves, and paniculate flowers, which are in half-whorls round the branches of the panicle. One species, *O. reniformis*, is not uncommon in alpine districts in Britain. [J. T. S.]

OXYSTELMA. A genus of *Asclepiadaceæ*, inhabiting tropical Asia, Africa, and Australia, and consisting of climbing glabrous shrubs, with narrow linear or lanceolate seldom ovate leaves, and racemose purplish flowers. The calyx is five-cleft, the corolla rotate and five-lobed, and the fruit oblong and smooth on the surface; whilst the seeds are small and have a feathery appendix. There is some doubt whether *O. esculentum*, termed Ourril Palay by the Malabar people, is really eaten. Both Roxburgh and Wight assert that they never saw the natives eat it; but in decoction it is used as a gargle for aphthous affections of the mouth and fauces. [B. S.]

OXYSTYLIS. A North American herbaceous plant, constituting a genus of *Capparidaceæ*, and having small yellow flowers arranged in axillary racemes. Sepals linear; petals oval; ovary two-celled, with two ovules in each cell. Fruit two-lobed, indehiscent, surmounted by the persistent style. [M. T. M.]

OXYTHECA. A genus of *Polygonaceæ*, containing an annual from Western North America and Chili, with the habit of the pedunculate *Eriogona*, but having a four or five-cleft involucre, with few flowers, which have a four or five-cleft perianth, and twice as many stamens as there are lobes. The segments of the involucre and calyx are spinulose-aristate. [J. T. S.]

OXYTROPIS. An extensive genus of

leguminous plants, closely allied to *Astragalus*, from which it is mainly distinguished by having the lower petals of the corolla or keel obtuse, and the lower suture of the legume inflexed. All the species have pinnate leaves, and bear their flowers, which are purplish cream-coloured or white, in spikes or clusters. The majority being alpine plants are of humble growth, and produce comparatively large flowers. Two species are indigenous to Scotland: *O. uralensis*, a stemless plant, the leaves of which are plentifully clothed with silky hairs, and the flowers bright purple, collected into heads, and which grows in dry pastures chiefly near the sea; and *O. campestris*, which has very short stems, yellowish capitate flowers, and inflated pubescent pods. The latter is a very rare native plant, being found only on the Clova Mountains. The species are principally employed for ornamenting rock-work.   [C. A. J.]

OYSTER-GREEN. A name commonly given to *Ulva Lactuca* from its bright-green tint, and its being frequently attached to the common oyster. It is also called Green Sloke. Other species, and one or two species of *Enteromorpha*, are probably included under the name.   [M. J. B.]

OYSTER PLANT. *Steenhammaria maritima.*

OZOTHAMNUS. A genus of *Compositæ* of the tribe *Gnaphalieæ*, only differing from *Cassinia* in the want of chaffy scales on the receptacle, and in the inner scales or bracts of the involucre being white coloured or scarious, and usually spreading in a ray. There are about thirty species known, of which three inhabit New Zealand, and the rest are Australian. They are all shrubby, with small scattered leaves, usually entire with the edges rolled back, and numerous small flower-heads in terminal corymbs or panicles.

PABS. In Scotland, the refuse of flax.

PACANE, or PACANIER. (Fr.) *Carya olivæformis.*

PACHANA. A bitter tonic infusion prepared in India from *Tinospora cordifolia.*

PACHIRA. A genus of tropical American trees belonging to the *Sterculiaceæ*, and differing from *Adansonia*, the baobab tree, in the calyx being cup-shaped and entire, not five-toothed. From the other genera of the family the disposition of the stamens is sufficient to distinguish it. The name *Pachira* was given to the plants of this genus in 1775, by Aublet, and about six years later the younger Linnæus gave them that of *Carolinea* without knowledge of the one already published. The former name, therefore, has precedence, but the plants are best known under the latter. They are either small or large trees, with digitate leaves somewhat like those of the horse-chestnut, but with the leaflets more leathery in texture. The large handsome flowers arise singly from the axils of the upper leaves, and are generally white but sometimes a deep rose or scarlet. The calyx is cup-shaped entire; the petals five, strap-shaped, varying from three inches to a foot in length, and often covered internally with soft white down; and the stamens very numerous, with their filaments united into a ring at the base, but divided upwards into many branching bundles; these being generally of a bright-red colour, add greatly to the beauty of the flowers, especially when the petals are white. The fruit is an oval woody one-celled capsule, which opens by a number of divisions, and contains numerous seeds.

One of the best-known species is *P. alba*, commonly called *Carolinea alba*, a native of many parts of South America. This is a tree growing twenty feet high, with flowers about six inches long. The petals are clothed with an olive-coloured down on the back, and covered internally with soft white silky hairs. According to Mr. Purdie, this is one of the most useful trees in New Grenada, the inner bark furnishing the entire country with cordage which is strong and durable.

The wool of the seeds of the Barrigon (*P. Barrigon*), is used in Panama to stuff pillows, cushions, &c., and the bark affords a useful fibre. Among the trees of that country which yield a useful timber, the Cedro Espinoso (*P. Fendleri*) is enumerated by Dr. Seemann. The largest-flowered species, *P. macrantha*, is found in Brazil; this tree attains a height of one hundred feet, and has flowers fifteen inches in length, the petals olive-green white within, and the stamens blood-red with yellow anthers. The name commemorates the Princess Sophia Caroline of Baden.   [A. A. B.]

PACHIRA DE CAYENNE. (Fr.) *Pachira aquatica.* — DU MARONI. *Pachira insignis.*

PACHYDENDRON. A section of the liliaceous genus *Aloe*, distinguished by the tubular slightly incurved perianth with an ascending bent limb, and by the stamens adhering to the base of the perianth. They are arborescent plants from the Cape of Good Hope, with crowded leaves at the top of the caudex, and nodding flowers in a terminal spike.   [J. T. S.]

PACHYLOBUS. An imperfectly known genus of trees, of the family *Amyridaceæ*. Don describes them as having compound leaves, and oval black bitter astringent fruits. These fruits are sold in the island of St. Thomas, Gulf of Guinea, under the names of Safu and Pasco.   [M. T. M.]

PACHYMA. A spurious genus of *Fungi* consisting of one or two doubtful productions. The most important of these will be briefly noticed under its native name, TUCKAHOO.   [M. J. B.]

PACHYNEMA. A genus of *Dilleniaceæ*, consisting of three leafless herbs or undershrubs from tropical Australia, with rush-like or flattened stems, and small yellow flowers on short lateral recurved branches,

3 H

They are well characterised by their stamens being never more than ten, with thickened ovoid filaments, very much resembling in shape the carpels of the ovary, and accompanied by two inner staminodia or barren stamens, which are still more like the carpels. To these has been added, as a section, the *Huttia* of Harvey, a West Australian species with the same rush-like stems, leafless except two or three small divided leaves at the base, and with larger flowers and the filaments broadly flattened instead of being ovoid.

PACHYNEURUM. A genus of *Cruciferæ* from the Altai, containing *Draba grandiflora*, which has the two outer sepals bulging at the base, and the pod linear-compressed, the valves with a thick nerve and prominent veins, and the seeds numerous, in two rows. [J. T. S.]

PACHYNOCARPUS. A lofty Borneo tree, with alternate entire coriaceous leaves, and deliciously fragrant flowers, in axillary and terminal panicles, forming a genus of *Dipterocarpaceæ*, closely allied to *Vatica*, but differing in the fruit. When ripe the calyx-lobes wear away, and the adnate tube enlarges and becomes thickened, almost enclosing the fruit, to which it closely adheres; whilst in *Vatica* the tube remains small, and the persistent lobes are reflexed under the fruit.

PACHYPHYLLUM. Epiphytal orchids of the tribe *Vandeæ*, allied to and with much of the habit of *Fernandezia*, having thick fleshy leaves arranged in two ranks, and overlapping each other. They bear axillary spikes of inconspicuous bifariously disposed flowers, which have a conniving perianth, with free equal sepals and petals, a free undivided sessile lip having a single tubercle at its base and two at its apex, a petaloid column, and two pollen-masses. All the species, about six in number, belong to tropical Western America. [A. S.]

PACHYPLEURUM. A genus of umbellifers, distinguished by having the petals in different flowers of the umbel of different shape; and each half of the fruit with five prominent thick ribs, the two lateral broader than the others. *P. alpinum* is the only species, a native of the Alpine parts of Europe. The name comes from Greek words indicating the thickened form of the ribs on the fruit. [G. D.]

PACHYPODIUM. A genus of dogbanes distinguished by having the calyx in five deep divisions, the corolla salver-shaped with its tube curved and five-angled, and the stamens inserted in the middle of the tube. The species are fleshy and spiny shrubs, with scattered leaves and milky juice. They are natives of the Cape of Good Hope. [G. D.]

The same name has been given to a genus of *Cruciferæ*, not sufficiently distinct from *Sisymbrium*, from which it differs only in the very long pods, cylindrical throughout, with a spongy partition destitute of a nerve. The species occur in Central Europe

and in the Mediterranean region. *Sisymbrium Columnæ* and *S. pannonicum* of authors belong to this group. [J. T. S.]

PACHYPTERA. A doubtful genus of *Bignoniaceæ*, the flowers of which are unknown. The fruit is an elongated flat capsule, divided into two cells by a partition placed parallel with the valves. The half-dozen species comprised in the genus are all South American shrubs, furnished with conjugate leaves, and climbing by means of tendrils. [B. S.]

PACHYRHIZUS. A genus of *Leguminosæ*: one species is common in the tropics of both hemispheres, another is confined to Japan, and two to Southern China. They are shrubby plants, with twining stems rising from large tuberous roots, and having leaves formed of three usually angular stalked leaflets, and racemes composed of clusters of violet-blue flowers on large glandular knobs. Each flower has two small bracts which soon fall off, a pitcher-shaped four-lobed calyx, a pea-like corolla, ten stamens (one of which is free) alternately shorter, and straight narrow flattened pods containing from seven to twelve roundish seeds.

P. angulatus is found in many parts of the tropics, such as tropical America, both the East and West Indies, Mauritius, Feejee Islands, &c. It has angular sharp-toothed leaflets, and long racemes of flowers. The roots generally run in a horizontal direction underground, and frequently attain six or eight feet in length and the thickness of a man's thigh. They are used for food in times of scarcity, and when cooked are of a dirty-white hue, and rather insipid. The Feejeans, who call the plant Yaka or Waynka, obtain a tough fibre from the twining stems, with which they make their fishing-nets. [A. S.]

PACHYSTEMON. A genus of *Euphorbiaceæ*, consisting of one or two Javanese trees, with the large peltate three-lobed leaves as well as most of the characters of a *Mappa*; but the male flowers have only a single stamen consisting of a three-celled anther, sessile on a thick column; and in the females the ovary is five-celled, with a hollow cylindrical five-lobed style.

PACHYSTICHOUS. Thick-sided; applied to cells only.

PACHYSTIGMA. The name of a small Natal shrub, constituting a genus of *Cinchonaceæ*. It is described as having a reddish bark, and axillary cymes of reddish flowers; a calyx-limb divided into four or five linear segments; a bell-shaped corolla with a somewhat globular tube, hairy in the interior, the limb divided into four or five lance-shaped segments; five stamens protruding from the corolla; and a five-celled ovary surmounted by a fleshy disk, the style terminated by a thick fleshy stigma—whence the name. [M. T. M.]

PACKMAN-RICH. A Scottish name for six-rowed barley.

PACOVA. A Brazilian name for the Banana.

PACUL. A wild variety of Plantain, from which some of the so-called Manilla hemp is obtained.

PADDLE-WOOD. A strong light elastic wood obtained in Guiana from *Aspidosperma excelsum.*

PADDOCK-PIPES. *Equisetum*, especially *E. limosum.*

PADDOCK-STOOLS. *Boletus* ; also *Agaricus.*

PADELION. *Alchemilla vulgaris.*

PADDY. Unhusked rice.

PADINA. A beautiful genus of dark-spored *Algæ*, of which *P. pavonia*, our Turkey-feather Laver or Peacock's Tail, is one of the most remarkable species, if indeed all are not reducible to that. The broadly fan-shaped frond, often proliferous, and circled round into a cup marked with concentric lines fringed at their upper margin, with heaps of spores between them, and partially covered beneath with chalky powder, at once indicate the species. It is common in tropical countries, extending

Padina pavonia.

to our *southern* coasts without any change of size or colour.   [M. J. B.]

PADOUK. A kind of Rosewood obtained in Burmah from *Pterocarpus indicus.*

PÆDERIA. A genus of *Cinchonaceæ*, consisting of four or five species, all Asiatic and mostly tropical, except one species which extends as far north as Japan. They are climbing shrubs with twining stems, opposite leaves with solitary stipules on each side, and small flowers disposed in loose two or three-forked cymes produced either from the angles of the leaves or at the ends of the branches. The flowers have a calyx with five small persistent teeth, a funnel-shaped corolla with short valvate lobes folded in the bud, five stamens included within the tube of the corolla, and a style with two short stigmas. The fruits are small berries covered with a thin brittle rind, and contain two one-seeded cells.

P. fœtida is a widely spread plant, common in most parts of India and all through the Malayan Archipelago, extending from the Mauritius northward to China and Japan. All parts of the plant give off a most offensive odour when bruised. Its leaves are usually heart-shaped at the base, but of variable width and outline ; and its flowers white or pale-pink marked with a pink star-like spot on the spreading limb. In Assam the plant is called Bedolee Sutta, and has lately been brought into notice as a fibre-yielding plant, its flexible stems yielding a tough fine fibre fit for spinning purposes. The Hindoos use the roots as an einetic.   [A. S.]

The chopped branches are known in China under the name of Jung-gala, and are used to destroy aphides on cabbages.

PÆDEROTA. A genus of *Scrophulariaceæ*, scarcely differing from *Veronica* in their more irregular almost two-lipped corolla. The habit is also that of the mountain species of *Veronica*, with terminal spikes. There are two species, both inhabiting the mountains of Çarinthia, Carniola, and Upper Italy : *P. Ageria*, an erect perennial of about six inches to a foot in height, with pale-yellow or straw-coloured flowers ; and *P. Bonarota*, a much lower but very ornamental plant, with blue or pink-coloured flowers.

PÆONIA. An extensive genus of handsome herbaceous plants, occasionally somewhat shrubby, belonging to the *Ranunculaceæ*, among which they are distinguished by producing their seeds in many-seeded follicles, and by bearing their stamens on a glandular disk. One species, *P. corallina*, has long been known to grow on an island called the Steep Holmes in the mouth of the Severn, but it is scarcely considered indigenous. *P. festiva*, or *officinalis*, is the Common Peony, with large single or double red or blush flowers, which decorates every cottage garden. *P. albiflora*, distinguished by its smooth recurved follicles, is a native of Siberia and the whole of Northern Asia : the roots of this are sometimes boiled by the natives, and eaten in broth ; they also grind the seeds and put them into their tea. French, *Pivoine* ; German, *Päonie.* See MOUTAN.   [C. A. J.]

PÆONY, or PEONY. *Pæonia.*

PÆSIA. A genus of Brazilian ferns, probably confined to one species, *P. viscosa*, a plant with large tripinnate glandular-pubescent fronds, and the general aspect of *Pteris aquilina* ; with which, moreover, it agrees so closely in its fructification as to have been named *Pteris scalaris.* The sorus of this plant, which was for a long time a pteridological puzzle, is either linear or roundish, with a double or two-valved indusium such as occurs in the bracken, which latter and its allies will probably have to be dissociated from *Pteris*, and combined with *Pæsia.* The latter has been generally referred to the *Dicksonieæ*, but it seems to fall rather in the vicinity of the *Lindseœ*, where it may form a distinct section, *Pdsieœ*. 　　　[T. M.]

PAGADOO. *Mimusops Elengi.*

PAGÆA. A genus of *Gentianaceœ*, represented by a South American herbaceous plant, with lance-shaped leaves, and purple funnel-shaped flowers, borne on nodding flower-stalks, that originate in the forks of the branches. It is closely allied to *Lisianthus*, but is distinguished by the stamens, which are attached to the tube of the corolla, and by the erect projecting anthers, which do not become twisted. The inflorescence also is peculiar in this family. The name is derived from the Greek *pagos*, a membrane, in allusion to the membranous texture of the calyx. 　　　[M. T. M.]

PAGARILLE. (Fr.) *Tropœolum aduncum.*

PAGINA. The surface of anything.

PAIGLE, PAGLE, or PEAGLE. *Primula veris.*

PAIN BLANC. (Fr.) *Viburnum sterile.* — DE COUCOU. *Oxalis Acetosella.* — DE CRAPAUD. *Alisma Plantago.* — DE GRENOUILLE. *Alisma natans.* — D'OISEAU. *Sedum reflexum.* — DE POULET. *Lamium purpureum.* — DE POURCEAU. *Cyclamen europœum.* — DE SAINT JEAN. *Ceratonia Siliqua.* — DE SINGE. *Adansonia digitata.* — VIN. Bread made from the seeds of *Lolium perenne.*

PAINTED. When colours are disposed in streaks of unequal intensity.

PAINTED-CUP. An American name for *Castilleja.*

PAIRED. The same as Conjugate.

PAJANELIA. A genus of *Bignoniaceœ*, confined to the East Indies, and consisting of two species, *P. multijuga* and *P. Rheedii*, both of which are gigantic trees, with imparipinnate leaves two to three feet long, ovate or cordate leaflets, and large panicles bearing purplish flowers. The calyx is distinctly five-cornered, and terminates in five acute teeth ; the corolla is leathery and bell-shaped ; the stamens are four in number; and the capsule is flat, and has two broad wings, by which the genus may at once be distinguished from *Cuspidaria*, which has four wings, and from all other *Bignoniaceœ*, destitute as they are of any wing-like appendices. 　　　[B. S.]

PALA. An Indian name for *Wrightia tinctoria.*

PALANDOO. An Eastern name for Onions.

PALAFOXIA. A genus of *Compositœ* of the tribe *Helianiheœ*, allied to *Gaillardia* in the naked receptacle and long filiform branches of the style, but the pappus scales are awnless, and the habit is very different. There are half a dozen species, natives of Mexico or Texas, herbs or suffruticose plants with a minute ashy pubescence, linear or lanceolate entire leaves,

and loosely paniculate or corymbose rather small flower-heads, with the florets white flesh-coloured or purple.

PALARIS. A root which is perfectly continuous with the stem. *Palari-ramose* is applied to a root which is palar, and produces numerous branches from its sides.

PALASA. An Indian name for *Butea frondosa.*

PALASS-GOOND. Bengal Kino, the produce of *Butea frondosa.*

PALATE. The prominent lower lip of a ringent corolla.

PALAVA, or PALAVIA. A genus of Peruvian herbaceous plants of the family *Malvaceœ*. The flowers are small, purple, on long axillary stalks, and unprovided with any outer calyx. This character, combined with the numerous one-seeded indehiscent carpels, suffices to distinguish the genus from its allies. 　　　[M. T. M.]

PALAWAH. A beautiful heavy red wood of Burmah.

PALAY. An Indian name for *Cryptostegia grandiflora.*

PALEACEOUS. Covered with paleæ, as the receptacle of many Composites.

PALEÆ, or PALES (adj. PALEACEOUS). Membranous scales resembling chaff. The inner scales of the flower in grasses are pales.

PALEÆFORM. Resembling paleæ or chaff, as Ramenta: which see.

PALEOLÆ. The hypogynous scales of grasses.

PALETUVIER. A French name for several woods of Guiana. —, MOUNTAIN. *Clusia flava.* —, RED. *Rhizophora Mangle.* —, SOLDIER. *Laguncularia racemosa.* —, WHITE. *Avicennia nitida.*

PALICOUREA. A genus of cinchonaceous shrubs, natives of tropical America, with opposite or whorled leaves, and yellow or white flowers variously arranged. The genus is nearly allied to *Psychotria*, differing mainly in the corolla, whose tube is distended or somewhat curved at the base and hairy within, and the limb with five short erect lobes. Two or three species are grown as stove-plants. 　　　[M. T. M.]

PALILLO. A Peruvian name for *Compananesia lineatifolia.*

PALISOTA. A genus of *Commelynaceœ*, with the perianth and ovary as in *Commelyna*, and having three stamens, one larger than the others, adherent to the ovary, with a thick filament and broad anther, the other two with filiform filaments and narrow lanceolate anthers. The habit is that of *Aneilema*. 　　　[J. T. S]

PALISSANDER. A name used in France for Rosewood ; and sometimes applied to Striped Ebony and Violet-wood.

PALIURUS. A genus of *Rhamnaceœ*,

P. aculeatus, commonly called Christ's Thorn, is a native of Southern Europe and Western Asia, and is a shrub, as also is *P. virgatus* a native of Nepal; while *P. Aubletii*, a Chinese species, is a moderate-sized tree. They have alternate simple three-nerved leaves, with stipules which ultimately become converted into prickles; and their flowers have a spreading five-cleft calyx, five petals, as many stamens, and a three-celled ovary half immersed in the flat disk, and bearing three oblong stigmas. The genus, however, is best distinguished by its dry hemispherical fruit; which is three-celled at the base and expanded at the top into a broad thin rim; the entire fruit resembling a head with a broad-brimmed hat on, giving rise to the French name, Porte-chapeau, given to *P. aculeatus.*

Some difference of opinion exists with regard to the identification of the plant which afforded the thorns used for plaiting the crown placed upon Christ's head before His crucifixion. Two common eastern plants usually bear the name of Christ's Thorn : one the *Zizyphus Spina-Christi*, and the other the present plant. This is a native of the countries bordering on the Mediterranean and of Western Asia to as far east as the Punjab. It has flexible branches, capable of being easily plaited ; and each leaf has two stout sharp spines at its base, one of which is straight and erect, and the other curved and bent downwards so as to form a hook. It is commonly used for hedges, and its seeds are considered medicinal by Turkish doctors, and are also used as a dye.   [A. S.]

PALM. The popular name for the plants belonging to the PALMACEÆ ; also popularly applied to *Salix Caprea* when in flower. —, ASSAI. *Euterpe edulis.* —, BETEL-NUT. *Areca Catechu* —, BOURBON. *Latania.* —, BROOM. *Attalea funifera*; also *Thrinax argentea.* —, BUSSU. *Manicaria saccifera.* —, CABBAGE. *Oreodoxa* or *Areca oleracea.* —, CARANA. *Mauritia Carana.* —, CARNAUBA. *Copernicia cerifera.* —, CATECHU. *Areca Catechu.* —, COCOA-NUT. *Cocos nucifera.* —, COHUNE. *Attalea Cohune.* —, COQUITO. *Jubæa spectabilis.* —, DATE. *Phœnix dactylifera.* —, DELEB. *Borassus(?)æthiopum.* —, DOOM, or DOUM. *Hyphæne thebaica.* — DRAGON'S-BLOOD. *Calamus Draco.* —, FAN. *Corypha.* —, —, EUROPEAN. *Chamærops humilis.* —, —, INDIAN. *Chamærops excelsa.* —, JAMAICA. *Sabal Blackburniana.* —, GEBANG. *Corypha Gebanga.* —, GOMUTI, or GOMUTO. *Saguerus saccharifer.* —, HEMP. *Chamærops excelsa.* —, IVORY. *Phytelephas macrocarpa.* —, ITA. *Mauritia flexuosa.* —, IU. *Astrocaryum acaule.* —, JARA. *Leopoldinia pulchra.* —, JUPATI. *Raphia tædigera.* —, MACAW. *Acrocomia sclerocarpa.* —, MIRITI. *Mauritia flexuosa.* —, MURUMURU. *Astrocaryum Murumuru.* —, NIBUNG, or NIBONG. *Oncosperma filamentosa.* —, OIL. *Elæis guineensis.* —, PALMETTO. *Sabal* or *Chamærops Palmetto.* —, PALMYRA. *Borassus flabelliformis.* —, PASHIUBA, or PAXIUBA. *Iriartea exor-*

rhiza. —, PATAWA. *Œnocarpus Batava.* —, PEACH. *Guilielma speciosa.* —, PIASSABA. *Attalea funifera*; also *Leopoldinia Piassaba.* —, PINANG. *Areca Catechu.* —, RATTAN. *Calamus Rotang, rudentum*, and other species. —, SAGO. *Sagus Rumphii* and *S. lævis.* —, TALIERA. *Corypha Taliera.* —, TALIPOT. *Corypha umbraculifera.* —, THATCH. *Sabal Blackburniana.* —, TUCUMA. *Astrocaryum Tucuma.* —, WAX. *Ceroxylon* or *Iriartea andicola*: —, of Brazil. *Copernicia cerifera.* —, WINE. *Cocos butyracea.* —, ZANORA. *Iriartea exorrhiza.*

PALM (adj. PALMARIS). Three inches, or the breadth of the four fingers of the hand.

PALMACEÆ. (*Palmæ, Palms.*) A natural order of petaloid monocotyledonous plants belonging to Lindley's palmal alliance of hypogynous Endogens. The flowers are bisexual unisexual or polygamous, on a terminal often-branched spadix, enclosed in a one or many-valved spathe. Perianth six-parted, the three inner segments often larger, and sometimes deeply connate ; stamens inserted into the base of the perianth; ovary free, usually composed of three carpels, more or less completely united. Fruit drupaceous or nut-like, or baccate, often with a fibrous covering ; seed with cartilaginous or horny albumen ; embryo small. They are arborescent plants, with simple rarely branched trunks, marked with the scars of the leaves, which are terminal, pinnate or fan-shaped, with plicate vernation and parallel simple veins, and often with spiny petioles. Natives of tropical regions chiefly, they impart to them much of their botanical physiognomy. Most of them have unbranched stems, attaining sometimes a height of 100 feet, and sending out clusters of large leaves, from the axil of which bunches of flowers proceed. Although the flowers are small, still the inflorescence, taken collectively, has often a most imposing aspect. Linnæus called them the Princes of the Vegetable Kingdom. Martius estimates the species at nearly 600, of which about one-sixth have fan-shaped leaves. They have been divided by him into various tribes, depending chiefly on the nature of the ovary ovules and fruit ; and sections are formed according as the leaves are pinnate or flabelliform, and the stems are spiny or not.

The properties of the plants of this order are very various. In the countries in which they grow they are used for supplying food and for forming habitations. The fruit of some is eatable. Many supply oil, wax, starchy matter, and sugar, which latter is fermented so as to form an intoxicating beverage. Their fibres are employed for ropes, and the reticulum surrounding their leaves is sometimes manufactured into brushes.

The Palm of the Bible seems to be *Phœnix dactylifera*, the drupaceous fruit of which supplies food to many of the inhabitants of Arabia and Africa. *Cocos nucifera*, the cocoa-nut palm, is one of the most useful, supplying food, clothing, materials for houses, and utensils of various kinds, ropes, and oil. The palm-oil imported from the West Coast of Africa is obtained by bruising the fruits of *Elæis guineensis* and *E. melanococca*. The betel-nut is the produce of *Areca Catechu*, and from it an extract is prepared of an astringent nature resembling catechu. Fine sago is said to be procured from *Sagus lœvis* and *S. Rumphii*, found in the eastern islands of the Indian Ocean. Sago, as well as sugar and a kind of palm-wine, are procured from *Caryota urens*. The date-sugar of Bengal is the produce of *Phœnix sylvestris*. *Ceroxylon* or *Iriartea andicola* yields wax, which forms a coating over its trunk. *Copernicia cerifera* is another wax-palm. *Calamus Rotang* is used as cane under the name of rattans. *Calamus rudentum*, the cable cane, a native of the East Indies, Cochin-China, and the Moluccas, grows sometimes to the length of 500 feet. The fruit of *Attalea funifera* is known by the name of coquilla-nut, and its hard pericarp is used for making umbrella-handles, &c. The spathe of *Manicaria saccifera* comes off in the form of a conical cap, and is used as a covering for the head in the West Indies. *Chamœrops humilis* is the only European species of palm. The doom-palm of Egypt (*Hyphœne-thebaica*) has a trunk which divides in a dichotomous manner; its pericarp is used as food, and has the taste of gingerbread. In the parched districts between the rivers Dande and Zenza, in tropical Africa, Welwitsch came upon a palm forest five leagues in length, which consisted exclusively of the crowded stems of a branched palm belonging probably to *Hyphœne*. Like most African palms, this yields an excellent wine. *Areca, Caryota, Sagus, Borassus, Corypha, Phœnix, Cocos*, and *Elœis* are examples of the genera. See Plates 7, 11, 12, 13, and 18 for illustrations of this family. [J. H. B.]

PALMA-CHRISTI. *Ricinus communis.*

PALMATE. Having five lobes, the midribs of which meet in a common point, so that the whole bears some resemblance to a human hand; as the leaf of the Maple.

PALMATIFID. Cut halfway down in a palmate manner. *Palmatilobed* means cut into shallow divisions in a palmate manner; *palmatiparted*, or *palmatisected*, cut nearly to the base in a palmate manner—a near approach to digitate.

PALM BUTTER. The same as Palm Oil.

PALMIFORM, PALMATIFORM. When numerous ribs of a leaf are arranged as in the palmate form, radiating from the top of the petiole.

PALMINERVED. The same as Palm-veined.

PALMELLEÆ. A natural order of green-spored *Algæ*, characterised by the plants being composed of free or merely conglomerated cells propagated by the organisation of their endochrome, which is mostly quaternary, and sometimes transformed into zoospores. In some species, as *P. botryoides*, though the propagation takes place by division of the endochrome, a portion of the original hyaline stem always separates at the same time, so that we have a dichotomous structure. The endochromes are not always green: indeed, various colours, as blue, yellow, &c., are assumed by some of the more obscure species. Many productions assigned to this order are doubtless mere transitional states of higher plants. The gonidia of some of the gelatinous lichens are multiplied like *Palmella* and *Hæmatococcus*, while the greater part follow *Nostochineæ*. *Protococcus nivalis*, or the Red Snow, is one of the most generally known examples of the order, though several, like the bloodstains at the base of walls, *Protococcus cruentus*, are amongst the commonest *Algæ*. [M. J. B.]

PALMETTO. A common name for several of the Fan-palms, but especially *Sabal Palmetto*. —, HUMBLE. *Carludovica insignis*. —, ROYAL. *Thrinax parviflora*, and *Sabal umbraculifera*. —, SILVER-LEAVED. *Thrinax argentea*. —, SMALL. *Carludovica*.

PALMIER À ÉVENTAIL, or P. NAIN. (Fr.) *Chamœrops humilis*.

PALMISTÉ. (Fr.) *Chamœrops*.

PALM-VEINED. Having the principal veins radiating from a common point.

PALMYRA-WOOD. A name given to the woody parts of the trunks of *Cocos nucifera* and *Borassus flabelliformis*.

PALO. A diuretic extract obtained from *Tinospora cordifolia*. — BLANCO. A Chilian name for *Flotovia diacanthoides*. — COTO. *Sargassum bacciferum*, and other South American seaweeds. — DE BUBA. *Jacaranda filicifolia*. — DE CRUZ. *Brownea grandiceps*. — DE LOS BRUJOS. *Lycioplesium pubiflorum*. — DE PAN. *Artocarpus incisa*. — DE SAN JUAN. *Lasionema roseum*. — DE VACA. *Brosimum Galactodendron*. — DE VELAS. *Parmentiera cerifera*. — MATO. *Lycioplesium pubiflorum*, the Tree of the Magicians. — NEGRO. *Euxenia grata*. — SANTO. A Paraguay name for Lignum-vitæ.

PALOMBINA. A sort of grape cultivated in Italy.

PALOMMIER. (Fr.) *Gaultheria*.

PALSYWORT. *Primula veris*.

PALUDOSE, PALUSTRIS. Growing in marshy places.

PALUNG. An Indian name for a native Beetroot.

PALUNGEO. An Indian name for the fibre of *Hibiscus cannabinus*.

PAMELLE. (Fr.) *Hordeum distichon*.

PAMEROON-BARK. *Moschoxylon Swartzii*.

PAMPELMOUSE, or **POMPELMOOSE.**

(Fr.) The fruit of the Shaddock, *Citrus decumana.*

PAMPHILIA. A genus of Brazilian trees of the family *Styracaceæ*. The surface of the plants is densely covered with ruddy-coloured woolly hairs; flowers in axillary clusters; calyx bell-shaped, five-toothed; corolla five-cleft, twice the length of the calyx, its segments bent inwards; stamens five, the filaments united below, shorter than the anthers, which are united at their backs by a membranous prolongation of the filaments: ovary free, three-celled: ovules erect, solitary; style one; stigma three-lobed.   [M. T. M.]

PANAIS. (Fr.) *Pastinaca.*

PANAX. A genus of *Araliaceæ*, comprising herbs, shrubs, or trees, natives of tropical and Northern Asia and America. The leaves are usually palmately compound with sheathing leafstalks; and their flowers greenish, arranged in an umbellate manner on branching flower-stalks. They have five spreading petals, five stamens, and eight styles, two with simple stigmas. The fruit is succulent, orbicular or divided into two lobes, rarely cylindrical, crowned by a fleshy disk, and divided internally into two one-seeded compartments.

The name *Panax* is an adaptation of the Greek word *panakés*, signifying a panacea, or remedy for all complaints, in allusion to the supposed or real virtues possessed by some of these plants. Thus the root of *P. Schinseng* is highly esteemed by Chinese physicians, who affirm that it is able to ward off or remove fatigue, to invigorate the enfeebled frame, to restore the exhausted animal powers, to make old people young, and in a word to render man immortal *if anything on earth can do so.* Hence the name Ginseng, which signifies 'Wonder of the World.' At Pekin it is said sometimes to have been worth its weight in gold. In Europe the root has failed to pro-

Panax quinquefolium.

duce any remarkable effects, though it is described as mucilaginous, bitter, and slightly aromatic. It is a native of Northern Asia. *P. quinquefolium*, a native of

North America, has been sometimes confounded with the foregoing. Its roots are exported from America to China, where they are highly valued. *P. fruticosum, P. cochleatum,* and *P. Anisum* have all aromatic properties. Some of the species are cultivated as objects of curiosity in this country.   [M. T. M.]

PANCE, PAUNCE, or PAWNCE. *Viola tricolor.*

PANCRAIS. (Fr.) *Pancratium.*

PANCRATIUM. A genus of *Amaryllidaceæ*, and the type of the pancratiform section of the order, distinguished by the presence of a cup or coronet, on which the stamens are borne. There are about

Pancratium maritimum.

half a dozen species found in South Europe, North Africa, Syria, Arabia, and Carolina, and as many more in India and the adjacent islands. They are bulbous plants, with lorate deciduous or persistent leaves, and an umbel of white flowers terminating a solid scape. The perianth tube is straight and elongated with a funnel-shaped throat, the limb six-parted and spreading, and the cup conspicuous funnel-shaped six-lobed, bearing six stamens between the lobes. The ovary is three-celled, with many ovules in each cell. The European *P. maritimum*, though not now regarded as official, has properties resembling those of the squill. It and *P. illyricum* may be grown at the foot of a wall. The tropical species form handsome stove-plants. Many of the latter are now separated under the name of *Hymenocallis.*   [T. M.]

PANDANACEÆ. (*Cyclantheæ, Freycinetieæ, Screwpines.*) A natural order of monocotyledonous plants, belonging to Lindley's aral alliance of Endogens. They are trees or bushes, sometimes with adventitious roots, long imbricated amplexicaul leaves, usually with spiny margins and backs, and unisexual or polygamous flowers, covering the whole of the spadix. Perianth none, or a few scales. Male flowers: stamens numerous; filaments with single two to four-celled anthers. Female flowers: ovaries one-celled, united in parcels; the ovules solitary or numerous, and the stigmas sessile, equal to the carpels in number. Fruit either fibrous drupes collected into parcels, or berries; seeds solitary in the drupes, numerous in the berries; embryo minute. They are natives of tropical regions, and are arranged in two sections:—*Pandaneæ*, with undivided leaves and no perianth; and *Cyclantheæ*, with fan-shaped or pinnate leaves, and scaly flowers. The limits of the genera are not very clearly settled, but examples occur in *Carludovica*, *Pandanus*, and *Nipa*. The flowers of some of the plants are fragrant; the seeds of *Pandanus* are used as food; and the juice has in some instances a stringent properties.　　　　　　　　[J. H. B.]

PANDANUS. One of the two simple-leaved genera of *Pandanaceæ*, and the principal genus of the order. It is distinguished by its male and female flowers being always on separate plants; and by the male inflorescence being a compound spadix made up of a number of short catkin-like spikes, each of which bears an immense number of little naked flowers, with indefinite stamens; and the female a globular or oblong head consisting of very numerous closely-packed ovaries, each containing a single ovule. There are a considerable number of species, perhaps thirty or more, all of which are confined to the eastern hemisphere, and a very large proportion of them to the islands of the Indian Archipelago, and the Mascaren Islands, abounding principally in the vicinity of the sea, and sometimes covering large tracts of country

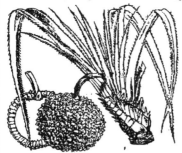

Pandanus utilis.

with an almost impenetrable mass of vegetation. Some grow to a large size, forming trees with much-branched stems, the latter being an uncommon circumstance amongst trees of the orders to which the *Pandanaceæ* are allied. The majority, however, are large bushes about ten or fifteen feet high. Their leaves—which are very long and narrow, tough and leathery, and armed along the midrib and edges with

sharp recurved prickles—are arranged in a triple spiral series towards the ends of the branches, forming dense tufts or crowns; it is from their resemblance to those of the pine-apple that the name Screwpine is derived. The lower parts of the branches and stem are naked, but densely marked with the annular scars left by the clasping bases of fallen leaves. Their fruits consist of a number of wedge-shaped clusters of drupes congregated into often large cone-like heads.

The species of *Pandanus* are remarkable for their aerial roots, with large cup-like spongioles. *P. Candelabrum* is the Chandelier-tree of Guiana, and is so called on account of its mode of branching. The most useful is *P. utilis*, the Vacona or Bacona of the Mauritius, in which island it is not only a very common wild plant, but is largely cultivated for the sake of its leaves, which are extensively consumed in the manufacture of the bags or sacks in which sugar is exported. It is of these sacks, when done with as sugar-sacks, that the well-known flat square fish-bags, commonly used in our markets, are made. The fruit of *P. fœtidus* is extremely fœtid, while the flowers of *P. odoratissimus* are very fragrant. The seeds of some are eaten. Several are very ornamental in our hothouses. See Plates 2 c, 6 g, 7 g, and 13 a.　　　[A. S.]

PANDIPAVE. (Fr.) *Momordica Charantia.*

PANDOREA. The only genus of *Bignoniaceæ* with twining branches, like those of a *Convolvulus*, and consisting of only three species: two of which, *P. australis* (*Bignonia* or *Tecoma australis* of some writers) and *P. jasminoides* (*Tecoma jasminoides* of Lindley), are widely distributed over the eastern part of New Holland; whilst a third species, *P. leptophylla* (*Tecoma leptophylla* of Blume), is confined to New Guinea. The two former species are inmates of our conservatories, and esteemed on account of their handsome pink flowers, and graceful branches. *P. australis* is a very variable plant in foliage, and goes under the various names of *Tecoma Oxleyi, floribunda, diversifolia,* and *ochromantha*. In Port Jackson, the children amuse themselves by launching the fruit, split in halves, in the water, and then term it 'boats and cargo.' *Pandorea* has a cup-shaped irregularly splitting calyx, a funnel-shaped corolla, five stamens (one of which is abortive, and two of the fertile ones shorter than the others), glabrous anthers, and an oblong two-celled capsule, the partition of which runs contrary to the direction of its valves, with winged seeds arranged in several rows on either side of the partition.　　　[B. S.]

PANDURATE, PANDURIFORM. The same as Fiddle-shaped.

PANGIACEÆ. (*Pangiads.*) A natural order of calycifloral dicotyledons belonging to Lindley's papayal alliance of diclinous Exogens. It is nearly allied to *Papayaceæ*, and by some is considered a suborder of that family. Trees with alternate stalked leaves, and axillary solitary or clustered unisexual flowers. Sepals five, rarely two three or four ; petals five, rarely six, with scales placed opposite them ; stamens five or numerous ; ovary free, one-celled ; ovules numerous ; placentas parietal. Fruit one-celled, succulent, indehiscent ; seeds numerous ; albumen oily ; embryo large. Natives of warm parts of India. *Hydnocarpus venenatus* bears poisonous fruit ; *Gynocardia odorata* yields chaulmoogra seeds, used in India for skin diseases. *Pangium, Hydnocarpus, Gynocardia,* and *Bergamia* are the only genera, and there are very few species. [J. H. B.]

PANGIUM. A Javanese tree, which gives its name to a small natural order, regarded by some botanists as a tribe of *Flacourtiaceæ,* differing in the petals bearing each a scale at the base. The leaves are alternate entire or three-lobed ; the flowers diœcious and axillary : the males in racemes, the females solitary. The tree, known in its native country under the name of Pangi, is said to have a hard solid wood ; the bark and leaves contain a poisonous principle, but the kernels of the seeds, when boiled, cut to pieces, and macerated in cold water to remove their noxious narcotic qualities, are occasionally used as a condiment, although rarely on account of their prejudicial effects on persons unaccustomed to them.

PANICAUT. (Fr.) *Eryngium.*

PANICLE. A branched raceme.

PANICUM. A very extensive genus of grasses, of the tribe *Paniceæ,* the essential character of which consists in the plants belonging to it having spikelets or locustæ, of two flowers, one perfect and the other imperfect, the latter having stamens only or neuter. Steudel describes 850 species under this genus, divided into eighteen sections, many of the heads of sections being distinct genera of other authors. Their geographical range is extensive, but they are chiefly natives of the tropical and subtropical regions of the earth, where in many instances one or other of the species constitute the principal fodder-grasses. For example, the Caapim de Angola, *Panicum spectabile,* grows from six to seven feet high in Brazil, according to Nees von Esenbach, as quoted by Dr. Lindley, whilst other equally gigantic species form the field-crops on the banks of the Amazons. *P. miliaceum,* called Warree, and *P. pilosum,* called Bhadlee, are both extensively grown in India ; while in the Deccan *P. frumentaceum,* called Shamoola, is also grown. [D. M.]

PANIZA. A Spanish name for Millet.

PANKE. *Gunnera scabra.*

PANJAM. The resinous gum of *Diospyros Embryopteris.*

PANMUHOOREE. An Indian name for *Fœniculum Panmorium.*

PANNA-MARAM. A Tamil name for *Borassus flabelliformis.*

PANNOSE. Having the texture of coarse cloth.

PANOCOCO. A French name for *Ormosia coccinea* ; also for *Swartzia tomentosa.*

PANSURI. Pens made from the midribs of the leaflets of *Arenga saccharifera.*

PANSY. *Viola tricolor.*

PANTOUFLE DE NOTRE DAME. (Fr.) *Cypripedium.*

PANUS. A genus closely allied to *Agaricus,* but of a more leathery persistent texture. Two or three species resemble *Agaricus ostreatus,* but are too tough to be eatable. *P. stypticus* is one of the most characteristic species, with its little fan-shaped mealy or bran-like brownish pileus and abrupt stem, growing gregariously on old oak-stumps or other wood. [M. J. B.]

PANYALA. An Indian name for *Flacourtia cataphracta.*

PAO CRAVO. A Portuguese name for *Dicypellium caryophyllatum,* which produces clove-bark. — D'ARCO. A species of *Bignonia.* — DE COBRA. The wood of *Strychnos colubrinum.* — DE GUARANA. Cakes prepared from *Paullinia sorbilis.* — DE ROSA. The beautiful rose-coloured wood of *Physocalymma floribunda.* — DE TINGUY. *Magonia pubescens.*

PAPANGAIE. (Fr.) *Luffa ægyptiaca.*

PAPANGAY, or PAPONGE. (Fr.) *Cucumis acutangulus.*

PAPAREH. (Fr.) *Momordica Charantia.*

PAPAVERACEÆ. (*Poppyworts.*) A natural order of thalamifloral dicotyledons, belonging to Lindley's ranal alliance of hypogynous Exogens. They consist of herbs or shrubs, usually with milky or coloured juice, having alternate exstipulate leaves, and long one-flowered peduncles. Sepals two, deciduous ; petals hypogynous, usually four, cruciate—sometimes a multiple of four, regular ; stamens hypogynous, usually indefinite ; ovary solitary, the style short or none ; stigmas two, or many and radiating ; ovules one-celled, anatropal. Fruit either siliquiform with two, or capsular with several, parietal placentas ; seeds numerous. The species are chiefly European, but are found scattered over tropical America, Asia, China, New Holland, Cape of Good Hope, &c. The order possesses well-marked narcotic properties. Opium is the concrete milky juice procured from the unripe capsules of *Papaver somniferum* and its varieties. There are about a score of genera, as *Papaver, Eschscholtzia, Argemone, Platystemon,* and *Chelidonium,* and nearly 150 species. [J. H. B.]

PAPAVER. A well-known genus typical of the *Papaveraceæ,* consisting of herbs with a milky juice, distributed over Europe and temperate Asia chiefly, though one or two are described as natives of Australia and South Africa. Some of the species, however, are to be met with in many other parts of the globe, to which they have been introduced by cultivation or commercial intercourse. The roots are fibrous; the leaves generally lobed or toothed, and hairy; the flower-stalks axillary, solitary without bracts, but terminated by a single flower, with two or three concave deciduous sepals, four or six petals, very numerous stamens, and an ovary of four or more carpels conjoined, and capped by a radiating compound stigma. The fruit is capsular, with parietal placentæ projecting into the interior, opening by pores or short valves, beneath the projecting margin of the stigma.

The Field Poppy, *P. Rhœas*, one of the most brilliant of our wild plants, decorating cornfields, railway-banks, and waste places with a perfect blaze of crimson flowers, is distinguished from the other British species by its smooth and globular fruits, and by the bristles which clothe the stem spreading out almost at right angles with it. The petals are collected for the purpose of making a coloured syrup, which has at the same time very slight narcotic properties. The seeds might possibly be used for the oil they contain, and they are by no means destitute of nutritive properties. Double-flowered varieties of various colours are not unfrequently grown in gardens as highly ornamental annual plants. *P. dubium*, frequently met with in some parts of the country, is a smaller more slender plant than *P. Rhœas*, and may be at once distinguished by the capsule which is twice as long as broad, and by the bristles which are flattened up against the stem. *P. hybridum* is less branched than the Field Poppy, which it greatly resembles, but differs in the filaments of the stamens, which are dilated from below upwards, and in the capsule, which, though globular, is covered with stiff bristles. This species is rare in this country. *P. Argemone* is the smallest of the British poppies; its capsule is in shape like that of *P. dubium*, but it has a few stiff hairs or bristles which are directed upwards. Several species are cultivated in English gardens for ornamental purposes, the most beautiful being *P. orientale*, and some varieties of the Opium Poppy. A variety of the former, with the petals united so as to form a funnel-shaped corolla, has been recently introduced.

The Opium Poppy, *P. somniferum*, is supposed originally to have been a native of the Levant, but is now widely distributed. The writer has observed it growing on the cliffs between Folkestone and Dover, and also in other places where it had more obviously been introduced. The plant varies much in the colour of its flowers and seeds, and in gardens double varieties are common. In general it forms an erect annual plant, slightly branched, about two feet in height, with the stem and leaves of a glaucous green colour, usually without bristles, but sometimes, especially in wild specimens, with a few straggling hairs. The leaves are oblong in shape, irregularly sinuous at the margin, and clasp the stem by their base. The flowers are usually of a light-violet colour with a purple centre. The Opium Poppy is cultivated in this country for the sake of its capsules, from which syrup of poppies is prepared, a favourite remedy for children when a sedative is required; but owing to the varying strength of the preparation, its liability to adulteration with laudanum, &c., and the frequent great susceptibility of children to the influence of opium in any shape, it should be used only with great caution, and its operation should be carefully watched. A decoction of poppy-heads is often employed as an anodyne fomentation, and with excellent effect; an extract of poppy-heads is also occasionally used in minute doses in place of opium.

The seeds contain a large quantity of oil, which is extracted as an article of food, and for the use of painters. Olive oil is stated to be adulterated with it; an intermixture of comparatively little consequence, as the oil is destitute of narcotic properties. The seeds themselves, in Greece, Poland, and elsewhere, are eaten as articles of food, and have an agreeable nut-like flavour.

It is, however, for producing opium that this plant is especially cultivated in India, Persia, Asia Minor, Egypt, &c., and it seems to have been cultivated for this purpose from the earliest times of which we have any record, at least so far as Greece is concerned. The word opium is derived from the Greek *opos*, juice, as being the especial juice, just as cinchona bark is called bark.

Two varieties of the plant are cultivated for the production of opium, one with violet-coloured or white flowers and black seeds, the other with white seeds and flowers. These two kinds are mentioned by Hippocrates. The latter is the one most generally cultivated in India. A very full account of the manufacture, as well as of the properties of opium, is contained in Dr. Pereira's *Materia Medica*, and in the *Pharmaceutical Journal* for 1852. From these sources, as well as from the *Kew Garden Miscellany* (vol. vi.), the following remarks have been condensed. The preparation of the drug seems to be conducted in much the same way in the various districts whence opium is obtained, but in some much greater care is taken than in others. In India a very large extent of country is devoted to the cultivation of the Opium Poppy, and at Behar and Benares are government agencies established for the purpose of regulating the manufacture, insuring the purity of the drug, &c. When the flowers are in bloom the first step is the removal of the petals, which are used in packing the prepared drug. After a few days the imperfectly ripened capsules are scarified from above downwards by two or three knives tied together and called 'nushturs.' These make a superficial incision, or series of incisions, into the capsule, whereupon a milky juice exudes, which is allowed to harden and is then removed and collected in earthen pots. The time of day chosen for slicing the capsules is about three o'clock in the afternoon, when the heat of the sun causes the speedy formation of a film over the exuded juice, great attention is also paid to the weather, prevailing winds, dew, &c., as all these causes modify the quantity, quality, or speediness of exudation of the opium.

The capsules are submitted to two or three slicing processes at intervals of a few days, and the drug is ultimately conveyed to the government factory, where it is kneaded into a homogeneous mass by native workmen. It is analysed by native examiners, whose tact and experience are such that the results of their examination differ but very slightly from those afforded by the more scientific investigation of the European officers. In this manner the quality of the drug is ascertained, its freedom from adulteration insured, and its strength reduced as nearly as may be to a uniform standard. When thus prepared, the drug is in a fit state for exportation; and it is then, by means of earthen cups, moulded into spherical masses of the size of a child's head, closely invested on the outside by the dried petals of the flower, compacted together by pressure and by immersion into the gummy fluid residue which drains off from the more solid opium during its preparation. It is remarkable that the natives and government officials, who thus are exposed to the fumes of this drug for several hours daily, and this at a temperature of 90° to 100° and upwards, are seldom injuriously affected: some of the operators are literally immersed in opium for several hours daily, so far as regards their legs and arms, and yet slight drowsiness at the end of the day is the sole inconvenience ever experienced, and this by no means frequently.

The Indian opium is exported in enormous quantities to China, in spite of the prohibition of the Chinese government, and its vigorous attempts to prevent the introduction of the drug. Comparatively little Indian opium finds its way into the British markets, where the most esteemed and most largely used kind is known as Smyrna or Turkey Opium. This is imported in irregular masses covered on the outside with dock-seeds. It is frequently adulterated. Other kinds of opium are occasionally imported, but in small quantities. Opium has been prepared of very good quality in this country, but its preparation is not profitable.

The chemical constitution of opium is somewhat intricate and variable; its medicinal effects, however, are mainly due to the presence of an alkaloid called *morphia*. To external appearance opium is a reddish-brown sticky gumlike substance, with a bitter taste, and a peculiar unmistakable perfume. It is beyond all doubt the most valuable of all drugs, and may be used with advantage in an immense number of conditions: to relieve pain, allay spasm, promote sleep, relieve restlessness, produce perspiration, or check excessive discharges. In small doses its effects are those of a stimulant, followed by depression; in larger doses constipation, perspi-

ration, contracted pupils, and somnolency are induced, and in still larger quantities coma and death. These matters, however, as well as the effects of the habitual use of opium internally, or by smoking as practised by the Chinese, hardly come within the limits of this article. The reader is referred to the works already mentioned, and to De Quincey's *Confessions of an Opium Eater*. It is necessary, however, to caution the general reader against accepting as ordinary occurrences those that are exceptional. [M. T M.]

PAPAW. A tropical fruit, the produce of *Carica Papaya*. — NORTH AMERICAN. *Asimina triloba*.

PAPAYACEÆ. (*Cariceæ, Modecceæ, Papayads*.) A natural order of calycifloral dicotyledons belonging to Lindley's papayal alliance of diclinous Exogens. They are trees or shrubs, not branching, with alternate lobed leaves supported on long slender petioles, and with unisexual flowers; and are found in South America and in other warm countries. Calyx minute, five-toothed; corolla monopetalous, inserted into the base of the calyx; in the males tubular and five-lobed, in the females divided nearly to the base into five segments; stamens ten, inserted into the throat of the corolla; ovary free, one-celled; ovules indefinite, attached to five parietal placentæ; stigma five-lobed, lacerated. Fruit usually succulent and indehiscent, sometimes capsular and dehiscent, one-celled; seeds indefinite, enveloped in a loose mucous coat, embryo in the axis of fleshy albumen. One of the most important plants of the order is *Carica Papaya*, the papaw-tree, which yields an acrid milky juice, and an edible fruit. The juice of the unripe fruit is anthelmintic. This tree is said to have the property of rendering meat tender. *Carica* and *Modecca* furnish examples of the few genera, which contain some score or more of species. [J. H. B.]

PAPAYER. (Fr.) *Carica*.

PAPEETA. An Indian name for the St. Ignatius Bean; see IGNATIA.

PAPER-TREE of Siam. *Trophis aspera*.

PAPERY. In texture, the same as Chartaceous.

PAPHINIA *cristata* is a very curious orchid belonging to the *Maxillaridæ* group, native of Trinidad and New Grenada. It forms a peculiar genus, technically distinguished from its allies by having its four pollen-masses attached in two pairs to a long caudicle, setaceous at its apex, and a minute subtriangular gland. The plant has oblong or ovate compressed, two or three-leaved pseudobulbs, from the base of which issue pendulous one or two-flowered peduncles; the flowers large and conspicuous, with similar and nearly equalsized fleshy, widely expanded, lanceolate sepals and petals, curiously streaked or barred and spotted with deep chocolate-brown or purple on a dull white ground, and a singular unguiculate three-parted smallish lip, of a chocolate-purple colour, tipped with a fringe of white filiform glands, and with four similar glands on the claw, and a crest between the side lobes.　　　[A. S.]

PAPILIONACEÆ. A suborder of leguminous plants, characterised by having the flowers papilionaceous, and the petals imbricated in æstivation, the upper one exterior. The flowers are like those of the pea, and consist of five irregular petals, the upper being the vexillum or standard which covers the rest in the bud, the two lateral being alæ or wings, and the inferior the carina or keel, consisting of two petals more or less completely cohering.

The plants of this suborder have frequently beautiful flowers, as in *Cytisus Laburnum, Wistaria, Lupinus, Clianthus, Erythrina* or coral-flower, &c. They are often nutritious, as in the various kinds of clover, bean, pea, medick, lucerne, sainfoin, melilot, &c. Many are used for their medicinal qualities, as in the case of *Glycyrrhiza glabra*, the liquorice; *Astragalus verus, creticus, gummifer*, and others, which yield gum-tragacanth; *Myrospermum peruiferum* and *M. toluiferum*, which yield balsam of Peru and balsam of Tolu; *Pterocarpus Marsupium* and *P. erinaceus*, which furnish kino, &c. Broom-tops, procured from *Sarothamnus scoparius*, are used as a diuretic; the hairs from the legumes of *Mucuna pruriens* in the West Indies, and of *M. prurita* in the East, under the name of cowhage or cowitch, are used as anthelmintics. Others are valuable in commerce and the arts, as furnishing food, dyes, fibres, timber. Various species of *Indigofera*, as *I. tinctoria* and *I. cærulea*, furnish the indigo of commerce; *Pterocarpus santalinus* yields red sandalwood, which is used as a dye; *P. Draco* yields gum-dragon; and, *P. dalbergioides* is said to yield Andaman redwood; *Baptisia tinctoria* gives a blue dye, and is the wild indigo of the United States; *Crotalaria juncea* supplies fibres, which are known as sunn or Bengal hemp; the fragrant seeds of *Dipterix odorata* are known as tonka-beans; a similar fragrance is given out by some species of *Melilotus*; *Arachis hypogæa* produces its legumes underground, and hence receives the name of ground-nut. *Robinia Pseud-acacia*, the locust tree, yields a hard durable wood; according to Bertoloni, a kind of ebony is the produce of *Fornarinia ebenifera*; rosewood is the timber of *Dalbergia, Machærium*, and *Triptolemæa*.

There are certain poisonous plants in this group: thus the seeds and bark of *Cytisus Laburnum* are narcotic, the roots of many species of *Phaseolus*, as *P. multiflorus* (the scarlet-runner) and *P. radiatus*, are poisonous; the branches and leaves of *Tephrosia toxicaria*, and the bark of the root of *Piscidia Erythrina*, are employed as fish-poisons. *Physostigma venenosum* yields the Calabar ordeal bean; *Gompholobium uncinatum* and *Gastrolobium grandiflorum* are deadly sheep poisons in the Australian

colonies. The suborder contains about 350 genera, and about 5,000 species. [J. H. B.]

PAPILIONACEOUS. Having such a corolla as that of the pea.

PAPILLÆ. Soft oblong superficial glands; also the aciculæ of certain fungals.

PAPILLOSE, PAPILLIFEROUS. Covered with minute soft tubercles or excrescences.

PAPOOSE-ROOT. The root of *Caulophyllum thalictroides*.

PAPPEA. A genus of *Sapindaceæ*, the only species of which is a small tree about twenty feet high, a native of the Cape of Good Hope, and hence called *P. capensis*. It has smooth leathery oblong leaves, with the edges bent backwards, and racemes of small unisexual flowers, both the leaves and the racemes of flowers being in clusters at the ends of the branches. The flowers have an unequally five-parted calyx, and four to six petals covered with hairs outside: the males containing eight to ten stamens inserted beneath a ring-like disk, and the females a three-celled ovary with a short style and trifid stigma. Its fruit, which is called Wilde Pruime i.e. Wild Plum) from its plum-like eatable flesh, is formed of three carpels, but two are frequently abortive, and the other contains a single seed. A vinous beverage and excellent vinegar are prepared from the pulp of the fruit, and an eatable though slightly purgative oil is extracted from the seeds, which, besides being used for food, is recommended as a remedy for scald-head and baldness. Its trunk affords a handsome wood, used for small articles of furniture and for ploughs, &c.　　　[A. S.]

PAPPOPHORUM. A genus of grasses of the tribe *Pappophoreæ*. The inflorescence is in contracted spike-like panicles, with the spikelets two to four-flowered, the lower flowers hermaphrodite, the upper sterile; glumes two, the outer shortest; pales two, membranaceous. Steudel describes twenty-seven species, which are mostly natives of New Holland, Africa, and parts of the East Indies.　　　[D. M.]

PAPPUS. The calyx of composites, in which that organ is reduced to a membrane, or scales, or hairs, or a mere rim. *Pappiform* means resembling a pappus.

PAPULÆ (adj. PAPULOSE). The same as Papillæ.

PAPYRACEOUS. Of a papery or chartaceous texture.

PAPYRUS. A genus of cyperaceous plants, belonging to the tribe *Cypereæ*. The inflorescence is in many-flowered spikelets, surrounded by long bracts; glumes imbricated, in two rows, one-flowered; style three-cleft; scales two, membranaceous; ovary without bristles underneath; seed three-cornered. *P. antiquorum*, the Paper Reed, is the plant which yielded the substance used as paper by the ancient

Egyptians. The soboles, or underground rootstocks, spread horizontally under the mud in places where the plant grows, continuing to throw up stems as they creep along. These stems are from eight to ten feet high, a portion of them being above the surface of the water. The paper was made from thin slices, cut vertically from the apex to the base of the stem, between its surface and centre. The slices were placed side by side according to the size required, and then, after being watered and beaten with a wooden instrument until smooth, were pressed and dried in the sun. The stems were likewise used for ornamenting the Egyptian temples, and crowning the statues of their gods. The Paper Reed grows naturally in the south of Italy, as well as on the banks of the Nile and Jordan, but in Britain it requires the aid of a stove to grow it properly, and then it must have a good supply of water. The stems of *P corymbosus* form the Indian matting, of which large quantities are imported. These plants are sometimes still retained in *Cyperus*, the Paper Reed being called *Cyperus Papyrus*. [D.M.]

PÂQUERETTE. (Fr.) *Bellis perennis.*

PÂQUEROLLE. (Fr.) *Bellium.*

PARABOLICAL. Ovate, very obtuse, contracted below the point.

PARACOROLLA. Any appendage of a corolla.

PARADISANTHUS *bahiensis* is a little terrestrial two-leaved stemless orchid, with simple erect spikes of milky-white flowers curiously marked with a succession of deep purple transverse stripes on the sepals and petals, forming circles round the centre of the flower. It has similar and nearly equal sepals and petals, the former connate at the very bottom, and the two lateral ones slightly unequal at the base; a three-lobed articulate lip with a curious pentagonal-mouthed sac on its hind part, at the base of which are a couple of diverging denticulate plates; a semiterete column abruptly bent forward above its middle; and four pyriform pollen-masses, sessile in two pairs upon a markedly transverse triangular gland. [A. S.]

PARAGRAMMA. A group of eastern tropical creeping-stemmed polypodiaceous ferns, usually associated with *Grammitis* or the net-veined *Polypodieæ*; but their constantly elongated sori parallel with the costæ connect them with the *Tæniideæ*. They have simple coriaceous fronds, non-indusiate linear-oblong submarginal sori, and immersed anastomosing veins having free veinlets in the areoles. [T M.]

PARAIBA. A Brazilian name for *Simaruba versicolor*

PARALLELINERVED, PARALLELI-VENOSE. Having the lateral ribs of a leaf straight, as in *Alnus glutinosa*; also having the veins straight and almost parallel but united at the summit, as in grasses.

PARANEMATA. The paraphyses of algals and other cryptogams.

PARAPETALUM. Any appendage of a corolla consisting of several pieces.

PARAPHYLLIA. Stipules.

PARAPHYSES. A name given to the barren threads which separate the asci or sporophores in such fungi as the *Pezizæ* and agarics. The term is also used for the bodies which accompany the archegonia in mosses, or the antheridia or analogous bodies in the fruit of *Balanophoræ*. These bodies are also sometimes called Paranemata. [M. J. B.]

PARASITES. A long treatise might be written on the parasites which affect vegetables, and are scarcely less injurious to them than similar enemies to the animal kingdom. Apart from all the depredations committed by external attacks, there are myriads of larvæ which live within plants, boring into the trunk, devouring the young pith on which the life of the plants depends, burrowing amongst the green cells of their leaves, or causing by their presence the extraordinary growths known under the common name of Galls. Others, as different species of *Vibrio*, exhaust their seeds or deform their roots, while all the fleshy fungi are sooner or later doomed to destruction by their peculiar parasites, even if other causes of decay should cease. Plants suffer, however, no less from members of their own kingdom. *Balanophoræ*, mistletos, *Loranthi*, and a host of other parasites live at their expense; mosses, lichens, and algæ smother their trunks and leaves; while multitudes of fungi live on their juices, or by their presence produce rapid decay. In fruit also, and succulent vegetables where vitality is low, yeast globules are formed from the spores of moulds, and true fermentation takes place, modified according to the different conditions of temperature. The mildew of corn, hops, grapes, and potatos are all so many examples. Death also arises in many instances from the spawn of various fungi, which first attacks the roots, and thence spreads into the inmost tissues. [M. J. B.]

PARASITIC. Growing into some other plant, and deriving food from its juices.

PARASOL CHINOIS. (Fr.) *Sterculia platanifolia.* — DU GRAND SEIGNEUR. *Salix babylonica.*

PARASPERMATIA. Small reproductive bodies found in some algals, and resembling spores.

PARASTAMEN, PARASTEMON. Any kind of abortive stamen.

PARASTYLI. Abortive styles.

PARATODA. A Brazilian name for *Pothomorphe umbellata.*

PARDANTHUS. A genus of *Iridaceæ*, consisting of a few herbaceous species, found in India, China, and Japan, and having rhizomatous stems, two-ranked ensiform leaves, and branching flower-stems bearing orange-coloured flowers spotted with purple. These consist of a six-leaved rotate perianth, with equal segments; three subsecund stamens, with subulate filaments and connivent anthers; a clavate style with three petaloid stigmas; and a three-celled ovary with numerous ovules.   [T. M.]

PARECHITES. A genus of *Apocynaceæ*, better known under the name of *Rhynchospermum*, which, however, must give place to that of *Parechites*, as it is already applied to a genus of *Compositæ*. The species are found in India, China, Japan, and Borneo, and are woody climbers with opposite elliptical or lance-shaped leaves, and yellow white or rosy jasmine-like flowers, arranged in axillary or terminal cymes. They have a five-parted calyx, with a ring of glands inside; a jasmine-like corolla with five arrow-headed stamens inserted about the middle of the tube; and a fruit consisting of two linear nearly cylindrical follicles or pods, four to nine inches long, each containing numerous beaked seeds with a tuft of silky hairs at their apex.

P. *Thunbergii*, well known in gardens as *Rhynchospermum jasminoides*, and cultivated in greenhouses for the sake of its sweet-scented white flowers, is a native of China and Japan. Its leaves are in size and form like those of the privet, only more rigid; while the flowers, which are produced in great profusion at the ends of the branches, are not unlike those of a jasmine, but with a shorter tube. [A. A. B.]

PAREIRA BRAVA. *Cissampelos Pareira.* —, WHITE. A name given by the natives of Cayenne to *Abuta rufescens.*

PARELLE. (Fr.) *Rumex Patientia.* — DES MARAIS. *Rumex Hydrolapathum.*

PARENCHYMA (adj. PARENCHYMATOSE). Cellular tissue which has a spheroidal, not tabular form.

PARIÉTAIRE. (Fr.) *Parietaria officinalis.*

PARIETAL. Growing to the walls or interior surface of an ovary.

PARIETARIA. A genus of herbaceous perennials belonging to the *Urticaceæ*, and distinguished from *Urtica* by having the calyx of the fertile flowers four-cleft, and the style prominent. It is represented in Britain by P. *officinalis*, the Common Pellitory-of-the-wall, a bushy plant from twelve to eighteen inches high, with reddish brittle stems, oblong ovate dull-green leaves, and tufts of small greenish flowers in the axils of the upper leaves. The structure of the flowers is very remarkable. The stamens in their early stage are curved inwards, but when ripe for discharging the pollen expand under the action of the sun or the irritation produced by the introduction of any foreign body, and discharge the pollen in the form of a little cloud of dust. The ashes of the plant are said to contain a quantity of nitre. French, *Pariétaire*; German, *Glaskraut.*   [C. A. J.]

PARIETES. The inside walls of anything.

PARINARIUM. One of the genera of *Chrysobalanaceæ* : it is divided into four sections, characterised by the form of the calyx, and the number of fertile stamens contained in the flowers. The calyx has a long or short tube and is five-cleft; the petals are five in number; the fertile stamens vary from seven to fifteen or an indefinite number, and are either disposed in a complete circle or in a semicircle with sterile ones opposite; and the ovary, which is two-celled, with its stalk adhering to the calyx-tube, ripens into a dry fruit with a thick rind surrounding a two-celled hard rough stone containing two seeds. About twenty species are known, all large trees with feather-veined leaves, and nearly all found in Guiana, Western Africa, and the Malayan Islands.

The fruit of P. *excelsum* is about the size of an Imperatrice plum, covered with a rough skin of a greyish colour, and commonly called the Rough-skin or Grey Plum. It is brought into the markets on the West Coast of Africa, but is not much esteemed on account of the small quantity of eatable matter it contains, which is only the dry farinaceous substance surrounding the large stone. P. *macrophyllum*, another West African species, with a larger fruit than the last, is called the Gingerbread Plum. The leaves of P. *laurinum*, a native of the Feejee and other Polynesian islands, supply the chief material used by the natives for covering the side-walls of houses, its stems also afford them tough spars for their canoes, and from its seeds they obtain a much-esteemed perfume. [A. S.]

PARIPINNATUS. The same as Equally-pinnate.

PARIPOU. *Guilielma speciosa.*

PARIS. An herbaceous perennial belonging to the *Trilliaceæ*, distinguished by having six to ten spreading or reflexed sepals, anthers with their cells fixed one on each side of an awl-shaped filament, and a three to five-celled berry. P. *quadrifolia*, Herb Paris, a native of moist shady woods in many parts of Great Britain, sends up, to the height of a foot, a simple stem, bearing near its summit four whorled large ovate acute leaves, and a single terminal large green flower. The leaves and stems were formerly used in medicine, and the juice of the berry, though considered poisonous, has been employed in curing inflammation in the eyes. French, *Parisette*; German, *Einbeere.*   [C. A. J.]

PARISHIA. A beautiful Malayan tree with pinnate leaves, and large terminal panicles of small flowers, forming a genus of *Anacardiaceæ*, remarkable for the calyx-lobes which after flowering are very much enlarged and foliaceous. In this respect it resembles at first sight *Melanorrhœa*, but in the latter genus it is the petals, not the sepals, that enlarge after flowering, and the flowers are pentamerous, not tetramerous as in *Parishia.*

PARISIOLE. (Fr.) *Trillium.*

PARITIUM. A genus of *Malvaceæ,* one of the many into which the old Linnæan *Hibiscus* has been divided by recent botanists. It is characterised by its flowers having the five-cleft calyx surrounded by an eight or ten-cleft or toothed outer calyx; by the column of stamens being five-toothed at the top, with the five-cleft style protruding out of it, and bearing five round velvety stigmas; and by the capsules being five-celled like those of *Hibiscus,* but having in addition to the five true partitions a spurious partition in the middle of each cell, through which they split open when ripe. The ten or twelve known species are tall trees or high shrubs, widely distributed throughout the tropics of both hemispheres. Their leaves are large entire or lobed, with prominent radiating nerves, one or three of which bear glands at the base.

P. elatum, the Mountain Mahoe, it has recently been ascertained, affords the beautiful lace-like inner bark called Cuba bast, at one time only known as a material used for tying round bundles of genuine

Paritium elatum.

Havannah cigars, but afterwards imported, particularly during the Russian war, as a substitute for the Russia bast used by gardeners for tying up plants. The tree, which is found only in Cuba and Jamaica, grows fifty or sixty feet high, and yields a peculiar greenish-blue timber, highly valued by the Jamaica cabinet-makers. All the species of *Paritium,* particularly *P. tiliaceum,* which is to be found in most tropical countries, afford more or less fibre, which the natives make into ropes, mats, clothing, &c.   [A. S.]

PARKBANE. *Aconitum theriophonum.*

PARKERIA. One of the synonyms of *Ceratopteris:* which see. It was proposed to be made the type of an order, *Parkeria-*

ceæ, but in reality is only a form of *Ceratopteris,* in which the striæ of the ring happen to be reduced to an almost rudimentary condition.   [T. M.]

PARKIA. A small but widely spread genus of *Leguminosæ,* having representatives in Western Africa, India, Java, Brazil, and Surinam. All the species are large unarmed trees, with twice-pinnated glandular-stalked leaves, composed of numerous pairs of leaflets, and small flowers collected into dense heads at the ends of long stalks, the lower ones being males and those above perfect. The tube of the calyx is cylindrical and two-lipped; the five petals are nearly equal, and joined to the middle or free; the ten stamens are connected by their bases; and the pods are stalked, clustered, flat with thick leathery valves, and contain a number of seeds enveloped in farinaceous pulp.

P. africana, the African Locust tree (Nitta or Nuita of the negroes), is a tree attaining thirty or forty feet in height, and having leaves with from twenty to thirty pairs of divisions, each having from thirty to fifty pairs of narrow downy leaflets, the main leafstalk bearing a large gland near the base. Its flower-heads are somewhat pear-shaped, and its pods contain from thirteen to fifteen seeds. The natives of Soudan, who call the tree Doura, roast the seeds and then bruise and allow them to ferment in water until they become putrid, when they are carefully washed, pounded into powder, and made into cakes which are excellent sauce for all kinds of food, but have an unpleasant smell. An agreeable beverage is prepared from the sweet farinaceous pulp surrounding the seeds, and sweetmeats are also made of it. The tree is not only a native of Western Africa but of tropical Asia, and has been carried to tropical America by the negroes.   [A. S.]

PARKINSONIA. A genus of *Leguminosæ,* comprising an ornamental spiny shrub, found in all parts of America between Montevideo and California, and in a cultivated state in most other tropical countries, and a species peculiar to the Cape of Good Hope. Both have abruptly pinnate leaves, with minute leaflets, and racemes of yellow flowers, which have a deeply five-parted calyx, five petals the upper of which is broader and long-clawed, ten distinct stamens bent downwards, and a sessile ovary with a thread-like style. Their narrow pods split into two valves, and contain few or many seeds separated from each other by constrictions in the pod.

P. aculeata—called in Jamaica the Jerusalem Thorn, and in the French West Indian Islands Genet épineux—though originally a native of some part of the American continent, is now found in nearly all tropical countries, where, from its spiny nature, it is used for making hedges; while in Mexico the Indians employ it as a febrifuge and sudorific, and also as a remedy in epilepsy. It grows from twelve to fifteen feet high, and has sweet-smelling flowers, and leaves with winged stalks and blunt leaflets, by which it is distinguished from the Cape of Good Hope species, which has round unwinged stalks and sharp-pointed leaflets. [A. S.]

PARK-LEAVES. *Hypericum Androsæmum.*

PARLATORIA. A genus of *Cruciferæ*, comprising a few annuals from the Levant, with the habit of *Cochlearia* or *Alliaria*, and with white flowers on peduncles which are deflexed after flowering. The pod is articulated to the thickened pedicel, two-valved, with the valves keeled and veined, the partition disappearing. [J. T. S.]

PARMELIACEÆ. An important natural order of lichens with an orbicular or kidney-shaped persistent not deliquescent disk, bordered by the thallus. It contains three very distinct groups :—
1. PELTIGERI, in which the thallus is horizontal, and the disk at first veiled, as in *Peltidea.*
2. EUPARMELIACEI, with the disk at first closed and a horizontal thallus, as in *Lecanora* and *Parmelia.*
3. USNEACEI, with the disk open from the first, and the thallus mostly centripetal, as in *Roccella, Ramalina,* and *Usnea.*

The species of the second division are extremely numerous, and constitute a great portion of the foliaceous lichens which abound everywhere on rocks and trees; while the third supplies the branched or braid-like lichens which hang down from their branches. This order contains almost all the lichens which are useful, either as esculents, medicines, or dyeweeds. [M. J. B.]

PARMELIA. The typical genus of *Parmeliaceæ,* containing an immense number of foliaceous lichens, some of which, as the yellow *P. parietina* and the grey *P. saxatilis,* occur on almost every tree. Many of the species are almost cosmopolites, though others are confined to temperate or tropical districts. Some afford excellent dyeweeds. *P. perlata,* for example, is estimated sometimes at from 190l. to 225l. a ton. [M. J. B.]

PARMENTIERA. A genus of *Crescentiaceæ,* consisting of two American species, and named in honour of the French botanist Aug. Parmentier, who did much for economic botany. *Parmentiera* has a spathaceous, deciduous calyx; an almost bell-shaped corolla, of a white or greenish colour; and a fleshy cylindrical fruit (which may be compared either to a cucumber or a wax-candle), with lentil-like seeds. Indeed, in the Isthmus of Panama, *P. cereifera* is termed the Candle-tree, or Palo de Velas, because its fruits, often four feet long, have quite the appearance of yellow wax-candles, and a person entering the forests which are composed of this tree almost fancies himself in a chandler's shop, for from all the stems and older branches these fruits are suspended. They

have a peculiar apple-like smell, which communicates itself in some degree to the cattle fattened with them, but which disappears if, a few days previous to killing, the food is changed. The fruit of *P. edulis* is eaten by the Mexicans, under the name of Quankhichotl or Cuajilote. Its surface, unlike that of *P. cereifera,* is rough. Both species are middle-sized trees, with either simple or trifoliated leaves, and serrated leaflets. [B. S.]

PARMENTIÈRE. (Fr.) *Solanum tuberosum.*

PARNASSIA. Herbaceous perennials forming a group of *Droseraceæ,* distinguished by having arranged intermediately with the stamens the same number of fan-like nectaries fringed with globular-headed filaments. *P. palustris,* Grass of Parnassus, common in bogs, especially among the mountains in the North of Britain, is a singularly beautiful plant. It bears from the root several bright-green smooth roundish leaves cordate at the base, among which rises to the height of about a foot a simple angular stem bearing below the middle a solitary small leaf, and at the summit a single large flower of a creamy-white colour delicately veined, and opposite each of the five petals a nectary of the same colour. Several species of similar habit are found in North America. The genus takes its name from Mount Parnassus, where, owing to the elegance of its form, it is fabled to have been produced. French, *Fleur du Parnasse*; German, *Einblatt.* [C. A. J.]

PAROLINIA. A genus of *Cruciferæ,* comprising a rigid undershrub from the Canaries, with lanceolate-linear entire leaves, pink flowers, and a cylindrical pod with keeled valves produced into a long bifid horn; seeds margined. [J. T. S.]

PARONYCHIACEÆ. The same as ILLECEBRACEÆ: which see.

PARONYCHIA. A large genus of *Illecebraceæ,* inhabiting the warmer parts of the temperate zone of both hemispheres. They are small perennials (rarely annuals) often cæspitose, with opposite or whorled leaves, white scarious interpetiolar stipules, and cymose heads or fascicles of small flowers, often hidden by the large white scarious bracts. The calyx is five-cleft, with a short funnel-shaped or cup-shaped tube; petals five, filiform, sometimes absent; stamens five (or fewer by abortion) with very short filaments; styles two; utricle indehiscent or opening by five slits at the base, one-seeded. [J. T. S.]

PAROPSIA. The name of a shrub of Madagascar, constituting a genus of *Passifloraceæ.* It attains a height of five to six feet, has alternate leaves, without stipules, and is likewise destitute of tendrils. The flowers are stalked, in axillary tufts, and have each a ten-parted perianth in two rows; within the inner row is a ring of thread-like processes, aggregated together into five bundles, placed opposite the inner segments. The stamens are five, opposite the outer segments of the perianth, and attached to the short stalk supporting the ovary, which is one-celled with three parietal placentæ. The seeds are provided with a cup-shaped arillus, which is described as being eaten in Madagascar, and as having a very sweet taste. [M. T. M.]

PARROTIA. A genus of *Hamamelidaceæ*, represented by *P. persica* (*Hamamelis persica*), a tree inhabiting Northern Persia and the Caucasus, and yielding a very hard timber. The leaves are alternate, oval, acuminate, and towards the point furnished with small teeth. The tube of the calyx is bell-shaped, and the border divided into five or seven lobes; the corolla is wanting; the stamens are from five to seven, the styles two; and the capsule is two-celled, each cell containing one seed. [B. S.]

PARROT'S-BILL. A New Zealand name for *Clianthus puniceus*.

PARROT-WEED. A West Indian name for *Bocconia frutescens*.

PARRYA. A genus of *Cruciferæ*, consisting of perennial herbs from the Arctic regions, with the leaves chiefly radical, fleshy, entire or toothed, and the flowers rose-coloured or purple. The pod is broadly linear or oblong, the valves veined, and the seeds in two rows, margined. [J. T. S.]

PARSLEY. *Petroselinum sativum.* —, BASTARD. *Caucalis.* —, BASTARD STONE. *Sison Amomum.* —, . BLACK. *Melanoselinum decipiens.* —, BUR. *Caucalis daucoides.* —, COW. *Chærophyllum temulentum.* —, DOG'S. *Æthusa Cynapium.* —, FOOL'S. *Æthusa.* —, HAMBURGH. A variety of garden parsley with a fleshy root, for which it is cultivated. —, HEDGE. *Torilis Anthriscus.* —, HEMLOCK. *Conioselinum.* —, HORSE. *Smyrnium Olusatrum.* —, MARSH. *Elæoselinum.* —, MILK. *Selinum.* —, MOUNTAIN. *Peucedanum Oreoselinum.* —, SQUARE. *Ptychotis heterophylla.* —, STONE. *Sison Amomum*; also *Libanotis vulgaris.* —, WILD. *Cardiospermum.*

PARSLEY-PIERT. *Alchemilla Aphanes*; also *Erica Aphanes.*

PARSNIP, or PARSNEP. *Pastinaca sativa.* —, COW. *Heracleum Sphondylium.* —, MEADOW. An American name for *Thaspium.* —, SEA. *Echinophora.* —, WATER. *Sium*, also *Helosciadium nodiflorum.*

PARSONSIA. A genus of *Apocynaceæ*, having a funnel-shaped corolla, the border of which is five-parted and bent back; the stamens inserted near the base of the tube; and the style single, dilated at the apex. The genus has representatives in the East and West Indies, and in Australia; and consists of twining shrubs with opposite leaves. The name was given in honour of Dr. Parsons, a physician and writer on Natural History. [G. D.]

PARTED, PARTITE. Divided into a determinate number of segments, which

extend nearly to the base of the part to which they belong. Thus, *bipartite* is parted in two, *tripartite* in three, and so on.

PARTHENIUM. A genus of *Compositæ* of the tribe *Helianthæ*, consisting of herbs or undershrubs, with alternate leaves, and small nearly globular heads of white flowers in a terminal flat corymb. The involucre has two rows of broad bracts, and contains five shortly obcordate female florets in the ray, and several tubular male ones in the disk; the receptacle has membranous scales. The achenes are flattened from front to back, with a callous margin, and a pappus of two small awnlike or broad scales. There are six species known, natives of Northern or tropical America, among which *P. Hysterophorus* with twice pinnate leaves, common in the warmer parts of America, has been introduced into our botanical gardens.

PARTIALIS. A secondary division; as in umbellifers, where the umbels of the second degree bear this name.

PARTIBLE. Capable of being divided, but not dividing spontaneously.

PARTITE. Divided nearly to the base: thus *partitions* are the deepest divisions into which a leaf can be cut without becoming compound.

PARTITIONED. Divided by internal horizontal partitions into chambers.

PARTRIDGE-BERRY. *Gaultheria procumbens*; also an American name for *Mitchella.*

PARTRIDGE-WOOD. The wood of certain South American and West Indian trees, one of which is supposed to be *Andira inermis.*

PARVATIA. A genus of *Lardizabalaceæ*, closely allied to *Stauntonia*, from which it is distinguished by its flowers having six lance-shaped petals, much smaller than the six sepals. The stamens of the male flowers are united into a tube; those of the female are free and barren, the latter containing, also, three egg-shaped ovaries terminated by oblong sharp-pointed styles. The only species, *P. Brunoniana*, is a tall climbing shrub, with long-stalked trifoliate leaves, and axillary racemes of small greenish flowers; it is a native of the Khasia mountains. [A. S.]

PASCALIA. A Chilian genus of *Compositæ*, related to *Heliopsis*, and represented by a single species, *P. glauca*, an erect perennial herb, with a resinous smell, and furnished with trinerved leaves, a single yellow-rayed flower-head nearly an inch across terminating each branch. The strap-shaped and female ray-florets have three-sided achenes; and in the tubular and perfect disk-florets the achenes are four-sided, surmounted by a minutely-toothed pappus crown, and nearly enveloped in the chaffy scales of the receptacle. The plant cultivated in England as *P. glauca* is evidently a species of sunflower, and has nothing to do with this genus. [A. A. B.]

PASCO. The fruits of a species of *Pachylobus*.

PASCUOUS. Growing in pastures.

PAS-D'ÂNE. (Fr.) *Tussilago Farfara*.

PASPALUM. An extensive genus of grasses belonging to the tribe *Paniceæ*. The inflorescence is in simple racemes solitary or fingered; inferior flower neuter, one-paled, membranaceous; superior flower hermaphrodite, two-paled. Steudel describes 262 species, which have a wide geographical distribution, chiefly in the tropical and subtropical regions. [D. M.]

PASQUE-FLOWER. *Anemone Pulsatilla*.

PASSAN-BATU. The Stone Oak, *Lithocarpus javensis*.

PASSE-FLEUR. (Fr.) *Lychnis coronaria*.

PASSE-PIERRE. (Fr.) *Crithmum maritimum*, and *Salicornia herbacea*.

PASSE-RAGE CULTIVÉ. (Fr.) *Lepidium sativum*. —, PETIT *Lepidium graminifolium*.

PASSERINA. A genus of heath-like shrubs of the order *Thymelaceæ*, natives for the most part of the Cape of Good Hope. The flowers are closely aggregated together towards the end of the branches, each having a pinkish funnel-shaped perianth, with a four-cleft limb and no scales; and eight stamens protruding from the tube of the perianth, those opposite to its lobes longer than the rest. The fruit is one-seeded, not enclosed within the base of the perianth, as that is deciduous. *P. tinctoria* is employed in the dyeing of wool yellow. [M. T. M.]

PASSE-ROSE. (Fr.) *Althæa rosea*.

PASSEROUS. (Fr.) *Valerianella coronata*.

PASSE-TOUT. (Fr.) A fine variety of *Hyacinthus orientalis*.

PASSE-VELOURS. (Fr.) *Celosia cristata*.

PASSIFLORACEÆ. (*Passionworts*.) A natural order of calycifloral dicotyledons belonging to Lindley's violal alliance of hypogynous Exogens. They are herbs or shrubs, often climbing, with alternate stipulate or exstipulate leaves; and are natives chiefly of warm climates in America, and in the East and West Indies. Sepals five, combined below into a tube; petals five, perigynous, often with filamentous or annular processes on their inside; stamens five, monadelphous, surrounding the gynophore, rarely indefinite; ovary one-celled, with a gynophore; ovules anatropal; styles three, stigmas dilated. Fruit often stipitate, one-celled, sometimes three-valved, opening by loculicidal dehiscence, or succulent and indehiscent. Seeds indefinite, arillate or strophiolate. There are upwards of a dozen genera, as *Passiflora*, *Tacsonia*, &c., and more than 200 species. [J. H. B.]

PASSIFLORA. The technical name of the genus to which the popular name Passion-flower is applied. It constitutes the typical genus of *Passifloraceæ*, and comprises a considerable number of herbaceous or shrubby plants of climbing habit, provided with tendrils, and of a few erect trees without tendrils. The leaves are lobed or entire, with or without stipules, and having axillary flower-stalks usually provided with three bracts, enveloping the base of the flower. The perianth has a short tube whose limb is divided into four or five segments, or more generally into ten coloured segments, arranged in two rows; intermediate between the inner segments of the perianth and the stamens are two or more rows of coloured thread-like processes, constituting the 'corona;' stamens four or five, opposite to the outer segments of the perianth, spreading widely apart above, but below united together, and so celled, with three parietal placentæ, and terminated by three cylindrical styles having rather large button-like stigmas at their extremities. The fruit is succulent within, and has a more or less hard rind; seeds numerous, partly imbedded in pulp, and provided with an arillus.

These singular and beautiful plants are chiefly natives of tropical America, a few being indigenous in Asia. The name was applied from the resemblance afforded by the parts of the plant to the instruments of our Lord's Passion and its attendant circumstances: thus the three nails—two for the hands, one for the feet—are represented by the stigmas; the five anthers indicate the five wounds; the rays of glory or, some say, the crown of thorns are represented by the rays of the 'corona;' the ten parts of the perianth represent the Apostles, two of them absent,—Peter who denied, and Judas who betrayed our Lord; and the wicked hands of His persecutors are seen in the digitate leaves of the plant, and the scourges in the tendrils.

On the leafstalks of these plants may frequently be seen small glands, which may possibly be the representatives of abortive lobes. The tendrils emerge from the axils of the leaves, and are probably to be considered in the light of abortive flower-stalks; at least it is by no means uncommon to find flower-buds on them. The ray or crown of these flowers has been the subject of much controversy, and it can hardly be said that its true nature is perfectly made out. It has been considered to consist of a series of modified petals or stamens, or as a perfectly distinct organ originating from the receptacle of the flower, between the petals and the stamens. To the writer, the crown of the Passion-flower appears to consist of a series of modified stamens, for the following reasons. Anthers have been occasionally seen on the end of the filamentous processes, as also on the edge of the membranous tube that results from their union in the adjacent genus *Murucuja*; again, the union of these filaments into a tube, in the genus just mentioned,

as well as in *Smeathmannia*, *Disemma*, and
other closely allied genera, may be compared with the united tubular stamens of
Melia, &c., or with the crown of *Narcissus*,
or the united filaments of *Pancratium*. The
peculiar arrangement of the filaments of
the corona in *Paropsia* may also be cited
in favour of this notion; in this latter
genus the rays are collected into five parcels, calling to mind the polyadelphous stamens of *Hypericum*, or the glands of *Parnassia*. The varying relative position of
the styles and stamens at different times
is a point to which Dr. Dresser has called
attention, and which had been strangely
overlooked. These differences in position
seem due to the process of fertilisation,
which of course demands the contact of
the pollen with the stigma; hence we see
in these flowers a difference in the relative
position of the stamens and styles before,
during, and after fertilisation.

Many of the species have edible fruits;
such are *P. filamentosa*, *P. pallida*, *P. lutea*,
P. maliformis, *P. coccinea*, *P. laurifolia* (the
Water Lemon of the West Indies), *P. edulis*,
P. alata, *P. Buonapartea*, *P. incarnata*, *P.
serrata*, *P. maliformis* (the Sweet Calabash
of the West Indies), *P. ligularis*, *P. ornata*,
P. tinifolia, *P. cærulea*, and *P. quadrangularis* (the Granadilla). The part that is eaten
is either the fleshy aril attached to the
seeds, or the juicy pulp in which the latter
are imbedded. This pulp has an agreeably
cool taste in some species, and a sweet
mawkish flavour in others. In the West
Indies the pulp is sucked through a hole
in the rind. Fruits of the Granadilla and
some other of the edible species are commonly seen in the Paris markets, and occasionally in Covent Garden, as they not unfrequently ripen in this country.

Although so many of the species furnish
edible fruits, they are nevertheless not devoid of suspicious qualities in other organs. Thus the root of *P. quadrangularis* is
stated to possess powerful narcotic properties, and to be used in the Mauritius as a
diuretic and emetic; the roots of *P. contrayerva* and *P. normalis* are considered as
antidotes to poison, and the flowers of *P.
rubra* are stated to be used in the form of
a tincture, for their narcotic effects, in the
West Indies. *P. foetida* has a reputation
as an expectorant, and as a remedy in hysteria and female complaints; its leaves are
also employed for poultices in inflammatory
affections of the skin. The bitter and astringent leaves of *P. laurifolia* are used as
anthelmintics, while those of some other
species are mentioned as being employed
in intermittent fevers.

A great number of species are cultivated
in this country for the beauty of their
foliage and flowers, or for their fruits.
Several have already been mentioned; other
valuable kinds have been produced by hybridisation. The flowers of some have exquisite fragrance. For ornamental purposes *P. alato-cærulea*, *P. kermesina Lemicheziana*, *P. Loudoni*, and *P. Buonapartea* are
deserving especial notice in a genus almost
all the species of which merit cultivation

for some reason or other. *P. cærulea* and
some of its varieties and hybrids are hardy,
and even produce their fruit in sheltered
situations in our climate. [M. T. M.]

PASSION-FLOWER. *Passiflora.*

PASSIONS. *Rumex Patientia.*

PASSIONWORTS. Lindley's name for
the *Passifloraceæ*.

PASTEL. (Fr.) *Isatis.* The same term
is applied to the colouring matter obtained
from *Isatis tinctoria*.

PASTÈQUE. (Fr.) *Citrullus vulgaris.*

PASTINACA. A genus of umbelliferous
plants, consisting of only two or three species, of which the most important is the
Common Parsnip, a well-known culinary
vegetable. The genus is distinguished
by having its fruit flattened from front to
back, as in *Heracleum*, from which it
differs in having the flowers small and
yellow, and the vittæ more slender and
descending down nearly to the base of the
fruit. The species are chiefly from the
Mediterranean region and West Central
Asia.

The Common Parsnip, *P. sativa*, is a biennial indigenous to Britain, and usually
found by roadsides where the soil is deep
and calcareous. In its wild state the
leaves are downy underneath, and the
root small and hard; but the cultivated
plant has large pinnated leaves of a rich
green colour, with oval toothed leaflets.
The flower-stem attains the height of
three or four feet, and bears a number of
yellow flowers disposed in large terminal
umbels. The root is white or cream-coloured, mild, sweet, and aromatic. In the
Channel Islands, where Parsnips are grown
to great perfection, the roots are often
eighteen inches long, and from four to five
inches in diameter.

As an esculent, Parsnips are known to
have been used from a very early period.
According to Pliny, they were held in such
repute by the Emperor Tiberius, that he
had them annually brought to Rome from
the banks of the Rhine, where they were
then successfully cultivated. They are in
great request by Roman Catholics during
Lent, and are dressed in various ways, and
eaten with salt-fish. They have been lately
recommended as a substitute for the potato, but, although they contain a large
portion of nutritive matter, they have been
found on analysis to be inferior to potatos
as an article of diet—the latter (according
to Dr. Lankester) having nearly twice the
amount of flesh-forming matter in their
composition. Notwithstanding this result,
we entertain a high opinion of this vegetable, and when thoroughly boiled, and
mashed with butter, it makes an excellent
dish, which is generally much esteemed.

In Holland Parsnips are used in soups,
whilst in Ireland cottagers make a sort of
beer by mashing the roots and boiling them
with water and hops, and afterwards fermenting the liquor. A kind of marmalade
preserve has also been made from them;

and even wine, which in quality has been considered to approach the famed Malmsey of Madeira.' [W. B. B.]

PASTISSON. (Fr.) *Cucurbita Melopepo.*

PATABEA. A genus of *Cinchonaceæ*, consisting of shrubs with oval pointed leaves, and axillary or terminal flowers, provided with four small bracts, arranged crosswise; calyx-limb short, entire, or slightly four to six-toothed; corolla with a short tube, and a limb of four to six oblong spreading lobes; anthers four to six, sessile within the throat of the corolla. Fruit succulent, two-celled, two-seeded, surrounded by the calyx. The species are natives of Guiana. [M. T. M.]

PATAGONULA. A small genus containing two species, natives of Jamaica, branching shrubs with alternate leaves, and small flowers in panicles without bracts. They have a very small calyx, increasing around the drupaceous fruit; a rotate corolla, with a short five-cleft limb; five stamens inserted in the throat of the corolla; and a simple style, doubly dichotomous, and having a stigmatic surface on each of the four divisions. The fruit is a subglobose drupe, with a one-celled stone.

The position of this genus is doubtful. It was referred to *Cordia* in *Hortus Kewensis*, and to *Cordiaceæ* by Chamisso, and doubtfully by Endlicher. Alph. Decandolle, from the examination of *P. bahiensis*, refers it to *Verbenaceæ*; while Schauer separates it from this order on account of its different habit, inflorescence, calyx, and fruit. [W. C.]

PATARA. A Tahitian edible tuber, probably that of *Dioscorea pentaphylla.*

PATATE. (Fr.) *Solanum tuberosum.* — DOUCE. *Batatas edulis.*

PATAWA. *Œnocarpus Batava.*

PATCHOULI. A perfume obtained from an Indian herb, *Pogostemon Patchouli.*

PÂTE D'AMANDE. (Fr.) The farinaceous matter which is left after the oil is expressed from almonds. — DE GUIMAUVE. A confectioner's name for a lozenge made from *Althæaofficinalis.*

PATELLA, PATELLULA. An orbicular sessile shield in lichens, surrounded by a rim which is part of itself, and not derived from the thallus.

PATELLIFORM. The same as Knee-pan-shaped.

PATENOTRIER. (Fr.) *Staphylea pinnata.*

PATENS, or PATENT. Spreading wide open; as petals from the calyx. *Patentissimus* is spreading open so much as to fall back.

PATERSONIA. A small genus of New Holland *Iridaceæ*, distinguished by having a hypocrateriform perianth, with six segments, the three inner of which are minute; three stamens, with their filaments connate into a tube; a hairlike style with three laminiform stigmas; and a three-celled prismatical ovary containing numerous ovules. They are perennial herbs, with fibrous roots, from which spring narrow ensiform leaves, and showy but very fugacious blue flowers. [T. M.]

PATHOLOGY. That part of Botany which relates to the diseases of plants.

PATIENCE. (Fr.) *Rumex Patientia.* — DES EAUX, GRANDE. *Rumex Hydrolapathum.* — DES JARDINS. *Rumex Patientia.* — SAUVAGE. *Rumex obtusifolius.*

PATISSON. (Fr.) A kind of Gourd.

PATMAWORTS. A name formerly proposed by Lindley for the *Rafflesiaceæ.*

PATONIA. A genus of Cingalese shrubs now referred by Drs. Hooker and Thomson to *Xylopia.*

PATRAQUE. (Fr.) *Solanum tuberosum.*

PATRINIA. A genus of *Valerianaceæ*, so named in compliment to a French botanical traveller in Siberia, who discovered some of the species. They are herbaceous plants, with tufted leaves, and yellow flowers in terminal corymbs. The main features of the genus are:—Calyx with an erect very short limb, which is sometimes entirely wanting; corolla regular, tubular with a three-lobed limb; stamens four or five; fruit membranous, crowned by the limb of the calyx, with two empty compartments, and a third containing a single seed. [M. T. M.]

PATTE D'ARAIGNÉE. *Nigella damascena.* — DE LAPIN. *Sedum villosum.* — DE LION. *Leontopodium alpinum.* — DE LOUP. *Lycopodium clavatum.* — D'OIE. *Chenopodium.* — D'OURS. *Acanthus mollis.*

PATULOUS. Spreading half open.

PATURIN. (Fr.) *Poa.* — À MANCHETTES. *Poa pilosa.* — COMMUN. *Poa trivialis.*

PAULIA. A genus of gelatinous lichens resembling *Sinalyssa*, an allied genus, in the gonidia being produced exactly in the same manner as *Palmella botryoides* is multiplied, a structure which obtains also in *Emericella.* [M. J. B.]

PAULLINIA. With the exception of two or three West African species, the whole of this large genus of *Sapindaceæ*, consisting of about sixty species, is confined to the tropical regions of the western hemisphere. Nearly all are climbing shrubs furnished with tendrils, and having variously divided compound leaves, with stipules at their bases, and axillary racemes of white flowers with two opposite tendrils below them. The flowers have five sepals either distinct or two of them united; four petals bearing scales inside near the base; eight stamens inserted on the inside of the two or four glands of the disk; and a short three-parted style. The genus, however, is distinguished from some of its allies by the fruit, which is a pear-shaped three-sided three-celled (or by abortion one-celled) capsule, with thin partitions, opposite which it splits open when ripe, each cell containing a solitary seed half enveloped in an aril.

From the seeds of the Guarana, *P. sorbilis*, several tribes of Indians on the Amazon prepare hard cakes called Pao de Guarana (i. e. sticks of Guarana), which form a considerable article of trade, and are carried into all parts of Brazil, where a cooling beverage is prepared from them. The ripe seeds are thoroughly dried, then pounded into a fine powder, which is made into dough with water and formed into cylindrical rolls, from five to eight inches long, which become excessively hard when dry. The beverage is prepared by grating about half a tablespoonful of one of the cakes into a glass of sugar-and-water. It is greatly used by the Brazilian miners, and is considered to be a preventive of all manner of diseases. Its active principle is a substance called *guaranine*, which is identical in its composition with the theine of tea.   [A. S.]

The Guarana is extensively used in Brazil, Guatemala, Costa Rica, and other parts of South America, as a nervous stimulant and restorative. The pounded seeds constitute Guarana. It is used both as a remedy for various diseases, and also as a material for making a most refreshing beverage. Not only is the active principle of Guarana identical with theine, but, as far as is known, no other substance yields it so abundantly; the amounts being 5·07 per cent. as against good black tea, which yields 2·13, and coffee from 0·8 to 1·00. The mode of using the Guarana is curious and interesting. It is carried in the pocket of almost every traveller, and with it the palate-bone or a scale of a large fish, the rough surfaces of which form a rasp upon which the Guarana is grated; and a few grains of the powder so formed are added to water, and drunk as a substitute for tea. The effect is very agreeable. *P. Cupana* also enters into the composition of a favourite national diet-drink; its seeds are mingled with cassava and water, and allowed to pass into a state of fermentation bordering on the putrefactive, in which state it is the favourite drink of the Orinoco Indians.   [T. M.]

PAULO-WILHELMIA. A genus of *Acanthaceæ*, containing a single species from Abyssinia. It is a shrub, with large ovate-cordate and petiolate leaves, and rose-coloured flowers in apparent whorls, crowded together so as to form a leafy spike. The calyx is unequally five-parted; the corolla funnel-shaped, with a long slender tube, and an equally five-cleft limb; the four exserted stamens have anthers with two equal parallel cells; the slender exserted style has a subulate stigma; and the capsule is narrow and four-sided, bearing near the base four compressed seeds, inserted on hooked retinacula.   [W. C.]

PAULOWNIA *imperialis* is a Japanese tree with the habit of *Catalpa*, and which was therefore originally published by Thunberg as a species of *Bignonia*, but it has much more the botanical character of *Scrophulariaceæ*, of which it is now considered as forming a distinct genus. It is a soft-wooded tree of moderate size, with a large dense spreading head, and broadly ovate-cordato entire or lobed opposite leaves. The flowers, nearly two inches long, in terminal panicles, are of a purplish-violet colour; the hard ovoid acuminate capsules, one to one-and-a-half inches long, open loculicidally in two valves, and contain numerous winged seeds. When first introduced, its rapid growth, large leaves, and the exaggerated accounts of the beauty of its flowers caused it to be much planted, but the somewhat hoary tint of the down which covers the leaves renders their green too dull; the flowers moreover come out too early to succeed well in our climate, and their colour is far from brilliant. It is indeed altogether inferior to the *Catalpa*, and scarcely more hardy.

PAUMELLE, (Fr.) *Hordeum distichon.*

PAVETTA. A genus of shrubs of the *Cinchonaceæ*, natives of tropical Asia, and also of tropical and Southern Africa. The flowers are white, in terminal corymbs, and differ little from those of the allied genus *Ixora*, except in the lobes of the corolla, which are twisted in the bud; and in the style, which projects for some distance from the corolla, and is terminated by a club-shaped stigma. Two or three species are grown as ornamental stove shrubs. The root of *P. indica* is bitter, and is employed as a purgative by the Hindoos. The leaves are likewise used medicinally, and for manuring; knife-handles are made from the roots.   [M. T. M.]

PAVIA. Shrubs or middle-sized deciduous trees belonging to the *Sapindaceæ*, and distinguished from *Æsculus* by having a smooth not prickly capsule. *P. rubra*, often called Red-flowered Horse-chestnut, is a slender-growing tree twenty to thirty feet high, from the mountains of Virginia and Carolina, and said also to be a native of Brazil and Japan. Several varieties are cultivated in England, differing in habit and in the form of their leaves. *P. flava*, also a native of North America, attains a larger size than the preceding, and is further distinguished by having the leaves downy beneath, and by the colour of its flowers. *P. discolor* is a shrub rarely exceeding the height of five or six feet, and as it bears numerous handsome flowers, is often planted as an ornament to the shrubbery. Other species are occasionally cultivated.   [C. A. J.]

PAVONIA. A genus of *Malvaceæ* named in honour of Don Josef Pavon, a botanical traveller in Peru, and joint author of the *Flora Peruviana*. The species are usually small shrubs, sometimes herbs, natives of America, and rarely of tropical Asia. Their leaves are various in form, sometimes having pellucid dots; the flower-stalks are axillary; and there is an involucel or outer calyx of five or more leaflets, distinct or united together, generally in one row, but occasionally in two. Calyx five-cleft; petals five, oblique; ovary sessile, five-lobed, five-celled, each compartment containing a single ovule; style ten-cleft: fruit of five one-seeded carpels.

P. diuretica is employed medicinally in Brazil, as also are P. *zeylanica* and *P. odorata* in the southern parts of India. Some of the species are grown in stovehouses in this country, but are not remarkable for beauty. [M. T. M.]

PAVOT. (Fr.) *Papaver.* — COQ. *Papaver Rhœas.* — CORNU. *Glaucium luteum.* — DES JARDINS. *Papaver somniferum.* — DU MEXIQUE. *Argemone mexicana.* — DE TOURNEFORT, or DU LEVANT. *Papaver orientale.* — EPINEUX. *Argemone mexicana.* — JAUNE DES PYRÉNÉES. *Meconopsis cambrica.* — PORTE-SOIE. *Papaver setigerum.*

PAXILLUS. A genus closely allied to *Agaricus*, but distinguished by the gills readily separating from the pileus. *P. involutus* is one of our commonest fungi, especially about fir-woods, being remarkable for its involute margin, and yellowish somewhat branched porous hymenium, which becomes brown when bruised. [M. J. B.]

PAXTONIA. A genus of orchids named in compliment to Sir Joseph Paxton, the well-known horticulturist. The only species, *P. rosea*, is one of the very few orchids which have the petals all similar, instead of one (called the lip) being strikingly unlike the others. It was established as a genus by Dr. Lindley, but further acquaintance shows reason to suspect that it is what is called a peloria or regular form of another orchid, *Spathoglottis spicata.* The plant is terrestrial, and has dense tufts of oblong three-leaved pseudobulbs marked with ring-like scars, and erect slender distantly-sheathed scapes, taller than the plicate leaves, and bearing upon its summit six or eight pretty rose-coloured flowers about an inch and a half across. These have a six-leaved perianth with the divisions alike, an erect almost terete column somewhat thickened towards the top, and eight narrow club-shaped unequal pollenmasses coherent at their apices. [A. S.]

PAYENA. A genus of *Sapotaceæ* named in honour of the celebrated French chemist. The species are shrubs with elliptical leaves, and axillary flower-stalks. Calyx four-parted, its segments ovate, externally pubescent: corolla tubular below, bell-shaped above, where it is divided into eight pieces; stamens eight, inserted into the tube of the corolla opposite to its lobes, and between them as many little teeth. The connective is prolonged into a fleshy point; the ovary is hairy, with eight compartments; and the style is smooth, twice as long as the calyx. [M. T. M.]

PAYPAYROLA. A genus of tropical American trees of the order *Violaceæ.* The flowers are in dense branching spikes or clusters; sepals and petals five, nearly equal, the latter coherent at the base after flowering; filaments combined into a short cup bearing the anthers; ovary sessile; style terminal, short, irregularly dilated or two-lobed at the top; fruit capsular, three valved. [M. T. M.]

PEA. *Pisum.* —, BLACK-EYED. A West Indian name for *Dolichos sphærospermus.* —, BUTTERFLY. *Clitoria Mariana.* —, CHICK. *Cicer arietinum*: the name was formerly written Cich or Ciche, sometimes Ramnies Ciches. —, CONGO. *Cajanus indicus bicolor.* —, EARTH. *Lathyrus amphicarpus.* —, EARTH-NUT. *Lathyrus tuberosus.* —, EGYPTIAN. *Cicer arietinum.* —, EVERLASTING. *Lathyrus latifolius.* —, FLAT. *Platylobium.* —, GLORY. *Clianthus.* —, HEART. *Cardiospermum Halicacabum.* —, HEATH. *Lathyrus macrrhizus.* —, HOARY. *Tephrosia.* —, MILK. *Galactia.* —, NO-EYE. *Cajanus indicus flavus.* —, ORANGE. The small immature fruit of the Curaçao orange used for flavouring wines. —, PARTRIDGE. *Heisteria*; also an American name for *Cassia Chamæcrista.* —, PIGEON. *Cajanus indicus.* —, ROSARY. The seeds of *Abrus precatorius.* —, SCURFY. *Psoralea.* —, SEA. *Lathyrus maritimus.* —, SPURRED BUTTERFLY. An American name for *Centrosema.* —, STURTS DESERT. *Clianthus Dampieri.* —, SWEET. *Lathyrus odoratus.* —, TANGIER. *Lathyrus tingitanus.* —, WOOD. *Lathyrus macrorrhizus.*

PEACH. *Amygdalus persica.* —, GUINEA. *Sarcocephalus esculentus.* —, NATIVE, of Australia. *Santalum acuminatum.* —, of Sierra Leone. *Sarcocephalus esculentus.*

PEACH-BLISTER. An affection to which peach-leaves are subject, the leaves becoming thick bladdery and curled. By some it is supposed to be produced by aphides; by others it is attributed to the action of cold winds when the leaves are expanding. In some cases it is undoubtedly produced by a minute fungus of the genus *Ascomyces.* If the leaves of a tree are once affected, the malady is very apt to recur in future seasons. [M. J. B.]

PEACH-WOOD. Nicaragua-wood, *Cæsalpinia echinata.*

PEACHWORT. *Polygonium Persicaria.*

PEACOCK'S TAIL. *Padina pavonia.*

PEA-FLOWER. A West Indian name for *Centrosema* and *Clitoria.*

PEAR. *Pyrus communis*; the name is also applied, generically, to species of *Pyrus* of the group *Pyrophorum*, consisting of the Pears proper. —, ALLIGATOR, or AVOCADO. *Persea gratissima.* —, ANCHOVY. *Grias cauliflora.* —, GARLIC. *Cratæva gynandra.* —, GRAPE. *Amelanchier Botryapium.* —, PRICKLY. *Opuntia vulgaris*, and *O. Tuna.* —, STRAWBERRY. *Cereus triangularis.* —, WILD. A West Indian name for *Clethra tinifolia.*

PEARL-EVERLASTING. *Gnaphalium margaritaceum.*

PEARL-FRUIT. The fruit of *Margyricarpus setosus.*

PEARL-GREY. Pure grey, a little verging to blue.

PEARL-MOSS. The same as Carageen.

PEARL-PLANT. *Lithospermum officinale.*

PEARLWEED, or **PEARLWORT.** *Sagina.*

PEARMAIN. A kind of Apple.

PEAR-SHAPED. Obconical, with the sides a little contracted.

PEAR-WITHE. A West Indian name for *Tanæcium Jaroba.*

PEASE. The seeds of the varieties of *Pisum sativum.*

PEA-TREE. *Sesbania.* —, **SIBERIAN.** *Caragana.*

PÊCHER. (Fr.) *Amygdalus persica.*

PECTIDIUM. The *Pectis punctata* has been distinguished under this name as a genus on account of a slight difference in the scales of the pappus, which are stiff hard awns, not at all dilated at the base.

PECTINARIA. *Stapelia articulata.*

PECTINATE. The same as Pinnatifid, but with the segments numerous close and narrow, like the teeth of a comb. *Pectinato-laciniate* is cut in a pectinate manner; that is to say, pectinate, with the lobes very long and taper-pointed.

PECTIS. A genus of *Compositæ*, comprising nearly thirty species, natives of South America, the West Indies, or Mexico, all glabrous herbs, with opposite leaves more or less marked with pellucid glandular dots, usually narrow and entire, bordered with a few long stiff hairs or bristles at the base. The flower-heads are usually small, with tubular involucres of a single row of bracts, the receptacle naked, the florets of the ray ligulate, those of the disk tubular. The achenes have a pappus of several scales or stiff bristles, varying in different species in number, and in being more or less dilated at the base. On this account the genus has been divided into four, *Pectidopsis*, *Pectidium*, *Pectis*, and *Lorentea*, but which may be much more conveniently regarded as sections. None of the species are of sufficient interest or beauty for cultivation.

PEDALIACEÆ. (*Pedalineæ*, *Sesameæ*, *Martyniaceæ*, *Pedaliads.*) A natural order of perigynous Exogens belonging to Lindley's bignonial alliance. It consists of herbaceous plants, with undivided angular or lobed exstipulate leaves, and large axillary flowers, solitary or clustered. The calyx is cut into five equal lobes; the corolla is monopetalous, irregular with a ventricose throat and bilabiate limb; the hypogynous disk is fleshy or glandular; the stamens didynamous with the rudiment of a fifth; and the ovary one-celled with parietal placentæ, becoming a bony or capsular fruit with four or six spurious cells formed by the splitting of the two placentæ and the divergence of their lobes; seeds wingless with an amygdaloid embryo. The order is allied to the *Bignoniaceæ*, but differs in the parietal placentæ and the wingless seeds. It is not very extensive, but is distributed over the tropics, most abundantly in Africa. The seeds of *Sesamum* yield an abundance of fixed oil of good quality, known as Gingilie oil. *Martynia*, *Uncaria*, and *Sesamum* are examples of the genera, which number about a dozen. [T. M.]

PEDALIS. Twelve inches long, or the length of a tall man's foot.

PEDALIUM. The order *Pedaliaceæ* takes its name from this genus, the only representative of which is *P. murex*, a tall succulent branching annual plant, common near the sea on the Coromandel and Malabar coasts of India, and in Ceylon. This plant has long-stalked opposite oval toothed leaves, and rather showy yellow flowers produced singly in the axils of the leaves, upon short stalks which are furnished with glands near the base. They have a small five-parted calyx with the upper lobe shorter than the others; a tubular corolla equal at the bottom and wide at the mouth, expanding into five round lobes the lowest of which is the largest; four stamens in pairs of different length with the anthers forming a cross; and a thread-like style bearing a bifid stigma. Its fruits, which do not open when ripe, are four-sided and of a somewhat pyramidal or conical shape, with four sharp prickles upon the corners near the base, and are divided into three cells, one of which is empty, while each of the others contains two pendulous seeds.

All parts of the plant give off a musky odour when rubbed; and the fresh branches possess the curious property of rendering water or milk mucilaginous by simply drawing them a few times round in the vessel containing it. In India the buttermilk sold in the markets is frequently adulterated by mixing with water thickened by this means. The seeds also are mucilaginous, and are used in India for making poultices. [A. S.]

PEDANE, or **PET D'ANE.** (Fr.) *Onopordon.*

PEDATE, PEDATIFID. The same as Palmate, except that the two lateral lobes are themselves divided into smaller segments, the midribs of which do not directly run into the same point as the rest. Hence: *pedatiform*, having a pedate form; *pedatilobed*, or *pedatilobate*, when a palmate leaf has the supplementary lobes at the base; *pedatinerved*, when the ribs are arranged in a pedate manner; *pedatipartite*, or *pedatisect*, when a pedate leaf has segments separated into so many distinct leaflets.

PEDDA-CANREW. A Molucca name for the fruit of *Flacourtia sapida.*

PEDDIEA. The name of a Nepal shrub

constituting a genus of *Thymelaceæ*. The flowers are terminal umbellate, perfect, with a coloured perianth, dilated below, contracted above, and having a four or five-cleft limb; stamens eight to ten; scales of the disk combined into a shallow tube surrounding the base of the ovary, which latter contains two pendulous ovules. Fruit succulent. [M. T. M.]

PÈ DE PERDIS. A Brazilian name for the diuretic decoction of *Croton perdicipes*.

PEDICEL, PEDICULE (adj. **PEDICEL-LATE, PEDICULATE**). A peduncle of a second or higher order, as in the raceme, where the principal flower-stalk is the peduncle, and the lateral secondary ones are pedicels. *Pediculus antheræ* is the filament of the stamen.

PEDICULARIS. A genus of herbaceous plants belonging to the *Scrophulariaceæ*, the characters of which are: calyx five-cleft, or unequally two to three-cleft, the segments sometimes leafy; corolla ringent, the upper lip flattened vertically. There are two British species—*P. palustris*, the Marsh Lousewort, an erect much-branched herbaceous plant, nine to twelve inches high, of a singularly pyramidal growth and purplish tinge, the leaves pinnate, and the flowers dull crimson; and *P. sylvatica*, the Pasture Lousewort, common on heaths and marshy meadows, which has prostrate or spreading stems, only branched near the base, the segments of the calyx leafy, and the flowers rose-coloured. Both these plants were formerly considered to be productive of the disease in sheep from which they derive their names; but in reality the localities in which they are abundant are little adapted for pasture-ground, being from their dampness unproductive of nourishing food. Upwards of fifty foreign species are described by botanists. *P. Sceptrum Carolinum*, or Charles's Sceptre, so called by Rudbeck in honour of Charles II., King of Sweden, from its manner of growth like a sceptre, attains the height of three or four feet, and bears golden-yellow flowers one inch long, the lower lip tinged with purple. It is common in Norway, Denmark, and Lapland. French, *Pédiculaire*; German, *Läusekraut*. [C. A. J.]

PEDILANTHUS. A genus of *Euphorbiaceæ*, very closely allied to *Euphorbia* itself in the structure of its flowers, and chiefly distinguished by the singularly irregular shape of the involucres, assuming almost the appearance of a slipper or shoe. There are two or three species, thick-stemmed half-shrubby plants with an acrid milky juice, natives of the warmer regions of America.

PÉDILONIE. (Fr.) *Wachendorfia*.

PÉDIVEAN. (Fr.) *Caladium*.

PEDUNCLE (adj. **PEDUNCULATE**). The stalk of a flower. *Pedunculares cirrhi* are tendrils proceeding from a peduncle.

PEERGRUG. An Indian name for *Cissampelos glabra*.

PEETHA. An Indian name for *Benincasa cerifera*.

PEETSAL. An Indian name for *Pterocarpus Marsupium*.

PEGANUM. The Greek word for rue, (*Ruta graveolens*), and apparently also applied by Dioscorides to the rue-like plant, which now bears the name, and constitutes a genus of *Rutaceæ*. *P. Harmala* is a common plant in Southern Europe and Asia Minor, and may now and then be met with in English gardens. It is a powerfully smelling herb, with alternate sessile entire or divided leaves, provided at the base with two hair-like stipules, but destitute of the pellucid dots generally seen among rueworts. The flower-stalks are opposite the leaves, and bear a terminal white flower with greenish nerves; stamens fifteen, with filaments dilated at the base, ovary on a short stalk surrounded by large disk, and having three compartments in the interior, each containing numerous ovules; style thread-like, becoming twisted. The fruit is capsular and opens by three valves, which have the partitions attached to them, and the albumen of the seed is horny. This plant derives its specific name from the Arabic word applied to it, and is interesting botanically, as combining in itself the characteristics of the order *Zygophyllaceæ*, in its stipulate not dotted leaves, and in the nature of the fruit; and those of *Rutaceæ* in the alternate arrangement of the leaves, the consistence of the albumen, and the general appearance of the plant. The seeds are used in Turkey as a vermifuge; they are collected by the Tartars in the Crimea for that purpose. [M. T. M.]

PEIGNE-DE-VENUS. (Fr.) *Scandix Pecten-Veneris*.

PELARGONIUM. A very extensive genus of *Geraniaceæ*, almost confined to the Cape of Good Hope, though a few occur in Australia, one in the Canary Islands, and another fine species (*P. Endlicherianum*) in Asia Minor. They are known in gardens as Geraniums, though very different from the genus of that name, in their spurred calyx, usually irregular corolla, and the number of perfect stamens, which varies from seven down to four.

The greater number of forms cultivated in gardens are hybrids, which are produced with great facility in this genus. The species possess more or less of the astringent properties of the order, but one species at least (*P. triste*) has tubers, which are eaten at the Cape; while some have fragrant foliage from which an essential oil may be extracted, as *P. roseum* and *capitatum*. They vary much in habit; some have a turnip-shaped rhizome and no proper stem: others have a distinct leafy stem, and a good number are undershrubs with thick fleshy stems. The leaves are opposite or the upper ones alternate, entire or variously divided, with leaf-like or scarious stipules at the base. The peduncles grow opposite the leaves or axillary;

and the flowers are usually in simple umbels with an involucre at the base; the calyx is five-parted, the upper segment having a spur which is adnate to the pedicel; corolla of five petals (sometimes four or two), more or less irregular; stamens ten, four to seven only with anthers; beaks of the fruit (styles) hairy inside, and spirally twisted when mature. *Pelargonium* is divided into the following subgenera:—

Hoarea: stemless with tuberous roots; petals five or four

Seymouria: stemless, with tuberous roots; petals only two.

Polyactium: caulescent, with tuberous roots; leaves lobed, or pinnately decompound; umbels many-flowered; petals subequal obovate, entire, or fimbriato-lacerate.

Otidia: stem succulent and knobby; leaves fleshy, pinnately or bipinnately compound; petals subequal, the upper eared at the base; stamens five.

Ligularia: stem either succulent or slender and branching; leaves rarely entire, mostly much cut or pinnately decompound; petals subunequal, spathulate, the uppermost tapering at the base; stamens seven.

Jenkinsonia: shrubby or succulent; leaves palmately nerved or lobed; two upper petals on long claws, very much larger than the lower; stamens seven.

Myrrhidium: slender suffruticose or annual; leaves pinnatifid or pinnatisect; petals four (rarely five), two upper largest; calyx-segments membranous, strongly-ribbed, and mucronate or taper-pointed; stamens five, rarely seven.

Peristera: herbaceous diffuse, annual or perennial; leaves lobed or pinnatifid; flowers minute; petals scarcely longer than the calyx. (Habit of *Geranium* or *Erodium*.)

Campylia: stem short, subsimple; leaves on long petioles, undivided entire or toothed; stipules membranous; flowers on long pedicels; two upper petals broadly obovate, three lower narrow; fertile stamens five, two of the sterile ones recurved.

Dibrachya: much-branched, with weak-jointed stems; leaves peltate or cordate-lobed, fleshy; petals obovate; stamens seven, the two upper very short. (The ivy-leaved race.)

Eumorpha: slender, suffruticose, or herbaceous; leaves on long petioles, palmately five to seven-nerved, reniform, lobed or pinnatifid; petals unequal, the two upper broad; stamens seven.

Glaucophyllum: shrubby; leaves carnose, simple or ternately compound, the lamina articulated to the petiole; stamens seven.

Ciconium: shrubby, with carnose branches; leaves either obovate or cordate-reniform, palmately many-nerved, undivided; petals all of one colour, scarlet, pink, or white; stamens seven, two upper very short.

Cortusina: caudex short, thick and fleshy; branches (if present) slender and half herbaceous; leaves reniform or cor-

date, lobulate, on long petioles; petals subequal, two upper broadest, stamens six or seven.

Pelargium: much-branched shrubs or subshrubs, not fleshy; leaves entire or lobed (never pinnatipartite); stipules free; inflorescence frequently panicled, the partial peduncles umbelled; two upper petals longer and broader than the lower; stamens seven. [J. T. S.]

PELEGRINE. (Fr.) *Alströmeria.*

PELEXIA. A small tropical American genus of terrestrial Orchids, belonging to the *Neotteæ*, and scarcely different from *Stenorhynchus*, except in having a membranous rostellum, and in the lateral sepals and lip being combined into a more conspicuous horn. [A. S.]

PELICAN-FLOWER. *Aristolochia grandiflora.*

PELIJURREE. An Indian name for the root of *Thalictrum foliolosum.*

PELIOS. In Greek compounds = livid.

PELIOSANTHES. A genus of *Liliaceæ*, of the section *Ophiopogoneæ*, from India. They have creeping rhizomes, with long-stalked oblong-lanceolate plicate radical leaves, and erect scapes with compact bracteated racemes or panicles of greenish flowers. The perianth is adherent to the ovary at the base, with a six-cleft rotate limb, and an annular crown at the throat: stamens six, with almost sessile anthers; seeds one to three, naked by the rupture of the ovary. [J. T S.]

PELLÆA. *Platyloma.*

PELL-A-MOUNTAIN. *Thymus Serpyllum.*

PELLETIERA. A genus of primworts, having the calyx five-parted; the corolla in three divisions, much shorter than the calyx; stamens three, inserted at the base of the corolla; and the seed-vessel round, two to three-valved, the seeds two. The only species is a small Brazilian herb, with a quadrangular stem, the leaves opposite, with solitary white flowers in the axils of the leaves. [G. D.]

PELLIA. A genus of frondose *Jungermanniaceæ*, belonging to the tribe *Haploläneæ*, in which it is distinguished by its dorsal fruit, and elaters which do not adhere to the tips of its valves. *P. epiphylla* is one of our commonest liverworts, growing on the margins of ponds, on the walls of wells, under bridges, or in other shady places. Some species of *Aneura* resemble it in habitat, but they have more divided and irregular ribless fronds. [M. J. B.]

PELLITORY. *Pyrethrum Parthenium*, also *Parietaria.* — OF SPAIN. *Anacyclus Pyrethrum.* — OF THE WALL. *Parietaria officinalis.*

PELLITUS. Skinned; deprived of skin, or seeming to be so.

PELORIA. A return from habitual irregularity to regular form, as in *Linaria vulgaris*.

PELOTTES DE NEIGE. (Fr.) The Gueldres Rose, a sterile variety of *Viburnum Opulus*.

PELTA. A target-like shield, found on the species of *Peltidea*; also a bract attached by its middle, as in peppers.

PELTANDRA. A North American genus of *Araceæ*, represented by an herbaceous plant, with a thick fleshy rootstock, from which are sent up arrow-shaped leaves, borne on long sheathing leafstalks. In the blade of the leaf the veins are numerous, and closely arranged in a somewhat parallel manner. The spadix emerges from between the sheaths of the leaves, and is invested by a green spathe, the lower portion of which is tubular and the upper portion expanded, with the point reflexed. The spadix itself is short, almost entirely covered with densely crowded flowers, except for a short space at the top. The uppermost and lowermost flowers are imperfect, while the central ones are perfect. The anthers are adherent one to another by means of their club-shaped large connectives. The ovaries taper into a very short style terminated by a depressed button-like stigma; they contain a small number of erect ovules placed on short ascending stalks. The rootstock of *P. virginica*, formerly *Arum virginicum*, contains a considerable amount of starch.   [M. T. M.]

PELTARIA. A genus of *Cruciferæ*, natives of Central Europe and Syria, and consisting of smooth erect perennials with ovate entire stalked root-leaves, and sessile arrow-shaped cauline ones. The racemes are numerous, disposed in a corymbose manner; the flowers small and white. Pouch indehiscent orbicular flat, with flat valves without wings, the partition vanishing; seeds two to four, or solitary by abortion. One species, *P. alliacea*, from Central Europe, has the odour of garlic. [J. T. S.]

PELTATE. Fixed to the stalk by the centre, or by some point distinctly within the margin; as the leaf of *Tropæolum*. *Peltatifid* is applied to a peltate leaf cut into subdivisions; and *peltato-digitate* to a digitate leaf with the petiole much enlarged at the setting on of the leaflets.

PELTIDEA. A genus of lichens the species of which are vulgarly confounded with *Marchantia* under the name of liverwort. The herbalists, however, distinguish them as Ground Liverwort. The marginal disks, which are either orbicular or reniform, are at first veiled, and often project from the thallus, retaining fragments of the veil at the margin; the underside of the frond is veined and attached to the ground, or whatever substance it may chance to grow upon, by numerous fibres. Their favourite place of growth is the top of a molehill or mudwall, where they have good drainage; in such situations they form handsome objects, especially when in fruit or studded with a little red parasite to which they are

subject. *P. canina* was once celebrated as a remedy against hydrophobia, but its virtues are quite imaginary.   [M. J. B.]

PELTIFORM. Having simple veins arranged as in a peltate leaf.

PELTINERVED. Having ribs arranged as in a peltate leaf.

PELTOBRYON. A genus of South American shrubs of the *Piperaceæ*, having oblong membranous leaves with glandular dots, and a smooth or slightly hairy surface. The stipules are opposite the leaves, lance-shaped or linear; the catkins are short-stalked, cylindrical, with membranous peltate bracts; the flowers are hermaphrodite, and have a cylindrical style, with three curved stigmas. Some of the species are made use of in South America in the same way as pepper.   [M. T. M.]

PELTOPHORUM. The plants now included in this genus were formerly referred to *Cæsalpinia*: two are natives of the West Indies, one of Brazil, and a fourth of the Cape of Good Hope. They are all unarmed trees of no great height, with abruptly bipinnate leaves, and large branching panicles of small flowers, which possess a five-parted calyx with nearly equal segments, five petals, ten stamens included within the petals and hairy at the bottom, and a broad shield-like smooth stigma. The pods have short stalks, and are flat and wingless, with one or a few seeds.

P. Linnæi, otherwise called *Cæsalpinia brasiliensis*, yields the orange-coloured dye-wood imported from Jamaica and San Domingo under the name of Brazilletto-wood. It is a small tree seldom exceeding fifteen feet high, and has leaves composed of four pairs of pinnæ, each of which has from six to eight pairs of small oval bluntish slightly downy leaflets, and small yellow flowers. From two to four hundred tons of Brazilletto-wood are annually imported for the use of our dyers, who obtain fine orange-red tints from it; turners also use it for various small articles, and violin-bows are sometimes made of it.

The wood of *P. Vogelianum*, which is a native of Brazil, is also called Brazilletto or Sobrazil. It is a larger tree than the last, attaining the height of about forty feet, with a great branching top, and the subdivisions of its leaves are more numerous, the number of pairs of pinnæ varying from twelve to sixteen, and the leaflets from twenty to thirty pairs, the entire leaf resembling the frond of a fern in appearance. The racemes of flowers are of a fine golden colour.   [A. S.]

PELTOPHYLLUM. A small slender leafless Brazilian annual, differing from *Triuris* in having six lobes to the perianth and six stamens instead of three, and forming part of the small group of *Triurideæ* nearly allied to *Alismaceæ*. The name *Peltophyllum* was given by Gardner from a peltate leaf which he believed to belong to the same plant. This has been proved by Miers

PELTOSTIGMA. The name of a genus of *Rutaceæ* to which Sir W. J. Hooker had applied that of *Pachystigma*. It is represented by a much-branched shrub, native of Jamaica, having its leaves ternate, its flower-stalks axillary, branched, with leafy bracts, and its flowers large white, fragrant, and hairy on the outside. The calyx consists of three overlapping segments, the innermost petal-like; petals four, concave; stamens numerous, inserted in two rows on to a large fleshy stalk supporting the ovary, which has eight compartments, each containing two ovules; stigma sessile, large, fleshy, irregularly lobed. Fruit of eight dry divergent carpels adherent by their bases, each two-valved with a single ~~seed~~ from the non-development of one of ~~ovules~~. [M. T. M.]

PELVIFORM. Like Cyathiform, but flatter.

PEMPHIS. A genus of *Lythraceæ*, inhabiting the shores of tropical Asia and Madagascar. They have shrubby stems, covered with short white down, opposite oblong-lanceolate entire leaves, and axillary solitary one-flowered peduncles with two bracts at the base. Flowers white, with a turbinate twelve-lobed calyx, the six inner erect, the six outer smaller and spreading; petals six, obovate; stamens twelve, alternately smaller; style short; stigma capitate; capsule membranous, six-valved, three-celled at the base, opening transversely; seeds numerous. [J. T. S.]

PENÆACEÆ. (*Geissolomeæ, Sarcocollads.*) A natural order of monochlamydeous dicotyledons belonging to Lindley's rhamnal alliance of perigynous Exogens. They consist of shrubs, with opposite entire exstipulate leaves, found at the Cape of Good Hope, and have no known properties of importance. Perianth coloured salver-shaped, with a four-lobed limb; stamens perigynous, four or eight, alternate with the lobes of the perianth; ovary superior, four-celled; ovules usually in pairs, anatropal, ascending or suspended; style simple; stigmas four. Fruit a four-celled four-valved capsule; seed erect or pendulous; nucleus a fleshy mass, without distinction of albumen or embryo. There are about half a dozen known genera, and twenty-one species. Examples: *Penæa, Geissoloma.* [J. H. B.]

PENÆA. As restricted in De Candolle's *Prodromus* this genus, the type of the order *Penæaceæ*, contains half a dozen little branching Cape shrubs, with small flat entire leaves, and solitary axillary flowers at the ends of the branches, where they usually form little heads, surrounded by coloured leaf-like persistent bracts. The flowers have a coloured calyx, with a tube scarcely longer than the limb, and no petals; four stamens with extremely short filaments, a thick connective, and the valves of the anther-cells thickly fringed; a smooth ovary with two erect ovules at the base of each of the four cells; and a four-winged style bearing four flat stigmas in the shape of a cross. The four-celled four-valved capsule is covered by the persistent enlarged calyx. A good many other species have been referred to it, but those are removed to other genera; and amongst them the plant called *Penæa Sarcocolla* in many works, from which the ancient gum-resin Sarcocolla is (without proof) said to have been derived. This is now placed in the genus *Sarcocolla.* [A. S.]

PENANG LAWYERS. A commercial name given to walking-sticks made from the stems of *Licuala acutifida.*

PENCIL-FLOWER. *Stylosanthes.*

PENGHAWAR DJAMBI. The name of a celebrated styptic afforded by the down or soft hair-like scales of the stem of some species of *Cibotium*. Its action is probably mechanical, as chemical analysis affords nothing peculiar. [M. J. B.]

PENGUIN. *Bromelia Pinguin.*

PENICILLARIA. A genus of grasses belonging to the tribe *Paniceæ*, the species of which are described by Steudel under *Pennisetum.* [D. M.]

PENICILLATE, PENICILLIFORM. Resembling a camel's-hair pencil; consisting of, or covered with, hairs which are nearly parallel with each other. Sometimes, marked with colour as if laid on in streaks with a camel's-hair pencil.

PENICILLIUM. A genus of naked-spored thread-moulds with a jointed stem branched at the top, each branch having a chain of spores either simple or divided. These spores are sometimes smooth, sometimes rough with little points. *P. glaucum* is one of the commonest of moulds, growing on all kinds of substances, and entering largely into the composition of yeast, but more especially of the Vinegar Plant. The species assume frequently very beautiful colours. A rose-coloured species, for instance, the agent in the destruction, some years since, of the barrack-bread at Paris, which was so much canvassed, attains its perfect growth a few hours after the bread comes from the oven. An apricot-coloured species occurs on fungi. Occasionally the same species will put on three or four different tints in the course of its growth. [M. J. B.]

PENNANTIA. A genus of *Anacardiaceæ* consisting of trees from New Zealand and Norfolk Island, with alternate simple leathery leaves, and small white or yellowish flowers in a corymbose panicle. The calyx is minute, cup-shaped, deciduous; petals five, lanceolate; stamens five, disk none; fruit fleshy, one-seeded. [J. T. S.]

PENNIFORM. Having the ribs of a leaf arranged as in a pinnated leaf, but confluent at the point, as in the Date-palm.

PENNINERVED, or PENNIVEINED. Having ribs or principal veins running straight from the midrib to the margin at equal distances.

PENNISETUM. A genus of grasses belonging to the tribe *Paniceæ*, and distinguished by the double involucre, composed of many bristles, the centre unequal, the inner pinnated, bearded. Spikelets two to four; glume two-valved, unequal; lower floret male, upper hermaphrodite, both sessile; pales cartilaginous. Steudel describes eighty-seven species, which are widely distributed, but mostly natives of subtropical countries. Several of them are very ornamental, and consequently cultivated in gardens. *P. longistylum* is sufficiently hardy to bear the winter in the open air in many parts of Britain, and is a very beautiful grass. [D. M.]

PENNY-LEAVES. *Cotyledon Umbilicus.*

PENNY-ROT. *Hydrocotyle vulgaris.*

PENNYROYAL. *Mentha Pulegium.* —, AMERICAN. *Hedeoma pulegioides.* —, BASTARD. *Trichostema dichotomum.* —, FALSE. *Isanthus cæruleus.* —, MOCK. *Hedeoma pulegioides.*

PENNYROYAL-TREE. *Satureja viminea.*

PENNYWORT. *Sibthorpia europæa*; also *Hydrocotyle, Cotyledon Umbilicus,* and *Linaria Cymbalaria.* —, MARSH. *Hydrocotyle vulgaris.*

PENSACRE. (Fr.) *Œnanthe crocata.*

PENSÉE or **P. ANNUELLE.** (Fr.) *Viola tricolor.* — DES JARDINS. *Viola tricolor hortensis.* — SAUVAGE. *Viola tricolor arvensis.* — VIVACE. *Viola altaïca.*

PENTA. In Greek compounds = five.

PENTACOCCOUS. Composed of five cocci, or shells splitting with elasticity, and falling off a central axis or column.

PENTADESMA *butyracea,* the Butter and Tallow tree of Sierra Leone, constitutes a genus of *Clusiaceæ,* allied to *Moronobea* and *Platonia,* but differing in its sepals passing gradually into the petals, which are imbricate but scarcely contorted. It is a large tree, yielding in several parts, especially in the fruit when cut, a yellow greasy juice, whence is derived its popular name. The leaves are opposite, coriaceous, and elegantly marked with numerous parallel veins; the flowers large and handsome, solitary and terminal. The fruits are said to be eaten in the country.

PENTAGLOTTIS. A name given by Wallich to an East Indian herb, which proves to be a species of *Melhania.*

PENTAPERA. A genus of heathworts, having the calyx equal and five-parted; the corolla ovate, its border five-cleft; the stamens ten, the anthers separate and without awns; and the fruit a five-celled capsule. The only species is a heath-like shrub, growing on calcareous rocks in Sicily; it was formerly known as *Erica Sicula.* The name is from the Greek, and indicates the repetition of the number five in the parts of the flower. [G. D.]

PENTAPETES. A genus of *Byttneriaceæ* of the tribe *Dombeyeæ,* now restricted to a single species, an East Indian erect more or less hispid annual, with narrow leaves, and rather showy red flowers on short axillary peduncles. The genus is distinguished from *Trochetia,* to which it is most nearly allied, by the more herbaceous calyx, and the style undivided to the top.

PENTAPHRAGMA. A genus of doubtful position, but usually referred to the order of bellworts. It is distinguished by having the seed-vessel connected with the calyx by means of prolongations to which the five stamens are attached. The only species is *P. begoniæfolia,* a native of Pulo-Penang; it is a creeping woolly herbaceous plant, with leaves like those of a *Begonia,* and clusters of white flowers. The name indicates the five prolongations on whi the stamens are inserted. [G. D

PENTAPTERA. An almost exclusively Indian genus of *Combretaceæ,* closely allied to and by some botanists considered to form a section of *Terminalia,* from which, however, it is readily distinguished by the thick leathery egg-shaped fruit having five or sometimes seven equal wings produced longitudinally and at regular distances all round. About a dozen species are known, all large trees, with opposite or nearly opposite entire leaves, furnished with two glands at the base, and axillary or terminal spikes of flowers without petals, and frequently with one of the sexes abortive. The tube of their calyx is egg-shaped and marked with five or seven ribs, which ultimately enlarge and form the wings of the fruit; and the limb is bell-shaped and five-cleft.

P. glabra is a large smooth-barked timber tree, with a trunk six or eight feet in diameter and from fifty to eighty feet high, without a branch. It is common in the teak forests of Pegu, and affords an excellent dark-brown timber, useful for mast-pieces, spars, and other purposes connected with shipbuilding. In Canara, on the western coast of the peninsula of India, the natives obtain a kind of lime by calcining the bark and wood, which they prefer to ordinary lime for eating with betel-nut, and also use for whitewashing. [A. S.]

PENTAPTEROUS. Having five wings.

PENTAPTERYGIUM. One of the genera into which *Vaccinium* has been somewhat unnecessarily divided. The species are Indian shrubs frequently found growing on trees. The flowers are axillary, solitary or in clusters; the calyx-tube provided with five wings (whence the name of the genus), and its limb is divided into five ovate segments; the corolla tubular, five-angled, five-lobed, the lobes short; stamens ten, distinct, the anthers sometimes provided with two short projecting points at the back, and prolonged into two long tubular processes opening at the top by a roundish hole; stigma truncate; berry subglobose, five-winged, five-celled, many-seeded, crowned by the limb of the calyx

P. flavum is remarkable for the yellow colour of its flowers, an unusual occurrence in the *Vacciniaceæ*. [M. T. M.]

PENTARHAPHIA. A genus of *Gesneraceæ*, composed of shrubby or half-shrubby plants inhabiting the West India Islands. The calyx is in shape like an inverted cone, and has five to ten ribs, and five long subulate lobes; the corolla is either tubular or nearly campanulate, and the stamens are projected above it. The stem and branches are resinous, the leaves oblong or obovate, generally toothed at the margin, and the flowers solitary or in umbels in the axils of the leaves. About fifteen species are recorded, but nothing is known about their uses. [B. S.]

PENTAS. A genus of shrubby *Cinchonaceæ*, natives of Western tropical Africa, and named in consequence of the parts of the flower being in fives. The segments of the calyx-limb are unequal, and have sometimes one or two small glands in the notches between them; corolla with a long tube, bell-shaped, the throat hairy in the inside, and the limb with five ovate smooth segments, which overlap one another in the bud; filaments short, bearing linear anthers; disk surmounting the ovary, thick; style simple, with two-lobed stigmas; capsule nearly globular, the apex free, two-celled, opening by valves; seeds numerous.

P. carnea is a favourite hothouse shrub with broad leaves and dense terminal tufts of pink flowers. Professor Oliver has pointed out a peculiarity in the hairs of the corolla of this plant; the upper ones lining the throat are of one cell, those occurring in the tube are of more than one cell, the constituent cells containing moreover a spirally coiled fibre. [M. T. M.]

PENTASACME. Erect glabrous herbs, with perennial roots, opposite ovate lanceolate or linear leaves, and axillary peduncles bearing two rather large yellowish flowers. The five-cleft calyx, rotate corolla, and narrow smooth elongated fruit, are amongst the leading features of this small genus of *Asclepiadaceæ*, of whose four species we know little except that they inhabit India and China. [B. S.]

PENTASPADON. A large Borneo tree, with pinnate leaves, and axillary panicles of small white flowers, forming a genus of *Anacardiaceæ*, distinguished from *Rhus* and its allies, chiefly by small spathulate or capitate staminodia alternating with the stamens, and by a depressed ovary with a short broad recurved stigma. The fruit is unknown.

PENTHORUM. A genus of *Crassulaceæ*, consisting of two species, both inhabiting swamps and ditches —*P. chinense* those of China, *P. sedoides* those of the United States and Canada. *P. sedoides* commonly goes by the name of Virginian Stonecrop in the United States. Like its congener, it is an erect herb, not succulent (like so many of the members of the order to which it belongs), with alternate membranaceous serrated leaves, and greenish-yellow flowers, unilateral on the simple branches of the cyme. The calyx has five sepals; the corolla either five petals or none; there are ten stamens; and the capsule is five-celled, and encloses numerous seeds. [B. S.]

PENTLANDIA. A Peruvian genus of *Amaryllidaceæ*, allied to *Stenomesson*, and consisting of a beautiful bulbous plant, *P. miniata*, which bears a solitary lanceolate leaf appearing before the blossoms, and a solid scape supporting an umbel of about half a dozen drooping vermilion-coloured flowers. The perianth is tubular, contracted and subcylindrical at the base, ventricose above, and terminating in six short somewhat spreading segments; there are six stamens without any connecting membrane, but alternating with six scales according to Kunth. The capsule is three-celled and many-seeded. [T. M.]

PENTSTEMON. Herbaceous perennials belonging to the order *Scrophulariaceæ*, characterised by having a rudimentary fifth stamen, from which the genus derives its name. In all the species the leaves are opposite. The handsome flowers, which grow in clustered panicles, are purple, blue, rose-coloured, white, pale yellow, or more rarely scarlet. The corolla is usually two-lipped oblong and tubular, in some species nearly campanulate. They are natives of America, and being very ornamental are much cultivated as border plants. [C. A. J.]

PEON. The Penang name for the straight spars of the Piney-tree, *Calophyllum angustifolium*.

PÉONE. (Fr.) *Pæonia.*

PEONY, or PIONY. *Pæonia.*

PEPERIDGE. *Nyssa aquatica.*

PEPEROMIA. An extensive genus of *Piperaceæ*, abundant in Central and Southern America, and found also in the Sandwich Islands, in the islands of the Pacific, in Southern Africa, and in the East Indies. They differ considerably in habit and general appearance, according to the situation in which they grow. The majority are small fleshy creeping plants, growing on trunks of trees or on damp rocks; others are erect, of a more or less shrubby character, and are terrestrial in their habits. The branches and leaves vary much in their arrangement; the latter are usually fleshy and stalked, rarely membranous, smooth or hairy, ribbed, green or coloured, occasionally with glandular dots. The spikes of flowers are variously disposed; the flowers scattered or crowded, with leafy and deciduous, or fleshy and persistent bracts, and perfect, each with two free stamens. Ovary ovate, with a roundish warty or somewhat brush-like stigma. Fruit sessile, or tapering at the base into a kind of stalk. Several species are cultivated for the sake of their foliage and as objects of curiosity rather than beauty, though the foliage of some and the graceful slender spikes of others render them desirable inmates of the stovehouse. [M. T. M.]

PEPINO. A Spanish name for *Cucumis sativus.*

PEPLAMOOR. An Indian name for the Long Pepper.

PÉPLIDE. (Fr.) *Euphorbia Chamæsyce.*

PEPLIS. An unpretending herbaceous aquatic belonging to the *Lythraceæ*, common in brooks and watery places on a gravelly or sandy soil in many parts of England. The stems, which are of a reddish hue, are prostrate, branched at the base, and only a few inches long; bearing in the axils of the upper leaves, which are smooth and obovate, inconspicuous flowers. *P. Portula*, or Water Purslane, occurs over the greater part of Europe. There are no other species worthy of notice. French, *Péplide*; German, *Zipfelblume.* [C. A. J.]

PEPO, PEPONIDA, PEPONIUM. A one-celled many-seeded inferior fruit, with parietal placentæ, and a pulpy interior, such as a Gourd.

PEPON. An Italian name for the Water Melon.

PEPPER. *Piper.* —, AFRICAN. *Habzelia aromatica.* —, ANISE. *Xanthoxylon mantchuricum.* —, BELL. *Capsicum grossum.* —, BETEL. *Chavica Betle.* —, BIRD. *Capsicum baccatum.* —, BITTER. *Xanthoxylon Daniellii.* —, BLACK. *Piper nigrum.* —, BONNET. *Capsicum tetragonum.* —, BOULON. *Habzelia æthiopica.* —, CAYENNE. A condiment prepared from the dried powdered fruits of several species of *Capsicum*, as *baccatum, frutescens, annuum.* —, CHINESE. *Xanthoxylon piperitum.* —, CUBEB. *Cubeba officinalis.* —, ETHIOPIAN. *Habzelia æthiopica.* —, GOAT. *Capsicum frutescens.* —, GUINEA. *Habzelia æthiopica*; also *Capsicum annuum*, and a name for Cayenne Pepper. —, JAMAICA. *Eugenia Pimenta.* —, JAPANESE. *Xanthoxylon piperitum.* —, JAVA. *Cubeba officinalis.* —, LONG. The fruit-spikes of *Chavica officinarum* and *C. Roxburghii.* —, MALAGHATTA. *Habzelia æthiopica.* —, MALAGUETTA or MELEGUETA. *Amomum Melegueta.* —, MONKEY. *Habzelia æthiopica.* —, MOUNTAIN. The seeds of *Capparis sinaica.* —, NATIVE, of New Holland. *Tasmannia aromatica.* —, NEGRO. *Habzelia æthiopica.* —, POOR MAN'S. The provincial name of *Lepidium latifolium.* —, STAR. *Xanthoxylon Daniellii.* —, WALL. *Sedum acre.* —, WATER. *Polygonum Hydropiper*, and *Elatine Hydropiper.* —, WHITE. The seeds of *Piper nigrum* deprived of their skins. —, WILD. An Indian name for the fruits of *Vitex trifolia.*

PEPPER-BRAND. The same as Bunt.

PEPPERBUSH, SWEET. An American name for *Clethra.*

PEPPERCORN. *Vibrio.*

PEPPER-CROP. *Sedum acre.*

PEPPER-DULSE. The common name of *Laurencia pinnatifida*, sometimes eaten in salads, but very inferior in point of quality to some other kinds of esculent seaweeds. [M. J. B.]

PEPPER-ELDER. A West Indian name for *Peperomia, Enckea,* and *Artanthe.*

PEPPERMINT. *Mentha piperita.* —, AUSTRALIAN. *Mentha australis.* —, SMALL. *Thymus Piperella.* —, TASMANIAN. *Eucalyptus amygdalina.*

PEPPERMINT-TREE. *Eucalyptus amygdalina,* and *E. piperita.*

PEPPER-POT. The man-dram, a West Indian appetizing preparation of capsicum, ochro, and other ingredients.

PEPPER-ROD. *Croton humilis.*

PEPPER-ROOT. *Dentaria diphylla.*

PEPPER-SHRUB. *Schinus Molle.*

PEPPER-TREE, AUSTRALIAN. *—mys aromatica.*

PEPPERWORT. *Lepidium*; also *Dentaria diphylla.*

PEPPERWORTS. Lindley's name for the *Piperaceæ.*

PER. When prefixed to Latin terms increases their force, as *persimilis* = very like.

PÉRAGU. (Fr.) *Clerodendron.* — À FEUILLES EN CŒUR. *Clerodendron infortunatum.*

PERAMA. A genus of tropical American annual plants belonging to the *Cinchonaceæ.* The stems are simple or branched, covered with straggling hairs, and having opposite or ternate sessile leaves, united at the base. The flowers are in terminal heads or spikes, with or without bracts; calyx-limb with only two leafy segments in front, the hinder ones being wanting, corolla funnel-shaped, hairy within, provided with three small scales, the limb divided into three or four ovate acute segments; stamens slightly protruding from the tube, the anthers bearded, at the base; ovary with three compartments, each containing a single ovule, the style slender, and the stigma divided into two teeth. Fruit capsular, surmounted by the persistent segments of the calyx and opening by a transverse slit, so as to detach the upper portion of the capsule from the lower, like a lid from a box. [M. T. M.]

PERAMAN. A resin obtained from a species of *Moronobæa* by the Orinoco Indians.

PERANEMA. A genus of polypodiaceous ferns typical of the *Peranemeæ*, and sometimes known by the name of *Sphæropteris.* The only species is a large tripinnate Indian fern, with stout roundish rhizomes, and herbaceous fronds bearing globose involucrate sori, but distinguished from all the other genera with sori of this character by having the involucres distinctly stalked. It has the veins free. [T. M.]

PERAPETALUM. The shaggy covering of such flowers as *Menyanthes*.

PERAPHYLLUM. A membranous expansion of the calyx formed after the fruit begins to ripen, or from the beginning.

PERAPHYLLUM. A low scrubby much-branched shrub, from the Blue Mountains of North-west America, with rigid lanceolate much-crowded leaves terminating the branches. It forms a genus of *Rosaceæ*, allied in many respects to *Amelanchier*, but the fruit contains two or sometimes three almost distinct carpels.

PERCE-FEUILLE. (Fr.) *Bupleurum rotundifolium*.

PERCE-MOUSSE. (Fr.) *Polytrichum*.

PERCE-MURAILLE. (Fr.) *Parietaria*.

PERCE-NEIGE. (Fr.) *Galanthus nivalis*; also *Leucojum vernum*, and *Primula veris*.

PERCE-PIER. (Fr.) *Alchemilla arvensis*.

PERCE-PIERRE. (Fr.) *Crithmum maritimum*. — DES CHAMPS. *Alchemilla arvensis*.

PEREBEA. An imperfectly known genus of *Artocarpaceæ*, represented by a tree, native of Guiana, which has alternate leathery serrated leaves, the younger ones being concealed within the convolute stipules. The flowers are diœcious. The males are undescribed; the females are placed upon a leathery receptacle, scaly on the outside, at first concave but ultimately reflexed, and have a tubular four-toothed perianth, a free ovate ovary with a terminal cylindrical style, and a two-lobed stigma. Fruit one-seeded, surrounded by the succulent perianth. [M. T. M.]

PERELLE D'AUVERGNE. (Fr.) *Lecanora parella*.

PERENNIAL, PERENNANS, PERENNIS. Lasting for several years, and yet flowering every year.

PÉRÉPÉ. (Fr.) *Clusia*.

PERESKIA (sometimes written *Pierescia*). A genus of *Cactaceæ*, unlike the rest of the order in that several of its species have broad flat veiny leaves like those of other plants, while the remainder have fleshy cylindrical or partially flattened leaves. The genus contains about a dozen species, a few of which are tree-like and have woody stems; but the majority are shrubs with fleshy stems, and round branches armed with tufts of spines, and bearing terminal solitary or clustered flowers, frequently upon short stalks. The calyx-tube is equal with the ovary, and divided into leafy segments, and the petals are broad and expanded in a rose-like manner; the stamens are numerous, free, and shorter than the petals, and the thread-like style bears a many-rayed stigma. The fruits are pear or egg-shaped, with a broad scar at the top surrounded by the leafy segments of the calyx.

In the West Indies, where it is indigenous, *P. aculeata* is called the Gooseberry shrub or Barbados Gooseberry. It grows about fifteen feet high, the stem armed with bundles of straight spines, and having trailing branches bearing oblong elliptical leaves and bunches of ornamental white flowers, which produce yellow eatable and pleasant-tasted fruits, used in the West Indies for making preserves in the same way that gooseberries are with us.

P. Bleo is called Bleo by the natives of New Grenada, in which country it is indigenous. It is a shrub growing eight or ten feet in height, with rather soft fleshy leaves about five or six inches long, of an elliptical form, sharp-pointed at the top, and tapering to the base; and handsome rose-coloured flowers, with ten petals in two series, the inner of which are the largest and deepest-coloured. The leaves are eaten as salad in Panama. [A. S.]

PERFECT. Complete in all the usual parts.

PERFOLIATE. When the two basal lobes of an amplexicaul leaf are united together, so that the stem appears to pass through the substance of the leaf.

PERGAMENEOUS. Having the texture of parchment.

PERGULARIA. Twining shrubs inhabiting India, the Moluccas, and Madagascar, having broad ovate or cordate leaves, and interpetiolar cymes bearing greenish or yellowish flowers, generally highly scented, constitute this genus of *Asclepiadaceæ*. The calyx is five-cleft, the corolla hypocrateriform, and the fruit smooth and ventricose. *P. odoratissima*, termed Liane Tonquin in Mauritius, Malatti Tunkat in Java, is a favourite in our hot-houses on account of its green sweetly scented blossoms, and is indigenous to the East Indies and Java. Together with *P. minor, montana, pallida, coromandeliana, accedens*, and *bifida*, it yields a blue dye. The young leaves of *P. edulis* are eaten as a potherb in Japan. *P. sanguinolenta*, from the West Coast of Africa, yields a kind of dragon's-blood, with which the dragon's-blood of commerce is adulterated. [B. S.]

PERI. In Greek compounds = around, or placed on something surrounding some other part.

PERI. The root of *Gastrodia Cunninghamii*.

PERIANTH. The calyx and corolla combined; that is to say, when they look so much alike that they cannot be readily distinguished, as in a hyacinth.

The same term is applied, among liverworts, to the membranous covering, consisting of one or more pieces, immediately surrounding the archegonium or veil which contains the ripe capsule. The perianth is sometimes wanting, and replaced by certain scales which are termed involucre. The involucre and perianth coexist sometimes in the same plant, showing that they are distinct from each other. [M. J. B.]

PERIANTHOMANIA. An unnatural multiplication of sepals, bracts, &c. Examples are afforded by the wheat-ear carnation, the curious sweetwilliam figured below, and the hose-in-hose primrose. In

Dianthus barbatus in a state of Perianthomania.

most cases the fertility of the plant is affected, and sometimes all attempt at the production of stamens and pistils is abortive. [M. J. B.]

PERIBLEMA *cuspidata* is the only representative of a genus of doubtful affinity, but provisionally classed with *Bignoniaceæ* or *Crescentiaceæ*. It is a native of Madagascar, is shrubby, has opposite simple and entire leaves, and axillary pedicels producing from one to three flowers. Its fruit is unknown. The calyx is five-cleft, and surrounded by a membranaceous rather inflated involucre; the corolla is funnelshaped and five-lobed; the stamens four in number, the anthers glabrous; and the ovary two-celled, each cell enclosing but two ovules. [B. S.]

PERICARP. The shell or rind of all fruits, taken as a whole. When it separates into layers, each layer may have a different name, but the whole is still the pericarp.

PERICARPIAL, or PERICARPIC. Of, or belonging to, a pericarp.

PERICARPIUM. The peridium of certain fungals.

PERICHÆTIUM (adj. PERICHÆTIAL). A collection of minute leaves surrounding the base of the seta of a moss.

PERICLADIUM. The dilated sheathing base of some petioles, especially among umbellifers.

PERICLINIUM. The involucre of composites.

PERICLINOIDES. A false involucre formed of paleæ of the receptacle in composites, surrounding the sides of an elevated receptacle having florets at its summit, as in *Evax*.

PERICLISTIA. A genus composed of two Guiana species of doubtful affinity, but provisionally classed with *Samydaceæ*. The *Periclistias* are shrubs with alternate ovate or oblong and quite entire leaves, and terminal flowers, having five sepals, petals, and fertile stamens, a simple style, and an ovary with numerous ovules. The fruit is unknown. [B. S.]

PERIDERM. The outer cellular layer of bark, below the epidermis.

PERICLYMENUM. *Lonicera Periclymenum.*

PERIDIOLUM. A membrane by which the spores of some algals are immediately covered; also the diminutive of *Peridium*, a secondary and interior peridium.

PERIDIUM. A term used for the outer coat or coats of certain *Fungi*, especially in the puffballs and other closely allied natural orders. In the puffballs and *Podaxinei* it is composed of interlaced threads with an admixture here and there of cells; and in these occasionally, as universally in the *Phalloidei*, the component threads are in parts highly gelatinous. In the myxogastres it is composed apparently of an amorphous substance which becomes gradually indurated and brittle, with a strong admixture in many cases of carbonate of lime. In such genera as *Geaster* the outer peridium is thick and composed sometimes of two separable coats, while in *Broomeia* it is represented by a thick corky stratum. In *Lycoperdon* it is resolved into warts, spines, or other excrescences, which are often intimately connected with the inner coat. In *Onygena*, which belongs to another series, it is simple and composed of threads and not of cells, as is the case with most perithecia. [M. J. B.]

PERIGONE, PERIGONIUM. Usually the same as Perianth.

PERIGYNIUM. The hypogynous setæ of sedges; the flask-like calyx in which the ovary of *Carex* is included; also the hypogynous disk of other plants.

PERIGYNOUS. Growing upon some part which surrounds the ovary, usually the calyx, though sometimes the corolla is also included within the meaning.

PERILLA. A genus of *Labiatæ*, having the calyx bell-shaped, unequally two-lipped, the upper three-cleft, the middle piece smallest; and the corolla about as long as the calyx, with its border in five nearly equal pieces. *P. nankinensis*, an annual species with deep purple leaves, is much used in the summer decoration of modern flower-gardens. [G. D.]

PERILOMIA. A genus of *Labiatæ*, distinguished by having the border of the corolla with its upper lip slightly bifid, the lower in three pieces, the middle of which is largest and notched, the others short and spreading; and the fruit dry, with a wing-like membranous border. The species are herbs or shrubs, natives of Peru and

Mexico, with solitary flowers springing from the axils of the ovate leaves. [G. D.]

PERINTEGER. Perfectly entire, or undivided.

PERIPHERIC. Of or belonging to circumference.

PERIPHERICO-TERMINAL. Belonging to the circumference and apex of a body; a term applied to stems which grow both at the sides, augmenting their diameter, and at the end, increasing their length.

PERIPHYLLIA. The hypogynous scales of grasses.

PERIPLOCA. A genus of *Asclepiadaceæ*, inhabiting Southern Europe and tropical parts of Africa and Asia, and consisting of about half a dozen twiners with ovate or lanceolate leaves, or without any leaves whatever. The flowers are arranged in axillary cymes. The calyx is five-cleft, the corolla rotate, and the fruit cylindrical and smooth. The milk of *P. græca*, a plant common in the hedges of Southern Europe and an inmate of our gardens, has been employed in the East for poisoning wolves. *P. linearifolia* is the Domaivo of Abyssinia. The roots of *P. vomitoria* and *P. ciliata*, two little-known plants, are used as emetics in Malabar; whilst a decoction of those of *P. viridiflora* is employed in the same country in ophthalmia, and the leaves for swollen feet. For other useful species formerly classed with *Periploca*, see HEMIDESMUS and CAMPTOCARPUS. [B. S.]

PERIPTEROUS. Surrounded by a wing-like expansion.

PERISPERM. The skin of a seed. Also the same as Albumen; thus *perispermic* is furnished with albumen.

PERISPORANGIUM. The indusium of ferns when it surrounds the spore-cases or sori.

PERISPORIACEI. A natural order of ascigerous *Fungi* characterised by the receptacles or perithecia being always closed except in decay, and the nucleus never softening into a gelatinous mass as in *Sphæriacei*. The asci are generally large, and sometimes solitary, and the sporidia less frequently eight or indeed definite than in neighbouring natural orders. The curious mycelium has been noticed under *Erysiphe*, now divided into several distinct genera. Most of the species are true parasites. See also OIDIUM. [M. J. B.]

PERISPORE, PERISPORIUM. The hypogynous setæ of sedges; also the skin of a spore.

PERISTACHYUM. The glumes of grasses.

PERISTERIA. A genus of *Orchidaceæ*, named from the Greek word *peristera*, a dove; the original species, *P. elata*, being known in Panama by the name *El Spirito Santo*, the Holy Ghost or Dove plant, in consequence of the resemblance of the column of the flower to a dove hovering with expanded wings, somewhat like the conventional dove seen in artistic representations of the Holy Ghost. Three other species are known; and several others have been referred to the genus, but are now placed in *Acineta*. All have fleshy pseudobulbs, large plicate leaves, and radical many-flowered scapes, with handsome neatly globular fleshy flowers. Their sepals are concave and connate at the base, and the petals resemble them, except that they are a little smaller; the lip has its lower half continuous with the column and sagittate at the base, and its upper half articulated with the lower, undivided, and bent down over the face of the column, which is short, fleshy, and wingless; and the two pollenmasses are furrowed, and sessile on a narrow gland.

P. elata, the Dove plant, has striated green pseudobulbs, as large as swan's eggs, bearing three to five lanceolate strongly ribbed and plicate leaves, sometimes upwards of a yard high and six inches across. Its flower-stem rises from the base of the pseudobulbs, and attains a height of from four to six feet; its upper portion, for about a third of its length, being occupied by a spike of almost globose very sweet-scented flowers, each about an inch and a half across, and of a creamy-white, with little lilac specks on the base of the lip. [A. S.]

PERISTOME. When the lid breaks off from the capsule of a moss, the edge of the cup is either naked, or is fringed with one or more whorls of variously fashioned teeth (the peristome), the outer of which is continuous with the inner layer of cells constituting the wall of the capsule, which is separated from the spore-cyst by a cavity traversed by a few articulated threads—the inner from the outer layer of cells in the spore-cyst. The tissues of this latter generate the spores, leaving mostly a barren cylinder in the centre, which is called the columella. The teeth consist of one or more layers of cells, and are mostly transversely articulate, and often striate longitudinally. They are usually definite in number, being four or multiples of four. They are variously combined, and often have transverse processes like little projecting beams on the inner side, called ' trabeculæ.' The teeth of the inner whorl may be separate, or connected at the tips and joined together by a common plicate membrane. Other modifications occur, and there is often a deciduous external ring of cells at the line of dehiscence of the capsule. [M. J. B.]

PERISTROPHE. A genus of *Acanthaceæ* containing a score of species, natives of India. They are herbs, with showy purple flowers included in a two-valved involucre, and arranged in axillary and thin terminal umbels. The calyx is five-cleft; the corolla two-lipped and resupinate, its lower lip being uppermost and three-toothed, the upper one entire or two-toothed; there are two stamens, with narrow two-celled anthers; and the capsule is two-celled with a long flattened seedless lower portion and four-seeded above.   [W. C.)

PERISTYLUS. According to Lindley the species of orchids collected under this genus, of which there are upwards of twenty, have all the characters of *Platanthera*, except that, instead of a galeate perianth and long slender spur, their calyx is always campanulate, and the spur very short and often pouch-like. Most of the species belong to the temperate regions of the northern hemisphere; but a few are found within the tropics, principally in Ceylon, Java, and the Mascaren Islands. Nearly all have at one time or other been referred to other genera, such as *Herminium* and *Habenaria*; and the two British species, P. *albidus* and P. *viridis*, are to be found under the latter genus in many of our local floras. [A. S.]

PERITHECIA. A word used to indicate those kinds of cysts or capsules which contain asci, and therefore not strictly applicable to those which merely give rise to sporophores producing naked spores. The Messrs. Tulasne have proposed for these the name of 'pycnidia,' and for the fruit that of 'stylospores.' Perithecia are of various colours, as yellow, blue, red, black, &c., and are mostly more or less decidedly cellular in structure, their walls being of greater or less density and thickness, and more or less decidedly different from the substance in which they are immersed when a stroma is present. In consequence, it is sometimes impossible to distinguish them from the stroma; and for this reason, in *Dothidea* the ascigerous cavities are called cells and not perithecia, the only distinctive mark of the genus. In some cases a third kind of cyst occurs in *Sphæriæ* and some other genera, which contains naked bodies supposed to have the function of pollengrains. In this case the cysts are called 'spermagonia,' and the enclosed bodies 'spermatia.'   [M. J. B.]

PERITROPAL. Directed horizontally as regards the axis of a fruit.

PERIWINKLE. *Vinca.*

PERLEBIA. A Brazilian tree said to be common in some parts of the province of Minas Geraes, having the appearance of a small-leaved *Bauhinia*, but differing from that genus, according to Martius, in the pod, which is divided into several cells, as in some *Cassias*, by transverse partitions between the seeds. It is only known as yet from a very short notice in Martius's Travels, and may possibly prove to be some described species of *Bauhinia*.

PERLIÈRE. (Fr.) *Gnaphalium.*

PERMAYRUTIE. An Indian name for the Malabar Catmint, *Anisomeles malabarica.*

PERNAMBUCO-WOOD. *Cæsalpinia echinata.*

PERNETTIA, or PERNETTYA. A genus of heathworts, distinguished by the presence of ten glands alternating with the stamens; by the convex and slightly five-lobed stigma; and by the five-celled fruit, each cell with many seeds. The species are small branched evergreen shrubs, with alternate leaves, and drooping white flowers. They are found in Peru and Mexico, and about the southern extremity of South America. The name was given in honour of Pernetty, a French navigator.   [G. D.]

PÉROLE. (Fr.) *Centaurea Cyanus.*

PERONATE. Laid thickly over with a woolly substance, becoming a sort of meal.

PERONOSPORA. A genus of naked-spored moulds, separated from *Botrytis* by Corda on very insufficient grounds, but in later times proved by Caspary and others to exhibit such characters as render its separation imperative. The mycelium or hyphasma (as it is often called) creeps amongst the loose tissue of living leaves, and rapidly causes its destruction. From the mycelium, erect threads are given off, and make their way into the surrounding air through the stomates. These threads are mostly inarticulate, and more or less branched and often forked above, and have at their tips large generally ovate spores. Amongst the threads of the mycelium globose sacs are produced, containing a single spore. This structure has, however, been observed in a few species only. *Peronosporæ* are most active agents in the destruction of vegetables, and it is to the ravages of P. *infestans* that the potato murrain is due. This species differs from all others in the curious swellings which exist on the upper branches. [M. J. B.]

PEROTIS. A genus of grasses belonging to the tribe *Agrostideæ*. The inflorescence is in nearly simple spikes; spikelets one-flowered; glume two-valved, the valves with bristles at the end; pale one, nearly as long as the calyx. There are about half a dozen species, natives of the East Indies, China, and New Holland.   [D. M.]

PERPIGNAN-WOOD. A name under which the wood of *Celtis australis* is used by the French.

PERRETTE. (Fr.) *Citrus Limetta.*

PERROQUET. (Fr.) *Alströmeria psittacina.*

PERROTTETIA. A genus of *Celastraceæ*, consisting of unarmed shrubs, with alternate ovate serrate leaves, and minute flowers in slender axillary panicles. The calyx-lobes and petals are five each, the ovary is free and two-celled, with two erect ovules in each cell, and the fruit a small globular berry. There are four species known, from the mountains of New Grenada, Mexico, and the Sandwich Islands.

PERSEA. The Alligator Pear of tropical America, and its allies, form a genus of *Lauraceæ*, characterised by their perfect flowers having a more or less downy six-parted calyx, which persists at the base of the fruit but at length falls away, the segments being either unequal or nearly equal ; and twelve stamens in four series, the inner one of which is sterile and the three outer fertile, with four-celled anthers, the inner series of fertile ones having two globular stalked glands at their bases. All the species are trees, with alternate entire arch-nerved leaves, and panicles of small flowers in clusters, producing large fleshy one-seeded fruits, supported upon a thickened stalk.

P. gratissima, the Avocado or Alligator Pear, is a common tree in tropical America and the West India Islands, where it attains the height of twenty-five or thirty feet. It has elliptical leaves, narrow towards the base and about six inches long, and bears large pear-shaped fruits covered with a smooth brownish-green or deep-purple skin. These fruits are highly esteemed in the West Indies and tropical America, though strangers at first do not relish them. They contain a large quantity of firm pulp possessing a buttery or marrow-like taste, and are hence frequently called *Vegetable Marrow* or *Midshipman's Butter*. It is usually eaten with spice, lime-juice, or pepper and salt. An abundance of oil, useful for illuminating purposes and for soapmaking, may be obtained from the pulp by expression. The seeds yield a deep indelible black stain, and are used for marking linen. [A. S.]

PERSIAN-BERRIES. The seeds of *Rhamnus infectorius.*

PERSICA. The Peach, *Amygdalus Persica.*

PERSICARY. *Polygonum Persicaria.*

PERSICAIRE. (Fr.) *Polygonum.* — DÛ LEVANT. *Polygonum orientale.*

PERSIL, or P. COMMUN. (Fr.) *Petroselinum sativum.* — À LARGES FEUILLES. *Petroselinum peregrinum.* — BÂTARD. *Caucalis latifolia.* — D'ÂNE. *Anthriscus sylvestris.* — DE MACÉDOINE. *Athamanta macedonica.* — DES MARAIS. *Apium graveolens.* — DES MONTAGNES. *Athamanta* ; also *Ligusticum Levisticum.* — FRISÉ. Curled Parsley — SAUVAGE. *Anthriscus vulgaris.*

PERSIMMON. *Diospyros virginiana.*

PERSISTENT. Not falling off, but remaining green until the part which bears it is wholly matured : as the leaves of evergreen plants.

PERSONATÆ. A name given by Linnæus to a natural order embracing certain plants which have irregular gamopetalous or monopetalous corollas: such as figworts, verbenas, bignonias, &c.

PERSONATE. A term applied to a monopetalous corolla, the limb of which is unequally divided : the upper division or lip being arched, the lower prominent and pressed against it, so that when compressed the whole resembles the mouth of a gaping animal ; as the corolla of *Antirrhinum.*

PERSOONIA. An extensive genus of *Proteaceæ*, distinguished by having a calyx of four equal sepals, sometimes only four-cleft, thickened at the base, which occasionally is enlarged into a small sac ; by having a stamen inserted on the middle of each sepal or segment ; by its filiform style, generally longer than the stamens, straight or curved, with an obtuse stigma ; and by its one or two-celled fruit being a drupe, with a leathery covering, and having a single seed in each cell. The flowers are generally solitary, but at times are produced in terminal spikes, often clothed with brownish hairs. The leaves are scattered, leathery in texture ; needle-shaped as in *P. microcarpa, pinifolia, tenuifolia,* and *Chamæpitys* ; linear as in *P. mollis* and *longifolia* ; lanceolate as in *P. angulata* and *daphnoides* ; obovate as in *P. elliptica, marginata, velutina,* and *cornifolia* ; and oval and acuminate as in *P. Cunninghamii.* They form trees or large shrubs, and are found in most parts of Australia. One species, *P. Toro,* a lofty tree, is found in New Zealand. [R. H.]

PERTUSARIA. A genus of lichens belonging to the natural order *Endocarpei*, which are characterised by a pale single or double perithecium piercing the horizontal thallus by a distinct ostiolum. *Pertusaria* is distinguished by the perithecia being sunk several together in wart-like processes, while in *Porina*, separated from it—the species of which are inhabitants of warm climates, while those of *Pertusaria* belong more especially to the temperate zones—the perithecia are solitary. *Pertusaria* has large sporidia, which become blue when treated with iodine. *P. communis* is one of our commonest lichens on the trunks of trees. When barren, the mealy disks called soredia, which are so common on lichens, abound to such a degree that it assumes a totally different habit, and with some other metamorphosed species constitutes the spurious genus *Variolaria.* This again, especially on old trunks, spreads with the growth of the bark for many inches, and the soredia predominating over the crust it assumes the name of *Lepraria.* [M. J.B.]

PERTUSE. Having slits or holes.

PERULE. The covering of a leaf-bud formed by scales ; also a projection in the flower of orchids formed by the enlargement of two lateral sepals. See MENTUM.

PERVENCHE. (Fr.) *Vinca.* — DU CAP. *Vinca rosea.* —, GRANDE. *Vinca major.* —, PETITE. *Vinca minor.*

PERVILLÆA. A genus of *Asclepiadaceæ*, consisting of only one species, *P. tomentosa,* a Madagascar twiner, with opposite broad oval or obovate leaves, tomentose on the under-surface, and cymose flowers, of a yellowish colour blotched with purple. The calyx is five-cleft, the corolla rotate, and the fruit oblong, covered with woolly hair, and enclosing comose seeds. [B. S.]

PESCATOREA. This genus of orchids was founded upon a species from Veraguas, originally referred to *Huntleya*, and another from New Grenada was afterwards added to it; but it is now abandoned as a genus by its author, Dr. Reichenbach, and is reduced to a section of *Zygopetalum*, distinguished from the other sections of that genus by its slender semiterete column with a triangular ear on each side at its base, and its lip with a replicate limb, and a thick broad numerously plaited and folded crest near its base.   [A. S.]

PESETTE. (Fr.) *Cicer arietinum.*

PESOMERIA *tetragona.* An orchid from the Isle of Bourbon, belonging to the *Bletidæ* division of *Epidendreæ*, remarkable on account of its deciduous bracts and sepals, which fall off spontaneously soon after the flower expands. Its sepals and petals are almost alike in shape, size, and colour; the lip is undivided, cucullate, parallel with and partly surrounding the column, with the lower part, of which it is adnate and forms a slight protuberance at the bottom; the column is semiterete and thickened upwards, with a four-toothed anther-bed; and the pollen-masses four, unequal and bifid. The plant is terrestrial, and has sharply four-cornered jointed stems a foot or more high, broad membranous long-pointed leaves, and lateral peduncles bearing a loose spike of eight or ten largish flowers, of a reddish-brown internally and greenish externally, except the lip, which is yellow streaked with orange-red. [A.S.]

PESSALOO. An Indian name for *Phaseolus Mungo.*

PESSE. (Fr.) *Abies excelsa;* also *Hippuris.* — D'EAU. *Hippuris vulgaris.* — DU CANADA. *Abies canadensis.*

PESTALOZZIA. A very curious genus of coniomycetous *Fungi*, consisting of large septate spores springing from an obscure mycelium, and crowned with two or three delicate hyaline short threads proceeding from the same point. They form little dark specks on leaves, as of oranges, camellias, &c. A few years since some leaves of camellias were sent to us, with a view to ascertain the nature of a little parasite which was doing immense damage in one of our first-rate nurseries. The fungus was clearly *P. Guepini*, and as the genus had not before occurred in England, we were anxious to ascertain the origin of the camellias. As we suspected, they had been obtained from Italy, and no doubt the pest had been imported with them. This little history is important as showing how easily new diseases may be introduced from abroad, and consequently as it bears on the vexed question of the origin of the potato and vine diseases. The same name has been given by Zollinger to a cucurbitaceous genus, near *Telfairea.* [M. J .B.]

PESTILENCE-WEED. *Tussilago Petasites.*

PETALOMANIA. An unnatural multiplication, repression, or alteration of petals. Each flower has its proper number of petals, which can be increased only by some cause, the consequences of which must be characterised as disease. All double flowers, therefore, which arise from multiplication of petals, must be regarded as diseased, however they may be prized by the florist, and the more so as the tendency is mostly to check fertility. Repression or extreme diminution of petals, as in many species of *Silene* and allied genera, though not affecting fertility, must be referred to the same head. How far the changes which occasionally take place in such genera as *Catasetum* amongst the orchids, by means of which three different types are exhibited in the same spike or truss, are due to diseased action or not, is at present uncertain. The same remark applies to the occurrence of regular or (as they are called) peloriold flowers in *Antirrhinum* and other plants.   [M. J. B.]

PETALOSTYLIS. An Australian genus of *Leguminosæ*, comprising a shrub with pinnate leaves, and axillary clusters of yellow flowers. Calyx of five equal pieces; petals five spreading, nearly equal; filaments five, three fertile, two without anthers; ovary few-seeded, terminated by a large petaloid three-lobed style. [M. T. M.]

PETALS. The divisions of the corolla, when they are not united to each other by their edges.

PETALINE, PETALOID, PETAL-LIKE. Having the colour and texture of a common petal.

PETANIELLE. (Fr.) *Triticum turgidum.* — ROUSSE. A kind of *Triticum.*

PETARKURA. An Indian name for the seeds of *Gynocardia odorata.*

PETASITES. A genus of *Compositæ*, established for three or four species of *Tussilago*, which have the flower-heads partially dioecious in racemes, sometimes branching into panicles. The essential characters which separate them from the common coltsfoot with one-headed scapes are very slight; and the foliage is the same. They are all European, and one species, *P. vulgaris* or *Tussilago Petasites*, is frequent in sandy meadows on the banks of streams in England, and known under the popular name of Butterbur.

PET D'ÂNE. (Fr.) *Onopordon.* — DE LÉOPARD. *Doronicum.* — DU DIABLE. *Hura crepitans.*

PETER'SWORT. A West Indian name for *Ascyrum hypericoides.*

PETIOLANEOUS. Consisting of petiole only.

PETIOLAR, PETIOLACEOUS. Inserted upon the petiole; as *cirrhus petiolaris*, a tendril inserted on a petiole.

PETIOLE (adj. PETIOLATE). The stalk of a leaf. —, COMMON. The first and principal leafstalk in compound leaves;

when they have secondary or tertiary petioles, these are called partial.

PETIOLULAR. Of or belonging to a petiolule.

PETIOLULES (adj. PETIOLULATE). Petioles of a second degree; that is, partial petioles, such as belong to the leaflets of compound leaves.

PETIT ABSINTHE. (Fr.) *Artemisia pontica.* — BASILIC. *Ocimum minimum.* — CERISIER DES HOTTENTOTS. *Celastrus lucidus.* — CORAIL. *Cratægus corallina.* — CYPRÈS. *Santolina Chamæcyparissus.* — CYTISE. *Cytisus sessilifolius.* — ÉPEAUTRE. *Triticum monococcum.* — FLAMBE. *Iris pumila.* — HOUX. *Ruscus aculeatus.* — LISERON. *Convolvulus.* — MARCEAU. *Salix aurita.* — MUGUET. *Asperula odorata.* — PASSE-RAGE. *Lepidium graminifolium.* — POIS. *Pisum sativum.* — SOLEIL. *Helianthus multiflorus.*

PETITE BOURRACHE. (Fr.) *Omphalodes verna.* — BUGLOSSE. *Lycopsis arvensis.* — CHÉLIDOINE. *Ficaria ranunculoides.* — CHÊNE. *Teucrium Chamædrys* and *Veronica Chamædrys.* — CIGUË. *Æthusa Cynapium.* — CONSOUDE. *Omphalodes verna.* — DOUVE. *Ranunculus Flammula.* — ÉCLAIRE. *Ficaria ranunculoides.* — ENDIVE. *Cichorium Endivia angustifolia.* — ÉSULE. *Euphorbia esigua.* — JACINTHE. *Hyacinthus nonscriptus.* — MARGUERITE. *Bellis perennis.* — MAUVE. *Malva rotundifolia.* — ORTIE. *Urtica urens.* — OSEILLE. *Rumex Acetosella.* — PERVENCHE. *Vinca minor.* — RADIAIRE. *Astrantia minor.* — SAUGE. *Salvia hispanorum.* — TITHYMALE. *Euphorbia exigua.*

PETIT-BAUME. A West Indian name for a liquor obtained from *Croton balsamiferum.*

PETIT-GRAIN. An essential oil obtained from the fruit and leaves of *Citrus Bigaradia.*

PETIVERIACEÆ. (*Petiverieæ.*) A natural order of monochlamydeous dicotyledons belonging to Lindley's sapindal alliance of hypogynous Exogens. Undershrubs or herbs with a garlic-like odour, alternate entire stipulate leaves, and racemose or panicled flowers. Calyx polysepalous; no corolla; stamens indefinite, alternate with the calycine leaves; ovary superior, one-celled, with one style, and a lateral stigma; ovules erect. Fruit one-celled, indehiscent and dry, with a wing at the back. Natives of the West Indies and tropical America. There are three genera, and about a dozen species. [J. H. B.]

PETIVERIA. The four species of this genus typical of the *Petiverieæ*, all natives of tropical America, are erect branching undershrubs, with alternate entire glabrous minutely stipulate leaves, and long whip-like terminal and axillary spiked inflorescence, bearing very small remote sessile flowers, each with three bracts at its base, the side ones of which are much smaller than the other. It is characterised by having a four-parted herbaceous calyx, by its fruit being armed with four to six subulate reflexed sharp bristles or spines, and by its seeds having thin eccentric albumen and a straight embryo. All the species are remarkable for possessing a garlic-like odour and more or less acidity. *P. alliacea*, a widely distributed species, extending from Carolina to Guayaquil and Rio Janeiro, called Guinea-hen Weed in the West Indies, and Raiz de Guiné in Brazil, is extremely acrid, and in the latter countries it is put into warm baths to restore motion to paralysed limbs. [A. S.]

PETRÆA. A genus of *Verbenaceæ*, containing thirteen species of twining shrubs or small trees, natives of tropical America. They have opposite coriaceous leaves, and large violet flowers in showy loose racemes. The epicalyx is three-leaved persistent, and increases to a large size around the fruit; it is coloured and united to the tube of the calyx, which is funnel-shaped with five teeth alternating with the leaves of the epicalyx; the deciduous corolla has a short cylindrical tube, and spreading limb divided into five roundish lobes; there are four included stamens inserted in the throat of the corolla, sometimes with the rudiment of the fifth; and the ovary is seated on a subcylindrical fleshy gynophore. The capsule is enveloped in the calyx, and covered by its bent-down teeth; it is two-celled, each cell containing a single large seed. [W. C.]

PETROCALLIS. A genus of *Cruciferæ*, the only species of which, *P. pyrenaica*—a pretty little tufted perennial peculiar to alpine places in the Pyrenees, and growing in dense patches like some of our saxifrages—is placed in *Draba* by Hooker and Bentham. The stems, an inch or two high, are densely clothed with wedge-shaped lobed leaves, and terminate in a raceme of rather large purplish flowers which are followed by small oval swollen netted two-celled silicules, with one or two seeds in each cell. The prominent netted veins on the fruit together with cut leaves distinguish this plant from other species of *Draba*. [A. A. B.]

PETROPHILA. A large genus of *Proteaceæ*, having a regularly four-cleft calyx bearing on each of its segments a nearly sessile anther; a filiform style with a spindle-shaped stigma, generally constricted in the middle and articulated; and the fruit a nut containing a single seed, either winged or having hairy margins. The flowers grow in heads, rarely in spikes; the leaves are rigid, round, and filiform, or sometimes plane and lobed. They are large shrubs, natives of most parts of extratropical Australia, but principally of the south-western portions. [R. H.]

PETROSELINUM. A genus of the order *Umbelliferæ*, distinguished by having each half of the fruit with five equal narrow ribs; and one oil-vessel in each furrow, the line of junction having two. The plants are herbaceous, natives of Eastern Europe chiefly.

The Common Parsley, *P. sativum*, is a well-known potherb, the generic name of which is said by botanists to have been derived from the Greek *petros*, a stone, from its being a native of rocky or stony places; but there is reason to think that its name had a widely different origin. Parsley has ever been an object of superstitious observances; for besides its being the assigned plant from beneath which came our brothers and sisters, we remember how it was always considered such ill-luck to transplant it, that but few people in the midland counties could be got to perform such an act. Mr. John Jones of Gloucester, who has published some interesting notes upon this subject, on asking a person to whom the order to remove a bed of parsley to another place had been vainly repeated, the reason for this neglect, received the following reply: 'He was quite willing to root it up and destroy it entirely, but transplant it he would not, nor did he know any one who would willingly take upon himself the consequences of such an act.' Mr. Jones thinks that it is probable this herb was dedicated to Persephone, as Queen of the Dead, presuming her to be identical with Hecate or Selene, the resemblance of its Greek name (Selinon) to that of the last-named divinity at once suggesting its direct derivation from her. The correctness of this supposition is supported by other etymological considerations, as thus —its Greek name being preserved with the prefix of Peter:—

Archaic Greek .	. Σελινον.
Latin . . .	. *Petroselinum.*
Italian . .	. *Petroselino.*
German . .	. *Petersilie.*
French . .	. *Persil.*
Welsh . .	. *Perllys.*
English . .	. *Parsley.*

These names our authority freely translates Peter's Moon-plant, and adds that the connection of the name of Peter with it is suggestive of the policy by which the prejudices of the rude people amongst whom Christianity was first introduced were met and modified, in the transference of objects of reverential regard from the tutelage of long-honoured Pagan divinities to that of Christian saints. Parsley, thus dedicated to funereal rites by the Greeks, was afterwards consecrated to St. Peter in his character of successor to Charon, and doorkeeper of Paradise.

We incline to believe in this archæological derivation of the name, and more especially as superstition in connection with Parsley is widely spread over Europe, which accounts for the name being so much alike in different languages, as well as the reverential regard in which the plant itself is held.

P. segetum, the Corn Parsley, formerly a rare plant in the cornfields of Sussex, is now frequently met with in arable fields throughout England, into which it has doubtless spread with crop-seeds. [J. B.]

PETROSUS. Growing in stony places.

PETTIGREE, or **PETTIGRUE.** *Ruscus aculeatus.*

PETUNIA. A word modified from the Brazilian *petun*, tobacco, and applied to a genus of *Solanaceæ* (or *Atropaceæ*) in consequence of its affinity with the tobacco genus. The species are natives of South America. They have sticky leaves, and axillary solitary flowers, with a calyx of five spoon-shaped segments; a funnel-shaped or somewhat salver-shaped corolla, the limb spreading and five-lobed; five included stamens of unequal length; and an ovary with two compartments supporting a simple style, and button-like stigma. The fruit is a two-valved capsule, containing numerous seeds.

One or two species, with numerous varieties and hybrid forms, are common in gardens, where they are much used as bedding-out plants. The colour of the flowers is white or some shade of violet or purple, and latterly some have been introduced whose flowers are marked with purple stripes on a white ground. Some of the varieties are sweet-smelling. Double flowers are frequently met with, the doubled condition arising from the substitution of petals for stamens, and sometimes from the multiplication or increased number of the petals themselves. In one variety the margin of the corolla is green and leaf-like, the other portions being of a violet hue; in this variety the stamens are also frequently replaced by leaves, the filament of the stamen answering to the stalk of the leaf, while the anther is replaced by the blade. [M. T. M.]

PETWOOD. *Berrya mollis.*

PEUCEDANUM. A genus of the umbellifer family with each half of the fruit five-ribbed, the two lateral ribs indistinct, the other three narrow; and having one or two oil-cells in each furrow of the fruit. The species are smooth perennial herbs, having white, yellow, or greenish-yellow flowers. The genus has representatives in different parts of the world; and some of the species have occasionally been employed in medicine. A resinous secretion is yielded by certain of them. [G. D.]

PEUPLIER. (Fr.) *Populus.* — BAUMIER. *Populus balsamifera.* — D'ITALIE. *Populus dilatata.*

PEWTERWORT. *Equisetum hyemale.*

PEYREYMONDIA. A genus of *Cruciferæ*, of the section *Schizopetaleæ*, comprising an annual herb from Chili, scarcely differing from *Schizopetalum*, except in having the embryo of the seed with two white cotyledons, which are incumbent and spathulate, thicker at the apex, the radicle dorsal and straight. [J. T. S.]

PEZIZA. A very large genus of ascomycetous *Fungi*. The hymenium lines the cavity of a fleshy membranous or waxy cup which, though sometimes closed at first, is always ultimately opened. The species present an immense variety in respect of form, size, colour, and clothing, and are generally remarkable for elegance. Some are mere specks, while others are several inches across. They grow on the naked ground, and upon all sorts of decaying vegetable substances, a few being essentially inhabitants of the dung of animals. Some of the large species approach very near to *Helvella*, and there is little doubt that such species as *P. Acetabulum* are equally wholesome with the esculent *Helvellæ*. A form of *P. cochleata* is sometimes sold as a substitute for morels. Amongst the most conspicuous in this country are *P. aurantia*, which grows about the stumps of old felled oaks, and is of the brightest orange ; *P. coccinea*, which grows on dead sticks supported by a decided stalk, is white externally and of a bright scarlet within ; while *P. onotica*, which is ear-shaped, is of the most delicate orange inclining to rose-coloured. Many other species might be quoted of almost equal beauty, though scarcely so brilliant and attractive in point of colour. In a few there is a large tuberous root, which, like the tuber of a phænogam, lies dormant for a time, and two or three species are almost strictly subterraneous. The *Pezizæ* have their maximum in the temperate zones, but the tropics produce some exquisite species. [M. J. B.]

PFEES. An Indian name for *Chamærops Ritchiana.*

PFEIFFERA. A name given to a genus of *Cactaceæ*, in honour of Dr. Pfeiffer, a German author of several works on that order of plants. The only known species, *P. cereiformis*, a native of Mexico, is an erect branching fleshy plant a foot or more in height, resembling a *Cereus* in general appearance, having a three or four-sided stem, and branches of the same shape, with the angles wavy, and bearing at short distances white downy cushions furnished with five to seven sharp bristly spines. The flowers are white tinged with rose-colour, and have two rows of erect segments, the outer ones or sepals being shorter and the inner lance-shaped and forming a funnel-shaped corolla ; their numerous stamens are shorter than the corolla, and the columnar style bears a five or six-rayed stigma. The young berries are bluntly five-sided, with tufts of spiny bristles on the angles, but become globular (about half an inch in diameter), pellucid, and of a reddish-violet colour, crowned with the withered flower. [A. S.]

PHACA. A genus of *Leguminosæ*, long adopted as distinct from *Astragalus*, in that the partition—which, in the latter genus, almost or quite completely divides the pod into two cells—is reduced in *Phaca* to a slightly prominent rib, or at most projects halfway across the pod. A considerable number of American and a few European and Asiatic species were referred to it ; but now that a much greater number of *Astragali* have been carefully examined, this difference in the pod is found to be in many instances so vague, and always to bear so little relation to habit and other characters, that the species of *Phaca* have now all been reunited with *Astragalus.*

PHACELIA. Annual or perennial herbs, with branched tufted stems, incised leaves, and spikes of blue flowers, which when in bud are circinate like those of heliotrope. They belong to the *Hydrophyllaceæ*, and are marked by the fugacious corolla and two-celled capsule. All are natives of America, and some of the annual species are cultivated as border-plants. [C. A. J.]

PHACIDIACEI. A natural order of ascigerous *Fungi* with a coriaceous or carbonaceous receptacle, and the disk at length exposed by the regular or irregular fissure of the outer coat. They are in fact *Helvellacei* as far as the hymenium is concerned, and *Sphæriacei* as regards the receptacle or perithecium. In the typical genus, *Phacidium*, the depressed receptacles burst above by a few angular laciniæ. The finest and most common of our British species, *P. coronatum*, occurs on dead leaves in woods, and is often very pretty with its yellow disk surrounded by black teeth. *Hysterium* borders very closely on *Opegrapha*, as does the genus *Sphæria* among the *Sphæriacei* on *Verrucaria.* [M. J. B.]

PHACOCAPNOS. A genus of *Fumariaceæ* from the Cape of Good Hope, consisting of a climbing herb with the habit of *Corydalis claviculata*, but differing from that genus in having the seeds without a strophiole at the hilum. [J. T. S.]

PHÆDRANASSA. A genus of *Amaryllidaceæ*, comprising a few bulbous plants of Peru and Quito. They have broadish ovate leaves, and terete scapes supporting an umbel of several drooping flowers. The perianth is tubular funnel-shaped, shorter on the lower side, the tube short, and the limb nearly erect, of spathulate convolute segments. There are six exserted stamens growing from the top of the tube ; a straight style with simple clavate stigma ; and a three-celled ovary with the ovules crowded in two rows in each cell. *P. chloracra* is a very handsome plant with flowers upwards of two inches long, the short tube green and the convolute limb segments purplish-rose, tipped with green. [T. M.]

PHÆNOCARPOUS. Bearing a fruit which has no adhesion with surrounding parts.

PHÆNOGAMOUS. Having manifest flowers.

PHÆO, PHAIOS. Prefixed to Greek compounds = fuscous.

PHÆOCORDYLIS. *Rhopalocnemis.*

PHÆOCYST. The name given by Decaisne to the Cytoblast.

PHÆOSTOMA. *Clarkia.*

PHAGNALON. A genus of the tribe *Astereæ* of *Compositæ*, readily recognised by its habit. Its essential character is found in the uniserial pappus of rough hairs, which are eight in number in the outer female florets, and ten in the inner perfect ones. There are seventeen species, distributed chiefly over the Mediterranean region, the eastern limit being Tibet, and the western the Canary and Cape de Verd Islands. They are perennial herbs with a woody rootstock, from which, in most species, are given off a great number of unbranched shoots about a foot high, each terminating in a single flower-head, and the whole forming a compact rounded mass. The stems and the under surface of the leaves are clothed with white down, and the flower-heads generally contain many tubular yellow florets, but in a few species are corymbose, and purple. [A. A. B.]

PHAJUS. The original species upon which this genus of orchids was founded by Loureiro is a cultivated Chinese plant, and all the other eighteen or twenty since added are natives of the tropical and subtropical regions of the eastern hemisphere. They are tall erect mostly terrestrial plants, with great broad plicate leaves, and radical leafless scapes bearing a few large showy flowers. Their sepals and petals are nearly alike, mostly spreading, and free; the lip entire or three-lobed, broad and convolute round the column, with the base of which it is adnate and formed into a spur; the column is long, semicylindrical, and dilated at its apex; and the anther four or obsoletely eight-celled, and containing eight pollen-masses attached in fours to an elastic membrane. [A. S.]

PHALACRÆA. A genus of *Compositæ*, consisting of two or three South American herbs, nearly allied to *Ageratum*, but without any pappus to the achenes.

PHALÆNOPSIS. The species of this genus rank amongst the most beautiful of the numerous orchids known to cultivators in this country. For a long time only a single species was known, but others have latterly been discovered, all natives of the islands of the Indian Archipelago; and the genus now contains about a dozen species. They are epiphytes, with scarcely any stems, few broad thick leathery two-ranked leaves, notched at the top, and perennial racemose inflorescence bearing numerous mostly large showy flowers. These have flatly-spread free sepals and petals, the latter of which are much larger and wider than the former; a three-lobed free lip continuous with the prolonged base of the column, and furnished with a callosity at its base; a semiterete column, thickened upwards; and a two-celled anther, containing two pollen-masses attached by a strap-shaped caudicle to a cordate gland. The best-known species in our gardens, that first introduced from Manilla, is the one referred to *P. amabilis* by Dr. Lindley, but which is now reported to be not the true *P. amabilis* of Blume. It has large and very thick tough dark-green somewhat elliptical leaves; and a long drooping stalk bearing at its extremity a raceme of a dozen or more large exceedingly beautiful almost entirely pure white flowers, the only colour about them being some streaks and spots of yellow and crimson on the lip, which is three-lobed, smaller than the petals, and has two three-toothed plates at its base, and two curious twisted tendrils at its tip. But the most magnificent species of the genus is *P Schilleriana*, which has not only beautiful flowers but beautiful leaves also, the latter being irregularly mottled all over with very deep green upon a lighter green ground, and the former tinged with delicate pinkish purple. At the base of its lip there are a couple of yellow callosities, and instead of being furnished with tendrils, its tip is prolonged into a pair of recurved horns. [A. S.]

PHALANGES. Bundles of stamens; a collection of several stamens joined more or less by their filaments.

PHALARIS. A genus of grasses of the tribe *Phalarideæ*. The inflorescence is in close spike-like panicles, the spikelets with one perfect flower, and generally the rudiments of two imperfect ones, which latter form minute scales between the outer empty glumes; glumes two, carinate; pales two, carinate on their backs. The score or more of described species are mostly from Central Asia. *P. canariensis* supplies the well-known canary-seed, so much used for singing cage-birds. [D. M.]

PHALLOIDEI. A natural order of gasteromycetous *Fungi*, distinguished by their soft cellular receptacle which bursts through a gelatinous volva, and by the sinuous hymenium melting down with the spores into an olivaceous fœtid semifluid mass. Many of the species are extremely beautiful, but their beauty does not compensate for their odious smell. A few species occur in temperate regions, but the order has its maximum in tropical regions, or at least in countries where the thermometer never descends very low. The gelatinous volva of one or two species is eaten where better food is scarce, and one, *Lysurus Mokusin*, has been prescribed when burnt as a remedy in ulcers. [M. J. B.]

PHALLUS. The typical genus of the *Phalloidei*, a natural order of *Fungi*. The pileus is conical, perforated at the apex, free at the base, slightly wrinkled or deeply pitted, and either naked beneath or furnished with a free flounce-like membrane, or with a bell of network. The species are sometimes tinted with pink or scarlet, and those with the network are objects of universal admiration where they occur. One species, *P. fœtidus*, is extremely common in some districts of England. It is the pest of the Kew pleasure-grounds, from its unsightly form and detestable smell. A doubtful species, said to have a bitter odour, occurs amongst sand on the coast of Suffolk. *Cynophallus*, of which we have one species, *C. caninus*, is distinguished by its imperforate adnate pileus. [M. J. B.]

PHALLUS. The peridium of certain fungals.

PHALOCALLIS. A genus of *Iridaceæ*, the one species, *P. plumbea*, having been separated by Dean Herbert from *Cyphella*, to which it was first referred ; and characterised by its short two-lobed transverse stigmas, which have the two outer crests petaloid and the inner scarcely perceptible ; and by its thin-skinned apparently indehiscent fruit, and nearly flat thin-edged seeds. The plant has a slender stem, a yard or more high, furnished with distant sword-shaped plicate leaves, and bearing upon its summit a solitary widely expanded lead-coloured flower, tinged with yellow in the centre, about three inches across, and so fugacious that it lasts only a few hours, expanding before sunrise and dying away by noon. It is a native of Mexico. [A. S.]

PHANEROGAMOUS. The same as Phænogamous. The term *Phanerogamia*, or *Phænogamia*, is applied to flowering plants in contradistinction to *Cryptogamia*, the name applied to flowerless plants.

PHANES, PHANEROS. In Greek compounds = manifest.

PHARBITIS. A genus of showy annual twining plants, belonging to the *Convolvulaceæ*, and allied to *Convolvulus*, from which they are distinguished by their three-celled capsules. *P. hederacea* (*Liseron de Michaux* of French horticulturists) is a pretty plant with numerous clear azure-blue flowers of a satiny texture, sometimes described under the name of *Ipomœa hederacea*. *P. hispida*, known also as *Convolvulus major*, has heart-shaped leaves, and large white, purple, blue, rose, or variegated flowers growing in clusters three to five together in the axils of the leaves. The above species are grown in the open air, but most of the others require protection. [C. A. J.]

PHARNACEUM. A genus of *Caryophyllaceæ*, of the tribe *Mollugineæ*, from the Cape of Good Hope, consisting of small herbaceous or shrubby plants, with slender usually terete or filiform bristle-pointed leaves, alternate below, and forming a coma above, with fringed stipules. The cymes are compound, the terminal ones stalked, the axillary often sessile, but sometimes the flowers are umbellate or solitary ; calyx five-parted, often coloured ; petals none ; stamens five, rarely six or seven ; styles three ; capsule three-valved, three-celled, many-seeded. [J. T. S.]

PHARUS. A genus of grasses of the tribe *Oryzeæ*. The inflorescence is in solitary spiked or compound panicles ; male and female flowers separate, the males slightly stalked, the females sessile. Steudel describes six species, which are large broad-leaved grasses, natives of South America. [D. M.]

PHASCEÆ. A natural order of acrocarpous mosses, distinguished by the capsule being mostly nearly sessile, having no proper lid, and therefore not opening by a horizontal fissure like other mosses. Almost all the species are small and insignificant annuals, though not without interest to the botanist. *Archidium* differs in its perennial growth, and the small number of its large angular spores. *Voitea*, which is also perennial, has a large hooded long-beaked veil, and a persistent columella, and has somewhat the habit of *Splachnum*. The only European species grows, like most *Splachnideæ*, on dung. [M. J. B.]

PHASCUM. A genus of annual mosses with an indehiscent capsule and fugacious columella. The species are for the most part stemless, and sometimes are of such rapid growth that the plant passes through every stage before the original germinating threads have vanished. The species are numerous, and are divided by authors into several distinct families. Their favourite place of growth is exposed fields and walltops. They are rather plants of the plains than of the mountains. [M. J. B.]

PHASEOLUS. A genus of *Leguminosæ*, of the suborder *Papilionaceæ*, easily recognised by the carina or lower petal of the corolla terminating in a long spirally-twisted point. It consists of annuals, or herbaceous perennials, with the rootstock often tuberous, and having annual stems, either erect and short or more frequently twining. The leaves have usually three leaflets, the lateral ones inserted on the common stalk at some distance from the terminal one ; the flowers are two or three together, on knot-like protuberances, along axillary peduncles, and often very showy. The calyx is campanulate with four or five teeth ; the stamens diadelphous, one free and the other nine united in a sheath ; and the pod straight or slightly curved, containing several seeds which are usually more or less flattened. There are nearly fifty species known, natives of hot climates, especially of Southern and Central America, with a few dispersed over Africa, Southern Asia, and the Southern States of North America.

Amongst them many have been long and generally cultivated for human food, and a few for ornament. The most remarkable are *P. vulgaris*, the Kidney or French Bean or Haricot, of uncertain origin, probably Asiatic, the most generally cultivated in Europe and other temperate climates. Amidst a number of varieties or races, often described as species, it may always be known by its few-flowered peduncles, and by the ovate striate bracts at the base of the calyx. *P. multiflorus* (*coccineus*), the Scarlet Runner, a native of Mexico, has a thick tuberous rootstock, and annual twining stems, showy scarlet or white flowers, numerous on the peduncles, and rough pods. *P. lunatus* is apparently wild in America, as well as in Asia and Africa, but so generally cultivated in hot climates that it is difficult to ascertain its origin. In Europe it is unknown, being too tender for our climate. It is much like the Common French Bean in general aspect, but the flowers are much smaller and more numerous ; and the pod is flat, short, broad, and somewhat crescent-shaped, with only two or three seeds. *P. perennis*, common in the Northern States of North America, is very near *P. lunatus*, but with a narrower pod: it does not appear to be cultivated. *P. Max*, of which *P. Mungo* is a variety, is a native of tropical Asia, and is much cultivated in India and some parts of Africa; like *P. vulgaris*, it is dwarf and erect or twining, but is very hairy with large stipules; and the narrow nearly cylindrical hanging pod is very hairy; the seeds are small, and the flowers insignificant. *P. semierectus*, a common maritime species in tropical countries, especially America, belongs to a section remarkable for the large size of the wings or lateral petals of the corolla. *P. truxillensis* is a showy species with large variegated flowers often transmitted as wild or cultivated from India as well as from many parts of South America. *P. Caracalla*, believed to be a native of Brazil, is often grown under the name of Caracol in the gardens of South America, Southern Europe, and sometimes in India, for its large showy and sweet-scented flowers. In all, the petals are twisted at the top with the carina into a corkscrew. Some other kidney-beans cultivated in hot countries, and formerly referred to *Phaseolus* or *Dolichos*, now form the genus *Vigna*.

The Common Kidney Bean, *P. vulgaris*, not unfrequently called the French Bean, is stated to have been introduced in 1597—although by some writers it is believed to have been first imported from the Netherlands about the year 1509, when the taste for gardening began to revive in England. The whole plant is slightly pubescent, with leaves composed of three oval pointed leaflets, having angular footstalks, knotted at the base, and small stipules. The flowers are axillary, clustered, white, rose, or lilac. The legume or pod is from three to six inches or more in length, compressed and pendulous, terminating in a small sharp point. The earliest notice we have of Kidney Beans is that given by Pliny, who calls them *Phaseoli*, and says the pod is to be eaten with the seed. Several kinds appear to have been known to Gerarde in 1590; and since that time cultivation has produced numerous varieties, which, although similar to one another in appearance, are very different in habit. Some are termed runners, from having stems which twine round stakes six or eight feet high for support; others are dwarf and bushy, while many hold a middle place between the two. Of some of these again the young green pods are eaten—of others the seeds; while in a third division both pod and seed may be used until nearly arrived at maturity. In this country it is the green pods in a young state which are most valued, and when properly dressed they are highly esteemed as a wholesome and excellent vegetable. On the Continent the ripe seeds, under the name of *Haricots*, are much used by cooks in the composition of a dish so called, as well as for a variety of soups and stews; and in Roman Catholic countries they are

well known to form the greater part of the food of the people during Lent. When very young the green pods are frequently preserved as a pickle by themselves, and also form an ingredient in 'mixed' pickles.

The Scarlet Runner Bean, *P. multiflorus*, is usually considered to be a half-hardy annual, and is treated as such, although in reality it is a tender perennial having tuberous roots which may be taken up and preserved during winter for planting in spring. It is a native of South America, and is stated to have been introduced in 1633. Although specifically distinct from *P. vulgaris*, yet in foliage and general appearance it differs but little from some of the varieties of that species. The whole plant is slightly pubescent, of a twining habit, and if supported will climb to the height of eight or ten feet. The flowers are produced in solitary racemes, about the length of the leaves, and arranged in pairs with bracts somewhat shorter than the calyx. They are very handsome, the upper part, or standard, being scarlet, while the wings and keel are of a pale red or rose-colour. The pods are pendulous, not quite so long as those of the Common Kidney Bean, but broader, compressed and more succulent, with a rougher surface.

As a culinary vegetable, the Scarlet Runner is much esteemed, and occupies a place in almost every garden—more particularly in that of the cottager, where during the summer and autumn it is not only one of its greatest ornaments, but is also one of the most productive and useful vegetables the cottager can possibly cultivate. The young green pods are dressed in the same way as those of the Kidney Bean. It is worthy of notice that the roots are narcotic and poisonous.　　　　[W. B. B.]

PHAUM. An Indian and Mauritian name for *Angræcum fragrans*.

PHEASANTS-EYE. *Adonis æstivalis*, and *A. autumnalis*.

PHEASANT-WOOD. The same as Partridge-wood.

PHEBALIUM. A name said to be derived from the Greek word *phibaleë*, a myrtle, in allusion to the appearance of some of the species. The genus is included among *Rutaceæ*, and consists of small trees or shrubs, natives of extratropical New Holland. The stems and leaves are clothed with star-shaped hairs, or silvery or reddish scales. The flower-stalks are axillary or terminal, arranged in an umbellate or corymbose manner; flowers small, with an entire or more or less five-cleft calyx; petals five lance-shaped, longer than the sepals; stamens ten, longer than the petals, five shorter than the remaining five; ovary five-lobed on a short stalk, with five compartments each containing two ovules, one ascending, the other pendent; styles five, confluent, with a five-furrowed stigma. Fruit of five two-valved one-seeded follicles.　　　　[M. T. M.]

PHEGOPTERIS. The name now sometimes applied to a large group of *Polypodium*, in which the fronds, instead of being articulated with a rhizome as in *P. vulgare*, are continuous and adherent to a caudex, which may be either short and erect as in *P. alpestre*, or elongated and creeping as in *P. Dryopteris*. Usually the sori are medial on the free veins. Generally speaking, the habit of growth is that of *Lastrea.* [T. M.]

PHELIPÆA. A genus of *Orobanchaceæ*, resembling the broomrapes in habit, and distinguished mainly by the tubular calyx, which is furnished with two or three bracts, and by the capsule opening at the top instead of the side. The genus thus characterised will include two British species of Broomrape—*Orobanche cærulea* and *O. ramosa*. [C. A. J.]

PHENACOSPERMUM. Endlicher has proposed to constitute under this name a genus of *Musaceæ*, comprising certain species from tropical America, which resemble *Heliconia* in general appearance. The flowers are not known, but the fruit is capsular, and contains numerous seeds arranged in several rows. From the allied genus *Ravenala* it is distinguished by its somewhat globular seeds, which are attached by means of a long stiff funicle or umbilical cord, which breaks up into a fibrous tow-like aril overlying or concealing the seed; hence perhaps the name, from the Greek *phenax*, an impostor. [M. T. M.]

PHILADELPHACEÆ. (*Syringas*.) A natural order of calycifloral dicotyledons belonging to Lindley's grossal alliance of epigynous Exogens. Calyx valvate with a persistent limb; petals alternate with the divisions of the calyx, and equal to them in number, imbricate; stamens indefinite; ovary adherent to the tube of the calyx; styles distinct; stigmas four to ten; ovules attached to a central placenta. Fruit a four to ten-celled capsule, free above, with indefinite scobiform pendulous seeds, with a loose membranous arillus. Shrubs with deciduous opposite exstipulate leaves without dots; flowers usually in trichotomous cymes. They are natives of the south of Europe, of North America, Japan, and India. They have no marked properties. The flowers of *Philadelphus coronarius* (Syringa) have a peculiar sweetish odour due to the presence of an oil, which to some persons is overpowering and disagreeable. *Deutzia scabra* has a scurfy matter on its leaves, which, under the microscope, is seen to consist of beautiful stellate hairs. There are five genera, including twenty-seven species. Examples: *Philadelphus, Deutzia*. [J. H. B.]

PHILADELPHUS. A genus of shrubs better known by the names Syringa and Mock Orange, giving name to the order *Philadelphaceæ*, and distinguished from *Deutzia* by having four petals. *P. coronarius* is the large bushy shrub so common in shrubberies and cottage gardens, and remarkable in early summer for its terminal tufts of large creamy-white flowers having a powerful odour, which at a distance is

thought to resemble that of orange-flowers; and known also by the flavour of its leaves, which is precisely that of cucumbers. The terminal flower in each tuft, it should be observed, has five petals. Other species with scentless flowers are less frequently cultivated. French, *Seringat*; German, *Pfeifenstrauch*. [C. A. J.]

PHILARIA. (Fr.) *Phillyrea.*

PHILESIACEÆ. (*Philesiads*.) A natural order of monocotyledonous plants belonging to Lindley's class of Dictyogens. They are nearly allied to *Roxburghiaceæ*, from which they differ in their trimerous symmetry, parietal placentæ, and orthotropal ovules. Most authors include them in that order. They are natives of Chili, and comprise the genera *Philesia* and *Lapageria*, each with a single species. [J. H. B.]

PHILESIA *buxifolia*, the Pepino of Valdivia, is a small evergreen box-leaved erect shrub, native of the extreme southern part of South America, from Valdivia to Magelhaens' Straits, bearing an abundance of large beautiful drooping, somewhat bell-shaped, bright rose-red, rather waxy flowers. By some botanists it is referred to *Smilaceæ*, while others place it and the apparently closely allied genus *Lapageria* in

Philesia buxifolia.

a separate order, styled *Philesiaceæ*. It is the only species of the genus, and is characterised by having a small three-leaved calyx and a large three-petaled corolla, monadelphous stamens, and an obscurely three-lobed stigma. In habit it is very different from *Lapageria*, being an erect stiff shrub instead of a scrambling climber, and having penninerved in place of five-nerved leaves. [A. S.]

PHILIBERTIA. *Sarcostemma.*

PHILIPPIA. A genus of heathworts, having eight stamens partly adherent to each other, and a four-celled four-valved seed-vessel, containing many seeds. The species are natives of the Cape, Madagascar, and Mauritius. They are shrubs, having the leaves in whorls of three or six; and the flowers small near the ends of the branches. [G. D.]

PHILIPPODENDRON. A name given by Poiteau, in honour of King Louis-Philippe, to a little tortuous shrub cultivated in the Paris Jardin des Plantes, and then believed to have been of Nepalese origin, and to be the type of a new natural order. A further investigation has, however, proved it to be the *Plagianthus betulinus*, a malvaceous plant from New Zealand.

PHILLYREA. Evergreen shrubs and trees introduced from the shores of the Mediterranean, and commonly planted in shrubberies and parks where it is desired to have a mass of foliage in winter. Many species and varieties are employed for this purpose, all of which agree in having oblong more or less serrated opposite leaves, and inconspicuous greenish-white flowers growing in axillary clusters. They belong to the order *Oleaceæ*, and are closely allied to the olive, but bear a globose berry. The species most commonly grown are *P. latifolia, P. media,* and *P. angustifolia*, from which numerous varieties have been derived. The Phillyreas with hollies and yews were formerly much employed as subjects for the topiary art; but they are now mostly allowed to retain their natural habit. —, CAPE. *Cassine capensis.* [C. A. J.]

PHILODENDRON. A genus of tropical American plants of the family *Araceæ*. They have mostly scrambling stems, which attach themselves to the trunks of trees, whence the name of the genus. The leaves are large, often irregularly lobed, the blades attached to the stalk by a kind of joint, and

Philodendron Simsii.

the veins very small and densely crowded. The spathe opens after the fertilisation of the flowers, and falls off when the fruit is ripe. The spadix is nearly of the same size as the spathe, wholly covered with flowers, the abortive ones being placed below the stamens; anthers sessile, opening at the summit; ovary many-celled, with numerous

ovules attached to the inner angle of each compartment by means of long threads. Several species are in cultivation as stove plants. [M. T. M.]

PHILOGLOSSA. A decumbent Peruvian herb, with yellow radiating flower-heads, constituting a genus of *Compositæ*, of the tribe *Heliantheæ*. It is technically placed near *Calliopsis*, but differs at first sight by the much more numerous narrow ligulate ray-florets. The branches of the style are also very hispid.

PHILOGYNE. One of Haworth's spurious genera of amaryllids, of which he described eight species, all founded upon well-known varieties of *Narcissus odorus*, the sweet-smelling Narcissus. [A. S.]

PHILOTHECA. A genus of *Rutaceæ*, consisting of heath-like shrubs, natives of the eastern extratropical parts of Australia. The leaves are linear, and the flower-stalks axillary and terminal, solitary with small scale-like bracts. The calyx is five-parted; petals five, stalked, much longer than the sepals; stamens ten, those opposite the petals shorter than the rest; the filaments hairy above, and combined below into a smooth tube; ovary on a short stalk, five-lobed, the styles combined into one. Fruit of five two-valved capsules or follicles, each with one seed. *P. australis*, with red flowers, is grown as an ornamental shrub in greenhouses. The name should be more correctly *Psilotheca*, from the Greek *psilos*, smooth, in allusion to the smooth sheath or tube formed by the lower part of the stamens. [M. T. M.]

PHILYDRACEÆ. (*Waterworts.*) A natural order of petaloid monocotyledons belonging to Lindley's xyridal alliance of Endogens. They are closely allied to *Xyridaceæ*, and differ chiefly in the want of an outer perianth, in the inner perianth being two-leaved, in having three stamens, two abortive, and in the embryo being large in the axis of the albumen. The flowers have spathaceous bracts; the roots are fibrous, the stem simple, leafy and often woolly, and the leaves ensiform and sheathing at the base. They are natives of New Holland, Cochin China, and China. [J. H. B.]

PHILYDRUM. The type of the *Philydraceæ*, and comprising a single species, native of wet marshy places in China and Australia. This plant, *P. lanuginosum*, is an erect annual attaining a height of two to three feet, with lance-shaped leaves dilated at the base, covered (as also are the outer portions of the perianth, and the capsules) with dense woolly hairs. The flowers are yellow, placed on long spikes, and protected by sheathing bracts. The genus is distinguished from *Hetæria*, the only other genus of the order, by the anthers, whose cells are somewhat spiral, and by the placentæ of the fruit, which are two-lobed and recurved, bearing the numerous seeds on the outer surface. The seeds, moreover, are marked externally with spiral striations, and have a little cap-like process at one end. The genus derives its name from the localities in which the species is found.

The flowers of this plant consist of a yellow perianth in two segments, and three stamens—one fertile opposite the lower segment of the perianth, two sterile and petaloid. Dr. Lindley describes the flower as wanting the calyx, and having a two-leaved corolla; but from the fact that the upper segment is frequently notched, and from the arrangement of the veins and the position of the stamens, it seems preferable to consider the parts of the perianth as constituting a calyx rather than a corolla. The leaves are equitant, spongy within, and with partitions of star-shaped cells. The structure of the flower-stalk is like that of an Exogen rather than an Endogen, being cellular on the outside and in the centre, while between the two layers a perfect circle of woody tissue occurs. The pollengrains are round, and cohere in groups of four.   [M. T. M.]

PHLEBODIUM. One of the net-veined genera separated from *Polypodium*, with which it agrees entirely in respect to the fructification. The veins are reticulated, with free included veinlets, which are excurrent; and the sori are placed on the converging apices of two or more of these veinlets occupying an elongated areole, the costal areole being transverse and void. The typical species is *P. aureum*. [T. M.]

PHLEBOMORPHA. The mycelium of certain fungals.

PHLEUM. A genus of grasses belonging to the tribe *Agrostideæ*. The inflorescence is mostly in oval spike-like panicles; glumes boat-shaped, keeled, with short awns at their points; paleos or inner glumes shorter than the outer, with a short awn on the back. Of this genus fourteen species have been described by authors, most of which belong to Northern Europe. *P. pratense* is the Cat's-tail or Timothy Grass of agriculturists, and a very valuable species, being one of the earliest and most productive among British grasses. This species is the badge of the Sutherlands. *P. alpinum* is an Alpine plant, and only found in one or two localities on the Scotch mountains, at great elevations.   [D. M.]

PHLŒUM. The cellular layer of bark below the epidermis.

PHLOMIS. A genus of the labiate order, having the border of the calyx entire or three-toothed, and the tube of the corolla short, the upper lip compressed, entire or notched, and the lower three-cleft and spreading. The species are herbs and shrubs, found in different parts of Europe and Asia, with wrinkled leaves, and flowers yellow, white, or purple. Several have been long known as garden plants. The name is adopted from one used by ancient Greek writers.   [G. D.]

PHLOX. Favourite showy herbaceous plants, mostly perennial, belonging to the *Polemoniaceæ*, and distinguished by the following characters:—calyx deeply five-cleft; corolla salver-shaped, with an elongated tube and wedge-shaped segments, which are twisted before expansion; stamens five, inserted above the middle of the tube; cells of the capsule one-seeded. Most of the species agree in sending up rod-like unbranched stems, one to four feet high, with opposite undivided leaves, and terminal panicles of handsome flowers, which are white, blue, some shade of red, or variegated. They are all natives of North America, and many species have been so long cultivated and hybridised that their specific names have given place in many instances to the names by which they are distinguished by horticulturists. *P. Drummondi*, an annual species, is among the most showy of the family, and from its low habit, and profusion of flowers of many hues, is deservedly popular. German, *Flammenblume*.   [C. A. J.]

PHOBEROS. *Scolopia*.

PHŒNICEOUS. Pure lively red, with a mixture of carmine and scarlet.

PHŒNIX. With the exception of two species found in South-eastern Africa, this genus of palms, of which about a dozen species are known, is confined to Northern Africa and tropical Asia, extending as far east as Hong Kong. As a genus it is readily distinguished by its pinnate leaves from the other genera of the tribe *Corypheæ*, which is characterised by the flowers possessing three distinct ovaries. Some species have scarcely any trunk, while others (as the Date Palm) rise to a great height, and have their trunks thickly covered with the scars of fallen leaves. The flower-spikes grow out from amongst the leaves and bear flowers of one sex only, the two sexes being upon distinct trees. Both kinds have a cup-shaped three-toothed calyx, and a corolla of three petals with their edges valvate in the male, and overlapping in the female; the former containing usually six (very rarely three or nine) stamens, with hardly any filaments and narrow erect anthers, and the latter three distinct ovaries with sessile hooked stigmas. Only one of the ovaries, however, comes to perfection, and ripens into a one-seeded fleshy fruit, the seed being composed of horny albumen with a groove down the front and the embryo placed at the back.

The Date Palm, *P. dactylifera*, is cultivated in immense quantities all over the northern part of Africa, and more sparingly in Western Asia and Southern Europe; and in some of these countries its fruit, though only known by us as an article of luxury, affords the principal food of a large proportion of the inhabitants, and likewise of the various domestic animals,—dogs, horses, and camels being alike partial to it. The tree usually grows about sixty or eighty feet high, and lives to a great age, trees of from one to two hundred years old continuing to produce their annual crop of dates. Numerous varieties are recognised by the Arabs and distinguished by different names, according to their shape, size, quality, and time of ripening. The fruit, however, is not the only valuable part of this widely dispersed tree, for, as with the cocoa-nut tree, nearly every part is applied to some useful purpose. The huts of the poorer classes are entirely constructed of its leaves; the fibre (*lif*) surrounding the bases of their stalks is used for making ropes and coarse cloth, the stalks themselves for crates, baskets, brooms, walking-sticks, &c., and the wood for building substantial houses; the heart of young leaves is eaten as a vegetable; the sap affords an intoxicating beverage (*lagbi*), though to obtain it the tree is destroyed; and even the hard and apparently useless stones are ground into food for camels.

Phœnix dactylifera.

Finally, we may mention that the Date was probably the Palm which supplied the 'branches of palm-trees' mentioned by St. John (xii. 13) as having been carried by the people who went to meet Christ on his triumphal entry into Jerusalem, and from which Palm-Sunday takes its name.

P. sylvestris, called the Wild Date, is supposed by some authors to be the parent of the cultivated date. It is common all over India, and, like the last, attains a considerable height. Large quantities of toddy or palm-wine are obtained from it, but the Asiatics, more skilful than the Africans, obtain it by merely cutting off the young flower-spike, by which means they do not destroy the tree. Date-sugar, so extensively used in India, is made by simply boiling the toddy. [A. S.]

PHŒNOCOMA. A generic name proposed by D. Don for the *Helichrysum proliferum,* a Cape species which differs from the others in the central florets of the head being males only and not hermaphrodite. It is a rather showy everlasting, with very small granular clustered leaves, and large solitary terminal flower-heads, having an involucre of many rows of scales, the outer of which are short and appressed, and the inner long radiating shiny and of a beautiful rose-purple colour. The tubular five-toothed florets are seated upon a naked receptacle. The pappus consists of a single row of rough bristles, those of the male club-shaped, and those of the female variously cohering. [A. S.]

PHOLIDIA. A genus of *Myoporaceæ,* containing two species from New Holland. They are shrubs with entire leaves, and flowers on very short solitary axillary peduncles. The calyx is deeply five-cleft, undergoing no change in fruiting; the corolla is funnel-shaped, with an unequally five-lobed spreading limb; there are four didynamous included stamens, with crescent-shaped anthers; and the ovary is oblong and four-celled, with a capitate emarginate stigma. The drupe has a four-celled and four-seeded stone. [W. C.]

PHOLIDOTA. A tropical Asiatic genus of orchids, the several species of which are all epiphytes either with pseudobulbs or fleshy jointed rhizomes, and having plicate leaves, and terminal usually imbricated and two-ranked drooping flower-spikes. Its flowers have equal distinct sepals; smaller petals; a concave entire or three-lobed lip parallel with the column, which is semicylindrical or winged; and a two-lipped two or four-valved anther, containing four distinct globose pollen-masses. [A. S.]

PHOLIOTA. A subgenus of *Agaricus* belonging to the series with brown or ferruginous spores, and characterised by the presence of a distinct woven veil, forming a ring on the stem. One or two are esculent, amongst which *A. pudicus* is much esteemed in Italy. *A. mutabilis* is sometimes confounded with the German Stockschwamm, *A. melleus,* but it is not clear that it is wholesome. [M. J. B.]

PHORADENDRON. An extensive genus of *Loranthaceæ,* confined to the New World, but extending from the United States to Brazil. It has diœcious or monœcious flowers: the males with a trifid perianth, and transversely two-celled anthers opening by pores or vertical slits (sometimes one-celled ones by confluence); and the females with a three-lobed perianth, and sessile obtuse stigma. The numerous species are parasitic usually leafy shrubs, and have catkin-like jointed spikes of sessile immersed flowers. One, which grows on elms and hickories in the United States, is known as the American Mistleto. [A. S.]

PHORANTHIUM. The receptacle of Compositæ.

PHORMIUM. The four species which have at different times been ascribed to this genus of *Liliaceæ* are now combined into one variable species, *P. tenax,* the New Zealand Flax, which is confined to New Zealand and Norfolk Island. This plant forms large tufts, and has sword-shaped leaves growing in opposite rows and clasping each other at the base; those of one variety being from five to six feet long, of a bright green above and glaucous underneath, and those of another only half as long and paler in colour. Its flower-spikes, which are large and alternately branched, rise up out of the centre of the leaves; those of the large-leaved variety reaching the height of sixteen feet and bearing deep orange-red flowers, while those of the other are not more than six feet high, and have yellow flowers tinged with red. The flowers have a tubular perianth of six erect pieces, the three inner of which spread out at the tip; six stamens projecting beyond

Phormium tenax.

the perianth, and alternately shorter; and a three-celled ovary bearing a three-sided style and simple stigma, ripening into a long bluntly triangular three-valved capsule, containing two rows of small flattened black seeds in each cell.

The leaves of this plant contain a large quantity of strong useful fibre, to which the name of New Zealand Flax has been given. When Captain Cook first landed in New Zealand, he found this flax in common use among the natives for making various articles of clothing, string, nets, &c.; and since the colonisation of that country various attempts have from time to time been made to render it an article of export, but hitherto without much success—the cost of preparation, owing to the presence of a viscid gummy matter in the leaves, being too great to allow of a remunerative profit. [A. S.]

PHORUS. A termination in Greek compounds, signifying a stalk, or support; a part which bears some other parts.

PHOTINIA. A genus of *Pomaceæ* allied to *Cratægus*; but the ovary is usually two-celled only, and the succulent fruit, crowned by the persistent lobes of the calyx, has the endocarp thin and cartilaginous, not forming the bony nuts of *Cratægus*. There are several species natives of the mountainous parts of Northern and Eastern India, of China, Japan, and North-west America. They are all erect unarmed shrubs, with evergreen laurel-like leaves, and numerous small flowers in terminal

panicles. One species, *P. serrulata*, a native of China and Japan, has long been an intimate of our shrubberies under the name of *Cratægus glabra*, and is very ornamental as an evergreen from its handsome shining foliage, but more particularly so when circumstances admit of its developing in perfection its rich panicles of innumerable small flowers of a pure white. *P. arbutifolia*, from California, has also been in cultivation, and some of the Himalayan species may be well worth introduction.

PHOTINOPTERIS. A genus of acrostichaceous ferns of scandent habit, with pinnate coriaceous fronds, which are fertile and contracted in the upper part, and have the pinnæ articulated with a basal auricle on the lower side. The venation is netted, with free divaricate clavate veinlets in the ultimate areoles. The fructification, as in this group, occupies the whole of the fertile pinnæ. *P. speciosa*, probably the only species, is found in the Malayan Archipelago. [T. M.]

PHRAGMA. A spurious dissepiment in fruits, i.e. one which is not formed by the sides of carpels; a partition, of whatever kind.

PHRAGMIFER, PHRAGMIGER. Divided by partitions.

PHRAGMITES. A genus of grasses belonging to the tribe *Arundineæ*. The inflorescence forms large spreading lax panicles, with three to six-flowered spikelets, in which respect this genus differs from some others that are nearly allied, but have spikelets with one flower in each. The flowers are enveloped with long silky hairs. Steudel describes eighteen species in his *Synopsis*; these range over various parts of the globe, from Western Europe to Japan. *P. communis* is the only native species, and is, besides, the largest British grass. Though not valuable for agricultural purposes, it is of great importance for binding the earth on river-banks with its extensively creeping rootstocks. [D. M.]

PHRIGANOPTOSIS. A name given by Rè to a disarticulation of vine-shoots that takes place principally when the previous summer has been cold and cloudy, and the wood imperfectly ripened. It may be observed most years in this country in the small lateral shoots, and was known to Pliny, who after Theophrastus calls it articulated. See CLADOPTOSIS. [M. J. B.]

PHRYNIUM. A genus of *Marantaceæ*, consisting of tropical Asiatic and American perennial plants with creeping roots, contracted stems, stalked leaves, and flowers in terminal heads or panicles. The inner lateral petals (abortive stamens) are larger than the outer or true petals; the lip is two-lobed; the filament is short, attached to the inner lateral segment of the corolla, the anther terminal; the ovary three-celled, with a single ovule in each compartment, a style curved above, and an incurved somewhat funnel-shaped stigma. Fruit capsular, three-celled, three-valved. Several species are grown in this country as stove plants; they are very similar in appearance to the species of *Calathea*. Some of them yield abundance of fibre. On the authority of Loureiro, the leaves are used in China for making vinegar with sugar and water or spirit of rice.　　　　　[M. T. M.]

PHTHIRIASIS. A disease produced by the presence of insects; lousiness.

PHU. *Valeriana Dioscoridis*.

PHULWARAH. An Indian name for *Bassia butyracea*.

PHURRA. An Indian name for the leaves of *Chamærops Ritchiana*.

PHYCELLA. A genus of South American *Amaryllidaceæ*, comprising some eight or ten handsome bulbous plants, with linear channeled leaves, and fistular terete scapes supporting umbels of numerous declinate flowers. The perianth is tube-like, six-parted with a short tube, and subequal convolute segments somewhat spreading at the apex; the stamens are six in number, inserted in the throat of the tube, with declinate filaments; the style filiform, declinate, with a simple stigma; the ovary three-celled, with many ovules in each cell disposed in two series. They are closely related to *Hippeastrum*, but the faucial membrane is not defective on the lower side. The flowers are red, and generally marked with yellow.　　　　　[T. M.]

PHYCOLOGY. That part of Botany which treats of the *Algæ* or Seaweeds.

PHYCOMATER. The gelatine in which the sporules of algals first vegetate.

PHYCOMA. The whole mass of an algal; its thallus and reproductive bodies.

PHYGELIUS *capensis* is a South African shrub, forming a genus of *Scrophulariaceæ*, very nearly allied to *Pentstemon*, but differing in the long curved tube of the corolla, in the barren stamen reduced to a small scale, and in the very oblique capsule, one cell being always much larger than the other. The leaves are opposite, quite glabrous; and the flowers in a terminal panicle, each fully an inch and a half long.

PHYKENCHYMA. The elementary tissue of algals.

PHYLICA. Handsome shrubs, with curious evergreen foliage, and the habit of a heath, belonging to the order *Rhamnaceæ*. The tube of the calyx is cylindrical and five-cleft; the stamens are protected by petal-like scales; and the seed-vessel contains three seeds. Most of the species are natives of South Africa, where, with their much-branched stems and narrow leaves, they inhabit dry sandy ground, to a certain extent simulating the heath tribe. The narrow leaves are for the most part white beneath, and revolute at the margins. The flowers are small, white, and arranged in heads or spikes. Upwards of twenty species have been described, and several are

cultivated, especially *P. ericoides*, called by the French *Bruyère du Cap*.　　[C. A. J.]

PHYLLAGATHIS *rotundifolia* is a somewhat herbaceous shrub, native of Sumatra, having large cordate-ovate denticulate and strongly seven to nine-nerved leaves, of a rich glossy metallic green on the upper side, and a bright red beneath; and a terminal head of small purple flowers, surrounded by large dark-purple bracts. The genus belongs to the *Melastomaceæ*, and has flowers with a campanulate four-lobed calyx having two or three bristles on the back of the lobes and others between them; four ovate pointed petals; eight stamens with subulate one-pored anthers without any prolongation of the connective; and an adherent four-celled ovary, bearing a slender style terminating in a punctiform stigma.　　　　　[A. S.]

PHYLLANTHUS. A genus of diœcious *Euphorbiaceæ*, characterised by its perianth of five or six imbricate divisions: the male flowers with three stamens, the filaments either free or united and surrounded by five or six glands; and the females with an ovary of three cells, two ovules in each, and a short three-branched style, each branch being again forked or divided. The species are very numerous, all natives of hot countries, and very variable in stature, from small prostrate annuals to moderate-sized trees. The leaves are usually small, alternate, entire, and so arranged in opposite rows along the smaller branches as to give them the appearance of pinnate leaves. The small green flowers, often with a yellowish or purple tinge, are usually clustered in the axils of the leaves, and very frequently one female is surrounded by several males in each axil. The fruit is a small depressed or globular capsule, separating into two-valved cocci.

Few species present any special interest. The section *Xylophylla* comprises several shrubs, chiefly West Indian, curious from their flattened leaf-like smaller branches without any other leaves than minute scales. *P. Niruri* and its allies, very abundant in tropical America, as well as Asia and Africa, and *P. Urinaria*, and others more specially limited to Asia, are low prostrate annuals, weeds of cultivation, and occasionally used medicinally. The leaves of *P. Conami* and some others are used in tropical America for poisoning fish. *P. natans*, from tropical America, is a very small species with the aspect of a *Salvinia*, usually found floating on the surface of still waters. None of the species have flowers sufficiently showy for cultivation for ornament. See EMBLICA and XYLOPHYLLA.

PHYLLARTHRON. A small genus of *Crescentiaceæ*, composed of shrubs or small trees confined to the islands of Eastern Africa, principally Madagascar. They have a very peculiar habit, in consequence of the leaves being narrow, and more or less linear, and made up of definite points one to two inches long. The calyx is five-cornered, ribbed and persistent; the corolla funnel-shaped; the stamens four in number; and the fruit cylindrical, very fleshy, and apparently many-celled. The branches are more or less glutinous, and often flat or angular; the flowers appear in terminal or axillary racemes, and are generally pink; whilst the fruit, about as long as the little finger, is dirty white. In Mauritius the fruit of *P. comorense* is used for jellies, and is also much sought after by birds; *P. Bojerianum* has likewise an edible fruit. Both are inmates of our stoves.   [B. S.]

PHYLLIDE. (Fr.) *Phyllis.*

PHYLLILESIA. In some plants a curl of the leaf is constitutional, as in *Salix annularis.* A similar condition, accompanied by more or less distortion or blistering, may be produced by aphides, parasitic fungi, or by particular conditions of the atmosphere. The affection called curl in potatos is of a different character. See CURL and PEACH BLISTER.   [M. J. B.]

PHYLLIS. This name, derived from the Greek *phyllon,* a leaf, is applied to a genus of *Cinchonaceæ,* the species of which have handsome foliage. The genus consists of shrubs, natives of the Canary Isles, with the leaves opposite or in whorls of three or four, and having membranous stipules prolonged into thread-like processes. The flowers are greenish in a terminal panicle; the limb of the calyx divided into two unequal deciduous lobes; the corolla wheel-shaped, five-parted, with a short tube allowing the five stamens to protrude beyond it; styles two, hairy; fruit of two dry indehiscent carpels.   [M. T. M.]

PHYLLITIS. *Scolopendrium.*

PHYLLOBRYON. The contracted pedicel of an ovary, such as occurs in some peppers.

PHYLLOCACTUS. Several species and varieties of this genus of *Cactaceæ* are cultivated in hothouses in this country for the sake of their fine white or crimson flowers, which are among the largest and most showy of the order. Some confusion exists in their nomenclature, owing to many of the species having formerly been referred to the genera *Epiphyllum* and *Cereus.* They are, however, distinguished from the latter by their curious flat broad leaf-like branches; and from the former by their flowers being produced from the notches or indentures along the edges of the branches instead of at the end, and having small sepal-like segments scattered wide apart on the tube, and numerous long petals variously expanded so as to form a rose-like, or a funnel- or salver-shaped corolla, with the stamens attached to the orifice of the tube, the outer ones being longer than the inner. The nine species described by botanists are found in Mexico, Central America, and Brazil. *P. Ackermanni,* a native of Mexico, has flowers measuring as much as seven inches across, and of a rich scarlet colour like those of some varieties of *Cereus speciosissimus,* with

broad, very sharp-pointed, slightly waved petals; its stems are rounded at the base and bear little tufts of short bristles, and its flat branches are from two to two-and-a-half inches broad and waved or deeply dented along the margin. *P. anguliger* is a West Mexican species, and is remarkable for having its flat branches deeply and sharply lobed so as to resemble pinnately cut leaves, the lobes almost forming right-angled triangles; its flowers, which are large and fragrant, have brownish outer petals, and pure white inner ones. [A, S.]

PHYLLOCARPUS. A genus of *Leguminosæ,* of the suborder *Cæsalpinieæ,* established by Tulasne on a Brazilian tree, with pinnate leaves and yellow flowers on short lateral peduncles, and remarkable for the long broad very flat and thin pod with a winged keel. Nothing is known of it beyond the dried specimens.

PHYLLOCLADUS. A singular genus of *Taxaceæ,* consisting of trees natives of Australia, New Zealand, and Borneo. On young seedling plants of this genus the true leaves are linear, sharply pointed, one-nerved, and glaucous on the under-surface; but in the adult plants, rhomb-shaped phyllodes are formed. These phyllodes, emerging from the axils of scaly leaves, seem to be formed partly of the branchlets, and partly of a number of linear leaves all united so as to form one leaf-like organ. The fruit consists of a few thick scales each bearing one ovule. The characters of the foliage and fruit serve to distinguish this genus from its near ally *Dacrydium. P. rhomboidalis,* the Celery-topped Pine, is in cultivation as an ornamental tree, as is also *P. trichomanoides,* the bark of which yields a red dye.   [M. T. M.]

PHYLLOCORYNE. A genus of *Balanophoraceæ,* whose species are natives of Jamaica. They have a lobed or branched rootstock, from which proceed a number of flower-stalks, densely invested with scales, and bearing cylindrical or oblong heads of flowers. The stamens are connate; and there are two styles. The genus is said by Dr. Hooker, its originator, to differ from *Helosis,* both in habit, and in the leafy flower-stalks.   [M. T. M.]

PHYLLODINEOUS. Resembling a leaf, as in the flattened branches of *Xylophylla* and *Ruscus.*

PHYLLODE, or **PHYLLODIUM.** That kind of leaf which results from an enlargement and flattening of the petiole and the loss of leaflets.

PHYLLOGLOSSUM. A curious genus of clubmosses, with the habit of an adder's-tongue. It has a tuberous root, short awl-shaped leaves, and a spike of capsules supported by a stem longer than the leaves. The capsules are axillary bivalved and subtended by a short ovate pointed bract. It is found in marshy ground in New Zealand, and is curiously connected with *Ophioglossaceæ* by the very similar Cape genus *Rhizo-*

glossum. It may be added that the germination of *Ophioglossum*, as far as is known, seems to confirm the affinity. [M. J. B.]

Phylloglossum Drummondi.

PHYLLOIDEOUS. The same as Foliaceous.

PHYLLOMA. The leaf-like thallus of algals, as in *Ulva*.

PHYLLOMANIA. The production of leaves in unusual numbers, or in unusual places.

PHYLLOPHORA. A genus of rose-spored *Algæ* belonging to the *Cryptonemiaceæ*, with compound nuclei, tetraspores collected in raised warts, and a flat flabelliform cleft frond. *P. rubens* is very common on our coast, and extremely beautiful when clear of parasites, but generally rough with *Melobesiæ* or zoophytes. Three others occur in our seas, of which *P. membranifolia* alone is at all common. [M. J. B.]

PHYLLOPTOSIS. As the leaves of plants are temporary organs, they are of course subject to decay. In some cases their continuation with the stems is so intimate that they hang on to it when dead, till decomposition due to atmospheric agents completely destroys them. In many cases they are articulated to the stem, and when vitality is reduced below a certain point by excess of heat, deficiency of moisture, old age, or any other cause, they fall off, and leave a scar behind. Schacht supposes that a layer of cork cells is formed at the point of division, which renders their separation easy and protects the scar. We have observed something like this in pears, but we cannot find that it is a universal condition. Trees lose their leaves at very different periods; in most cases they fall the first year; the Scotch fir retains them three years, and the silver fir and spruce eight or ten years. [M. J. B.]

PHYLLOTA. A genus of *Leguminosæ*, of the suborder *Papilionaceæ*, consisting of Australian shrubs with heath-like leaves and yellow flowers. They have the habit of *Dillwynia*, and their characters are intermediate between that genus and *Pultenæa*.

PHYLLOTAXIS. The manner in which leaves are distributed over a stem.

PHYLLULA. The scar left on a branch by the fall of a leaf.

PHYLLUM. A sepal. In Greek compounds = a leaf.

PHYMATODES. *Pleopeltis*.

PHYSALIS. This name, derived from the Greek *phusa*, a bladder, is applied to a genus of herbs and shrubs of the family *Solanaceæ*. The calyx is five-cleft, and greatly increases in size after the corolla falls off, so that the fruit is enclosed within a large leafy bladder, whence the name. The corolla is folded in the bud, bell-shaped or wheel-shaped, and conceals the five stamens within its tube; the anthers open by long slits; and the fruit is succulent, two-celled, enclosed within the distended calyx. The species are widely distributed in tropical countries, both of the Old and New World, and one is found even in the southern and middle districts of Europe.

Several species are grown in English gardens, the best known being the hardy European species, *P. Alkekengi*, better known as the Winter Cherry, a name which it has received in consequence of its scarlet cherry-like fruit enclosed within the enlarged calyx, which also assumes a bright red colour, and thus renders the plant very ornamental in the beginning of the winter season. The calyx of this plant is frequently macerated so as to separate and preserve the fibrous network of veins by which it is traversed, in the same manner as in the skeleton leaves. In Arabia, and even in Germany and Spain, the fruits, which have a slightly acid taste, are eaten for dessert. The fruits of *P. peruviana* are likewise edible, as well as those of *P. pubescens*, the Camaru of Brazil.

Several of the species are considered to possess medicinal properties; those already mentioned are said to be useful as diuretics, while *P. somnifera* has, as its name implies, narcotic properties, on which account it was mentioned by Dioscorides. The leaves of this plant steeped in warm castor-oil are employed in India as an application to carbuncles and other inflammatory swellings. They are very bitter, and are given in the form of infusion in fevers. The seeds are stated to be employed to coagulate milk. According to Kunth, the leaves of this plant have been found with the Egyptian mummies. [M. T. M.]

PHYSEMATIUM. *Woodsia*.

PHYSEUMA. The branch of a *Chara*.

PHYSIC, CALVER'S. A North American name for *Veronica virginica*. —, INDIAN. An American name for *Gillenia trifoliata*.

PHYSIOLOGY. That part of Botany which treats of the functions of plants.

PHYSOCALYMMA. The beautifully striped rose-coloured wood imported from Brazil, and called Tulip-wood by our cabinet-makers, the Rosenholz of the Germans, Bois de Rose of the French, and Pão de Rosa of the Portuguese—a wood which has of late been used in considerable quantities for inlaying costly pieces of furniture, for making various articles of small-ware, for turnery, &c.—is the produce of *P. floribundum*, the only plant belonging to this genus of *Lythraceæ*. It is a tree, with opposite oval rough leaves; and large terminal opposite-branched panicles of purplish flowers, which are produced while the tree is leafless. Each flower has two large roundish concave bracts, which entirely enclose the bud before it expands; the bell-shaped eight-toothed coloured calyx is inflated and persists round the ripe fruit; the eight wavy petals are inserted between the teeth of the calyx; the twenty-four stamens are long and projecting, two of them being placed opposite each of the teeth of the calyx and one opposite each petal; and the four-celled hemispherical or four-sided ovary bears a simple long style and round-headed stigma, and by the obliteration of the partitions ripens into a one-celled fruit, with a free central column to which numerous flattened winged seeds are attached. [A. S.]

PHYSOCALYX. A genus of *Scrophulariaceæ*, consisting of two species only, both of them Brazilian shrubs, with opposite or alternate entire ovate or obovate leaves, and orange-coloured flowers in terminal racemes. Their calyx is large and inflated; the corolla is tubular with five spreading nearly equal lobes; the stamens are didynamous, included in the tube, with bearded and awned anthers; and the capsule opens in two entire valves. Both species are said to be showy, but are unknown in cultivation.

PHYSOCHLAINA. The species of this genus are so like those of *Hyoscyamus*, that they might with great propriety be classed with them, as they were originally. They are herbaceous perennials, natives of Siberia, &c.; and have the calyx slightly inflated and five-toothed; the corolla funnel-shaped below, widening above into the shape of a bell, its limb slightly five-lobed; the stamens five, protruding from the corolla, hairy at the base; and the fruit that of the henbane. *P. orientalis*, better known as *Hyoscyamus orientalis*, a native of Siberia, may be occasionally met with in gardens. It produces its violet-coloured flowers early in the season. *P. physaloides* is also in cultivation. [M. T. M.]

PHYSOLOBIUM. A genus of *Leguminosæ* of the suborder *Papilionaceæ*, closely allied to *Kennedya*, from which it is scarcely sufficiently distinguished by its broad orbicular vexillum without appendages at the base, giving a somewhat different shape to the flower; and by the more turgid pod. It consists of two or three species from South-west Australia, with the trailing or twining habit of *Kennedya*, and scarlet flowers, usually two or three only on each peduncle. Two species have been introduced to our gardens, but they do not appear to maintain themselves, not being so showy as the allied species of *Zichya*.

PHYSOMYCETES. A small section of *Fungi*, distinguished from *Ascomycetes* by the total absence of anything like an hymenium, and the vesicular fruit which encloses an indefinite mass of sporidia. The habit is the same as that of many *Hyphomycetes*. It contains two natural orders only: *Antennariei* analogous to *Dematiei*, and *Mucorini* analogous to *Mucedines*. The threads are either free or closely felted, and in one subterraneous genus, *Endogone*, they form a little ball. In *Acrostalagmus* the sporidia grow from a definite point within the vesicular fruit. *Antennariei* flourish most in hot countries, and the species are so intimately connected with *Capnodium*, that it is not certain whether all of them are true species. [M. J. B.]

PHYSORHYNCHUS. A genus of *Cruciferæ* of the tribe *Isatidæ*, from Scinde, comprising a glaucous biennial, with the racemes arranged in a panicle. The fruit has a very large ovate acuminate persistent beak, and two small valves at the base; and the seeds, two in number, are contained in the beak. [J. T. S.]

PHYSOSPERMUM. A genus of the umbellifer order, distinguished by having each half of the fruit nearly kidney-shaped, with five slender equal ribs, and one broad oil-cell in each furrow. The species are perennial herbs, chiefly natives of Southern Europe and Eastern Asia. Their lower leaves are usually much divided, and the upper ones are in some mere scales; their flowers are white, the umbels surrounded by bracts. The name, signifying 'bladder-seed,' indicates the loose outer coat of the fruit in its early stage. [G. D.]

PHYSOSTEGIA. The generic name of plants belonging to the labiate order; having the calyx bell-shaped and much inflated; and the corolla with the upper lip entire or notched, and the lower in three round lobes, the middle one of which is notched. The species are herbs, natives of North and South America, of handsome appearance, and acquisitions to gardens. The name indicates the bladder-like character of the calyx. [G. D.]

PHYSOSTELMA. A genus of *Asclepiadaceæ*, confined to India and Java, and comprising two species of twining plants, with opposite fleshy ovate or oblong leaves, lateral long-stalked umbels, a five-cleft calyx, a rotate five-lobed corolla of comparatively large size, and a corona composed of five leaflets. The fruit is unknown. [B. S.]

PHYSOSTEMON. One of the genera of *Capparidaceæ*, the name of which is expressive of a peculiarity in the stamens, consisting in a bladder-like thickening of the top of the filament. The species are natives of Brazil, with annual stems, sparingly provided with leaves, and yellow flowers arranged in clusters; sepals and petals four; stamens six or eight, of unequal length, some of them bent downwards, the two or four uppermost distended in the way before mentioned; ovary on a very short stalk bent downwards, and ripening into a two-valved pod. The kidney-shaped seeds are attached to a replum or false partition, which remains behind after the two valves of the fruit have fallen away.   [M. T. M.]

PHYSOSTIGMA. The Ordeal-bean of Old Calabar, the Eséré of the natives, is the type of a genus of *Leguminosæ* of the tribe *Phaseolæ*, approaching *Canavalia* in the character of its seeds, but with flowers very like *Phaseolus*, except that its bearded style is terminated by a great oblique hood covering the blunt stigma. It is upon the presence of this hood that the genus depends for its character and name. This plant, called *P. venenosum*, is a great twining climber, with pinnately-trifoliate leaves, and axillary pendulous racemes of purplish bean-like flowers. Its seeds, in which the popular interest in the plant centres, are borne two or three together in dark-brown pods about six inches in length, and are of an oblong or somewhat hemispherical form, about an inch long, roughish but a little polished, blackish-brown with a long dark sunken hilum surrounded by a lighter-coloured elevated border. These seeds are extremely poisonous, and are employed by the natives of Old Calabar as an ordeal; persons suspected of witchcraft or other crime being compelled to eat them until they vomit or die—the former being regarded as a proof of innocence, and the latter of guilt. Recent investigations in this country have proved them to possess valuable medicinal properties.   [A. S.]

PHYSURUS. The majority of the species of this genus of orchids, of which there are a considerable number, are natives of the New World, the exceptions being a few found in the islands of the Indian Archipelago. It is the type of one of the divisions (*Physuridæ*) of the tribe *Neottæ*, and consists of small terrestrial plants with slender succulent roots, and slim stems bearing loosely-sheathed stalked leaves, often beautifully marked with veins, and usually dense terminal spikes of inconspicuous flowers. They have nearly equal sepals and petals, the lateral sepals placed beneath the lip, and the dorsal agglutinated to the petals. Their lip is parallel with the column, concave, constricted below the apex, and extended downwards into a frequently swollen spur; and their column is free or adnate to the bottom of the lip, straight and attenuated into an ultimately bifid rostellum, having the anther at the back, containing two sectile pollen-masses attached to an oblong or subulate gland. Some of the species are grown in this country on account of the beauty of their leaves.   [A. S.]

PHYTELEPHAS. The Ivory Plant of South America, *P. macrocarpa*, producing the nuts known as Marfil Vejetal or Vegetable Ivory in commerce, is the representative of a curious genus closely allied to palms, and having their habit; but differ-

ing from them in having an indefinite number of stamens, and on that account regarded by some botanists as the type of a separate natural order, *Phytelephanteæ*. The plant has a creeping rooting caudex or trunk, terminal pinnatifid leaves, and axillary flowers emitting a powerful perfume. The male and female flowers are on separate trees, and the trunk of the male plant is always more erect and taller than that of the female. The inflorescence of the male plant is a simple fleshy cylindrical spadix four feet long, with four or five spathes, and crowded with flowers; while that of the female plant, which also forms a simple but much shorter spadix, bears from six to seven flowers, of a pure white. The ovary is from six to nine-celled, each cell containing a solitary ovule. The style is elongated, and divided into six, seven, eight, or even nine branches. The fruit consists of a collection of six or seven drupes, forming clusters which are as large as a man's head, the drupes being covered

Phytelephas macrocarpa.

outside with hard woody protuberances. Each drupe contains from six to nine seeds, the Vegetable Ivory of commerce, fashioned by the American Indians, as well as by European turners, into knobs, reels of spindles, toys, &c. The seed at first contains a clear insipid fluid, with which travellers allay their thirst: afterwards this same liquor becomes milky and sweet, and it changes by degrees until it becomes as hard as ivory. Bears, hogs, and turkeys devour the young fruit with avidity. Enclosing the seeds is a yellow sweet oily pulp, which is collected at the proper season, and sold, under the name of Pipa de Jagua, for one real (6d.) a pound at Ocaña, New Granada. With the leaves the Indians thatch their huts. In 1854 one thousand nuts were sold in London for 7s. 6d., but the price is very fluctuating. The Ivory Plant has for some years been grown in our hothouses. It is confined to the northern parts of South America. [B. S.]

PHYTEUMA. A genus of bellworts, having the corolla wheel-shaped, its border generally in five deep narrow pieces; the stigma two to three-cleft; and the seed-vessel with two to three cells, and opening at the sides. The species are perennial herbs, natives of the temperate parts of Europe and Asia; they are generally handsome, and some are well known in cultivation. [G. D.]

PHYTOCHLORE. Green colouring matter; chlorophyll.

PHYTOCRENACEÆ. A natural group of thalamifloral dicotyledons belonging to Lindley's urtical alliance of diclinous Exogens. They are climbing shrubs with entire or palmate leaves, and small unisexual flowers in panicles or clusters. The males have four to five sepals, four to five valvate petals alternate with the sepals, and four to five introrse stamens, the filaments arising from an androphore. The females have four to five sepals and petals, abortive stamens, a one-celled ovary on a gynophore, with two ovules, a thick style, and a large stigma. Fruit a series of drupes collected into a large globular mass; seed albuminous; cotyledons large and leafy. They are all natives of warm climates. The group is, however, by some botanists regarded as a tribe of *Olacaceæ*. [J. H. B.]

PHYTOCRENE. A genus of climbing shrubs, with stalked heart-shaped or palmate alternate leaves; and small flowers, in small pea-shaped heads, on racemes that emerge from near the base of the trunk. The flowers are diœcious, arranged on globular fleshy receptacles. The males have a four-parted calyx and corolla, with four stamens united below, and attached to a short stalk supporting the rudimentary pistil. In the females the pistil is stalked, with a large and thick style terminated by a cushion-shaped stigma. The fruit is fleshy, one-celled, one or two-seeded. The wood of these shrubs is soft and porous, and of peculiar structure. When living it is full of a limpid watery sap, which is drunk by the natives of Martaban. The name of the genus, signifying 'plant-fountain,' denotes this quality. [M. T. M.]

PHYTOEROSIA. That part of Botany which relates to the diseases of plants.

PHYTOGELIN. The gelatinous matter of algals.

PHYTOGRAPHY. That part of Botany which teaches the art of describing plants.

PHYTOLACCACEÆ. (*Rivinaceæ, Phytolaccads.*) A natural order of monochlamydeous dicotyledons belonging to Lindley's chenopodal alliance of hypogynous Exogens. They are undershrubs or herbs, with alternate entire often dotted leaves; and are natives of warm countries in America, Asia, and Africa. Perianth four to five-parted; stamens indefinite, or alternate with the perianth segments; ovary of one or several carpels, distinct or combined, each with one ovule. Fruit fleshy or dry, indehiscent, sometimes samaroid; seeds solitary. There are twenty known genera, including *Phytolacca* and *Rivina*, and comprising about eighty species. There is frequently much acridity in the plants of

this order, and some of them act as irritant emetics and purgatives. [J. H. B.]

PHYTOLACCA. The typical genus of the *Phytolaccaceæ*, distinguished by its flowers having a six-parted calyx with coloured petal-like or thin green segments, which have membranous edges and are at length reflexed under the ripe fruit; by the stamens varying from five to twenty-five in number, of which five are exterior and alternate with the calyx-segments and the rest opposite them; and by the compound ovary being composed of from five to twelve carpels arranged in a whorl round a concave torus, with their sides growing together throughout their whole length so as to form a solid ovary, which is crowned by five to twelve separate short styles curved outwards. It is distributed throughout the tropical and subtropical regions of both hemispheres, but is most abundant in the western. About ten species are known, which are mostly tall herbs or rarely shrubs, with alternate entire feather-veined leaves, and simple spike-like racemes of flowers opposite the leaves, producing succulent berry-like many-celled fruits of a somewhat globular shape but usually flattened at the top, each cell containing a single brittle-shelled seed.

P. decandra, the Pocan, or Virginian Poke or Poke-weed, is a branching herbaceous plant, with a smooth green or sometimes purplish stem, from six to twelve feet high, with large green or purplish leaves, and erect flower racemes longer than the leaves, the flowers having ten stamens and ten carpels. Its dark-purple berries, called Raisin d'Amérique by the French, contain a purplish-red juice somewhat resembling red ink, and hence it is sometimes called the Red-ink Plant. A tincture of them has acquired a reputation in the United States as a remedy for some forms of chronic rheumatism, and was once a celebrated remedy for cancer. The root is an emetic and cathartic; and the young shoots, though extremely acrid, are rendered harmless by boiling, and are eaten in the United States in the same way as asparagus. It is found not only in the United States, but in the Azores, North Africa, and China.

P. icosandra is a much smaller plant than the last, seldom growing more than two or three feet high. It has a shrubby stem, and long smooth reddish-tinted herbaceous branches, bearing elliptical sharp-pointed leaves from three to six or more inches in length, and long graceful drooping racemes of flowers, which contain from ten to twenty stamens and as many carpels, and produce dark-purple or almost jet-black berries about the size of peas but flat at the top. It is widely spread over the American continent, extending from Rio de Janeiro to Mexico, and is also found in several of the West Indian islands.

In the island of Oahu the natives cook and eat the leaves of a species of *Phytolacca*, which they call Poporo-tumai, and is perhaps *P. brachystachys*; and in the West Indies the berries of *P. octandra*, the Verbachiina of the Mexicans, are used for washing like soap.　　[A. S.]

PHYTOLITHES. See CARPOMANIA.

PHYTOLITHS. Fossil-plants.

PHYTOLOGY. That part of Botany which treats of plants in general.

PHYTON. A rudimentary plant, out of numbers of which perfect plants are made up, according to Gaudichaud.

PHYTOS. In Greek cómpounds = a plant.

PHYTOTOMY. That part of Botany which teaches anatomical structure.

PIA-PIA. A Tahitian name for a sort of gum extracted from the trunk of *Cocos nucifera.*

PIASSABA, PIASSAVA, or PIAÇABA. A stout woody fibre, obtained in Bahia from the leafstalks of *Attalea' funifera*, much used in the manufacture of brooms, brushes, &c. —, PARA. A finer and more valuable kind of Piassaba, obtained from *Leopoldinia Piassaba.*

PICEA. A subgenus of *Coniferæ*, usually included in *Abies* (which see), but by some regarded as a distinct family. The Silver Fir, *Abies Picea*, otherwise *Picea pectinata*, is the type, and the principal other species are *A. cephalonica, Pinsapo, Pichta, Nordmanniana, balsamea, grandis, amabilis, nobilis, bracteata, Webbiana, Pindrow, firma, religiosa,* &c. Their chief distinguishing feature is the erect cylindrical thin-scaled cones.　　[T. M.]

PICEUS. Black, changing to brown.

PICHOLINE. (Fr.) A kind of olive.

PICHOT. (Fr.) A name for the Cherry.

PICKEREL-WEED. *Pontederia.*

PICKERINGIA. A small much-branched Californian shrub, described as a distinct genus of *Leguminosæ* of the suborder *Papilionaceæ*. The structure of the flowers is as in *Baptisia*, and the pod is unknown; but the shrubby not herbaceous habit, and the red not yellow flowers, lead to the conclusion that the genus may be maintained.

PICKPURSE. *Capsella Bursa-pastoris;* also a Norfolk name for *Spergula arvensis.*

PICKTOOTH. *Ammi Visnaga.*

PICOTEE. One of the florist's varieties of *Dianthus Caryophyllus.*

PICOTIANE, or PICQUOTIANE. (Fr.) *Psoralea esculenta.*

PICRÆNA-WOOD. The bitter wood sold as Quassia. See PICRASMA.

PICRAMNIA. A rather extensive genus of *Simarubaceæ*, confined to tropical America and the West Indies. Most of the species are tall shrubs, with alternate unequally pinnate leaves, the leaflets of which are usually alternate and more or less unequal at the base. They have small reddish flowers, in clusters forming long slender racemes; the two sexes growing on different plants, and the females producing olive-shaped berry-like fruits divided into two cells, each of which contains a pendulous seed. In both sexes there is a three or five-parted calyx, and as many narrow pointed petals : the males contain three or five stamens with the filaments naked and destitute of scales : and the females, imperfect scale-like stamens, and a two or rarely three-branched style.

Like the rest of the order of quassiads, the plants belonging to this genus are intensely bitter, its generic name being derived from the Greek word *picros*, in allusion to that quality. In Brazil the bark of *P. ciliata*, a small tree, is employed as a substitute for Cascarilla ; and in the West Indies the negroes use an infusion of *P. Antidesma*, a shrub about eight feet high, as a cure for colic and other complaints, under the name of Majo-bitters.　　[A. S.]

PICRASMA. A genus of *Simarubaceæ*, containing about half a dozen species very widely dispersed in both hemispheres, one being found in Brazil, another in the West Indies, two in Nepal, one in China, and one in Java. They are small trees, with unequally pinnate leaves, and axillary stalked cymes of small diœcious or polygamous flowers, which have the calyx four or five-parted, minute ; the petals egg-shaped, agreeing in number with the divisions of the calyx, those of the female being persistent and often becoming larger and thicker ; the stamens as many as, and alternate with, the petals, and having hairy filaments but no scales ; and three to five distinct ovaries elevated on the thickened disk, each containing a single ovule, having the styles united, and ultimately ripening into pea-like drupes. The trees have the aspect and foliage of the species of *Ailantus.*　　[A. S.]

P. excelsa yields the bitter wood known as Jamaica Quassia, in contradistinction to that furnished by *Quassia amara* or Surinam Quassia. This bitter-wood tree is very common in the lowlands of Jamaica, where it attains the height of fifty or sixty feet. The leaves are composed of four or five pairs of short-stalked oblong blunt leathery leaflets, and an odd terminal one. Jamaica Quassia, which is that commonly met with in the shops, is of a whitish or yellow colour, and has an intensely bitter taste. Hence an infusion or tincture is much used in cases of weak digestion, where a simple bitter is required. It is remarkable that the drug appears to act on animals as a narcotic poison, though such effects have not been witnessed in the human subject : and hence the tincture is also used as a fly-poison. The Bitter Cups, so extensively sold of late in this country, are, when genuine, made of Quassia-wood, and water allowed to remain in them for a short time acquires tonic properties. Brewers are said to employ the chips as a substitute for hops.　　[M. T. M.]

PICRIS. A genus of herbaceous plants belonging to the tribe *Cichoraceæ* of compound flowers, distinguished by having numerous scales outside the involucre, a naked receptacle, and transversely striated seeds, which are scarcely beaked, but furnished with a pappus of which the inner hairs are feathery. *P. hieracoides*, the only British species, is a common wayside plant in England, but not in Scotland, two to three feet high, with bristly branched stems, rough oblong toothed leaves, and corymbs of bright-yellow flowers. French, *Picride*; German, *Bitterkraut*. [C. A. J.]

PICRORHIZA. The sole representative of this genus of *Scrophulariaceæ* is *P. Kurroa*, a small perennial herbaceous plant found in Kumaon, at Gossain, and other parts of the Himalaya mountains, where its roots, which are called Hooling in Tibet, and have a powerfully bitter taste, are used as a febrifuge by the natives, and also sent down to the bazaars of Bengal, where they form one of the many bitter roots sold under the name of Teeta. The plant grows six inches high, and has scarcely any stem, its leaves rising from the summit of the thick root; as also do its flower-stalks, which are from four to six inches high, and bear a dense spike of small bluish flowers at the top. The leaves are somewhat wrinkled, oblong, entire and tapering to the base but round-toothed above. The flowers have a five-parted calyx, a corolla with a short tube and four somewhat spreading entire segments, and four diverging nearly equal stamens three times as long as the corolla; and they produce small two-celled fruits about half an inch in length, which split, both through the partition and through the cell-walls, into four valves, and contain numerous small seeds covered with a loose netted transparent shell. [A. S.]

PICTUS. The same as Painted.

PIDDINGTONIA. A genus of *Lobeliaceæ*, represented by a Nepalese creeping herbaceous plant, with serrated leaves downy on the under surface, and purplish flowers on axillary stalks. The limb of the calyx is divided into five linear equal lobes; the corolla is two-lipped, the upper lip divided into two linear erect segments, the lower divided into three ovate acute lobes, the tube split along the top; the two lowermost anthers are terminated by bristles; the stigma is two-lobed; and the berry is thick ovoid, two-celled. One species, *P. nummularia*, is cultivated in this country as a pretty stove annual fitted for bedding-out. It is perhaps best known under the name of *Pratia begoniæfolia*. [M. T. M.]

PIED D'ALOUETTE. (Fr.) *Delphinium*. — DE CANARD. *Podophyllum*. — DE CHAT. *Gnaphalium dioicum*. — DE CHEVRE. *Ægopodium Podagraria*. — DE COQ. *Ranunculus repens*. — DE CORBEAU. *Ranunculus aconitifolius*. — DE CORNEILLE. *Plantago Coronopus*. — D'ELEPHANT. *Elephantopus scaber*; also *Testudinaria elephantipes*. — DE GRIFFON. *Helleborus fœtidus*. — DE LIÈVRE. *Trifolium arvense*, and *T. Lagopus*. — DE LION. *Alchemilla vulgaris*. — DE LOUP.

Lycopus europæus. — DE PIGEON. *Geranium columbinum*. — DE POULE. *Cynodon Dactylon*. — DE SAUTERELLE. *Campanula Rapunculus*. — DE VEAU. *Arum maculatum*; also *Richardia æthiopica*. — D'OIE. The name of several species of *Chenopodium*. — D'OISEAU. *Ornithopus perpusillus*; also *Trigonella ornithopodioides*.

PIERARDIA. A small tropical Asiatic genus doubtfully referred to *Sapindaceæ* by some authors, and to *Euphorbiaceæ* by others. They are small trees, with alternate simple leaves; and long slender racemes of unisexual flowers, with a four-parted perianth—some species bearing the two sexes in separate racemes on the same tree, and others on different trees. The males contain eight short stamens; and the females a three-celled ovary, bearing three sessile somewhat two-lobed stigmas, and ultimately ripening into a three-celled fruit with a corky rind, each cell containing one or two seeds enveloped in a juicy eatable aril. *P. dulcis* is a Malayan species, and is distinguished by having both the sexes upon the same tree, and by its smooth entire leaves, being of a somewhat elliptical form, but broader and rounded at the top, and with a short blunt point. Its fruits, which are rather larger than a cherry, nearly round, and of a yellowish colour, contain a luscious sweet-tasted pulp, and are greatly eaten in Sumatra, where the tree is called Choopah, and also in Malacca, where it goes by the name of Rambeh. *P. sapida*, an allied species, with the two sexes on different trees and with oblong leaves, is found in Tipperah and Pegu, and produces eatable fruits like those of the last. It is called Lutco by the Hindoos. [A. S.]

PIETRA FUNGAJA, or FUNGUS STONE. The Italian name of *Polyporus tuberaster*, whose mycelium is remarkable for collecting the surrounding earth into a large ball, which year after year yields a crop of esculent fungi. These balls are articles of commerce, and transported from place to place, as they are almost always fertile if put in a proper situation and well watered. There is a fine specimen in the herbarium of the British Museum, which was raised in Messrs. Lee and Kennedy's garden at Hammersmith many years since. The ball has been considered as a kind of truffle, but this is decidedly a mistake, as we can safely assert after examination of fine specimens in our possession. [M. J. B.]

PIGAMON. (Fr.) *Thalictrum*.

PIGEON-WOOD. Zebra-wood, of which there are several kinds, some of which come from Brazil. —, JAMAICA. *Guettarda speciosa*.

PIGGESNIE. An old name corrupted from Pink-seen-eye, and assigned by Dr. Prior to *Dianthus Caryophyllus*.

PIGNON, or PINONE. The edible seed of the cones of various pines, as those of *Pinus Pinea*, which are eaten in Italy. — D'INDE. The seed of *Jatropha Curcas*.

— DOUX. A South European name for the seed of *Pinus Cembra* and *P. Pumilio.*

—, PETIT. The seed of *Croton Tiglium.*

PIGONIL. A Quito name for *Festuca quadridentata*, which is said to be poisonous to cattle.

PIG'S FACES. The fruit of *Mesembryanthemum æquilaterale.*

PIGWEED. *Chenopodium.*

PILARIS. Composed of small hairs.

PILEA. A genus of *Urticaceæ*, consisting of annual or perennial herbs or undershrubs, mostly with the aspect of *Parietaria*, but very different in the structure of their flowers. The leaves are always opposite, although sometimes one of each pair is very much smaller than the other. The flowers are small and greenish, in little axillary loose cymes or clusters; the males have a four-cleft perianth and four stamens; the female perianth has three divisions, of which one is much the larger and thickened or mushroom-shaped at the top, the ovary has a single ovule, and is crowned by a tufted stigma. There are about 180 species known, almost all confined or nearly so within the tropics, in the New as well as in the Old World. One species, however, extends rather far into North America. No one species presents any peculiar interest, except it be *P. serpyllifolia*, the Artillery Plant; and most of them are insignificant weeds.

PILEANTHUS. A small genus of *Chamælauciaceæ*, consisting of shrubs, with club-shaped leaves, found in South-west Australia. They are distinguished by having a ten-parted calyx with white roundish lobes; a corolla of five petals; twenty stamens, all fertile, the filaments occasionally forked; and a single style having an obtuse stigma. The flowers are white, axillary or terminal, and surrounded by an involucre. [R. H.]

PILEATE, PILEIFORM. Having the form of a cap; or having a pileus.

PILEOLUS. A little cap or cap-like body; also the diminutive of Pileus; also the receptacle of certain fungals.

PILEORHIZA. The cap of a root, a membranous hood found at the end of the roots of *Nuphar* and other plants, and distinct from the spongiole.

PILEUS. A convex expansion terminating the stipes of agaricaceous fungals, and bearing the hymenium.

PILEWORT. *Ficaria ranunculoides.*

PILI. Hairs. *Pili polycephali* are hairs divided at the end into several arms.

PILICORDIA. *Cordia.*

PILIDIUM. An orbicular hemispherical shield in lichens, the outside of which changes to powder; as in *Calycium.*

PILIFEROUS. The same as Hair-pointed.

PILINGRE. (Fr.) *Polygonum Persicaria.*

PILITIS. A genus of *Epacridaceæ*, containing a single species, *P. acerosa*, having a sharp-pointed leafy calyx, a corolla with a hood which finally breaks away, and stamens not attached to the corolla. The flowers are terminal, surrounded by sharp-pointed ovate bracts. It is a shrub, having needle-shaped leaves with broad bases, and is found in Tasmania. [R. H.]

PILLCORN, or PILCORN. *Avena nuda.*

PILL DE BRETAGNE. (Fr.) *Lolium multiflorum.*

PILLWORT. *Pilularia.*

PILOBOLUS. A genus of vesicular moulds, consisting of two or three species, which grow on dung. When young they are of a bright-yellow hue; the short stem, however, gradually loses its colour, swells above like the hood of a Cobra, and bears a little vesicle at the apex filled with close-packed dark spores. Accounts have been given of curious motions observed in these plants, but it is believed that they are due to some little worm. [M. J. B.]

PILOCEREUS. The well-known Old Man Cactus and a few allied species have been separated under this name from the genus *Cereus*, but, as in other genera of *Cactaceæ*, the distinguishing characters are scarcely of generic importance. The principal differences consist in the flower-bearing portion of the plant being unlike the rest, usually forming a dense woolly head at the summit of the stem, and having more numerous, longer and thinner, often hair-like spines; and the flowers themselves being smaller and having fewer divisions, with the stamens attached to the whole surface of the tube. All the species are from Mexico and tropical America. As seen in our hothouses, the Old Man Cactus, *P. senilis*, is usually a cylindrical-stemmed plant, a foot or more in height; but in Mexico, its native country, it attains a height of twenty or twenty-five feet, with a diameter of nine or ten inches, and its fluted character gives it somewhat the appearance of an architectural column. The stem is divided into thirty or forty narrow furrows, with corresponding ridges, which are furnished at very short distances with tufts of white spines surrounded by numerous long flexible white hairs resembling the grey hairs of an old man's head; hence has arisen not only the common name of the plant, but also its scientific appellation. When young the stems are fleshy and succulent, but as they get old their tissue becomes filled with an extraordinary quantity of small sand-like grains composed of oxalate of lime, not less than from sixty to eighty per cent. having been found in individual stems. [A. S.]

PILOSE. Covered with hairs; covered with somewhat erect loose distant hairs; having the form of hairs. *Pilosity* is a general term for hairiness; and *pilosiusculus* means somewhat hairy.

PILOSELLE. (Fr.) *Hieracium Pilosella.*

PILOSTYLES. A genus of *Rafflesiaceæ*, the species of which are without stem or true leaves, but consist solely of small diœcious flowers, encircled by an outer and inner series of bracts. These little flowers burst forth from the bark of trees, in Chili and Brazil, and hence have been thought, but erroneously, to be deformed flowers of *Bauhinia* or *Adesmia*, the trees on which they are parasitic. The flowers are described as diœcious; the males, which alone are known, have a four-leaved perianth surrounding a column, the summit of which is covered by small pimple-like lobes, beneath which is a dense row of one-celled anthers. [M. T. M.]

PILOT-WEED. *Silphium laciniatum.*

PILULA. A cone like a Galbulus; any spherical inflorescence.

PILULAIRE (Fr.) *Pilularia globulifera.*

PILULARIA. One of the four genera of *Marsileaceæ*, characterised by having quill-shaped leaves or footstalks, which are circinate when young, and pill-shaped receptacles embraced by the stalk, and formed by the tips of the transformed footstalk, or from the limb of the leaf which is not in other cases developed. This is divided into two or four cells filled with spore-like antheridia and spore-cases, each spore-case containing only a single spore. The germination resembles that of *Marsilea*. The genus occurs in Tasmania, and in the north of Africa, as well as in Europe. *P. globulifera* is not uncommon in Great Britain in marshy places amongst sedge, but requires a practised eye to discover it; *P. minuta* is sometimes cultivated. [M. J. B.]

PILUMNA. A genus of the *Brassidæ* tribe of orchids, consisting of only two species, both from the vicinity of Popayan, and both epiphytes with sheathed one-leaved pseudobulbs, and radical scapes of largish green and white flowers. It has equal uniform spreading sepals and petals; an unguiculate convolute almost entire lip, adnate to the base of the column, which is club-shaped, with a thin fringed hood at the back of the anther-bed and a fleshy rounded ear on each side in front; and two pollen-masses, with a short caudicle attached to an ovate or linear gland. [A. S.]

PIMELEA. A genus comprising some seventy or more slender branching shrubs, with entire leaves, usually opposite but occasionally alternate, and white rose or yellow flowers in terminal or rarely axillary heads, surrounded by an involucre of bracts of different shape from that of the leaves. It is included among *Thymelaceæ*, and may be recognised by the funnel-shaped perianth with a four-cleft limb unprovided with scales, one or two stamens attached to the throat of the perianth, a lateral style, and a capitate stigma. The fruit has a thick rind, or is succulent and berry-like. They are natives of Australia, Tasmania, New Zealand, &c.; and have tough stringy bark, like the other members of the *Daphne* family. Several kinds are grown in this country as ornamental greenhouse shrubs: among the best are *P decussata*, *P. spectabilis*, and *P. Hendersoni*. The name is derived from the Greek *pimele*, fat, in allusion to the oily seeds. [M. T. M.]

PIMENT. (Fr.) *Capsicum*; also *Chenopodium Botrys.* — CERISE. *Capsicum cerasiforme.* — DE LA JAMAÏQUE. *Eugenia Pimenta.* — DE MOZAMBIQUE. *Capsicum luteum.* — DES ABEILLES. *Melissa officinalis.* — ROYAL. *Myrica Gale.*

PIMENTELLA. A genus of cinchonaceous shrubs, natives of the mountains of Peru. Its characters are not perfectly known; the more important among them seem to be the cup-shaped persistent limb of the calyx; and the linear capsule dividing from above downwards into two valves, and containing numerous very small winged seeds, attached to the margins of the valves. [M. T. M.]

PIMENTO. The dried berries of the West Indian *Eugenia Pimenta* and *E. acris.*

PIMIA *rhamnoides* is the sole representative of the only genus of *Byttneriaceæ* as yet discovered in the tropical parts of Polynesia, and the easternmost member of the natural order to which it belongs. It is found in the Feejees, and is a timber tree forty to fifty feet high, with ferrugineous branches and foliage, alternate oblong entire leaves, a five-cleft calyx, five very minute cordate petals, five stamens, no staminodia, a five-celled ovary, and an echinate capsule resembling that of *Commersonia*. Its nearest ally is *Lasiopetalum*. It was named in honour of the Arctic explorer, Captain Bedford Pim, R.N. [B. S.]

PIMIENTO. The Spanish name for Capsicum

PIMPINELLA. A genus of umbellifers, the fruit of which is ovate in general outline, each half with five equal narrow ribs, the furrows between which have several oil-vessels. The species are European herbs, usually having the lower leaves more deeply divided than the upper; and the flowers white. The name is an alteration of *bipennula*, or twice-pinnate, in allusion to the form of the leaves. [G D.]

PIMPERNEL. *Anagallis.* —, BASTARD. *Centunculus.* —, FALSE. An American name for *Ilysanthes gratioloides.* —, RED or SCARLET. *Anagallis arvensis.* —, SEA. *Honkenya peploides.* —, WATER. *Samolus Valerandi*; also *Veronica Beccabunga*, and *V. Anagallis.* —, YELLOW. *Lysimachia nemorum.*

PIMPINEL. *Pimpinella Saxifraga.*

PIMPLED. The same as Papillose.

PIMPLOES. A West Indian name for the Prickly Pear, *Opuntia Tuna* and *O vulgaris.*

PIMPRENELLE. (Fr.) *Poterium*; also *Rosa pimpinellæfolia.* — AQUATIQUE.

Samolus Valerandi. — D'AFRIQUE. *Melianthus major.* — DES JARDINS. *Poterium Sanguisorba.* — DES PRÉS. *Sanguisorba officinalis.*

PIN. (Fr.) *Pinus.* — À GROS FRUIT. *Pinus Coulteri.* — ALVIEZ. *Pinus Cembra.* — À TROCHET. *Pinus Pinaster minor.* — BLANC. *Pinus halepensis.* —, BON. *Pinus Pinea.* — CHÉTIF. *Pinus inops.* — COMESTIBLE DES INDES. *Pinus Gerardiana.* — COMMUN. *Pinus sylvestris.* — CRIN. *Pinus Mughus.* — CULTIVÉ. *Pinus Pinea.* — D'ALEP. *Pinus halepensis.* — DE BORDEAUX. *Pinus Pinaster.* — DE BRIANÇON. *Pinus Mughus.* — DE CORSE. *Pinus Laricio.* — D'ÉCOSSE. *Pinus sylvestris.* — DE GENÈVE. *Pinus sylvestris genevensis.* — DE HAGUENAU, *Pinus sylvestris haguenensis.* — DE JÉRUSALEM. *Pinus halepensis.* — DE LA ROMAGNE. *Pinus Laricio caramanica.* — DE L'ENCENS. *Pinus Tæda.* — DE MARAIS. *Pinus palustris.* — DE MÂTURE. *Pinus sylvestris rigensis.* — DE MONTAGNE. *Pinus Mughus.* — DE PIERRE. *Pinus Pinea.* — DE RIGA, or DE RUSSIE. *Pinus sylvestris rigensis.* — DES LANDES. *Pinus Pinaster.* — DE TARARE. *Pinus sylvestris genevensis.* — DE WEIMOUTH. *Pinus Strobus.* — DOUX. *Pinus mitis.* — DU LORD. *Pinus Strobus.* — DU MANS. *Pinus Pinaster minor.* — ÉCAILLEUX. *Pinus sylvestris scariosa.* —, GRAND. *Pinus Pinaster.* — HÉRISSÉ. *Pinus rigida.* — JAUNE. *Pinus mitis.* — LOURD. *Pinus ponderosa.* — MARITIME. *Pinus Pinaster.* — NAIN. *Pinus Pumilio.* — NAZARON. *Pinus pyrenaica.* — NOIR D'AUTRICHE. *Pinus austriaca.* — PIGNON. *Pinus Pinea.* — PINCEAU. *Pinus Pinaster minor*; also *P. pyrenaica.* — PINSOT. *Pinus Pinaster minor.* — PINIER. *Pinus Pinea.* — PLEUREUR. *Pinus excelsa,* and *P. Gerardiana.* — ROUGE DE CANADA. *Pinus resinosa.* — RUDE. *Pinus rigida.* — SAUVAGE. *Pinus sylvestris.* — SUFFIS. *Pinus Mughus.* — TINIER. *Pinus Cembra.* — TROCHETS. *Pinus Pinaster minor.*

PINACEÆ. A name adopted by Lindley for the CONIFERÆ; which see.

PINA-CLOTH. The pineapple cloth of the Philippine Islands.

PINANG. A Malay name for the Betel-nut palm, *Areca Catechu.*

PINANGA. A genus originally founded upon species previously referred to *Areca,* but Dr. Martius, whose work on the order of palms is so justly celebrated, afterwards combined it with and made it a section of *Seaforthia,* which is synonymous with *Ptychosperma* of other authors, so that some species have at one time or other gone under four distinct generic names. All the species belong to the islands of the Malayan Archipelago, and are usually low slender-stemmed palms, with smooth unarmed ringed stems, and terminal pinnate leaves. Regarded as forming a section of *Seaforthia,* they are characterised by the flower-spikes having in most instances only one spathe, the flowers being disposed in straight lines, in whorls, or in spirals composed of few turns, by the male flowers having their sepals connected at the base and scarcely overlapping, and containing a short rudimentary pistil or none at all, and by the albumen of the seeds being marked like a nutmeg. [A. S.]

PINASSE. (Fr.) *Pinus sylvestris.*

PINASTER. *Pinus Pinaster.*

PINATHA. A kind of Jackwood, or probably a *Laurus,* obtained in Burmah.

PINŒNECTITIA. A name under which some plants allied to *Cordyline* and *Dasylirion* have been sent out by Belgian horticulturists. It is supposed to have arisen from the blunders of ignorant gardeners, who mistook the plant for a *Freycinetia,* but wrote the name so badly that it was read as above. The species with two others have been recently described by Lemaire as a genus of *Liliaceæ* of the tribe *Asparagineæ,* under the name of BEAUCARNEA; which see. The *B. recurvata,* the only one that has flowered, produced a panicle a yard long and a yard and a half in circumference, crowded with thousands of small white slightly scented flowers. By further blunders it has been spelt *Pincinectia* and *Pincecnitia.*

PINCKNEYA. A genus of small trees, natives of the Southern States of North America, and belonging to the *Cinchonaceæ.* The flowers are in tufts in the axils of the uppermost leaves. One of the five lobes of the calyx is usually expanded in the form of a coloured leaf; the corolla is funnel-shaped, with a five-cleft spreading limb, beyond which the five stamens project; style simple; stigma somewhat two-lobed; fruit capsular, the upper portion free from the calyx, dividing into two valves when ripe. *P. pubens* is grown in this country in sheltered situations. Its red downy flowers, and large downy ovate leaves, render it a handsome plant for a south wall. [M. T. M.]

PINDAIBA. A Brazilian name for the highly aromatic fruit of *Xylopia sericea.*

PINDALS, PINDARS. American and West Indian names for the Ground Nut, *Arachis hypogæa.*

PINE. *Pinus.* —, AMBOYNA. *Dammara orientalis.* —, BASTARD GROUND. *Teucrium Pseudo-Chamæpitys.* —, BHOTAN. *Pinus excelsa.* —, BLACK. *Pinus austriaca.* —, —, of New Zealand. *Podocarpus ferrugineus.* —, BRAZILIAN. *Araucaria brasiliensis.* —, BROOM. *Pinus australis.* —, CANDLE-WOOD. *Pinus Teocote.* —, CELERY-TOPPED. *Phyllocladus rhomboidalis.* —, CHILI. *Araucaria imbricata.* —, CHINESE WATER. *Glyptostrobus heterophyllus.* —, CLUSTER. *Pinus Pinaster.* —, COWRIE, or KAURI. *Dammara australis.* —, CYPRESS. *Frenela verrucosa.* —, DAMMAR. *Dammara orientalis.* —, IMOU. *Dacrydium cupressinum.* —, FRANKINCENSE. *Pinus Tæda.* —, GROUND. *Ajuga Chamæpitys.* —, HIGHLAND. *Pinus sylvestris horizontalis.* —, HUON. *Dacrydium Franklinii.* —, JERSEY. *Pinus inops.* —, KING. *Abies Webbiana.* —, KNEE. *Pinus Pumilio nana.* —, LABRADOR. *Pinus Banksiana.* —, LACE-BARK. *Pinus Bungeana.* —, LOBLOLLY. *Pinus Tæda.* —, MORETON BAY. *Araucaria Cunninghamii.* —, NEOZA. *Pinus Gerardiana.* —, NORFOLK ISLAND. *Araucaria excelsa.* —, NUT. *Pinus Fremontiana.* —, OYSTER BAY. *Callitris australis.* —, PITCH. *Pinus rigida*; also *P. australis.* —, POND. *Pinus serotina.* —, PRINCE'S. An American name for *Chimaphila umbellata.* —, RED. *Pinus australis*; also *Pinus resinosa.* —, —, of New Zealand. *Dacrydium cupressinum.* —, SAP. *Pinus rigida.* —, SCOTCH. *Pinus sylvestris.* —, SCREW. *Pandanus.* —, SCRUB. *Pinus Banksiana.* —, SEASIDE. *Pinus maritima.* —, SPEY-SIDE. *Pinus sylvestris horizontalis.* —, STONE. *Pinus Pinea.* —, —, SWISS. *Pinus Cembra.* —, —, SIBERIAN. *Pinus Cembra sibirica.* —, SWAMP. *Pinus palustris.* —, TARTARIAN. *Pinus Pallasiana.* —, TWISTED. *Pinus Teocote.* —, VIRGINIAN. *Pinus palustris.* —, WEST INDIAN. *Pinus occidentalis.* —, WEYMOUTH. *Pinus Strobus.* —, WHITE. *Pinus Strobus*; also *P. Tæda.* —, —, of New South Wales. *Podocarpus spinulosus.* —, YELLOW. *Pinus mitis*; also *P. australis.*

PINE. A general name for various kinds of timber obtained from coniferous trees; also applied especially to that of *Pinus Strobus.* Baltic, Riga, Norway, Red, or Memel Pine is the timber of *Pinus sylvestris* as grown in the north of Europe. New York Pine is the wood of *Pinus mitis*, Pitch Pine that of *Pinus rigida*, and Georgia Pitch Pine that of *Pinus australis.*

PINEAPPLE. *Ananassa sativa.*

PINEDA. The genus so named by Ruiz and Pavon is now referred to *Banara* of Aublet.

PINE-DROPS. An American name for *Pterospora.*

PINE-KNOTS. A United States name for the cones of pines.

PINELIA *hypolepta.* A minute and little-known Brazilian orchid of doubtful alliance. It is a tufted epiphyte, only two inches high, the pseudobulbs bearing single fleshy ovate leaves, three-toothed at their apices, and a terminal slender solitary-flowered peduncle clothed with three distant sheaths. The flower is comparatively large, like a miniature *Cattleya*, but green, with free spreading petaloid sepals, the lateral ones unequal at the base, similar but smaller petals, a large undivided lip continuous with and adnate to the base of the column, which is short almost horizontal, and has petaloid edges.   [A. S.]

PINE-SAP. *Monotropa Hypopitys.*

PINE-WEED. *Hypericum Sarothra.*

PINE-WOOL. The fibre obtained from the leaves of *Pinus sylvestris*, and from which vegetable flannel is made.

PINEY-VARNISH. The resin or dammar obtained from *Valeria indica.*

PINEY-TREE. *Calophyllum angustifolium.*

PINGUICULA. A family of small stemless herbaceous plants belonging to the *Lentibulariaceæ*, well marked by bearing close above the root a tuft of spreading leaves, of membranous texture, incurved at the edges, and greasy to the touch. Several species are natives of the British Isles, of which two are common: namely, the Common Butterwort, *P. vulgaris*, and *P. lusitanica.* The former sends up from the tuft of leaves several slender leafless stalks six to eight inches high, each bearing a solitary drooping violet-purple flower, which is two-lipped and spurred; it is frequent in boggy ground in the North, and is highly ornamental. The latter is a plant of similar habit, but smaller in all its parts, and with pale pink inconspicuous flowers; this is very frequent in Devonshire and Cornwall, in Ireland, and in the Hebrides. Both systematic and English names were probably given to these plants from the unctuous matter found on the leaves, which the ancient herbalists perhaps fancied to have some affinity with butter. The leaves are said to coagulate milk; and Gerard tells us that the 'oilous juice' was used in his time, in Yorkshire, to anoint the wounded teats of cows. French, *Grassette*; German, *Fettkraut.*   [C. A. J.]

PINGUIN, PEN-GWYN. *Bromelia Pinguin*, a fence plant used in the West Indies.

PINHA. A Brazilian name for *Anona squamosa.*

PINK. *Dianthus.* —, CLOVE. *Dianthus Caryophyllus.* —, CUSHION. *Silene acaulis.* —, DWARF. An American name for *Hedyotis.* —, GARDEN. *Dianthus plumarius.* —, MAIDEN, or MEADOW. *Dianthus deltoides.* —, MOSS. *Phlox subulata.*

PINK-NEEDLE. *Erodium moschatum.*

PINK-ROOT. An American name for *Spigelia marilandica*; also called Carolina Pink-root. —, DEMERARA. *Spigelia Anthelmia.*

PINK-WEED. *Polygonum aviculare.*

PINNÆ. The primary divisions of a pinnated leaf; its leaflets.

PINNATE. When simple leaflets are arranged on each side a common petiole. *Imparipinnate* is pinnate with an odd leaflet; *paripinnate* is pinnate with an equal number of leaflets.

PINNATIFID. Divided almost to the axis into lateral segments, something in the way of the side divisions of a feather. It is compounded with other words thus: *Pinnatifido-incised*, pinnatifid with very deep segments; *pinnatifido-laciniate*, pinpatifid with the segments laciniated ; *pin-natifido-sinuate*, pinnatifid with the segments sinuated—and so on.

PINNATILOBED,   PINNATILOBATE. When the lobes of a pinnatifid leaf are divided to an uncertain depth.

PINNATIPARTITE. Having the nervures pinnated, the lobes separated beyond the middle, and the parenchyma uninterrupted ; as in *Polypodium aureum*.

PINNATISECT. When the lobes are divided down to the midrib, and the parenchyma is interrupted.

PINNULES, or PINNULÆ. The secondary divisions of a pinnate leaf.

PINOCCHIO. Edible pine-seeds.

PIN-PILLOW. *Opuntia curassavica*.

PINSAPO. *Abies Pinsapo*.

PINUS. The true Pines form a very extensive genus of *Coniferæ*, numbering perhaps about seventy species. They are confined solely to the northern hemisphere, and, with the exception of one Canarian species, to Europe, Asia, and America—abounding principally in the temperate and cold regions, and occurring only very rarely within the tropics. All the species are trees, a very great many growing to a large and some to an immense height and size ; and being of gregarious habit, growing together in masses, they form extensive forests, especially in North America and Northern Europe.

Generically the Pines are well distinguished from the firs, spruces, cedars, and larches, which some botanists combine with them, by having their leaves in little clusters of twos, threes, or fives, sheathed at the base by thin chaff-like scales ; and by the persistent woody scales of which their cones are formed being thickened into a more or less pyramidal elevation at the top, with a boss in the centre, which is often very prominent and hooked. The leaves are evergreen, and what is called needle-shaped, varying from little more than an inch to a foot or more in length, but never much thicker than a stout needle, and usually very sharp-pointed. The two sexes of flowers are borne on the same tree, and appear in the spring ; the male catkins being clustered round the lower part of the young current year shoots, forming dense compound spikes ; and the females solitary or in clusters at the apex of young shoots. The former are made up of numerous closely imbricated anthers inserted round a common axis, and consisting of two cells adnate to a scale-like connective ; and the latter of numerous imbricated scales, each bearing two inverted ovules at its base. The cones ripen in the autumn of the second or third year after the flowering season, and consist of the enlarged and hardened scales of the female catkins, with the two ovules matured into nut-like seeds, which are nearly always furnished with thin wings.

The genus is of immense economic im-

portance to mankind, more particularly in the constructive arts, its chief products being timber and turpentine. The following are some of the most useful species:—

Pinus sylvestris, the typical Pine of Europe, especially of the northern and central parts, has a very extensive geographical range, reaching from the Mediterranean and Caucasus to lat. 74° north in Scandinavia, and eastward across Siberia to Kamtschatka. In this country it is known as the Scotch Pine, the highlands of Scotland being the only part of the British Isles where it is truly indigenous at the present day It is the badge of the M'Gregors. The tree varies much in size according to the soil and situation of its place of growth, at high elevations being a mere stunted shrub, and in more favourable localities a tree fifty or one hundred feet high, furnishing extremely valuable timber, the different varieties of which are known in commerce as Red, Norway, Riga, or Baltic Pine. It also affords a great part of the Wood Tar of Northern Europe, and some Turpentine.

Pinus australis, or *P. palustris*, as it is sometimes called, is the Pitch Pine of the Southern States of North America, where it forms a great portion of what are there termed ' pine-barrens,' which are extensive and monotonous tracts of country covered with pines to the exclusion of nearly all other trees. Before the outbreak of the American civil war, nearly all the Turpentine consumed in this country came from the Southern States, and was principally the produce of this species of Pine. It also affords the timber known to builders as Georgia Pitch Pine.

Pinus Pinaster, the Cluster Pine or Pinaster, is indigenous to the European countries bordering on the Mediterranean, but has been introduced into some Asiatic

Pinus Pinaster.

and other countries. It is one of the species that flourish close to the sea, and on that account is of vast importance in such districts as the French departments of Landes and Gironde, where, by means of plantations formed of it, enormous tracts of land adjacent to the seacoast and formerly occupied by rolling sands, have been reclaimed and rendered useful for agricultural purposes. It is also extremely valuable on account of the great quantity of Turpentine it yields; and since the blockade of the ports of the Southern States of America, it has supplied the bulk of the turpentine used in this country.

Pinus Pinea, the Stone Pine, is a native of Southern Europe and the Levant. This is one of the species of which the seeds are eaten. They are called *Pignons* by the French, and *Pinocchi* by the Italians, and are commonly eaten for dessert, or made into sweetmeats. Several other species also yield eatable seeds; such as *P. Sabiniana*, the seeds of which are collected in immense quantities by the Californian and Oregon Indians as an article of winter food;

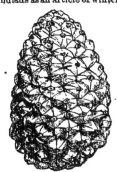

Pinus Pinea.

P. Gerardiana, the Neosa Pine of the Himalayas, affording the Neosa or Chilgoza seeds sold as food in the bazaars of Upper India; and *P. Cembra*, the Siberian Cedar, whose seeds are largely consumed by the Russians, as we eat nuts. The Canary Island Pine is shown at Plate 11e.   [A. S.]

PINWEED. *Lechea.*

PINXTER-FLOWER. An American name for *Azalea nudiflora.*

PIONANDRA. A group of about twenty tropical American *Solanaceæ*, collected together by Mr. Miers; but in the latest monograph of that order, the majority of them are combined with the older genus *Cyphomandra*, and the remainder referred to *Solanum*. They are small trees or treelike shrubs, with dichotomous branches, usually entire and mostly cordate leaves, borne in pairs, one of each pair always smaller than its fellow, and extra-axillary racemes, with small campanulate flowers arranged all on one side.   [A. S.]

PIONNE. (Fr.) *Pæonia officinalis.*

PIPE-DE-TABAC. (Fr.) *Aristolochia Sipho.*

PIPE, INDIAN. An American name for *Monotropa.*

PIPE-TREE. *Syringa.*

PIPERACEÆ. (*Pepperworts.*) A natural order of monochlamydeous dicotyledons, belonging to Lindley's piperal alliance of hypogynous Exogens. They are shrubs or herbs, with articulated stems, opposite verticillate stipulate or exstipulate leaves, sometimes alternate by abortion; and hermaphrodite spiked or racemose flowers without perianth, supported on a bract; stamens from two to six; anthers with or without a fleshy connective; ovary solitary free, one-celled, with a solitary erect ovule, orthotropal. Fruit somewhat fleshy, indehiscent; seed erect, with the embryo in a fleshy vitellus. They are natives of the hottest quarters of the globe, and occur commonly in South America and India. The wood is often arranged in wedges, with medullary rays, but without concentric zones. They have pungent, acrid, and aromatic properties; most of them contain an acrid resin, and a crystalline principle called *piperin*, in which their active qualities reside; some are narcotic and astringent. The substance called matico, or matica, consists of the leaves and unripe fruit of *Artanthe elongata*. There are about a score of genera, and upwards of 600 species—*Piper, Artanthe*, and *Peperomia* affording the best-known examples. [J. H. B.]

PIPER. This name was employed by the Romans to designate the Pepper-plants, and was derived by them from the Greek word *peperi*. The Greeks, in their turn, must have derived it from the Hindoos. Botanically, it is applied to the typical genus of *Piperaceæ*, the species of which are for the most part climbing shrubs, with alternate stalked leaves; stipules adherent to the leafstalk or opposite and deciduous; spikes solitary stalked, pendulous, opposite the leaves, with diœcious or perfect flowers, protected by oblong decurrent bracts. The species are indigenous in India, the islands of the Indian Ocean, the Sandwich Islands, &c., and some of them are abundantly cultivated in the tropical countries of the New as well as of the Old World.

P. nigrum yields the Pepper of commerce, a condiment that has been held in high esteem from the earliest times. It is frequently mentioned by Roman writers of the Augustan age, and it is related that in the fifth century Attila demanded, among other things, 3,000 lbs. of pepper in ransom for the city of Rome. Pepper is cultivated in the East and West Indies, Sumatra, Java, &c., but that which comes from Malabar is held in the highest esteem. The pepper-vine will, if left to itself, attain a height of twenty or more feet, but in cultivation it is found more convenient not to allow it to exceed the height of twelve feet. The plants are placed at the base of trees that have rough or prickly bark, in order that they may the more readily attach themselves to the trunk. In three years they produce their spikes of fruits, and continue to do so for some seven or eight years, after which time they become less productive. The fruit when ripe is of a red colour; it is gathered before it is fully ripe, and spread on mats in the sun, when it loses its red colour and becomes black and shrivelled, as we see it in the peppercorns of the shops: this is Black Pepper. White Pepper is the same fruit, freed from its outer skin by maceration in water and subsequent rubbing; occasionally it is rendered of a yet paler colour by being submitted to the action of chlorine.

Sir John Mandeville, who travelled in the years 1322 to 1356, has given us an account of the Pepper, which, with some exceptions, applies as well now as then. 'The Peper growethe,' he writes, ' in maner as doth a wylde vine, that is planted fast by the trees of the wodee for to susteynen it by, as doth the vyne, and the fruyt thereof hangethe in manere as Reysinges: and the tree is so thikke charged, that it semethe that it wolde breke: and when it is ripe it is all grene, as it were Ivy berryes; and then men kytten hem as men doe the vynes and than thei putteh it upon an owven, and there it waxeth blak and crisp.'

Piper nigrum.

Pepper is imported into this country in enormous quantities, and is used as a condiment. Medicinally it is employed as an acrid stimulant in cases of weak digestion, and it has also been recommended in cases of ague to ward off the paroxysm, a practice recommended by Celsus. Pepper is also sometimes employed externally. Pepper on chemical analysis is found to contain a hot acrid resin, and a volatile oil, as well as a tasteless crystalline substance called *piperin*, which has been recommended as a substitute for quinine. This piperin is especially contained in some large coloured cells in the interior of the fruit. Ground Pepper is frequently adulterated, according to Dr. Hassall, with linseed, mustard-seed, wheat-flour, pea-flour, and ground rice: sago has also been mentioned as being employed for this purpose. All such admixtures can be readily detected by the microscope. At one time, when a very heavy duty was levied on this substance, factitious peppercorns were manufactured of oilcake, clay, and a small portion of cayenne. Pepper-dust, known in the trade as P. D. or H. P. D. (hot pepper-dust), consists of the sweepings of the floors of the warehouses wherein pepper is stored, or of the siftings of the pepper. It is used to mix with genuine ground pepper, also for pickling. The root of the Pepper-plant is employed by the natives of India as a tonic stimulant and cordial.

P. trioicum, a nearly allied species to *P. nigrum*, yields also some little of the Pepper of commerce. Dr. Roxburgh, who first cultivated this plant, observed that the pepper of the female vines did not ripen properly, but dropped when green, and was deficient in pungency; but the pepper of those plants which had hermaphrodite and female flowers mixed on the same spike was very pungent, and reckoned by the merchants as equal to the best Malabar Pepper.

Long Pepper is the produce of *Chavica Roxburghii*. The Betel Pepper-leaf is also the produce of another species of *Chavica*, *C. Betel*; while Cubebs, another fruit formerly referred, like the two last-mentioned, to the genus *Piper*, is now considered to form a distinct genus, *Cubeba*. See CHAVICA and CUBEBA.   [M. T. M.]

PIPERITOUS. Having a hot biting taste.

PIPEWORT. *Eriocaulon*. Pipeworts is the name given by Lindley to the *Eriocaulaceæ*.

PIPI-PODS. The astringent legumes of *Cæsalpinia Pipai*.

PIPITZAHUAC. A drastic product of *Dumerila Alamanni*.

PIPPERIDGE, or PIPRAGE. *Berberis vulgaris*.

PIPPIN, NORMANDY. Sun-dried apples, pressed and stored for winter use.

PIPPUL, or PEEPUL. An Indian name for *Ficus religiosa*.

PIPSISSEWA. *Chimaphila umbellata*.

PIPTADENIA. In the character of its flowers this genus of *Leguminosæ* does not differ from *Entada*, though readily distinguished by its pods, which are seldom more than six or nine inches long and not very broad, flat and membranous or somewhat leathery, sometimes contracted between the seeds but without partitions inside, and ultimately separate into two pieces, which have the seeds attached to them by thread-like funiculi. The genus is entirely confined to tropical South America, and contains about thirty species, some trees, and others large sometimes prickly shrubs, with twice-pinnate leaves, and small white or greenish flowers, either in spikes or round heads, growing from the axils.

P. peregrina is one of the tallest trees of the genus, and has leaves composed of from fifteen to thirty pairs of pinnæ, each with from thirty to eighty pairs of minute leaflets; and rough leathery moniliform pods about six inches in length. The Indians of Venezuela and Brazil prepare a kind of snuff, called Niopo in the former and Parica in the latter country, by pounding the roasted seeds and mixing the powder with lime. It produces a peculiar kind of intoxication almost amounting to frenzy, and is taken by help of an instrument made of the leg-bones of birds. On the Rio Negro this is formed by joining two pieces, so that when one end is placed in the mouth the other reaches the nostrils, and the snuff is blown with great force up the nose; but in Venezuela it consists of a bone seven inches long, with a short piece joined on towards the top, so as to form a fork, which is applied to the nostrils, and the lower end being dipped into the snuff the mull, the snuff is drawn up the nose.   [A. S.]

PIPTANTHUS. A Himalayan shrub forming a genus of *Leguminosæ* of the suborder *Papilionaceæ* and tribe *Podalyrieæ*, very nearly allied to *Anagyris*, and with the same trifoliolate leaves, and rather large pale-yellow flowers; but the standard or upper petal has the sides closely folded back on each other. The free stamens and flat-stalked podare as in *Anagyris*. The only species known, *P. nepalensis*, has been introduced to our botanic gardens, where, however, it requires to be grown against a wall.

PIPTATHERUM. A genus of grasses belonging to the tribe *Stipeæ*, and now included under *Urachne*.   [D. M.]

PIPTOLÆNA. A genus of dogbanes, having the calyx tubular, shortly five-cleft, and falling off after flowering; its tube lined inside with several rows of fleshy scales; and the stigma capitate, two-lobed, subtended by four recurved lamellæ. It is an African tree, with opposite short petiolate leaves, wedge-shaped at the base; and bears its flowers in the axils of the upper leaves.   [G. D.]

PIPTOSTEGIA. A genus founded on *Ipomœa operculata*, and published without a technical description. The plant is well known, being used in medicine on account of its purgative qualities: it is imported into Europe under the name of Gomma da Batata.   [W. C.]

PIRATINERA. The plants formerly included under this generic name are now referred to *Brosimum*. One of the species yields Snakewood, or *Bois des Lettres*, which is exceedingly hard, and derives its name from its peculiar markings.   [M. T. M.]

PIRCUNIA. A genus of *Phytolaccaceæ* separated from *Phytolacca*, and characterised by the five segments of the calyx being of a thick leathery texture and green colour, and either ascending or reflexed under the ripe fruit; by the stamens varying from five to thirty, and more particularly by the five to twelve ovaries being distinct, or cohering only by their bases, but never throughout their whole length like those of *Phytolacca*. The species are tall herbs, with leaves and flower-spikes resembling those of *Phytolacca*, except one which attains the height

of a tree, and has the two sexes of flowers on different plants. They are found in America, Africa, and the East Indies.

P. dioica, the arborescent species just mentioned, is distinguished not only by its size and unisexual flowers, but by the racemes being pendulous and the carpels united by their bases. It is a native of Buenos Ayres, from whence it has been introduced and partly naturalised in Spain and Portugal, where it grows very rapidly to the height of twenty or twenty-five feet, forming a handsome leafy tree with a very thick trunk of remarkably soft spongy wood, and short branches spreading so as to form a rounded head. Its leaves are of an elliptical form, on longish stalks, and measure about six or eight inches in length and from one to two inches in breadth.

P. esculenta was recommended some twelve or more years ago for cultivation in France as a culinary vegetable, but does not appear to have met with much success. Its leaves cooked as spinach, and its young shoots as asparagus, were both said to possess an excellent flavour. The plant is herbaceous, and grows from three to five feet high, with a thickish pale-green smooth stem, and branches bearing elliptical leaves from five to seven inches long and two to two-and-a-half inches broad, and erect racemes of perfect flowers, with the ovaries cohering by their bases.   [A. S.]

PIRI-JIRI. The New Zealand *Haloragis citriodora*.

PIRITU. A Venezuelan name for *Guilielma speciosa*.

PISAILLE. (Fr.) *Pisum arvense*.

PISANG. An Indian name for *Musa paradisiaca*.

PISCIDIA. A West Indian tree constituting a genus of *Leguminosæ*, with the foliage habit and flowers of *Lonchocarpus*, but the pod bears four projecting longitudinal wings. The pounded leaves and young branches of this tree, *P. Erythrina*, like those of some other allied arboreous *Papilionaceæ*, are used for poisoning fish.

PISHAMIN. *Carpodinus*.

PISIFORM. Pea-shaped.

PISONIA. A genus of tropical trees and shrubs of the family *Nyctaginaceæ*, named in honour of a Dutch physician who wrote a folio volume on the Natural History of Brazil in 1648. The flowers are arranged in cymes, provided with very small bracts, but no general involucre, and are for the most part diœcious. The perianth is coloured and funnel-shaped, the limb either entire or more or less five-lobed; stamens six to ten, free, of unequal length, protruding; ovary one-celled, with a single erect ovule; fruit angular, enclosed within the persistent and hardened tube of the perianth, its angles frequently rough and prickly. Some of the species are in cultivation as stove plants, but have little to recommend them: *P. fragrans* and other species have emetic properties. *P. aculeata,* a scrambling tree with reclining thorny branches, is described as offering serious annoyance to travellers in the West Indies by its strong hooked spines, which become entangled in the clothes or flesh of the wayfarer. The glutinous bur-like fruit adheres to the wings of birds to such an extent as to prevent them from flying, and allow of their easy capture. [M. T. M.]

PISSABED. *Taraxacum Dens-leonis.*

PISSBLUME. *Armeria vulgaris.*

PISSENLIT. (Fr.) *Taraxacum.*

PISSE-SANG. (Fr.) A vulgar name for Fumitory.

PISTACHE. (Fr.) The Pistachio-nut. — DE TERRE. *Arachis hypogœa.*

PISTACHIER. (Fr.) *Pistacia.*

PISTACIA. The *Pistacias* or Turpentine trees form a genus of *Anacardiaceæ*, dispersed through the temperate zone of the northern hemisphere, extending in the Old World from the south of Europe and North Africa through Western Asia and the north of India to China, while a solitary species is found in Mexico. They are mostly small trees, seldom more than twenty or thirty feet high, and have pinnate leaves with or without a terminal leaflet, and axillary panicles or racemes of small unisexual apetalous flowers, those bearing the female being looser than the male, and the two sexes being produced on separate trees; the males five-parted, with a stamen opposite and inserted into each segment; the females three or four-parted, closely investing a one- (rarely three-) celled ovary. The fruits are dry egg-shaped drupes, containing a one-seeded stone with a bony shell, the seed having thick fleshy oily cotyledons.

P. Lentiscus, the Mastic tree, is a native of Southern Europe, Northern Africa, and Western Asia. It is a small tree about

Pistacia Lentiscus.

fifteen or twenty feet high, with evergreen pinnate wing-stalked leaves without a terminal leaflet. Mastic or Mastich is the resin of the tree, and is obtained by making

transverse incisions in the bark, from which it exudes in drops and hardens into small semitransparent tears. It is principally produced in the island of Scio and in Asiatic Turkey, and is consumed in large quantities by the Turks for chewing to sweeten the breath and strengthen the gums : hence its name, which is derived from *masticare,* ' to chew.' In this country it is used for varnishing pictures, and by dentists for stopping teeth.

P. Terebinthus, the Chio or Cyprus Turpentine tree, is likewise found in Southern Europe, Northern Africa, and Asia. It has deciduous pinnate leaves, usually with three pairs of lance-shaped leaflets and an odd terminal one ; and produces small dark-purple roundish furrowed fruits. The turpentine flows from incisions made in the trunk, and soon becomes thick and tenacious, and ultimately hardens. It is collected in the islands of the Greek and Turkish Archipelagos, but seldom comes to this country. Curious horn-shaped galls, caused by the punctures of insects, are found in large numbers upon the Terebinth-tree, and are collected for dyeing and tanning purposes—one of the varieties of Morocco leather being tanned with them.

P. vera, the Pistacia tree, which yields the eatable Pistachio-nuts, is a native of Western Asia, from whence it has been introduced into and is greatly cultivated in Southern Europe. Its leaves are composed of three or five (occasionally one) broad egg-shaped leaflets ; and its fruits are much larger than in the last, oval, sometimes nearly an inch long, and containing a seed with bright-green cotyledons. Pistachio-nuts are greatly eaten by the Turks and Greeks, and also in the south of Europe, either simply dried like almonds, or made into articles of confectionary. Galls are also collected from this and other species ; those from Cabul and Bokhara, called Gool-i-Pista, being the produce of *Pistacia Khinjuk.* It is probable that the Chinese Galls (Woo-pei-tsze) may also be obtained from one of the species. [A. S.]

PISTIACEÆ. (*Lemnaceæ, Lemnads, Duckweeds.*) A natural order of monocotyledons belonging to Lindley's aral alliance of Endogens. They are floating plants, with lenticular or lobed leaves or fronds, bearing one or two monœcious flowers enclosed in a spathe, but with no perianth ; stamens definite, often monadelphous ; ovary one-celled ; ovules one or more, erect or horizontal. Fruit indehiscent, membranous, one or more seeded. They are natives both of cool and warm regions. *Pistia* and *Lemna* are examples of the few genera, which comprise some two dozen species. *Lemna* forms the green covering of pools in Britain, while *Pistia* floats on ponds in warm countries. [J. H. B.]

PISTIA. *Stratiotes* is a very common tropical water-weed, out of which many species and even separate genera have been made. It is referred to the same order as duckweed (*Lemna*), whence it is sometimes called Tropical Duckweed, but is very different in appearance; indeed, its common West Indian name, Water Lettuce, is much more expressive of its general resemblance. Like duckweed, it propagates itself with great rapidity, and frequently completely covers tropical ponds and water-tanks with a coating of verdure, keeping the water beneath fresh and cool. It floats on the water, and sends down a quantity of long feathery roots, which do not always reach the bottom. The plant consists of a rose-shaped tuft of wedge-shaped slightly concave notched or round-topped leaves, two to five inches long, of a delicate pale pea-green, covered with fine hairs. Each plant sends out several runners, and upon the ends of these other similar plants are formed, which, again, send out runners, until in a short time the surface of the water is covered. Its flowers are very small, and borne in little spathes at the base of the leaves, each spathe containing one male and one female flower attached to an adnate spadix. The former occupies the upper-part, just within the mouth of the spathe, and consists of three to eight four-celled anthers adnate to a short column seated in a cup-shaped disk; while the latter is nearly concealed within the spathe, beneath the male, from which it is separated by a scale-like appendage, and consists of a single one-celled ovary terminated by a thick style and cup-shaped stigma, and containing numerous ovules along its inner face. [A. S.]

PISTIL. The female part of a flower, consisting of ovary, style, stigma, and ovules.

PISTILLARY CORD. A channel which passes from the stigma through the style into the ovary.

PISTILLIDIA. Young spore-cases, the archegonia in ferns; organs in the muscal alliance, which have the appearance of pistils.

PISTILLIGEROUS. Bearing a pistil.

PISTOLOCHIA. *Aristolochia Pistolochia.*

PISTORINIA *hispanica* is the only representative of a genus of *Crassulaceæ* inhabiting Spain and the Barbary coast of the Mediterranean. It is an erect annual or biennial herb, with nearly terete oblong and sessile leaves, and pinkish flowers arranged in umbels. The calyx is five-cleft, the corolla monopetalous, hypocrateriform, with its border divided into five lobes; and there are ten stamens, five scales, and five carpels. [B. S.]

PISUM. A genus of *Leguminosæ* of the tribe *Vicieæ*, distinguished by its triangular style keeled above, subfalcate and geniculate at the base. Three species have been referred to it, but they may all be reduced to the one grown for culinary purposes. It is, however, scarcely sufficiently distinct from *Lathyrus.*

The Common Pea, *P. sativum,* is a hardy annual of the greatest antiquity, and one of the most valuable of cultivated legumes.

Its native country is unknown, but is generally understood to be the south of Europe, from whence it is supposed to have been introduced into this country, by way of Holland or France, about the time of Henry VIII. During the long period it has been in cultivation numerous varieties have been produced, some of which seldom exceed a foot in height; while others, if allowed to attach themselves to stakes by their tendrils, will climb as high as eight feet or more. The whole plant is covered with a delicate glaucous bloom. The stem is round, furnished with numerous alternate compound leaves, the leaflets of which are roundish oval entire, and of a rich deep green, often marked with blotches of a paler colour. At the base of the footstalk each leaf has a pair of stipules, which resemble the leaflets but are much larger, rounded below, and have small convex teeth; while the extremity of the footstalk is terminated by a small round branching tendril, which clasps for support round anything near it. The peduncle is axillary, sometimes one but more generally two-flowered. The flowers are large, pure white or pale violet. The pods are pendulous, smooth, deep green, and variable in size, but for the most part oblong compressed somewhat scimitar-shaped terminating in a small hooked point. The peas when ripe are also variable—some being white and round, others blue and wrinkled, and a few large irregular and dull green.

The use of Peas is familiar to every one. In their dried state they are split and used for soups, or ground into meal for puddings, &c. In either case they form an agreeable and nourishing food, containing upwards of one-seventh more of nourishing matter than is found in the same weight of wheaten bread. But it is in a green state that peas are most valued for culinary purposes, and more particularly when they are quite small and young. In Queen Elizabeth's time (about 1570), we are told, they were occasionally brought from Holland, and considered 'a dainty dish for ladies—they came so far and cost so dear.' For many years their culture does not appear to have been much attended to, but after the Restoration of Charles II. in 1660, the taste for green peas became fashionable, and has continued to be so up to the present time—enormous prices being still paid for young peas very early in the season, when they are scarce and regarded as a great delicacy. To have peas in the highest perfection, they should not be allowed to get too old or too large. When the pods become full and hard, the peas are then more suitable for soups than a vegetable dish.

Besides the varieties of Peas whose seeds are edible, there is a section denominated Sugar-peas, which is remarkable in that the pods are destitute of the inner film peculiar to the pods of the other kinds of Peas. They are consequently more fleshy and crisp, and admit of being cut and dressed in exactly the same manner as French-beans. [W. B. B.]

The original Grey Pea, *P sativum arvense* of authors, supposed to be wild in Greece and the Levant, is probably the original parent both of the few sorts of peas grown by the farmer, and the countless numbers of still increasing sorts of the garden. Formerly varieties of the Grey Pea were almost exclusively planted on the farm: now, however, several garden varieties are introduced to field culture, as the White and Blue Prussian, Dwarf Blue and Green Imperial, the Scimitar, and others. Peas formerly took their place on the farm as a seeding crop, but at present in the neighbourhood of large towns even farmers cultivate green peas. Before the spread of the potato, peas formed a great part of the food of the working-classes, especially in the country; and a seed so rich in nitrogen was doubtless the cause of that superior muscular development which obtained among the peasantry in the last century. So important was this crop held to be, that in the letting or taking of a farm the acreage of Siddaw land (the term by which soil that would grow good boiling peas was known in Gloucester, Hereford, and Worcester) was always taken into consideration.

Field peas are often drilled with horsebeans, the mixture being known in country vernacular as Poulta—no doubt a corruption of Pulse. A greater breadth of peas is grown in the counties of Sussex and Essex than we have seen elsewhere, and in the former county we have observed roasted peas always ready in the hucksters' shops. Pea-straw is highly esteemed as fodder, its large amount of flesh-forming matter rendering it superior in regard to its feeding properties to the straw either of wheat or barley.   [J. B.]

PITA. *Agave americana* and the allied species. Pita-fibre and Pita-thread are names for the fibre, called also Aloe-fibre, obtained from the leaves of the larger Agaves, such as *A. americana* and *A. mexicana.*

PITANGA, PITANGUEIRA. Names applied to Brazilian fruit-bearing species of *Eugenia.*

PITCAIRNIA. A genus of tropical American herbs belonging to the *Bromeliaceæ.* They have linear spiny leaves, and flowers in clusters; perianth of six pieces, the three outer lanceolate keeled erect, the three inner ones larger, combined into a tube below, arching above or spreading, and scaly at the base within; stamens six, inserted into a ring encircling the partially adherent ovary; capsule three-celled, three-valved; seeds numerous. Several species of this handsome genus are in cultivation, and have for the most part scarlet or yellow flowers.   [M. T. M.]

PITCH. The residuum obtained in the distillation of wood-tar from *Pinus sylvestris* and *P. Pinaster*; the resin of pine, extracted by fire and inspissation. It is commonly known as Black Pitch. —, AMBOYNA. The resin of *Dammara australis.*

—, BURGUNDY. The purified resinous sap of *Abies excelsa.*

PITCHER. A hollowed-out leaf, furnished with a distinct extremity or lid; the latter being the lamina, the former the petiole; as in *Nepenthes.*

PITCHER-LEAF. *Nepenthes Phyllamphora.*

PITCHER-PLANT. *Nepenthes*; also *Saracenia.* —, AUSTRALIAN, or NEW HOLLAND. *Cephalotus follicularis.* —, CALIFORNIAN. *Darlingtonia californica.*

PITCHER-SHAPED. The same as Campanulate, but more contracted at the orifice, with an erect limb; as the corolla of *Vaccinium Myrtillus.*

PITCH-TREE. *Abies excelsa.* —, AMBOYNA. *Dammara orientalis.*

PITH. The same as Medulla.

PITHECOLOBIUM. The majority of the species now included in this genus of *Leguminosæ* were referred by old authors to *Inga*, from which they are not distinguishable by their flowers, but by their leaves and pods. Thus the *Ingas* have simply pinnate leaves, and straight or only slightly curved thick-edged pods, which do not open at maturity; while the leaves of *Pithecolobium* are twice-pinnate, and the pods either spirally twisted or very much curved, sometimes so much as to form rings, not thickened at the margin, and when ripe splitting into two valves. The seeds are usually surrounded by a thin pulp. Nearly a hundred species are described, the greater number of which belong to the tropics of the Western hemisphere, and the remainder to tropical Asia, with the exception of one found in Eastern Australia.

P. dulce, a large tree native of the hot regions of Mexico, produces cylindrical irregularly swollen pods curled at the top, containing a sweet edible pulp, which the Mexicans, who call the tree Guamuchil, boil and eat. The Spaniards introduced it into the Philippine Islands, from whence it has been carried to India; and it is now planted along the lines of railway in the Madras Presidency, where the fruit is known as Manilla Tamarinds. Other species, such as *P. Saman* in Brazil and Venezuela, also yield eatable pods, which are given to cattle like the Carob pods of Europe. Those of *P. cyclocarpum* possess saponaceous properties and are used as soap in Caraccas, as also is the bark of *P. bigeminum,* or an allied species, in Cochin China; while the bark of *P. unguis-cati* is astringent.   [A. S.]

PITHYUSA. *Euphorbia Pithyusa.*

PITO. A sort of beer made from the fermented seeds of *Zea Mays.*

PITS. Depressions on the inside of cells or tubes, formerly taken for pores, which they resemble.

PI-TSI. *Scirpus tuberosus.*

PITTE (Fr.) *Fourcroya gigantea.*

PITTED. Having numerous small shallow depressions or excavations.

PITTOMBA. *Sapindus esculentus.*

PITTOSPORACEÆ. (*Pittosporads.*) A natural order of thalamifloral dicotyledons belonging to Lindley's berberal alliance of hypogynous Exogens. They are trees or shrubs, with simple alternate exstipulate leaves, and regular symmetrical occasionally polygamous flowers, found chiefly in Australasia. Many of them are resinous, and in some instances the berries are eaten. Sepals and petals four or five, imbricated; stamens five, alternate with the petals; ovary two to five-celled, with axile and parietal placentæ. Fruit capsular or berried, with many-seeded cells, which are sometimes incomplete; seeds often enveloped in a glutinous or resinous pulp. *Pittosporum, Billardiera,* and *Sollya* are some of the genera, of which there are about a dozen, including some eighty or more species. [J. H. B.]

PITTOSPORUM. A genus of *Pittosporaceæ,* having a calyx of five sepals; a corolla of five petals, the claws of which are united into a tube; five stamens alternating with the petals; a single style crowned with numerous stigmas; and a smooth or hairy five-valved one-celled capsule, the seeds covered with a resinous pulp. They form large shrubs or small trees, with entire permanent leaves, and white or yellowish flowers with a spreading limb, disposed in terminal cymes or racemes. The larger number of species are natives of Australia, but some occur in Madeira, the Canaries, Cape of Good Hope, Japan, &c. [R. H.]

PITUITAIRE. (Fr.) *Delphinium Staphisagria.*

PIVOINE. (Fr.) *Pæonia.* — EN ARBRE. *Pæonia Moutan.* — DES JARDINS, or P. FEMELLE. *Pæonia officinalis.* — MÂLE. *Pæonia corallina.*

PIWARRIE. An intoxicating beverage prepared from Cassava, *Manihot utilissima.*

PIXIDELLE. (Fr.) *Lindernia.*

PIXIE-STOOLS. *Chanterellus cibarius.*

PIZIUBA. *Iriartea exorrhiza.*

PLACEA ornata. A pretty little Chilian amaryllidaceous plant, forming a genus allied to *Eurosia,* and having a petaloid perianth of six equal reflexed spreading divisions, the two lower of which are widely separated; a coronet of six notched narrow pieces cohering into a tube at the bottom; three long and three short declinate stamens; and a curved style and truncate stigma. It has a small bulb, from which rise a pair of narrow leaves; and a flower-stem a span or so high, bearing about six flowers, which are snow-white outside and striped with brilliant vermilion lines inside. [A. S.]

PLACENTA. The place or part on which ovules originate.

PLACENTA-SHAPED. Thick, round, and concave on both the upper and lower surface; as the root of *Cyclamen.*

PLACENTATION. The manner in which the placenta is constructed or placed.

PLAGIANTHUS. A small genus of *Sterculiaceæ,* confined to South Australia, Tasmania, and New Zealand. One species is a tall tree, and the others large shrubs, with very tough bark, and more or less covered with star-like down. Their leaves are alternate or in clusters, and very variable in shape; and their small whitish flowers are borne in little racemes or clusters in the axils of the leaves, and are usually unisexual with the two sexes sometimes on separate plants, but occasionally perfect. The fruit consists of from one to five one-celled cocci, which ultimately burst irregularly and separate from the central column. *P. betulinus,* also sometimes called *P. urticinus,* when full-grown forms a tree seventy feet high, but it is more frequently a straggling bush of no great height. The inner bark of the young branches yields a very fine tough fibre, sometimes called New Zealand Cotton, though more like flax than cotton: it is the Akaroa of the New Zealanders. *P. sidioides* is one of several plants with fibrous bark, which in Tasmania and New South Wales bear the native name Kurrajong or Currajong. The present, a shrub ten or twelve feet high, yields a tough fibre, of which good cordage and twine for fishing-nets are made. [A. S.]

PLAGIOCHILA. A charming genus of *Jungermanniaceæ,* characterised by the free terminal herbaceous perianth, which is generally exserted but sometimes concealed by the involucre, though in that case distinct. The leaves, moreover, have their anterior margin concealed by the posterior margin of the next in succession. In *Plagiochila* the perianth is two-lipped and laterally compressed. The species belong principally to warm countries, but we have a fine representative, *P. asplenioides,* in this country. Should *Jungermanniæ* ever become objects of cultivation, the species of *Plagiochilæ* must be in the first class. Some of them are very large and elegant, as, for example, the New Zealand *P. Stephensoniana,* which attains a length of eight or nine inches, and is as beautiful in structure as the most delicate *Hymenophyllum.* [M. J. B.]

PLAGIOCHILUS. A genus of *Compositæ* of the tribe *Anthemideæ,* consisting of low herbs from the Andes of South America, mostly with the prostrate stems, much-cut leaves, and small flower-heads of *Soliva,* but remarkable for the external florets of each head being deeply and unequally three-lobed. There are several species, insignificant weedy-looking plants of no special interest.

PLAGIOLOBIUM. A name given by Sweet to *Hovea chorozemæfolia* and its variety *ilicifolia,* which have broader leaves than other *Hoveas*, often bordered by prickly teeth, and a broader and more oblique pod. They are natives of South-west Australia, and are to be met with in many of our collections of Australian papilionaceous plants. The flowers are of a deep purplish-blue as in other *Hoveas*, and are rather ornamental.

PLAITED. Folded lengthwise, like the plaits of a closed fan; as in the leaves of the fan-palm.

PLANE. Flat or perfectly level; as in many leaves.

PLANE. (Fr.) *Acer platanoides.*

PLANERA. Trees, natives of Asia and North America, belonging to the *Ulmaceæ*, and closely allied to the elms, from which they may be distinguished by their fruit, which is roundish, gibbous, pointed, two-celled, and two-seeded. *P. Richardi*, the Zelkona tree, attains in its native country a great size, growing to the height of seventy or eighty feet, with a trunk of the diameter of four feet. The bark resembles that of the hornbeam more than the elm, and instead of becoming rugged is shed in scales like that of the plane. The foliage strongly resembles that of the elm; the flowers are small, of a greenish-brown colour, and smell like those of elder. The fruit is about the size of a pea, and contains two seeds. The trunk is straight and upright, and is of equal circumference from the surface of the ground to a height of twenty-five or thirty feet, where it throws out its first branches. The timber is much prized. The sapwood, which is of a light colour and very elastic, is used for the purposes in which ash-timber is employed. The heartwood, which occupies two-thirds of the whole trunk, is reddish, heavy, and when dry exceedingly hard: hence it takes a good polish, and is valued for making domestic furniture. *P. Gmelini*, a native of the Southern States of America, is a small tree, to which no particular value is attached. Either of the above may be grafted on the elm. French: *Orme de Sibérie.* [C. A. J.]

PLANE-TREE. *Platanus.* —, MOCK, or SCOTCH. *Acer Pseudo-Platanus.*

PLANIUSCULUS. Nearly flat.

PLANK PLANT. *Bossiæa Scolopendrium.*

PLANTAGINACEÆ. (Ribworts.) A natural order of corollifloral dicotyledons belonging to Lindley's cortusal alliance of perigynous Exogens. They are herbs, often stemless, with radical ribbed leaves, and spiked hermaphrodite flowers, or solitary unisexual ones. Calyx four-parted, persistent; corolla monopetalous, scarious, with a four-parted limb; stamens four, alternate with the segments of the corolla; disk inconspicuous; ovary free, two to four-celled, with a simple style and hispid stigma. Fruit an operculate capsule. The species are chiefly found in temperate and cool regions. The three genera, of which

Plantago and *Littorella* are examples, comprise over 100 species. [J. H. B.]

PLANTAGO. A genus of stemless herbaceous plants giving name to the order *Plantaginaceæ*, represented in Great Britain by several common species. *P. major*, the Greater Plantain, abundant by waysides and in the corners of fields, is known by its broad strongly ribbed leaves tapering towards each extremity, from the centre of which rise, to the height of two to six inches, several cylindrical leafless stalks bearing each a long spike of greenish flowers, succeeded by many-seeded capsules, which when ripe are much sought after by bird-fanciers as food for canary-birds. *P. media*, the Hoary Plantain, has the leaves similar but smaller, and they are remarkable for being pressed so closely to the ground as to injure seriously any crop among which it may be growing by stifling the young plants; hence it is a great pest in pastures and on lawns. *P. lanceolata*, the Rib-grass, has narrow strongly ribbed leaves, and bears brown spiked heads of flowers at the summit of a furrowed stalk; it is sometimes sown as an ingredient in a crop of meadow-grass, but with doubtful propriety. *P. Coronopus* grows on sea-cliffs, and is distinguished by its pinnate toothed leaves, which radiate so as to resemble a star, whence it is sometimes called Star of the Earth. There are numerous foreign species, but none of particular interest. The name Plantain is frequently applied to the Banana of the tropics, MUSA: which see. French: *Plantain*; German: *Wegerich.* [C. A. J.]

PLANTAIN. *Musa paradisiaca.* —, BASTARD. *Heliconia Bihai.* —, GREATER. *Plantago major.* —, INDIAN. An American name for *Cacalia.* —, MUD. *Heteranthera reniformis.* —, RATTLESNAKE. *Goodyera.* —, ROBIN'S. *Erigeron bellidifolium.* —, WATER. *Alisma.* —, —, of Jamaica. *Pontederia azurea.*

PLANTAIN. (Fr.) *Plantago.* — AQUATIQUE. *Damasonium Alisma*, alias *Actinocarpus Damasonium.* — D'EAU. *Alisma Plantago.* — EN ARBRE. *Musa.*

PLANT D'AIX. (Fr.) A kind of olive.

PLANTIA. A genus of irids, allied to *Sisyrinchum* and *Moræa*, consisting of a Cape species, *P. flava*, of which very little is known. It has a single narrow stem-clasping leaf, and a many-flowered stem bearing pretty yellow flowers. [A. S.]

PLAQUEMINIER. (Fr.) *Diospyros.* — D'ORIENT. *Diospyros Lotus.*

PLATANACEÆ. (Planes.) A natural order of monochlamydeous dicotyledons, referred to Lindley's urtical alliance of diclinous Exogens, and consisting only of the genus PLATANUS: which see. [J. H. B.]

PLATANAIRE. (Fr.) *Sparganium.*

PLATANTHERA. An extensive genus of orchids, belonging to the tribe *Ophrydeæ*, and closely allied to *Habenaria*, from which it is distinguished by the absence of the two fleshy processes of the lower lip of the stigma, characteristic of that genus. The numerous species are nearly all natives of the temperate and cold regions of the northern hemisphere, in Europe, Asia, and America, very few extending to the warmer regions—the exceptions being one or two in Java, and as many in Ceylon. Two—viz. *P. bifolia* and *P. chlorantha*—are British, and are frequently referred to *Habenaria* in local floras. [A. S.]

PLATANUS. A genus bearing some resemblance to the urtical and amental families, but so different that it has been separated from them as distinct, under the name of *Platanaceæ*, placed by Lindley in the urtical alliance. It consists of five or six species, nearly resembling each other, natives of Europe, Asia, North Africa, and the temperate parts of North America. Most of them are lofty trees, with dense foliage and massive trunks, the bark of which annually scales off, leaving the surface smooth. The leaves are alternate, with sheathing stipules, the lamina being pentangular or palmate. The flowers are monœcious, in globular heads somewhat resembling catkins: the males usually consist of a mass of apparently irregular sepals and stamens, but when fully developed the flower is found to consist of four sepals and four stamens alternate with them; frequently, however, only three or two are present. The heads of female flowers also have commonly the same appearance of irregularity, from which the ovary has been regarded as consisting of a single carpel; but when they are perfect each flower proves to consist of four sepals, four barren stamens alternate with them like minute petals, and from four to eight distinct carpels—the latter character being more obvious in *P. occidentalis*. Each of the carpels contains one or two pendulous ovules, and becomes a single-seeded fruit. The embryo, which has an inferior radicle, is enclosed in a small quantity of albumen. For a further description of the flowers, and for figures, see *Ann. Nat. Hist.*, Third Series, i. p. 10 *et seq.*

Different opinions have been formed as to the position of this genus in the natural system; the ovary, however, together with the general appearance of the trees, brings it near *Aceraceæ*, 'Sycamore,' which is a species of *Acer*, being one of the names by which *P. occidentalis* is known in America.

P. orientalis, the Oriental Plane-tree, so common in the parks and plantations of this country, is when fully grown from seventy to ninety feet high, forming when standing separately a majestic object. It is distinguished from *P. occidentalis* by the leaves being more deeply divided and indented, and by the absence of membranous bracts around the female flower. The wood is used in the Levant and in Asia, in carpentry, joinery, and cabinet-making, and is said to make beautiful furniture on account of the smoothness of its grain,

and its susceptibility of receiving a high polish. *P. acerifolia*, the tree commonly grown as *P. occidentalis*, is as large and magnificent as the Oriental Plane, the trunk having been known to become upwards of thirteen feet in diameter. The wood in seasoning becomes of a dull red colour; it is used in carpentry, but is not much esteemed.

P. racemosa, the Californian Plane—remarkable for its deeply five-lobed leaves, the under-surface of which, even when they become old, is copiously clad with woolly hairs—has a wood far preferable to that of *P. occidentalis*, as it is much harder and more durable, being also less liable to warp. [B. C.]

PLATEAU. (Fr.) *Nuphar luteum.*

PLATENIA. A genus of *Palmaceæ* closely allied to *Cocos* and *Syagrus*, lately established upon a palm found upon the banks of the River Magdalena in New Grenada, and principally characterised by its flower-spikes being furnished with only one spathe, which splits lengthways along the back, by the female flowers not having barren stamens, and by the bony stone of the fruit being smooth or marked with three small channels. *P. Chiragua*, the palm in question, grows from fifty to seventy feet high, and has pinnate leaves measuring twelve feet in length, with very numerous narrow sharp-pointed smooth segments as much as two feet in length. Its flower-spikes are simply branched, and bear female flowers, with one or two males adjoining them on the lower and males alone on the upper part; the females producing fleshy orange fruits about the size of pigeons' eggs, and containing a single horny seed with a cavity in the centre. [A. S.]

PLATONIA *insignis*. A beautiful Brazilian tree forming a genus of *Clusiaceæ* closely allied to *Moronobea*, and differing chiefly in the five bundles of stamens consisting of much more numerous filaments, not spirally twisted round the ovary. The tree is very large with a hard wood; the leaves coriaceous, elegantly marked with numerous parallel veins; the flowers large, of a light red colour, solitary at the ends of the small branches. The fruit, called Pacoury-uva in Brazil, is said to be very sweet and delicious, whilst the seeds have the flavour of almonds.

PLATYCAPNOS, A genus of *Fumariaceæ*, native of the Mediterranean region, differing from *Fumaria* by the erect not climbing stem, and by the fruit being oval, compressed, two-valved, the epicarp separable from the membranous endocarp. [J. T. S.]

PLATYCARPUM. A genus of doubtful affinity provisionally classed with *Bignoniaceæ*, but inclining strongly towards *Rubiaceæ* and *Loganiaceæ*. Unlike most *Bignoniaceæ*, the five-cleft calyx is semi-inferior; the funnel-shaped corolla encloses five fertile stamens; the capsule is woody, flat, and at the top and base cordate, whilst two winged seeds are enclosed in each of the two cells into which the fruit is divided by a very narrow partition. Only one species, *P. orinocense*, is known; this grows on granitic rocks on the banks of the Orinoco, and is a tall timber tree, with simple oblong leaves, furnished with stipules, and terminal panicles bearing rose-coloured blossoms. Its nearest allies are the various species of *Henriquezia*, also inhabitants of the Orinoco region.　　[B. S.]

PLATYCARYA. *Fortunæa.*

PLATYCERIUM. A very distinct and remarkable genus of ferns commonly associated with the *Acrosticheæ*, but which it has been proposed to place in a separate section, from its producing its sori in large amorphous patches, not as in the true *Acrosticheæ* universal over the fertile portions. The species are few in number, chiefly Eastern or Australian, and for the most part tropical. They have heteromorphous coriaceous laciniate or lobate fronds, clothed with stellate hairs, and the fertile ones are

Platycerium Wallichii.

articulate. The broad fronds are traversed by several furcate ribs, between which there is a close network of finer buried veins. The large shapeless masses of spore-cases are attached to a plexus of crowded veins, and are quite naked. In *P. biforme* they occupy a separate scutiform lobe, but in the other species they are variously situated near the margin.　　[T. M.]

PLATYCODON. A genus of bellworts, having a funnel-shaped corolla, with a broad five-lobed border, and the filaments of the anthers broad at the base. The species are perennial shrubs, natives of Eastern Asia. Their leaves are alternate and sessile; and the flowers large and handsome. The name is from the Greek words signifying 'broad' and 'bell,' in allusion to the conspicuous corolla. [G. D.]

PLATYCRATER. A genus of *Hydrangeaceæ*, growing on moist rocks in the north of Japan. It forms a small shrub, with procumbent or rooting branches, ob-

long acuminate serrate leaves, and a loose terminal branched corymb of flowers, of which the lower ones of each branch are sterile with an expanded coloured calyx, as in *Hydrangea*; but the fertile flowers have indefinite stamens inserted on an epigynous disk or ring.　　[J. T. S.]

PLATYLEPIS. A genus of cyperaceous plants belonging to the tribe *Hypolytreæ*. The inflorescence is in solitary or compound many-spiked heads. It contains six species, which are either natives of South Africa or Brazil.　　[D. M.]

PLATYLOBIUM. A genus of *Leguminosæ* of the suborder *Papilionaceæ* and tribe *Genisteæ*, consisting of Australian shrubs with opposite simple leaves, and yellow pea-shaped flowers in the axils of the leaves. The calyx is remarkable for its two upper lobes uniting into a large rounded upper lip. The pod is very flat, bordered by a rather broad wing on the upper side, and contains several seeds. Two species, *P triangulare* and *P. Murrayanum*, with acutely triangular leaves, both from Tasmania and South-eastern Australia, are occasionally to be seen in our greenhouses, and are handsome plants, while *P. formosum*, from the same country, has ovate leaves.

PLATYLOMA. A genus of polypodiaceous ferns, often erroneously associated with *Pterideæ* or *Cheilantheæ*, but in reality very distinct, and now representing a separate group, the *Platylomeæ*. They are pinnate or bipinnate plants, with free venation, and furnished with marginal oblong sori the receptacles of which lie transversely, being formed of the parallel apices of the contiguous venules, the spore-cases becoming laterally confluent into a broadish continuous marginal band, quite different from the continuous linear receptacle of *Pteris*. They are spuriously indusiate; that is, the margin is somewhat inflected over the outer portions of the band. Some of the species referred to *Pellæa* by authors belong here, the rest chiefly to *Pteris*. [T. M.]

PLATYMISCIUM. A genus of *Leguminosæ* of the tribe *Dalbergieæ*, consisting of South American trees or shrubs, with pinnate leaves always opposite—almost the only instance of this arrangement amongst trees of this order with compound leaves. The flowers are yellow, disposed in racemes either solitary in the leaf-axils, or clustered on the older branches. Their structure is nearly the same as in *Pterocarpus*, whilst the pod, broadly oblong and very thin and flat, is like that of some species of *Lonchocarpus*. There are about a dozen species, some of them probably supplying part of the hard woods used in or exported from Brazil.

PLATYNEMA. The name of some tropical Asiatic trees, supposed to constitute a genus of *Malpighiaceæ*. They have opposite elliptical leaves; flowers in terminal clusters; a five-parted glandless calyx; five flat-stalked entire petals; ten stamens, alternately long and short, with dilated filaments; and an ovary with three projecting keel-like wings; and the styles combined into one thread-shaped column, longer than the stamens. The name is derived from Greek words signifying 'flat-thread,' in allusion to the dilated filament.   [M. T. M.]

PLATYPODIUM. A genus of Leguminosæ of the tribe Dalbergieæ, with the flowers nearly of Pterocarpus and of Tipuana, while the pod is samara-like as in the latter genus; but the wing, instead of being a dilatation of the style and consequently placed above the seed-bearing part, is an expansion of the stalk and below the seed. It is like a Tipuana pod attached by the wrong end. The genus consists of three Brazilian trees, with pinnate leaves, and yellow flowers growing in handsome loose racemes in the axils of the upper leaves. They probably supply some of the hard woods used in Brazil.

PLATYS. In Greek compounds = broad.

PLATYSEMA. A little-known Brazilian bean, formerly proposed by Bentham as a distinct genus of the tribe Phaseoleæ, but most probably a species of Centrosema.

PLATYSTEMMA. A somewhat dubious genus of Gesneraceæ of the tribe Cyrtandreæ, represented by a single species, P. violoides, inhabiting Nepal, and having the habit of a violet. It is a low herb, the stem of which bears towards the apex one or two cordate and crenate leaves. The peduncle has from one to four flowers; the calyx is five-cleft; the corolla has a short tube and is bilabiate, the upper lobe being two-cleft, the lower five-cleft; there are four stamens; the style is filiform; the stigma acute; and the fruit a two-celled oblong capsule.   [B. S.]

PLATYSTEMON. Annuals belonging to the Papaveraceæ, among which they are distinguished by having three sepals, six petals, dilated filaments (whence the genus derives its name), and numerous distinct many-celled capsules. Two species have been described: P. californicus, a hairy spreading plant with lanceolate leaves arranged in threes, solitary stalked yellow flowers, and hairy capsules; and P. leiocarpus, a native of Siberia, distinguished by its yellowish-white flowers, and smooth capsules.   [C. A. J.]

PLATYSTIGMA. A Californian annual belonging to the Papaveraceæ, distinguished by its three sepals, four to five petals, thread-like filaments, three erect divergent stigmas, and its one-celled three-valved capsule opening from top to bottom. The stems, which are very short, are densely crowded with linear entire leaves, from among which rise on slender hairy stalks the solitary yellow flowers. The whole plant grows to the height of about six inches.   [C. A. J.]

PLATYTHECA. A genus of Tremandraceæ, consisting of a couple of species inhabiting the sandy plains of South-west Australia. They are elegant little evergreen shrubs, with linear leaves arranged in whorls somewhat resembling those of Galium. The pedicels bear one flower of a purplish-lilac colour, and only opening once on a bright day, but never when the sky is overcast or night is approaching; whilst in its ally, Tetratheca, the flowers open and close repeatedly on bright days, closing on the approach of night or showers of rain, as Dr. Steetz has well observed. The calyx is five-cleft, the corolla five-petalous, the stamens ten in number, the capsule two-celled and two-valved. P. galioides (Tremandra verticillata) is an inmate of our greenhouses.   [B. S.]

PLATYZOMA. The only species of this genus, P. microphyllum, is a curious dwarf linear-fronded fern of the Australian continent, with minute sessile suborbicular pinnæ, having the margins so decidedly revolute that the sori, which are non-indusiate, consisting of from two to four sessile spore-cases, are with great difficulty discovered. These pinnæ readily fall off, leaving the crowded rigid stipites and rachides standing like so many coarse bristles. The plant belongs to the Gleichenineæ, and indeed its fronds most nearly resemble single branchlets of those small-pinnuled species of Gleichenia which have saccate or pouch-formed segments.   [T. M.]

PLECOLEPIS. An involucre of composites, in which the bracts are united into a cup.

PLECOSTIGMA. A genus of Liliaceæ from Siberia, founded upon Gagea pauciflora, which is separated from the others on account of the stigma being three-cleft, each lobe longitudinally folded within, and the seeds oblong-trigonous. The flowers are yellow, one to three in a raceme, with two bracts at the base. Bulb simple; root-leaves few, filiform, at length elongated, stem-leaves scattered linear.   [J. T. S.]

PLECTOCOMIA. A genus of palms, of which two species are confined to Malacca, Penang, Java, and Borneo, and three are found in Assam, Khasia, and the Himalayas. They are allied to the rattans (Calamus), and like them are inhabitants of forests. Their climbing stems, though stouter than the generality of Calami, require other trees for their support; and in order that they may take a firm hold among the branches, their large pinnate leaves are furnished with long whip-like tails, beset on the under-side with excessively strong compound spines shaped something like a mole's foot, with the claws directed downwards. The genus is best distinguished by the flower-spikes, which are produced from the axils of the leaves, and are divided into numerous very long tail-like branches, clothed with two opposite rows of overlapping spathes, each of which encloses a short spike of flowers—the two sexes being upon separate trees. The fruits, like those of all other Calameæ, are densely covered with overlapping scales, but the scales, instead of being highly polished as in most genera, are rough and fringed at the edges, and give the fruit a prickly appearance; they contain a single seed with hard even albumen and basilar embryo.

In Java the formidably armed tails of the leaves of *P. elongata* are used for catching rogues and vagabonds and run-a-muck Malays. For this purpose pieces of the tails are attached to the inside of a forked stick, which is thrust so as to include the body of the man and take firm hold of his clothes or flesh. [A. S.]

PLECTRANTHUS. The generic name of plants belonging to the order *Labiatæ*, having the long tube of the corolla with a dilatation or short spur below; the border has the upper lip three to four-cleft, the lower entire, concave. The species are herbs and shrubs, natives of the warmer parts of Africa, South America, and Asia. The name is from the Greek words signifying 'spur' and 'flower,' indicative of the character of the corolla. [G. D.]

PLEEA. A genus of *Melanthaceæ*, inhabiting the warmer parts of North America. The species have tufted rhizomes, throwing up rush-like stems; the leaves are chiefly radical, two-ranked, evergreen, very narrow and acute; and the racemes are simple, with spathaceous bracts similar to the uppermost leaves. Perianth coloured (brownish), with six segments united at the base, and spreading; stamens nine to twelve, the filaments subulate, and the anthers linear; ovary three-lobed, with three short styles; capsule leathery, ovate, three-lobed, three-celled, [J. T. S.]

PLEIONE. A group of half a dozen spe-

Pleione maculata.

cies of *Orchidaceæ*, which, instead of forming a separate genus, are now considered only as a section of *Cœlogyne*, distinguished more by habit than by constant or well-marked technical characters. They are dwarf epiphytal plants, with handsome large membranous and generally richly-coloured flowers, which appear either before the leaves or after very quickly decidous leaves, so that the flowering plants

are leafless. All are alpine, being found growing at considerable elevations in the mountains of Northern and North-eastern India. [A. S.]

PLEIOPHYLLOUS. A name given to such nodes as have no manifest buds.

PLEIOS. In Greek compounds = more than one; several.

PLEISTOS. In Greek compounds = most; a great many.

PLENUS. Double, as in double flowers.

PLEOCNEMIA. A fern genus of the aspidioid group, in which it is known by its sori having reniform indusia affixed at the sinus, by its fronds being monomorphous or conformable, and by its veins being reticulated and arcuately anastomosing so as to form elongated costal areoles. It includes a few large much-divided tropical eastern species, some of which are said to have a subarboreous caudex. *P. Leuzeana* is the type. [T. M.]

PLEOPELTIS. A name originally proposed for a few ferns of the polypodioid type, in which the sori, not covered by any proper indusium, were invested with a few peltate stipitate scales, which grew up among the spore-cases. This group has not been maintained, and the name, as being the oldest available, has been transferred to a large group in which these scale-invested species are included, and to which the names *Phymatodes* and *Drynaria* have also been given. Thus extended, it forms the largest genus amongst the net-veined *Polypodieæ*, distinguished by compoundly reticulated venation, in which the areoles contain divaricate free veinlets, by the fronds being free from a clothing of stellate hairs (present in *Niphobolus*), by the sori being compital and polycarpous, and by the fronds being articulated with the rhizome, and monomorphous in character. *P. percussa, lycopodioides, irioides, crassifolia, Phymatodes, tridactyla,* and *juglandifolia* are types of so many subdivisions. The species are mostly tropical, a large number from India or the Eastern Archipelago, others from South America or the West Indies, extending to Chili, and a few from South Africa or New Zealand. [T. M.]

PLEROMA. This genus of *Melastomaceæ* is now generally made to contain all the *Lasiandras*, and numerous species formerly referred to *Chætogastra, Rhexia,* and some other genera, so that it numbers nearly one hundred species, natives of tropical South America, especially of Brazil. The principal part consists of shrubs or undershrubs, with large thick entire five-nerved leaves, and generally large terminal panicles, but sometimes solitary large purple violet or white flowers, with their floral envelopes in fives. They have a more or less oblong urceolate or campanulate calyx-tube and deciduous teeth or lobes; obovate, entire or retuse, often one-sided petals; ten unequal stamens, with smooth hairy or bearded filaments and long narrow subulate curved anthers, opening by single pores, having the connective prolonged at the base, and furnished with a couple of knobs at its junction with the filament; and a five-celled hairy-topped ovary bearing a slender curved style. Several species are grown in hothouses in this country on account of their beautiful large showy flowers. [A. S.]

PLEURACHNE. A genus of cyperaceous plants, belonging to the tribe *Scirpeæ*. *P. secunda*, the only species, is now referred to *Ficinia* by Steudel. [D. M.]

PLEURANDRA. A genus of *Dilleniaceæ*, usually distinguished from *Hibbertia* by the stamens being all inserted on one side of the ovaries; but as the relative arrangement of the stamens and ovaries in these genera and their immediate allies has now been found to be of a purely artificial character, separating species otherwise very similar, *Pleurandra* has been reduced to a section of *Hibbertia*. The species are all Australian, low shrubs or much-branched undershrubs, with yellow flowers.

PLEURENCHYMA. The woody tissue, consisting of tough slender tubes, out of which the woody parts are mainly formed.

PLEURISY-ROOT, *Asclepias tuberosa*.

PLEUROCARPI. One of the great divisions of true mosses, containing *Hypnum* and other genera which bear their fruit on the sides of the branches; the base of the peduncle, or rather the short portion of the axis which supports it, being rough, with a few leaves which differ generally from the others, and are called perichætial. The distinction is not, however, absolute, as acrocarpous and pleurocarpous species may occur in the same genus. [M. J. B.]

PLEURODISCOUS. Growing on the sides of the disk.

PLEUROGYNE. A genus of Arctic and mountain plants with herbaceous stems, leafless flowerstalks, and blue flowers. Corolla wheel-shaped, fringed at the throat; stamens five, inserted into the throat of the corolla; anthers not becoming twisted; ovary one-celled, the style wanting, and the stigmas two, prolonged downwards along the edges of the ovary valves; fruit capsular. The genus belongs to the *Gentianaceæ*. The generic name expresses the peculiarity of the stigma. [M. T. M.]

PLEUROGYRATE. A term employed for those ferns whose spore-case has a ring carried round the sides.

PLEUROPETALUM. A genus of *Amaranthaceæ*, from the Galapagos Islands. It comprises an erect glabrous somewhat shrubby plant, with alternate elliptical-lanceolate veiny leaves, and terminal and lateral racemes of flowers, each with three bracts, and a five-leaved deciduous perianth; stamens eight, united into a cup at the base, with subulate filaments, two-celled anthers, and no staminodes; ovary

one-celled, with numerous ovules; style short, with four stigmas. This genus was at first referred to *Portulaceæ*, the bracts being supposed to be sepals, and the sepals petals. [J. T. S.]

PLEUROPHORA. A genus of *Lythraceæ*, consisting of annuals or undershrubs from Chili. They have four-sided branches; opposite oblong-lanceolate or linear entire leaves, often sharp-pointed; and terminal flower-spikes with the bracts densely imbricated, each flower with bractlets, often spinescent. Calyx tubular, ten or fourteen-toothed, the inner ones ovate, mucronate, erect, or connivent—the outer spiny and spreading; petals five to seven; stamens generally as many as the petals; ovary stipitate, unequal-sided and excentric, one-celled, with few ovules. [J. T. S.]

PLEUROPHYLLUM. A genus of *Compositæ*, of the tribe *Asteroideæ*, consisting of two species from the Auckland and Campbell Islands in the Antarctic regions. They are both tall erect herbs, densely covered with a white or silvery shining silky wool. The leaves are alternate, the lower ones very large, and the flower-heads large and handsome, with purple florets, and growing in a close terminal raceme. The involucral scales are numerous and narrow, the outer florets radiating, the disk ones tubular, the receptacle without chaff, and the pappus consisting of numerous stiff bristles.

PLEUROTHALLIS. One of the most extensive genera of orchids, comprising nearly three hundred species, the whole of which are confined to tropical America and the West Indies. By various authors it has been split up into a dozen smaller genera, but these have all been reunited. The species are epiphytes, and are very variable in habit: the majority have erect one-leaved stems, either nearly naked or closely sheathed, rising from a creeping rhizome; but in one section the stems are scarcely at all developed, and in another they bear numerous alternating leaves. Their flowers, which proceed from spathes and are solitary or racemose, have the lateral sepals usually coherent and enlarged at the base, the petals free, and the lip articulate with the prolonged base of the column, which is terete or thin-winged and truncate, or has the anther-bed thin-edged, and the lid-like anther either at the top or a little towards the back. The pollen-masses, of which there are two or rarely four, are free, waxy, and obovate or pyriform. [A. S.]

PLEUROTUS. A subgenus of *Agaricus*, containing those white-spored species which have an excentric or lateral stem. In a few the stem is at length or from the beginning obsolete, and the pileus is resupinate; while in other cases it is at first cup-shaped, and the margin on one side at length turns over. The subgenus contains a few esculent species, as *A. ostreatus*, which is so common in autumn on laburnums and other trees. A species is also raised on coffee made at Naples, allied to *A. tignatilis*, which is said to be excellent. *A. ostreatus* must be distinguished with care from the tarragon-scented *A. suaveus*, which has pale-pink spores, and is sometimes dangerous. [M. J. B.]

PLEXAURE *limenophylax*. A very small terrestrial orchid, with about six narrow lanceolate equitant broad-based striped fleshy leaves, and a dense spike of extremely minute inconspicuous flowers, hardly so large as grains of millet. It was described as a new genus by Endlicher in his Flora of Norfolk Island, where alone it is found, but it has since been shown to belong to the older genus *Phreatia*. [A. S.]

PLEXEOBLASTUS. An embryo whose cotyledons are not developed in the form of true leaves, although they rise above the earth and become green.

PLICA. An excessive multiplication of small twigs, instead of branches.

PLICÆ. The lamellæ of certain fungals.

PLICATE, PLICATIVE. Plaited lengthwise like a lady's fan. The term *plicate* is usually employed in speaking of æstivation.

PLICATILIS. Capable of being plaited.

PLINTHUS. A genus of *Tetragonaceæ*, consisting of a small prostrate Cape of Good Hope shrub, with adpressed silky down, small imbricated ovate triquetrous leaves, and very small axillary sessile flowers. The calyx is tubular, five-cleft, with erect unequal lobes, coloured within; petals none; stamens five, with capillary filaments; style three-parted; capsule ovoid, membranous at the base, rounded and woody at the apex, papillose, three-celled, three-valved; seeds solitary in each cell, pear-shaped and shining. [J. T. S.]

PLOCAMIUM. A beautiful genus of rose-spored *Algæ*, belonging to the *Rhodymeniaceæ*, distinguished by its linear compressed fronds, which are pinnate with comb-like teeth, the branchlets being disposed alternately on either side in threes or fours. The nucleus of spores is compound, and formed of several more or less confluent nucleoli, the spore-bearing threads radiating in several tufts from a basal placenta; and the tetraspores are divided transversely, and contained in certain of the marginal divisions of the frond. The genus is widely diffused, as is the species *P. coccineum*, which is one of the best-known rose-coloured *Algæ* on our coasts, and collected by every seaside wanderer, attracting attention by its brilliant colour and curious ramification. Though common on the Atlantic shores of Europe, and distributed freely in the Southern Ocean, it is a very rare inhabitant of the Atlantic coast of America. [M. J. B.]

PLOCOSTEMMA. A genus of *Asclepiadaceæ*, allied to *Hoya*, and inhabiting the forests of Borneo and Java. There are only two species, both twiners, with opposite coriaceous glabrous leaves, oblong or ovate in shape, and umbellate flowers. The calyx and corolla are five-cleft, the corona five-leaved, and the stigma apiculate. The fruit is unknown. [B. S.]

PLÖSSLEA. A Nubian tree described by Endlicher as a new genus of *Sapindaceæ*, but which on further examination has proved to be a species of *Bursera*.

PLUKENETIA. A genus of *Euphorbiaceæ*, consisting of woody climbers with alternate cordate leaves, and small green flowers in axillary racemes, the lowest one of each raceme female, the others male. The perianth is four-cleft, with eight to sixteen stamens in the males; and in the females a four-celled ovary with a simple style and a four-lobed stigma, and one ovule in each cell of the ovary. There are very few species, all tropical, both in the New and the Old World. The leaves of *P. corniculata*, from tropical Asia, are said to be aromatic and to be used as a potherb.

PLUM. The well-known *Prunus domestica* and its varieties. —, BLACK, of Illawarra. *Cargillia australis*. —, BLOOD, of Sierra Leone. *Hæmatostaphis Barteri*. —, BULLACE, *Prunus insititia*. —, CHICASAW. *Cerasus Chicasa*. —, COCOA. *Chrysobalanus Icaco*. —, DATE. *Diospyrus Lotus*, and *D. virginiana*. —, GINGERBREAD. *Parinarium macrophyllum*. —, GREY. *Cargillia arborea*; also *Parinarium excelsum*. —, GUINEA. *Parinarium excelsum*. —, HOG. The fruits of several species of *Spondias*, as *S. purpurea, S. Mombin, S. lutea*, &c. —, JAMAICA. *Spondias lutea*. —, JAVA. *Calyptranthes Jambolana*. —, MAIDEN. *Cynocladia integrifolia*. —, MALABAR. *Eugenia Jambos*. —, ORLEANS. A cultivated variety of *Prunus domestica*. —, QUEENSLAND. *Owenia venosa*. —, PORT ARTHUR. *Cenarrhena nitida*. —, ROUGH-SKINNED, of Sierra Leone. *Parinarium excelsum*. —, SAPODILLA. *Achras Sapota* and allied species. —, SEBESTEN. The dried pulpy fruit of two species of *Cordia*, employed as pectoral medicines in India. —, SPANISH. *Spondias Mombin*. —, SUGAR. A Sierra Leone name for *Malpighia saccharina*. —, SWEET. *Owenia cerasifera*. —, TAMARIND. *Dialium indicum*. —, WILD, of New South Wales. *Achras australis*.

PLUMBAGELLA. A genus of *Plumbaginaceæ*, containing a single species, a native of Siberia. It is an annual herb, with small flowers arranged in subcapitate spikes. The ovate calyx is five-ribbed and five-parted, with lanceolate acute segments, scarcely membranaceous at the margins, and increasing very little around the fruit; corolla tubular divided into five lanceolate lobes; stamens five included, the filaments dilated and united at the base; ovary oblong with a slender style, and five filiform stigmas. The utricle is oblong; the lower part, included in the calyx, is membranaceous, and the upper exposed part coriaceous and falling off like a calyptra in dehiscence. The capsule contains a single ovate acute seed. This genus differs from *Plum-

bago in the structure of the calyx, the form of the corolla, and the place of rupture in the capsule. [W. C.]

PLUMBAGINACEÆ. (*Plumbagineæ, Leadworts.*) A natural order of corolliflferal dicotyledons belonging to Lindley's cortusal alliance of perigynous Exogens. They are herbs or undershrubs, with alternate or fasciculate exstipulate leaves, and panicled or capitate flowers. Calyx tubular, persistent, sometimes coloured; corolla monopetalous or pentapetalous, regular; stamens five, hypogynous when the corolla is gamopetalous, attached to the base of the petals when they are separate; ovary free, one-celled, with a solitary pendulous ovule, and five styles. Fruit utricular. They inhabit sea-shores and salt-marshes, chiefly in temperate regions. There are eleven genera, and nearly two hundred and fifty species. Examples : *Plumbago, Statice, Armeria.* [J. H. B.]

PLUMBAGO. A genus of *Plumbaginaceæ*, containing several species of herbaceous

Plumbago europæa.

plants or shrubs, natives of Europe, Asia, and Africa. They have subsessile flowers in more or less elongated spikes. The herbaceous calyx is tubular and five-toothed; the corolla gamopetalous, with a rotate five-parted limb; there are five included hypogynous stamens, inserted opposite the corolla lobes. The ovary is one-celled, and contains a single anatropal ovule, pendulous from the point of an umbilical cord which rises from the bottom of the cell; the style is single, but has five filiform stigmas; and the five-sided one-celled capsule is included in the persistent calyx. Many of the plants of this genus are acrid and caustic in the highest degree. The root of *P. scandens*, the Herbe du Diable of San Domingo, is a most energetic blistering agent when fresh; so also is that of *P. rosea.* The beggars employ *P. europæa* to raise ulcers upon their body to excite pity, and used internally it is said to be as effectual an emetic as ipecacuanha. [W. C.]

PLUMBEUS. Lead-coloured.

PLUMEAU. (Fr.) *Hottonia.*

PLUME-NUTMEGS. Lindley's name for the *Atherospermaceæ.*

PLUMET. (Fr.) *Stipa.*

PLUMIERIA. The name of a genus of *Apocynaceæ*, having the corolla funnel-shaped, with a long slender tube, and the segments of its border unequal; and the style short, ending in a thick and notched stigma. The species are trees or shrubs, with fleshy leaves growing in tufts at the ends of the branches. They occur in Peru and other parts of South America. *P. rubra* has the flowers so deliciously scented that it is called Red Jasmine in the West Indies. The genus was named in honour of Plumier, a French traveller and writer on Botany. [G. D.]

PLUMOSE. The same as Feathery.

PLUMULE. The bud of a seed; the youngest bud in a plant—placed between the cotyledons if the plant has more than one, or on one side if the cotyledon be solitary.

PLURI. In composition = more than one; thus *plurilocularis* signifies containing more than one cell; *pluriceps* having more than one head, as the crown of many roots.

POA. A genus of grasses belonging to the tribe *Festuceæ.* The inflorescence is either in spreading or close panicles, the spikelets of which are for the most part several-flowered and without awns; outer glumes unequal and generally keeled, many-nerved; lower pales keeled, five-nerved, sometimes with three intermediate nerves; upper pales shorter and narrower, with inflexed membranous margins. This large genus contains, according to Steudel, 192 species, which range over most parts of the world. Some of those belonging to the British Flora are valuable for agricultural purposes, especially *P. trivialis* and *P. pratensis. P. nemoralis* is one of the few grasses which grow well under the shade of trees; and *P. distans, P. maritima,* and *P. procumbens* are the kinds which constitute the pasture grasses on salt-marshes near the sea. *P. laxa* and *P. alpina* grow on the tops of the highest mountains in Britain. [D. M.]

POAYA, P. BRANCA, or P. DA PRAJA. *Ionidium Itubu.* — DO CAMPO. *Ionidium Poaya.*

POCAN-BUSH. *Phytolacca decandra.*

POCKWOOD-TREE. *Guaiacum officinale.*

POCOCKIA. A genus of *Leguminosæ*, closely allied to *Medicago* and *Trigonella,* but differing in the pod, which is very thin and flat, rather broad, more or less falcate, and often fringed on the edge. There are three or four species, low decumbent herbs, natives of the Eastern Mediterranean region.

POCULIFORM. Cup-shaped, with a hemispherical base and an upright limb; nearly the same as Campanulate.

POD. The capsule or seed-case of leguminous and cruciferous plants, those of the former being called legumes, and those of the latter siliques, and silicules.

PODALYRE. (Fr.) *Baptisia australis.*

PODALYRIA. A genus of *Leguminosæ* of the suborder *Papilionaceæ* and tribe *Podalyrieæ*, consisting of South African shrubs, more or less silky or silvery pubescent, with small simple alternate and entire leaves, and purple pink or bluish-white flowers, usually one or two on axillary peduncles. The calyx is widely campanulate, remarkably indented at its insertion on the stalk, the vexillum or upper petal broad, the stamens all free, and the pod turgid, with several seeds. There are seventeen species known, one or two of which are occasionally to be met with in our greenhouses in collections of Cape shrubs.

PODANTHES. A synonym for *Stapelia*, sometimes used in gardens.

PODAXINEI. A natural order of gasteromycetous *Fungi*, consisting of a few genera confined to warm countries, reaching the south of Europe in the northern and New Zealand in the southern hemisphere. All of them are stipitate with a distinct peridium, which often when ruptured forms a sort of volva at the base of the stem. The hymenium is sinuated and convolute, and in one genus only, *Montagnites*, gill-shaped. When old the spores form frequently a dusty mass, and in *Polyplocium* are mixed, as in the puffballs, with a few threads. The hymenium is, however, in general far more persistent. The genus *Secotium* contains one or two esculent species; one is highly prized at the Swan River. These, like *Lycoperdon giganteum*, must be used when quite young. *Podaxon carcinomalis* is employed for dressing ulcerous cancers.   [M. J. B.]

PODAXON. The typical genus of the natural order *Podaxinei*. The head is more or less conical or clavate, traversed by the elongated stem, and covered by the distinct peridium, which breaks off from the base of the stem. The spores are mixed with fibres, which grow from the top of the stem. In *P. pistillaris* the threads have a spiral structure. The species grow on ant-hills, or on the naked soil, and are confined to hot countries. In *P. pistillaris* the colours are bright, approaching that of dried saffron; in *P. carcinomalis* the pileus is dirty-white and the spores brown. No one has had an opportunity as yet of examining young specimens.   [M. J. B.]

PODEENA. An Indian name for *Mentha viridis.*

PODETIA. A name applied in lichens to the erect branched or simple growths springing from the horizontal thallus, which bear the fruit. In *Cenomyce* the thallus and podetia are to a certain extent distinct, though in some species thalloid horizontal processes are given out from the podetia. The term is applied, but less correctly, to all shrubby or erect growths.   [M. J. B.]

PODICILLUM. A very short podetium.

PODISOMA. A genus of *Pucciniei*, distinguished by the clavate gelatinous masses into which the stalked uniseptate protospores which germinate at different points, are packed. They grow exclusively on species of juniper, on which they appear year after year till the plant is killed. In this country *P. fuscum* grows on the savin, and two other species on the common juniper. *P. macropus* forms on *Juniperus virginiana*, in Pennsylvania, curious gall-like tubercles, studded with scars from which the fungus has fallen. These excrescences are called Cedar Apples, and are esteemed, though apparently without any reason, as a remedy against worms. Those trees which have been clipped for garden purposes are the most subject to the parasite. *Gymnosporangei*, which is closely allied, differs in the still more gelatinous expanded tremelloid masses.   [M. J. B.]

PODIUM, PODUS. A stalk, or receptacle, or torus; only used in Greek compounds.

PODOCARPUS. Under this name are grouped a number of trees, natives of various tropical countries, and especially of New Zealand and other extratropical parts of the southern hemisphere. They constitute a genus of *Taxaceæ*, and have usually linear leaves arranged in two rows or sometimes overlapping. The male flowers are borne on terminal cylindrical catkins, with sessile overlapping anthers, the cells opening at the sides; the females axillary, solitary, the ovule inverted and placed upon a lobed disk. The fruit is succulent, borne on a thick fleshy stalk, whence the name of the genus.

Several of these trees furnish good timber, *P. cupressina* is noted as one of the best timber trees of Java; while *P. Totara*, a New Zealand species, having a light durable tough wood, has been frequently the subject of contention and strife among the natives; its bark is made use of for roofing purposes, and its fruits are eaten. Several species are grown in conservatories in this country, and one or two Japanese or Chinese kinds are sufficiently hardy to stand out of doors with slight protection from frost.   [M. T. M.]

PODOGYNIUM (adj. PODOGYNOUS). An elevation in the centre of a flower, on the summit of which the ovary stands; it is in reality an internode.

PODOLEPIS. A genus of *Compositæ* of the tribe *Gnaphalieæ*, consisting of erect Australian herbs, mostly annuals, with entire narrow or stem-clasping leaves, and yellow or purple rather large and often showy flower-heads growing singly on terminal peduncles. The involucres are composed of numerous scarious or transparent bracts, the inner ones on slender claws.

The outer florets are ligulate and radiating, the inner ones tubular and hermaphrodite; the achenes have a pappus of simple bristles. Two species are in cultivation: *P. gracilis*, with purple flowers and stem-clasping leaves like those of a *Manglesia*; and *P. chrysantha*, with yellow flowers.

PODOLOBIUM. A genus of *Leguminosæ* of the suborder *Papilionaceæ* and tribe *Podalyrieæ*, with the general habit, opposite leaves, yellow flowers, and most of the characters of *Oxylobium*; but the leaves are divided into three or five prickly lobes, the axillary racemes are usually looser, and the pod is borne on a much longer stalk. There are two species known, both from New South Wales.

PODOPHYLLUM. A small genus of *Ranunculaceæ*, comprising a United States and a Himalayan species, both herbaceous plants with thick creeping rootstocks which send up in spring a stem bearing two leaves, with a solitary flower between them. The leaves are large, deeply palmate-lobed, and peltate; and the flowers are composed of six thin sepals which fall off before the flower expands; six or nine spreading petals; as many or double as many stamens; and an egg-shaped ovary crowned by a large thick-crested peltate stigma, and containing numerous ovules attached in several rows to a broad placenta down one side. The ovary ultimately becomes a fleshy berry, enclosing numerous seeds enveloped in pulp. *P. peltatum*, the American species, grows in damp shady places in woods, and is distinguished by the stamens being double the number of the petals. Its leaves are from five to nine-lobed; its flowers large white and nodding; and its fruits egg-shaped and yellowish, somewhat resembling a small lemon, and hence sometimes called Wild Lemon, but more generally May Apple. The plant is also known by the name of Mandrake. Its herbage is narcotic and poisonous, but the acid pulp of the fruit is eatable though of a mawkish flavour; and its rhizomes possess active medicinal properties, a resinous extract from them called *podophyllin* being much in use among American 'eclectic' practitioners as a substitute for mercurials; it has lately been introduced into this country as a cathartic.   [A. S.]

PODOSPERM. The cord by which some seeds are connected with their placenta. The same as Funiculus.

PODOSPERMUM. A genus of *Compositæ* nearly related to *Tragopogon*, but differing in the beakless achenes, as well as in the involucral scales being in many instead of one series; and from all others in the achenes being each supported on a short hollow swollen stalk. There are about a dozen species known, chiefly natives of the Mediterranean region. One of the commonest is *P. laciniatum*, a perennial herb with a root like the dandelion, a tuft of pinnatisect (rarely entire) leaves close to the ground, and arising from their midst a simple or branching flower-stem

three inches to a foot high with a few leaves below, each branch terminating in a pale-yellow flower-head. The achenes have a white feathery pappus; they have a very weedy appearance. The generic name refers to the stalked fruit.   [A. A. B.]

PODOSTACHYS. A name given by Klotzsch to two Brazilian herbs belonging to the order *Euphorbiaceæ*, and which other botanists consider as forming a section of *Croton*.

PODOSTEMACEÆ. (*Podostemads*.) A natural order of monochlamydeous dicotyledons belonging to Lindley's rutal alliance of hypogynous Exogens. They are herbaceous branched floating plants, furnished with capillary linear lacerated or minute and imbricated leaves; the flowers naked, or with an imperfect perianth, bursting through an irregularly lacerated spathe; stamens hypogynous, distinct or monadelphous; ovary free, two to three-celled; ovules numerous. Fruit slightly pedicellate, capsular, two to three-valved, the seeds indefinite. They are natives chiefly of South America, and of the islands to the east of Africa. There are a score of genera, including *Podostemon* and *Lacis*, and about a hundred species.   [J. H. B.]

PODOSTEMON. A genus of herbs found in rivers and moist places in South America, Madagascar, and other warm climates. They attach themselves to rocks, the roots of trees, &c.; and have a rootstock varying in shape, linear or finely divided leaves which clasp the stem at their base, and solitary terminal or axillary flowers. These have a tubular involucre, two stamens, and a ribbed capsule with two unequal valves. The genus gives its name to the order *Podostemaceæ*.   [M. T. M.]

PODOTHECA. A genus of *Compositæ* of the tribe *Gnaphalieæ*, consisting of erect glabrous or nearly glabrous annuals, with alternate entire decurrent or stem-clasping leaves, and solitary terminal heads of yellow florets. The genus is allied to *Helichrysum*, but remarkable for the long green cylindrical imbricate involucre, and for the florets being all tubular and hermaphrodite. There are two species known, natives of South-west Australia, not nearly so handsome as most of the allied plants.

POE. The Sandwich Island name for the fermented corms of *Colocasia esculenta*, which are eaten.

PŒCILANDRA. A handsome Guiana shrub, with alternate oblong smooth and shining evergreen leaves, and bright yellow flowers in a terminal panicle. It constitutes a genus of *Ochnaceæ*, distinguished amongst its allies chiefly by having two rows of staminodia outside the stamens, those of the outer row short and spathulate, the inner ones long and filiform.

PŒCILOCHROMA. A genus of Peruvian shrubs of the order *Solanaceæ*. The flowers are axillary solitary or in pairs, the flower-stalks dilated at the top and coloured. The calyx is persistent, and as the fruit ripens it bursts irregularly in two or three places; its tube is leathery, coloured, deeply contracted at the throat, and its limb divided into five very short teeth; corolla thick, bell-shaped with a short tube, the limb plaited, five-lobed; stamens five, within the corolla, the anthers opening lengthwise; ovary two-celled; stigma club-shaped, two-lobed on the end of the style, which equals the stamens in length. The fruit is pea-shaped, succulent, and of a red colour. The generic name is derived from the Greek words *poikilos* and *chroma*, signifying varied or spotted colour; and alludes to the corolla, which is described as handsome, of an orange-colour with reddish spots. So showy a plant is not likely long to be absent from our greenhouses. [M. T. M.]

POECILOPTERIS. A genus of tropical mostly Eastern ferns of the tribe *Acrosticheæ*. They have pinnate often viviparous fronds, and the usual dimorphous character of the group, in which they are principally distinguished by their venules being arcuato-angularly united between the pinnate primary veins, and furnished with excurrent veinlets. It is the same as *Cyrtogonium* and *Heteroneuron*. [T. M.]

POEROU. The Tahitian name for *Hibiscus tiliaceus*.

POGON. A beard; in Greek compounds = any collection of long hairs.

POGONETES. A South-west Australian genus of *Goodeniaceæ*, founded upon the *Scævola spinescens*. The plant is shrubby, spinescent, with quite entire oval or obovate leaves, and solitary-flowered axillary peduncles. [R. H.]

POGONIA. Terrestrial orchids with spherical tubers, and either having one or a few sessile leaves upon an erect stem at the period of flowering, or leafless till after flowering, and then producing a solitary stalked leaf from an underground stem. Their flowers are solitary or loosely racemose, and have free conniving or somewhat ringent sepals and petals, either all nearly equal or the petals smaller; a free erect undivided or lobed lip, with its disk crested papillose or bearded; a long semiterete clavate column, eared or winged at the top; and a sessile or very shortly stalked two-celled anther, containing two furrowed pollen-masses. The genus belongs to the *Arethuseæ* tribe, and contains about fifteen or twenty species, widely spread throughout America and Asia. [A. S.]

POGOSTEMON. A rather numerous genus of *Labiatæ*, consisting of tall herbs found in various parts of tropical Asia, but principally in India and Ceylon. They have opposite stalked leaves, and flowers collected into dense clusters or whorls forming terminal interrupted spikes or close panicles. The flowers have an unequally five-toothed calyx; a somewhat two-lipped corolla, with the upper lip three-lobed and the lower entire and rather longer; and four nearly equal stamens longer than the corolla, and sometimes slightly bent downwards, the filaments usually covered with long hairs, and the anthers one-celled.

P. Patchouly affords the celebrated Patchouli perfume or Pucha-pat of the Hindoos. It is a shrubby herb about two feet high, a native of Sylhet, Penang, and Malacca; and has broadly egg-shaped stalked leaves between three and four inches in length, with the margins slightly lobed and round-toothed; and both terminal and axillary dense spikes of small whitish flow-

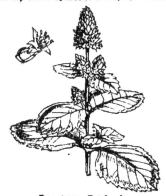

Pogostemon Patchouly.

ers tinged with purple. Although the odour of Patchouli is certainly peculiar, and even disagreeable to some people, it is highly popular not only in Europe but in India, where it is one of the commonest perfumes found in the bazaars. The odoriferous part of the plant is the leaves and young tops, and by distillation these yield a volatile oil from which essence of Patchouli is prepared; sachets of Patchouli, however, are made of the coarsely-powdered leaves. Genuine Indian shawls and Indian ink were formerly distinguished by their odour of Patchouli, but since the perfume has become common in Europe the test does not hold good. Ill effects, such as loss of appetite and sleep, nervous attacks, &c., have been ascribed to the excessive employment of Patchouli as a perfume. [A. S.]

POHUTU-KAWA. A useful New Zealand timber tree, *Metrosideros tomentosa*.

POIL DE LOUP. (Fr.) *Poa rigida*; also *Festuca ovina*.

POINCIANA. A genus of *Leguminosæ* of the suborder *Cæsalpineæ*, closely allied to *Cæsalpinia* itself, and originally distinguished from it by the great length to which the stamens project from the corolla. It is now, however, more properly confined to two trees—*P. elata* from India and Arabia, and *P. regia* from Madagascar—in which the calyx is valvate in the bud, whilst in the true *Cæsalpinias* it is much imbricated. Both the above trees are very handsome, with twice-pinnate leaves bearing numerous small leaflets, and showy orange or yellowish flowers in terminal racemes with long richly coloured stamens. *P. pulcherrima* of Linnæus, a prickly shrub, so much planted for hedges as well as for its great beauty in most tropical countries, is now considered as a species of *Cæsalpinia*, as is also *P. Gilliesii*, from South America, often to be seen in our greenhouses, and which some botanists have proposed to establish as a genus by itself, to which they have given the name of *Erythrostemon*, derived from the rich crimson stamens, which are longer than in any other species.

POINCILLADE. (Fr.) *Poinciana.* — FAUSSE. *Adenanthera.*

POINSETTIA. A name given by Graham to a South American euphorbiaceous shrub, frequently to be seen in our stove collections, and still more common in the gardens of the south of Spain, where it is known by the name of Flor de Pasqua. The large richly-coloured red bracts which surround the small green flower-heads are very showy, and were made use of to characterise the genus. It is now found, however, that there is nothing else to distinguish it from *Euphorbia* itself, and that many other species of that genus have similar bracts, although less conspicuous; and *Poinsettia* has therefore been recently reunited with *Euphorbia.*

POINTE DE FLÉCHE. (Fr.) *Pontederia.*

POINTLETTED. The same as Apiculate.

POIRE. (Fr.) The fruit of the Pear-tree. — D'AIL. *Cratæva.* — D'ANCHOIS, *Grias.* — D'AVOCAT. *Persea gratissima.* — DE TERRE. The tubers of *Helianthus tuberosus.*

POIREAU, or POREAU. (Fr.) *Allium Porrum.* — D'ÉTÉ, or DU LEVANT. *Allium Ampeloprasum.*

POIRÉE, or PORÉE. (Fr.) *Beta Cycla.*

POIRETIA. A genus of *Leguminosæ* of the suborder *Papilionaceæ* and tribe *Hedysarieæ*, consisting of half a dozen South American herbaceous twiners or perennials, with pinnate leaves of four or rarely three leaflets, and yellow flowers in axillary racemes or terminal panicles. The stamens are strictly monadelphous, and the flat pod consists of several joints either square or oblong. The whole plant is always dotted with small resinous glands. Some species might be ornamental, but are not in cultivation, and no other interest is attached to them.

POIRIER. (Fr.) *Pyrus.* — D'AIL. *Cratæva.* — D'AVOCAT. *Persea gratissima.* — DES ANTILLES, or DE LA MARTINIQUE. *Tecoma pentaphylla.* — DES INDES. *Psidium.*

POIS. (Fr.) *Pisum.* — À BOUQUETS. *Lathyrus latifolius*; also *Pisum sativum umbellatum.* — À FLEURS, *Lathyrus odoratus.* — AGNEAU. *Pisum arvense.* — À GRATTER. *Mucuna pruriens.* — BRETON. *Lathyrus Cicera.* — CAFÉ. *Tetragonolobus purpureus.* — CARRÉ. *Pisum sativum quadratum.* — CICHE. *Cicer arietinum.* — CORNU. *Lathyrus Cicera.* — D'ANGOLE. *Cajanus indicus.* — DE BREBIS. *Lathyrus sativus*; also *Pisum arvense.* — DE CHINE. *Lathyrus latifolius.* — DE CŒUR, or DE MERVEILLE. *Cardiospermum Halicacabum.* — DE PIGEON. *Pisum arvense*; also *Ervum.* — DE SENTEUR. *Lathyrus odoratus.* — DE SERPENT. *Lathyrus Aphaca.* — DOUX. *Inga Burgoni.* — GOULUS, or MANGE-TOUT. *Pisum sativum saccharatum.* — MABONIA. *Capparis cynophallophora.* — MUSQUÉ, or ODORANT. *Lathyrus odoratus.* — PATATE. *Pachyrhizus tuberosus.* — QUENIQUES. The seeds of *Moringa pterygosperma.* — SABRÉ. *Canavalia ensiformis.* — SANS PARCHEMIN, or SUCRES. *Pisum sativum saccharatum.*

POISON, ARROW. The juice of *Euphorbia heptagona, virosa*, and *cereiformis* in Africa, and of *E. cotinifolia* in Brazil. Also the Woorali Ourari, or Curara poison, derived from *Strychnos toxifera* by the savages of Guiana; and the Tieuté Tjettch or Tschittich poison, prepared by the Javanese from *Strychnos Tieuté.* Also the poisonous juice of *Hippomané Mancinella.*

POISON-BERRY. A West Indian name for *Cestrum.*

POISON-BULB. *Buphane toxicaria.* — , ASIATIC. *Crinum asiaticum.*

POISON-WOOD. An American name for *Rhus venenata.*

POITÆA. A genus of *Leguminosæ* of the suborder *Papilionaceæ* and tribe *Galegeæ*, consisting of two or three shrubs from San Domingo, having the habit of *Robinia.* They are also nearly allied to that genus, but the long narrow petals, with the upper one or vexillum shorter than the wings, give the flower an oblong shape, very different to that of *Robinia.* The leaves are pinnate, the flowers white or pink in axillary racemes.

POITRON. (Fr.) A kind of yellow plum.

POIVRE. (Fr.) The fruit of the Pepper. — D'AFRIQUE. *Habzelia æthiopica.* — D'AMÉRIQUE. *Schinus Molle.* — D'EAU. *Polygonum Hydropiper.* — DE GUINÉE. *Capsicum annuum.* — DE LA JAMAÏQUE. *Eugenia Pimenta.* — DE MURAILLE. *Sedum acre.* — D'OISEAU, or DE POULE. *Capsicum baccatum.* — DU COMMERCE. *Piper nigrum.* — INDIEN. *Habzelia æthiopica.* — LONG. *Capsicum annuum.*

POIVREA. Climbing shrubs of the order *Combretaceæ*, natives of the tropics of both hemispheres. They have opposite or alternate entire leaves, and spiked axillary and terminal inflorescence. Their flowers have a funnel-shaped five-lobed deciduous calyx, five petals, ten protruded stamens, and a two or three-ovuled ovary bearing a slender protruded style; and their fruit is ovial or oblong or five-winged, and contains a solitary pendulous five-angled seed with irregularly convolute cotyledons, the latter character and the quinary division of its flowers distinguishing the genus from *Combretum*, to which it is closely allied. [A. S.]

POIVRETTE. (Fr.) *Nigella sativa.*

POIVRIER. (Fr.) *Piper.* — D'AMÉRIQUE, or DU PÉROU. *Schinus Molle.*

POIVRON. (Fr.) *Capsicum annuum.*

POKE, INDIAN. *Veratrum viride.* —, VIRGINIAN. *Phytolacca decandra.*

POKE-ROOT. *Veratrum viride.*

POKEWEED. *Phytolacca decandra.*

POLANISIA. This name, applied to a genus of *Capparidaceæ*, is compounded of the Greek words *polus* 'many,' and *anisos* 'unequal,' in allusion to the stamens. The species are herbaceous plants, natives of the warmer parts of Asia and America, with palmate leaves, and terminal clusters of flowers. Sepals and petals four; stamens eight or more, unequal in length, some of them occasionally destitute of anthers, all inserted on a short hemispherical receptacle; ovary sessile or shortly stalked; style as long as the ovary; stigmas blunt; fruit a two-valved pod, the valves separating from a persistent replum or partition. Some of the species are pungent and acrid, so as to be used in India, Cochin China, and the United States as an irritant application, and as a vermifuge. The leaves of *P. icosandra* are eaten by the natives with other herbs as a salad; they have an acrid pungent taste. The leaves of *P. felina* are esteemed in India as tonic and expectorant; their juice mixed with oil is used as a remedy in ear-ache. [M. T. M.]

POLAO. A Chilian name for a kind of Mint.

POLAR PLANT. *Silphium laciniatum.*

POLBA. A Russian name for Spelt Wheat.

POLCHE. (Fr.) *Hibiscus populneus.*

POLEMONIACEÆ. (*Polemonideæ*, *Cobæaceæ*, *Phloxworts*.) A natural order of corollifloral dicotyledons belonging to Lindley's solanal alliance of perigynous Exogens. They consist of herbaceous or climbing plants, with opposite or alternate simple or compound leaves. Calyx inferior, in five divisions, persistent; corolla regular, five-lobed; stamens five, free, alternate with the segments of the corolla, the pollen often blue; disk lobed; ovary free, three-celled, with axile placentæ; style simple; stigma trifid. Fruit a three-celled three-valved capsule; seeds angular or oval, or winged; embryo straight in the axis of a fleshy or horny albumen; cotyledons foliaceous. They inhabit temperate countries chiefly, and abound in the north-western parts of America. Many of them have showy flowers. The mucous covering of the episperm of various species of *Collomia* contains numerous spiral cells, which, when the seeds are moistened with water, become uncoiled. *Polemonium*, *Phlox*, and *Cobæa* are examples of the genera, of which about seventeen are known, comprising upwards of one hundred species. [J. H. B.]

POLEMONIUM. A genus of erect herbaceous perennials, with alternate pinnate leaves, and terminal panicles of handsome blue or white flowers, giving name to the order *Polemoniaceæ*. The characters of the genus are:—calyx bell-shaped, five-cleft; corolla with a very short tube and erect limb; stamens inserted in the throat of the corolla; capsule many-seeded. *P. cæruleum*, the Greek Valerian, or Jacob's Ladder, is to be found in most cottage gardens, growing about a foot and a half high, with stiff erect scarcely branched angular stems, bright-green smooth leaves, pinnate with an odd leaflet, and terminal corymbs of pretty blue or white flowers. It grows seemingly wild in some of the northern counties, but is not generally admitted to be indigenous. French: *Valériane grecque*; German: *Speerkraut.* [C. A. J.]

POLE-REED, or PULL-REED. *Phragmites communis.*

POLE-RUSH. The Bulrush.

POLIANTHES. The Tuberose, a favourite conservatory plant belonging to the order *Liliaceæ*. The leaves are linear lanceolate; the flower-stalk, which is two to three feet long, bears towards its summit numerous creamy-white very fragrant flowers, which are funnel-shaped and incurved; the stamens are inserted in the throat of the tube. The species most commonly cultivated, *P. tuberosa*, is a native of the East Indies, but the plants grown in England are for the most part annually imported from Italy, those with double flowers being the most prized. The English name, often but improperly pronounced as a word of two syllables, is no doubt a corruption of the Latin adjective *tuberosa*, and has reference to the form of the root. This plant has been observed in a sultry evening after thunder, when the atmosphere was highly charged with electric fluid, to dart sparks of lucid flame in abundance from such of its flowers as were fading. French: *Tubéreuse*; German: *Tuberose.* [C. A. J.]

POLITUS. Having the appearance of a polished substance; as the testa of many seeds.

POLLEN. The powdery or other matter usually contained in the cells of an anther, by whose action on the stigma the fertilisation of the ovules is accomplished. *Pollen-cells* are the cavities of an anther, in which the pollen is formed; *pollen-grains* or *granules* the separate particles of pollen; and *pollen-tubes* membranous tubes emitted by pollen, and conducting the fluid which the pollen secretes down the style.

POLLEX (adj. POLLICARIS). The first joint of the thumb; an inch.

POLY. *Teucrium Polium.* —, MOUN-
TAIN. *Bartsia alpina.*

POLY. In Greek compounds = numerous.

POLYACTIS. A genus of filamentous
moulds characterised by their threads being partially of a dark hue as if scorched,
and by their naked hyaline spores situated
at the tops of the ramifications which are
confined to the upper part of the plant.
P. vulgaris with one or two others are
amongst the commonest moulds on all
sorts of decaying phænogams, and recognisable by their sparkling white spores
and dark grey-brown threads. [M. J. B.]

POLYADELPHOUS. Having many parcels of stamens.

POLYANTHUS. An umbellate-flowered
variety of *Primula vulgaris*, cultivated as
a garden flower.

POLYBOTRYA. A genus of tropical
ferns of the tribe *Acrosticheæ*, occurring
both in the eastern and western hemispheres. It is known by the dimorphous
pinnate or bi-tripinnate fronds, the fertile
ones having linear contracted segments,
with one or both surfaces covered by spore-
cases; the veins are simple or forked, or
pinnate from a central costa. *Rhipidopteris*
differs in its flabellately-forked veins, and
Elaphoglossum and *Lomariopsis* in the parallel forked veins; these with *Polybotrya*
being the only free-veined genera of the
tribe *Acrosticheæ.* [T. M.]

POLYCARPON. A small genus of *Illecebraceæ* found in the warmer parts of the
temperate zone in both hemispheres. They
are small plants (usually annual), with opposite or verticillate oblong ovalor obovate
leaves, and extremely numerous minute
flowers in dense corymbose very compound
cymes; the stipules and bracts small and
scarious. *P. tetraphyllum*, which has three
stamens, and the lower leaves four in a
whorl, occurs in the south-western counties of England. [J. T. S.]

POLYCARPOUS. Having the power of
bearing fruit many times without perishing; also, and more properly, bearing
many distinct fruits or carpels in each
flower.

POLYCHORION. A polycarpous fruit
like that of *Ranunculus.*

POLYCHROA. A name given by Loureiro to a procumbent herb found wild in
China and Cochin China, and also cultivated
there for its dense variegated spikes of
flowers. From Loureiro's imperfect description it has been supposed by some
botanists to be a species of *Amaranthus*,
which others consider as very doubtful.

POLYCLADIA. The same as Plica.

POLYCNEMUM. A small genus of *Amaranthaceæ*, found in Europe and temperate
Asia. They are procumbent branched pu-
berulent annuals, with sessile somewhat
imbricated awl-shaped mucronate leaves,
scarious at the margin; and axillary nearly
sessile flowers, with two bracts at the base;
calyx of five sepals; stamens three (rarely
one to five); styles two; ovary one-celled;
capsule oval-compressed, indehiscent, one-
seeded. [J. T. S.]

POLYCOTYLEDONOUS. Having more
cotyledons than two.

POLYFLOROUS. A barbarism for Multiflorous.

POLYGALACEÆ. (*Polygaleæ, Krameriaceæ, Soulameæ, Trigoniaceæ, Milkworts.*)
A natural order of thalamifloral dicotyledons belonging to Lindley's sapindal alliance of hypogynous Exogens. Shrubs or
herbs with alternate or opposite exstipulate leaves; sepals five, very irregular,
three exterior of which one is superior,
two interior usually petaloid, lateral; petals unequal, usually three, of which one
is anterior and larger, and two alternate
with the upper and lateral sepals, the anterior petal, called the keel, is often crested; stamens eight, monadelphous or diadelphous; anthers clavate, usually one-
celled, opening by pores; ovary mostly
two-celled, the ovules solitary, rarely two;
seeds pendulous, strophiolate at the hilum.
They are found in all quarters of the globe.
The flowers have a resemblance to *Papilionaceæ*; they are distinguished, however,
by the odd petal being inferior, and the
sepal superior. They are generally bitter,
and their roots yield a milky juice. There
are about a score of genera, and over 500
species. Examples: *Polygala, Securidaca,
Trigonia*: see also KRAMERIA. [J. H. B.]

POLYGALA. A well-known and extensive genus of plants constituting the type
of the *Polygaleæ.* The technical name,
signifying 'much milk,' was applied from
the fact that the lacteal secretion of animals
that feed on these plants is increased thereby. Some of the Milkworts, moreover, possess milky juice in their roots. The species
are distributed widely over most parts of
the globe, and occur as herbaceous plants
or shrubs, with entire leaves, and very irregular flowers arranged in racemes. Sepals five, persistent, the two lateral ones
(sometimes called wings) larger than the
others, and frequently petal-like; petals
three to five, the lowest keel-shaped, all
united below to the tube of the stamens;
stamens eight, united below, dividing above
into two parcels, each bearing four anthers
opening by pores; ovary and capsule flat,
two-celled, with a single seed in each compartment. The seeds are downy, and have
a small wart-like process at one end.

Many of the species have medicinal properties. Thus *P. vulgaris, P. amara, P. glandulosa, P. Poaya, P. sanguinea*, and many
others, are mentioned as having more or
less powerful emetic properties. *P. rubella*
is esteemed as an excellent bitter tonic
and diaphoretic. *P. amara* and *P. vulgaris*
have been used in cases of long-standing
catarrh. *P. Chamæbuxus* is stimulant,
tonic, and expectorant. *P. tinctoria* is so
called from its yielding a purple dye like

indigo; its seeds are a vermifuge. The root of *P. thesioides* has diuretic properties. *P. tenenuta*, a Javanese plant, is reported to be intensely poisonous; merely touching a leaf of this plant is sufficient to produce violent sneezing and faintness, according to Commerson.

Of all the species, however, which are used medicinally, that best known in this country is *P. Senega*, the root of which is used as a stimulant diaphoretic and expectorant, especially in cases of chronic bronchitis. In large doses it produces symptoms of acrid poisoning. The root, as met with in commerce, is remarkable for having a prominent ridge extending along its whole length on one side. The active properties appear to depend upon an acid substance found principally in the rind of the root, and called polygalic acid, or sometimes *senegin*. This root was introduced into medical practice by Dr. Tennant, a Scotch physician residing in Pennsylvania, as a remedy for snake-bites. Several other species, besides many of those already mentioned, are described as having similar virtues as antidotes to snake-bites. They seem to act as stimulant emetics, purgatives, and diaphoretics, and relieve the embarrassed breathing which occurs in such cases.

Several species are in cultivation as greenhouse plants, *P. cordifolia*, *P. latifolia*, and *P. oppositifolia*, all Cape species, being among the handsomest. The purple petal-like sepals and fringed keel-like petal give these plants a singular and elegant appearance. *P. Chamæbuxus* is a dwarf-growing evergreen shrubby species, with comparatively large yellow flowers. It grows wild in Central Europe, and is frequently met with in the borders of shrubberies, &c. *P. vulgaris* is a common British plant, especially on chalky or limestone soil. Its branches are numerous, slender, ascending, clothed with more or less linear leaves, the lowermost obovate or even roundish, and bearing flowers of a bright-blue or sometimes pink or white. *P. amara* is generally considered as a mere variety of *P. vulgaris*, which indeed differs very much in the shape of the leaves and sepals, their colour, &c. in different situations.   [M. T. M.]

POLYGAMOUS. Having, on the same plant, some flowers male, others female, and others hermaphrodite. Its sign is ☿ ♂ ♀.

POLYGONACEÆ. (*Buckwheats.*) A natural order of monochlamydeous dicotyledons, belonging to Lindley's silenal alliance of hypogynous Exogens. They are herbaceous, rarely shrubby plants, with alternate stipulate or exstipulate leaves, and often unisexual flowers. Perianth inferior, often coloured; stamens definite, inserted into the bottom of the perianth; ovary free, usually formed by three carpels; ovule solitary, orthotropal; styles and stigmas equal to the carpels in number. Fruit a nut, usually triangular, naked or covered by the persistent perianth; seed erect, with farinaceous albumen. They are found in almost all parts of the world, more especially in the temperate regions of the northern hemisphere. They grow in fields, waste grounds, ditches, mountains, &c., and have astringent and acid properties—some being purgative, and a few acrid. Their astringency depends on the presence of tannin, and their acidity chiefly on oxalic acid. The fruit of *Polygonum aviculare* is emetic and purgative. The fruit of *Fagopyrum esculentum*, and other species of buckwheat, is used as food; the plant is cultivated in some northern countries. The leaves of *Rumex Acetosa*, sorrel, and of *R. Acetosella*, field sorrel, are acid and astringent. The roots of *Rumex aquaticus*, and *R. Hydrolapathum*, the water docks, and of other species, are used as astringents and alteratives; those of *R. alpinus*, under the name of Monk's Rhubarb, were formerly employed as purgatives. One of the most important plants of the order is the rhubarb plant.   [J. H. B.]

POLYGONATUM. The Solomon's Seal: a genus of liliaceous but not bulbous plants, with axillary cylindrical six-cleft flowers, the stamens inserted in the top of the tube, and the fruit a globose three-celled berry with two seeds in each cell. *P. multiflorum*, the most frequent species in England, grows profusely in certain situations where it has taken possession of the soil, but cannot be called a common plant. It sends up, to the height of about two feet, stoutish simple green stems, of which the lower half is bare of leaves, the upper curved towards a horizontal direction, and bearing numerous broad sessile leaves; and from their axils slender flowerstalks with drooping green and white flowers in clusters of two to four. These are succeeded by small bluish-black berries. Less frequent species are *P. verticillatum*, found in Scotland, which bears its leaves in whorls; and *P. officinale*, resembling the first in habit but smaller, and bearing solitary fragrant flowers. Several foreign species are described. French: *Sceau de Salomon*; German: *Weisswurz*.   [C. A. J.]

POLYGONELLA. A genus of *Polygonaceæ*, inhabiting dry plains in the warmer parts of North America. Small branched smooth shrubs, with short ochreæ, small thick linear or spathulate subsessile leaves, and small perfect or polygamous white or rose-colour spicately racemose flowers, adpressed to the rachis. Perianth coloured, five-leaved, the two outer segments unchanging, at length reflexed, the three inner enlarging and enclosing the fruit.   [J. T. S.]

POLYGONUM. A very extensive and generally distributed genus of *Polygonaceæ*, consisting of annual or perennial herbs, more rarely undershrubs, found throughout the whole world but rare within the tropics. They have alternate leaves, with ochreate stipules; and the flowers are usually in spikes or racemes, sometimes contracted into heads, sometimes so lax that they may be regarded as axillary. The perianth is funnel-shaped or bell-shaped, usually pink-white or red, five-cleft, the segments somewhat unequal, persistent, and usually increasing in size after flowering: stamens five six or eight (very rarely four or nine); styles two to three; nut lenticular in the species with two, and three-edged in those with three styles. Several of the species are astringent, as Bistort, *P. Bistorta*, which is occasionally used in medicine; others are acrid, as the Water-pepper, *P. Hydropiper*; and some furnish a blue dye, as the Chinese *P. tinctorium*. The genus is divided into the following sections:—*Bistorta*, the British species of which are *P. Bistorta* and *P. viviparum*; *Amblygonum*, of which the garden Persicary, *P. orientale*, is a good example; *Persicaria*, represented by *P. amphibium, lapathifolium, laxum, Persicaria, mite, Hydropiper*, and *minus*; *Echinocaulon* and *Cephalophilon*, both extra-European; *Aconogonon*, of which one species, *P. alpinum*, occurs in Europe; *Tiniaria*, comprising the British *P. Convolvulus* and *dumetorum*; and *Avicularia*, of which three species occur in Britain, *P. aviculare, Raii*, and *maritimum*. [J. T. S.]

P. Convolvulus, the Climbing Buckwheat, is often a great weed-pest, as it twists around the stems of the crop, and not only strangles it, but keeps away sun and air by reason of its large leaves. *P. aviculare*, the Knot-grass, and *P. Persicaria* and *lapathifolium*, Persicary, are three very troublesome agrarian weeds, and more especially where manure is much employed. These species, indeed, will always be found growing on exposed dung-heaps, where they seed freely, and from which these plants are doubtless for the most part spread over our fields. *P. Hydropiper*, the Biting Persicaria, derives its trivial name from its acrid and biting taste. It has been employed in medicine as a diuretic, for which purpose the green herb is used, as its properties are lost in drying.

The Snakeweed, *P. Bistorta*, is a pretty species which is not uncommon in old-fashioned gardens, where it was probably grown not only as a flower, but as a medicine. It occurs frequently growing in large circular patches in meadows, and especially those near villages, from which it may be inferred that it has become naturalised as a British plant. We are informed by Mr. Robert Holland, that the green tops are eaten in Cumberland under the name of Easter Man Giants (? Easter-eating — Fr. *mangeant*). The roots were formerly much used in medicine: as they are highly astringent, their decoction in water is found useful as an astringent injection, and as a gargle in sore-throats. See also FAGOPYRUM. [J. B.]

POLYGYNIA. Having many distinct styles.

POLYIDES. A genus of rose-spored *Algæ*, consisting of a single species which is so like *Furcellaria fastigiata* that it is not easy to distinguish it except when in fruit. This forms a spongy mass composed of

vertical articulate threads containing numerous globose compound nuclei, the spores of which are large and obconical and radiate from a central point, and is so singular that the genus is referred to a distinct natural order, *Spongiocarpeæ*. *P. rotundus*, not uncommon on our coasts, occurs also in the United States. [M. J. B.]

POLYLEPIDOUS. Having many scales.

POLYMERIA. A small genus of Eastern Australian *Convolvulaceæ*, distinguished from *Convolvulus* by its four to six acute stigmas, and by having only one ovule in each of the two ovary-cells. [A. S.]

POLYMEROUS. Consisting of many parts.

POLYMNIA. A genus of *Compositæ* of the tribe *Heliantheæ*, consisting of erect herbs with alternate or opposite leaves, often large or deeply lobed, and terminal corymbose flower-heads with a yellow ray and usually a dark-purple disk. The involucre has five outer spreading leafy bracts and several inner smaller ones embracing the achenes. The ray-florets are female, producing obovate achenes without any pappus; the disk-florets all male with linear abortive achenes. *P. Uvedalia* and *P. canadensis* are common in some of the hilly districts of North America, and about half a dozen more species are South American.

POLYPETALOUS. Having the petals perfectly distinct from each other.

POLYPHORE. A receptacle which bears many distinct carpels, as in *Crowfoots*.

POLYPODE, or **P. DE CHÊNE.** (Fr.) *Polypodium vulgare.*

POLYPODIACEÆ. A natural order of ferns, comprising nearly all that are known, the other orders, *Marattiaceæ* and *Ophioglossaceæ*, being of very limited extent. The chief distinguishing feature consists in the presence of an elastic jointed ring nearly surrounding the spore-cases. By this peculiarity they may at once be recognised in all cases, except in the genera *Osmunda* and *Todea* in which the ring is always, and in *Ceratopteris* in which it is sometimes, more rudimentary. In all these cases, however, the ring is present; and hence the *Polypodiaceæ* are called annulate ferns, while the *Marattiaceæ* and *Ophioglossaceæ*, in which the ring is absolutely wanting, are called exannulate. See FILICES. [T. M.]

POLYPODIUM. The typical genus of the *Polypodieæ*, and known at once by having its fronds plane not indusiiform at the edge, its veins free, and its sori globose and naked. It is an extensive genus, of the most varied aspect, and distributed all over the world, presenting itself in some half-dozen distinctive forms: as, for example, with terminal sori and articulated fronds, as in *P. vulgare*; with terminal sori and articulated fronds and pinnæ, as in *P. tenellum*; with terminal sori on obovate receptacles and adherent fronds, as in

P. hymenophylloides; with terminal sori on punctiform receptacles and adherent fronds, as in *P. suspensum*; with medial sori and adherent fronds, as in *P. Phegopteris*; and with basal sori and adherent fronds, as in *P. tenuisectum.* The fronds vary from simple to decompound in form, and from membranaceous to coriaceous in texture; while their size is equally varied. [T. M.]

POLYPODY. *Polypodium.* — of the Oak. *Polypodium vulgare.* —, COMMON. *Polypodium vulgare.* —, FEMALE. *Athyrium Filix-fœmina.* —, MALE. *Lastrea Filix-mas.*

POLYPOGON. A genus of grasses belonging to the tribe *Agrostideæ.* The inflorescence is in densely contracted panicles; glumes unequal, more or less hairy and compressed, with bristles or very sharp points; pales shorter than the glumes, the lower with a bristle under the apex. There are twenty-four species described by Steudel, which have a considerable geographical range, extending from Western France to Central Asia. *P. monspeliensis* and *P. littoralis,* the only species belonging to the British Flora, are confined to England. There are several handsome grasses among them, though mostly worthless for agricultural purposes. [D. M.]

POLYPORUS. An enormous genus of pore-bearing *Fungi* distinguished from *Boletus* by the tubes not separating from each other or from the pileus. The species vary much in point of substance, a few being so soft as to be esculent, and others hard and woody or corky. Our European species are numerous, but while the tropics have many species in common with other zones, they have hosts of species which require a high temperature. *Polypori* are frequently resupinate, and glued down to the matrix; the margin alone in others becomes free; then the whole is free but sessile; then the pileus contracts behind, acquires a short stem, by easy gradation becomes central, and finally is borne like an umbrella on a tall well-formed stem. One of the finest, *P. sacer,* is an object of worship in Guinea. Some of the species are of a brilliant scarlet, others lilac, yellow, orange, &c., but the predominant colours are tints of brown. The pores vary much in size, being sometimes almost invisible to the naked eye. A few, as *P. ovinus,* afford a grateful food; but in general, like *P. squamosus,* they are not only coarse, but tough and indigestible. *P. tuberaster,* which springs from the Fungus Stone (see PIETRA FUNGAJA), is esteemed in Italy, and a species is raised from pollard-hazels by roasting them gently before the fire and then keeping them properly irrigated. *P. fomentarius* supplies the best Amadou of commerce, though inferior kinds are produced from other species. *P. officinalis* was once a celebrated drug, but it is now little used, though still to be obtained in the herb-shops; it grows almost exclusively on Larch. *P. destructor* and some others are the pest of wooden struc-

tures, while the spawn of *P. hybridus* is the dry-rot fungus of oak-built ships. *P. betulinus,* when cut into strips, forms excellent razor-strops. [M. J. B.]

POLYSACCUM. A genus of puffballs remarkable for containing a multitude of small partial peridia within the common irregularly bursting envelope. These in an early stage are pulpy, but they are soon indurated and ultimately contain a mass of threads and spores, the latter of which are larger than in most *Lycoperdinei* : the mature plant is extremely rigid and brittle. The species are divisible into two sections—the first of which includes the larger kinds which have a stout stem, divided and rooting at the base, with a clavate or rounded head; the second those with a short abrupt stem, giving off a few roots only. Fries gives a third section consisting of ill-known species in which there are neither stems nor roots. The species inhabit sandy tracts in warm countries, a single specimen only having occurred on common soil in the neighbourhood of London. In Italy one species at least is said to produce a yellow dye. [M. J. B.]

POLYSARCIA. An excess of sap, giving rise to unnatural growth, &c.

POLYSIPHONIA. A large genus of rose-spored *Algæ* belonging to the natural order *Rhodomelaceæ,* characterised by its thread-shaped articulated fronds with the surface-cells arranged in transverse rows so as to produce a pretty striated appearance. The species occur in all parts of the world from the polar seas to the equator, and are abundant on our coasts. Sections of the stem are pretty objects under the microscope, resembling wheels with a nave and radiating spokes. *P. fastigiata* is perhaps the most familiar species, forming brown bushy tufts on *Fucus nodosus* in America as well as in this country. A section of the stem has the peculiarity of showing a dark endochrome in the midst of the nave. [M. J. B.]

POLYSPOROUS. Containing a great many spores.

POLYSTACHYA. Chiefly an African genus of orchids, the main exceptions being two West Indian and tropical American species, one of which is also found in Ceylon. It belongs to the *Maxillaridæ* group of *Vandeæ,* and is characterised by having its lateral sepals broader than the other and adnate to the prolonged foot of the short semiterete column, its lip three-lobed, cushioned on its disk, and articulate with the column, and its four collateral pollen-masses attached by a setaceous caudicle to a minute gland. The species are epiphytes, usually of small size, with or without pseudobulbs, and small not showy flowers in simple or compound terminal spikes. [A. S.]

POLYSTEMMA *viridiflora* is the sole representative of a genus of *Asclepiadaceæ* inhabiting the mountains near Orizaba, in Mexico. It is a twiner, with densely tomentose branches, cordate hirtellous leaves, and umbels bearing rather large green flowers. The calyx is five-cleft, the corolla bell-shaped, and the corona consists of twenty-five leaves. The fruit is unknown. [B. S.]

POLYSTEMONOUS. Having a much larger number of stamens than petals.

POLYSTICHUM. One of the principal genera into which the old genus *Aspidium* is broken up by modern pteridologists. It is separated from the rest by its free veins, globose sori, and peltate indusia, no other ferns having these peculiarities combined. The fronds are in general rigid and coriaceous, with the margins mucronato-serrate; and hence they have a distinct aspect, which serves to distinguish them almost as clearly as their technical characters. They are included in *Aspidium* by those who do not admit the genera founded on diversity of venation. The species are numerous and widely dispersed, some few occurring in Britain. [T. M.]

POLYTÆNIA. A genus of umbellifers, having an oval and smooth fruit, each half of which has five obscure ribs, with two oil-cells in each furrow, and six on the line of junction. *P. Nuttallii* is the only species, a native of Arkansas in the United States; it is an herb with yellow flowers. The name was given in allusion to the numerous oil receptacles of the fruit. [G. D.]

POLYTOMOUS. Pinnate, but without having the divisions articulated with the common petiole.

POLYTRIC OFFICINAL. (Fr.) *Asplenium Trichomanes.*

POLYTRICHEI. A natural order of acrocarpous mosses, characterised by the mouth of the capsule being closed by a flat membrane formed by the top of the columella and confluent with the tips of the teeth, and a calyptra rough with dependent silky hairs which were originally a sort of paraphyses, though distinct from the true attendants on the archegonia. The order is remarkable for containing some of the finest genera among mosses, as *Dawsonia, Lyellia, &c.*: the former an Australian genus extending to New Zealand, with an oblique capsule, and an indefinite number of concentric teeth in the peristome, which are either quite free or partly connected with the top of the columella; and the latter a Nepalese genus with a similarly shaped capsule whose mouth is entirely closed with a membrane, from which a central orbicular portion separates, together with the columella which contracts within the capsule. *Polytrichum,* the typical genus, contains many common British species, known at once from all other mosses by their peculiar habit and veil. *Atrichum undulatum,* which is common in grassy shady places, is distinguished from the rest by the absence of hairs on the veil. [M. J. B.]

POLYTRICHUM. A fine genus of acro-

carpous mosses with a peculiar rigid habit, a veil rough with dependent hairs, and the mouth of the capsule closed with a flat membrane continued from the tips of the teeth. The capsule is angular, and furnished with a little apophysis below. The spore-sac is sometimes separated from the columella as well as from the walls of the capsule. The species are numerous, and occur in all parts of the world. In *P. dendroides* the stem is highly developed, and shows scalariform markings in some of its tissue, accompanied by lighter-coloured cells which con-

Polytrichum commune.

tain starch-grains. *P. commune,* though attaining its largest size in marshy heaths, is not confined to them; it is sometimes formed into brushes or plaited into mats for the feet. [M. J. B.]

POLYXENA. A genus of *Liliaceæ* from the Cape of Good Hope, allied to *Massonia,* but differing in the funnel-shaped perianth with the stamens inserted in the tube (not a prolongation of it upwards), and by the perianth being circumscissilely deciduous; seeds one or two in each of the three cells; leaves lanceolate, somewhat fleshy; flowers racemed, pale violet or rose. [J. T. S.]

POLYZONE. A South-west Australian genus of *Chamælauciaceæ,* consisting of shrubs with whorled branches, needle-shaped three-angled leaves, and flowers in sessile terminal heads surrounded by a many-leaved coloured involucre. This with *Genetyllis* and *Hedaroma* are now referred to *Darwinia.* [B. H.]

POMACEÆ. (*Appleworts.*) A natural order of calyciflora dicotyledons belonging to Lindley's rosal alliance of perigynous Exogens. The plants are often considered as a suborder of *Rosaceæ.* They are trees or shrubs with alternate stipulate leaves, and solitary or cymose regular flowers; calyx superior, five-toothed, the odd segment superior; petals five, the odd one inferior; stamens numerous; disk lining tube of calyx; ovaries one to five; ovules anatropal; styles one to five. Fruit a one to five-celled pome; seeds exalbuminous. Common in temperate climates in Europe, North America, and Northern Asia. The apple, pear, medlar, quince, and several other edible fruits belong to the group, of which there are sixteen genera and about two hundred species. Examples: *Pyrus, Mespilus, Cratægus.*   [J. H. B.]

POMADERRIS. A genus of *Rhamnaceæ*, of which about twenty species are known, all of them found in Eastern extratropical Australia and Tasmania, or in New Zealand. It is distinguished from *Cryptandra* and other allied genera, by the flowers being destitute of bracts, by the stamens being longer than the petals, and by the three one-seeded pieces into which the fruit separates not splitting in halves, but having a large opening on the inner face. The plants are erect branching shrubs, or rarely small trees, woolly with star-like hairs, and have alternate entire or toothed leaves, and small flowers possessing a hairy calyx with a short tube and five spreading lobes, five small stalked petals with as many stamens opposite them, and a trifid style. The fruits are loosely invested by the tube of the calyx; hence the generic name, which is derived from the Greek words *poma,* ' a covering,' and *derris,* ' skin.'

Several species, such as *P. apetala, P. discolor, P. betulina, P. elliptica* (the Kumahou of the New-Zealanders), and others, are occasionally met with in greenhouses in this country; they produce a profusion of small yellowish-brown or whitish flowers. *P. apetala* forms a small tree in New South Wales, and yields a hard close-grained wood, there called Cooper's wood. [A. S.]

POMARIA. A little-known South American shrub, described as constituting a genus of *Leguminosæ* of the suborder *Cæsalpinieæ*, differing from *Cæsalpinia* itself chiefly in its short two-seeded very glandular pod, and the glandular hairs with which the whole plant is covered. If really a good genus, it should probably include five or six South Brazilian or Chilian species which have been published under the names of *Cladotrichum* and *Zuccagnia*, all low rigid undershrubs or shrubs with twice-pinnate leaves, very small rigid and not very numerous leaflets, and yellow flowers in terminal racemes.

POMAROSA. A Central American name for *Jambosa vulgaris*.

POMAX. A genus of Australian annual plants of the family *Cinchonaceæ*. The leaves are opposite, with leaf-like stipules, and the flowers umbellate surrounded by floral leaves and their stipules as by an involucre. There are about three flowers in each head, all conjoined by the fusion of their respective calyx-tubes; between them passes a central axis dilated above into a flat disk common to all the flowers, and surmounting the ovary. The corollas have each a three to five-lobed limb, and are attached below to the disk; stamens one to five, generally protruding beyond the corolla; ovaries combined within the united

calyx-tubes, each one-celled with a single ovule; style very short; stigmas two, elongated, filiform. Fruit leathery crowned by the common calyx, three-celled with three erect seeds. The epigynous disk before mentioned separates from the axis supporting it like a little lid, whence the name of the genus from the Greek *poma*, 'a lid,' or operculum. One of the species is in cultivation as a greenhouse plant. This genus, with its near ally *Opercularia*, is very curious in a botanical point of view, as the nature of their inflorescence shows an affinity to that of *Umbelliferæ* or *Compositæ*; with *Valerianaceæ* they are connected by their variable number of stamens, single ovules, and other characters, while they resemble some species of *Lonicera* in the fusion of their flowers by means of the calyx-tube.   [M. T. M.]

POME. An inferior fleshy many-celled fruit, like that of the Apple.

POMEGRANATE. *Punica Granatum.*

POMELLE, or PAMELLE. (Fr.) *Hordeum distichon.*

POMELLOES. A name under which Forbidden-fruit, the smaller-sized Shaddocks, are sometimes sold in this country.

POMERANGE. A German name for the Orange.

POMERIDIAN. Occurring in the afternoon.

POMME. (Fr.) The fruit of the Apple, *Pyrus Malus*. — D'ADAM. A variety of *Citrus Limetta*. — D'AMOUR. *Lycopersicum esculentum.* — DE FLAN. *Anona muricata.* — DE LIANE. *Passiflora laurifolia.* — DE MAI. *Podophyllum peltatum.* — DE MERVEILLE. *Momordica Balsamina.* — DE PIN. The Cone of the Pine-tree. — DE TERRE. *Solanum tuberosum.* — ÉPINEUSE. *Datura Stramonium.* — ÉTOILÉE. *Chrysophyllum.* — ROSE. *Jambosa vulgaris.*

POMMETTE DE DOUX-CLOSES. (Fr.) *Cratægus Azarolus.*

POMMIER. (Fr.) The Apple, *Pyrus Malus*. — DE LA CHINE. *Pyrus spectabilis.* — PORTE-BAIES. *Pyrus baccata.*

POMPADOURA. (Fr.) *Calycanthus floridus.*

POMPELMOUSE, or PAMPELMOUSE. (Fr.) The Shaddock, *Citrus decumana* : especially applied to the larger-sized fruits.

POMPION. The Pumpkin, *Cucurbita Pepo.*

POMPOLEON. The larger-sized fruits of the Shaddock, *Citrus decumana.*

PONCEAU. (Fr.) *Papaver Rhæas.*

PONCELETIA. An epacridaceous genus containing a single species, *P. sprengelioides*, which has a five-leaved calyx surrounded by small bracts; a short campanulate five-cleft smooth corolla; short stamens included within the corolla, with beardless anthers, peltate beneath the middle; and a five-celled capsule. A dense shrub, with solitary erect flowers, the leaves cucullate at the base and sharp-pointed. It is a native of New South Wales. [R. H.]

PONCIRADE. (Fr.) *Melissa*.

PONCIRE. (Fr.) A large variety of Lemon.

PONDEUSE. (Fr.) *Solanum ovigerum*.

PONDWEED. *Potamogeton*; also *Lemna*. —, HORNED. *Zannichellia*. —, TASSEL. *Ruppia*.

PONERA. From the Greek *poneros*, 'unhappy,' in allusion to the thin appearance of the plants of this genus of orchids. All the species have simple slender lanky stems, very narrow grass-like leaves, and small axillary flowers in tufts upon the young leafy or the old leafless stems. They have erect fleshy sepals, the lateral ones largest and connate with the elongated foot of the column; free petals: a naked two-lobed wedge-shaped lip articulate with the foot of the column, which is short and terete; and a membranous four-celled anther, containing four pollen-masses adhering in pairs by means of two powdery caudicles. The species are natives of Central America and the West Indies. [A. S.]

PONGAMIA. Several species have from time to time been included in this genus of leguminous plants, but they are now referred to *Derris* and other genera, and only the original species (*P. glabra*) upon which it was established, remains. As a genus, however, it is scarcely distinguishable from the tropical American and African *Lonchocarpus*, its flowers agreeing perfectly with those of that genus, and of *Derris*, *Piscidia*, and *Mullera*; but its pods are somewhat different, being of an oblong form, from an inch and a half to two inches long, and an inch broad, flattened but thick and hard, and with rounded not winged edges; and they contain only one seed, which is thick and kidney-shaped.

P. glabra is a tree extensively diffused throughout Southern India, Pegu, Malacca, and the Indian Archipelago, and also found in Southern China, North Australia, and the Feejee Islands. It has smooth pinnate leaves, composed of five or seven egg-shaped or broadly elliptical leaflets, arranged in pairs with a terminal odd one; and loose axillary racemes of flowers. In India an oil, called Karunj, or Poonga oil, is expressed from the seeds, and greatly used for mixing with lamp-oil, or by the poorer classes for burning without any admixture. It is of a deep-yellow colour inclining to reddish-brown, and is fluid at temperatures above 60° Fahr., but below that it becomes solid. The tree has been recommended as suitable for forming avenues in the south of France. [A. S.]

PONOPILINO. *Pedilanthus tithymaloides* and *P. padifolius*.

PONTEDERACEÆ. (*Pontederads*.) A natural order of monocotyledons belonging to Lindley's lilial alliance of Endogens. They are aquatic or marsh plants, with sheathing parallel-veined leaves, which are sometimes cordate or sagittate, and have inflated petioles, and spathaceous flowers. Perianth tubular, coloured, six-parted, circinate in æstivation; stamens three to six, the anthers introrse; ovary free, or slightly adherent, three-celled; style one; stigma simple. Fruit a three-celled three-valved capsule, with loculicidal dehiscence; seeds indefinite, attached to a central axis. They are natives of North and South America, the East Indies, and Africa, and are unimportant in regard to properties. There are six genera, including *Pontederia* and *Leptanthus*, and about thirty species. [J. H. B.]

PONTEDERIA. A genus of *Pontederaceæ*, now restricted to those species which have two of the cells of the ovary barren, and a one-celled utricular fruit with a single seed. They are stout American herbs, growing in shallow water, with creeping rhizomes, long-stalked leaves (generally heart-shaped at the base), and a one-leaved stem, terminated by a raceme of purplish-blue flowers which are two-lipped, the upper three segments united to form the three-lobed upper lip, and the three lower spreading; stamens six, the three upper shorter and often sterile. *P. cordata*, the Pickerel-weed, is a common North American aquatic, with the leaves somewhat arrow-shaped, and a dense spike of blue flowers. [J. T. S.]

PONTHIEVA. Of the two species of this genus of the *Neotteæ* tribe of orchids, one is exclusively West Indian, and the other West Indian and American, from Carolina to Ecuador. They are both terrestrial plants with tufted roots, broad veiny radical leaves, and many-flowered terminal scapes clothed with glandular pubescence. Their flowers have the lip posterior and adnate to the column together with the petals, a beaked column, and a dorsal oblong linear stalked anther, containing two bilobed pollen-masses. [A. S.]

PONY. *Tecoma serratifolia*.

POOAH, or PUYA. An Indian name for *Böhmeria Puya*, from which a valuable fibre is obtained.

POODINA. An Indian name for *Mentha sativa*.

POOL-REED. *Phragmitis communis*.

POOL-RUSH. *Typha*.

POON-WOOD. An Indian wood, the produce of one or two species of *Calophyllum*.

POOR-MAN'S PARMACETTY. *Capsella Bursa Pastoris*.

POOR-MAN'S TREACLE. *Allium*.

POOR-MAN'S WEATHERGLASS. *Anagallis arvensis*.

POP. A United States name for some varieties of Maize.

POPE'S-HEAD. *Melocactus communis.*

POPLAR. *Populus.* —, YELLOW, of North America. *Liriodendron tulipifera.*

PÖPPIGIA. A tall tree, a native of the West Indies and tropical South America, with simply pinnate leaves, having many leaflets like those of a *Robinia*, and numerous yellow flowers in terminal panicles. It forms a genus of *Leguminosæ* of the suborder *Cæsalpinieæ*, and is chiefly characterised by five nearly equal narrow petals, ten nearly equal free stamens, and a long thin flat and rather narrow pod, with a narrow wing along the upper suture, much like the pod of a *Robinia.*

POPPY. *Papaver.* —, CALIFORNIAN. *Eschscholtzia californica.* —, CELANDINE. *Stylophorum.* —, CORN. *Papaver Rhœas.* —, GARDEN. *Papaver somniferum.* —, HORNED. *Glaucium luteum.* —, OPIUM. *Papaver somniferum.* —, PRICKLY. *Argemone mexicana.* —, RED. *Papaver Rhœas.* —, SEA. *Glaucium luteum.* —, SPATLING. *Silene inflata.* —, WELSH. *Meconopsis cambrica.*

POPPYA. A name synonymous with *Luffa*, a genus of the *Cucurbitaceæ* embracing the Towel-gourds. *P. Fabiana* of gardens is *Luffa cylindrica.* [A. A. B.]

POPPY-SEED. The seed of *Papaver somniferum.*

POPPYWORTS. Lindley's name for the *Papaveraceæ.*

POPULAGE. (Fr.) *Caltha.*

POPULUS. The Poplar: a family of deciduous trees, often attaining a considerable height, natives of temperate climates in both hemispheres. They belong to the *Salicaceæ*, and are botanically distinguished by bearing both barren and fertile flowers in catkins, the scales of which are jagged. There are no nectariferous glands as in *Salix*; the number of stamens varies from four to thirty, and these organs, as is also the case with the style in the fertile flower, are contained in a cup-shaped perianth.

The Poplars are trees of rapid growth; consequently their timber is soft, light, and of a loose texture: they are remarkable for a greater or less amount of tremulous motion in the leaves, occasioned by the length and slenderness of the leafstalk, which instead of being flattened horizontally, or in the same plane with the leaf, as is the case with the generality of trees, is compressed vertically, so that the plane of the leaf and that of the stalk form a right angle with each other. The barren catkins are conspicuous in early spring by their length, and the red tint of the numerous stamens, and, a little later in the season, the fertile catkins become remarkable from the quantity of white cottony down which envelopes the seeds.

P. fastigiata, the Lombardy Poplar, is the formal cypress-shaped tree with perpendicular slender branches so common in suburban gardens, but scarcely ornamental except when its taper head rises above a mass of round-headed trees and breaks or relieves a too continuous horizontal line. It is indigenous in Lombardy, Persia, and the Himalayas, and attains a height of from 100 to 150 feet. Its timber is of little use, except for packing-cases. *P. monilifera*, the Black Italian Poplar, is a native of North America, though now common in Italy and Switzerland and extensively planted in England. It is the fastest-growing of all the Poplars, and sends up a remarkably straight stem; but the branches are far more diffuse than those of the Lombardy Poplar, with which, however, it is closely allied. *P. alba*, or Abele, the White Poplar, and *P. canescens*, the Grey Poplar, are allied species: the former having four yellow stigmas and the fertile catkins oval; and the latter eight purple stigmas, and the fertile catkins cylindrical. These trees are thought to be natives of Britain, France, and Germany, as well as the Caucasus, Barbary, and Persia. They often attain a large size, and are remarkable for their roundish deeply toothed leaves, which are downy and white beneath. The Abele is the badge of the Fergusons. The timber of *P. alba* is of little value; that of the Grey Poplar, a tree of slower growth, is used by the carpenter, turner, and millwright for many purposes. *P. tremula*, the Aspen, is a native of most parts of Britain in wet soils. This is also a fast-growing tree, with a smoothish grey bark and spreading branches, which in age become pendulous; the leaves are nearly circular, almost smooth on both sides, and are especially liable to the tremulous motion peculiar to the family. *P. nigra*, the Black Poplar, so called apparently in contradistinction from the White Poplar, is considered by Sir W. J. Hooker to be merely a variety of the Lombardy Poplar. *P. balsamifera*, the Tacamahac, a native of North America, is remarkable for its fine foliage in early summer, and the pleasant balsamic odour of its buds and leaves. For other species and varieties see Loudon's *Arboretum.* French: *Peuplier*; German: *Pappel.* [C. A. J.]

PORANTHERA. A genus of *Euphorbiaceæ*, of the tribe *Phyllantheæ*, consisting of small Australian shrubs, usually glabrous and much-branched, with alternate entire narrow often heath-like leaves, and small flowers in dense clusters surrounded by a few involucral leaves. The calyx is coloured and five-cleft, with five minute petals; the male flowers have five stamens remarkable for their four-celled anthers, and the females a three-celled ovary with two ovules in each cell, and three two-cleft styles. There are not many species, and none of any special interest.

PORCAL. A large plum grown in Spain.

PORCELLE. (Fr.) *Hypochæris.*

PORCUPINE-WOOD. The hard outer portion of the trunk of *Cocos nucifera.*

POREWORTS. Lindley's name for the *Tremandraceæ*.

PORI (adj. POROSE). Apertures in the covering of anything; as in the anthers for the emission of pollen (hence *porandrous*), or in the skin, when they are also called stomates. Also, appendages of the pileus among fungals in the form of cylindrical or angular tubes, placed side by side, open at one end, and containing in their cavity the organs of reproduction.

PORILLON. (Fr.) *Narcissus poeticus.*

PORION. (Fr.) *Narcissus poeticus* and *N. Pseudo-Narcissus.*

PORLIERA. A genus of shrubs of the *Zygophyllaceæ*, named in honour of a Spanish botanist. The species are met with in Peru and Chili. Their pinnate leaves are provided with small spiny stipules; the flowers grow in tufts, and have a four-parted calyx, four petals, eight stamens inserted below into a little scale, and a four-lobed ovary placed on a short stalk, with four ovules in each of the four compartments; fruit fleshy, four-lobed, each compartment containing but a single seed, owing to the suppression of the remaining three. *P. hygrometrica* is grown in this country as a stove shrub. Its specific name is given in allusion to the power that the linear leaflets have of expanding in fine and closing in wet weather. [M. T. M.]

POROPHYLLUM. A genus of *Compositæ* of the tribe *Heliantheæ*, allied in many respects to *Tagetes* and *Pectis*. It consists of from twelve to fifteen South American herbs or undershrubs, all glabrous and more or less glaucous, with entire or toothed leaves almost always marked with pellucid oblong glands. The flower-heads, always without rays, are singly pedunculate, with tubular involucres of five often united bracts. The florets are tubular, the style-branches linear nearly as in *Vernoniaceæ*, and the achenes elongated as in *Tagetes*, with a pappus of simple bristles.

PORPHYRA. A genus of *Ulvaceæ*, with a membranous flat frond, and dark-purple spores arranged in fours, though its natural affinities are clearly with the green-spored *Algæ*. The species have undoubtedly been multiplied needlessly, and *P. vulgaris* and *P. laciniata*, which supply the Laver of commerce, run manifestly into each other, though extreme forms seem distinct. When very young they closely resemble *Bangiæ*. The tint varies from a clear rose to a livid purple, but though occasionally slightly olivaceous is never green.   [M. J. B.]

PORPHYREUS. Brown, mixed with red; a warm red.

PORPHYROCOMA. A genus of *Acanthaceæ*, containing a single species, a shrubby plant, with opposite lanceolate almost sessile leaves, and sessile flowers in terminal aggregate spikes, which have a very showy appearance from their large crowded purple bracts. The small calyx consists of five subulate sepals, placed within three bracts, the outer one being very large; the corolla is tubular and two-lipped, the upper lip erect and two-lobed, the lower reflexed and three-lobed; there are two stamens, with anthers having two diverging cells; and the ovary is surrounded by a disk, and bears a long slender style and obtuse stigma. The fruit, concealed by the large persistent bracts, is unguiculate two-celled and two-valved. There are four flattened seeds on hooked retinaculæ.   [W. C.]

PORTE-BANDEAU. (Fr.) *Sparganophorus Vaillantii.*

PORTE-CHAPEAU. (Fr.) *Paliurus aculeatus.*

PORTE-COLLIER. (Fr.) *Osteospermum moniliferum.*

PORTE-FEUILLE. (Fr.) *Asperugo procumbens.*

PORTE-NOIX. (Fr.) *Caryocar.*

PORTE-SUIF. (Fr.) *Stillingia.*

PORTLANDIA. The Duchess of Portland, a great lover of Botany, is commemorated by this very handsome genus of cinchonaceous shrubs. The species are West Indian, and have elliptical leaves with broad triangular stipules; and very large whitish flowers, borne on axillary flower-stalks, in groups of two or three. The limb of the calyx is divided into five persistent leafy segments; corolla funnel-shaped, with a five-angled tube, and a limb divided into five blunt lobes; stamens attached to the throat of the corolla; style thread-like, as long or longer than the tube of the corolla; stigma undivided; capsule ribbed, surmounted by the limb of the calyx and bursting from above downwards, through the middle of the valves; seeds numerous, rough. Some of the species possess properties similar to those of the true cinchona. The bark of *P. hexandra* is used instead of cinchona in French Guiana; and that of *P. grandiflora* is exceedingly bitter. Two or three species are in cultivation as hothouse plants, and their splendid flowers are very ornamental; *P. grandiflora* is the one commonly met with. *P. platantha*, a species of more recent introduction, flowers in a dwarf state, and is almost always in bloom—two great recommendations.   [M. T. M.]

PORTLAND-POWDER. A medicine consisting of equal parts of the roots of *Aristolochia rotunda* and *Gentiana lutea*.

PORTULACACEÆ. (*Purslanes.*) A natural order of calycifloral dicotyledons belonging to Lindley's sfienal alliance of hypogynous Exogens. They are succulent shrubs or herbs, with alternate seldom opposite exstipulate leaves; sepals two, cohering; petals usually five, rarely wanting; stamens usually perigynous, ovary free or partially adherent, formed by three united carpels; stigmas several. Fruit capsular, one-celled, opening by circumscissile dehiscence, or by three valves, occasionally monospermous and indehiscent. They are found in various parts of the world—chiefly, however, in South America and at the Cape of Good Hope—and always inhabit dry parched places. They have a great affinity to *Caryophyllaceæ*, from which they are chiefly distinguished by their bisepalous calyx, perigynous stamens, and transversely dehiscent capsule. Genera eighteen ; species 196. Examples : *Portulaca, Talinum, Claytonia.*   [J. H. B.]

PORTULACA. The typical genus of *Portulacaceæ.* It contains between thirty and forty species, fully two-thirds of which belong to the tropics and subtropics of the western hemisphere, and the remainder to tropical Africa, India, Australia, and the Sandwich Islands ; while the Common Purslane, *P. oleracea,* is naturalised in most warm parts of the world. All are low succulent herbs, with alternate or irregularly opposite flat or nearly cylindrical leaves, often with tufts of bristles in their axils, and the upper ones forming an involucre around the solitary or clustered flowers ; the latter being yellow purple or rose-coloured and very ephemeral, expanding only once, and that only in direct sunshine during the forenoon.

P. oleracea, the Common Purslane, is a prostrate annual seldom more than six inches high, glabrous, with small oblong wedge-shaped leaves destitute of bristles in their axils, and small stalkless clustered or solitary yellow flowers above the last leaves on the branches. Purslane has been cultivated from very ancient times, and is now spread over the tropics and both temperate zones. It possesses antiscorbutic properties, but is not much employed in this country, though its young shoots are sometimes put in salads, and the older ones used as a potherb or for pickling. Three varieties, the Common Green, the Golden, and the large-leaved Golden, are grown in gardens.   [A. S.]

POSO. A sort of beer made of the fermented seeds of *Zea Mays.*

POSOQUERIA. A genus of shrubs or small trees, natives of Guiana, the West Indies, &c., and included among the *Cinchonaceæ.* They are remarkable for their very long white hanging flowers, the corolla of which is funnel-shaped, with a very long tube, a hairy throat, and a five-parted limb ; stamens five, protruding from the corolla and attached to its throat, the filaments wavy ; style thread-like, concealed within the tube of the corolla ; stigma with two slender lobes. Fruit succulent, crowned by the limb of the calyx, two-celled. Some of the species with long white flowers are cultivated as stove plants in this country. The generic name is a modification of the native name applied to *P. longiflora* in Guiana.   [M. T. M.]

POSTICOUS. Turned away from the axis of a flower, as some anthers whose dehiscence takes place next the petals ; also, stationed on that side of a flower which is next the axis.

POTALIA. A genus of *Loganiaceæ* allied to *Fagræa,* but well characterised by the great number (usually ten) of the lobes of the corolla and of the stamens, whilst that of the lobes of the calyx is four only. There is probably but one South American species, a weak shrub or undershrub, quite glabrous, with long opposite rather thick leaves, and axillary flowers. The juice is bitter and acrid, as in *Gentianaceæ* ; and an infusion of the leaves, slightly mucilaginous and astringent, is used in North Brazil as a lotion for the eyes. The tropical African *Anthocleista* differs in so few essential points that it might be considered as a second species of *Potalia.*

POTAMOGETONEÆ. The same as *Juncaginaceæ.*

POTAMOGETON. The Pondweed : a genus of submersed or partially floating aquatics belonging to the order *Juncaginaceæ,* of which the characters are :—Flowers perfect, four-cleft ; stamens and styles four ; seed-vessels four, sessile. There are nearly twenty species of Pondweed indigenous in our lakes, ponds, and rivers, all having very cellular stems and leaves, and unattractive greenish flowers often collected into a spike. One group is represented by *P. natans,* of which the lower leaves when present are submersed very long and narrow ; the upper broadly elliptical, of a coriaceous texture distinctly marked with longitudinal veins, of a glossy green hue, and furnished with long flaccid stalks by means of which they accommodate themselves to a varying depth of water, and are always in a floating position. *P. crispus, P. densus, P. perfoliatus,* &c., have only submersed leaves which are alternate and pellucid, resembling when artificially dried a thin animal membrane. *P. zosteræfolius* and *P. gramineus* have only submersed leaves, which are very long and narrow and of a texture resembling that of *Zostera. P. pusillus* and others bear also submersed leaves of an olive-brown hue, and so narrow as to present scarcely any plane surface. Some of these species are less common than others, but there is scarcely a pond, canal, or any large body of still water, which does not contain some of them. In canals they sometimes grow so profusely as to impede navigation ; and in autumn, when they shed their leaves, the latter are liable to be carried away by the current, and choke the sluices of mills. The herbage and seeds afford food to many water-birds and myriads of aquatic insects. French : *Potamot* ; German : *Saamkraut.*   [C. A. J.]

POTATO. A highly esteemed esculent consisting of the tuber of *Solanum tuberosum.* —, CANADA. *Helianthus tuberosus.* —, MADAGASCAR. *Solanum Anguivi.* —, NATIVE, of Tasmania. *Gastrodia sesamoides.* —, SEASIDE. *Ipomæa pes capræ.* —, SPANISH, or SWEET. *Batatas edulis.* —, TELINGA. *Amorphophallus campanulatus,* much cultivated in India as an esculent. —, WILD. The West Indian name for *Ipomæa fastigiata.*

POTATO MURRAIN. A formidable disease in potatos, which appeared first in this country in the year 1845, but was previously known in America. It is characterised by the rapid putrescence of the leaves and haulm, which is first indicated by the presence of a little mould, *Peronospora infestans*, which preys upon the tissues, spreading rapidly in every direction. The tubers also exhibit brown spots on their surface and within their tissue, and, according to circumstances, decay with greater or less rapidity. It is now admitted by most persons that the mould is the primary cause, but as it attacks the tissues before it appears externally it is almost impossible to apply a remedy. Many plans have been adopted, but the two most important, though far from infallible, are powdering the sets well with flower of sulphur; and early planting, with the removal of the haulm as soon as the mould appears. The disease has been equally bad in the wettest and hottest seasons, and has baffled the researches of all practical and scientific men. It was in many districts as bad in 1860 as it was on its first appearance—the worst year perhaps being 1846, when its sudden inroad produced a fearful famine in Ireland, which resulted in the loss by death of thousands; and, as good often comes out of evil, it also led to the repeal of the Corn Laws.

German authors distinguish two forms, the wet and dry rot. It is, however, to be observed that these diseases, which are characterised not only by the peculiar condition of the tubers, but by the presence of *Fusisporium Solani tubcrosi*, were prevalent in this country before 1845; the brown mottled appearance of the tubers, and the presence of *Peronospora* on the leaves and the exposed tissues, being previously unknown. [M. J. B.]

POTELÉA. (Fr.) *Hyoscyamus niger.*

POTENTILLA. A genus of shrubby or herbaceous plants belonging to the *Rosaceæ*, and allied to the Strawberry, from which they are mainly distinguished by having their seeds in a dry not pulpy receptacle. The British species of most frequent occurrence are *P. Fragariastrum*, a humble hedge plant, with ternate leaves made conspicuous in early spring by its small white flowers, which are often mistaken for those of the Wild Strawberry; *P. anserina*, the Silver Weed, a roadside plant well marked by its pinnate leaves, glossy with white silky down, and large yellow flowers; *P. reptans*, distinguished by its slender creeping 'runners,' quinate leaves, and large yellow flowers; and *P. Tormentilla*, a humble slender trailing plant, of which the lower leaves are quinate, the upper ternate, and the flowers, which are yellow, have four or five petals. *P. fruticosa* has pinnate leaves and yellow flowers; it grows in bushy places in the North, but is rare. Many species are cultivated, of which *P. nepalensis, atro-sanguinea, Thomasii,* and *hæmatochrus* have furnished varieties of all shades of purple and crimson. French: *Quintefeuille*; German: *Fünffingerkraut.* [C. A. J.]

POTERIUM. A genus of *Rosaceæ* named from the Latin *poterium*, a 'drinking cup,' as its herbage, which has much the flavour of cucumber, was employed in the old English drink known as a cool tankard. Its flowers are monœcious, its separated male and female florets being compounded into more or less compact heads, from which depend little tassel-like bunches of bright pink stamens. Of this plant the botanist recognises two forms, probably only varieties:—*P. Sanguisorba*, the Lesser Burnet, which has an angular stem about a foot high, pinnate leaves with serrated leaflets, and seeds somewhat acutely quadrangular: this occurs in calcareous soil; and *P. muricatum*, the whole plant of which is much larger than the preceding, the seeds four-winged, and more or less pitted with raised tooth-like elevations. The latter seems to be apparently wild in districts where sainfoin has been cultivated, and is probably a foreign plant introduced with continental seed; or else, from agrarian cultivation, burnet may have become the coarse plant which farmers have lately had so much reason to complain of from its being sown with their sainfoin. At first this evil was overlooked, as the intended crop only afforded a sample of the burnet here and there; and as both possessed pinnate leaves, the farmer scarcely distinguished them, though in the burnet the leaflets are serrated, while in the sainfoin they are entire at the edges. In order to distinguish the seeds of these two plants, reference should be made to the particulars given in treating of Sainfoin. [See ONOBRYCHIS.] The colour of the seeds is a light brown, and the wrinkled aspect of both is so much alike that the pest is often overlooked by the buyer of sainfoin-seed, or we should hardly find what should be sainfoin turn out as much as fifty per cent. of burnet. To prevent this the best plan is to sow only decorticated seed. [J. B.]

POTHERB, WHITE. *Valerianella olitoria.*

POTHOMORPHE. A genus of *Piperaceæ*, consisting of undershrubs having somewhat the appearance of some of the species of *Pothos*, whence the name. They are natives of the tropics of the Old and New World, delighting in damp shady situations. They are studded with pellucid glands, and have large membranous heart-shaped sometimes peltate leaves. The spikes emerge from the axils of the leaves, above one or two branches, that proceed from the same spot. The stipules are small, opposite to the leaves; the flowers perfect; the fruit very small. [M. T. M.]

POTHOS. The name of a genus of climbing shrubs of the family *Orontiaceæ*. They are natives of India, China, Madagascar, New Holland, &c.; and have for the most part cord-like stems, sending out false roots here and there, and attaching themselves to trees. The leaves are in the adult state stalked, provided below with a permanent sheath; the blade of the leaf varies in shape in the different species, being sometimes entire, at other times palmately lobed, sometimes perforated. The spathe is persistent, and ultimately bent backwards. The spadix is clothed with perfect flowers, each of which has a six-leaved perianth, short filaments, and a sessile stigma. Several kinds are grown in stove-houses for the sake of their foliage. The generic title is said to be an adaptation of the Cingalese name for these plants. [M. T. M.]

POTIRON. (Fr.) *Cucurbita maxima* or *C. Pepo;* also sometimes applied to the esculent *Boleti.*

POT-PLANT. *Lecythis Ollaria.*

POTTIACEÆ. A natural order of acrocarpous mosses, with pedunculate straight oval capsules, which are generally without any peristome, and large-celled leaves. *Pottia* comprises several of the old *Gymnostomas.* *P. truncata* grows on almost every mud-wall, and *P. Heimii,* which is found at the Cape, and is widely distributed elsewhere, is not uncommon on old ant-hills. *Gymnostoma* has the reticulation of the leaves much more compact. [M. J. B.]

POTTSIA. A genus of the dogbane order, distinguished from its allies chiefly by the style and stigma, the former of which is broad at the base, and narrower upwards; and the latter is somewhat round and five-angled. The only species is a Chinese shrub, with hairy branches, oval stalked smooth leaves, and few small flowers. [G. D.]

POUCHBELL. *Glossocomia.*

POUCH-SHAPED. Hollow, and resembling a little double bag; as the spur of many orchids.

POUDRE À VERS. (Fr.) *Artemisia judaica.* — DE CHYPRE. A cosmetic wash-powder prepared from the starch of *Arum maculatum.*

POUKENEL, or POWKE-NEEDLE. *Scandix Pecten-Veneris.*

POULARD. (Fr.) *Triticum turgidum.*

POULE QUI POND. (Fr.) *Solanum Melongena.* — GRASSE, or MÂCHE. *Valerianella.*

POULIOT. (Fr.) *Mentha Pulegium.* — DE MONTAGNE. *Teucrium Polium.* — THYM. *Mentha arvensis.*

POUPARTIA. A genus of *Anacardiaceæ,* two of the species formerly included in which have been referred to *Evia* and *Dracontomelum,* so that it is now restricted to the solitary species upon which it was founded. This, *P. borbonica,* is a middle-sized tree a native of the island of Bourbon, where it is called Bois de Poupart by the French, whence the generic name. It has unequally pinnate or sometimes simple leaves; and axillary and terminal racemes of dark-purple flowers, which are distinguished from those of allied genera by being unisexual, and by having their petals overlapping in the bud, and afterwards spread very wide open. The fruit has a hard bony stone divided into two cells, each of which contains a single seed. [A. S.]

POUROUMA. A genus of *Artocarpaceæ,* consisting of tropical American trees marked with circular scars, indicating the position of the stipules. The leaves are entire or palmately lobed, smooth or rough, sometimes woolly; flowers diœcious, in corymb-like cymes or clusters at the extremities of the branched flower-stalks. In the females the stigma is peltate, and the ovule partially inverted. [M. T. M.]

POURPIER. (Fr.) *Portulaca.* — DE MER. *Atriplex Halimus.* — MARRON. A Madagascar name for several species of pepper-bearing succulent fruits.

POURPIÈRE. (Fr.) *Peplis Portula.*

POURRETIA. A genus of *Bromeliaceæ* named in honour of the Abbé Pourret, a French botanist. The habit and general appearance of these plants do not materially differ from those of the other genera of this order. Perianth six-parted, the outer three segments equal, the inner three convolute at the base, spreading above, rolling up spirally when withered; stamens six, the filaments awl-shaped; ovary three-cornered, with a thread-like style, and three linear spirally-twisted stigmas; fruit capsular, cartilaginous, three-valved. The species are natives of South America. Some are in cultivation, and have blue or red flowers. [M. T. M.]

POUZOLZIA. A genus of *Urticaceæ,* consisting of herbs shrubs or small trees, with the characters nearly of *Böhmeria,* except that the stigmas are deciduous, but frequently with the habit approaching more to that of *Parietaria.* The leaves are alternate three-nerved and entire; the flowers small, green and monœcious, in axillary or spicate clusters, the males and females usually intermingled; the former with a three to five-cleft perianth and three to five stamens; the females with a tubular perianth enclosing the fruit, and often winged. There are rather more than twenty species known, natives of both worlds within the tropics. Amongst them *P. indica* is a common herb in waste places in India, where it replaces our common *Parietaria,* which it much resembles in aspect. A considerable number of species formerly included in *Pouzolzia* now constitute the genus *Memorialis.*

POWDERY. Covered with a fine bloom or powdery matter, as the leaves of *Primula farinosa.*

POW-ITCH. An Indian name for the fruit of *Pyrus rivularis.*

POZOA. A genus of the order *Umbelliferæ,* distinguished by having the fruit four-angled, each half with five ribs, the three middle of which are close together and remote from the other two; there are no oil-cells. The only species is a smooth herbaceous plant, a native of Chili, with stalked and wedge-shaped radical leaves; the flowers in dense umbels, surrounded by large bracts. The genus was named after Pozo, a Spanish botanist.   [G. D.]

PRÆCOCITAS. A constitutional condition in peculiar individuals or varieties of plants, in consequence of which the natural time of flowering or fruiting is anticipated, as in the Glastonbury Thorn. Such varieties are often extremely valuable to gardeners. Most trees when raised from seed are many years before they yield perfect seed, though they may produce flowers at an early period. The Scotch Fir and Larch, for instance, bear fruit about the sixteenth year, the Spruce about the fortieth, the Silver Fir and the Beech scarcely before the fiftieth. We do not know what the usual age of seeding is in the *Wellingtonia*, but we have seen two three-year-old seedlings out of a great quantity with a single cone on each.   [M. J. B.]

PRÆCOX. Appearing early in the year, or earlier than others related to it.

PRÆFLORATION. The arrangement of the parts of the flower when unexpanded. See ÆSTIVATION.

PRÆFOLIATION. The arrangement of leaves in a leaf-bud.

PRÆMORSE. The same as Truncate, except that the termination is ragged and irregular, as if bitten off.

PRÆUSTUS. Looking as if burnt, owing to the formation of a brown matter in the interior.

PRANGOS. The greater number of species forming this genus of umbellifers are found in Persia and Asia Minor, and extend from thence into Northern India, Africa, and Southern Europe. They are perennial herbs, with round tapering stems, and much-divided compound leaves, having very narrow segments; and they bear numerous umbels of yellowish flowers, which have a five-toothed calyx, entire egg-shaped petals rolled inwards at the point, and the style-bearing disk depressed. The fruits are scarcely at all flattened, being nearly of a taper form; the face by which the half-fruits cohere is broad, the half-fruits themselves each having five longitudinal ridges at the back, which are thick at the base but decrease to a thin wing; and the seeds are covered with numerous oil-cells.

The Hay-plant of Tibet, or the Prangos Hay-plant, *P. pabularia*, was some twenty or more years ago greatly lauded as a forage plant, and various attempts were made to introduce it among the agricultural plants of this country, but without success. Its high reputation appears to have been undeserved; for although extremely valuable in the cold and arid regions of Tibet, where it is indigenous and where forage of a better quality is not obtainable, it is not so much esteemed in Kashmir and other more fertile countries,

where grass-pasture exists. It was first discovered by Mr. Moorcroft during his travels in Tibet, and was spoken of by him as being extensively employed as winter fodder for sheep, goats, and frequently for neat-cattle, producing fatness in a very short space of time, and proving very destructive to the liver-fluke so fatal to sheep. The late Dr. Royle was of the opinion that this plant was probably the kind of *Silphium* mentioned by Arrian in his account of the wars of Alexander: 'In this part of the Caucasus' (the modern Hindoo Kush) 'nothing grows except pines and silphium; but the country was populous, and fed many sheep and cattle, for the sheep are very fond of the silphium. If a sheep should perceive the silphium from a distance, it runs to it and feeds on the flower, and digs up the root and eats that also.' The other kinds of *Silphium* mentioned by Greek writers have been referred to plants of the same natural order.   [A. S.]

PRASINUS. Grass-green.

PRASIOLA. A rather pretty genus of *Ulvaceæ*, comprising the species which grow on rocks or on the naked soil, whether impregnated more or less with salt, or quite saltless. They form exquisite objects under the microscope, from the symmetry of the cells of which the frond is composed, these being disposed in fours or multiples of four. Some of them when young are very narrow, and, like the cognate *Porphyra*, look like *Bangia*. They are all natives of cold regions. *P. crispa*, which is not uncommon in Europe, occurs in Cockburn Island in lat. 60° S.   [M. J. B.]

PRASIUM. A genus of *Labiatæ*, having the calyx bell-shaped, with the border two-lipped; the upper lip short, three-cleft, the lower deeply two-cleft, and all ovate and leaf-like; and corolla with a short tube, its upper lip ovate and entire, and the lower three-cleft, the middle piece largest and entire. *P. majus*, the only species, is an evergreen shrub, native of Europe and Northern Africa. The name is adopted from the Prasion of Dioscorides, a plant like horehound or marjoram.   [G. D.]

PRATENSIS. Growing in meadows.

PRATIA. A small genus of *Lobeliaceæ*, natives of the southern parts of South America, Australia, Tasmania, New Zealand, and India. They form little creeping herbaceous plants, growing usually in marshy places; and having prostrate stems, small rounded or oblong sinuate or toothed leaves, and axillary single-flowered peduncles. It is distinguished from *Lobelia* by its fleshy indehiscent fruits.   [A. S.]

PRATLING PARNELL. *Saxifraga umbrosa*.

PRAYER-BEADS. The seeds of *Abrus precatorius*.

PRÊLE. (Fr.) *Equisetum*. — DES TOURNEURS. *Equisetum hyemale*.

PREMNA. A large genus of *Verbena*

ceæ, limited to the tropical and subtropical regions of the Old World, extending to Northern Australia and the Pacific Islands. They are shrubs or trees, with small flowers in terminal trichotomous panicles, or in opposite cymes or clusters forming a spike-like thyrse. The calyx is truncate or sinuately toothed; the corolla tube is short, and the limb spreading, with four or rarely five lobes which are nearly equal or slightly two-lipped; there are four stamens, usually shorter than the corolla; and the ovary is four-celled, with pendulous or laterally attached ovules, the style having two acute stigmatic lobes. The fruit is a drupe. [W. C.]

PRENANTHES. A genus of *Compositæ* of the suborder *Cichoraceæ*; nearly allied to *Crepis*, and with a similar sessile pappus; but the slender cylindrical involucre has only four to six nearly equal bracts or scales surrounded by a few small ones at their base, and contains only three to five florets. The genus is now restricted to a very few European or Asiatic herbs. Amongst them *P. purpurea*, common in mountainous or hilly woods in Central and Southern Europe, is a tall erect herb with oblong-lanceolate stem-clasping leaves; and a large loose terminal panicle of elegantly drooping purple flower-heads.

PREPUSA. A genus of the family *Gentianaceæ*, represented by a Brazilian shrub, with handsome flowers arranged in terminal leafy clusters. The calyx is bell-shaped, coloured, six-cleft, and winged; the corolla bell-shaped, with a short tube, deciduous; stamens six, inserted into the throat of the corolla; ovary one-celled, surrounded at the base by a fleshy disk; fruit two-valved. *P. Hookeriana* bears fine crimson and whitish flowers. The generic name is derived from the Greek word *prepo*, 'I am handsome.' [M. T. M.]

PRESCOTTIA. A small tropical American and West Indian genus of the *Neotteæ* tribe of orchids, the species of which are terrestrial, and have tufted roots, rosulate or single leaves, and a terminal sheathed scape bearing a dense cylindrical spike of green flowers, which have the lateral sepals connate with the lip into a sac, the lip being fleshy cucullate and entire, with a couple of ears at its base. [A. S.]

PRESLIA. A genus of *Labiatæ*, having the calyx ovate equal and four-toothed, and the border of the corolla of four entire and equal lobes. The only species is a prostrate herbaceous plant, growing in marshy places in the southern parts of Europe, having sessile narrow leaves, and whorls of pale-purple flowers. The genus was named after C. B. and J. S. Presl, botanists of Prague. [G. D.]

PRETREA. A genus of *Pedaliaceæ*, consisting of only one species, *P. zanzibarica*, inhabiting the sandy shores of Eastern Africa. It is a procumbent herb, with opposite sinuato-pinnatifid leaves, the lobes of which terminate in spines, and axillary peduncles producing one flower of a pink colour; a five-cleft calyx, a nearly campanulate corolla, four stamens, and a nut-like fruit with two horns, and one or two seeds. [B. S.]

PRIAPÉE. (Fr.) *Nicotiana rustica.*

PRICKET, or **PRICK-MADAM.** *Sedum acre, album*, and *reflexum.*

PRICKLES. Hard conical sharp elevations of the epidermis or epiphlœum; hence *prickly*, furnished with prickles, as the stem of a rose.

PRICKLE-YELLOW. The *Xanthoxylon Clava Herculis.*

PRICKLY-PEAR. *Opuntia Tuna*, and *vulgaris.*

PRICKLY-POLE. A West Indian name for *Bactris Plumieriana.*

PRICKLY-WITHE. *Cereus triangularis.*

PRICK-TIMBER, or **PRICKWOOD.** The wood of *Euonymus europæus.*

PRIDE OF INDIA. *Melia Azedarach.*

PRIESTLEYA. A genus of *Leguminosæ* of the suborder *Papilionaceæ* and tribe *Genisteæ*, consisting of South African shrubs, with alternate simple and entire leaves without stipules, and yellow flowers in terminal heads or racemes, or rarely scattered in the axils of the leaves. They have a five-lobed calyx; a rounded vexillum and curved carina; the stamens are diadelphous, the upper one free, the others united in a sheath; and the pod is flat, with several seeds. There are fifteen species known, none of them of any special interest, although some are rather showy.

PRIESTLEY'S GREEN MATTER. A name given to the green organised crust which occurs at the base of walls or shaded trees and leaves, or in other situations where the direct sunlight does not penetrate. It consists either of the infant condition of certain lichens and algæ, or of minute species of *Palmelleæ*. It has been considered by the advocates of spontaneous generation as mere organisable gelatine, waiting for conditions favourable to its development into plants or animals, or into germs capable of mutations from one kingdom, genus, or species into another. Such notions, however, depend for the most part either on imperfect observations or on imperfect knowledge. [M. J. B.]

PRIEST'S-CROWN. *Taraxacum Densleonis.*

PRIEST'S-PINTLE. *Arum maculatum.*

PRIMARIUS. The first part developed; or the principal division of any organ.

PRIMEROLE, or **PRIMET.** *Primula vulgaris.*

PRIMEROLLE. (Fr.) *Primula vulgaris.*

PRIMEVÈRE. (Fr.) *Primula.* — CAN-

DÉLABRE. *Primula sinensis* or *prænitens.* — EN ARBRE. *Œnothera.*

PRIMIGENIUS, PRIMORDIAL. The earliest part developed in a plant. Primordial leaves are the first leaves produced by the plumule.

PRIMINE. The exterior integument of the ovule.

PRIMORDIAL UTRICLE. The first layer of protoplasm thrown down over the interior of a cell.

PRIMPRINT, or PRIM. *Ligustrum vulgare.*

PRIMROSE. *Primula*: specially, the popular name of *P. vulgaris.* —, BIRD'S-EYE. *Primula farinosa.* —, EVENING, or NIGHT. *Œnothera.* —, PEERLESS. *Narcissus biflorus.*

PRIMULACEÆ. (*Lysimachiæ, Primworts.*) A natural order of corollifloral dicotyledons belonging to Lindley's cortusal alliance of perigynous Exogens. They consist of herbaceous plants, with usually opposite, frequently radical, exstipulate leaves, and flowers on simple or umbellate scapes. Calyx five rarely four-cleft, regular, persistent ; corolla monopetalous ; stamens inserted on the corolla, and opposite its segments ; ovary free, one-celled ; style one. Fruit a capsule ; seeds numerous, attached to a free central placenta. They are natives chiefly of temperate and cold regions in the northern hemisphere ; in the tropics occupying lofty situations. *Primula, Androsace, Glaux, Trientalis, Anagallis,* and *Samolus* occur amongst the genera, which are over thirty in number, and comprise about 250 species. Few of them have any important medicinal properties, though acridity is more or less present. They are cultivated as showy garden annuals and perennials. [J. H. B.]

PRIMULA. A genus of primworts, having the calyx tubular or bell-shaped, and five-toothed ; the corolla salver-shaped, its tube cylindrical, and the mouth open ; and the seed-vessel splitting into ten teeth at the end. The species are herbaceous, and natives of Europe and Asia, some being alpine ; they are rare in North America. The leaves are usually clustered below, and the flowers are in umbels. The name is from the Latin *primus,* 'first,' to indicate the early opening of the flowers in some of the species.

Primroses are deservedly favourites, as many of them are among the finest of our garden plants. In their native localities they fail not to attract special notice, from the little *P. scotica* of our own northern shores, to the more prominent *P. sikkimensis* of the Himalayas, which latter forms a notable feature of the vegetation at from 12,000 to 17,000 feet elevation, and has leaves a foot long, and a tall scape of yellow flowers.

The fine forms of Auricula are derived from the yellow *P. Auricula,* a native of the Swiss Alps. The British species are *P.*

veris the Cowslip, the flowers of which are said to be narcotic ; *P. elatior* the Oxlip, *P. vulgaris* the Primrose, *P. farinosa,* and *P. scotica.* [G. D.]

PRIMWORTS. Lindley's name for the *Primulaceæ.*

PRINCE'S FEATHER. *Amaranthus hypochondriacus* ; also an American name for *Polygonum orientale.*

PRINCEWOOD. A light-veined brown West Indian wood, the produce of *Cordia gerascanthoides* and *Hamelia ventricosa.*

PRINGLEA. The sole representative of this genus of Cruciferæ is *P. antiscorbutica,* a remarkable cabbage-like plant confined to insular Kerguelen's land, and hence often called the Kerguelen's-land Cabbage. The genus is characterised by its oblong seedpods being composed of two convex or boat-shaped valves without a partition between them, and by the seeds, which are numerous and in two rows, being heart-shaped at the bottom, but prolonged into a short beak at the top, and having accumbent cotyledons.

The plant has a thick round root, often three or four feet long, and two inches in diameter, which lies along the ground and bears at its extremity a large cabbage, closely resembling the common cabbage of this country, having a dense white heart and loose green outer leaves ; its flower-stems grow out from below the principal leaves, and are from two to three feet high, with their lower part more or less leafy. The whole plant abounds with essential oil, and when cooked the cabbage tastes like tough mustard and cress. Being a powerful antiscorbutic, it is invaluable to the crews of ships touching at Kerguelen's land. Dr. Hooker says : ' During the whole stay of the Erebus and Terror in Christmas Harbour, daily use was made of this vegetable, either cooked by itself or boiled with the ship's beef, pork, or pea-soup. The essential oil gives a peculiar flavour, which the majority of the officers and the crew did not dislike, and which rendered the herb even more wholesome than the common cabbage ; for it never caused heartburn, nor any of the unpleasant symptoms which that plant sometimes produces.' [A. S.]

PRINOS. The Greek word applied to the holly has been employed to designate a genus of shrubs closely allied thereto. Its flowers are four or six-cleft, with six stamens, usually diœcious or polygamous ; and the fruit is succulent, with six to eight stones. The species are natives of North America, the West Indies, and the warmer parts of Asia. Some of them are evergreen, while others are deciduous ; and some have scarlet berries, while in others they are purple or black. Several are in cultivation in English shrubberies.

The bark of *P. verticillatus* is bitter, and has been employed in the treatment of fever, and, in the form of lotion, as an application in cases of gangrene, &c. The berries are tonic, and sometimes emetic.

The leaves of *P. glaber* are stated to be used in place of those of *Ilex paraguayensis* for the preparation of Maté or Paraguay Tea. [M. T. M.]

PRINSEPIA *utilis* is a prickly shrub common in the most barren places of the Himalaya, forming a genus of *Rosaceæ*, and referred by Royle, who first described it, to the *Chrysobalanaceæ*, because as the fruit enlarges it does so very unequally, and the seed of the style remains at the base as in the true genera of that group; but at the time of flowering the style is terminal, and the genus is in fact nearly allied to *Prunus*. The leaves are small, serrate; the flowers very abundant, growing three or four together in the upper axils, and not unlike those of our blackthorn; the berries are usually very numerous, small, and purple. They are not edible, but the seeds yield a useful oil.

PRIONIUM. A very remarkable South African plant, the Palmiet or Palmet of the Dutch colonists, *P. Palmita* of botanists, is the only representative of this genus of *Juncaceæ*. In its botanical characters it is scarcely distinguishable from *Juncus*, to which, indeed, the plant was once referred. The principal differences consist in the three stigmas being sessile upon the three-celled ovary, in the ovules being confined to the lower half of the cells, and in the seed having a very large club-shaped embryo; but in habit and general aspect it presents more the appearance of one of the *Bromeliaceæ*, having a tuft of sword-shaped channelled leaves, between two and three feet long, about an inch broad at the base, and tapering upwards to a point, with the margins sharply serrated. In South Africa it grows in the beds of rivers, and often increases to such an extent as to choke them. It has a trunk-like partially submerged stem, from five to ten feet in length and about the thickness of a man's arm, principally composed of the remains of the sheathing bases of the leaves; and the branching panicle of flowers is produced from the centre of the tuft of leaves. The leaf-sheaths contain a network of strong black fibre suitable for brush-making, or, when curled, as a substitute for horsehair; the leaves themselves are useful for plaiting and thatching, and also yield very good fibre; while the heart, or cabbage, is eatable. [A. S.]

PRIONOTES. A genus of *Epacridaceæ*, having a five-parted calyx without bracts; a tubular corolla, with an open throat and a five-parted smooth limb; five stamens, the filaments adhering by half their length to the tube; and a five-celled seed-vessel. They are smooth much-branched shrubs, with oval serrated leaves, and single-flowered axillary peduncles. The genus contains only two species—*P. cerinthoides*, a native of Tasmania, and *P. americana*, found in Staten Island. This latter species has also been described under the names of *Lebetanthus* and *Allodape*. [R. H.]

PRIORIA. A large and handsome tree from Central America and some of the West Indian Islands, with pinnate leaves and large terminal panicles of small flowers. It forms a genus of *Leguminosæ* of the suborder *Cæsalpinieæ*, allied to *Copaifera*, but differing in its large more petal-like sepals, and in its large broad flat strongly-veined pod.

PRISCO. The Spanish name for a kind of Peach.

PRISMATIC. Prism-shaped; having several longitudinal angles and intermediate flat faces, as the calyx of *Frankenia pulverulenta*.

PRISMATOCARPUS. Pretty little annuals formerly arranged with *Campanula*, but distinguished by having a rotate corolla, and an elongated prismatical capsule. *P. hybrida*, a plant from six to twelve inches high, has a slightly-branched erect stem, oblong roughish leaves which are wavy and toothed at the edges, and a few terminal solitary flowers which expand only in fine weather. It occurs occasionally in cornfields. [C. A. J.]

PRISMENCHYMA. Prismatical cellular tissue.

PRITZELIA. A genus of *Umbelliferæ*, having five unequal petals, the two smaller in pairs, the fifth large and radiant, all ovate acute and entire; and one half of the fruit usually abortive, the fertile half with ribs, not winged, and no oil-vessels. The only species is an herb, native of the Swan River district in Australia; it is erect, with scattered bristles; the umbels simple, of eight to twelve white or pale rose-coloured flowers. It was named in honour of Pritzel, who wrote on the genus *Anemone*. [G. D.]

PRIVA. A genus of *Verbenaceæ*, containing a few species, natives of America, Africa, and India. They are perennial herbs, with a woody or tuberous rhizome, opposite serrate leaves, and subsessile flowers in axillary and terminal spikes; the calyx is tubular, ventricose, and five-toothed; the corolla tube cylindrical, and the limb unequally quinquefid; stamens four included didynamous, with erect two-celled anthers bifid at the base; and the ovary four-celled with an ovule in each cell. The capsule is surrounded by the enlarged calyx; when mature it dehisces into two cocci which are two-celled, or one-celled by abortion. [W. C.]

PRIVET. *Ligustrum*. —, BARREN. *Rhamnus Alaternus*. —, EGYPTIAN. *Lawsonia alba*, —, GARDEN. *Ligustrum vulgare*.

PROBOSCIDEOUS. Having a hard terminal horn, as the fruit of *Martynia*.

PROCERUS. Very tall.

PROCESS, PROCESSUS. Any extension of the surface.

PROCESSION-FLOWER. *Polygala vulgaris.*

PROCKIA (including *Kellettia*). A genus of tropical shrubs erroneously placed amongst *Flacourtiaceæ,* but belonging really to the *Tiliaceæ. P. Crucis (Kellettia odorata),* a native of the West Indies and the Isthmus of Panama, may be regarded as the type of the genus; and has sweet-scented flowers, reminding one of the odour of linden-blossoms. The plants have a three to five-cleft calyx, no corolla, an indefinite number of stamens, and a dry berry enclosing from four to six nearly round seeds. The leaves are alternate, quite entire or toothed; and the flowers appear in small racemes, and are occasionally unisexual.   [B. S.]

PROCRASSULA. A name applied to some species of *Crassula,* e.g. *C. rubens,* but not generally adopted.   [B. S.]

PROCRIS. A genus of *Urticaceæ,* consisting of undershrubs or shrubs remarkable for their foliage. The leaves are distichous, that is to say, arranged in pairs on opposite sides of the branch and in the same place, but not quite opposite, those of each pair being very unequal in size, the small one inserted a little higher up than the large one. The flowers are small green and axillary, the males in small clusters or cymes, with a five-cleft perianth and five stamens, the females crowded on a globular or club-shaped fleshy receptacle in a small head, which as it ripens assumes somewhat the aspect of a strawberry. There are about half a dozen species known, natives of the East Indies, and of the islands of the Indian and Pacific Oceans.

PROCUMBENT. Lying flat upon the ground.

PROEMBRYO. The reproductive part of a spore; the youngest thallus of a lichen.

PROLIFERATIO. The production of one organ by a very different one; as that of cup-like appendages by leaves, or of branches by flowers.

PROMENÆA. The five species of this genus of orchids were formerly included in *Maxillaria;* but on the revision of that genus some years ago, they were separated under the above name, and characterised as follows:—Sepals spreading; lip three-lobed, crested or much tuberculated at its middle; column short, semiterete; pollen-masses four, sessile in two pairs on an ovate gland. Reichenbach considers it a section of *Zygopetalum.* They are small plants with one or two-leaved pseudo-bulbs, and radical one or rarely two-flowered peduncles.   [A. S.]

PRONAYA. A West Australian genus of *Pittosporaceæ,* containing only one species, *P. elegans,* which has a five-leaved calyx with acuminate sepals; five obovate petals, their apices slightly revolute; five erect stamens with arrow-headed anthers; and a short round style and acute stigma; the fruit being a cylindrical many-seeded berry. They are climbing or erect shrubs, with alternate oblong-linear leaves, and blue flowers in racemes at the ends of the branches.   [R. H.]

PROPAGINES. Deciduous axillary bulbs formed on the stem of some plants.

PROPAGO. The branch that is bent down in the operation of layering.

PROPAGULA. The powder-like grains which constitute the soredia of lichens.

PROPAGULUM. A runner or slender branch proceeding from the surface of the ground, ending in an expanded leaf-bud, and capable of propagation, as in the houseleek. See OFFSET.

PROPHET'S-FLOWER. The name given by Indian Mussulmans to *Arnebia echioides.*

PROPHYSES. The abortive pistillidia of the muscal alliance.

PROSARTES. A genus of *Melanthaceæ,* consisting of downy herbs, inhabiting North America, with the stems divergingly branched above, and having sessile ovate leaves, and drooping greenish-yellow flowers on terminal peduncles, solitary or a few in a simple umbel. The perianth is bell-shaped, with six equal deciduous leaves; filaments long; style undivided, with three short stigmas; berry ovoid or oblong, red with three to six seeds.   [J. T. S.]

PROSCOLLA. A viscid gland on the upper side of the stigma of orchids, to which the pollen-masses become attached.

PROSENCHYMA. Short cellular tissue, having acute extremities.

PROSERPINACA. A small genus of perennial aquatic plants belonging to the *Haloragaceæ,* inhabiting North America. Stems creeping at the base, with alternate serrate or pectinate leaves, and axillary flowers, solitary or two or three together; tube of calyx three-sided, the limb three-parted; petals none; stamens three; stigmas three; fruit bony, three-angled, three-celled, three-seeded.   [J. T. S.]

PROSOPIS. A genus of *Leguminosæ,* of the suborder *Mimoseæ,* consisting of trees or shrubs often armed with hooked prickles or with stout axillary spines, or with both. The small green or yellowish flowers are closely sessile in little heads or spikes, and have the valvular corolla and ten stamens with glandular anthers of *Entada;* but the pod, more or less thickened, and either straight or variously twisted, is indehiscent, with a thick endocarp, and filled in between the seeds with a pulpy succulent or sometimes mealy or pithy substance. The leaves are twice-pinnate, generally rigid and of a glaucous hue, with only one or two pairs of pinnæ, but with a considerable number of leaflets.

There are several species scattered over the warmer regions of America, Asia, and Africa. Amongst them *P. dulcis,* with several varieties often described as distinct species, is widely spread over Central and Southern America, and is sometimes planted for its sweetish succulent pods, used for cattle-feeding, called Algarobo after the Spanish Algarobo or *Ceratonia*, which it resembles in flavour. The *P. spicigera*, in the East Indies, has also a sweet pod there compared to the Algarobo. *P. Stephaniana*, sometimes separated as a distinct genus under the name of *Lagonychium*, is a scrubby prickly bush, common in Syria and Northern Persia, with an irregularly curled or twisted pod. *P. torquata*, and some other South American shrubby species, have a very curious spirally twisted pod like a corkscrew. The pods of several species supply a large quantity of tannin.

P. glandulosa, the Mezquit of Texas and the regions to the west, in some situations forms a tree thirty feet high, and yields excessively hard and durable timber, and likewise affords a large quantity of gum resembling gum-arabic. *P. pubescens*, also a native of Texas, New Mexico, and California, is the Screw-bean or Screw Mezquit of the Americans, and the Tornillo of the Sonora Mexicans, and is so called from the screw-like form of its pods.

PROSTANTHERA. A genus of *Labiatæ*, having the corolla somewhat bell-shaped, the upper lip bifid, the lower three-lobed, the middle lobe largest; and the anthers furnished with spurs beneath. The species are Australian shrubs, with a powerful odour. *P. lasianthos* has been long known in cultivation, having been one of the earliest of the species introduced; its leaves are lanceolate and serrate, the corolla hairy. The name is from the Greek for 'appendage' and 'anther,' in allusion to a prominent character of the genus.   [G. D.]

PROSTEA. A large tree from tropical Africa, proposed by Cambessedes as a genus of *Sapindaceæ*, but now considered as a species of *Deinbollia*.

PROTEACEÆ. (*Proteads*.) A natural order of monochlamydeous dicotyledons belonging to Lindley's daphnal alliance of perigynous Exogens. Perianth four-parted, valvate; stamens four (one sometimes sterile), opposite the segments of the perianth, the anthers bursting lengthwise; ovary superior, one-celled; ovules erect, the style simple, and the stigma undivided; seed exalbuminous. They form shrubs or small trees, with hard dry opposite or alternate exstipulate leaves; and are natives principally of Australia and the Cape of Good Hope. In general they occur in land unfit for cultivation, and seldom attain to a considerable size. In the section *Nucumentaceæ* the fruit is nucumentaceous and indehiscent; and in *Folliculares* it is follicular and dehiscent. *Protea, Persoonia, Grevillea, Hakea, Banksia*, and *Dryandra* are examples of the genera, some forty-six in number, comprising over 600 species. They have no medicinal properties of importance, but present great diversity of appearance—hence the name of the order;

and they are cultivated for their handsome habit, and the peculiarity of their flowers. The clustered cone-like heads of the flowers of *Banksia* are very remarkable. In *Grevillea* the style is at first bent downwards, and the discoid stigma is enclosed within the upper part of the perianth where the anthers are placed; but after the pollen has been scattered the stigma is emancipated, and the style rises upwards. The fruit and seeds of a few plants of the order are eaten, and the wood is used for economical purposes. *Guevina Avellana* yields nuts, which are sold in Chili under the name Avellano. *Protea mellifera* is called Sugar-bush, on account of the honey furnished by its flowers. *Leucadendron argenteum* is the Witteboom of the Cape.   [J. H. B.]

PROTEA. A large chiefly South African genus of *Proteaceæ*, one species, *P. abyssinica*, being a native of Abyssinia. The genus is distinguished by having an elongated unequally divided two-parted calyx, the broader lip bearing three nearly sessile stamens, the narrower lip one; and by the awl-shaped style having a cylindrical acuminate stigma. Fruit a hairy nut containing a single seed. The flowers are terminal or axillary, in large heads six to eight inches in diameter, surrounded in some species by coloured bracts four inches in length and half an inch broad, their apices crowned with long silky hairs. The plants themselves form small trees or shrubs with very variable foliage. In *P. speciosa, P. mellifera, P. longifolia, P. coccinea, P. neriifolia*, the leaves are oblong with a narrow base; in *P. cordata, P. latifolia, P. spectabilis, &c.*, they are heart-shaped; in *P. caffra, P. abyssinica, P. pencillata, &c.*, they are lanceolate; and in *P. pulchella, P. formosa, P. acerosa, P. scabra, &c.*, they are linear and sharp-pointed.   [R. H.]

PROTERANTHOUS. Having leaves which appear before the flowers.

PROTHALLUS. A term intended to indicate the first results of the germination of the spores in the higher cryptogams. In ferns it is a little kidney-shaped or rounded membrane; in adder's-tongues a little bulb-like body; in horsetails a bundle of adnate threads; in *Selaginella, Isoëtes*, and *Marsileaceæ*, a cellular expansion confluent with the spore. In all these cases the new plant springs from the impregnation of a cell in peculiar organs called archegonia. The term Prothallus is not applied to the germinating threads in mosses and liverworts, which produce the plant at once without impregnation, that process resulting in the formation of a capsule, and not of a new plant.   [M. J. B.]

PROTOCOCCUS. A genus of chlorospermous *Algæ*, consisting of plants composed of a single cell propagated by the organisation of the endochrome, which is repeatedly divided into four, the individual spores for a time moving about by means of flagelliform appendages. The species collected under the name do not probably present the same structure as the Red Snow, and one or two allied *Algæ*. [M. J. B.]

PROTOPHYLLUM. The first leaf of a cryptogamic plant after germination.

PROTOPHYTA. A name given by Perleb to the simpler cryptogams, as being the most imperfect plants, and the first efforts of nature in the production of the vegetable kingdom. [M. J. B.]

PROTOPHYTOLOGY. That part of Botany which treats of fossil plants.

PROTOPLASM. The matter which is deposited over the inside walls of a cell subsequent to the formation of the cell itself.

PROTOSPORE. As the apparent spores in *Pucciniei* are not the true reproductive bodies, but merely preparatory organs analogous to a prothallus, and as the name of prothallus cannot conveniently be applied to them, the term protospore is proposed as a convenient name. [M. J. B.]

PRUD'HOMME. (Fr.) *Salvia verbenaca.*

PRUINA (adj. PRUINOSE). A coarse granular secretion found on the surface of some plants.

PRUMNOPITYS. A name proposed by Philippi for the *Podocarpus andina* from Chili, but not founded on characters of sufficient importance to justify its separation as a distinct genus.

PRUNE. The dried fruits of certain varieties of the Plum, *Prunus domestica*. —, WILD. A Cape of Good Hope name for *Sapindus Pappea.*

PRUNEATIER. (Fr.) *Prunus insititia.*

PRUNELET. A liquor made from Sloes or Wild Plums.

PRUNELLA. A genus of herbaceous plants belonging to the *Labiatæ*, distinguished by a two-lipped calyx, the upper lip truncate three-toothed, the lower bifid ; stamens ascending ; style bifid. The species are common wayside weeds throughout the temperate zone in both hemispheres. *P. vulgaris*, or Common Selfheal, is a plant of frequent occurrence in the British Isles, growing to the height of a few inches, of a straggling habit, and bearing stalked ovate leaves, and dense spiked heads of deep purple flowers, with a pair of leaves at the base of each head. Selfheal was highly commended by the old herbalists for its vulnerary properties, but is now held in no repute. French, *Brunelle* ; German, *Prunelle*. [C. A. J.]

PRUNELLIER. (Fr.) *Prunus spinosa.*

PRUNES. (Fr.) The fruits of the Plum-tree. — NOIRES D'AMÉRIQUE. *Spondias.* — VIERGES. *Comocladia.*

PRUNE-TREE of the West Indies. *Prunus occidentalis.*

PRUNIER. (Fr.) *Prunus.* — ÉPINEUX D'AMÉRIQUE. *Ximenia.* — ICAQUE. *Chrysobalanus.* — JAUNE D'ŒUF. *Lucuma.*

PRUNUS. A Latin epithet borrowed from the Greek word signifying Plum, and used to designate the genus whose species furnish that fruit. It is included in the *Drupaceæ*, and consists of trees and shrubs, natives of temperate regions in both hemispheres, many of them spiny in the wild condition, but losing their thorns when cultivated. The flowers are in umbel-like clusters, or sometimes solitary, produced before or after the leaves ; and the margins of the young leaves are rolled inwards. The fruit is covered with mealy bloom or velvet-like down ; the stone is pointed at one or both ends, and furrowed along the edge.

P. spinosa is the Common Sloe or Blackthorn, whose white blossoms are the ornament of our hedges in March and April. The leaves are elliptical, produced after the flowers, and the branches dark-purple in colour (whence the name Blackthorn), and terminating in a sharp spine. The roots are creeping, and throw up numerous suckers, on which account it is ill-adapted for a hedge-plant ; these suckers, however, grow into upright branches, much sought after for walking-sticks. The wood is of no great value, but the bark has been used as a febrifuge. The leaves are used extensively to adulterate tea ; the fruits are globose, dark-purple in colour, and very sour and rough in taste. It is said that they are employed in the manufacture of a fictitious portwine ; by the poor they are made into a palatable preserve. This shrub is the badge of the clan M'Quarrie.

P. insititia, the Bullace, is sometimes distinguished from the foregoing by its narrower leaves, more downy on the under-surface ; the flowers not solitary, but produced in pairs ; and the fruits larger and less rough to the palate. They are extensively used in this country. A variety occurs with yellowish fruit, which latter are sold in London as White Damsons.

P. Cocomilia, a native of Calabria, yields a bark which is considered a specific remedy in the fevers of that country. The kernel of *P. brigantiaca* yields an oil known in France as Huile des Marmottes, which is used instead of almond or olive oil. The fruit of *P. myrobolana* is used in India to dye black. The fruits of some of the cultivated varieties of *P. domestica*, dried in the sun or by artificial means, are known as Prunes. Those for table-use are from the St. Catherine or Reine Claude varieties. Another esteemed sort takes its name from Guimaraes, a village of Portugal, where they are principally prepared. Those intended for medicinal purposes are obtained from the St. Julien Plum. Prunes are used as mild laxatives ; the fresh fruit when ripe is also slightly laxative, but eaten in moderation it is not so injurious as is usually supposed. The fruit of the Apricot, *P. Armeniaca*, is used in the East as a remedy in fevers. *P. sibirica* is like the common Apricot tree, but smaller. It blooms earlier, and when in flower is highly ornamental. Among the species of *Prunus* in cultivation for ornamental purposes, there is a small greenhouse shrub, which bears in spring a profusion of double white blossoms. This (*P. sinensis*) is deservedly a great favourite.　　[M. T. M.]

The Apricot, *P. Armeniaca*, forms a tree twenty to thirty feet high, with a round head, heart-shaped or ovate glossy leaves, and sessile flowers, with roundish white petals, appearing before the leaves. The fruit is roundish, pubescent, orange or brownish-orange, with a more or less deep orange-coloured flesh: the kernel in some is bitter, as in the well-known variety called Moorpark; in others, like the Breda, it is as sweet as a nut. The Apricot, sometimes considered as the type of a distinct genus *Armeniaca*, obtained its name from having been considered indigenous to Armenia; but it also grows wild in the north but more especially in the middle of that chain (Pallas, *Fl. Ross.*) Reynier found it in the oases of Upper Egypt, and Munby in Algeria, both wild and cultivated; but Alph. Decandolle remarks that the trees in these cases were probably naturalisations from cultivated varieties.

The Apricot was the *Mela armeniaka* of the Greeks, the *Malum-armeniacum* and the *Præcocia* of the Romans. It does not appear to have been known to the Greeks in the time of Theophrastus, for according to him the only tree which put forth its flowers before the leaves was the almond; therefore he could have known neither the peach nor the apricot, for both of them do so. Dioscorides, 300 years later, in the beginning of the first century, mentions the Apricot under the name of *Armeniaca*,' and which the Romans call *Præcocia*.' Pliny, writing about the same time, states that the *Præcocia* ripens in summer, and had been introduced into Italy about thirty years. The modern Greeks named the Apricot *prichochehia* and *berichochchia*; the Italians generally *albicocca* or *albicoceo*, according to Alph. Decandolle, who observes that 'all these and other modern names have certainly the appearance of being derived from *Armeniaca*, from *Præcocia*, or sometimes from *Arbor præcox*.' The French name *Abricot*, the German *Apricose*, and our Apricot are doubtless corruptions of the classical appellation. By our early authors on Horticulture, it was formerly written *a-precoke*, which is closer to the original than our present name for this fruit. The Apricot tree is said to have been introduced from Italy into England in 1524, by Woolf, gardener to Henry VIII. The varieties are somewhat numerous; but those most worthy of cultivation may be comprised in a dozen sorts. These may include the Large Early, Royal, Moorpark, and Turkey for walls, and the Breda for standards; from which, although not large, the fruit is rich and excellent for the confectioner, forming, in the opinion of many, the richest of all preserves. Its kernels are sweet, as are likewise those of the Musch-Musch, a variety grown in the oases of Upper Egypt, where the fruit is dried and forms an article of commerce. Various sweet-kerneled varieties have also

been obtained of late years from Syria; and their kernels, like those of the Breda or Amande Aveline, may be eaten like filberts.

The cultivated Plum-tree, *P. domestica*, grows to the height of fifteen to twenty feet, its branches generally spineless, but by no means uniformly so; therefore there is no real distinction between this and the *P. insititia* of some botanists. In *P. domestica* the leaves are simple ovate or lanceolate, alternate stipulate deciduous, convolute when unfolding; and the flowers are solitary or in pairs, white, appearing generally before the leaves. The fruit is round oblong or obovate, fleshy, glabrous, and covered with a glaucous bloom; the stone compressed, acute at both ends.

The Plum is a native of the Caucasus and Asia Minor, naturalised at least in Greece, and in most temperate regions of Europe. The various common names which it anciently had indicate, says Alph. Decandolle, that it had a very extended primitive existence in Europe and in Western Asia. The great majority of the Latin and Germanic names are derived from *proune* of the Greeks: the Sclavonian languages have derived the name from quite a different root: in Bohemia it is called *Sliva*, and *Slivonik* in Russia; by the Tartars and Turks, *Erik* and *Uruk*; the Celtic words *Eiran* and *Eirin* are employed by the Welsh, and these are not very different from the Turkish and Tartarian. The Greek name *kokkumelea* appears to have left no trace in modern languages. Cultivated varieties, according to Pliny, were brought from Syria into Greece, and thence into Italy. 'Several varieties of the garden plum,' says Professor Targioni, 'were introduced from the East since the days of Cato, who was born 232 years before the Christian era. Such was, for instance, the Damson or Damascene Plum, which came from Damascus in Syria, and was very early cultivated by the Romans. Muratori says that the Italian name for the plum, *Susine*, was derived from Susa, in Persia, whence it had been introduced into Italy. But the most ancient Latin name was *Prunus*, and with the Greeks *Coccymela*.' From all these statements it may be certainly inferred that the cultivated plum existed at a very early period in Western Europe, where it had sown itself abundantly, as it does at the present day. Even in Britain seedling plums are frequently met with in our hedges, and occasionally some of them are found worthy of cultivation. Formerly, however, our finest varieties were introduced from France and Italy, and among them one, the quality of which has not been excelled—the well-known Green Gage. In France this is known by the name of Reine Claude, from having been introduced to that country by the queen of Francis I. It was brought to this country by one of the Gage family, after whom it was called, the name by which it was obtained from the Chartreuse at Paris having been lost. This excellent variety occasionally reproduces itself from the stone. Many varieties appear to have been introduced from France centuries ago. The Orleans Plum is supposed to have been brought over when the English held possession of that French city *temp.* Henry V. There are now more than 300 sorts, and their number is still increasing.

A few of the finest for dessert are the Green Gage, Purple Gage or Reine Claude Violette, Jefferson, Kirke's, Royal Hâtive, Washington, and Coe's Golden Drop. Many others, however, possess great excellence. Some are employed for making preserves, and others dried form the Prunes of the shops. The Prunes which come from Brignoles, in the south of France, are prepared from a variety called the Perdrigon. The neighbourhood of Tours is celebrated for the quantity of Prunes which it furnishes. The German Prunes are prepared from an oblong purple variety called Zwetsche, or Quetsche, a Slavonian name originally, which is spelled variously on the Continent. Damsons are plums well-known and much used in this country for preserves, and so are the small round nearly wild sorts called Bullaces.

P. myrobolana, which is named Cherry Plum, probably from its colour, is a species from Canada. It flowers very early, and bears a medium-sized heart-shaped fruit, in great abundance and of tolerably good quality, but not equal to the European varieties. [E. T.]

PRURIENS. Causing an itching sensation.

PSALLIOTA. A subgenus of *Agaricus*, belonging to the series with purple-black spores, amongst which it is distinguished by the presence of a ring, which adheres to the stem. It contains many of our best esculent *Fungi*, especially *Agaricus campestris* and the allied mushrooms. Though capable of enduring cold, some of the species flourish where the temperature is high, provided there is sufficient moisture in the air. [M. J. B.]

PSAMMA. A genus of grasses belonging to the tribe *Arundineæ*, described by Steudel under *Calamagrostis*, and by other authors under *Ammophila*. It is the well-known Bent-grass of the sandhills near the sea-shores of Britain. [D. M.]

PSAMMISIA. The species of this genus of *Vacciniaceæ* are American shrubs with large leathery ribbed leaves, and axillary inflorescence in the form of stout corymb-like racemes, the pedicels of which are thickened in the upper part, jointed, and provided with a small scale-like bract. The limb of the calyx is leathery and cup-shaped; the corolla tubular; and the upper part of the anthers attached at the back to the filaments. *P. Hookeriana* is in cultivation under the name of *Thibaudia pichinchensis*. Most authors consider the species of the present genus to form part of the genus *Thibaudia*. The name is derived from Psammis, King of Egypt! [M. T. M.]

PSEUDANTHUS. A name which has been applied both to a genus of *Amaranthaceæ*, and to one of *Euphorbiaceæ*.

PSEUDATHYRIUM. A name proposed for *Polypodium alpestre* on account of its close resemblance to the *Athyrium* or Lady Fern. [T. M.]

PSEUDEPIDENDRUM *spectabile*. A Central American orchid, erected into a genus by Reichenbach, but afterwards abandoned and now called *Epidendrum pseudepidendrum* by the same author. The genus was characterised by having two-edged somewhat falcate pollen-masses, the two outer much larger than the two inner, with a deeply three-toothed caudicle turned back upon them. It is a tall erect-stemmed plant, with sheathed leaves, and a panicle bearing a very few large green flowers with a scarlet lip. [A. S.]

PSEUDERIOPSIS. One of the many genera of orchids proposed and afterwards abandoned by Reichenbach. The sole species referred to it is a British Guiana plant, which is now said to be identical with *Eriopsis biloba* of Lindley. [A. S.]

PSEUDIOSMA. The name applied to a small tree, native of Cochin China, and forming a genus of *Xanthoxylaceæ*. The leaves are alternate, entire; the flowers yellow, in terminal panicles. Sepals five, spreading; petals five, larger than the sepals; anthers five, sessile; ovary five-lobed, girt by a thick disk; style as long as the anthers; stigma simple; follicles five, stalked, one-seeded. [M. T. M.]

PSEUDO. In Greek compounds = spurious.

PSEUDOBULB. A stem having the appearance of a bulb, but not its structure, seen in the thickened above-ground stem of many orchids.

PSEUDOCENTRUM *macrostachyum*. A Peruvian terrestrial orchid, forming a genus allied to *Pelexia* in *Neotteæ*; but nothing is at present known of it except the flowers, which are borne in a dense cylindrical spike, and have the front sepal small lanceolate and spreading, and the two lateral ones large triangular and excessively produced at their base, forming a long curved sheath, within which lies the sessile hastate three-lobed lip, the middle lobe of which is as long as the sheath, narrow and channelled. [A. S.]

PSEUDOCOSTATE. Having the curved and external veins, both or either, in a reticulated leaf, confluent into a line parallel with the margin, as in many *Myrtaceæ*.

PSEUDOCOTYLEDONEÆ. A name applied to some of the higher cryptogams, from a notion that there is some analogy between the results of germination and cotyledons. It is essential to cotyledons that they should exist in the embryo ready formed. False cotyledons must be aftergrowths on the axis, and it is clear that the organs in question are of such a different character that the name is wholly inapplicable. [M. J. B.]

PSEUDO-GYRATE. Falsely ringed; when an elastic ring is confined to the vertex of the spore-cases of Ferns.

PSEUDO-HYMENIUM. A covering of sporidia resembling the hymenium of fungals.

PSEUDO-MONOCOTYLEDONOUS. Having two or more cotyledons consolidated into a single mass, as in the Horse-Chestnut.

PSEUDO-PARASITES. False parasites, including those plants which only attack dead tissues, as many Fungi. Such plants are pseudo-parasitic. See EPIPHYTES.

PSEUDO-PERIDIUM, PSEUDO-PERITHECIUM. A covering of sporidia, resembling the péridium.

PSEUDO-PYRENIUM. The perithecium of certain fungals.

PSEUDOSCORDUM. A genus of *Liliaceæ* sometimes called *Nothoscordum*, differing from *Allium* in having the style terminal, not contained in a central canal, and the ovules several in each cell. [J. T. S.]

PSEUDO-STROMA. The receptacle or perithecium of certain fungals.

PSIADIA. A genus of *Compositæ* of the tribe *Asteroideæ*, consisting of a small number of species natives of Mauritius or of Madagascar, all shrubby and mostly glutinous, with alternate coarsely toothed or entire leaves, and small flower-heads in compound corymbs. The involucral bracts are imbricate, and the ray-florets ligulate and numerous, but usually so small as to make the head appear discoid. The pappus consists of simple bristles. *P. glutinosa* is frequently cultivated in Continental botanic gardens.

PSIDIUM. A most extensive but exclusively tropical American genus of *Myrtaceæ*, consisting of trees or shrubs with opposite entire feather-veined leaves, and large white flowers, growing either singly or a few together on axillary stalks, and producing fleshy berries crowned with the remains of the calyx-lobes, and containing numerous small hard kidney or horse-shoe-shaped seeds nestling in pulp. The flowers have an egg-shaped calyx, with the lower part cohering with the ovary, and the upper free part entire and closed in the bud, and at length coming off entire or bursting into five or rarely four lobes; four or five free petals; numerous stamens; and a two or more celled ovary with many ovules in each cell.

P. Guaiava, the Guava tree, produces the well-known Guava fruits of tropical countries. It is a small tree, seldom more than fifteen or twenty feet in height, and has downy four-sided branchlets; egg-shaped or oblong short-stalked leaves, covered with soft down underneath, and with the principal veins very prominent; and axillary short stalks bearing one or three flowers, each about an inch in diameter. Several varieties of this species are known, the two most common, distinguished by the shape of the fruit, being sometimes described as distinct species. They are: 1, *pomiferum*, with a round apple-shaped fruit; and 2, *pyriferum*, with pear-shaped fruit. Both are natives of tropical America and the West Indies, from whence they have been introduced into and become naturalised in India and other Eastern countries; and they also flourish and produce very good fruit in hothouses in this country. Their fruits have a thin bright-yellow rind, and are filled with a pulpy yellowish or red flesh, which has a pleasantly acid-sweet flavour; but the pear-shaped variety is sweeter and more agreeable in a raw state than the apple-shaped, though both make a very good jelly or preserve. Guavas are of too perishable a nature to permit of their being brought to this country in their natural state; but considerable quantities of guava-jelly and guava-cheese are brought by the West India mail-steamers. The wood of the Guava-tree has a fine close grain, and has been experimented upon as a substitute for boxwood for engraving purposes; but it proved too soft to stand the pressure of printing, especially when engraved with fine lines.

P. Cattleyanum, the Purple Guava, though originally brought to Europe from China, is most probably a native of Brazil. It has smooth round branchlets, smooth leathery leaves, and short one-flowered stalks. The fruits—which are produced in great abun-

Psidium Cattleyanum.

dance, and are readily distinguished from the common Guavas by their deep claret-coloured pitted rind—are filled with a juicy pale flesh of a very agreeable acid-sweet flavour. [A. S.]

PSILOCARYA. A genus of cyperaceous plants belonging to the tribe *Rhynchosporeæ*. The inflorescence is in many-flowered spikelets; scales all fertile, imbricated on every side, membranaceous or papery; stamens two, with long persistent filaments; styles cleft in two. Steudel describes thirteen species, which are all American. [D. M.]

PSILOS. In Greek compounds = thin.

PSILOTUM. A genus of clubmosses with a three-sided stem, three-celled axillary capsules, and small bristle-pointed leaves. The stem is erect and dichotomous. The only species, *P. triquetrum*, grows on the trunks of trees in tropical or equable climates, and extends through Brazil and Central America to the Southern United States. It bears cultivation well, and is not uncommon in hothouses. The spores burst when placed in water, and emit a cloud of microscopic particles. [M. J. B.]

PSILURUS. A genus of grasses belonging to the tribe *Rottboelleæ*. The inflorescence is in rounded slender spikes; spikelets two-flowered, the lowest flower sessile and hermaphrodite, the upper stalked and minute; glume one, very small, oval, and membranous; pales two, membranaceous, the lowest one-nerved with a short awn at the point, the upper a little longer, and two-keeled; stamen one; stigmas two. Only one species is described, *P. nardoides*, which is an annual grass, native of the south of Europe. [D. M.]

PSOPHOCARPUS. A genus of *Leguminosæ*, founded upon an East Indian and Mauritius plant previously referred to *Dolichos*, and two others from Western Africa have since been added to it. They are tuberous-rooted herbs, with herbaceous twining stems, trifoliate leaves, and racemes with a few flowers at the end. These have an unequally two-lipped calyx, with the upper lip two-lobed and rather larger than the lower, which is three-parted; a papilionaceous corolla, with a roundish reflexed upper petal spurred at the base but destitute of callosities; and ten stamens, nine of which are united and one free. The pods are furnished with four thin longitudinal wings at the angles, and contain from four to eight roundish seeds. *P. tetragonolobus*, also called *Dolichos tetragonolobus*, is grown in India for the sake of its eatable seeds. [A. S.]

PSORALEA. A very large and most extensively dispersed genus of *Leguminosæ*, consisting of nearly a hundred species, spread over most parts of the American continent, and also found in great abundance at the Cape of Good Hope, more sparingly in Australia, and still more so in Asia. The genus is named from the Greek word *psoraleos*, 'scurfy,' in reference to the plants belonging to it being for the most part sprinkled all over or roughened with glandular dots or wart-like points. They are chiefly small shrubs or perennial herbaceous plants, sometimes with tuberous farinaceous roots, and usually have compound leaves composed of from three to five leaflets with the stipules adhering to the stalk, though occasionally the leaves are simple; and their blue white or purple flowers are borne in short spikes or racemes. The

calyx is five-cleft and persistent, the tube covered with glands, and the lowest lobe longer than the others; and nine of the ten stamens are joined together, the tenth being generally free but sometimes joined to the others at the bottom, and the five alternate anthers often imperfect. The one-seeded pods are seldom longer than the calyx, thick and often wrinkled, and do not split open at maturity.

P. corylifolia is an East Indian erect herbaceous plant growing about two feet in height, having simple egg-shaped leaves, slightly heart-shaped at the base, and pale bluish flowers in dense short spike-like racemes on long axillary stalks. The pods, which are very small, flat and oval or kidney-shaped, have an aromatic taste, and are employed medicinally by the native doctors in India; they also yield an oil, and under the name of Bawchan-seeds have been sent to this country for pressing.

P. esculenta is a native of Wisconsin, Missouri, and other parts of North-west America, where its tuberous roots, known as Indian or Prairie turnips (Pomme Blanche or Pomme de Prairie), form a great part of the food of the indigenous population, but when boiled are rather insipid. It is a hairy herbaceous plant about a foot high, with leaves composed of five leaflets disposed in a palmate manner, and roundish heads of blue flowers.

In Chili the leaves of *P. glandulosa*, there called Culen, are used as a substitute for tea under the name of Jesuit's Tea; but their infusion is not very aromatic, and appears to be valued more for its medicinal properties than as an agreeable beverage, being a powerful vermifuge and likewise a stomachic; they are also used by the Chilians for making poultices to apply to wounds, and an infusion of the root is emetic and purgative. The plant has been introduced into the Mauritius, and has there lately acquired a reputation as a remedy for diseases of the respiratory organs. It forms a dwarfish shrub, with trifoliate leaves, and long-stalked racemes of striped bluish and white flowers. [A. S.]

PSYCHINE. A genus of *Cruciferæ*, from Mediterranean Africa, containing a hispid annual, with oblong toothed leaves, those of the stem amplexicaul, and racemes of white violet-veined flowers opposite the leaves, with leaf-like bracts. The pod is triangular, laterally compressed, with a very narrow septum and a beak formed by the persistent style, which is four-sided at the base, and filiform at the tip; valves keeled, winged at the apex; seeds numerous, with folded cotyledons. [J. T. S.]

PSYCHOTRIA. The etymology of this name is somewhat obscure: the generally received opinion is, that it is derived from Greek *psyche*, 'the soul,' 'life,' in allusion to the active properties possessed by some of the species. Botanically it is applied to a genus of *Cinchonaceæ*, consisting of shrubs found in tropical countries, especially in America. The more important characters of the genus are: a nearly entire or slightly five-toothed calyx limb ; a funnel-shaped corolla with a regular tube, and a spreading or reflected five-lobed limb; five stamens, concealed within the corolla or slightly protruding; and a fleshy fruit surmounted by the calyx, and having two smooth or ribbed stones. The flowers are mostly in terminal panicles. Several species are in cultivation ; the flowers of most of them are white or yellowish, and of no great beauty. One is said to grow upon trees as an epiphyte. Emetic properties are assigned to the roots of some of the species, especially to those of *P emetica*, a Peruvian plant, which furnishes what is called Striated Ipecacuanha, a substance less valuable than the true ipecacuanha. The roots of *P. tinctoria* and *P. sulphurea* have been used as dyes. [M. T. M.]

PTÆROXYLON *utile*, a small timber tree about thirty feet high, a native of the Cape of Good Hope, is the only plant belonging to this genus of *Sapindaceæ*. It has pinnate leaves, composed of five or seven pairs of thick unequal-sided entire leaflets, with or without a terminal one ; and axillary bunches of flowers, which are unisexual by abortion, and have a calyx of four sepals, four petals without appendages, four free smooth stamens, and a two-celled flattened ovary, bearing two distinct or united styles, and two round-headed stigmas ; and its ripe fruit contains two winged seeds, one in each cell. The timber of *Ptæroxylon* is handsome, durable, and takes a good polish, and is used at the Cape for making articles of furniture and agricultural utensils. It is called Niesbout or Sneezewood by the Dutch colonists, from its possessing the property of causing the sawyers to sneeze violently when employed upon it. On account of its not being much affected by moisture, it is used for mill-work and bridges; and it is said to burn readily, even when green. [A. S.]

PTARMICA. A genus proposed for the *Achillea Ptarmica*, and some other large-flowered chiefly alpine species, which differ from the others in some very trifling characters.

PTELEA. The Greek name for the elm, and applied by Linnæus to a genus of shrubs or small trees, natives of North America and Asia, and included in *Xanthoxylaceæ*. It may be briefly characterised by its monœcious flowers, which have a four to five-parted calyx, four to five petals, and in the male flowers as many stamens ; in the female flowers, the two to three-celled ovary is placed on a short stalk. The fruit is turgid in the centre, and surrounded by a broad membranous wing, like that of the fruits of the elm.

P. trifoliata, the Shrubby Trefoil of North America, is frequently grown in shrubberies in this country. Its leaves are of a rich green colour, with three unequal leaflets. In autumn these leaves assume a fine yellow tinge. The flowers are greenish, arranged in corymbs less conspicuous than the curious winged fruits, which ripen in October. In Canada the young green shoots are used as an anthelmintic in the form of infusion. The fruits are bitter and aromatic, and have been used as a substitute for hops. [M. T. M.]

PTERANDRA. A genus of *Malpighiaceæ*, consisting of tropical American shrubs, with large stipules in the axils of the leaves. Flowers pink, variously disposed towards the end of the branches, their stalks jointed and provided with two small bracts, five-parted; petals nearly regular, stamens ten, all fertile, one or sometimes both sides of the anthers expanded into a crest-like appendage—whence the name of the genus ; ovaries three, slightly adherent ; styles three. [M. T. M.]

PTERIDOGRAPHIA. That part of Botany which treats of Ferns.

PTERIDOPHYLLUM. A genus of *Fumariaceæ*, comprising a stemless herb from Japan, with a thick præmorse rhizome, pectinate-pinnatisect stalked leaves with scaly petioles and numerous linear-oblong subfalcate segments (the terminal one three-lobed), and racemose flowers. Calyx two-sepaled, deciduous ; petals four, the two outer ones folded, the inner plain ; stamens four; ovary orbicular, compressed, one-celled ; style filiform, with a capitate two-lobed stigma. [J. T. S.]

PTERIS. A genus of polypodiaceous ferns typical of the *Pterideæ*. It is known by having linear marginal sori, on a continuous linear receptacle, and covered by a membranaceous indusium of the same form, combined with free veins. The plants vary greatly in size and form, some having pedate and others decompound fronds ; and they are distributed over the temperate and tropical regions, though most plentiful in the latter. In the true species the vernation is terminal ; but in *P. aquilina*, the Common Bracken, not only is the vernation lateral, but the indusium is double ; that is to say, the spore-cases lie between two—an inner and an outer membrane. Hence it is not improbable that this species will have to be eventually removed. See PÆSIA. The Bracken is the badge of the Robertsons. [T. M.]

PTERIS. In Greek compounds = a wing or membranous expansion.

PTEROCARPUS. With the exception of one South African species, this genus of *Leguminosæ* is confined within the tropics, but has representatives in Asia, Africa, and America. The fifteen described species are all trees, frequently of large size, and have alternate pinnate leaves with alternate or irregularly opposite leaflets, and simple racemes or loose panicles of showy yellow flowers, which have a five-toothed somewhat two-lipped calyx narrowed or top-shaped at the base, and a papilionaceous corolla with glabrous petals, and contain ten stamens united into a sheath, which is split on the upper or both sides (sometimes nine are united and one free), and an ovary with from two to six ovules. The pods are flat, nearly round or oval, and somewhat one-sided—usually thick and hard in the middle or seed-bearing part, but more or less attenuated into a thin wing at the edges all round ; and they contain from one to three seeds separated by thin woody partitions.

Gum Kino is obtained from trees of this genus: in India from *P. Marsupium*, and in Africa from *P. erinaceus*. Both these species are large trees, affording valuable hard timber ; that of the former being extensively used in India in the manufacture of cotton-gins, while that of the latter is known in Western Africa as Rosewood. Kino is obtained by making V-shaped incisions in the bark, from which the juice exudes and hardens into a brittle mass, easily broken into little angular shining fragments of a bright ruby colour. It is highly astringent, and is used medicinally in diarrhœa, &c., and in India for dyeing and tanning. Another species, *P. santalinus*, yields the deep red dyewood known as Red Saunders, large quantities of which are annually exported from India. [A. S.]

PTEROCARYA. A small genus of *Juglandaceæ*, containing Caucasian, Chinese, and Japanese species, all of them trees with pinnate leaves composed of about a dozen pairs of leaflets. It is distinguished by its two-winged indehiscent fruits.　　[A. S.]

PTEROCEPHALUS. A genus of *Dipsacaceæ*, founded on the *Scabiosa plumosa* and some others from the Mediterranean region, in which the calyx when in fruit is converted into a pappus of numerous soft feathery bristles.

PTEROCOCCUS. A genus of *Polygonaceæ*, from Southern Russia and Siberia, distinguished from *Calligonum* and *Calliphysa* by having the four-angled nut with each angle produced into a double papery or leathery wing, and by being smooth between the wings. They are leafless shrubs, with articulated branches, ochreate stipules, and flowers with a five-parted coloured perianth. *P. aphyllus*, or *Calligonum Pallasia*, has suborbicular toothed wings to the fruit, and reddish flowers. The roots when pounded are said to furnish a mucilaginous edible substance resembling gum tragacanth.　　[J. T. S.]

PTERODISCUS *speciosus*, the only known representative of this genus of *Pedaliaceæ*, is an herbaceous plant with tuberous roots, confined to Southern Africa, and now an inmate of our gardens. The leaves are opposite, oblong sinuato-dentate, the flowers axillary and of a purple colour, which renders them very ornamental. The calyx is small and five-cleft, the corolla funnel-shaped with a five-lobed border ; the stamens are four, the stigma bilabiate, and the fruit an indehiscent capsule, round, compressed, with two broad wings at the edge, small tubercules at the surface, and two or apparently six-celled, two of the cells containing isolated pendulous seeds. [B. S.]

PTEROGLOSSIS. The name of a Chilian perennial constituting a genus of *Scrophulariaceæ*. The stems are numerous, slender, branched ; leaves pinnately divided ; flower-stalks axillary in loose panicles ; calyx tubular, ten-nerved ; corolla funnel-shaped, contracted below, dilated above, the limb unequally five-lobed and somewhat two-lipped ; stamens four, filaments dilated ; anthers notched at the top, and opening by a chink at the notch ; ovary on a short stalk surrounded at the base by a fleshy lobed disk; the style dilated at its upper portion and the stigma notched, with a viscid gland in the notch, keeled on the upper, flat on the lower surface, the margins dilated into broad membranaceous wings that overlap the two lower stamens ; capsule two-valved, concealed by the persistent calyx.　　　[M. T. M.]

PTEROPHYLLA. A genus of *Cunoniaceæ*, forming a tree from the Moluccas, with pinnate leaves, and terminal erect aggregated spike-like racemes. Calyx four-cleft, deciduous ; petals four; stamens eight ; ovary woolly, two-celled ; style very short, incurved.　　　[J. T. S.]

PTEROPODIUM. A doubtful genus of *Bignoniaceæ*, probably identical with *Jacaranda*, consisting of two South American species, trees with pinnated or bipinnated leaves, and large panicles of purple flowers. The calyx is bell-shaped or tubular, the corolla funnel-shaped, the stamens four in number, with the rudiment of a fifth, the anthers glabrous ; fruit unknown. [B. S.]

PTEROSPERMUM. A genus of *Sterculiaceæ*, of the tribe *Helictereæ*, in which the ovary is borne on a stalk closely combined with the staminal column, and the anthers are stipitate as in *Helicteres* ; but the anther-cells are linear and parallel, and the capsule is almost woody, containing numerous winged seeds. There are about fourteen species, tropical Asiatic trees or shrubs, with more or less of a scaly or stellate tomentum. The leaves are alternate coriaceous entire or toothed, and usually very oblique. The flowers are on short axillary peduncles, usually large white and fragrant, sometimes attaining several inches in length, although their beauty is diminished by a want of breadth and expansion.

PTEROSPORA. A genus of fir-rapes, distinguished by having its calyx five-parted, the corolla with a five-toothed border, and the seeds numerous, small, each with a wing-like membrane. *P. Andromeda* is the only species, an annual with flowers like *Andromeda*, and the whole plant dotted with viscid hairs ; it is a native of Canada. The name is indicative of the *winged seed*, a prominent characteristic of the genus.　　　[G. D.]

PTEROSTEGIA. A genus belonging to the order *Polygonaceæ* and tribe *Eriogoneæ*, in which the flowers are enclosed in an involucre. It differs from others in the involucre being formed of two leaves, which enclose one flower. There are two known species, both natives of California—*P. drymarioides* and *P. macroptera*. The first is a smooth trailing much-branched annual herb, with opposite stalked leaves having rounded or bilobed blades, and small involucres single in the axils of the leaves, their margins crested with slender teeth. In *P. macroptera* the involucral leaves enlarge as the fruit ripens, so that when mature they are half an inch across. In both the involucral leaves are formed like the valves of an oyster-shell. [A. A. B.]

PTEROSTYRAX. The name applied to a Japanese shrub, constituting a genus of *Styracaceæ*. The shrub is covered with stellate hairs, has sharply serrated ovate leaves, and bears axillary and terminal panicles of flowers. The tube of the calyx is adherent for a short distance to the ovary; the stamens are ten, five longer than the rest, all partially united below into a tube; the ovary contains numerous ovules, arranged in two rows; the style being awl-shaped, jointed above the base, and the stigma somewhat five-lobed. Fruit dry, somewhat woody, partially adherent to the tube of the calyx, the limb of which is expanded, and forms, as it were, five wings to the fruit, whence the name of the genus. [M. T. M.]

PTEROZONIUM. A genus of ferns belonging to the *Gymnogrammeæ*, and separated indeed from *Gymnogramma* itself, where some botanists still retain it. The only species, *P. reniforme*, a South American species, of dwarf stature, with simple reniform coriaceous fronds, has the sori

Pterozonium reniforme.

placed in so remarkable a position, that it has been made the type of a distinct genus. The sori are linear, and radiato-furcate, but laterally approximate, so that they soon become confluent into a broad horseshoe-shaped band on the back of the reniform frond. This confluence of the contiguous lines of spore-cases indicates a considerable approach towards the structure of *Platyloma*. [T. M.]

PTERYGIUM. Any wing or membranous expansion of seeds.

PTERYGODIUM. A genus of Cape orchids, small terrestrial leafy plants, with sheathing-based leaves, and solitary or racemose pale-yellow or greenish flowers, which have their upper sepal agglutinated to the petals and forming a hood, whence one species is called Monk's Cowl. The two lateral sepals are free and spreading; and the lip adnate to the face of the column, and furnished with a large tongue-formed appendage at its base. [A. S.]

PTERYGOTA. A name under which it is proposed to separate *Sterculia alata* from the rest of the genus on account of its winged seeds. It is an East Indian tree, of which the seeds are said to be narcotic.

PTILOTA. A beautiful genus of rose-spored *Algæ* belonging to the natural order *Ceramiaceæ*, and distinguished by their compressed inarticulate frond, which is repeatedly pinnate. *P. plumosa* is confined to our northern coast, growing constantly on *Laminaria digitata*. *P. sericea* is more finely divided, and is common on our coasts, growing on rocks, and occasionally on *Fucus serratus*. It is one of the plants often used for making up seaweed pictures. A species which occurs at the Cape is one of the most beautiful of *Algæ*, and there are other southern species. The genus does not apparently occur on the shores of the United States. [M. J. B.]

PTILOTUS. A genus of *Amaranthaceæ*, consisting of glabrous annuals from Australia and the Moluccas, with narrow alternate leaves, and terminal heads of flowers with shining scarious bracts; perigone of five sepals, with three bracts at the base; stamens five, united at the base, without intermediate staminodes; anthers two-celled; utricle indehiscent one-seeded, enclosed in the woolly sepals. [J. T. S.]

PTISAN. A medicated drink prepared from the flowers of *Malva sylvestris*.

PTYCHODE. An internal membrane overlying the external skin of a cell internally; the protoplasm.

PTYCHOMERIA. A genus of *Burmanniaceæ* consisting of six or seven small slender leafless annuals from tropical Brazil and Guiana. They are allied to *Dictyostegia*, but remarkable for the long slender tube of the perianth, its three outer lobes being more or less three-cleft, whilst the three inner ones are very small or entirely deficient.

PTYCHOTIS. A small genus of annual or biennial plants belonging to the *Umbelliferæ*, found in the south of Europe, on the borders of the Mediterranean, in Egypt, Arabia, and India. It is distinguished by the compound umbels of white flowers being surrounded by a few-leaved involucre, by the margin of the calyx being five-toothed, and the petals notched or slit at the apex, with a long inflexed point proceeding from the sinus and cohering with the middle vein; and by the two halves of the rough laterally compressed fruit, having each five equal thread-like ribs with single vittæ between them. All the species have the stem-leaves more or less minutely cut into numerous hair-like segments.

P. Ajowan is a small plant, with erect forking stems, and very few leaves, the lower of which are cut into numerous narrow segments and the upper are simply pinnate; and produces umbels composed of from seven to nine rays surrounded by an involucre of narrow entire leaflets. It is very much cultivated during the cold season in Bengal, where it is called Ajowan or Ajouan, or Javanee, and valued for its aromatic fruits, which are commonly used for culinary and medicinal purposes. They are very small, somewhat like caraways, rough on the surface and strongly ribbed, and remarkable for their strong odour of thyme.   [A. S.]

PUBERA (Ætas). The period in the duration of a fruit succeeding to the fertilisation of the ovules.

PUBLIC-HOUSE PLANT. Asarum europæum.

PUCCINIA. An important genus of coniomycetous Fungi, and the type of the natural order Pucciniæi. It is distinguished by the uniseptate stipitate protospores, which are not bound together by gelatine. The species are all parasitic, growing on the different parts of phænogams, and in a few rare instances on cryptogams. The mycelia creep amongst and penetrate the cells of the mother-plants, exhausting their juices and appropriating them to the nourishment of the large protospores. The species are therefore more or less destructive to the mother-plant, unless where they tend to repress overluxuriance. P. graminis, which occurs in almost every part of the world on grasses, and especially on cereals, is the common wheat mildew, one of the most formidable diseases of wheat, and one for which no remedy has as yet been found. Were it even possible to devise any plan which might destroy every particle of wheat mildew, there would still be a fresh supply in the fields from the wild grasses. Most species of Puccinia, besides the proper protospores, produce others which are unicellular, and which are generally assigned to Uredo or its allied genera. These, it is to be observed, are distinct from the young protospores before the septum is formed. Occasionally two distinct species exist together on the same plant. [M. J. B.]

PUCCINIÆI. A natural order of coniomycetous Fungi, formerly restricted to those parasitic species which have septate protospores, but now extended to those which consist of a single cell, provided there be no true peridium, as in Æcidium. In Xenodochus and Aregma the septa are numerous; in Triphragmium there is occasionally a vertical septum; in the sections Uredinei and Ustilaginei they are mostly unicellular; and in the latter the mother-threads vanish at a very early stage of growth. In Cystopus they are chained together, and are of two kinds, a circumstance which occurs also in the rose rust referred to the genus Coleosporium. In all, the protospores germinate either from some indifferent point by the protrusion of the inner membrane, or from definite points like many pollen-grains. Some of the species, as mildew and smut, are cosmopolites, but one or two genera have at present occurred only in tropical or subtropical countries. Podisoma and Gymnosporangium differ merely in their abundant gelatine.   [M. J. B.]

PUCCOON. The Blood-root, Sanguinaria canadensis. —, HAIRY. Lithospermum hirtum. —, HOARY. Lithospermum canescens. —, YELLOW. Hydrastis canadensis.

PUCELAGE. (Fr.) Vinca.

PUCELLE. (Fr.) Galanthus nivalis.

PUCHA-PAT. The Patchouli, Pogostemon Patchouly, used in India as an ingredient in tobacco for smoking, and for scenting the hair, clothes, &c.

PUCHIRIM. A South American name for Sassafras.

PUCIÈRE. (Fr.) Plantago Psyllium.

PUCKFIST, PUCKBALL, or BALL-FIST. Evidently a corruption of the German word Bofist, applied generally to the larger puffballs. According to Withering, they are sometimes called Bunt. [M. J. B.]

PUDDING-PIPE TREE. Cassia Fistula.

PUDIS. (Fr.) Pistacia Terebinthus.

PUERARIA. A tall woody twiner from the Himalayas, described as constituting a genus of Leguminosæ of the suborder Papilionaceæ, having the foliage and flowers of Phaseoleæ, with the jointed pod of Hedysareæ. This point has not, however, as yet been satisfactorily ascertained, and it is possible that the genus may be the same as the more recently established Neustanthus.

PUETTE. (Fr.) Lepidium ruderale.

PUFFBALL. Lycoperdon.

PUINE. (Fr.) Cornus sanguinea.

PULAS. An Indian name for Butea frondosa and B. superba.

PULICAIRE. (Fr.) Pulicaria vulgaris.

PULICARIA. A genus of herbaceous plants, belonging to the tribe Corymbiferæ of compound flowers. The flowers are conspicuously rayed, all yellow; the florets of the ray forming a single row, and destitute of a pappus; and those of the disk furnished with a hairy pappus, which is surrounded by a cup-like membrane. P. dysenterica, the Common Fleabane, received its name from the supposed virtue of its smoke when burnt in driving away fleas. It is a common plant in marshes and by the sides of rivers in England, where it is conspicuous in autumn by its numerous bright-yellow flower-heads, and wrinkled downy oblong leaves. It grows to the height of about one foot. *P. vulgaris* is a much smaller plant, growing in moist sandy places, but is less frequent and unpretending in appearance. [C. A. J.]

PULLEY-SHAPED. Circular, compressed, contracted in the middle of its circumference so as to resemble a pulley; as the embryo of *Commelyna communis*.

PULLIPUNTA. A Peruvian name for *Phytelephas macrocarpa*.

PULLOM. An African name for *Bombax Ceiba*.

PULL-PIPES. A local North of England name for the stems of some of the larger *Equiseta*.

PULLUS. Black, with a strong lustre.

PULMONAIRE. (Fr.) *Pulmonaria*. — DE CHÊNE. *Sticta pulmonacea*. — DES FRANÇAIS. *Hieracium pulmonarium*. — DES MARAIS. *Gentiana Pneumonanthe*. — DE VIRGINIE. *Pulmonaria virginica*.

PULMONARIA. The Lungwort: a genus of *Boraginaceæ*, occurring in Europe and North America, consisting of hispid perennials, with creeping rhizomes, and large ovate root-leaves, often marked with white blotches; the stems short, with smaller leaves, and a terminal raceme of blue flowers, which are red while in bud. Calyx five-sided tubular five-toothed, bell-shaped in fruit; corolla funnel-shaped and salver-shaped, with an open throat without scales; stamens included; nuts free, smooth, affixed to the receptacle by the truncate bases. Two species occur in Britain: *P. officinalis*, with ovate root-leaves, probably an introduced plant; and *P. angustifolia*, with elliptical root-leaves narrowed at the base, which appears to be wild in the Isle of Wight. [J. T. S.]

The *Pulmonaria* formerly held a place in almost every garden, under the country name of Jerusalem Cowslip, its purple flowers and spotted leaves recommending it to notice; whilst it was held in great esteem for its reputed medicinal qualities in diseases of the lungs, and was hence called Lungwort. It is occasionally found in woods and thickets. Its former use in diseases of the lungs was indicated to our forefathers by the well-defined white spots on the leaves of the *P. officinalis*. These spots were supposed so far to imitate those of the lungs, as to have been designed by Nature to point out its uses, especially in consumption. Sir J. E. Smith says that 'every part of the plant is mucilaginous; but its reputation for coughs arose not from this circumstance, but from the speckled appearance of the leaves resembling the lungs!' The Lungwort, however, offers an interesting instance of a plant which, though having been used as a remedy from the most superstitious motives, yet fortunately possessed those demulcent qualities, which from their beneficial effects were confirmation of the belief in a wrong theory. [J. B.]

PULP. The juicy tissue found in the interior of plants; sometimes applied to the succulent hymenium of fungals.

PULQUE. The fermented juice of *Agave*.

PULSATILLE. (Fr.) *Anemone Pulsatilla*, sometimes called *Pulsatilla vulgaris*.

PULSE. A common name for the seeds of many cultivated *Leguminosæ*, such as peas, beans, &c.

PULTENÆA. A genus of *Leguminosæ* of the suborder *Papilionaceæ* and tribe *Podalyrieæ*, consisting of Australian shrubs, with alternate entire or two-lobed small sessile leaves, small brown stipules, and yellow or orange-coloured flowers in terminal heads or in the upper axils, always surrounded by small brown or scarious bracts. The calyx-lobes are nearly equal, the stamens all free, the pod small, more or less flattened, containing one or two seeds. There are between fifty and sixty species, two or three of which are occasionally grown in greenhouses amongst other Australian papilionaceous shrubs.

PULVEROUS. Powdery; consisting of powdery matter.

PULVERULENT. Covered with dust or powdery matter.

PULVINULI. Spongy excrescences in Lichens, sometimes rising up from the thallus and often resembling minute trees, as in *Parmelia glomulifera*.

PULVINULUS. A heap of naked spores, such as occur in the genus *Spiloma*.

PULVINUS (adj. PULVINATE, PULVINIFORM). A cushion-like enlargement at the base of some leaves, or at the apex of some petioles.

PULVIS. Powder, dust, &c.

PUMICIN. (Fr.) Palm-oil.

PUMILUS. Short, close-growing, as compared with other species of the same genus or family.

PUMPKIN. A species of Gourd, *Cucurbita Pepo*. The name is sometimes loosely applied to other gourds.

PUN. An Indian name for the leaves of *Typha elephantina*.

PUNCHUDE. (Fr.) A kind of olive.

PUNCTATA VASA. Dotted vessels; tubes having dot-like appearances on their sides. See BOTHRENCHYMA.

PUNCTATE. Dotted; marked with some colour disposed in very small round spots or points.

PUNCTUM VEGETATIONIS. The growing point of a leaf-bud.

PUNGA-PUNGA. A kind of bread made from the pollen of the Raupo, *Typha angustifolia*.

PUNGENT. Terminating gradually in a hard sharp point, as the lobes of the Holly leaf.

PUNICA. Owing to the singular structure of its fruit, this genus, which contains only one species, *P. Granatum* (the Pomegranate), was by some botanists formed into a separate order *Granateæ*; but it is now more generally considered to belong to the *Myrtaceæ*. The peculiarity of the fruit resides in its being composed of two

Punica Granatum.

whorls of carpels, one placed above the other, the lower consisting of three or four and the upper of from five to ten

Punica Granatum (fruit).

carpels; and its seeds also differing from the rest of the order in having a pellucid pulpy coating.

The Pomegranate is a native of Northern Africa and Western Asia, and is usually a tree varying from fifteen to twenty-five feet high, with oblong or lance-shaped entire leaves, destitute of dots, and without the marginal vein usual in *Myrtaceæ*; but there is a dwarf variety with narrower leaves, sometimes called *P. nana*, naturalised in the West Indies. Its flowers are usually scarlet, though sometimes white or yellowish, and have a leathery top-shaped calyx divided at the top into five to seven valvate lobes, and as many or, in certain double-flowering varieties, a larger number of petals. Pomegranates are greatly valued in warm countries on account of their delicious, cooling, and refreshing pulp. Numerous varieties are grown, some being sweet and vinous, and others acid or of a bitter astringent taste; and the colour of their pulp is also much redder in some than in others. They are generally about the size of the fist, and have a tough leathery rind of a beautiful deep golden colour tinged with red, and are crowned with the remains of the calyx-lobes. The rind, espe-

cially that of the bitter kind, contains a large quantity of tannin, and is used for tanning the celebrated morocco-leather, and also as an astringent medicine; the flowers likewise yield a red dye. [A. S.]

PUNICEUS. The same as Phœniceus.

PUNICIN. A peculiar principle, obtained from the bark of the root of *Punica Granatum*, which has the appearance of an oleo-resin.

PUNK. Touchwood or vegetable tinder.

PUNNEERIA. A genus of *Solanaceæ* containing only one species, *P. coagulans*, common in rocky and cultivated soil throughout Scinde, Afghanistan, and Beloochistan, and well known to the natives of those countries on account of its berries having the property of coagulating milk, in the same manner as rennet, for which they are substituted by the Beloochees and Afghans, who call them Puneer-bund, *i.e.* cheesemaker. It is a shrubby plant, growing from one to three feet high, clothed in all parts with a down formed of star-like hairs, which give it an ash-grey hue. Its leaves sometimes grow in pairs, and are thickish and of the same colour on both surfaces, oblong or lance-shaped and unequal-sided; and bear in their axils two or three small drooping flowers, which are unisexual by abortion, the sexes being borne on distinct plants. Both have a five-cut calyx, that of the female increasing in size after flowering and closely enveloping the ripe fruit; and their bell-shaped corolla has a five-parted limb. The males contain five fertile stamens as long as the corolla-tube, and an imperfect ovary; and the females five short barren stamens, and a perfect two-celled ovary bearing a simple style and two broad flat stigmas. [A. S.]

PUNOWUR PAIT. A Malayan name for *Eurycoma longifolia*.

PUPUNHA. A name used in the Amazon district for *Guilielma speciosa*.

PURA-AU, or **PURATRURA.** A Tahitian name for *Cratæva religiosa*.

PURDIÆA. A handsome shrub, with alternate sessile entire glabrous and coriaceous leaves, and pink flowers in an elegantly drooping terminal raceme. The calyx consists of five very unequal sepals, which as well as the bracts are thin and scariose; there are five distinct petals, and ten stamens with the anthers opening in terminal pores as in *Ericaceæ*; the fruit is a four-celled nut with one seed in each cell. It forms a genus of the little group of *Cyrillaceæ* nearly allied to *Ericaceæ*, although polypetalous. It was named after M. Purdie, the collector, who discovered it near La Cruz in New Grenada.

PURGA MACHO. *Ipomœa batatoides.* — DE GENTIO, or DA PAULISTAS. *Anda Gomesii.*

PURKINJIA. A generic name applied by Presl to some specimens of a Mexican shrub figured by him, but which appear to be a diseased state of some species of *Myrsinaceæ*, probably an *Ardisia*.

PURPLE. Dull red with a slight dash of blue.

PURPLE-HEART, GUIANA. *Copaifera pubiflora* and *C. bracteata*. —, TRINIDAD. *Peltogyne paniculata*. —, WEST INDIAN. *Copaifera officinalis*.

PURPLE-LIP. *Vanilla claviculata*.

PURPLES. *Vibrio*.

PURPLEWORT. *Comarum palustre*.

PURPURASCENS. Having a purplish colour.

PURRET. *Allium Porrum*.

PURSE-TASSELS. *Muscari comosum*.

PURSHIA. A shrub from the Oregon district in North-west America, with small villous three-toothed or three-lobed leaves, and solitary nearly sessile yellow flowers, forming a genus of *Rosaceæ*, allied in many respects to *Geum*.

PURSILL. A Scotch name for *Alaria esculenta*.

PURSLANE, or PURCELLAINE. *Portulaca oleracea*. —, MILK. *Euphorbia maculata*. —, SEA. *Atriplex* or *Obione portulacoides*; sometimes used as a common name for *Obione*. —, SEASIDE. A West Indian name for *Sesuvium Portulacastrum*. —, WATER, *Peplis*; also *Isnardia palustris*. —, WILD. *Euphorbia Peplis*.

PURSLANE-TREE. *Portulacaria afra*.

PUS, PODUS. In Greek compounds = foot or stalk.

PUSCHKINIA. A genus of *Liliaceæ*, with the habit of *Scilla*, but having the segments of the perianth cohering at the base, and the filaments united into a tube forming a six-lobed crown. It is a small bulbous plant, with two narrow leaves, and a scape supporting a lax raceme of campanulate rotate pale-blue flowers. It is a native of Southern Russia. [J. T. S.]

PUSILLUS. Very small. See PERPUSILLUS.

PUSSLY. A name used in the North American prairies for Purslane.

PUTAMEN. The hard bony lining or stone of the fruit of many plants, as of the Plum, Cherry, &c.

PUTCH-LEAF. A Malayan name for Patchouly.

PUTCHUK. An Eastern name for the roots of the Costus, *Aplotaxus Lappa*.

PUTERA. An Indian name for *Typha elephantina*.

PUTIET. (Fr.) *Cerasus Padus*.

PUTRANJIVA. A large timber-tree, with a white close-grained very hard wood, from the mountainous districts of Central and Peninsular India, forming a genus of *Euphorbiaceæ* closely allied to *Phyllanthus*, and chiefly distinguished by the fruit, which is always one-seeded only, although derived from a three-celled ovary with two ovules in each cell.

PUTTERLICKIA. A genus of *Celastraceæ* founded on the *Celastrus pyracanthus* and an allied species, both from the Cape Colony, which differ from the other species of *Celastrus* in having about six ovules in each cell of the ovary instead of two only. The genus is not adopted by all botanists.

PUTTY-ROOT. *Aplectrum hyemale*.

PUTWA. An Indian name for string and ropes made from the fibre of *Bauhinia racemosa*.

PUYA. This is the same as *Pourretia* of Ruiz and Pavon, and is a tropical and southern subtropical genus of *Bromeliaceæ*, the species of which have simple sometimes almost arboreous leafy stems, with narrow spiny leaves, and simple or compound bracteated flower-spikes. Its flowers have a six-parted perianth, with the divisions in two series, the outer calycine and the inner petaloid. [A. S.]

PUYA. *Böhmeria Puya*.

PYA. A name used in the Sandwich Islands for *Tacca oceanica*.

PYCNANTHEMUM. The generic name of the Mountain Mints of the United States. These are closely allied to our own mints, but have evidently two-lipped corollas, in common with the great mass of the *Labiatæ*, while in *Mentha* the corolla has an almost equally four-lobed border. About a dozen species are known, perennial herbs with erect four-angled stems, furnished with opposite mint-like or hyssop-like leaves smelling like those of spearmint or pennyroyal, and small white or lilac flowers disposed in terminal dense cymose bracted heads. To this the generic name (derived from the Greek *pyknos* 'dense,' and *anthemon* 'a flower') alludes. The chief features of the genus are the shortly tubular two-lipped and ten to thirteen-nerved calyx, naked in the throat; the two-lipped corolla; and the four perfect stamens. [A. A.) B.]

PYCNIDIA. Many species of *Sphæria* and allied genera have a second kind of fruit resembling in some measure the perithecia, but instead of producing asci generating naked spores. These organs are called pycnidia to distinguish them from perithecia. In *Erysiphe* two kinds of pycnidia are sometimes present, the one like the normal fruit, the other produced by a transformation of one or more cells of the short chains of spores produced on the white spawn. Pycnidia require to be cautiously distinguished from spermogonia, and indeed are in many cases to be recognised only by observing whether the granules to which they give rise are capable of germination. [M. J. B.]

PYCNOCOMA. A genus of *Euphorbiaceæ*

consisting of three or four trees or shrubs from tropical Africa, with alternate oval or oblong leaves, often one to two feet long, and numerous small flowers in dense compound racemes in the upper axils ; the terminal flower female, the lower ones in clusters, either all males or with a female one in the centre of each cluster. Nothing is known of them beyond their botanical characters.

PYCNOPTERIS. *Lastrea.*

PYCNOS. In Greek compounds = close, dense, compact : hence *pycnocephalus*, close-headed, a term sometimes applied to very compact kinds of inflorescence.

PYCNOSORUS. A genus of *Compositæ* of the tribe *Gnaphalieæ*, founded on an Australian cottony undershrub, with oblong-linear alternate leaves, and very small but exceedingly numerous flower-heads, densely clustered into a doubly compound globular head of about an inch diameter.

PYCNOSPORA. A decumbent or ascending weedy perennial, constituting a genus of *Leguminosæ* of the suborder *Papilionaceæ*, having the habit foliage and nearly the flowers of a *Desmodium*, but which on account of the pod, which is not jointed but ovoid and inflated like that of a *Crotalaria* or of a *Flemingia*, must be classed in the tribe *Flemingiæ*. It is common in South-eastern Asia, the Indian Archipelago, and Northern Australia.

PYCNOSTELMA *chinense,* or *Asclepias paniculata,* is the sole representative of a genus of *Asclepiadaceæ* inhabiting the mountain-slopes of Northern China. It is an erect perennial herb, with opposite linear leaves, terminal panicles of green flowers, a five-cleft calyx, a rotate corolla deeply cut into five lobes, and a simple corona composed of five leaflets. The fruit is unknown.   [B. S.]

PYGEUM. One of the few genera of *Drupaceæ*, consisting of trees, natives of tropical Asia, with entire leaves, and axillary and lateral clusters of flowers more or less covered with woolly hairs. The flowers are six-parted, a circumstance which with the characters presented by the dry fruit, with a somewhat kidney-shaped stone contracted in the middle, serves to distinguish the genus from its congeners.   [M. T. M.]

PYRAMIDAL. Having the figure of an angular cone, but more frequently used as an equivalent for Conical ; as the prickles of some roses, the root of the carrot, and the heads of many trees.

PYRENA. The stone found in the interior of the drupe and of similar fruits, caused by the hardening of the endocarp.

PYRENACANTHA. An Indian climbing shrub, with milky juice, thread-like stems, and stalked elliptic entire alternate leaves, has been so named, and is considered to constitute a genus of itself, whose position is doubtful. Lindley refers it to *Artocar-*

paceæ ; others to *Stilaginaceæ.* The flowers are small, diœcious, arranged in spikes or heads. Calyx four-parted ; stamens four ; ovary detached with two pendulous ovules ; stigma sessile. The fruit is drupe-like, its stone pitted on the outside, internally spiny, the spines projecting into the seed ; albumen fleshy. The name of the genus is expressive of the above-mentioned peculiarity of the stone of the fruit.[M. T. M.]

PYRENIUM. Either the receptacle or perithecium of certain fungals.

PYRENOMYCETES. A name given by Fries to the *Fungi* included in this volume under the natural orders *Sphæriacei* and *Phacidiacei*.   [M. J. B.]

PYRÈTHRE. • (Fr.)   *Anacyclus Pyrethrum.*

PYRETHRUM. One of the genera of *Compositæ*, very nearly allied to *Chrysanthemum*, and with difficulty distinguished from it. The distinctive features reside in the presence in *Pyrethrum* of a pappus, in the form of an elevated membranous border, and in the achenes or fruits being angular but not winged. The species are abundant in the temperate countries of the Old World ; and many of them are in cultivation as ornamental greenhouse or hardy plants.

P. Parthenium is frequently met with in a wild state in this country, but it is esteemed a doubtful native, and is considered to have escaped from cultivation. It is an erect branching plant, a foot or more in height, with somewhat downy pinnate leaves ; and the flower-heads less than half an inch across, arranged in a terminal loose corymb ; the florets of the ray white, those of the disk or centre yellow. The plant has bitter tonic properties, like those of chamomile (*Anthemis nobilis*) ; and is a popular remedy in slight fevers, whence it has received the name of Feverfew, in common with some other allied plants. The smell of the whole herb is said to be particularly offensive to bees. The plant producing the root known in shops as *Radix Pyrethri*, or Pellitory of Spain, used as an irritant and for the relief of toothache, &c., is included in ANACYCLUS : which see. The name of the present genus is derived from the Greek appellation of the last-named plant,—from *pur* ' fire,' in allusion to the hot taste of the root.   [M. T. M.]

PYROLACEÆ. (*Wintergreens.*) A natural order of corollifloral dicotyledons belonging to Lindley's erical alliance of hypogynous Exogens. They are herbs with simple leaves, and racemose or solitary flowers ; sepals five, persistent ; corolla regular deciduous, four to five-parted ; stamens hypogynous, eight to ten, free and perfect, the anthers opening by pores ; ovary four to five-celled ; style one, declinate. Fruit a four to five-celled capsule with central placentæ ; seeds numerous, albuminous ; embryo minute. Natives of temperate climates in Europe, North America, and the north of Asia. There are half a dozen genera, and about a score of species. Examples: *Pyrola, Moneses.* [J. H. B.]

PYROLA. The typical genus of the order of Wintergreens, chiefly distinguished from its allies by having the margins of the valves of the capsule connected by a web. The species are small plants, natives of Northern Europe and of North America, of very graceful aspect when in flower. The name is a diminutive of *pyrus*, a 'pear-tree,' from the resemblance of the leaves to those of the Pear. [G. D.]

PYROLIRION. A genus of *Amaryllidaceæ*, consisting of a few Peruvian bulbous plants, with linear leaves, and fistular scapes, bearing a solitary erect orange-coloured flower, similar to *Zephyranthes*. The perianth is campanulately funnel-shaped from a short tube, with a six-parted regular limb, bearing six scales in the throat: stamens six subequal, inserted below the scales in the throat of the perianth; style declinate, with a trifid stigma; ovary three-celled, with many ovules. It differs from *Zephyranthes* in the cochleariform apices of the lobes of the stigma. [T. M.]

PYRRHOSA. Under this name a genus of *Myristicaceæ* has been designated, but Drs. Hooker and Thomson consider it to form rather a subdivision of the genus *Myristica*, including those species with flowers arranged in axillary panicles, whose perianth is two to four-lobed, smooth, concealing the column of stamens, which is somewhat globular, concave at the top, and covered with anthers. The mace of one species, *M.* (*Pyrrhosa*) *tingens*, is stated by Blume to stain the fingers of a reddish colour. The natives of Amboyna make a pigment of it with the addition of lime, for the purpose of staining their teeth red. The name is probably derived from the fiery-red colour of the mace. [M. T. M.]

. PYRROCOMA. A name given by Decandolle to a genus of *Compositæ* which has since been reduced to *Aplopappus.*

PYRROS. In Greek compounds = flame-coloured or fiery.

PYRULARIA. A genus of sandalworts, having the stamens on one plant, and the pistils on another; the former are surrounded by five deep revolute divisions, five glands alternate with them, and five stamens opposite to them; the fertile flowers have the calyx adherent to the seed-vessel, and its border five-cleft. The species are North American shrubs, with the leaves and branches alternate, the former oblong ovate and hairy; and the flowers very small, arranged in spikes. [G. D.]

PYRUS. A genus of *Pomaceæ*, consisting of trees or shrubs with entire or pinnately-divided leaves, and showy flowers, either proceeding with a few leaves from buds or spurs on a former year's wood, or in simple or branched corymbs at the ends of the year's shoots. The calyx-tube adheres to the ovary, and the five small divisions generally persist on the top of the fruit. There are five petals, numerous stamens, and five or fewer ovaries and styles, which at the time of flowering are often distinct from each other, although enclosed within the calyx-tube; but as the fruit enlarges the ovaries become completely united, and, with the thickened calyx-tube, form a fleshy mass divided in the centre into five or fewer cells of a leathery or cartilaginous consistence, called the core—each cell containing one or two seeds or pips. It is the consistence of this core alone that separates *Pyrus*, as a genus, from *Cratægus* and others which have the cells hard and bony.

There are a considerable number of species, natives of the temperate or mountainous regions of the northern hemisphere, chiefly in Europe and Central Asia; and several are in very extensive cultivation. Amongst those with undivided leaves, *P. communis*, the Pear, and *P. Malus*, the Apple, the badge of the Lamonts, have been in cultivation since the times of the ancient Greeks and Romans. The Siberian Crab, *P. prunifolia*, is planted sometimes in our shrubberies.

Amongst the cut-leaved species the most important are the White Beam-tree, *P. Aria*; the Wild Service-tree, *P. torminalis*; the Mountain Ash or Rowan-tree, the badge of the M'Lachlans, *P. Aucuparia*; and the cultivated Service-tree, *P. Sorbus*—all natives of Europe and temperate Asia, and, except the last, indigenous to Britain. The above trees mostly supply a hard wood, although few of them attain a sufficient size to be considered as timber-trees. One species, *P. Chamæmespilus*, not unfrequent in the mountains of Central Europe, is never more than a bush, and sometimes flowers and fruits when not above six inches or a foot from the ground.

The Apple, *P. Malus*, is called in its wild state the Crab, and from this the vast number of cultivated varieties have originated. The leaves are acutely serrated or crenated, more or less downy beneath; and the flowers grow in corymbs, and have glabrous styles. The fruit, generally concave at the base, is well known; in some varieties it is sweet, in others acid; and some of the cider-apples are a mixture of bitter and sweet, or, as termed by the French, amer-doux. The tree is deciduous, and attains the height of from twenty to forty or fifty feet. The Apple was called by the Greeks *Mela*, by the Romans *Malum*: the latter, it may be observed, applied the term Pomum to any round fleshy fruit. Decandolle states (*Géographie Botanique*, p. 890) that the root of nearly all the names of the apple is *Ab, Ap, Al, Aff*: for example, the Bretons *Aval* or *Avelen*, the Welsh *Afalen*, the Germans *Apfel*; and analogous to this is our English name, and those of other nations in the north of Europe—as Saxon, *Appl* or *Appil*; Dutch, *Appel*; Danish, *Aeble*; Swedish, *Aple*.

The Apple in its wild state exists in most countries of Europe, and also in the region of the Caucasus. Its cultivation extends to the most northern extremity of Britain. We learn from a *Synopsis of the Vegetable Products of Norway*, by Dr. Schübler, and from specimens sent to the International Exhibition in 1862, from that country, that 'the Crab Apple grows wild in the lowlands as far north as Drontheim (lat. 63° 25′). Even in Romsdal (lat. 62° 25′), specimens are found growing wild from twenty to thirty feet in height, with stems of two feet in diameter. Cultivated apple-trees grow as standards up to lat. 65° 10′, and the earlier sorts will undoubtedly ripen farther north against walls. Beyond this degree of latitude scarcely any apple-trees are to be found in any other part of the world.' It appears from this statement that the Apple will grow in a very high latitude, and that it is amongst the hardiest of our fruit-trees. Its blossoms, however, are more susceptible of cold than are even those of the peach and nectarine; the latter naturally expand earlier than those of the apple, appearing when the winter is scarcely over—in March; whereas the apple does not bloom till May, when the nights are in general much warmer than when the peach comes in flower; and not being adapted to bear the vicissitudes to which the latter is subject, its blossoms more readily perish with a slight degree of frost.

Although the Apple exists in high latitudes, its fruit in such is but small—not from the excessive cold to which the tree is exposed in winter, but for want of sufficient heat in summer; for in Nova Scotia, where the winters are long and intensely cold, the apples are large and of splendid colour; but there the summers, though short, are very hot. In tropical climates the Apple does not succeed; but its cultivation extends from the far north, as we have mentioned, to the warmer parts of the temperate zone, thus extending over a vast portion of the globe. According to Royle, it is cultivated in the north of India, but more abundantly in Kashmir and adjoining countries. It is perfectly naturalised in America; in the northern and middle portions of the United States, its produce is very fine; in Canada likewise, as will be recollected by those who saw the Canadian specimens at the International Exhibition of fruits at South Kensington. Large quantities of American apples are regularly exported in the ice-ships from Boston, in the United States, to the seaports of India and other Eastern countries, where the apple-tree is not grown; and being packed in ice they are landed in excellent condition, and are esteemed a great luxury by the European inhabitants. In the southern hemisphere, in Australia and in New Zealand, where, in the memory of the present generation, nothing better in the way of fruits than a few wild berries were to be met with, and where of apples there were none, the latter are now abundant, and attain great perfection.

When this most useful fruit was first cultivated in Britain is uncertain—probably by the Romans, to whom twenty-two varieties were known in Pliny's time. Many kinds of cider-apples appear, from their names, to have been introduced from Normandy; but many are doubtless seedlings that have sprung up from pips, and, without grafting, have been found to answer the purpose of cider-making. From their names, we can trace the origin of many of our dessert and kitchen varieties in cultivation at the present day to Holland, and to France; but on the whole the varieties of English origin are the best for our climate, and the most suitable to English taste. Many of the foreign kinds have a mawkish sweetness; whereas we prefer not sweetness alone, but a brisk subacid sugary apple, and of such we have a vast number. The collection of the Royal Horticultural Society contains upwards of 1,500 varieties of dessert, kitchen, and cider apples, and more are continually being raised. Many of the above are, however, considered no longer worthy of cultivation, but some of English origin have acquired almost universal celebrity; for instance, the Golden Pippin, Ribston Pippin, Court of Wick, Scarlet Nonpareil, Blenheim Pippin, &c.; and recently Cox's Orange Pippin has been brought into notice, and is likely to supersede even the Ribston Pippin.

The uses of the Apple are familiar to every one. For a great part of the year it can be employed for pies, tarts, sauces, and in confectionery, &c. The fermented juice forms cider, of which great quantities are made in England and in foreign countries, especially those in which the vine cannot be grown successfully for wine-making. The circumstance of the Apple being so easily cultivated, so generally liked, and so useful in various ways to all classes, rich and poor, accounts for the extensiveness of its cultivation wherever it was known in old countries, and likewise for the eagerness with which it is obtained and rapidly propagated in our new colonial settlements.

The Common Pear-tree, *P. communis*, grows to the height of thirty to sixty rarely seventy feet, and assumes generally a pyramidal form of growth. The branches are thorny, and the leaves ovate and serrated. Under cultivation the thorns disappear, and fruit-buds are formed instead; and the leaves are less sharply serrated, sometimes only crenated, and frequently almost entire. The flowers come in corymbs of from five to nine, all of which sometimes set their fruit; but in that case, from being so numerous, the fruits do not attain a large size if they all hang on to maturity. Generally a few only of each corymb take the lead, and in some cases only one; the rest, unable to compete, drop off at an early stage of their growth.

The name of *Pyrus* is derived from the Celtic *Peren*, and to this most of the European names of the Pear may be easily traced. Thus in Italian and Spanish the Pear is called *Pera*; in German, *Birn*;

Dutch, *Peer*; French, *Poire*; Danish, *Päre*; Swedish, *Päron*. The Pear is a native of Europe, Circassia, Central Asia, and the north of China; but it is not met with in Southern India. As regards its hardiness, it is not found, like the Apple, in a wild state in Norway, nor has its cultivation been extended so far north as that of the Apple by 120 miles; it stops at Drontheim (lat. 63° 25'), and even there it must have the shelter of a wall.

From the Wild Pear have arisen improved varieties in different countries, which instead of being hard and gritty, as the earlier cultivated sorts generally were, become at maturity as melting as a peach. Many of the French Pears, raised upwards of two centuries ago, are no longer reckoned worthy of cultivation. A collection of them, consisting of fifty sorts, existed at Chelsea 150 years ago, and are figured in an early volume of the *Transactions of the Horticultural Society*. Most of the kinds imported from France have been superseded by Belgian varieties, which have proved in general of better quality, and more suitable for the climate of England. Some of these improved varieties, only known comparatively recently in this country, existed in the latter part of the last century chiefly in the gardens attached to numerous religious establishments in Belgium; and it was only after the close of the war in 1815 that they were obtained in England and other countries. The varieties of Pears are now very numerous. After excluding a vast number of worthless kinds, upwards of a thousand still exist in some collections; and amongst these the kinds possessing great excellence are too numerous to be noticed here. We may, however, mention the names of a few of established merit, such as Passe Colmar, Glou Morceau, Winter Nelis, Beurré Bosc, Thompson's, Louise Bonne, Fondante d'Automne, Comte de Lamy, Easter Beurré, Bergamotte d'Esperen, Joséphine de Malines, and Beurré Rance. Mr. Knight, when President of the Horticultural Society, devoted great attention to crossing and raising new pears from seed. A considerable number of those which he obtained were very good, but perhaps the best is Knight's Monarch. Besides its use for dessert, the Pear is employed for stewing, baking, compôtes, and for the making of perry.

The True Service-tree, *P. Sorbus*, has the leaves imparipinnate and serrated; and the flowers cream-coloured, about the size of those of the common hawthorn. The fruits,—of which there are two principal varieties, the apple-shaped *P. S. maliformis*, and the pear-shaped *P. S. pyriformis*,—are about as large as a moderate-sized gooseberry, of a dull greenish-brown with sometimes a reddish tinge, and marked with ferruginous specks; the flesh is acid and austere in the unripe state, and only fit to be eaten when it becomes soft and mellow, in a state of incipient decay like the medlar. The tree grows to the height of from twenty to sixty feet. It is a native of France and Italy, and has been found in some parts of Barbary—also in the mountainous districts of Cornwall. It is said to be of slow growth, and to be sixty years before it comes into bearing; but this is not the case, for in the Gardens of the Horticultural Society, where both the apple and pear-shaped varieties have borne fruit abundantly, the growth was as rapid as that of most trees of the genus *Pyrus*. It appears not so well adapted for the climate of Britain as it is for that of France. It lives to a great age: Loudon states that some specimens of it are believed to be upwards of 1,000 years old, and that it is the hardest and heaviest of all indigenous woods. It has a compact fine grain, and takes a high polish; it is much sought after in France by millwrights for making cogs to wheels, rollers, cylinders, blocks, &c.; it is preferred to all other kinds of wood for making the screws to winepresses, and it is also in repute for mathematical rulers. Its properties are such as to justify the opinion that it would answer exceedingly well for certain kinds of wood-engravings where the fineness of boxwood is not required. [R. T.]

PYTHONIUM. This genus, as is also the case with some of its allies, owes its name to the snake-like appearance of its spadix, &c. It is classed under the *Araceæ*, and consists of Nepalese herbs with a somewhat globular fleshy rootstock, whence emerge the much-divided leaves and the inflorescence—the latter consisting of a spadix, elevated on a long stalk, and surrounded by a spathe. The spadix is thickly beset with male and female flowers; its upper extremity has a number of wart-like neutral flowers on it; the anthers open by two pores; and the ovaries are one-celled, with a long style, terminated by a three to four-lobed fleshy stigma.

One species, best known under the old name of *Arum bulbiferum*, is cultivated in hothouses, and is remarkable for the presence of little bulb-like buds on the leaves just at the junction of the stalk with the blade of the leaf. These bulbs become detached, and thus serve to perpetuate the species. This plant has also been described under the name *Thomsonia*. The odour of the spadix of some of these plants is most disgusting, and has been compared to that of putrid salt-fish. [M. T. M.]

PYXIDANTHERA *barbulata* is a small prostrate creeping evergreen, native of North America, and one of the two genera forming the order *Diapensiaceæ*. It has narrow oblanceolate awl-pointed crowded leaves, bearded near the base, the lower ones opposite and the upper mostly alternate; and very numerous solitary sessile white or rose-coloured flowers, which are distinguished from those of *Diapensia* by their transversely-opening anthers having an awn on the lower valve. [A. S.]

PYXINEI. A natural order of lichens, with an orbicular superficial disk, contained in an excipulum which is at first closed, distinct from the thallus, which is horizontal foliaceous and for the most part fixed in the centre. It comprises the lichens known in the Arctic regions as Tripe de Roche. In *Gyrophora* the disk produces a number of partial disks on the hymenial surface, giving it a curious convolute appearance. *Pyxine*, which is a tropical or subtropical genus, has a thallus like that of *Parmelia*.   [M. J. B.]

PYXIS, PYXIDIUM (adj. PYXIDATE). A capsule opening by a lid, as in *Hyoscyamus* or *Anagallis*.

QUADRETTE. (Fr.) *Rhexia*.

QUADRI. In Latin compounds = four times.

QUADRICRURIS. Having four legs or arms, as in the retinaculum of some asclepiads.

QUADRIFOLIATE. When the petiole bears four leaflets from the same point.

QUADRIHILATE. Having four apertures, as is the case in certain kinds of pollen.

QUADRIJUGUS. Consisting of four pairs (of leaflets).

QUAKERS AND SHAKERS. *Briza media*.

QUALEA. A genus of trees or shrubs of Brazil and Guiana, belonging to the *Vochyaceæ*, and remarkable for their unsymmetrical flowers, which have but one petal and one fertile stamen (rarely two of each), as well as for the numerous winged seeds of the fruit. There are about thirty species known, some of them attaining a height of 130 feet; the bark of the trunk is somewhat corky, and the young branchlets often four-sided and covered with gum. They have opposite or whorled, lance-shaped or oblong, laurel-like leaves, with the blades frequently marked with numerous nerves running at right-angles to the midrib; and the flowers are exceedingly handsome and numerous, disposed in axillary or terminal panicles. The flowers have a five-parted calyx, one of the segments being much larger than the others, petal-like, and prolonged behind into a spur as in the balsam, a single fan-shaped petal with the fertile stamen alternating with it; and an ovary which when ripe is a three-celled angular woody capsule, with many winged seeds in each cell.

Many of the species have primrose-scented flowers, yellow white blue or rose-coloured, and the petal is usually marked with a yellow or white line in the centre. Perhaps the most handsome when in flower is *Q. pulcherrima*, a tree about fifty feet high, discovered by Mr. Spruce. It has sessile beautifully veined leaves, in size and shape like those of the Portugal laurel, and when first met with by Mr. Spruce—who remarks he had never seen a more striking object—the crown of the tree was 'a complete mass of blue and red, in which did not appear a single green leaf.' The calyx is blue, the petal red, marked with a yellow line in the centre, rather more than half an inch long, and shaped like the lower petal of a violet. The largest-flowered species is *Q. macropetala*, in which the large fan-like petal is white marked with a yellow line in the centre, and about two-and-a-half inches across. It also is Brazilian.   [A. A. B.]

QUAMASH. The North American name for the edible *Camassia esculenta*. —, EASTERN. An American name for *Scilla esculenta*.

QUAMOCHITL. *Inga Unguis Cati*.

QUAMOCLIDION. A genus of *Nyctaginaceæ*, established by Choisy for some Mexican species of *Mirabilis*, which have usually three flowers instead of only one in each involucre, but it has since been again reduced to a section of *Mirabilis*.

QUAMOCLIT. A genus of *Convolvulaceæ*, containing several species of annual twiners, natives of tropical America and Asia. They are herbs with alternate cordate leaves, and red or crimson flowers on axillary one or many-flowered peduncles. The sepals are mostly mucronate or awned; the corolla cylindrical, tubular, with a small five-lobed spreading limb; the stamens and style are protruded; and the stigma is capitate and two-lobed. The capsule is four-celled, with a single seed in each cell.   [W. O.]

QUAMOCLIT. (Fr.) *Ipomœa*. — CARDINAL. *Quamoclit vulgaris*.

QUANDANG. The edible fruit of *Santalum acuminatum*.

QUAPALIER. (Fr.) *Sloanea*.

QUAPOYA. The name formerly given to a few tropical American trees belonging to the *Clusiaceæ*, and now referred to *Clusia*.

QUÁQUARA. *Smilax China*.

QUARANTIN. (Fr.) *Cheiranthus annuus*.

QUARTINE. A fourth integument, counting from the outside, supposed to occur in some ovules; but in reality a mere layer of either the secundine or nucleus.

QUARTINIA. The generic name of an Abyssinian plant belonging to the *Lythraceæ*, found growing attached to stones in the beds of rivers, and having capillary submerged leaves like those of the water crowfoot densely packed on the stems. The minute flowers are in naked racemes, each consisting of an eight-toothed bell-shaped calyx, four stamens, a two-celled germen, and a simple style. The genus bears the name of M. Quartius Dillon, a French botanist and traveller in Abyssinia. *Q. repens* is the only known species. [A. A. B.]

QUASI-RADIATE. Slightly radiant; a term applied to the heads of some composites, whose ray-florets are small and inconspicuous.

QUASSIA. Linnæus applied this name to a tree of Surinam in honour of a negro, Quassi or Coissi, who employed its bark as a remedy for fever, and enjoyed such a reputation among the natives as to be almost worshipped by some, and suspected of magic by others. The tree now forms a genus of *Simarubaceæ*. Its distinguishing characteristics reside in the presence of hermaphrodite five-parted flowers, of ten stamens longer than the petals, and of five fleshy drupes in the fruit.

Q. amara is a lofty tree, described as similar in appearance to the common ash. The leaves are unequally pinnate, the common stalk being winged and jointed; and the flowers are large, red in colour, and arranged in terminal clusters. It is cultivated in the West Indies, &c., and may occasionally be seen in the hothouses of the curious. The wood of this plant was at one time employed in this country, under the name of Surinam Quassia; but it appears to be no longer imported for medicinal purposes, the Quassia in use being furnished by the allied *Picræna excelsa*. The wood is destitute of smell, but has an intensely bitter taste, on which account it was used as a tonic. The root has been considered a valuable remedy in dysentery, as also the bark. The flowers too are stated to have been employed as stomachics in Surinam. It is probable that many of the uses and virtues ascribed to this plant are more properly to be referred to the Jamaica Quassia, PICRÆNA, or to the SIMARUBA; which see. [M. T. M.]

QUASSIA-CHIPS. The wood of *Picræna excelsa*.

QUATELÉ. (Fr.) *Lecythis*.

QUATERNI, QUATERNATE. Growing in fours.

QUATRE-ÉPICES. (Fr.) *Nigella sativa*; also *Calycanthus*.

QUEEN-OF-THE-MEADOWS. *Spiræa Ulmaria*.

QUEEN-OF-THE-PRAIRIE. *Spiræa lobata*.

QUEEN'S-CUSHION. A provincial name for *Saxifraga hypnoides*.

QUEEN'S-DELIGHT, or QUEEN'S-ROOT. A North American name for *Stillingia sylvatica*.

QUEKETTIA. A vandeous genus of orchids related to *Ionopsis*, but with the habit of a *Pleurothallis*. It consists of a single species, *Q. microscopica*, a little Brazilian epiphyte with terete leaves, and a terminal panicle of minute flowers, which have thin erect equal sepals and petals, the lateral sepals slightly joined and gibbous at the base; an undivided lip convolute round the column, and furnished with a couple of callosities in its excavated base; a long narrow column with two long membranous recurved ears hanging down from its apex; and a one-celled anther containing two spherical pollen-masses, hollowed out behind, and attached by a narrow caudicle to a minute gland. Its flowers abound in raphides, and are beautiful objects under the microscope; whence the specific

name of the plant, and whence, also, the genus has been named after Mr. Quekett, the eminent microscopist. [A. S.]

QUELTIA. A subgenus of *Narcissi*, of which *Narcissus montanus* may be taken as the type. They are distinguished by their subcylindrical perianth-tube and their short coronet; by their filaments being unequally adnate to the upper part of the tube; and by their attenuated style. They are called Mock *Narcissi*. [T. M.]

QUENNERON. (Fr.) *Anthemis Cotula*.

QUÉNOT. (Fr.) *Cerasus Mahaleb*.

QUENOUILLÉ. (Fr.) *Typha latifolia*.
— DES PRÉS. *Cirsium oleraceum*.

QUENOUILLÉTTE. (Fr.) *Atractylis*.
— LAINEUSE. *Kentrophyllum lanatum*.

QUERCITRON. *Quercus tinctoria*.

QUERCUS. The technical name of the Oak, derived it is said from the Celtic *quer* 'fine,' and *cuez* 'tree.' The genus belongs to the order *Corylaceæ*, and consists of trees and shrubs which bear monœcious flowers, the males in long slender pendulous catkins, with five to twelve stamens surrounded by narrow scales, sometimes united into an irregular perianth; and the females solitary or clustered, each placed within an involucre, or capsule, which is covered with small overlapping scales on the outside, which involucre forms the 'cup' of the ripe fruit or acorn. The perianth of the female flower is adherent to the ovary, and is more or less six-lobed. The ovary itself has three cells or compartments, each containing two pendulous ovules, and is surmounted by a three-lobed style. As the ovary ripens into the fruit, two of the three compartments and five of the six ovules become obliterated, so that in the ripe fruit or acorn there is but one cavity containing a single seed.

The genus comprises numerous species, distributed widely over the northern hemisphere, and found also in Java and the mountains of Mexico and South America. Although much variety exists in the outward appearance of these trees, yet the acorns and their cups are sufficient to distinguish the genus from its allies. One species from Guatemala, however, *Q. Skinneri*, is remarkable for presenting a resemblance to the Walnut (*Juglans*) in its lobed and wrinkled seed-leaves or cotyledons.

As these trees vary extremely not only in the form of their leaves and general appearance, but also in the shape of their fruits, there is great difficulty in discriminating the species, and a like discrepancy between the opinions of various botanists as to their limits. The chief points relied on as furnishing distinctive characters are the following: viz., the time required for the maturation of the acorns, one or two years as the case may be; the nature of the cup and its investing scales; and the shape and colour of the acorns. The leaves also furnish important characters: for instance, they may be deciduous or evergreen, entire spiny or pinnate; while in autumn, when decaying, they assume varying shades of brown, yellow, crimson, purple, &c., according to the species. The roughness or smoothness of the bark also affords a means of discriminating one species from another. The cup arises from the hollowing out of the top of a small branch, on the sides of which are developed small leaves in the shape of scales.

Quercus pedunculata.

Few trees possess so much interest as the various kinds of Oak: the historical traditions connected with them, their varied uses to mankind, their great age, vast size, and noble appearance in some instances, all contribute to render them of more than common interest. The most valuable species, as affording timber, are the European *Q. pedunculata* and *Q. sessiliflora*, the former of which supplies the greater portion of the oak used in this country for shipbuilding and other pur-

Quercus sessiliflora.

poses. There is a considerable difference in the appearance of the wood of these two trees, but, according to Dr. Lindley, the value of their timber for constructive pur-

poses is about equal. The wood of *Q. sessiliflora*, or Durmast as it is called, is described as darker, heavier, and more elastic than that of *Q. pedunculata*, less easy to split, not so easy to break, yet the least difficult to bend. These characteristics depend in some degree on the small proportion of silver-grain clash or flower (terms used by joiners and others to signify the medullary rays of botanists) possessed by the wood of the Durmast in comparison with that of the other kind. On this account, the wood of the Durmast has been frequently confounded with that of the sweet chestnut; and for this reason it is less valuable for the purposes of the cabinetmaker than the wood of *Q. pedunculata*, in which the silver-grain is much more conspicuous. The wood of the Durmast has been stated, on insufficient grounds, to be less durable than that of the Common Oak. The wood of these trees, when stained green by the growth of a peculiar fungus, *Peziza æruginosa*, is highly prized by cabinetmakers and makers of Tunbridge-ware.

Some of the American kinds also furnish valuable timber. Such are *Q. alba*, the White or Québec Oak, the wood of which is used in shipbuilding, and by wheelwrights, coopers, and others. *Q. virens*, the Live Oak, also yields excellent timber for naval purposes. The wood of *Q. Ilex*, a Mediterranean species, is said to be as good as that of the common oak. *Q. Cerris*, the Turkey Oak, supplies a wood much in favour with wheelwrights, cabinetmakers, turners, coopers, &c. Mr. J. G. Veitch mentions several Japanese oaks, the timber of some of which he describes as 'splendid,' and as likely to prove equal to any oak in the world for practical purposes. The False Sandalwood of Crete is the produce of *Q. abelicea* (?). This wood is of a reddish colour, and has an agreeable perfume. The less valuable kinds furnish excellent charcoal and firewood.

Next in importance to the wood is the bark of these trees, as from its astringency it is valuable for dyeing and other purposes; while that of *Q. Suber*, a native of Southern Europe and Northern Africa, furnishes cork. The outer layers of bark in this tree increase annually, and after eight or nine years fall off, but for commercial purposes they are purposely removed one or two years previously. The bark is removed by incisions round the top and bottom of the tree, and by a long one connecting these two, which allows the bark to be stripped off. The barking of the trees is effected when the bark is most firmly adherent to the wood, in order that the innermost layers of bark may not be injured, nor the health of the tree impaired; indeed, it is said that the removal of the corky layers is beneficial to the tree. The layers of cork, when stripped off, are thrown into pits and soaked in water; by these means, and by placing heavy weights above them, they become flattened. The outer surface is subsequently charred to close the pores, as may be seen in bungs.

The largest quantity and best quality of cork is exported from Spain. In that country cork is said to be employed on floors in lieu of carpets, and on walls in lieu of tapestry. The Romans are said to have used cork for the same purposes as we ourselves, not excepting even cork soles. In some of the Greek islands cork is used for beehives. A floorcloth now coming into extensive use, from its deadening the sound of footsteps, and called Kamptulicon, is said to be manufactured from cork and caoutchouc. Burnt cork or Spanish-black is used for dyeing purposes, and was formerly employed in medicine. Some of the kinds of elm also produce cork, though not in sufficient quantity to be of much use : see ULMUS. The name *Suber* is supposed, with reason, to be derived from the Greek *suphar*, 'bark.'

Several species furnish bark of much value for tanning and dyeing purposes ; this arises from the presence of tannic and gallic acids. The common oaks of this country are barked or peeled in spring and early summer, a period when the bark contains the most astringent matter, and is also most readily separated from the wood. The slabs of bark as they are removed 'are stacked in large heaps to dry. Oak-bark is very largely employed in this country in the manufacture of leather. After it has been used for this purpose, it is still serviceable to gardeners for the warmth it generates, and is largely used by them under the name of Tan ; it has, however, the objection of favouring the growth of certain fungi, which are occasionally very deleterious to the plants. Refuse tan is also less creditably employed in the adulteration of chicory and coffee. In Brittany tan, compressed into cakes, is used as fuel. Oak-bark also is employed for dyeing black, in conjunction with salts of iron, With alum, oak-bark yields the dyer a brown tint ; with a salt of tin, a yellow colour ; with a salt of zinc, Isabella yellow.

Q. tinctoria, a North American species, yields Quercitron Bark, employed for dyeing yellow. *Q. aquatica*, also a native of North America, supplies a bark made use of by the tanners of that country. The bark of the South European *Q. Ilex* is also used by tanners, while the American Indians are said to dye their skins red by means of the bark of *Q. Prinus*. The cups of other kinds are also employed by tanners and dyers. Foremost in importance in this respect are those of *Q. Ægilops*, a native of the Mediterranean regions. These cups are sometimes very large, at other times smaller ; they are used for ornamental purposes in the East, and are imported in enormous quantities from the Levant for tanning purposes under the name of Valonia. Camata and Camatina are also furnished by this tree ; they are simply the undeveloped acorns, enclosed within the partially ripened cups. Camatina is the least developed of the two. *Q. sinensis* supplies a dye in China.

Few trees are so subject to the formation of the morbid growths called galls as are the various kinds of Oak. The galls are various in appearance, and result from the puncture of different species of gall-flies (*Cynips* and *Aphis*). The common oaks of this country are much affected by them—sometimes on the leaves, where they form the so-called oak-apples: sometimes on the shoots, where they do great mischief by checking and distorting the growth of the tree. The galls of commerce are imported from the Levant, and are produced by *Q.*

Quercus infectoria (with galls).

infectoria. They are largely used in the manufacture of ink, for dyeing purposes, and for the preparation of tannic and of gallic acids. The same tree also furnishes the galls known as Mecca Galls, which are supposed to be the Dead Sea or Sodom Apples, ' the fruit that never comes to ripeness,'—the fruit so pleasant to the eye, so bitter to the taste.

Q. coccifera, a native of the Mediterranean region, affords a bark used by tanners, and gives sustenance to an insect like the cochineal insect, and which is used as a crimson dye under the name kermes. This was much employed prior to the introduction of cochineal, and is still largely used in the East. The name kermes is derived from the Arabic word for worm, and is the parent of the French *cramoisi*, and the English crimson.

The medical properties of the various Oaks are due to the astringency imparted by the tannic and gallic acid they contain. Thus common oak-bark is employed as an astringent and tonic ; so also is that of *Q. coccifera*. The leaves of *Q. falcata* are stated to have been employed as astringent applications in gangrene. Galls also are used as tonics and astringents, and as an antidote to certain vegetable poisons, whose activity they lessen by the combination of their tannic acid with the organic alkali of the poison. Tannic and gallic acids are of great service in certain forms of hæmorrhage, and are employed in various ways in the arts.

In olden times the rude inhabitants of Britain and other northern countries prized the Oak for the food furnished by the acorns, not only to their herds of swine but also to themselves. The right of feeding swine in the oak-woods was among our Saxon forefathers a highly-valued privilege, the infringement of which by the Normans constituted one of the most severely-felt hardships that were inflicted on the conquered race. To this day the acorns of some of the species are eaten as food. There is a variety of the common oak which produces sweet edible acorns; this variety is supposed to be the *Æsculus* of Virgil. The acorns of *Q. Ballota*, and of its variety *Q. Gramuntia*, are eaten in Barbary, Spain, and Portugal, under the name of Belotes: in Arabia also they are eaten cooked, and an oil is extracted from them. The acorns of *Q. Æsculus* are eaten in Syria; these retain their green colour even when ripe, and are boiled by the Arabs. The leaves of *Q. mannifera* yield a manna-like exudation in Kurdistan.

The vast size and great age of some Oaks add to the interest that is attached to this family of trees. There still exist some fine specimens in this country. Humboldt refers to an oak in the Département de la Charente Inférieure, measuring nearly ninety feet in circumference near the base. Near Breslau an oak fell, in a storm in July 1857, measuring sixty-six feet in circumference at the base. These large trees are for the most part decayed and hollow in the interior, their 'tops bald with dry antiquity:' their age has been estimated at from one to as many as two thousand years. The famous Oak of Mamre, Abram's Oak, has been recently figured in the *Transactions of the Linnæan Society* by Dr. Hooker.

Abram's Oak.

It is a fine tree of the species *Q. pseudococcifera*, and is popularly supposed to indicate the spot where grew the oak or lentisc under which the patriarch pitched his tent. There is a superstition that any person who cuts or maims the oak will lose his firstborn son.

The Romans employed branches of the Oak to form the chaplets wherewith the heads of citizens eminent for their civic virtues, especially for having saved the life of a fellow-citizen, were crowned. The Druids venerated the Oak, as being the tree on which the sacred mistleto grew; or, possibly, the latter plant was regarded as the more sacred from growing on the Oak. At present the mistleto is rarely found on the Oak, but that it does grow on this tree is sufficiently attested. To this day the custom is kept up, in many places in the country, of gathering and displaying branches of Oak on May 29, in commemoration of the concealment of Charles II. in the oak at Boscobel. Much difference of opinion prevails as to our British Oaks; some considering that there are three species, some two, and others (as M. Decandolle in his recent revision of the genus) one only. The generally accepted opinion is that there are two, *Q. pedunculata* and *Q. sessiliflora*, distinguished one from the other by the following characters, *Q. sessiliflora*, or Durmast, has long yellowish leafstalks, and sessile or shortly stalked acorns; it grows more quickly than the other species, is more ornamental, and will thrive on poorer soil. *Q. pedunculata* has either stalkless leaves, or the leafstalks are short and of a greenish or reddish hue, while the acorns are on long stalks. This last is the badge of the Camerons. The difference in the timber of these two species has been before mentioned.

A large number of the species mentioned are in cultivation in this country. *Q. Ilex*, the Holm or Evergreen Oak, is more like a huge shrub than a tree. The Lucombe and Fulham Oaks are also nearly evergreen. *Q. Cerris* forms a very handsome tree. *Q. coccinea* is valuable for its foliage, which assumes a crimson tint in autumn, and remains on the tree during the greater part of the winter. A valuable frost-proof species, *Q. sinensis*, has been recently introduced from China by Mr. Fortune. It has evergreen leaves, resembling those of the sweet chestnut.   [M. T. M.]

The Oak appears in all ages to have been an object of veneration, from the time of the 'Oak of Mamre,' under which Abraham sat in the heat of the day, down to that of the Greeks, by whom it was held sacred, and the Romans, who dedicated it to Jupiter. To come nearer home, the Druids worshipped beneath its shade; and even we ourselves view the mighty King of the Forest with mingled feelings of veneration and gratitude, which this age of ironclad ships will not wholly eradicate. Still do we retain the name of Gospel Oak in many of our English counties, pointing to the time when penitential psalms and Gospel truths were breathed beneath their shade; and, they became notable objects as resting-places in the beating of the parish-bounds, a practice supposed to have been derived from the feast to the god Terminus. Our English custom was thus described more than two centuries since by Withers:

That every man might keep his own possessions,
Our fathers used, in reverent processions,
With zealous prayers, and with praiseful cheere,
To walk their parish limits once a year;
And well-known marks (which sacrilegious hands
Now cut or breake) so bordered out their lands,
That every one distinctly knew his owne,
And brawles now rife were then unknowne.

This ceremony was performed by the minister and parochial authorities, accompanied by the people, going the boundaries of the parish, and stopping at the most remarkable sites (oak-trees being considered the most worthy), and reading passages from the Gospels, and there also asking blessings for the people. Herrick makes a lover say :—

> Dearest, bury me
> Under that holy oke or Gospel Tree ;
> Where, though thou see'st not, thou mayst think upon
> Me, when thou yearly go'st Procession.

It is not a little remarkable that though the name of Gospel Oak has not been newly bestowed for many generations, yet that so many trees with that appellation still remain in different parts of England, so that most people have an acquaintance with one or more ancient trees bearing this appellation.

In the midland counties there is always much speculation as to whether the leaves of the oak or those of the ash will appear first, as the following proverb is implicitly relied upon :—

> If the oak 's before the ash,
> Then you'll only get a splash ;
> If the ash precedes the oak,
> Then you may expect a soak.

Considering the different habits of the two trees, there may be reason in the rhyme. The Oak sends its root deep into the soil, and its leafing is advanced or retarded by a warm or cold spring. The roots of the ash are nearer the surface, and so a wet spring hastens its growth, while a dry one would retard it. Rain, moreover, does not affect the oak so much as it does the ash.　　　　[J. B.]

QUERIA, QUERIACEÆ. *Queria hispanica* is a small South European annual, intermediate in many respects between *Caryophyllaceæ* and *Illecebraceæ* ; having the petalless flowers and solitary ovule of the latter, with the capsule opening in valves as in *Caryophyllaceæ*. It is therefore usually considered as constituting a tribe of that order, or is sometimes proposed as an independent one under the name of *Queriaceæ*.

QUERNALES. An alliance proposed by Lindley to include the *Corylaceæ* and *Juglandaceæ*, and distinguished from *Amentales* by the inferior ovary.

QUETSCHE. A name used in Germany for the long egg-shaped varieties of the Plum.

QUEUE D'ARONDELLE. (Fr.) *Sagittaria.* — DE CHEVAL. (Fr.) *Equisetum Telmateja* ; also *Ephedra.* — DE LÉZARD. *Saururus.* — DE LIÈVRE. *Lagurus.* — DE LION. *Leonotis.* — DE PAON. *Tigridia Pavonia.* — DE POURCEAU. *Peucedanum officinale.* — DE RAT. *Myosurus* ; also *Equisetum arvense,* and *Pothos acaulis.* — DE RENARD. *Alopecurus* ; also *Equisetum sylvaticum,* and *Amaranthus caudatus.* — DE SCORPION. *Scorpiurus.* —DE SOURIS. *Myosurus.*

QUICK. The Florin, *Agrostis stoloni-*

fera ; also *Triticum repens* ; and the Quickset, *Cratægus Oxyacantha.*

QUICKEN, or **QUICK-BEAM.** *Pyrus Aucuparia.*

QUICK-IN-HAND. *Impatiens Noli-tangere.*

QUICKSET, or **QUICK.** The Whitethorn, *Cratægus Oxyacantha,* more especially when used as a hedge-plant.

QUILLAJA. A small genus of South American trees belonging to the *Quillaia* or wing-seeded section of *Rosaceæ,* and remarkable for possessing soap-like properties. Five species are described—three Chilian, one Peruvian, and one Brazilian. They are large evergreen trees, with undivided scattered leaves upon stalks bearing two small stipules, which, however, soon drop off ; and their flowers grow four or five together upon stalks produced from the leaf-axils or at the ends of the branches, some being unisexual and others perfect. The calyx is five-parted, and is furnished with a star-like fleshy disk having five elevated notched lobes ; the five petals are spatula-shaped ; the stamens are ten in number, five inserted along with and opposite the petals, and five in the middle of the calyx-segments ; and the five single-celled ovaries, containing numerous ovules in two rows, cohere together but are tipped with distinct spreading styles.

Quillaja differs from its nearest ally, *Kageneckia,* in the calyx segments not overlapping each other in the bud, as well as in the ten stamens being in two instead of one row.

Q. Saponaria, the Quillai or Cullay of the Chilians, is a tree from fifty to sixty feet high, with smooth shining short-stalked oval leaves ; and usually terminal white flowers, either solitary or from three to five upon a stalk. Its bark, called Quillai or Soap-bark, is rough and dark-coloured externally, but internally consists of numerous regular whitish or yellowish layers, and contains a large quantity of carbonate of lime and other mineral matters. It is also rich in *saponine,* a vegetable soap-principle found likewise in plants belonging to the cloveworts, soapworts, and a few other orders ; and on this account it is commonly used as a substitute for washing clothes, two ounces of the bark being sufficient to wash a dress. It is also said to remove all spots or stains, and to impart a remarkable lustre to wool ; and it is used to wash the hair, for which purpose it is powdered between stones, then rubbed with the hands in water, making a foam like soap. A preparation of it has lately been brought into use in this country for promoting the growth of the hair. The Brazilian species, *Q. Selloviana,* which has similar properties, has also been called *Fontenellea brasiliensis.*　　　　[A. S.]

QUILLWORT. *Isoëtes.*

QUIN, QUINQU. In composition = five in number.

QUINA. The South American name applied to several kinds of Cinchona-bark; also the Brazilian name for some other febrifugal barks, as those of *Discaria febrifuga*, *Esenbeckia febrifuga*, *Ticorea febrifuga*, *Hortia brasiliana*, and *Solanum Pseudoquina*. — BLANCA. A Mexican name for Cascarilla-bark. — DE SERRA. The bark of *Remijia ferruginea* and *Vellozii*. — DE LA ANGOSTURA, or DE LA GUAYNA. A Venezuelan name for the bark of *Galipea Cusparia*. — DE REMIJO. The same as Quina de Serra. — DO CAMPO. The bark of *Strychnos Pseudoquina*.

QUINANCY-WORT. *Asperula cynanchica*.

QUINAQUINA. *Cinchona Condaminea*.

QUINATE. Growing in fives; as when a petiole bears five leaflets from the same point; it is then, however, digitate.

QUINCE. *Cydonia vulgaris*. —, BASTARD. *Pyrus Chamæmespilus*. —, BENGAL. *Ægle Marmelos*.

QUINCHAMALIUM. A genus of *Santalaceæ*, consisting of Chilian herbs said to be parasitical upon roots of other plants, like our *Thesiums*. The flowers have a long tubular perianth with five short lobes, and each perianth is surrounded at the base by a small four-toothed involucre often taken for an external calyx, and which distinguishes the genus from others of the tribe *Thesieæ*, to which it belongs. There are three or four species known, of little general interest.

QUINCUNCIAL. A kind of æstivation, in which out of five parts two are exterior, two interior, and the fifth covers the interior with one margin, and has its other margin covered by the exterior; as in the calyx of the rose.

QUINOA. *Chenopodium Quinoa*.

QUINQUENERVIS. When there are five ribs all proceeding from the same point of the base.

QUINQUINA. (Fr.) *Cinchona*. —, BRAZILIAN. The bark of *Cosmibuena hexandra*. — COLORADO. The same as Brazilian Quinquina. — DE PIAUHI. The bark of *Exostemma Souzanum*. — DES ANTILLES. The same as Quinquina Piton. — FAUX. *Iva frutescens*. — INDIGÈNE. A Mauritian name for *Mussænda Landia*. — PITON. The febrifugal emetic bark of *Exostemma caribæum* and *E. floribundum*.

QUINQUINO. *Myrospermum peruiferum*.

QUINSY-BERRY. The Black Currant, *Ribes nigrum*.

QUINSYWORT. *Asperula cynanchica*.

QUINTEFEUILLE. (Fr.) *Potentilla reptans* and other species. — BÂTARDE. *Sibbaldia*. — ROUGE DES MARAIS. *Comarum palustre*.

QUINTINE. A supposed integument of an ovule, the fifth counting from the exterior; but in reality the skin of the nucleus.

QUINTINIA. A genus of *Escalloniaceæ*, nearly related to the well-known *Escallonias* of our gardens, and differing from them in the three to five instead of two-celled ovary. Four species are known, two from New Zealand, and two from South Australia; all of them bushes or small trees, with elliptical or lance-shaped leaves, often covered with scurfy scales, and white flowers the size of those of the privet, disposed in axillary or terminal racemes or panicles. Each flower consists of a calyx with a five-toothed border, five petals, a like number of stamens, and a three to five-lobed style crowning the ovary, which when ripe is a small angular capsule with numerous delicately winged seeds. The genus bears the name of LA Quintinie, a French writer on Horticulture. [A. A. B.]

QUINTUPLED. Multiplied by five.

QUINTUPLE-NERVED. When of five ribs the four lateral spring from the middle one above its base.

QUISQUALIS. A genus of *Combretaceæ*, confined to tropical and subtropical Asia and Africa, and consisting of scandent shrubs with opposite rarely alternate leaves, and axillary or terminal spikes of flowers which change from white to red. The five-cleft calyx is deciduous; the corolla has five oblong petals; the stamens are ten in number, and project beyond the corolla; whilst the fruit is a five-angled one-seeded drupe. *Q. indica* is an inmate of our hothouses. According to George Bennett, a species of this genus, perhaps *Q. chinensis* of Lindley, grows about Macao, and is used by the Chinese as a vermifuge under the name of Tot-chee-fa. [B. S.]

QUITCH. The Couch Grass, *Triticum repens*; also *Agrostis stolonifera*.

QUIVER-TREE. *Aloe dichotoma*.

QUIVISIA. A genus of *Meliaceæ* confined to Mauritius and Bourbon, and consisting of four species, all of which are shrubs or trees, with alternate or nearly opposite simple leaves, either quite entire or on the same branch lobed, and axillary flowers generally arranged in racemes or corymbs. The calyx is urn-shaped, and has from four to five teeth; the corolla is composed of four to five short externally silky petals; the stamens are from eight to ten; the stigma capitate; and the fruit a dehiscent capsule, with four or five valves and cells, each cell containing two seeds. [B. S.]

QUOYA. A West Australian genus of *Verbenaceæ*, having the habit as well as the woolly stems and leaves of some of the small shrubby species of *Stachys*. The leaves are opposite and sessile, and the flowers are disposed in short-stalked close verticils proceeding from the axils of the upper reduced leaves, and forming a long terminal compound raceme, or raceme-like panicle. They have a deeply two-lipped villous calyx, a blue bell-shaped corolla; four perfect stamens; and a filiform style forked at top, and crowning a four-celled ovary. [A. A. B.]

QUUNA. Tropical American trees or shrubs usually classed with the *Clusiaceæ*, but differing in having stipules accompanying the opposite leaves, which are often toothed, and in one species pinnatifid, whilst in all other *Guttiferæ* they are simple and entire. The glossy blades are three to twelve inches long by one to six inches broad, marked with prominent primary veins running at right angles to the midrib; and the small yellow or white flowers are disposed in raceme-like cymes in the axils of the leaves. Each flower has a calyx of four to five rounded sepals, four to eight petals, numerous stamens, and a two to four-celled ovary, which when ripe is a small oblong berry. The pinnatifid-leaved species, *Q. guianensis*, was described by Aublet as a separate genus with the name *Touroulia*. [A. A. B.]

RAAB. A kind of jaggery, or coarse Indian sugar.

RABANA. (Fr.) *Sinapis arvensis*.

RABANNES. A kind of matting made in Madagascar from coarse grass, or the fibre of *Raphia Ruffia*, and imported into the Mauritius for covering floors, or wrapping goods, &c.

RABBIT-BERRY. *Shepherdia argentea*.

RABBIT-ROOT. *Aralia nudicaulis*.

RABELAISIA. This genus of *Rutaceæ* commemorates the well-known French humourist, and consists of shrubs, natives of the islands of the Malayan Archipelago. The branches, inflorescence, and leafstalks are covered with scales; the leaves are waxy at the margins, on long stalks; the flowers are small dioecious—the males arranged in small closely-packed heads on a branched inflorescence, the females more closely crowded on a very short spike. The calyx and corolla have each three segments; and in the male flowers there are three stamens, with globose anthers. The fruit is triangular, three-celled, and opening partially by three valves, each cell containing a single seed. [M. T. M.]

RABÈS. (Fr.) *Carlina acaulis*.

RABES, or RABETTE. (Fr.) *Brassica Napus*.

RABIOULE. (Fr.) *Brassica Rapa*.

RABONE. *Raphanus sativus*.

RACEME. An inflorescence in which the flowers are arranged singly on distinct pedicels, along a common axis.

RACHIS. The divisions of the petiole of the leaves of ferns; also the axis of an inflorescence.

RACHITIS. An abortion of the fruit or seed—a disease.

RACINE D'ABONDANCE. (Fr.) A variety of the Beet-root. — AMÈRE. *Lewisia rediviva*. — D'AMÉRIQUE. *Monsonia ame-*

ricana. — D'ARMÉNIE. *Rubia.* — DE CHARCIS. *Dorstenia Contrayerva.* — DE CHINE. *Smilax China.* — DE COLOMBO. *Jateorhiza palmata.* — DE DISETTE. The same as Racine d'Abondance. — DE MÉCHOACHAN. *Batatas Jalapa.* — DE PYRÈTHRE. *Anacyclus Pyrethrum.* — DE SAINTE HÉLÈNE. *Acorus Calamus.* — DE SANAGROEL. *Aristolochia Serpentaria.* — DE SERPENT. *Ophiorrhiza.* — DE SERPENT À SONNETTES. *Polygala Senega.* — DU BRÉSIL. *Psychotria emetica.* — DU DICTAME BLANC. *Dictamnus albus.* — DU SAINT ESPRIT. *Archangelica officinalis.* — SALIVAIRE. *Anacyclus Pyrethrum.* — VIERGE. *Tamus communis.*

RACLE. (Fr.) *Cenchrus*.

RACOMITRIUM. A genus of acrocarpous mosses belonging to the natural order *Grimmiei*, resembling *Grimmia*, but looser in habit, with a mitræform veil variously split at the base (from whence the name), awl-shaped above, a straight awl-shaped lid, and a single peristome with sixteen twice or thrice-cleft teeth. The leaves are either obtuse or hair-pointed. The species are rather numerous. *R. lanuginosum* forms thick broad beds on the sides of mountains, which are hoary from the long diaphanous hair-like points of the leaves. Some other species are common in subalpine countries, but the genus scarcely exists in lowlands except on sandy heaths and in wild exposed stony places. [M. J. B.]

RADAMÆA. A genus of *Scrophulariaceæ*, containing two small prostrate shrubs from Madagascar, with opposite entire scabrous leaves. The tube of the corolla is slender; and the four stamens with short filaments are included. The short axillary pedicels are furnished with two bracts below the calyx. [W. C.]

RADE-KANE. An Indian name for *Panicum miliaceum*.

RADIAIRE. (Fr.) *Astrantia major*. —, PETITE. *Astrantia minor*.

RADIAL. Growing on the circumference of a circle.

RADIATE. Diverging from a common centre, like rays; as the arms of an umbel, or the ligulate florets of any composite.

RADIATING, or RADIANS. Spreading from a common point, or from the circumference of a circle: also forming apparent rays in the circumference of a circle by the enlargement of the exterior parts; as the outer florets in the umbels of many umbelliferous plants.

RADICAL. Arising from the root, or from its crown.

RADICANS. Throwing out roots; usually applied to stems or leaves.

RADICATE. Having a root.

RADICATIO. The manner in which roots grow, or are arranged.

RADICELLA. A very small root; the young tiny root which appears from the lower part of a young plant at the period of germination.

RADICIFORM. Being of the nature of a root.

RADICLE, RADICULA. The first root of a plant, rudimentary in the embryo.

RADICOSE. Having a large root.

RADII. The peduncles of secondary umbels, or of the flowers of simple umbels. — MEDULLARES. The medullary rays.

RADIOLA. A genus of *Linaceæ*, differing from *Linum* only in the sepals, petals, and stamens being four each, in the sepals being deeply trifid, in the stamens being quite distinct, and in the capsule being eight-celled. *R. Millegrana*, which is indigenous to England and the Continent, is a very small annual, having a much-branched stem, with opposite leaves, and minute white flowers. [B. C.]

RADIS. (Fr.) *Raphanus.* — PETITE-RAVE. *Raphanus sativus.*

RADISH. The well-known esculent root of *Raphanus sativus.* —, HORSE. *Cochlearia Armoracia.* —, SEA. *Raphanus maritimus.* —, WATER. *Nasturtium amphibium.* —, WILD. *Raphanus Raphanistrum.*

RADIUS. The circumference or outer side of the circle formed by umbels or capitules or of other such parts.

RADIX. The root; the descending axis; that part which is the development of a radicle. It differs from a stem not only in its origin, but in not branching symmetrically, and having no normal leaf-buds.

RADULA. A genus of *Jungermanniaceæ* which is noticed here as containing *R. complanata*, a species common in woods on almost every tree. The lobe at the underside of the leaves is remarkable for sending roots into the substance on which it grows. It belongs, like *Madotheca*, in which the lobes are without radicles, to the division *Platyphyllæ.* [M. J. B.]

RAEE, RAI. Indian names for Mustard-seed, *Sinapis nigra, S. ramosa,* &c.

RAFFLESIACEÆ. (*Rafflesiads.*) A small order of parasitical plants, the position of which in the natural system has been the subject of considerable difference of opinion, but which Lindley places amongst Rhizogens. The plants which compose it have no stem, but consist of flowers only, sometimes of gigantic size, surrounded by a few scales, and sessile on the stems or rhizomes of woody or perennial plants. These flowers consist of a campanulate or globular five-cleft perianth, with numerous anthers on a central column. The ovary is inferior, one-celled, with many-seeded parietal placentæ, and as many styles as placentæ, more or less united within the column, where the flowers are hermaphrodite, or in the centre of female flowers. The fruit is indehiscent, with numerous seeds, and the embryo undivided, with or without albumen. The principal genera are *Rafflesia* and *Brugmansia* in tropical Asia, and *Pilostyles* and *Apodanthes* in South America.

RAFFLESIA. The name of a genus of parasitical plants, natives of Java and Sumatra. The species have great interest, both for the botanist and for the general public, owing to their peculiar structure and appearance. The *Rafflesias* were first made known in 1818. Sir Stamford Raffles, at that time Governor of Bencoolen, was on a tour in the interior of Sumatra, accompanied by Lady Raffles, Dr. Arnold, and others, when the party lighted upon a flower of enormous size, more than a yard across. Descriptions and drawings of this vegetable prodigy were sent to this country, and the plant was named by the celebrated Robert Brown, in honour of its discoverers, *Rafflesia Arnoldi.* Since then several other species have been discovered, but none of equal size with that just mentioned, which indeed still retains its character as being the largest flower known. The genus, with one or two allies, is now comprised in a distinct family, *Rafflesiaceæ.*

The true *Rafflesias* have no proper stems or leaves, but consist solely of flowers, varying in diameter from two or three inches to as many feet, enveloped at the base by a few bluish or brownish scales, and emerging from the roots and trunks of various species of *Cissus.* The unexpanded flower-buds in *R. Arnoldi* are roundish, and resemble a close cabbage in shape. The flowers appear to be diœcious, and have a perianth which is tubular below, but whose limb is divided into five entire fleshy lobes, which partially overlap one another in the bud, but afterwards spread widely. The perianth is flesh-coloured and mottled, and has a foul odour of tainted meat, by which insects are attracted. Within is a thick fleshy rim or corona lining the upper part of the tube; and within this corona, in the male flowers, and occupying the centre, is a thick fleshy column, adherent to the perianth-tube, having one or more projecting rims surrounding its base, and at the top a wide flat plate, the overhanging margin of which is rolled round like the capital of an Ionic column. On the revolute margin is placed a ring of anthers, which are sessile, each one opening by a single pore, although it is divided in the interior into many compartments; the pollen-grains are round. In the female flowers, the deep cup-shaped perianth and corona are like those of the male flowers; the central column is also similar, but there are no anthers. The ovary is adherent to the base of the tube of the perianth, has a single compartment containing numerous ovules attached to its walls, and is surmounted by several styles, which are blended with the central column.

Three or four species are known, differing greatly in size, but little in essential characters. The corona and summit of the column are in some species studded with tubercles and scales. The outer portions of the flower are brownish or flesh-coloured, the central portions pinkish or yellowish. Dr. Arnold describes the first flower seen by him as being more than a yard across, the petals or lobes of the perianth as being a foot long, and varying in thickness from three-quarters to one-quarter of an inch, and the cup of the flower as calculated to hold twelve pints. The weight of the whole flower was estimated at fifteen pounds.

It appears from the subsequent investigations of Mr. Jack, M. Blume, M. de Vriese, and other botanists, that the growth of these flowers occupies a few months. They first appear as round knobs protruding from the bark of various species of *Cissus*. The flowers remain expanded only for a few days, and then gradually putrefy. Their fetid scent may be conducive to their fertilisation, by means of the insects which are attracted by the smell. This is the more probable, as the stamens and pistil are in different flowers. It was at first considered that these plants grew only on the roots of their foster-parents, and hence they were called Rhizanths or Root-flowers; but it is now known that they grow also on the stems, in some cases at some feet above the ground, though in others the stems are prostrate and thus resemble roots. The parasites develope their flowers at a season when the leaves and flowers of the *Cissus* have withered. A stringent and styptic properties are assigned by the Javanese to these singular plants. One species, *R. Rochusseni*, discovered in Java in 1850 by two Dutch botanists, MM. Teysmann and Binnendijk, was in cultivation in 1851 at the Botanic Garden at Leyden. See Hooker's *Journal of Botany*, 1851, p. 217; also *Transactions of Linnæan Society*, xiii. p. 201, and xix. p. 221. See also PLATE 14 a for *R. Rochusseni*. [M. T. M.]

RAFINESQUIA. This genus of *Compositæ* is nearly related to *Scorzonera*, and differs from it chiefly in the single series of feathery pappus hairs, and the distinctly beaked achenes. The two known species, *R. californica* and *R. neo-mexicana*, are annual weeds with runcinate or lyrately-pinnatifid leaves, those of the stem linear; the cylindrical flower-heads terminate the twigs, and each contain from ten to fifteen rose-coloured florets, all fertile, and enclosed in an involucre of membranaceous scales surrounded at the base by a few short narrow bracts. The genus bears the name of C. S. Rafinesque, a Sicilian by birth, who chose America as his adopted country, and wrote many works on the botany of the United States. [A. A. B.]

RAFNIA. A genus of South African shrubs of the same group of *Leguminosæ* as our own broom, and readily known among its allies by the perfect smoothness of its parts, the usually pea-green leaves, which are not strongly nerved as in *Borbonia*, and the forked instead of racemed inflorescence. There are about twenty species, divisible into two groups by the form of

their leaves, which are either lance-shaped oval or elliptical, or heart-shaped embracing the stem. The flowers are axillary, the pedicels usually forked and bearing a number of flowers, while at the point of forking there are opposite leaf-like bracts. The flowers are yellow, mostly as large as those of the broom. The genus bears the name of O. G. Rafn, a Danish botanist. [A. A. B.]

RAGATELUS. *Trichomanes*.

RAGEE. *Eleusine coracana*.

RAGGED ROBIN. *Lychnis Flos-cuculi*.

RAGIOPTERIS. *Onoclea*.

RAGOUMINIER. (Fr.) *Cerasus pumila*.

RAGWEED. *Ambrosia trifida*.

RAGWORT. *Senecio Jacobæa*. —, AFRICAN. *Othonna*. —, SEA. *Cineraria maritima*.

RAIFORT. (Fr.) *Raphanus*. — AQUATIQUE JAUNE. *Nasturtium amphibium*. — DES BOUTIQUES. *Cochlearia Armoracia*. — DES PARISIENS. *Raphanus sativus*. — GRAND, or SAUVAGE. *Cochlearia Armoracia*.

RAIPONCE. (Fr.) *Campanula Rapunculus*.

RAISIN D'AMÉRIQUE. (Fr.) *Phytolacca dodecandra*. — DES BOIS. *Vaccinium Myrtillus*. — D'OURS. *Arctostaphylos uva-ursi*. — DE MARS. *Ribes rubrum*. — DE MER. *Ephedra distachya*. — DE RENARD. *Paris quadrifolia*.

RAISINIER. (Fr.) *Coccoloba*.

RAISINS. Sun-dried Grapes.

RAISIN-TREE. *Ribes rubrum*.

RAIZ DA CHINA. A Brazilian name for the knotty roots of *Smilax glauca*. — DE PIPI. A Brazilian name for *Petiveria tetrandra*. — DE TIHU. A Brazilian name for *Jatropha officinalis*. — DO PADRE SALERMA. A Brazilian name for the medicinal *Gomphrena officinalis* and *G. macrocephala*. — PRETA. A Brazilian name for Cabinca, a drug obtained from *Chiococca racemosa*, *densifolia*, and *anguifuga*.

RAJANIA. The celebrated English naturalist John Ray, whose system of grouping plants was published in 1703, and who is considered as the founder of the natural system, is commemorated in this genus. The species are West Indian climbing shrubs, having a great resemblance to those of *Dioscorea*, or yam, from which genus the present is distinguished by having only one ovule in each of the three compartments of the ovary. The membranaceous capsular fruit, moreover, has but one fully-formed compartment, owing to the arrest of the growth of the other two. The fertile compartment is flattened and prolonged into a wing, but does not split when ripe. It contains a single wingless seed. One or two species are cultivated as stove climbers, but have little to recommend them. The genus belongs to the order *Dioscoreaceæ*. [M. T. M.]

Plate 14

F. Adlard sc

MOUNTAIN VEGETATION OF JAVA.

(AFTER DE VRIESE.)

a Rafflesia Hochussoni b. A Vanilla
c A Freyrinetia   d. A Selligura.

RAJIKA. A Sanscrit name for Black Mustard seed.

RAJ-JEERA. An Indian name for *Amaranthus frumentaceus*, the seeds of which are edible.

RAL. The balsamic resin of *Shorea robusta*.

RALEIGHIA. A Brazilian shrub, resembling in habit some species of *Weinmannia*, having opposite undivided stipulate leaves, and small flowers in dense terminal racemes. It forms a genus of *Cunoniaceæ*, nearly allied to *Belangera*, but differing chiefly in the one-celled ovary with parietal placentas.

RAMAL. Of or belonging to a branch.

RAMALINA. A small genus of lichens with flat fronds like stag's horns, or nearly cylindrical like *Clavaria*. The frond is alike all round, without any distinct under-side, in which the genus differs from *Evernia*. *E. fraxinea* grows everywhere on the trunks of ash-trees, and *R. farinacea*, with its narrow mealy spotted fronds, is almost equally common. Others are marine in their habits like *Roccellæ*. *R. polymorpha* and *scopulorum* are good dye-weeds. [M. J. B.]

RAMASTRA. The secondary petioles or petiolules of compound leaves.

RAMBEH. *Pierardia sativa*, a Malacca fruit.

RAMBIYA. A Malayan name for the Sago Palm.

RAMBUTAN, or RAMBOOTAN. The fruit of *Nephelium lappaceum*.

RAMEAL, RAMEOUS. Of or belonging to the branches.

RAMEAU D'OR. (Fr.) *Cheiranthus Cheiri*.

RAMENTA. Thin membranous expansions found upon the surface of plants, and resembling hairs in composition, except that they are not composed of a single longitudinal series of cells, but of many series of cells arranged on the same plane.

RAMENTACEOUS. Covered with ramenta, as the stems of many ferns.

RAM-GOAT. *Fagara microphylla*.

RAMIPAROUS. Producing branches.

RAMONDIA. A genus of monopetalous plants of doubtful affinity, and provisionally classed with *Cyrtandraceæ*, from the greater number of which it differs in having five fertile stamens. It is a stemless perennial herb, occupying rocks in the Pyrenees, and also in the Piedmontese Alps. The leaves are radical, ovate, and forming rosettes, and the scape bears from one to six flowers of a purplish colour. The calyx is five-cleft; the corolla rotate, and nearly regular; the stamens are five, their filaments short and glabrous; whilst the style is simple; and the capsule oblong, one-celled, enclosing numerous seeds. [B. S.]

RAMOON-TREE. *Trophis*.

RAMOSE. Divided into many branches.

RAMPE. *Arum maculatum*.

RAMPION, or RAMPS. A garden name for *Campanula Rapunculus*.

RAM'S-HEAD. An American name for *Cypripedium arietinum*; also the seeds of *Cicer arietinum*.

RAMSONS, or RAMSIES. *Allium ursinum*.

RAMSTED. An American name for *Linaria vulgaris*.

RAM-TIL. An Indian name for the Black Til, *Guizotia oleifera*.

RAMTURAI. An Indian name for the Ochro, *Abelmoschus esculentus*.

RAMULUS (adj. RAMULOSE). A twig; a small branch—the least which a plant produces.

RAMUS. A branch; any division of the stem.

RAMUSCULI. The mycelium of certain fungals.

RANALES. An alliance proposed by Lindley for the hypogynous polypetalous families which have indefinite stamens and a minute embryo enclosed in a large quantity of fleshy or horny albumen. It includes *Magnoliaceæ*, *Anonaceæ*, *Dilleniaceæ*, *Ranunculaceæ*, *Sarraceniaceæ*, and *Papaveraceæ*.

RANDIA. A genus of *Cinchonaceæ* named in honour of Isaac Rand, formerly Præfectus of the Botanic Garden of the Society of Apothecaries at Chelsea. The species are small trees or shrubs, natives of the tropical regions of both hemispheres. They have axillary spines, and, so far as the construction of their flowers goes, they are very nearly allied to *Gardenia*. The main differences are to be sought in the ovary, which is two-celled, and surmounted by a disk. The fruit has a dry rind, is surmounted by the limb of the calyx, and is internally divided into two compartments, containing numerous seeds imbedded in pulp. Moreover, the tube of the corolla is usually shorter in this genus than in *Gardenia*. *R. dumetorum* is used as a hedge-plant in India. Its fruit is emetic, and is used to stupefy fish, so as to allow of their ready capture; the rind of the root is also used medicinally. The seeds of *R. scandens* furnish in China a scarlet dye. The fruit of *R. aculeata* is employed in the West Indies as a blue dye; its wood is used for cask-staves, ladders, and other purposes. Some of the species are in cultivation in this country as stove shrubs; the flowers are whitish or yellowish in colour. [M. T. M.]

RANKNESS. A condition often assumed by fruit-trees in gardens and orchards, in consequence of which great shoots, or feeders as they are called, are given out with little or no bearing wood.

Excessive richness of soil, and a too copious supply of manure, are generally the moving causes, though some varieties are naturally so luxuriant that they require grafting, or something which may check their growth. Pears, for this reason, are beneficially grafted on quince stocks; but where this has not been done, lifting and root-pruning are indispensable. We do not, however, recommend gardeners to adopt root-pruning as a system without reference to the nature of the soil or condition of their trees. If the soil is naturally sterile, and the growth moderately luxuriant, root-pruning may induce permanent mischief, as we can ourselves bear witness. In this case, as in many others in horticultural matters, 'a little knowledge is a dangerous thing.'　　　[M. J. B.]

RANUNCULACEÆ. (Ranunculi, Podophyllaceæ, Cronofoots.) A considerable order of polypetalous dicotyledons, characterised chiefly by definite deciduous sepals, indefinite hypogynous stamens, several free ovaries, seeds without an arillus, and a homogeneous albumen with a minute embryo. With the exception of Clematis, the species are almost all herbaceous, with radical or alternate leaves, very frequently much cut or divided; the sepals are generally four or five, and more or less coloured; the petals always free when present, but often small and scale-like, or spurred or otherwise deformed, or altogether wanting; the carpels of the fruit either single-seeded and seed-like, or capsular with several seeds, often opening into follicles. The species are numerous in Europe and Northern Asia, less so in North America; and there are several in the temperate regions of the southern hemisphere, but very few within the tropics, except in mountain districts. Throughout the order there is a tendency to an acrid, caustic, and more or less poisonous principle, very volatile in the foliage and herbaceous parts, but sometimes very virulent in the roots. There are about forty genera, of which the principal are: Clematis, Thalictrum, Anemone, Ranunculus, Caltha, Trollius, Helleborus, Nigella, Aquilegia, Delphinium, Aconitum, Actæa, and Pæonia.

RANUNCULUS. An extensive genus of herbaceous plants giving name to the order Ranunculaceæ, and distinguished by the following characters:—Sepals five, not prolonged at the base; petals five, with a nectariferous scale at the base; fruit without awns. There are reckoned to be about twenty British species, which may popularly be arranged into several groups. The common meadow weeds with glossy yellow flowers, known by the names Buttercups, Golden-cups, and King-cups, belong to one or other of the following species—R. acris, R. bulbosus, and R. repens, of which the first may be discriminated by its slender cylindrical flower-stalk and spreading calyx; the second by its furrowed flower-stalk, reflexed calyx, and bulbous root; the third by its furrowed flower

stalk, spreading calyx, and creeping scions. R. auricomus approaches nearest to R. acris in habit, but grows in woods, has the calyx coloured, frequently has one or more of its petals abortive, and has the upper leaves smooth and divided into very narrow segments. R. sceleratus is a coarse succulent aquatic, with glossy divided leaves, small yellow flowers, and oblong heads of fruit. R. arvensis, common in cornfields, is a slender plant about a foot high, sufficiently marked by its large prickly fruit. All the above have divided leaves and yellow flowers. R. Lingua and R. Flammula, Greater and Lesser Spearwort, have lanceolate undivided leaves, and grow in watery places—the former two to four feet high with large yellow flowers; the latter also with yellow flowers six to eighteen inches high. R. aquatilis, the Water Crowfoot, with its varieties, by some botanists considered species, is the common aquatic with showy white flowers, long flexible stems, bearing numerous leaves, of which the submersed ones are capillary, while the upper are plane, variously lobed, and floating; when growing in swift-running water, the upper leaves and flowers are not developed, and the lower may be compared to a tuft of bright green hair waving to and fro in the current. The Lesser Celandine, the showy star-like yellow flower which enlivens every bank in early spring, is by some botanists called R. Ficaria, by others FICARIA: which see. Most of the above have very acrid properties, which renders their presence in meadow-lands objectionable; but the herbage of R. aquatilis is not only innoxious, but nutritive to cattle.

Among cultivated species R. asiaticus affords the endless varieties of Ranunculus grown by florists. White Bachelor's Buttons (Fr. Boutons d'Argent) are the flowers of R. aconitifolius, and Yellow Bachelor's Buttons (Fr. Boutons d'Or) are those of a double variety of R. acris. Several species of humble growth, but having comparatively large flowers, grow in the Arctic regions, or high up on the mountains in most parts of the world. French: Renoncule; German: Ranunkel.　　　[C. A. J.]

RAOULIA. A genus of Compositæ nearly related to Gnaphalium and Helichrysum, and, according to Dr. Hooker, differing mainly from these in their peculiar habit, and the narrow receptacle of the flower-heads. The species, mostly from New Zealand, grow in dense tufts in rocky mountainous places, and have the aspect of mosses, their short branches being densely clothed with minute smooth or woolly leaves. Sitting at the apex of each short twig is a single white starry flower-head closely surrounded with leaves. In some species, as R. grandiflora, where the heads are three-quarters of an inch across, the inner scales of the involucre are white, and have the appearance of ray-florets, which, however, are tubular and fertile, the disk-florets being also tubular and perfect. The achenes are smooth or downy, and crowned with a pappus of one series of rough hairs. The name of Vegetable Sheep(!) is given by the settlers in New Zealand to *R. eximia*, because, from its growing in large white tufts on elevated sheep-runs, it may be readily mistaken for the sheep. The genus is dedicated to M Raoul, a French naval surgeon who wrote on New Zealand plants. [A. A. B.]

RAPA. The name given by Tournefort to the genus which he constituted to contain the common turnip, *Brassica Rapa*, which he separated even from the colza, *B. Napus*; though some botanists now include both these under *B. campestris*, considering that the differences are not sufficient to establish even their specific distinction. [J. T. S.]

RAPATEA. A genus of *Juncaceæ*, consisting of four or five species from tropical South America. They are stout and rather coarse herbs, with long flat radical leaves and erect simple scapes, often much flattened at the top; and bearing a head or dense umbel of yellow flowers in an involucre of two leafy bracts, broad at the base with long points. Each flower is surrounded by several imbricated scales, and consists of three outer stiff chaff-like erect sepals, and three inner spreading petals, with six stamens and a three-celled three-valved capsule, with one seed in each cell.

RAPE, SUMMER. *Brassica campestris.* —, WINTER. *Brassica Napus.*

RÂPETTE. (Fr.) *Asperugo procumbens.*

RAPHANISTRUM. A genus of *Cruciferæ* combined with *Raphanus*, from which it differs only in the more slender-beaded pods, which break transversely into one-seeded joints, the lower joint persistent, empty, not obliterated, and the substance of the pod woody not spongy throughout. The flowers are pale-yellow or white. The pod has a beak formed by the conical persistent style. The Wild Radish, *Raphanus Raphanistrum*, a common weed in cultivated ground, is the type. [J. T. S.]

RAPHANUS. A genus of *Cruciferæ* containing only two or three species, of which the most important is the Common Radish. The genus is characterised by the pod, which is more or less elongated thick pointed and indehiscent, more or less contracted or even jointed between the seeds, without any longitudinal partition when ripe, but containing several seeds separated by a pithy substance filling the pod.

The Garden Radish, *R. sativus*, is unknown in the wild state; but some varieties of *R. Raphanistrum* on the Mediterranean coast come sufficiently near to suggest the possibility that it is merely a cultivated race of the wild plant. It is a hardy annual, and in the time of the Pharaohs was extensively cultivated in Egypt, from whence it gradually found its way into Europe, but does not appear to have reached this country until A.D. 1548. Gerard

mentions four varieties as being known in A.D. 1597. The root is fleshy and variable in form, in some varieties fusiform, in others round like a small turnip, or semi-globular, and either of a reddish-purple, white, yellowish, or deep brown colour. The leaves are rough, lyrate, or partly divided transversely into segments, the outer one being much larger and broader than the rest. The flower-stem is round erect and branching, about three feet high, and bearing moderate-sized flowers, varying from white to pale-violet, with strong dark-coloured veins. The seed-pods are smooth, ending in a short pointed beak. When plump, and while young and green, these pods are used for pickling, alone or with other vegetables, and are considered a tolerable substitute for capers.

It is, however, as a salad-root that radishes are chiefly grown, and for this they have been used from time immemorial. They are of rapid growth, and in perfection when of a moderate size and quite young. The flesh is white, crisp, and tender, and abounds in a peculiar nitrous juice, which is much relished by vegetarians, and considered to be a powerful antiscorbutic. Radishes are usually eaten raw with salt, vinegar, &c., or cut into slices and mixed in salads. When too large for a salad they make an excellent dish if dressed and served like asparagus. Although a favourite vegetable with all classes, it is generally admitted to possess but a very small amount of nutritive matter. [W. B. B.]

RAPHE. The cord of fibro-vascular tissue which connects the base of the nucleus of an ovule with the placenta.

RAPHIA. The species forming this genus of Palms are confined to three very limited but widely separated localities— one, *R. tædigera*, being found only on the banks of the Lower Amazon and Pará

Raphia Ruffia.

Rivers in Brazil; another, *R. vinifera*, on the West Coast of tropical Africa; while

tho third, *R. Ruffla*, is only known as a cultivated plant in Madagascar and the neighbouring islands. All three inhabit low swampy lands in the vicinity of the sea, or river-banks within the influence of the tides. They have stout unarmed ringed trunks of no great height, and bear gigantic pinnate spiny leaves, often fifty or more feet in length, and erect, so that the entire trees are sometimes sixty or seventy feet high. The flower-spikes are also of large size and much-branched, hanging down from amongst the leaves, and measuring as much as six feet in length; the branches being arranged in two opposite rows, and the ultimate ones bearing the flowers resembling flattened catkins. Both sexes are borne on the same spike. The fruit-spikes sometimes weigh as much as 200 lbs. or 300 lbs., and bear a large number of one-seeded fruits rather larger than eggs, covered with shining bony overlapping scales.

The Jupati Palm, *R. tædigera*, has cylindrical leafstalks, which measure from twelve to fifteen feet in length, and are used by the natives of the Amazon for a variety of purposes; the walls and partitions of their houses being often constructed of them, while baskets, boxes, &c., are made of strips of the smooth outer portion. *R. vinifera*, the Bamboo Palm, is employed for similar purposes by the Africans, who also make very pliable cloth and neat baskets of the undeveloped leaves. Palm-wine is obtained from it, whence its Latin specific name. [A. S.]

RAPHIDA, RAPHIDES. Crystals of various salts formed in the interior of plants by the combination of vegetable acids with alkaline bases. They derive their name from being in many cases acicular, or needle-shaped.

RAPHIOSTYLIS. A name proposed by Planchon for a tropical African tree of the order *Olacaceæ*, which has since been united with *Apodytes*, differing from the other species of the latter genus only in its axillary inflorescence.

RAPHISTEMMA. A genus of *Asclepiadaceæ*, consisting of two species from Eastern India and Java. They are both tall climbers, with large opposite cordate leaves, and rather showy white campanulate flowers in axillary corymbs. The genus is chiefly characterised by the staminal corona, consisting of five distinct ligulate petal-like scales, inflected at the top, and as long as the tube of the corolla.

RAPISTRUM. A genus of *Cruciferæ* inhabiting Southern Europe and Central Asia; annuals or perennials, with a more rigid habit, and much shorter pods in larger racemes, than *Raphanus*. The pods are two-jointed with one-celled joints, the lower stalk-like obconic one-seeded or empty; the upper subglobose one-seeded, terminated by the filiform style. [J. T. S.]

RAPONCULE. (Fr.) *Phyteuma*.

RAPONTIQUE. (Fr.) *Rheum*. — DES

MONTAGNES, or DES MOINES. *Rumex alpinus*. — VULGAIRE. *Centaurea Jacea*.

RAPPADURA. A coarse kind of sugar made in Mexico.

RAPUNCULUS. *Campanula Rapunculus*

RAPUNTIUM. *Lobelia*.

RAQUETTE. (Fr.) *Opuntia vulgaris*.

RARAK. The Malayan name for the Soap-berry, *Sapindus emarginatus*.

RARE, RARUS. Thinly placed; the reverse of such terms as dense, approximated, &c.

RASAMALA. An Eastern name for *Liquidambar Altingia*.

RASPAILIA. A genus of *Bruniaceæ*, distinguished by the calyx being free, its tube bell-shaped, and its border having five acute segments with hard ends. The corolla consists of five petals, which are obovate and erect; the ovary is free and two-celled. The only species is a small shrub, a native of the Cape. The genus was named after Raspail, a French writer on Botany, &c. [G. D.]

RASPBERRY. The fragrant subacid fruit of *Rubus Idæus*.

*RASPBERRY-JAM TREE. The Stinking *Acacia* of Central and Western America, from which is obtained a hard heavy wood, with an odour resembling raspberry jam.

RATA. A New Zealand name for one of the hardwooded species of *Metrosideros*.

RATANHIA. A Peruvian name for the drug called Rhatany-root, the root of *Krameria triandra*.

RATIBIDA. A synonym of *Obeliscaria*, sometimes used in gardens.

RATMARA. An Indian name for one of the dyeing lichens.

RATONIA. A genus of *Sapindaceæ*, consisting of a few pinnate-leaved trees of East Tropical Australia, the Philippines, and the West Indies. Some of the species were formerly placed in *Cupania*, from which, as now defined by Dr. Hooker, they differ in the calyx-segments being valvate in the bud, instead of overlapping each other. The leaves are smooth, formed of two to seven pairs of oblong-lanceolate leaflets; and the minute greenish flowers, disposed in axillary or terminal panicles, have five calyx-segments, five scale-like petals (or none), eight to ten stamens, and a trifid style surmounting a three-celled ovary, which becomes a two or three-lobed leathery capsule, each cell with a single black seed having a yellow aril at its base. *R. apetala*, a common West Indian plant, forms a tree of about twenty feet high, and is known in Jamaica as Bastard Locust. [A. A. B.]

RATOON. The young shoots of the Sugar Cane.

RATSBANE, or **RAT-POISON.** A West African name for *Chailletia toxicaria.*

RATTAN. A commercial name for the long trailing stems of *Calamus Royleanus, Rotang, rudentum, viminalis,* and other species, which form a considerable article of import from India and the Eastern Archipelago. —, **GREAT.** *Calamus rudentum.* —, **GROUND.** *Rhaphis flabelliformis.*

RATTANY, or **RHATANY.** The powerfully astringent root of *Krameria triandra.* — **SAVANILLA.** The root of the New Grenada variety of *Krameria Ixina.*

RATTLE, RED. *Pedicularis sylvatica.* —, **YELLOW.** *Rhinanthus Crista galli.*

RATTLE-BOX. *Rhinanthus Crista galli;* also an American name for *Crotalaria.*

RATTLESNAKE-HERB. An American name for *Actæa.*

RATTLESNAKE-ROOT. The root of *Polygala Senega;* also an American name for *Nabalus.*

RATTLESNAKE'S MASTER. An American name for *Liatris scariosa* and *squarrosa.*

RATTLESNAKE-WEED. *Eryngium virginicum.*

RATTLEWORT. *Crotalaria.*

RAUCHE. (Fr.) *Typha latifolia.*

RAUPO. *Typha angustifolia.*

RAUWOLFIA. This genus of *Apocynaceæ,* so called in honour of a botanical traveller, consists of tropical American shrubs, having the leaves opposite or whorled, and the flowers in corymbs. The corolla is funnel-shaped, with a hairy throat, and a limb divided into five oblique segments; the ovary is two-lobed, surrounded at its base by a circular thickened rim; and the fruit is fleshy, divided into two halves each containing a stone, in which is enclosed a single seed. The fruits of *R. canescens* contain a black juice which has been used as a dye in the West Indies. These plants are more or less poisonous. Some of them are used medicinally as cathartics or emetics, as for instance *R. nitida,* of which the root is thus employed. [M. T. M.]

RAVE. (Fr.) *Brassica Rapa.* — **DE SAINT ANTOINE.** *Ranunculus bulbosus.*

RAVENALA. A splendid Madagascar plant constituting a genus of *Musaceæ.* The trunk is like that of the palm, and is built up of the sheaths of the leafstalks, the other portions of the leaves having fallen off. The upper leaves are in two rows on long stalks, and they diverge from the upper portion of the stem somewhat in the same manner as the ribs of a fan, from its centre. The flowers are closely crowded in the axils of large bracts or spathes, which are ranged in two rows along the terminal flowerstalks. In botanical characters the flowers are similar to those of the species of *Musa* and *Strelitzia,* but they differ in the stamens which are six in num-

ber. The fruit also is woody, capsular, three-celled, and three-valved; and the seeds are arranged in two rows, in each of the compartments of the fruit, and have a pulpy blue arillus surrounding them.

This noble plant is called by the French the Traveller's Tree, probably on account of the water which is stored up in the large cup-like sheaths of the leafstalks, and which is sought for by travellers to allay their thirst. The broad leaves are used as thatch to cover the huts in Madagascar. The seeds are edible, and the blue pulpy aril surrounding them yields an essential oil. The blades of the leaves are oblong in form, and are larger in size than those of any known plant, being simple, except the *Victoria regia.* [M. T. M.]

RAVEN-BLACK. See PULLUS and CORACINUS.

RAVENCHBENY. An Indian name for Gamboge.

RAVENELLE. (Fr.) *Raphanus Raphanistrum.* — JAUNE. *Cheiranthus Cheiri.*

RAWUND, or **REWUND.** Indian names for Rhubarb.

REAUMURIA, REAUMURIACEÆ. The first of these names represents a small genus of dicotyledons, closely connected through *Hololachna* with *Tamarix,* and considered by several botanists as belonging to the family of *Tamaricaceæ,* whilst others, relying upon its affinities with *Hypericaceæ,* propose it as the type of the small independent order *Reaumuriaceæ.* The foliage, the free erect distinct placentæ, and the seeds, connect the genus with *Tamaricaceæ,* from which it differs chiefly in the more numerous stamens, and in the placentæ, which, although free from the sides of the ovary, rise up to the top of the cavity, with which they are often united there as well as at the base. The few species are small diffuse or much-branched saline shrubs, natives of the eastern shores of the Mediterranean, or of the salt-plains of Central Asia; and bearing solitary conspicuous flowers, which have a five-cut bell-shaped calyx surrounded by numerous overlapping bracts, five egg-shaped petals with two fringed scales at their bases on the inside, numerous stamens with narrow awl-shaped filaments cohering together in five bundles, and a sessile ovary terminating in five thread-like styles, and divided into five cells each containing four ovules. The five-celled fruits contain one or two hairy seeds in each cell. The bruised leaves of *R. vermiculata* are used at Alexandria as an external application for the cure of the itch. [A. S.]

REBENTA CABALLOS. A Spanish American name for *Isotoma longiflora.*

RÈBLE, or **RIÈBLE.** (Fr.) *Galium Aparine.*

RECCHIA. A little-known Mexican shrub, *R. mexicana,* is the only representative of this genus of *Dilleniaceæ* which is allied to *Curatella;* but distinguished from it by the five sepals being equal and widely spread, and by the stamens being only ten in number. It has twisted branches, oval or oblong leaves, and short-stalked yellow flowers produced along the upper part of the young angular branches, and forming a kind of raceme. [A. S.]

RECEPTACLE. A general term expressive of a part which receives or bears other parts: as the receptacle of flowers or *clinanthium*, the receptacle of fruits or *torus*, the receptacle of ovules or *placenta*. Receptacles of oil are cysts formed among the cellular tissue of plants and containing an oily secretion, as in the so-called dotted leaves of the orange. Receptacles of secretion are those cavities of the interior of a plant into which natural secretions are drained.

RECESS. The same as Sinus.

RECHSTEINERA. A genus of *Gesneraceæ* inhabiting Brazil, of which *R. allagophylla* (*Gesnera allagophylla* of the gardens) is the type. They have large tubers, an erect hairy stem, opposite or ternate linear or oblong leaves, and a terminal spike of fine scarlet or yellow flowers. The nearly bilabiate corolla is scarcely double the length of the five-cleft calyx; and the ovary is surrounded by five glands, two of which are larger than the rest. *R. allagophylla* has long been a favourite in our hothouses, on account of its gay orange-scarlet flowers. [B. S.]

RECLINATE, RECLINING. Bent down upon some other part; falling gradually back from the perpendicular, as the branches of many trees.

RECONDITE. Concealed; not easily to be seen.

RECTEMBRYÆ. A suborder of *Solanaceæ*, consisting of those plants in which the embryo is straight, as distinguished from *Curvembryæ*, in which it is curved.

RECTINERVIS, RECTINERVIUS. The same as Parallelinervis.

RECTIVENIUS. Straight-veined; having all the veins parallel, as in the leaves of a grass.

RECTUS. In a right line; not wavy or curved, or deviating from a straight direction in any way.

RÉCURE DE CRAPAUD. (Fr.) *Elatine Alsinastrum.*

RECURVATE, RECURVED, RECURVUS. Bent, but not rolled backwards.

RED. The common term for any pure red.

RED-BROWN. See PORPHYREUS.

RED-BUD. *Cercis Siliquastrum*; also *C. canadensis.*

RED-COAT. *Erythrochiton.*

RED GUM, RED RAG, RED ROBIN, RED RUST are all so many synonyms of Rust.

RED-HEAD. *Asclepias curassavica.*

RED-INK PLANT. *Phytolacca decandra*

RED-KNEES. *Polygonum Hydropiper.*

RED-LAC. *Rhus succedanea.*

RED-LEGS. *Polygonum Bistorta.*

RED MOROCCO. *Adonis autumnalis.*

REDOUL. (Fr.) *Coriaria.*

RED-ROOT. A popular name for the fleshy rhizomes of *Sanguinaria canadensis*; also the root of *Geum canadense*, and of *Ceanothus americanus*; also an American name for *Lachnanthes.*

RED-ROT. *Drosera.*

RED-SHANKS. *Polygonum Persicaria*; also *Geranium Robertianum.*

RED SNOW. The common name of *Protococcus nivalis*, which in an incredibly short space of time produces large patches of a brilliant scarlet on the surface of snow in the Arctic regions or amongst the Alps. A species of *Protococcus*, which is almost identical with *P. pluvialis*, is common upon leaves, straws, little pebbles, &c. where water has rested; and has given occasion to Shuttleworth, Cohn, and others for a tolerably perfect study of this strange production, which before the discovery of the propagation of so many *Algæ* by zoospores must undoubtedly have been referred to the animal kingdom. The endochrome is divided into a definite number of cells, each of which becomes a new individual. Some become naked active cells moving by two flagelliform processes, or these cells are surrounded by a hyaline sac, and within the sac are definitely divided into a number of new individuals. Occasionally the division goes so far that their number is apparently indefinite. It is impossible within our limits to trace each further change, for which we must refer to Cohn's paper (*Nachträge zur Naturgeschichte des Protococcus pluvialis*). The spores, as in many other minute *Algæ*, are in some stages green, in some scarlet. [M. J. B.]

RED-TOP. An American name for *Agrostis vulgaris.* —, FALSE. *Poa serotina.* —, TALL. *Tricuspis seslerioides.*

REDUPLICATIVE. Doubled back: a term of æstivation, when the edges are valvate and doubled back.

REDWARE. *Laminaria digitata.*

RED-WATER TREE. *Erythrophleum guineense.*

RED-WEED. *Papaver Rhœas*; also *Phytolacca.*

RED-WITHE. *Combretum Jacquini.*

REDWOOD. An East Indian dye-wood, the produce of *Pterocarpus santalinus*; also *Erythroxylon.* The Redwood of the Turks is *Cornus mascula*; that of the timber trade is furnished by *Sequoia sempervirens.* —, ANDAMAN. The timber of *Pterocarpus dalbergioides.* —, BAHAMA. *Ceanothus colubrinus*, or *Colubrina ferruginosa*. —, JAMAICA. *Gordonia Hæmatoxylon.*

REDWOOD-TREE. *Soymida febrifuga.*

REED. *Arundo* and *Phragmites.* —, AROMATIC, of Scripture. *Andropogon Calamus aromaticus.* —, BUR. *Sparganium.* —, CANARY. *Digraphis arundinacea.* —, COMMON. *Phragmites communis.* —, EGYPTIAN. *Papyrus antiquorum.* —, INDIAN. *Canna.* —, SEA. *Ammophila arundinacea.* —, SMALL. *Calamagrostis.* —, TRUMPET. *Arundo occidentalis.* —, WATER. *Arundo* or *Phragmites.*

REED-MACE. *Typha.*

REEPERS. Laths, or longitudinal sections of the Palmyra Palm, used for building purposes in the East.

REEVESIA. A genus of *Sterculiaceæ*, comprising a few evergreen bushes with alternate stalked ovate or lance-shaped leaves, somewhat like those of a laurel; and terminal cymes of white blossoms, appearing at a distance like those of a *Viburnum*, and remarkable for their protruding staminal tube, which terminates in a round knob, consisting of fifteen sessile anthers. The chief features of the genus are:—A bell-shaped three to five-lobed calyx, five-clawed petals, and a long stamen-tube enclosing a stalked ovary, which is tipped with a sessile five-lobed stigma, and when ripe is an inversely pear-shaped capsule about an inch long, with five cells and one or two winged seeds in each. *R. thyrsoidea* was introduced from China in 1818 by John Reeves, Esq., F.R.S., whose name the genus bears, and is cultivated as a greenhouse shrub. Two other species are known from the Khasya mountains in India.   [A. A. B.]

REFLEXED. Curved backwards excessively.

REFRACTUS. Curved or directed backwards suddenly.

REGELIA. A genus proposed by Schauer for the *Melaleuca sprengelioides*, and an allied species, both of them myrtaceous shrubs from South-western Australia, differing slightly from *Beaufortia* in the dehiscence of their anthers, and in the ovary having several ovules instead of a single one in each cell.

The same name has been also applied in Continental gardens to a fine Seychelles Palm, which Wendland has since designated *Verschaffeltia splendida*.

RÉGLISSE. (Fr.) *Glycyrrhiza.* — BÂTARDE or SAUVAGE. *Astragalus glycyphyllos.* — DES ALPES or DES MONTAGNES. *Trifolium alpinum.*

REGMA. A tricoccous fruit like that of spurges; also any such fruit, whether the number of cocci is three or not.

REGRESSUS. In Morphology, signifies the change from one organ into the form of the organs that immediately preceded it; as of petals into sepals.

REGULAR. Having all the parts of each series of a flower of a similar form and size.

REHMANNIA. A genus of the cyrtandraceous division of *Gesneraceæ*, containing a single species, a Northern Chinese herbaceous plant, with obovate coarsely serrated alternate leaves decreasing in size towards the top of the plant, and solitary axillary long-stalked flowers. These have a campanulate five-cleft calyx; a corolla with a long compressed ventricose tube, and a two-lipped nearly equally five-lobed limb, the two upper lobes of which are bent back and the three lower spread out; two long and two short included stamens with diverging anther-cells; a one-celled ovary with two two-lobed parietal placentas; and a slender style bearing a stigma of two broad equal plates. [A.S.]

REICHENBACHIA. A small little-known shrub from the Rio Magdalena in tropical South America, with alternate lanceolate leaves, and small tubular flowers in terminal cymes, which forms a genus of *Nyctaginaceæ* allied to *Salpianthus*.

REIDIA. A genus of *Euphorbiaceæ* allied to *Phyllanthus*, of which it has entirely the habit, differing chiefly in the calyx of the sterile flowers consisting of four instead of five sepals, and the stamens being two instead of three in number. There are about a dozen known species distributed over tropical India and Java. They are small bushes having slender twigs, furnished with numerous small unequal-sided ovate or oblong smooth entire leaves, bearing in their axils, either singly or in clusters, small green or whitish pink-tipped flowers, fertile and sterile in the same cluster (the fertile larger than the sterile), and with slender drooping stalks an inch or more in length. The calyx in the females is of four to six deep triangular divisions often fringed; and inside these an equal number of glands surrounding the ovary, which is tipped with three forked styles. The fruits are little trilobed capsules of the size of peas, with three cells and two seeds in each. *R. glaucescens* is a very neat bush cultivated in hothouses. Its slender twigs are furnished with elliptical pea-green leaves about half an inch long, arranged in a two-ranked manner so that the twigs have the aspect of pinnate leaves. When this plant is covered with its slender-stalked drooping neatly fringed blossoms of a pinkish hue, it is really an extremely pretty object. This plant is a native of Java. M. Baillon unites the genus with the West Indian *Epistylium*, which however embraces plants of a very different aspect, although the structure of the flower is very similar. He also refers here a Javanese plant known under the name of *Eriococcus*. [A. A. B.]

REIMARIA. A genus of grasses belonging to the tribe *Paniceæ*, which has the inflorescence in racemes, the spikelets of which are subsessile and two-flowered; lower flowers neuter, one-glumed and three-nerved; hermaphrodite flowers two-glumed, membranaceous, shining, the lower glume three-nerved acute, the upper obsoletely three-nerved; stamens two; styles two; ovary smooth. This genus contains but two species, *R. acuta* and *R. conferta*, both natives of Brazil. [D. M.]

REINECKIA. The generic name of a Chinese liliaceous plant related to *Sansevieria*, but more so to *Ophiopogon*, from which it is hardly recognisable. *R. carnea* is a tufted plant with a creeping rootstock, thick fibrous roots, grassy leaves six inches to a foot long; and rising from their midst a flower-spike three to four inches high, bearing a number of sessile rose-coloured fragrant flowers, each seated in the axil of a bract. They have a tubular perianth with a six-lobed flat border, six stamens opposite the lobes, and a three-celled three-lobed ovary with four ovules in each cell. *Sanseviera carnea* was the name first given to this plant when introduced to English gardens about the year 1792; afterwards it was named *Sansevia carnea*; and now *Reineckia*. [A. A. B.]

REINE-CLAUDE. (Fr.) The Green Gage Plum.

REINE DES BOIS. (Fr.) *Asperula odorata*; also *Diahella ensifolia*. — DES PRÈS. *Spiræa Ulmaria*. — DES PRÈS DU CANADA. *Spiræa lobata*. — MARGUERITE. *Callistephus chinensis*.

REINWARDTIA. The name given to a genus of *Linaceæ* peculiar to the mountainous regions of India, and consisting of three species which were formerly included in *Linum*; from which they differ in having three or four instead of five styles, as well as in the glands at the base of the petals being unequal or entirely deficient. *R. trigyna* is a very common erect branching deciduous-leaved bush often cultivated in hothouses in England for the sake of its handsome yellow flowers, which are nearly one inch and a half across. The ash-coloured twigs are furnished with ovate or lance-shaped leaves two to three inches long, and the flowers are solitary or two or three together from the apex of the shoots. It is readily propagated by cuttings or pieces of the creeping root, which renders it a troublesome weed in some parts of India. This plant, which has been in cultivation for upwards of sixty years, and is often called *Linum trigynum*, has been named in honour of G. C. Reinwardt, a celebrated Dutch botanist. [A. A. B.]

REISSEKIA *cordifolia* is the only species of a genus of *Rhamnaceæ*, which is most nearly related to *Gouania*, differing chiefly in the flowers being disposed in umbels instead of racemes. It is a scrambling Brazilian bush, with slender branches, having tendrils like a vine, and alternate stalked heart-shaped leaves, bearing in their axils umbels of minute yellowish

flowers much like those of the common buckthorn. These are succeeded by three-celled three-winged capsules, having the wings papery in texture, and a single seed in each cell. It was named in honour of M. Reissek, a Continental botanist. [A. A. B.]

RELBUN. The roots of *Calceolaria arachnoidea*, which are largely collected in Chili for dyeing woollen cloths crimson.

RELHANIA. A South African genus of *Compositæ*, comprising six species, three of which are small bushes with an abundance of heath-like leaves covered with white down underneath, and solitary yellow flower-heads terminating the twigs; while the others have smooth rigid oblong leaves with recurved tips, and their yellow flower-heads are in terminal corymbs: each head with numerous florets intermixed with chaffy scales, the ray-florets strap-shaped and female, and those of the disk tubular and perfect. The genus differs chiefly from its near allies in the minutely-toothed crown-like pappus which surmounts the narrow achenes. [A. A. B.]

RELIQUIÆ. The withered remains of leaves which do not fall off, but perish upon a plant and adhere to it.

REMIJIA. A genus of *Cinchonaceæ* closely allied to *Cinchona* itself, but differing in the structure of its seed-vessels, and its peltate seeds, as well as in its inflorescence and habit. They form slender shrubs, with oblong or ovate revolute leaves, lanceolate stipules, long interrupted axillary racemes of flowers, and a corolla which is woolly outside, and has five linear limb-segments. In Brazil, where the plants are found, some of the species, as *R. ferruginea*, and *R. Vellozii*, are called Quina de Serra, or Quina de Remijo, and their bark is used as a substitute for that of *Cinchona*. [T. M.]

REMIREA. A genus of sedges belonging to the tribe *Cypereæ*. The inflorescence is in heads or clusters, the spikelets of which are one-flowered; glumes four to five, the lower empty and blunt, the uppermost containing the flower sharp-pointed; stamens three; styles three-cleft. The few species described under this genus are natives of subtropical countries, ranging from South Africa to China. [D. M.]

REMORS. (Fr.) *Scabiosa succisa*.

REMOTE. Separated by intervals longer than usual.

REMUSATIA. A genus of *Araceæ*, comprising a solitary species formerly known under the name of *Caladium viviparum*. This is an Indian plant with a tuberous rootstock, from which are sent off long branches bearing small bulbs, which after a while fall off and grow into distinct plants; subsequently the peltate leaves are produced. The spadix is short, entirely covered with flowers, and completely encircled below by the yellow spathe; above it is exposed, owing to the spreading open and bending downwards of the spathe.

The anthers are one-celled, and between them and the ovaries are placed a number of rudimentary flowers. The ovaries are numerous, and partially three-celled, and contain numerous ovules. *R. vivipara* is in cultivation. [M. T. M.]

RENANTHERA. A genus of vandeous orchids very nearly allied to *Vanda* itself, from which it is technically distinguished by its lip being articulated not continuous with the column, and saccate or spurred at its middle instead of at its base. The original species of the genus is a native of Cochin China, but those since added, eight or ten in number, are all confined to the large islands of the Malayan Archipelago. As ornamental plants they take rank with the most beautiful of the orchid tribe, in which they are also amongst the largest-growing, their long branching and rooting stems climbing on trees to a considerable height. They have thick leathery strap-shaped leaves regularly arranged in two opposite rows; and their flowers are disposed in long panicles proceeding from the sides of the stems. The most magnificent and certainly the most remarkable species of the genus yet known in this country, is *R. Lowii*, formerly *Vanda Lowii*, a native of Borneo. This species grows to a great height, and has leaves from half a yard to a yard in length; and from near the top of its stem it sends out several long slender pendulous flower-spikes, ten or twelve feet in length, clothed with numerous rather large conspicuous flowers. These are of two kinds, at least all the spikes that have as yet come under notice have been furnished with a couple of tawny-yellow crimson-spotted flowers at their base; while all the rest, forty or fifty in number, have been of a pale-greenish hue, marked inside with very large irregular blotches of reddish-brown. [A. S.]

RENEALMIA. A genus of *Zingiberaceæ* named after the French botanist Renealme. The species are tropical American herbs, with creeping rootstocks, from which are thrown up the two-ranked leaves, and panicled inflorescence. The flowers are concealed within large bracts, and partake for the most part of the botanical characteristics of those of *Alpinia*. The lip of the corolla, however, is erect, and embraces the very short flattened filament; and the three-celled capsule splits into three pieces when ripe. They have white flowers. [M. T. M.]

RENGGERIA. A genus of *Clusiaceæ* nearly related to *Clusia*, from which, according to Mr. Bentham, it differs chiefly in having from five to ten instead of a much greater number of stamens to the sterile flowers; and from most others in having many instead of few ovules to each cell of the ovary, which when ripe is a capsule. The four known species, found in Brazil, Peru, and Guiana, are scrambling semiparasitical trees of low growth, with opposite entire leathery leaves, the twigs terminating in panicles of yellowish flowers, the sterile and fertile on different trees.

R. peruviana was at one time separated as a genus under the name *Rengifa*. [A. A. B.]

RENIFORM. The same as Kidney-shaped.

RENNELLIA. A genus of *Cinchonaceæ* whose species inhabit Sumatra. The inflorescence is a terminal spike, the flowers crowded and united one to another by the confluence of the calyx-tubes. The free margin of the calyx is unbroken; the corolla is tubular, its limb divided into four spreading segments; stamens four; style thread-like, surrounded at the base by a fleshy disk, and dividing above into two stigmas. Fruit of irregular shape, consisting of several ovaries combined, and surmounted by the persistent calyces and disks. [M. T. M.]

RENONCULE. (Fr.) *Ranunculus.* — DES JARDINS. *Ranunculus asiaticus.*

RENONCULIER. (Fr.) *Cerasus avium flore-pleno.*

RENOUÉE. (Fr.) *Polygonum.* — ACRE. *Polygonum Hydropiper.* — DU LEVANT. *Polygonum orientale.*

RENOUELLE. (Fr.) *Eriogonum.*

REPAND. Having an uneven slightly wavy or angular margin.

RÉPARÉE. (Fr.) *Beta maritima.*

REPENT. Creeping; lying flat upon the ground, and emitting roots at the same time.

REPLICATE, REPLICATIVE. When the upper part of a leaf is curved back and applied to the lower, as in the Aconite.

REPLUM. The valve of a door—applied in Botany as if it signified a door-frame; the frame left in certain fruits by the dropping-off of the valves in the act of dehiscence.

REPRISE. (Fr.) *Sedum Telephium.*

REPTONIA. This genus is interesting because of its botanical affinities. It is usually placed in the *Myrsinaceæ*, with which it accords in the one-celled ovary; but on the other hand it is close to the *Sapotaceæ*, having five sterile filaments alternating with the five fertile ones which are opposite the corolla-lobes; the leaves have no transparent dots, as have most *Myrsinaceæ*; and the seeds, with ruminated albumen, are unlike any in either of the two families. *R. buxifolia*, the only known species, is found in Affghanistan and on the shores of the Persian Gulf opposite to Muscat; it is a rigid evergreen hardwooded bush, with alternate entire leaves, and short lateral shoots terminating in spiny points like those of the sloe. The small yellowish flowers, arranged in clusters in the axils of the leaves, have each a five-cleft calyx with rounded lobes, a shortly tubular corolla, and an ovary remarkable for its slender style being protruded while the flower is yet in the bud. According to Griffith, the rounded black edible drupes, of the size of marbles, are considered heating by the Affghans, who sell them in their bazaars under the name of Goorgoora. The fruit is mainly occupied by the seed, which is not eaten. *Edgworthia buxifolia* and *Monotheca mascatensis* are synonyms of this plant. [A. A. B.]

REREE. *Typha angustifolia*, the leaves of which are used in the north-western provinces of India for making mats.

RESEDACEÆ. (*Weldworts*.) A small order of polypetalous dicotyledons allied to *Capparidaceæ*, from which they differ chiefly in their irregular scale-like usually fringed petals, and in the fruit which is most frequently open at the top before it is ripe. They are mostly herbs or small spreading undershrubs, with alternate entire or pinnately divided leaves, and minute gland-like stipules. The flowers, usually green white or of a greenish-yellow and not showy, are in terminal racemes or spikes ; sepals and petals usually five or six each ; stamens definite, or at any rate not numerous, and inserted on a broad fleshy hypogynous disk. The ovary is one-celled with three parietal placentas, and bears three distinct stigmas ; and the seeds have a curved embryo without albumen. The species are for the most part inhabitants of Europe, Northern Africa, and Western Asia, but a very few occur also in Southern Africa and North-west America. The order consists chiefly of the Linnæan genus *Reseda*, and some small ones which have been separated from it by modern botanists, and to these has been added *Ochradenus* with an exceptionally baccate fruit.

RESEDA. Herbaceous or slightly shrubby plants giving name to the order *Resedaceæ*, well marked by the calyx being divided almost to the base into from four to six narrow segments, an equal number of cloven petals, and a bladdery three to four-horned many-seeded capsule open at the top. *R. odorata*, the Mignonette, a native of Egypt and Northern Africa, is a universal favourite which needs no description. When cultivated it is usually treated as an annual, but if protected during winter and properly trained may be made to last several years, and to attain a large size. *R. Luteola*, the Weld, Yellow-weed, or Dyer's Weed, is a common wayside plant, one to three feet high, with numerous lanceolate glossy leaves, and terminal spikes of greenish-yellow flowers nodding at the top. Dyers formerly made great use of this plant, as it affords a beautiful yellow dye. A paint is also made from it called Dutch-pink. *R. lutea* is a native of many parts of Britain ; it has to some extent the habit of *R. odorata*, but is more erect in growth, and the flowers are scentless. Other foreign species are sometimes cultivated. [C. A. J.]

RÉSÉDA. (Fr.) *Reseda odorata*. — RAIPONCE. *Reseda Phyteuma*. — SAUVAGE. *Reseda lutea*.

RES HERBARIA. Botany ; whatever relates to that subject.

RESIN. The residue of the process for obtaining oil of turpentine ; also a general term for certain vegetable secretions insoluble in water, which become solid either by the evaporation of their volatile constituents or by the absorption of oxygen, and are distinguished from balsams by the absence of benzoic acid, and from gum-resins by the absence of gum. —, CARANA. The product of *Bursera acuminata*. —, COPAL. The product of *Rhus copallina*. —, COUMIA. The product of *Icica Tacamahaca*. —, ELEMI. The product of *Amyris Plumieri*. —, GUAIAC. The product of *Guaiacum officinale*. —, HEMP. Churras, the narcotic product of *Cannabis sativa*. —, CHIBOU or CACHIBOU. The product of *Bursera gummifera*. —, MANAWA. The product of *Avicennia tomentosa*. —, MASTICH. The product of *Pistacia Lentiscus*. —, MAYNAS. The product of *Calophyllum Calaba*.

RESIN-BUSH. A colonial South African name for *Euryops speciosissimus*.

RÉSINE DE GOMMART. (Fr.) A resinous product of *Bursera acuminata* or *gummifera*.

RESTANS. The same as Persistent.

RESTENCLE. (Fr.) *Pistacia Lentiscus*.

RESTHARROW. *Ononis arvensis*.

RESTIACEÆ. (*Restiads*.) An order of monocotyledons having usually the habit of rushes or sedges, and closely allied in character both to *Juncaceæ* and *Cyperaceæ*. They differ from *Juncaceæ* by the more glume-like segments of their perianth, usually fewer than six ; from *Cyperaceæ* by their more perfectly formed perianth ; and from both by their pendulous seed, and lenticular embryo, placed at the extremity of the albumen most remote from the hilum. They are usually stiff herbaceous plants, with narrow simple leaves having longitudinally slit sheaths, or in some species the leaves are reduced to these sheaths or entirely wanting. The flowers are frequently unisexual, usually gathered into heads or clusters with glume-like bracts ; the perianth has from two to six segments ; the stamens are usually two or three but sometimes twice those numbers ; and the ovary has one two or three one-seeded cells, and bears two or more styles or stigmas. The order is divisible into two suborders, sometimes considered as distinct orders : the true *Restiaceæ* distributed into about twenty-four genera, all natives of the southern hemisphere, chiefly South Africa and Australia, with the exception of a very few tropical Asiatic species ; and the *Eriocaulaceæ* : which see.

RESTIBILIS. A plant with a perennial root and annual stems : an herbaceous plant.

RESTIO. A genus of *Restiaceæ* comprising all the true rush-like leafless *Restiaceæ* in which the style is elongated, with two long linear stigmas. There are a large number of species known, more than two-thirds of which are natives of Southern Africa, the remainder being found in Australia. None are of any special interest or deserving of cultivation.

RESTREPIA. A genus of orchids closely allied to *Pleurothallis*, but having the hind sepal and petals always extended into long tapering glandular points, a long slender column, a hooded anther-bed, and a linear membranous-bordered stigma. It embraces about a dozen tropical American species, small mostly epiphytal plants, with either one-leaved stems or stems with one-leaved branches, always furnished with large membranaceous sheaths, and bearing largish generally spotted flowers, solitary on long stalks. [A. S.]

RESUPINATE. Inverted in position by a twisting of the stalk—as the flowers of *Orchis*; also said of those agaricaceous Fungals whose hymenium is placed uppermost instead of undermost.

RETAMA. A genus of *Leguminosæ* whose species were formerly included in *Genista* and *Sarothamnus*, from which they differ in having rounded or oval somewhat berried pods about the size of damsons, which do not open when ripe, and contain but one or two seeds, instead of being thin, dry, bursting, and containing numerous seeds. There are about ten known species, distributed over the Mediterranean region and the Canary Isles, all of them much-branched bushes, the twigs angular or round and rush-like, the younger sometimes having a few lance-shaped leaves, but usually entirely leafless, and thickly covered in the summer months with short clusters of yellow or white flowers sometimes tinged with lilac. Rætem is the name given by the Arabs to a white-flowered species, *R. Rætam*, which grows in Arabia and Syria. According to Forskål, an infusion of its bitter roots is drunk by the Arabs for internal pains, and the shoots macerated in water are applied to wounds. The Arabic name Rætem, altered slightly into *Retama*, is the common appellation of the plants of this genus in Spain.

Don remarks of *R. monosperma* : ' The use of this shrub along the shores of Spain in stopping the sand is great. It converts the most barren spots into a fine odoriferous garden by its flowers, which continue for a long time. The young shoots are eagerly eaten by goats, and the twigs are used for tying bundles.' These remarks seem to apply better to *R. sphærocarpa*, a yellow-flowered species which is common on the Spanish coast, while *R. monosperma* is comparatively rare. The latter species is sometimes cultivated in greenhouses in England, or on sheltered borders with a southern aspect. It has slender shoots covered with short silky hairs, which give the plant a silvery appearance. The flowers are white, the centre of the standard and the calyx tinged with lilac. [A. A. B.]

RETICULARIA. A genus of the semigelatinous myxogastrous *Fungi*, distinguished by its simple expanded stemless peridium, and flat-branched flocci amidst the multitudinous spores. Corda has shown that these are at first developed in little bundles on oranchlets of the threads. *R. maxima* is sometimes a troublesome plant in hotbeds from its rapidly-growing slimy spawn enclosing everything in its way, and the abundance of its dark dust-like spores. [M. J. B.]

RETICULATE, RETIFORM. Having the appearance of network.

RETICULATO-VENOSE, RETINERVIS, RETINERVIUS. Having veins with the appearance of network.

RETICULUM. A membrane consisting of crossing fibres, found in palm-trees at the base of the petiole, either on its side or between it and the stem.

RETINACULUM. A viscid gland belonging to the stigma of orchids and asclepiads, and holding the pollen-masses fast.

RETINOSPORA. A small Japanese genus of the *Cupresseæ* division of *Coniferæ*, closely allied to and by some botanists regarded as a section of the North American genus *Chamæcyparis*, from which it is distinguished by the integument of its seeds being furnished with evident resinous channels, whence the generic name. One species, *R. obtusa*, the Japanese Cypress, is a very fine forest tree, eighty or

Retinospora obtusa.

more feet high, with a straight trunk occasionally as much as five feet in diameter at its base, yielding a useful fine-grained light-coloured timber. Its Japanese name is Hinoki, which signifies Tree of the Sun, it being dedicated by them to the God of the Sun. The other species are either smaller trees or largish shrubs. [A. S.]

RETOMBET. (Fr.) *Passerina Tartonraira*.

RETROCURVUS. The same as Recurved.

RETROFLEXED. The same as Reflexed.

RETRORSE. Backwards: thus, *retrorsa folia* are those leaves which are pressed backwards against the stem ; *retrorsum hamulosus*, having a number of little hooks directed backwards.

RETROVERSIO. A bending backwards; an inversion, or turning upside down.

RETTI or RATI-WEIGHTS. The seeds of *Abrus precatorius.*

RETUSE. Terminating in a round end, the centre of which is depressed.

RETZIACEÆ. Three shrubs or undershrubs from South Africa — *Retzia* with rather long erect verticillate leaves, and two species of *Lonchostoma* with small crowded ones,—all with sessile flowers, which although not small are almost concealed by the leaves, have been attached by different botanists to *Convolvulaceæ*, to *Hydroleaceæ*, or to *Solanaceæ.* Their technical characters are those of the latter order, but their habit is so different that they have been proposed by some as a distinct group under the above name of *Retziaceæ.*

REVALENTA ARABICA. The prepared farina of the Lentil, sold also as Ervalenta.

RÉVEILLE-MATIN. (Fr.) *Euphorbia helioscopia* and other species.

REVENTA-CAVALLOS. *Isotoma longiflora.*

REVOLUTE. Rolled backwards—*i.e.* out of the direction ordinarily assumed by other similar bodies; as certain tendrils, and the sides or ends of some leaves.

REVOLUTIVE. When the edges are rolled backwards spirally on each side, as in the leaf of the rosemary; a term of æstivation.

REWUND, or RAWUND. Indian names for Rhubarb.

REYNAUDIA. A genus of grasses belonging to the tribe *Agrostideæ.* The inflorescence is in simple panicles, the spikelets of which are one-flowered; outer glumes compressed, cleft below the points, with short bristles; flowering glumes one half shorter, three-nerved; pales with very short bristles below their points, the lower five-nerved, the upper one-nerved; stamens two; styles two. Only one species is described, *R. filiformis*, a native of San Domingo and Cuba. [D. M.]

REYNOLDSIA. A genus of *Araliaceæ*, consisting of two trees from the islands of the Pacific Ocean, with simply pinnate leaves, and small flowers in compound terminal or lateral panicles. They have the entire calyptra-shaped corolla of the American *Sciadophyllums*, but differ from that genus in foliage, in the perfectly consolidated stigmas, and in the drupe consisting of from eight to eighteen pyrenes.

RHABÂBATH. An Arabian name for the fruit of *Ruscus aculeatus.*

RHABARBARUM. *Rheum.*

RHABDIA. The generic name of two stiff branching erect shrubs three to four feet high, with the habit of some *Lyciums*, belonging to the *Ehretiaceæ*, and most nearly allied to *Ehretia* itself—differing mainly from that genus in the style being entire instead of forked. *R. viminea* is very common in India, and is found also in Ceylon and Borneo, always growing in the rocky or sandy beds of rivers. It has reddish twigs furnished with an abundance of alternate spathulate leaves, and in their axils a few small rose-coloured flowers disposed in corymbs. Each flower has a five-parted calyx with narrow segments, a shortly tubular corolla with a five-lobed border, five stamens arising from the tube, and an ovary ending in a slender style with a two-lobed stigma. The fruit is a scarlet berry with four to six seeds. *R. lycioides* is a Brazilian species growing in similar situations, and very like the former in habit, but having broadly lance-shaped leaves. [A. A. B.]

RHABDOCALYX. *Cordia.*

RHABDOTHAMNUS *Solandri* is the sole representative of a genus of *Cyrtandraceæ* peculiar to New Zealand, forming a slender twiggy much branched shrub, two to four feet high, with opposite leaves, and pretty yellow and red striped flowers. Calyx five-cleft; corolla with a bell-shaped tube and a two-lipped border; fertile stamens four, the anthers united; ovary broadly ovate; style long, slender, and curved towards the apex. The shrub is found in the northern island of the New Zealand group, from the Bay of Islands as far as the east coast. [B. S.]

RHABDUS. The stipe of certain fungals.

RHÆO. A name proposed by Hance for the *Tradescantia discolor*, a commelynaceous plant long since introduced into our stoves from the countries bordering on the Gulf of Mexico, and which differs from the other *Tradescantias* in its dense umbels on very short scapes from the midst of long broad radical leaves, and in the ovules being always solitary in each cell of the ovary. There is little beauty in its flower, but it is sometimes grown on account of the rich purple colour of the underside of the leaves.

RHAGADIOLUS. A genus of cichoraceous *Compositæ* nearly allied to *Lapsana*, readily recognised when in fruit by the involucral scales, which are about eight in number, being spread out in a star-like manner, and the margins of each incurved so as to clasp in its embrace one of the cylindrical achenes of the outer row: so that in looking at a flower-head with ripe achenes, there appears to be nothing but the involucral scales left. There are but two species, *R. stellatus* and *R. Hedypnois*, the former common through the Mediterranean region, the latter extending eastwards to Affghanistan. Both are annual weeds six inches to a foot high, with lyrate and toothed or sinuate radical leaves, and numerous small yellow flower-heads, those situated where the branches fork being sessile, the others stalked. [A. A. B.]

RHAGODIA. A genus of Australian shrubs or herbs belonging to the *Chenopodiaceæ.* They have alternate leaves, and spicate bractless flowers with a five-parted perigone unchanged in fruit, one to five stamens, and a bifid style. The fruit is depressed, with a horizontal seed. [J. T. S.]

RHAMNACEÆ. (Rhamni, Rhamnads). An order of polypetalous dicotyledons, comprising trees or shrubs resembling Celastraceæ in their small green or yellowish flowers with a fleshy disk, and stamens equal in number to the sepals, but differing usually in their valvate sepals, and in their more decidedly perigynous and sometimes superior stamens; and always in these stamens being alternate with the sepals, and in the petals when present being small concave or hoodshaped, opposite the stamens, and often enclosing them. The leaves are alternate or very rarely opposite, entire or more frequently toothed, and sometimes reduced to minute scales. The branches are frequently thorny or prickly; the flowers in axillary or terminal clusters, cymes, panicles, or rarely racemes; their parts are in fours or in fives; the ovary is two three or four-celled, with solitary erect ovules in each cell; and the seeds have a straight embryo in a fleshy albumen, which is rarely wanting. The order is spread over the greater part of the globe, and consists of above forty genera, of which the principal are Zizyphus, Rhamnus, Ceanothus, Colletia, Phylica, Pomaderris, and Gouania.

RHAMNUS. The Buckthorn: a large genus typical of the Rhamnaceæ, and, with the exception of a few species inhabiting mountainous regions within the tropics in India and Abyssinia, confined to the temperate countries of the Northern Hemisphere. The majority of them are shrubs varying from one to eight or ten feet high, though some occasionally grow as high as fifteen or twenty feet and form small trees, and many of them are armed with stout spines. Their leaves, which are thick and evergreen in some species, but thin and deciduous in others, are almost always alternate short-stalked and simple, and usually smooth and feather-veined; and their small greenish short-stalked flowers are borne in clusters or umbels proceeding from the leaf-axils. They have a four or five-cleft calyx, the lower or entire part of which is cup-shaped or hemispherical and lined with the thin disk, and has the petals and stamens (agreeing in number with the segments of the calyx) inserted into its summit; the former, however, are sometimes absent, but when present they are usually nearly flat and notched at the top. The ovary is free from but generally shorter in the calyx-tube, from two to four-celled, and bears a two to four-branched style. The fruits are fleshy, and contain from two to four small one-seeded hard-shelled stones. Several species afford useful products, particularly dyes, and the fruits of many possess violent purgative properties.

The Alaternus, R. Alaternus, is an evergreen shrub or small tree, native of the South of Europe and North of Africa, of which several varieties are grown for ornamental purposes in English gardens. It has smooth serrated leaves varying from egg-shaped to elliptical or lance-shaped, and flowers of separate sexes, without petals.

R. catharticus, the Purging Buckthorn, indigenous to Britain, is a stiff very much branched shrub growing from five to ten feet high, frequently having the branches terminating in a sharp thorn-like point. It has deciduous yellowish-green egg-shaped leaves, and dense clusters of yellowish-green flowers, which produce a crop of little shining black fruits about the size of peas. These fruits, which resemble corns of black pepper when dry, were formerly in great demand as a purgative medicine, and are still employed by rustic practitioners; but on account of the violence of their action, they have deservedly fallen into disrepute, although Syrup of Buckthorn is included in our pharmacopœias. The pigment known as sap or bladder-green is prepared by mixing the fresh juice of buckthorn berries with lime and evaporating to dryness. The bark likewise possesses active purgative properties.

The Alder Buckthorn, R. Frangula, also affords a colouring-matter, and its wood yields a superior charcoal for making gunpowder. But the most important commercial product of the genus is the dyeing material used by calico-printers, and known as Yellow-berries or Persian berries, considerable quantities of which are annually imported from Asiatic Turkey, and from Persia by way of Trebizonde. Although usually ascribed to R. infectorius, they are probably collected indiscriminately from several species—the unripe fruits alone being gathered.

From the bark of two species lately described under the names R. chlorophorus and R. utilis, the Chinese prepare a beautiful green dye, called by them Lo-kao, and in this country Chinese Green Indigo, considerable quantities of which have been imported into Lyons and used for dyeing silks, the shades of green imparted by it being exceedingly beautiful, especially when seen under the influence of artificial light. A similar dye has since been extracted from R. catharticus. [A. S.]

RHAPHIDOPHORA. A genus of Orontiaceæ, consisting of Indian herbaceous plants differing from Calla in their flattened filaments and linear stigmas, and in the presence of only a single ovule in the ovary. From Monstera they are distinguished by their one-celled ovaries, with only one ovule in each, and by the linear stigma; from Scindapsus by their flattened filaments; and from each by the persistent spathe. The leaves of some of the species are perforated with holes, for an account of which see SCINDAPSUS. [M. T. M.]

RHAPHIOLEPIS. A genus of evergreen bushes belonging to the Rosaceæ, and numbering three species found in China and Japan. They are nearly allied to Cratægus, but are readily distinguished by the flowers being disposed in racemes or panicles instead of cymes, as well as by the funnel-shaped calyx, the upper free portion of which falls off when the flower withers. *R. indica*, varieties of which are known in our greenhouses as *rubra*, *salicifolia*, and *phœostemon*, is a nearly smooth evergreen bush, having alternate ovate or lance-shaped leaves, and short terminal panicles of white or pink-tinted flowers, the size of those of the hawthorn. These have a calyx-border of five narrow segments, five petals, numerous stamens, and two styles crowning a two-celled ovary, which when ripe is a small black berry with two cells and one or two seeds in each. *R. japonica* is a beautiful large-leaved species forming, according to Siebold, a bush from six to ten feet high, and commonly cultivated by the Japanese, who plant it either with azaleas and other bushes, or singly, as it forms a beautiful object when covered with its innumerable bouquets of dark red flowers. The generic name refers to the narrow bracts, which are often seen on the panicles mixed with the flowers. [A. A. B.]

RHAPIS. The genus *Rhapis* is closely allied to *Chamœrops* in its botanical characters, and belongs to the same section of *Palmaceæ*, but it differs in general appear-

Rhapis flabelliformis.

ance, the four or five species referred to it, all of which are confined to Eastern Asia, being of dwarf habit, and having thin reed-like stems growing together in dense tufts rising from the same roots. Their leaves are fan-shaped but deeply cut into segments, which are usually toothed at the top, and the sheathing-bases of their stalks are split into a fibrous network. The flower-spikes have spreading branches, and their stalks are sheathed in incomplete spathes. Some plants bear flowers of only one sex, while others have both sexes and also perfect flowers. The latter have

a cup-shaped shortly trifid calyx, a tubular or bell-shaped trifid corolla, six stamens with thread-like filaments and egg-shaped anthers, and three distinct ovaries, all or only one or two of which ripen into one-seeded fruits.

R. flabelliformis is commonly called the Ground Rattan Palm, and is said to yield the walking-canes known by that name in this country; but as its stems are seldom more than three or four feet high and not much thicker than the finger, this is probably a mistake, though it is possible they may be the produce of one of the larger species. It is a native of Southern China, and is also cultivated in Japan, where it is known by the name of Kwanwortsik, and in European gardens plants of this species from Japan are sometimes called *Rhapis Kwanwortsik*. [A. S.]

RHAPONTIQUE. (Fr.) *Rheum Rhaponticum.*

RHAPONTICUM. A genus belonging to the thistle-tribe of the *Compositæ*, and comprising nine species distributed over Southern Europe and Northern Africa, Siberia and Mandchuria. Some of them have the aspect of *Centaurea*, but the florets are all equal and perfect. They are related to *Serratula*, but differ in the membranaceous tips of the involucral scales; and to *Leuzea*, from which they are recognised by the rough instead of feathery pappus-hairs. All are perennials, and the stems (which in a few are three to five feet high and slightly branched) are furnished with lance-shaped or pinnatifid leaves usually clothed with white down underneath; while the large knapweed-like yellow or rose-coloured flower-heads, sometimes as much as two inches across, are solitary at the ends of the twigs. *R. acaulis*, an Algerian species, has a rosette of pinnately-parted much-cut leaves lying close on the ground, and seated in their midst a large head of yellow flowers which smell like those of the sweet *Acacia Farnesiana*. The root also, according to Desfontaines, is eatable and not unpleasant to the taste. [A. A. B.]

RHAPTOSTYLUM. A name given by Kunth to a South American tree which has been since shown to be a species of *Heisteria*.

RHATANY. The root of *Krameria triandra*. —, SAVANILLA. The root of the New Grenada variety of *Krameria Ixina*.

RHAZYA. The two species of this genus of *Apocynaceæ* are small shrubby plants, with alternate entire short-stalked leaves, natives of South-western Asia. Their flowers have a five-parted calyx ; a corolla with a long tube and five egg-shaped or oblong lobes, the tube being wide in the middle and constricted at the top and hairy inside, particularly in the throat, but destitute of scales; five stamens rising from the middle of the corolla tube, with very short filaments and longish anthers; two ovaries connected at the bottom ; and a style bearing a roundish stigma, and girded by a reflexed cup-shaped membrane. Their fruits consist of a pair of erect tapering follicles, containing a number of flattened seeds.

R. stricta is widely distributed through Western Asia, from Yemen in Arabia to the North-west Provinces of India. Its leaves, which are very bitter, are collected and sold in the bazaars in Scinde, the natives using them in the preparation of cool drinks in the hot weather. It is a stiff-growing plant with erect stems two or three feet high, and upright thickish smooth leaves, placed rather close together on the stem. [A. S.]

RHEA. *Böhmeria nivea* and *B. utilis.*

RHEEDIA. A genus of trees or shrubs found in Madagascar and tropical America belonging to the *Clusiaceæ*, and numbering about a dozen species, most of which were formerly included in the Asiatic genus *Garcinia*, from which they differ in having a calyx of two instead of four rounded sepals to each flower. They have opposite stalked entire leaves, with lance-shaped or ovate oblong blades very leathery in texture and sometimes a foot in length; and the flowers are small, white or greenish, the males and females on the same or on different trees, and arranged in clusters in the axils of the leaves: the sterile with numerous free stamens, and the fertile with a three to five-celled ovary crowned with a shield-like stigma, succeeded by ovoid berries with few seeds. The fruits of the Wild Mamme of Jamaica, *R. lateriflora*, are one to four inches long, yellow when ripe, and have a pleasant acid taste, as have also those of *R. edulis*, a Panama species with fruits the size of hazel-nuts. [A. A. B.]

RHETSA-MAUN. A name used by the Telingas for *Xanthoxylon Rhetsa.*

RHEUM. The technical name of the genus more familiarly known as Rhubarb. It is said to be derived from *Rha*, the ancient name of the Volga, on whose banks the plants grow: but according to others it comes from the Greek *rheo* ' to flow,' in allusion to the purgative properties of the roots. The genus is included in the *Polygonaceæ*, and consists of several species, natives for the most part of Central Asia. They are perennials, with large rootstocks, from which the large sheathing leaves and flower-stalks are given off. The infloresence consists of much-branched panicles bearing a great number of whitish greenish or pinkish flowers, which have a petaloid six-parted perianth, enclosing nine stamens attached to its base. The three-sided ovary is surmounted by three spreading styles. The three-cornered fruit is winged and encircled at the base by the withered remnants of the perianth.

Owing to the fact that great part of the district where the plants grow is as yet unexplored by travellers, and to the jealous reticence of the Chinese, the exact species yielding the best medicinal Rhubarb is not known with anything like certainty. What is known in English commerce as the best

Turkey Rhubarb in reality comes from China through Russia by way of Kiachta. It was formerly imported from Natolia, whence the name Turkey Rhubarb. The root is said by Pallas to be dug up in the summer, washed, bored with a hole, strung on a thread, and dried in the sun. In this state it is sent to the chief towns of China and to the Russian frontier-town Kiachta: at the latter place the drug undergoes careful examination by the agents of the Russian Government, and all inferior or decayed specimens are rejected. The odour of the best samples is so delicate, that it is stated that the assistants in the wholesale drug-warehouses are not permitted to touch it without gloves. The pieces are covered with a fine yellow powder, and when broken present a mottled red-and-yellow colour, owing to the passage of a number of wavy carmine-coloured streaks through the yellowish-white matrix. Here and there are small spots of a darker colour.

The best Rhubarb has a bitter astringent and somewhat aromatic taste, and feels gritty to the teeth owing to the abundance of small crystals of oxalate of lime which are contained in it. Genuine powdered rhubarb of this description is rarely to be had, being generally mixed with the powder of inferior sorts, such as Chinese and English Rhubarb; the latter being principally grown near Banbury in Oxfordshire, and the species being *R. Rhaponticum*. It is chiefly used to adulterate the more highly-priced Rhubarb and is the sort sold by itinerant vendors, some of whom carry the delusion still further by arraying themselves in Oriental costume. English Rhubarb is of a light spongy texture; its taste is astringent and mucilaginous, but destitute of the aromatic and gritty qualities possessed by the more highly-esteemed kinds. It is probable that with greater care in the preparation, this kind might be looked upon with more favour, as it appears that there is very little difference in the medicinal effects of home-grown and foreign Rhubarb. In the Himalayas *R. Emodi* and *R. Webbianum*, and possibly other kinds, furnish Indian Rhubarb, which however is not esteemed in this country.

Rhubarb is largely employed medicinally as a mild purgative, in addition to which its tonic and slightly astringent properties render it useful as a stomachic in cases of indigestion. These properties are said to be due to the presence in the drug of certain resinous and crystalline substances. Several species and varieties are cultivated in this country for the sake of their leaf-stalks, which form so agreeable a substitute for fruit in pastry, etc. The leaves themselves are made use of in the fabrication of fictitious cigars and tobacco. The shape of the hairs however, as seen under a microscope, is amply sufficient to enable the observer to detect the presence or absence of tobacco, but it is not so easy to determine the source of the fraudulent admixtures. Some of the species are very handsome owing to the boldness of their foliage and the elegance of their inflorescence. They have not however found much favour in an ornamental point of view.

One Sikkim species mentioned by Dr. Hooker has such a singular and showy appearance that its introduction into this country is greatly to be desired. Dr. Hooker thus describes the plant :—'The individual plants of *R. nobile* are upwards of a yard

Rheum nobile.

high, and form conical towers of the most delicate straw-coloured shining semitransparent concave imbricating bracts, the upper of which have pink edges; the large bright glossy shining green radical leaves, with red petioles and nerves, forming a broad base to the whole. On turning up the bracts the beautiful membranous fragile pink stipules are seen like red tissue-paper, and within these again the short-branched panicles of insignificant green flowers. The root is very long, often many feet, and winds among the rocks; it is as thick as the arm, and bright yellow inside. After flowering, the stem lengthens, the bracts separate one from another, become coarse red brown, withered and torn; finally, as the fruit ripens they fall away, leaving a ragged-looking stem, covered with panicles of deep-brown pendulous fruits. In the winter these naked black stems, projecting from the beetling cliffs or towering above the snow, are in dismal keeping with the surrounding desolation of the season.' The natives, it is said, eat the pleasantly acid stems and call them *Chuka*. [M. T. M.]

R. Rhaponticum and its varieties form the Common Rhubarb used for culinary purposes. It is a hardy perennial found on the borders of the Volga River, and has been grown in this country since 1573. The plant has large broad heart-shaped smooth deep-green leaves, strongly veined beneath. The footstalks are long, thick and fleshy, channeled above, and rounded at the edges. *R. undulatum* also yields some of the forms of

garden Rhubarb, especially those with red leafstalks.

In Queen Elizabeth's time Rhubarb-leaves were used as a potherb, and considered superior to spinach or beet. The use of the tender leafstalks is comparatively of modern date; for although they are now so common during the spring and early part of summer, it was not until the beginning of the present century that they came to be employed for tarts, and were found so valuable for various other culinary preparations. They are excellent, either stewed alone, or with rice; and a capital preserve has been made from them, in the form of a jam which is equal in flavour to that made from currants. When too large and old for cooking they undergo a process by which the juice is expressed from them and made into a delicious wine similar to that from green gooseberries, and closely resembling champagne: indeed, it may be suspected that much of the so-called champagne commonly drunk is no other than a preparation from the stalks of Rhubarb. The juice is stated to contain oxalic acid, as well as nitric and malic acid in abundance; and it is these which give an agreeable taste to the stalks when cooked, but which render them ill-suited to persons of weak digestion.

In the *Gardener's Chronicle* for 1846 (p. 5) Mr. A. Forsyth first directed attention to another part of Rhubarb as being suited for culinary purposes, and to which he gave the name of Rhaflower. This is the large globular pouch of unopened flowers, which is described as being of a beautiful colour when dressed in the same manner as Rhubarb, of a milder flavour, and forming altogether a dish of great delicacy. [W. B. B.]

RHEUMATISM-ROOT. *Jeffersonia diphylla.*

RHEXIA. A small North American genus of *Melastomaceæ*, the species of which are low perennial often bristly herbs, commonly called Deer-grass, or Meadow-beauty, and have sessile three to five-nerved bristle-edged leaves, and large showy cymose flowers. It has an urn-shaped calyx-tube and four persistent teeth shorter than the tube; four obovate somewhat retuse petals; eight equal or nearly equal stamens, with mostly narrow curved blunt one-pored anthers, somewhat thickened at the base and prolonged beyond the insertion of the filament, above which they are nearly always armed with a sharp spur or a tubercle; and a four-celled ovary, adherent at its base. Its fruit is invested by the permanent calyx, and contains numerous seeds of a coiled pyramidal form, like a snail-shell. [A. S.]

RHIGOZUM. A South African genus of *Bignoniaceæ*, in which it is remarkable for having five or rarely six to seven perfect stamens to the flower, instead of four fertile and one sterile, as is usually the case. The two known species, *R. trichotomum* and *obovatum*, are rigid bushes, with short lateral branchlets terminating in spiny points, and furnished with ternate leaves having obovate entire leaflets. The flowers, arising from the axils of the leaves, are either solitary or two or three together, and have yellow funnel-shaped corollas with a border of five rounded lobes nearly three-quarters of an inch across. The fruits are thin compressed elliptical capsules with two cells, separated from each other by a partition which runs contrary to the boat-like valves; and each cell has a number of flattened orbicular winged seeds. [A. A. B.]

RHINACANTHUS. A genus of *Acanthaceæ*, containing a few Indian species, all of them having the habit and structure of *Justicia*, except that the small white flowers are arranged in trichotomous terminal spikes. The roots of *R. communis*, better known as *Justicia nasuta*, are used by the Hindoos for the cure of ringworm. [W. C.]

RHINACTINA. This genus, belonging to the same group of *Compositæ* as *Aster*, differs from that in the rough pappus-hairs being in two series, the outer shorter than the inner; and from its nearer ally, *Diplopappus*, in the tubular florets of the disk being somewhat two-lipped instead of regularly five-toothed, one of the lips four-toothed, the other narrow and undivided. There are two species, *R. uniflora* and *R. limoniifolia*, both natives of desert regions along the Altai mountain range. The first is a tufted nearly stemless perennial, with a rosette of spathulate hoary leaves, and a short flower-stalk bearing a single purple-rayed flower-head; the other has branching stems six to eight inches high. [A. A. B.]

RHINANTHACEÆ. An order of dicotyledons, originally established by Jussieu under the name of *Pediculares*, and adopted by many subsequent botanists with some modifications under that of *Rhinanthaceæ*, but now with general assent incorporated with *Scrophulariaceæ*.

RHINANTHERA. *Scolopia.*

RHINANTHUS. A genus of European annuals belonging to the *Scrophulariaceæ*, of which the characters are:—Stamens four, two longer than the others; calyx with four divisions; upper lip of corolla compressed laterally; calyx inflated. *R. Crista galli*, the Yellow Rattle, is a common weed in meadows and pastures, with a rigid smooth spotted stem, either simple or branched, oblong tapering serrated leaves, and yellow flowers in the axils of the upper leaves; these are made conspicuous by the large light-green inflated calyx, which is persistent, and if brushed against or shaken when the seeds are ripe makes a rattling noise: hence the name. *R. angustifolius* grows in cornfields in the North of England, and is distinguished by its more bushy habit, and by the acuminated bracts and upper leaves. French: *Cocrête des prés*; German: *Hahnenkamm.* [C. A. J.]

RHINOCARPUS. The name often given to a noble tree of Columbia and British Guiana, where it is called the Wild Cashew. Like the common cashew, which it much resembles, it belongs to the genus *Anacardium*. It grows to a height of 160 feet, yields an excellent tough durable timber, and a pleasant edible fruit like the cashew. In Panama, according to Seemann, the tree is called Espave, and its bark is said to be used in stupefying fish. Caracoli is the name of the tree in New Grenada: see ANACARDIUM. [A. A. B.]

RHINOPETALUM. A liliaceous plant from the Ural Mountains, with the bulb and habit of a small *Fritillaria*, but differing from that genus in the simple undivided stigma. It has not the beauty of the majority of its allies.

RHIPIDODENDRON. By some writers separated from the genus *Aloe* in consequence of the stamens not being adherent to the tube of the perianth. The species are natives of the Cape of Good Hope, and have a woody forked stem, bearing towards the extremities of the branches a number of closely-packed fleshy tongue-shaped leaves, arranged in two rows on either side of the branch, so that a fan-like appearance is presented by them: whence the name, from the Greek words signifying 'fan-tree.' The Hottentots extract a kind of aloes from the leaves, and employ the stems as quivers for their arrows. [M. T. M.]

RHIPIDOPTERIS. A small group of ferns of the section *Acrosticheæ*, allied closely to *Polybotrya* in their free veins and wholly fertile fronds, but differing altogether in habit and aspect. They are curious little creeping plants, with small fronds from one to three inches high, the sterile ones flabellately parted and dichotomously wedge-shaped, and the fertile ones either roundish and entire, or two-lobed. The veins are flabellately forked. They are confined to the West Indies and South America. [T. M.]

RHIPSALIS. One of the genera of *Cactaceæ*, with rotate or wheel-like flowers, that is, flowers with wide-spreading segments and scarcely any tube. The segments in the present genus vary from twelve to eighteen, the outer ones or sepals being small greenish and scale-like, and the inner or petals larger and whitish. Its flowers contain numerous stamens of nearly equal length, and a narrow style bearing a three to six-rayed stigma; and they are succeeded by little smooth berries about the size of peas, bearing the withered remains of the flowers and becoming pellucid when ripe. It consists of a considerable number of small fleshy jointed-branched leafless plants, usually growing upon trees but varying considerably in general appearance, some having cylindrical and others angular stems and branches, while those of others, again, are flat and leaf-like; the flowers are produced from the sides of the branches, or from little notches along the edges in the flat-branched kinds. All the species are natives of the warmer parts of the Western Hemisphere, extending from Mexico to Buenos Ayres. Several are met with in hothouses in this country.

R. Cassytha is a common species in the West Indies, where it grows from one to six feet long, and hangs from the branches of trees. It has whorls of cylindrical branches with blunt ends, the ultimate branchlets being about three inches in length. *R. platycarpa*, a native of Brazil, has flat leaf-like branches resembling those of the genus *Phyllocactus*, the joints being from four to eight inches long and about one-and-a-half broad, with small distant notches from which the dirty white flowers are produced. [A. S.]

RHIZANTHEÆ. One of the five classes into which Lindley divides the vegetable kingdom. It consists of plants destitute of true leaves, but with short amorphous stems parasitical on roots. The flowers, which in some instances are very large, are various in their structure; and the three orders composing the class, the *Balanophoraceæ*, *Cytinaceæ*, and *Rafflesiaceæ*, are by some botanists placed far from each other in the vegetable system.

RHIZINA. The young roots of mosses and lichens.

RHIZOBLASTUS. A term applied to embryos which develope roots.

RHIZOBOLACEÆ. (*Rhizobols.*) A small order of dicotyledons, consisting only of the two genera *Caryocar* and *Anthodiscus*, which have been compared with *Clusiaceæ* on account of the extraordinary size of the radicle of the embryo with very minute cotyledons, and the opposite leaves of one genus. The leaves are, however, alternate in the other genus, and the structure of the flowers is so nearly that of *Ternströmiaceæ*, among which there is sometimes an approach to the same disproportion in the parts of the embryo, that the *Rhizobolaceæ* are now proposed to be considered as a tribe of that order, differing both from it and from *Clusiaceæ* in their digitately compound leaves. The few species known are all tropical American trees.

RHIZOBOLUS. *Caryocar*.

RHIZOCARPÆ. The same as *Marsileaceæ*.

RHIZOCARPOUS, RHIZOCARPICUS. Having a perennial root, but a stem which perishes annually; as herbaceous plants. The sign of these is ♃.

RHIZOGENS. *Rhizantheæ*.

RHIZOGLOSSUM. *Ophioglossum*.

RHIZOID, or RHIZOIDEOUS. Resembling a root.

RHIZOMA, RHIZOME. A prostrate rooting stem, progressively throwing up leaves. The name is applied among ferns to the creeping stem, which may be either superficial or covered with the soil, and in such a case must not be confounded with the true roots. The fronds are sometimes articulated with the rhizome, and such ferns are called by Smith *Eremobrya*; sometimes they are permanently attached, and

the ferns in which this is the case are called *Desmobrya*. The distinction is, however, not of the same importance as in phænogams; and if this character were adopted as distinctive, closely allied genera would be widely separated. The rhizomes of ferns, like real stems, exhibit very different arrangements of their several constituent tissues. When these differences have been more extensively studied, they will very probably afford good characters for sectional divisions. For an account of these we refer to Berkeley's *Introduction to Cryptogamic Botany*, p. 514. [M. J. B.]

RHIZOMANIA. An unnatural development of roots. Many plants, as ivy, screwpines, figs, &c., without any indication of disease whatever, send out roots from various parts in the same way as trees so commonly produce adventitious buds. In the common garden fig, wherever it is nailed to the wall, roots are sent out within the band which surrounds the stem. Their development, however, as in the vine and common laurel, usually indicates something wrong about the ordinary roots, in consequence of which sufficient moisture is not supplied to the stems and leaves, and rootlets are thrown out from the stem in search of it. In the laurel this generally ends in death. Roots again are frequently developed in little bundles on the stems of apple-trees; and as they retain moisture amongst them, and their tips in process of time decay, decomposition is set up, extending inwards till canker is produced. [M. J. B.]

RHIZOMORPHA. A spurious genus of *Fungi*, comprising a great number of root-like productions which are nothing more than particular states of *Polypori*, *Hypoxyla*, &c. Many of these owe their peculiar flattened character to the circumstance of their growing between the bark and wood of our forest trees, and thus being strongly compressed in the course of their growth. Other matters have been referred to the same genus, which are merely the roots of willows, elms, &c., or even of herbaceous plants filling up drain-tiles or other cavities where there is a constant supply of water. Fries indeed thinks that there is one good species of *Rhizomorpha* produced in mines, a bad situation for an autonomous plant. One great peculiarity of the supposed species which grow in mines, or of some of them at least, is their highly luminous character, which is not exceeded by *Agaricus olearius*, or any other luminous fungus. In the coal-mines near Dresden the species are described as giving those places the air of an enchanted castle; the roof, walls, and pillars are entirely covered with them, their beautiful light almost dazzling the eye. The light (which is apparently phosphorescent) is found to increase with the temperature of the mines. [M. J. B.]

RHIZOMORPHOUS. Resembling a root.

RHIZOPHORACEÆ. (*Rhizophoreæ*, *Mangroves*). An order of polypetalous dicotyledons, allied in some respects to *Cuno-*

niaceæ, but still more to *Lythraceæ*. It consists of tropical trees or shrubs, with opposite entire leaves, and axillary flowers, either solitary or in cymes or clusters. The calyx is often superior, with the lobes always valvate; the petals inserted on the calyx are often fringed or divided; and the stamens as many or twice as many as the petals, rarely more, inserted within them with erect anthers. The ovary has two or more cells; and the fruit, either inferior or enclosed in the calyx, has one or few seeds. The order contains about fourteen genera and is divided into two distinct tribes: *Rhizophoreæ* proper consisting of the genus *Rhizophora*, and a few small ones separated from it, all maritime trees known as mangroves, whose seeds are without albumen and almost always germinate before falling off; and *Legnotideæ* (which see), trees or shrubs not strictly maritime, with usually smaller flowers, and albuminous seeds not germinating before they fall. The chief genera of this tribe are *Carallia*, *Gynotroches*, and *Anstrutheria* in Asia and Africa, and *Cassipourea* in America and Africa.

RHIZOPHORA. This genus gives its name to the family *Rhizophoraceæ*, and is more familiarly known by that of Mangrove. The species are trees, inhabiting the muddy swamps close to the sea-shore in tropical climates. Botanically they are distinguished from neighbouring genera by their four-parted calyx, four sharply-pointed petals, eight to twelve stamens, with short filaments and anthers containing several little pits filled with pollen, and a partially adherent ovary, the adherent portion containing two cavities each containing two ovules, and the free portion solid fleshy and gradually tapering into a style.

Their chief interest, however, arises from their peculiar mode of growth and of germination. Dr. William Hamilton has published an interesting account of them in the *Pharmaceutical Journal*, from which we extract the following: 'In the economy of Nature the Mangrove performs a most important part, wresting annually fresh portions of the land from the dominion of the ocean, and adding them to the domain of man. This is effected in a twofold manner: by the progressive advance of their roots, and by the aërial germination of their seeds, which do not quit their lofty cradle till they have assumed the form of actual trees, and drop into the water with their roots ready prepared to take possession of the mud, in advance of their parent stems. The progression by means of the roots is effected by fresh roots, which issue from the trunk at some distance above the surface of the water, and arching downwards penetrate the mud, establishing themselves as the pioneers of fresh invasions of the retiring element. In this manner the plants, after their descent from the parent trees, continue during their early years to advance steadily forward, till they have attained a height of about fifteen feet, and gained a position considerably in advance of their parent trunks. After this, fewer additions are made to the roots, but the head begins to expand in every direction, spreading its branches on all sides. These branches in their turn send down long slender roots, like those of the banyan-tree (*Ficus indica*), which rapidly elongating descend from all varieties of height, and reaching the water penetrate the mud, becoming in time independent trees: thus a complicated labyrinth is at length formed.'

These mangrove-bogs are the certain indicators of a malarious locality, inasmuch as they prevent the escape of the unhealthy miasma. The natives scramble along from root to root, without ever trusting their weight to the boggy soil below. To these roots the oysters and other molluscs adhere, and are brought into view as the tide goes down, thus verifying the statement of old travellers that oysters grew on trees.

All parts of these trees contain an abundance of tannin, and hence they are very serviceable to tanners. The bark is likewise employed by dyers, yielding with salts of copper and iron, olive, brown, rust and slate-coloured tints. The bark has also been used medicinally as an astringent remedy. In the West Indies and the Mauritius the leaves and roots of some of them are employed by the fishermen as poultices for wounds caused by certain fish and venomous animals.

The fruit of *R. Mangle* is said to be sweet and edible, and the fermented juice to be made into a kind of light wine. In Borneo mangroves furnish the best firewood, and a coarse bitter salt is extracted from their aërial roots. In the Philippines, and also in the West Indies, the bark of some of the species is used as a febrifuge. The genus well deserves its technical name of 'root-bearer.'   [M. T. M.]

RHIZOPHYLLUM. A name proposed by Newman for the *Polypodieæ* referred to *Phlebodium* and *Pleopeltis*.

RHIZOPOD, or RHIZOPODIUM. The mycelium or spawn of fungals.

RHIZOPOGON. A genus of hypogynous *Fungi*, agreeing with *Melanogaster* in having root-like fibres running over the surface, though not moist within, but dry like a piece of porous bread-crumb). We are not aware that the British species are eaten, though sometimes produced in abundance. *R. provincialis* is greedily devoured by the peasants in Provence. One species is found in the United States, and the genus occurs also at the Swan River.   [M. J. B.]

RHIZOS. In Greek compounds = root.

RHIZOSPERMA. *Azolla*.

RHIZULA. The young root of mosses and lichens.

RHODACTINIA. The well-known *Barnadesia rosea* has been separated from the others of that genus under this name. It differs from *Barnadesia* in having straight instead of spirally twisted hairs on the receptacle, free in place of monadelphous stamens, and no central tubular florets: see BARNADESIA. [A, A. B.]

RHODALSINE. A genus of Caryophyllaceæ, proposed for Alsine procumbens, which differs from the other species of the genus in having the cotyledons accumbent not incumbent. It is a small glandular plant inhabiting the Mediterranean region; and has oblong leaves, and small flowers with entire rose-coloured petals, ten stamens in two rows, three styles, and compressed kidney-shaped seeds. [J. T. S.]

RHODANTHE. A beautiful genus of Compositæ, found in Western Australia. The only species is R. Manglesii, of which there are several varieties differing from each other mainly in the size and colour of their flower-heads, which have the dry character of what are commonly called 'everlasting' flowers.' It is an annual plant, rising from a foot to a foot and a half high, with an erect branching stem, oblong blunt entire stem-clasping leaves of a glaucous green colour, and flower-heads on slender stalks arranged in a corymbose manner. The flower-heads have a top-shaped involucre of numerous dry scales, which are small and silvery at the base, but gradually increase upwards in size and depth of tint till they become radiate and of a colour varying from pale rose to deep purple. Each head contains numerous florets, all similar and borne upon a naked receptacle, the florets themselves having a five-cut tubular corolla, and a pappus of distinct feathery bristles in a single row. The achenes are woolly and beakless. By some the plants called atrosanguinea and maculata are regarded as distinct. [A. S.]

RHODEA (or ROHDEA) japonica. A curious Japanese monocotyledon formerly described as an Orontium, of which it has somewhat the appearance, but from which it is widely different in structure. It constitutes a genus of Liliaceæ of the tribe Aspidistreæ, remarkable for the flowers and afterwards the baccate fruits being densely aggregated in a compact oblong spike, resembling the spadix of several Aroideæ.

RHODES-WOOD. The Candlewood of the West Indies, Amyris balsamifera.

RHODIOLA. A succulent herbaceous perennial, which by some authors is separated from Sedum on account of its bearing fertile and barren flowers on distinct plants. R. rosea, the Rose-root, may be considered as a species of Sedum with plane leaves and a thick root, having the habit of S. Telephium. It grows on wet rocks on the high mountains of Scotland and the North of England and Ireland, as well as on sea-cliffs. The stems are unbranched, about a foot high, the leaves broad thick fleshy and glaucous, and the flowers yellow, crowded at the summit of the stem. The root, when bruised and even when dried, yields a scent like that of a rose. The Rose-root is the badge of the clan Gunn. [C. A. J.]

RHODO. In Greek compounds = red.

RHODOCALYCE. (Fr.) Rhodochiton.

RHODOCHITON. A genus of Scrophulariaceæ, founded on R. volubile, a climber from Mexico, which differs little from Lophospermum, except that the calyx is less divided and the corolla is not so open, and has the two lips cut into nearly equal segments. [W. C.]

RHODOCHLAMYS. A genus of Labiatæ, the leading characters of which are:—Calyx inflated, the upper lip entire, the lower bifid; tube of the corolla inflated about the middle, its upper lip short and entire, the lower tricrenate; filaments of the lower pair of stamens dilated and partly joined. R. speciosa is a Mexican shrub with red flowers, hoary and glandulose above. The name is from the Greek words signifying 'red' and 'a covering,' in allusion to the appearance of the corolla. [G. D.]

RHODOCOMA. A genus proposed by Nees for a species of Restiaceæ from the Cape Colony, but which is probably not sufficiently distinct from Elegia.

RHODODENDRON. The generic name of a group of showy plants belonging to the Ericaceæ. In their flowers the corolla is funnel-shaped, sometimes slightly irregular, five-lobed; and the stamens are ten in number, rarely fewer, and usually declined.

The species are shrubs or low trees, with entire alternate leaves, and showy clusters of flowers. The name is from the Greek, and literally means 'rose-tree.' The plants of this genus have been long favourably known to cultivators, combining, as most of them do, beauty profuseness and fragrance of flower with handsome foliage. Some also have the additional recommendation of bearing a succession of flowers for a considerable time: R. Maddeni, for example, flowering for eight or more weeks. The flowers of R. Edgeworthi attain a diameter of five inches, are white with a shade of delicate pink, and so fragrant that a few are sufficient to scent a large room. The snow-white flowers of R. Griffithianum present a beautiful contrast with the large leaves, six to twelve inches long, which are bright-green with a pale-yellow edge.

In the size attained by the species there is a wide contrast. The small and humble R. lapponicum is a prostrate shrub, with branches a few inches long; while R. Rollissonii of Ceylon attains a height of thirty feet, and a girth of four feet; and R. Falconeri is sometimes fifty feet high, with leaves nineteen inches long.

The genus is widely diffused: R. lapponicum occurs in the Arctic Zone, R. maximum and R. catawbiense are plentiful in some parts of North America. The genus has also representatives in Europe and in China, but in India we find the greatest number. Dr. J. D. Hooker observed forty-three species in Sikkim, most of which were new: and in Bhotan they also abound. R. lapponicum is one of the brightest floral ornaments on the shores of Davis's Straits near the sea-level; on the other hand *R. nivale*, the most alpine of woody plants, flourishes at an elevation of 17,000 feet. Respecting it and some others Dr. Hooker reports the following interesting facts :—*R. nivale* ripens its fruit in two months; *R. anthopogon*, at 13,000 to 14,000 feet, requires four months ; *R. campanulatum*, at 11,000 to 12,000 feet, six months; and *R. argenteum*, at 8,000 to 9,000 feet, eight months. Some are epiphytes or false parasites, growing attached to the stems of other plants. Such is the *R. Brookeanum* of Sarawak, whose large fleshy roots are admirably suited to such a habitat.

As regards properties, some are looked on with suspicion. It is long since poisonous qualities were attributed to honey collected by bees from flowers of *R. ponticum*, and the same is reported of some Indian species. Goats are said to die after eating the leaves of *R. cinnabarinum*; and when used as fuel it produces swellings of the face and inflammation of the eyes. Notwithstanding this, a jelly is prepared in India from the boiled-down flowers of *R. arboreum*. The Siberian *R. chrysanthum*, of which a figure is given, is narcotic in its properties and is used medicinally.

The discoveries of Dr. J. D. Hooker have added greatly to our knowledge of the species, and enriched our collections with several which are highly prized by cultivators. *R. ciliatum* may be mentioned as an example; it grows in the rocky valleys of *Sikkim*, at 9,000 to 10,000 feet elevation, and of all Indian species is probably most easily cultivated; while its moderate size and abundant flowers are further recommendations. The process of hybridising has been extensively used between species of this genus—for example, between *R.*

Rhododendron chrysanthum.

ciliatum and *R. Edgeworthi*, *R. formosum*, and *R. Dalhousiae*; but we must refer to professedly horticultural treatises for details respecting the results in such cases. The beautiful epiphytal *R. Dalhousiae*, just mentioned, is represented in its natural habitat in Plate 1.   [G. D.]

RHODOLÆNA *altivola* is the only

known representative of a genus of *Chlœnaceæ* peculiar to Madagascar. It is a climbing shrub, the fruit of which is unknown; and has oval leaves, axillary peduncles and large purple flowers, with three sepals, six petals, an indefinite number of stamens, quadrangular anthers, and a three-celled ovary, containing numerous ovules in each cell.   [B. S.]

RHODOLEIA *Championi* is a beautiful shrub or small tree, a native of the island

Rhodoleia Championi.

of Hong-Kong, forming a genus of *Hamamelidaceæ*, allied to *Bucklandia*, but remarkable for the flower-heads being surrounded by several rows of imbricated bracts, whilst the bright pink petals of all the five or six flowers of the head are arranged round the circumference, giving it the appearance of a handsome semidouble *Camellia*. The evergreen coriaceous leaves, too, are also not unlike those of some *Camellias*. The plant was introduced a few years since, and has flowered at Trentham. A second species of the genus has been found in Java.

RHODOMELACEÆ. A natural order of rose-spored *Algæ*, belonging to the division in which the spore-threads are tufted. The nucleus is lodged in an external oval or globose conceptacle, which is hollow and has the placenta at the base; and the spores are confined to the terminal cell of the spore-threads. *Rhodomelaceæ* are either jointed, or have a jointed many-tubed axis, and the surface divided into little areæ. It contains some of the most beautiful genera, and especially *Amansia*, while others are dark in colour and inelegant. Several of them contain many species, *Polysiphonia* numbering two or three hundred. *Odonthalia dentata*, one of our most beautiful *Algæ*, does not extend further south than the Isle of Man; while some genera, as *Amansia*, are tropical and subtropical, and others have representatives in every part of the globe. Some are attached to peculiar plants. For example, wherever we find *Fucus nodosus* we are sure to find *Polysiphonia fastigiata*.   [M. J. B.]

RHODOMYRTUS. This genus of Myrtaceæ differs but little from Myrtus, except in the flowers, which are rose-coloured (whence the name); and in the seeds, which are compressed, flat, and arranged in two rows in each of the compartments of the fruit. R. tomentosa, a native of China, is in cultivation as a greenhouse plant. It much resembles the common myrtle, save in the colour of the flowers, and in the fact of the leaves being downy on their under-surface.   [M. T. M.]

RHODORA. Rhododendron.

RHODORRHIZA. A small genus of Convolvulaceæ confined to the Canary Islands, and by most authors regarded as identical with Convolvulus. It derives its name from the rose-like smell peculiar to the rootstocks and lower part of the stems, which yield a kind of Rosewood (lignum rhodii). From them is extracted by distillation the powerfully-scented oil known as Oleum ligni Rhodii æthereum, used in some countries for ointment, but more frequently for the adulteration of attar of roses. This Rosewood is called by the French Bois des Rhodes des Parfumeurs, and must not be confounded with the so-called rosewood of commerce used for furniture. Rhodorrhiza is composed of two species: R. scoparia (Convolvulus scoparius) and R. florida (Convolvulus floridus), both having woody erect stems, linear leaves, terminal panicles of flowers, five sepals, a bell-shaped corolla, a single style bearing two stigmas, and a two-celled capsule, each cell of which has two or by abortion one seed.   [B. S.]

RHODOSPATHA. A genus of Orontiaceæ, comprising certain Peruvian herbaceous plants, throwing down roots from their trailing stems, having large leaves and very large rose-coloured spathes, whence the name of the genus. It differs from Calla and Monstera in the definite stamens, and in the structure of the fruit. [M. T. M.]

RHODOSPERMEÆ. The Rhodosperms form one of the three great divisions of Algæ, distinguished by their rose-coloured spores, which are of two kinds—the one contained in capsular bodies of various structure and denomination, external or immersed; the others of spores, always four together (tetraspores), formed by the cell-division of the endochrome of a single cell, which is generally globular, but sometimes cylindrical. Antheridia are also found in many genera, and probably are universal. One or two genera which are not of this group, as Bangia and Porphyra, have spores of a similar colour, but they have not the double fructification. It has been questioned which is the true fruit. At present the tetraspores are regarded as gemmæ not requiring impregnation.

The Rhodosperms divide naturally into two great tribes, Desmiospermeæ and Gongylospermeæ, in the former of which the spores are formed in a joint or joints of the spore-threads; in the other they are congregated without order in a hyaline mucous or membranaceous mother-cell. The genera depend partly on the structure of the frond, and partly on the nature of the fruit, whether capsular or tetraspored. It is to the younger Agardh especially that we are indebted for the present improved arrangement, which has been diligently followed out by Montagne, Harvey, and others. Kützing also has done a good deal, but unfortunately has not clear notions as to the extent of genera and species. Rhodosperms are found in all parts of the world; but, like other bright-coloured productions, their maximum is attained in warmer climes, however abundant they may be elsewhere.   [M. J. B.]

RHODOSTOMA. A genus of Cinchonaceæ, of which one species is in cultivation in hothouses, but whence obtained is doubtful. It is a small shrub, with smooth somewhat glossy leaves, white or pinkish flowers in terminal cymes, the small branches of which are of a rich flesh-colour. The five lobes of the calyx are reflected; the corolla is funnel-shaped, with a long tube concealing the stamens; the ovary is two-celled, adherent to the calyx, and surrounded by a fleshy disk. The plant is a pretty stove-shrub, and known under the name of R. gardenioides.   [M. T. M.]

RHODOTHAMNUS. A genus of Ericaceæ, distinguished by its wheel-shaped and five-lobed corolla, and by the ovary being two-celled, and when ripe opening through the backs of the cells into five valves. The only species has been long known as Rhododendron Chamæcistus, a small handsome shrub with solitary rose-coloured flowers, and alternate oval leaves. The generic name expresses the general reddish tint of the plant.   [G. D.]

RHODYMENIA. The typical genus of the natural order of rose-spored Algæ, Rhodymeniaceæ, which are characterised by an inarticulate membranaceous frond composed chiefly of many-sided cells, the surface-cells forming a continual coating, and the nucleus lodged in an external conceptacle, and either single or compound; spores at first moniliform. Rhodymenia itself has a flat forked or irregularly cleft frond with a simple nucleus. R. palmata, which is common everywhere on our coasts, and is parasitical on Fuci and Laminariæ, &c., in the United States, is the Dulse or Dillisk of the Scotch; and though tough and of a parchment-like texture, is not an unacceptable food to hungry men, as we have ourselves experienced in former days amongst the Western Islands, when travelling was not so easy as it is now. It varies much in width, and is sometimes wider than it is long.   [M. J. B.]

RHOMBEUS, RHOMBOID, RHOMBOIDAL. Oval, a little angular in the middle, as the leaf of Hibiscus rhombifolius.

RHOPALA. A proteaceous genus of trees or large shrubs, natives of South

America, having simple or pinnate coarse and generally toothed leaves, and flowers in axillary or terminal racemes, often covered with a rich brownish wool. These flowers have a straight cylindrical club-shaped calyx of four linear sepals, with concave apices, which become recurved; four stamens, one inserted above the middle of each sepal, with linear anthers; and a straight filiform persistent style having a club-shaped stigma. The seed-vessel is a woody or leathery oval two-seeded follicle, containing oblong compressed winged seeds.   [R. H.]

RHOPALOSTYLIS. A name given by Klotzsch to a scandent bush of the *Euphorbiaceæ*, found in Northern Brazil and Guiana, and better known to botanists as *Dalechampia micrantha*. It merely differs from *Dalechampia* in the leaves being undivided instead of more or less lobed; and in the sunk instead of projecting stigmas at the apex of the club-shaped style, which is much longer than the flowers. The ovate and alternate stalked leaves are smooth and five-nerved, while the inconspicuous flowers are borne on short axillary peduncles.   [A. A. B.]

RHUBARB. *Rheum*. —, BUCHARIAN. *Rheum undulatum*. —; ENGLISH. *Rheum Rhaponticum*. —, FRENCH. *Rheum Rhaponticum undulatum* and *compactum*. —, HIMALAYAN. *Rheum Emodi* and *Webbianum*. —, MONK'S. *Rumex alpinus*; also *R. Patientia*. —, POOR-MAN'S. *Thalictrum flavum*. —, TURKEY. *Rheum palmatum*.

RHUBARBE. (Fr.) *Rheum*. — DES MOINES. *Rumex Patientia*. — DES PAUVRES. *Thalictrum flavum*.

RHUS. A large and widely-spread genus of *Anacardiaceæ*, found abundantly in the temperate countries of both hemispheres, especially in North America and at the Cape of Good Hope, and more sparingly within the tropics. The greater number of the species are shrubs from six to ten feet high, but some are low bushes, while others again grow to a considerable height and form trees. With few exceptions their leaves are compound, either composed of three leaflets or pinnate with a terminal leaflet. The Venetian Sumach and a few others, however, have simple leaves. Their flowers are small, and most frequently have only one sex perfectly developed; the male and female flowers sometimes occurring on separate trees, and very few species having uniformly perfect flowers. Their fruits are small, and are either nearly dry or slightly juicy, and contain a single bony one-seeded stone.

Most of the species of *Rhus* possess poisonous properties in a greater or less degree. Some American species indeed, such as *R. venenata* and *R. Toxicodendron*, produce effects almost rivalling those once fabulously imputed to the Upas-tree of Java (*Antiaris*), the hands and arms, and sometimes even the whole body, becoming greatly swollen from simply touching or

carrying a branch of one of these plants, and the swelling being accompanied with intolerable pain and inflammation, and ending in ulceration. These effects, however, are not felt by everyone, some people

Rhus Toxicodendron.

being able to handle the plants with impunity. *R. venenata*, called the Poison Sumach or Poison Elder, is a tall shrub with pinnate leaves composed of eleven or thirteen smoothish leaflets; while *R. Toxicodendron* is a rambling shrub, either trailing along the ground and rooting at intervals, or climbing up trees or on walls and attaching itself like ivy, and has leaves composed of only three leaflets.

Some species, however, yield useful products, such as *R. Coriaria*, the Tanning Sumach, which affords commercial Sumach or Shumac. This species is a native of the European countries bordering the Mediterranean, and when allowed to grow to its full size attains a height of fifteen or

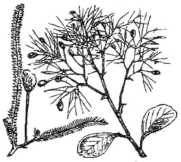

Rhus Cotinus.

twenty feet; but in a cultivated state the young shoots are cut off annually for the sake of their leaves, and it is consequently seldom seen higher than four or five feet. Its leaves are hairy and composed of from five to seven pairs of leaflets and a terminal odd one, the leaflets somewhat resembling the leaves of the common elm. The Sumach of commerce is the finely-ground young leaves: it is extensively employed for tanning and dyeing purposes, from 12,000 to 18,000 tons being annually imported, chiefly from Sicily.

R. *Cotinus*, another South European species, called the Venus or Venetian Sumach, yields the yellow dyewood called Young Fustic, which in olden times was supposed to be the young branches of the true Fustic-tree (*Maclura*). This is a shrub with simple smooth shining green leaves, and a very remarkable feathery inflorescence.

The Japan wax recently brought in considerable quantity to this country, is the produce of the fruits of *R. succedanea*, a small tree or tallshrub, with smooth branches and leaves, the latter being pinnate, and consisting of from eleven to fifteen shining green leaflets from two to three inches long, and of an oblong form with a long taper point. R. *vernicifera*, another small Japanese tree, yields the famous lacquer so extensively employed by the inhabitants of that country for lacquering various articles of furniture and small-ware. It exudes from wounds made in the tree, and is at first milky-white, but becomes darker and ultimately black on being exposed to the air. Nothing certain is known respecting the mode of preparing it for use, and it is said that the Japanese themselves have lost the secret of its preparation, for the lacquer-ware at present manufactured is greatly inferior to the ancient. [A. S.]

RHYNCHANTHERA. A genus of *Melastomaceæ*, consisting of herbs undershrubs or shrubs, from Guiana, Brazil, and other parts of tropical America, usually hirsute and glandular, with opposite cordate or oblong leaves, and for the most part showy flowers in the upper axils, or in terminal panicles. They belong to the tribe of *Lavoisiereæ*, in which the fruit is free and capsular, and the seeds not curved; and are distinguished from allied genera chiefly by the anthers, of which five are perfect, ending in a long beak and auricled at the base, whilst the other five are small and often imperfect. One of the five perfect ones is also in many species much longer than all the others. There are nearly thirty species known, several of which might be ornamental if introduced to our hothouses. The name has also been given to an orchidaceous plant now referred to *Corymbis*.

RHYNCHOCORYS. A small genus of annuals from the South of Europe and East of Asia, separated from *Rhinanthus* because the flowers have a distinctly two-lipped calyx. [W. C.]

RHYNCHOGLOSSUM. A small genus of *Cyrtandraceæ* inhabiting the East Indies and Java, having a fleshy herbaceous stem, alternate ovate leaves, terminal racemes bearing blue flowers, a tubular five-cleft calyx, a tubular corolla with a bilabiate border, two fertile and two sterile stamens, and an ovate capsule. [B. S.]

RHYNCHOLACIS. A genus of *Podostemaceæ*, consisting of aquatic herbaceous plants, with very short thick hardened stems, unbranched or repeatedly forked; flowers on long stalks or in whorls; and broad membranous leaves, lacerated at the margins. The principal diagnostic mark of the genus resides in the capsule, which consists of two equal valves, each provided with a keel and projecting beak. The species are natives of Guiana. [M. T. M.]

RHYNCHOLEPIS. A genus of *Piperaceæ*, the species of which are shrubs inhabiting the Philippine Islands. The branches are jointed, hairy; the leaves ovate and oblique, their stipules very hairy; and the flowers diœcious, borne on cylindrical catkins, the bracts of which are stalked, peltate, fleshy, and elongated into a long thread-like process. [M. T. M.]

RHYNCHOPETALUM. A genus of *Lobeliaceæ*, represented by an Abyssinian herbaceous plant, with a hollow stem about a foot high, bearing a crowded tuft of lance-shaped leaves at the top, and flowers in long clusters. The five lobes of the calyx are leafy; the tube of the corolla is split on the upper edge, and its lobes are confluent one with another so as to resemble the prow of a boat. This latter circumstance has given the name 'beak-petal' to the genus. [M. T. M.]

RHYNCHOSIA. A genus of *Leguminosæ* the species of which are very numerous, and occur in India and other parts of Southern Asia, in Australia, the West Indies, and the warmer parts of America. They are herbs or undershrubs, usually with twining stems, and often sprinkled with small yellow resinous or glandular dots. Their leaves generally consist of three leaflets, the middle one of which has a long stalk, very rarely of a single leaflet; and their flowers are in most instances disposed in racemes produced from the angles of the leaves, and nearly always of a yellowish colour. They have a bell-shaped four or five-lobed calyx; a papilionaceous corolla, the upper petal of which is roundish, and has two round lobes or ears at the bottom, but no hard swellings as in some allied genera; ten stamens, nine being united into a sheath, and the tenth or upper one free from the bottom; and a stalkless ovary with a smooth style. Their flattened unequal-sided or sickle-shaped pods are without divisions, and contain two (rarely one) round or somewhat kidney-shaped seeds.

R. *precatoria* has pretty little half-black and half-scarlet or yellow shining seeds, which the Mexicans string into necklaces and rosaries—whence its Latin name. It is a tall climbing plant, with hairy stems, and broadly egg-shaped or almost rhomboid three-nerved leaflets covered with soft short hairs or down; its flower-spikes are about the same length as the leaves, and its pods scarcely one inch long, constricted between the seeds, and covered with glandular hairs. It is a native of Mexico and Panama. [A. S.]

RHYNCHOSPERMUM *verticillatum* is a Javanese composite plant related to *Erigeron*, from which it differs in the shortly-beaked achenes, as well as in the pappus-hairs being twisted or inflexed at the apex. It is described as being a smooth perennial, the ultimate branches whorled, the leaves shortly stalked and lanceolate, and the stalked terminal flower-heads almost the size of peas, with strap-shaped and fertile outer florets in two or three series, and tubular perfect inner florets. Only one species is known. For the well-known *Rhynchospermum jasminoides* of gardens, see PAREOHITES. [A. A. B.]

RHYNCHOSPORA. A genus of *Cyperaceæ* belonging to the tribe *Rhynchosporeæ*. The inflorescence is generally in clustered spikelets forming terminal or axillary heads. Each spikelet contains from one to nine flowers; glumes imbricated round the axis, the lower or outer empty, the upper containing flowers; stamens three, rarely two or one; styles cleft flattened and thickened at the base. Steudel describes 121 species, which are distributed over North and South America, Australia, &c. The European representatives, *R. alba* and *R. fusca*, grow on wet spongy bogs, the former frequent but the latter rare in Britain, and hitherto only observed in a few places. [D. M.]

RHYNCHOSTEMON. A name given to two small West Australian bushes belonging to the *Byttneriaceæ*, differing from *Thomasia* only in the anthers being prolonged into a short beak—whence the name, signifying ' beaked stamen.' They have alternate stalked leaves with spear-shaped blades, clothed, like the young twigs, with glandular hairs; and their pretty pink flowers are disposed in racemes towards the ends of the twigs, and greatly resemble those of *Thomasia*. [A. A. B.]

RHYNCHOTHECA. A genus of *Oxalidaceæ* peculiar to the Andes of South America, and consisting of two species, both spiny shrubs, with square branches, oblong leaves, and pedunculate flowers crowded towards the apex of the branches. The calyx is composed of five sepals, the corolla is entirely wanting, the stamens eighteen, the style very short, and the carpels five, each containing two ovules. *R. diversifolia* grows in hedges. [B. S.]

RHYTACHNE. A genus of grasses belonging to the tribe of *Rottboelleæ*, and having the inflorescence in solitary terminal spikes; spikelets two-flowered, inserted in notches on the rachis—the lower flower hermaphrodite, the upper male; glume one, thick, transversely wrinkled and awned; stamens three. Only one species is described, *R. rottboellioides*, which is a native of the West Indies. [D. M.]

RHYTIDOMA. A formation of plates of cellular tissue within the liber or mesophlœum.

RHYTIDOPHYLLUM. A small genus of shrubby West Indian *Gesneraceæ*, with sparse leaves, hairy beneath and bullate above, and long axillary flower-stalks bearing a corymbose inflorescence. The calyx has the tube adnate to the ovary, and a five-parted limb; the corolla is obliquely campanulate, broad at its mouth and somewhat constricted at its middle, and has a five-lobed limb; the stamens are inserted high up on the corolla, and are two short and two long, with the rudiment of a fifth; and the disk upon the top of the ovary is thick annular and sinuose. The capsule is concrete with the calyx, and splits into two valves at its top. [A. S.]

RHYTIGLOSSA. A very large genus of herbaceous or shrubby plants belonging to the *Acanthaceæ*, widely dispersed through the tropical and warm countries of the Western Hemisphere, and found also at the Cape of Good Hope. Most of the species have terminal flower-spikes and reddish flowers, usually with narrow bracts resembling but shorter than the divisions of the calyx, or rarely with broad overlapping bracts. The calyx is four or five-parted; the corolla two-lipped; the stamens two; and the stigma simple and sharp-pointed. *R. pectoralis* is one of the commonest of the American species, being found in most of the West India Islands, and in various parts of tropical America, from Southern Mexico to Brazil. In some of these countries an infusion or tea made of the leaves is drunk to relieve chest affections, or a stomachic syrup is prepared by boiling them with sugar. In Martinique the French call it Herbe au Charpentier. [A. S.]

RHYTISMA. A genus of phacidiaceous *Fungi*, with a thin stroma, and superficial irregular wrinkle-like more or less confluent perithecia. The two most common species are *R. salicinum* of the willow, and *R. acerinum* of the sycamore—especially the latter, which forms large shining black orbicular patches on the leaves, conspicuous all the winter, and fructifying in the spring. [M. J. B.]

RIB. The principal vein or nervure which proceeds from the petiole into a leaf; also any firm longitudinal elevation.

RIBAND-WEED. The common name in some districts of the ordinary form of *Laminaria saccharina*. [M. J. B.]

RIBAS. An Eastern name for *Rheum Ribes*.

RIBBON-TREE. *Plagianthus betulinus*.

RIBES. The principal genus of *Grossulariaceæ*, characterised by its flowers having a five-parted coloured calyx, five small distinct petals, as many free stamens rising from the throat of the calyx-tube alternately with the petals, and a two to four-cleft style; and by its juicy one-celled berries, which are crowned with the remains of the flower, and contain numerous seeds suspended in pulp by long threads. Upwards of sixty species are described, two-thirds of which are found in the temperate parts of the American continent, where they extend from the Straits of Magellan to the Arctic Circle; while the rest are confined to the temperate regions of Europe and Asia. They are all shrubs, varying from one or two to five or six feet high, sometimes spiny, and have lobed alternate leaves, and either solitary or axillary racemes of flowers.

R. sanguineum, the Red-flowered Currant, a native of North America, is the species most frequently grown in our gardens for ornamental purposes, and when covered with a profusion of racemes of rich deep rose-red flowers in early spring, it forms a most beautiful object. It belongs to the section of the genus without prickles, and forms a bushy shrub sometimes as much as eight feet in height, having five-lobed serrated leaves, heart-shaped at the base, and downy underneath; and racemes usually twice as long as the leaves, containing numerous flowers, the conspicuous part of which is the richly-coloured calyx, which has a long bell-shaped tube, and blunt spreading segments much larger than the small paler-coloured petals.   [A. S.]

Those well-known and extensively cultivated fruits, the Gooseberry and Currant, are included in this genus. The rough or hairy Gooseberry has been called *R. Grossularia*, and the smooth Gooseberry *R. Uva crispa*; but there is no difference between them except as regards the surface of the fruit, for seeds from one bush will produce both rough and smooth-fruited plants. The Gooseberry is called in Cheshire and in the North of England *Feaberry* (according to Gerarde, a contraction of *Feverberry*, the fruit being considered a sort of specific against fevers); in Norfolk it is called *Feabes*; in Scotland *Grozet* or *Grozerts*; by the Germans *Krausel-beere*, or *Stachelbeere*; by the Dutch *Kruisbes*, or *Kruisbezie*; and by the Danes and Swedes *Krusbaar*, which is nearly identical with the Dutch name. The French call it *Groseille*, formerly written *Groiselle*, or *Groisseletz* according to Decandolle, and these names bear much analogy to the old Scotch name *Grozet*. The French use the fruit for making a sauce for mackerel, and hence call it Groseille à Maquereau; and we find it frequently stated in books that it is called Gooseberry from being used as a sauce for young or green geese. This, however, must be an error; for when Queen Elizabeth received the news of the destruction of the Spanish Armada, on September 29, she was eating goose, and that day has since been noted as about the time when young geese are in season; but there are then no green gooseberries to be had for sauce.

The Gooseberry is indigenous in this country, as well as in many other parts of Europe, and it has been found, according to Royle, in Nepal. Dr. Schübeler states that 'it is found wild here and there in Norway, in the lowlands, up to lat. 63°. Finer varieties, when cultivated, will ripen as far north as 66½° at least.' It therefore appears that it will succeed 16° north of London, but it will not thrive so far to the south. Even in southern parts of England, under a hot sun, the fruit of some of the varieties becomes as if parbolled. The cooler climates of the North of England and Scotland suit it best. It is an important plant for millions of the manufacturing population; for it supplies abundant fruit for tarts, pies, sauces, &c. at an early period of the season, and before any other can be had in quantity for these purposes. By competition for prizes in Lancashire and the adjoining counties, the size of the berries has been enormously increased, although some of the old sorts, such as the Red Champagne, are yet unsurpassed in quality. The varieties are exceedingly numerous, and are divided into sections according to their colour—red yellow green and white; and again from their surface being hairy downy or smooth.

Of the Red Currant, *R. rubrum*—which has cordate bluntly three to five-lobed leaves, yellowish-green flowers, and bright-red fruit in pendulous racemes,—there are several varieties, the most distinct of which are the pale-red, the flesh-coloured or champagne, the striped, and the white; but the red and the white are the most extensively cultivated. The original form of the species has undergone very great improvement. The Currant is indigenous to Britain, Central and Northern Europe, Siberia, and Canada. According to Dr. Schübeler (*Synopsis of the Vegetable Products of Norway*), it is generally to be found wild as far north as Finmark, and even under the seventieth parallel of latitude it produces annual shoots twenty inches in length. It may therefore be said that it possesses all the hardiness that need be desired. But, like the gooseberry, it is not suited for so warm a climate as the South of Europe—otherwise it would have extended into Italy, and would have become known to the Greeks and Romans, which does not appear to have been the case. It was only in the Middle Ages that its cultivation was introduced into the South of Europe. It is called *Ribs* in Danish, *Risp* and *Reps* in Swedish; and the Latin name of the genus, *Ribes*, is believed by Alph. Decandolle to have had a northern origin. The English name of Currant originated from the similarity of the fruit to the Corinth or Zante Grape, the currant of the shops. Improved varieties of the Currant appear to have been introduced from Holland, and the Red Dutch and the White Dutch are amongst the best in cultivation at the present day. These fruits are always in demand for making wine, tarts, jellies, jams, &c., and the quantities grown for that purpose have greatly increased since the price of sugar has become reduced. The refrigerant juice is also very grateful to the parched palates of persons suffering from fever.

The Black Currant, *R. nigrum*, bears short lax racemes of large black berries, which are much prized for domestic use, both as a preserve and medicine. [R. T.]

RIBESIACEÆ. Another name for the *Grossulariaceæ*.

RIBWORT. *Plantago lanceolata.*

RIBWORTS. Lindley's name for the *Plantaginaceæ.*

RICCIACEÆ. A natural order of liverworts with a valveless capsule sunk in the substance of the frond, rarely free, surrounded by or adnate with the veil, with or without additional envelopes, at length bursting irregularly, or opening by a terminal pore, and producing numerous spores without elaters. Most of the plants are horizontal, but *Riella* has an erect frond. At first sight they might seem to have some affinity to *Endocarpon*, but the vegetation and formation of the fruit (which take place, as in the case of pollen-grains, by repeated cell-division) are entirely different; besides which the structure of the frond is diverse from that of the thallus of any lichen. Warm countries are their favourite abode, but there are some which delight as much in temperate regions. Most of them grow upon the surface of the soil like *Marchantia*, but several are always immersed in or float freely on the surface of water, while a few grow on the trunks of trees. In *Corsinia* there is a chaffy compound involucre; in *Cronisia* the involucre consists of two or sometimes of three boat-like leaves. [M. J. B.]

RICCIA. The typical genus of the natural order *Ricciaceæ*, with a horizontal more or less forked lichen-like frond, which adheres closely to the soil or to the trunks of trees, or floats on the surface of pools. The same species may exist in all the three situations with slight modifications. *R. glauca* is extremely common on calcareous soil, though often overlooked, while *R. natans* and *fluitans* are common in fen-ditches. The latter has a narrow repeatedly forked frond, the former a shorter broader frond with numerous flat processes beneath hanging down into the water, which make admirable subjects for the microscope, especially when treated with various chemical substances. [M. J. B.]

RICCIN. (Fr.) *Ricinus communis.*

RICE. *Oryza sativa.* —, CANADA. *Zizania aquatica.* — FALSE. An American name for *Leersia*. —, HUNGRY. *Paspalum exile.* —, INDIAN. An American name for *Zizania*. —, MILLET. *Panicum colonum.* —, MOUNTAIN. An awnless upland variety of *Oryza sativa*, grown without irrigation on the Himalayas, in Cochin China, &c.; also an American name for *Oryzopsis*. —, PETTY. A Peruvian name for the seeds of *Chenopodium Quinoa.* — WATER, or WILD. *Zizania aquatica.*

RICE-PAPER. A peculiar kind of transparent paper manufactured in China from the pith of *Aralia papyrifera*, and used for painting on by native artists. —, MALAY *Scævola Taccada.*

RICHARDIA. A genus of *Araceæ*, containing a well-known species often cultivated as a drawing-room ornament under the name of the White Arum or Trumpet Lily. It is a native of the Cape of Good Hope, and throws up from the root a number of hastate leaves borne on long sheathing stalks; the spadix is also stalked, its spathe large, rolled round below but flattened and bent backwards above, and of a dead-white hue. The spadix itself is completely covered with flowers. At the upper part are the very numerous yellow anthers, which have a wide wedge-shaped connective between their two cells, and which open by two pores. The ovaries occupy the lower part, and are mixed up with a number of barren stamens; each ovary has three parietal placentæ, and is partially subdivided into three compartments; the style is short, the stigma roundish and glandular. The fruits consist of one-celled few-seeded berries. This plant is deservedly a favourite from its elegant appearance, and the contrast presented by its deep-green leaves, its snow-white spathe, and its bright yellow spadix. The genus is named in compliment to an eminent French botanist. [M. T. M.]

RICHARDSONIA. A genus of tropical American herbs belonging to the *Cinchonaceæ*. They are trailing plants, with woody roots, covered with a thick rough rind. The flowers are clustered together in heads at the ends of the branches, and are invested by an involucre of four bracts. The calyx-limb is divided into from four to seven nearly equal teeth; the corolla is funnel-shaped, and its limb divided into from three to five lance-shaped segments; there are from three to five stamens protruding from the throat of the corolla, near to which they are attached; and the stigma is divided into three or four thick almost club-like divisions. The fruit is membranous, and divides into three or four one-seeded segments, which are themselves indehiscent. The root of *R. scabra* has emetic properties, and has been employed in medicine under the name of White Ipecacuanha. These roots are smaller than those of the true Ipecacuanha, destitute of the circular rings characteristic of the genuine drug, and less certain and active in their effects. [M. T. M.]

RICHEA. The four species of this genus of *Epacridaceæ* are found in the mountains of Tasmania, one only, *R. Gunnii*, occurring elsewhere, and that only in the neighbouring mountains of Victoria in South Australia. Some grow to a considerable height, and are crowned with a tuft of long ribbon-like leaves resembling those of screwpines, while others are scarcely more than a foot high, and have short erect leaves; in all the species, however, the leaves are hard stiff and sharp-pointed, and are without stalks, their broad bases clasping the branches and overlapping each other, leaving a circular scar when they fall away Their flowers are disposed in spikes or in simple or branched racemes; and have a small five-lobed or five-parted thin calyx without bracts; a cap-like corolla, which ultimately becomes detached near the bottom and falls away in a single piece; five stamens rising from below the ovary with scales between them; and a five-celled ovary containing numerous ovules hanging from the top of the central column.

R. pandanifolia is in general appearance widely different from the usual character of epacrids, though in the structure of its flowers it perfectly agrees with them. It has a long slender naked stem, marked with circular rings like those of many palms, attaining a height of from thirty to forty feet with a diameter of about nine inches, and crowned with a dense tuft of shining wavy sword-shaped leaves from three to five feet in length, with their edges sharply toothed like a saw — the whole plant having very much the appearance of a screwpine.　　　[A. S.]

RICHELLE DE MARS. (Fr.) A *Triticum*.

RICHWEED. *Pilea pumila.*

RICINELLE (Fr.) *Acalypha.*

RICINOCARPUS. A genus of small erect euphorbiaceous bushes found in the temperate parts of Australia and Tasmania; and related to *Jatropha*, from which they differ in the numerous stamens of the sterile flowers. *R. pinifolia*, one of the commonest species, is found in Eastern Australia and Tasmania, and is a rosemary-like bush two to four feet high, with numerous alternate rigid linear revolute leaves. The flowers are sterile and fertile on the same plant, and are borne singly in the axils of the upper leaves, the sterile with slender stalks the length of the leaves, the fertile with shorter and stouter stalks. They have a four to six-parted calyx, a corolla of a like number of narrow white petals, a cone of numerous stamens in the sterile, and a three-celled ovary crowned with three forked styles in the fertile flower. The fruits are rough three-celled and three-lobed capsules, with one seed in each cell. The fruits are somewhat like those of *Ricinus*, and from this resemblance the genus receives its name. There are eight species, all very similar in habit. [A. A. B.]

RICINUS. A genus of *Euphorbiaceæ*, comprising various species inhabiting tropical Asia and Africa. The principal generic characters are as follows:—Flowers monœcious; calyx with three to five segments; corolla absent; stamens very numerous, their filaments combined into a number of separate bundles; style short, divided into three forked feathery stigmatic branches; fruit globular, prickly, ultimately dividing into three one-seeded segments.

The best-known species is *R. communis*, the seeds of which yield castor-oil. The plant is a native of India, but is now widely distributed over the warmer regions of the globe and throughout the Mediterranean region. It is even cultivated in this country as an annual, and is known under the name of Palma Christi.

.Ricinus communis.

In our climate the stems do not attain a height of more than from three to five feet; in India, however, they grow from eight to ten feet, while in Spain, Crete, Sicily, and elsewhere the plant is stated to become a small tree. The stem is jointed, of a purplish-red colour, and covered with a glaucous bloom like that of a plum. The leaves are large stalked palmate, deeply divided into seven lance-shaped segments; and at the junction of the blade with the stalk of the leaf is a small saucerlike gland. The flowers are in spikes, the males being placed below, the females above.

There are several varieties of this plant, differing in sundry slight particulars, and amongst others in the size of the seeds. These latter are oval, flattened, of a greyish colour mottled with brownish blotches. At the upper end of the seed is a small sponge-like excrescence. It is stated that the best oil for medicinal purposes is derived from the small seeds; that procured from the large seeds is coarser, and in India employed for lamps and in veterinary practice. A still prevalent error is that the acrid purgative principle resides in the seed-coats and in the embryo only, while the albumen is destitute of it. The oil is extracted by boiling the seeds and by pressure in an hydraulic press; the latter process yields the most esteemed oil. After expression the oil is purified by being allowed to stand, by decantation, and by filtration. In India the oil, after having been obtained by pressure, is mixed with a certain proportion of water, and boiled till the water has evaporated. In France the oil is obtained by macerating the bruised seeds in alcohol, but the process is expensive, and the product inferior. The larger quantity of the oil used in this country is imported from India. Castor-oil is very largely used as a gentle and efficient purgative; its nauseous taste is, however, a great objection to its use. This may partially be overcome by mixing it with

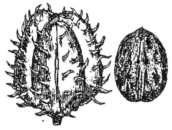

Ricinus communis (fruit and seed).

orange-wine, gin, or peppermint-water, or by making it into an emulsion with the yolk of an egg or mucilage. The leaves are used for various purposes, for which their size and coolness render them serviceable, and topically as an application in rheumatism. [M. T. M.]

RICOTIA. A genus of *Cruciferæ*, consisting of annuals from the Levant, with pinnatifid leaves, and purplish flowers having the outer calyx-segments bulging at the base. The pod is oblong or linear-oblong. One of the species resembles *Lunaria* in the pod and flower, but another is more like *Cardamine*. [J. T. S.]

RIEBLE. *Galium Aparine.*

RIEDLEA. *Onoclea.*

RIELLA. A most curious genus of *Ricciaceæ*, with an erect stem and flat membranous frond twining round it in a spiral. The male and female fruit are on different plants, the former occupying the edge of the frond, and the latter axillary with a perianth and globose sporangium, in which peculiarity it departs from the distinctive characters of the order. *Riella* was named after a distinguished soldier and botanist, Durieu de Maisonneuve, by whom it was first discovered perfecting its fruit, like *Subularia*, beneath the surface of the water. The frond is attached to the stem exactly in the same manner as the network of the curious seaweed *Dictyurus*, a near relative of *Polysiphonia*. [M. J. B.]

RIESENBACHIA. A genus of *Onagraceæ*, in which the calyx is of four narrow lanceolate divisions, the posterior one longer than the others. There is no corolla, and but a single stamen, which is opposite the anterior lobe of the calyx. The only species is a Mexican shrub, with lanceolate serrated leaves. [G. D.]

RIGIDELLA. A genus of *Iridaceæ*, consisting of Mexican herbs, with equitant plaited leaves and fasciculate terminal flowers. The perianth is three-parted,

the segments imbricated at the base, constricted below the middle, with a concave revolute limb; stamens three, the filaments united in a long-exserted tube, and the anthers linear erect; ovary three-celled, with many ovules, and three biparted stigmas with an appendage at the back; capsule papery. They are very pretty plants, especially *R. flammea*, which has flame-coloured flowers marked at the base of the reflexed limb with dark-purple stripes. [T. M.]

RIMA. The cleft-like ostiolum of certain fungals.

RIMOSE. Marked by chinks or cracks on the surface.

RIMU. *Dacrydium cupressinum.*

RINDERA. A genus of *Boraginaceæ*, native of South-eastern Russia and Siberia. The plants are herbs, with the leaves lanceolate oblong or ovate, and the inflorescence racemosely paniculate. The calyx is five-parted; the corolla tubular, with five narrow lobes to the limb, and the throat without scales; the anthers are nearly sessile in the throat of the corolla; and the nuts four, depressed, with a broad-winged margin, adhering to the style by an internal angle at the base. [J. T. S.]

RINGED. Surrounded by elevated or depressed circular lines or bands, as the roots or stems of some plants, the cupule of several oaks, &c.

RINGENT. The same as Personate.

RINGWORM-SHRUB. *Cassia alata.*

RIOCREUXIA *torulosa* is a South African twiner, the only known representative of a genus of *Asclepiadaceæ*. It has cordate leaves, and terminal or axillary umbels of flowers. The calyx is small, and divided into five lobes; the corolla is ventricose at the base and five-lobed, the lobes joined together at their tips; the fruit is long slender and twisted. Its nearest ally is *Ceropegia*. [B. S.]

RIPARIOUS. Growing by water.

RIPIDIUM, *Schizæa.*

RIPOGONUM. This name, compounded of two Greek words signifying 'osier-like' or 'flexile twig,' is applied to a genus of *Smilaceæ*, the species of which are climbing plants, natives of Australia and New Zealand. The stem is spiny, the leaves cordate, destitute of tendrils, and the flowers disposed in axillary clusters. The flowers differ chiefly from those of *Smilax* in the segments of the perianth being equal, and in the filaments of the stamens being awl-shaped. Two species are in cultivation as greenhouse climbers. [M. T. M.]

RISHTA, RITAH. Indian names for *Sapindus emarginatus*; also of an Indian medicinal oil obtained from the Soapnut, the seed of *Acacia concinna.*

RITCHIEA. A genus of tropical African climbing shrubs of the *Capparidaceæ*, named in honour of Ritchie the African traveller. The leaves are ternate, and the flowers in terminal racemes. The calyx has four concave sepals; the corolla an equal number of stalked petals, placed on the margin of a hemispherical fleshy receptacle; and the stamens are twelve to sixteen, inserted with the petals; the ovary is placed on the end of a long stalk, and is capped by a sessile orbiculate stigma. *R. fragrans* is a handsome stove-climber with white flowers.   [M. T. M.]

RIVACHE LAITEUX, R. DES MARAIS, or R. SAUVAGE. (Fr.) *Peucedanum sylvestre.*

RIVEA. A genus of *Convolvulaceæ* found in the tropics of both hemispheres, and composed of about a dozen species, all of which are shrubby climbers of great beauty, generally having cordate leaves and being more or less covered with hair. The calyx has five sepals; the corolla is tubular or funnel-shaped, and often purple; the style is solitary, and bears at the apex a capitate or almost two-lobed stigma; the ovary is four-celled, with one ovule in each cell; and the fruit is succulent and indehiscent, in which respect the genus differs from most other members of the *Convolvulus* tribe. Several species are cultivated in our gardens.   [B. S.]

RIVER-WEED. An American name for *Podostemon.*

RIVINA. This genus comprises about eight or ten species, all American, except one which is doubtfully Asiatic. It is characterised by having a somewhat corolla-like four-parted calyx, with equal ultimately erect or rarely reflexed segments, and mostly only four stamens, and by its berries at length becoming dry and juiceless. The species are undershrubs, with usually erect stems, alternate stalked minutely stipulate leaves, either quite entire or obsoletely crenulate, and terminal and lateral racemes of small flowers.

R. humilis, a common plant in hothouses, has beautiful racemes of little bright scarlet berries, which before drying up contain a very fine scarlet juice, the colour of which, however, is very evanescent. It is a native of the West Indies and of the continent of America from Texas to Brazil.   [A. S.]

RIVULARIA. A genus of green-spored *Algæ* belonging to the natural order *Oscillatoriei,* in which the gelatinous element is so predominant that the plant presents itself in masses of a more or less definite form. These are attached to rocks, plants, &c., or float loosely on the surface of the water, and have been sometimes confounded with *Tremellæ.* The structure is very beautiful. Each branchlet is obtuse at the base, and much attenuated upwards till it becomes a mere colourless hair-like point. The outer coat is very thick and gelatinous, and at the base of each is a large connecting cell, which was diverted from the mother-thread or branch, and from which it was originally developed. The mass of threads, therefore, exhibits a very curious mode of branching, which it is at first very difficult to comprehend. The species grow both in fresh and salt-water, and where there is much carbonate of lime in solution the frond becomes sometimes very hard and crystalline. [M. J. B.]

RIWASOH. An Eastern name for *Rheum Ribes.*

RIZ. (Fr.) *Oryza.* — D' ALLEMAGNE. *Hordeum Zeocriton.*

ROASTBEEF-PLANT *Iris fœtidissima.*

ROBIN DÉCHIRÉ. (Fr.) *Lychnis Flos-cuculi.*

ROBINET. (Fr.) *Lychnis dioica.*

ROBINIA. A great number of species have at different times been placed in this genus, but it is now restricted to a few North American trees and shrubs, one of which, commonly called Acacia in this country, is a well-known object of ornament. All the species have deciduous pinnate leaves, frequently with prickly spines at their bases in place of stipules, each leaf consisting of from five to ten pairs of leaflets and an odd terminal one, the leaflets being furnished with stipels (secondary stipules) at their bases, and usually of an egg-shaped or oblong form. Their flowers, produced in conspicuous usually pendulous racemes from the leaf-axils, vary from white to rose-coloured, and are succeeded by narrow flat thin-shelled pods containing several seeds, and having the seed-bearing edge thicker than the other parts. They have a short five-toothed slightly two-lipped calyx; a pea-like corolla, with the large rounded upper petal turned back in the fully expanded flowers; one free and nine united stamens; and a slender downy style.

R. Pseud-Acacia, the Common or False Acacia, or North American Locust, is a large tree from fifty to eighty feet high, with smooth naked young branches, and loose slender racemes of sweet-smelling white flowers, producing smooth pods. It is a native of the United States, from Pennsylvania southward to Carolina. *R. viscosa*—so called because its young branches, instead of being smooth like those of the last, are covered with a sticky substance—is a much smaller tree, and differs also in having nearly scentless flowers tinged with rose-colour, and crowded together in shorter racemes, and in the pods being covered with glandular hairs. It is a native of the Southern States of North America. *R. hispida,* the Rose Acacia, has large deep rose-coloured scentless flowers in loose racemes; besides which it differs from the above two species in size, seldom growing higher than six or eight feet, and in its young branches and leafstalks being thickly clothed with bristles. It also is a native of the Southern States of America.

The North American Locust or False Acacia has had the most extravagant praises bestowed upon it as a timber-tree, and was one of the plants which the celebrated Cobbett on his return from America unsuccessfully endeavoured to cultivate as a profitable speculation in this country. It is largely grown in the United States, and its timber is there extensively employed for posts, pales, and similar purposes, and also by carpenters and cabinet-makers, and to a more limited extent by shipwrights; but it is seldom of sufficient size to afford planks suitable for ship-building, its principal use being for the manufacture of treenails, for which it is so admirably adapted, that considerable quantities of these 'locust treenails' are exported to this and other European countries. It is also cultivated in the South of France, where it is used for vine-props. The timber is of a yellowish colour, more or less tinged with reddish-brown in the centre. The roots have the taste and smell of liquorice, but are a dangerous poison, and accidents have occurred from their being mistaken for liquorice-roots. [A. S.]

ROBIN-RUN-IN-THE-HEDGE. *Nepeta Glechoma.*

ROBINSONIA. This genus comprises four species of arborescent *Compositæ*, which, with a few others of the same family, give a character to the vegetation of the island of Juan Fernandez. They are branching trees ten to fifteen feet high, having grey bark marked with the semicircular scars of old leaves, these being sessile, linear or lanceolate, and smooth. The small unisexual flower-heads —not unlike those of some groundsels— are arranged in corymbs or panicles, each head having a bell-shaped involucre of numerous scales united by their margins and enclosing a number of florets, the outer row of which are strap-shaped, the inner tubular. The stamens are imperfect in the fertile flowers, the ovary in the sterile; and the cylindrical achenes are crowned with a single series of rough pappus-hairs. From some of the species a resin exudes which is in repute in Chili and Peru as a remedy for headache. *Balbisia*—a nearly allied genus from the same island, differing in having three instead of many flowers to each head—is, like this genus, remarkable in the family in having the seed-lobes (cotyledons) rolled inwards. M. Decandolle has dedicated these plants to Defoe's Robinson Crusoe! (Alexander Selkirk), who was wrecked on the island of Juan Fernandez. [A. A. B.]

ROBLE. A shipbuilding wood obtained from *Catalpa longissima*; also *Platymiscium platystachyum.*

ROCAMBOLE. *Allium Ophioscorodon.* —, WILD. *Allium Scorodoprasum.*

ROCCELLA. A genus of lichens belonging to the usneoid section of *Parmeliaceæ.* Like *Ramalinæ,* they are flat or cylindrical, and are distinguished by the disk, which is open from the earliest stage of growth, being seated on a carbonaceous stratum. The species are of a dull-grey tint, and spring like seaweeds from a little peltate disk. They are valuable dyeweeds. See ORCHELLA WEED, ORCHIL.

R. fuciformis is said to be very inferior to *R. tinctoria.* The latter afforded the first dye for blue British broadcloths, which were once so universally used, and to this was due their purple tints when viewed against the light. [M. J. B.]

ROCHEA. A genus of *Crassulaceæ* inhabiting the Cape of Good Hope, and consisting of fleshy shrubs, with opposite connate and quite entire leaves, and umbellate-cymose flowers of a white pink or scarlet colour. The calyx is five-lobed; the five petals are connate, forming a hypocateriomorphous corolla; the stamens are five in number, and alternate with the petals: there are also five glands and five carpels. Several species are favourites in our gardens, both on account of their strange leaves and bright flowers. [B. S.]

ROCHELIA. A genus of *Boraginaceæ* inhabiting Southern Europe, Northern Africa, and Siberia, and differing from the other genera of the order in the ovaries being only two, adnate to the style. They are small hispid annuals or biennials, with the habit of *Echinospermum,* and have a five-parted calyx with the tips incurved after flowering; a funnel-shaped five-lobed corolla, closed by five scales at the throat; and two oblique nuts adhering to the style and to each other. [J. T. S.]

ROCKCIST. *Helianthemum.*

ROCKET. *Hesperis*; also *Eruca,* especially *E. sativa.* —, BASE. *Reseda lutea.* —, BASTARD. *Brassica Erucastrum.* —, CRESS. *Vella.* —, DAME'S. *Hesperis matronalis.* —, DYER'S. *Reseda Luteola.* —, FALSE. *Iodanthus.* —, GARDEN. *Hesperis matronalis*; also *Eruca sativa.* —, LONDON. *Sisymbrium Irio.* —, SEA. *Cakile maritima.* —, WHITE. *Hesperis matronalis.* —, WINTER, or YELLOW. *Barbarea vulgaris.*

ROCOU. (Fr.) Annotto, *Bixa Orellana.*

RODDON-TREE. A Scotch name for *Pyrus Aucuparia.*

RODRIGUEZIA. A small tropical American and West Indian genus of epiphytal orchids, with leathery or thin plicate leaves, and a one-sided spiked inflorescence. Its flowers have spreading nearly equal sepals and petals, the lateral sepals joined beneath the lip, which is entire and clawed, and furnished with a horn at its base and a callosity in the middle; the column is terete and bearded at the apex; and the anther is fleshy and one-celled, containing two pollen-masses attached by an elastic caudicle. [A. S.]

RODWOOD. A Jamaica name for *Lætia Guidonia.* —, BLACK *Eugenia pallens.* —, RED. *Eugenia axillaris.* —, WHITE. *Calyptranthes Chytraculia.*

ROËA. A genus of *Leguminosæ* of the suborder *Papilionaceæ* and tribe *Podalyrieæ*, consisting of two low herbs or undershrubs from Swan River, with ascending simple almost rush-like stems, and alternate narrow simple leaves. The flowers are yellow, in a loose terminal raceme, of no beauty. They are distinguished from the allied genera, which like them have two ovules only to the ovary, chiefly by the small globular pod, borne on a distinct stalk.

ROEBUCK-BERRY. The fruit of *Rubus saxatilis*.

REGNERIA. A genus of grasses belonging to the tribe *Festuceæ*. The spikelets are distant, few-flowered; the outer glumes three-nerved, the superior five-nerved; flowering glume subcompressed, lengthened out into a long awn-shaped apex, obsoletely three-nerved, the margin hairy. This genus contains only one species, *R. caucasica*, which inhabits woods in Daghestan.　　　　[D. M.]

ROELLA. The name of a genus of *Campanulaceæ*, whose chief character is derived from the capsule, which is elongated and two-celled, opening by a hole at the apex. The species are chiefly undershrubs, rarely herbaceous plants, having alternate narrow and usually rigid leaves. They are natives of the Cape of Good Hope. The genus was named in honour of Roell, an Amsterdam professor.　[G. D.]

RŒSTELIA. A curious genus of parasitic *Fungi* with an elongated peridium, the component cells of which at length separate from each other so as to form ragged laciniæ. In *R. cornuta* and *lacerata*, which grow on the mountain-ash and hawthorn, these are separate at the apex so as to expose completely the mass of spores joined to each other like the beads of a necklace; but in *R. cancellata* they remain attached above, so as merely to leave a passage for the spores between their interstices. All of them produce at the same time, generally on the opposite side of the leaf, little cysts or pycnidia, which are filled with minute naked spores. Some imagine these bodies to have sexual functions. *R. cancellata*, which is the pest of pear-trees, produces curious rugged swellings on the leaves, through each elevation of which a peridium bursts out. The only method of mitigating the evil is to handpick every leaf as soon as it shows any sign of the swellings and burn it. It may be too late if the peridia have made their appearance and dispersed their spores.　　[M. J. B.]

ROGATION-FLOWER. *Polygala vulgaris*.

ROGERIA. A small genus of *Pedaliaceæ*, having the habit of *Pedalium*, and consisting of annual herbs found in tropical Africa and Brazil. The calyx is five-cleft; the corolla tubular and funnel-shaped; the stamens are four in number, and do not project beyond the border of the corolla; the fruit is almost nut-like, opens towards the point, has from four to eight spines, and appears to be from four to six-

celled, the cells having either an indefinite number or only solitary seeds. Their uses are unknown.　　　　　[B. S.]

ROGIERA. A genus of *Cinchonaceæ* named in compliment to M. C. Rogier, late Minister of the Interior of Belgium, and an active patron of horticulture. They are shrubs somewhat resembling the laurestine; but the leaves are covered with soft hairs, while the salver-shaped corollas are rose-coloured, and closed at the throats by a tuft of golden hairs. The genus differs from *Rondeletia* in the absence of the thick ring in the corolla-throat.　　　　　[M. T. M.]

ROHUNA. An Indian name for *Soymida febrifuga*.

ROI DES ARBRES. (Fr.) *Quercus Robur*.

ROLLANDIA. This name has been given to two shrubby milky-juiced Sandwich Island plants belonging to the *Lobeliaceæ*, which are described as differing generically from *Delissea* in the staminal tube being adnate to the tube of the corolla on one side, instead of free from it. This is supposed to be an error by Dr. Asa Gray, who unites the genus with *Delissea*: which see.　　　　　[A. A. B.]

ROLLINIA. An almost exclusively Brazilian genus of *Anonaceæ*, composed of about twenty species of shrubs or small trees, closely allied to *Anona*, from which, however, they are distinguished by their flowers having the petals cohering and forming an almost globose corolla, which is open and shortly six-lobed at the top, and is drawn out at the back into three very blunt concave wings. They have alternate entire short-stalked leaves, from near the axils of which solitary or rarely several flowers are produced, and are succeeded by scaly fruits formed of a number of one-seeded carpels cohering together.

The arboreous species, such as *R. multiflora*, *R. longifolia*, and others, afford a light tough wood resembling lancewood; that of the first-mentioned being used by the natives of Guiana and Brazil for making spears. They seldom grow above twenty-five or thirty feet high.　　　[A. S.]

ROMAINE. (Fr.) The Cos Lettuce.

ROMANZOVIA. A genus of *Hydrophyllaceæ*, consisting of low many-stemmed pilose herbs, with cordate radical leaves on long petioles, small alternate cauline leaves, and terminal one-sided racemes. The calyx and corolla are five-parted; the five stamens are included in the tube of the corolla; and the style, unlike the other members of the order, is simple and furnished with a capitate stigma. They are natives of Arctic America.　　　[W. C.]

ROMARIN. (Fr.) *Rosmarinus*. —
SAUVAGE, *Ledum palustre*.

ROMERIA. A genus of *Papaveraceæ*, named in honour of J. Römer, a botanist, and editor of some of the works of Linnæus. The genus is intermediate between *Papaver, Glaucium,* and *Chelidonium.* The distinctive characters reside in the ovary and the fruit. The ovary is elongated cylindrical one-celled, and contains numerous ovules; the stigma is sessile, with two to four divisions; and the fruit is capsular, bursting from above downwards into two or four valves, the thread-like placentas also becoming after a time detached and separate. The species are small herbs,with yellow juice, and divided leaves, whose narrow segments are frequently terminated by a hair-like joint, and large solitary violet flowers. They are natives of the Mediterranean regions, and some are cultivated as annuals in this country, a purpose for which their large purple flowers well fits them. *R. hybrida* is occasionally found wild in cornfields in this country, having been introduced with foreign seeds. It is said to be well established in Cambridgeshire. [M. T. M.]

ROMNEYA. A genus of *Papaveraceæ,* forming a link between *Nymphæaceæ* and *Sarraceniaceæ.* The ovary is divided into numerous compartments, and the ovules are distributed over the whole surface of the dissepiments. The only species is a Californian herb, with stalked divided leaves, and handsome white flowers. [M. T. M.]

ROMULÉE. (Fr.) *Trichonema.*

RONCE. (Fr.) *Rubus.*

RONDELETIA. An extensive West Indian and tropical American genus of the many-seeded division of *Cinchonaceæ.* Most of the species are shrubs, but a few grow to the size of trees. They have opposite entire leaves, with triangular or narrow lance-shaped stipules between them; and usually dense flat-topped more or less branched heads of flowers, produced either from the angles of the leaves, or at the ends of the branches. The calyx has a nearly globose tube, and is four or five-parted, the segments being either minute and toothlike, or as long as the tube itself; and the corolla a cylindrical tube slightly swollen towards the top, and a flat expanded part consisting of four or five roundish lobes, which overlap in the bud. The stamens have very short filaments or none at all, and are entirely enclosed within the tube: and the slender style bears a two-lobed stigma. Their fruit is a two-celled roundish capsule, containing minute seeds and splitting, when ripe, through the cells into two pieces.

R. versicolor is so called in consequence of its deep rose-coloured flowers becoming paler after they expand. It is a native of Veraguas in Central America, where it forms a shrub from twelve to fifteen feet high, with an extremely bitter bark. Its leaves are five or six inches long and two or three broad. The sweet-scented *R. odorata,* a native of Cuba and Mexico, is a straggling shrub with brilliant vermilion-coloured flowers having a yellow or orange centre. The perfume sold as Rondeletia

takes its name from this plant, but is not prepared from any part of it. [A. S.]

RONDELLE, or RONDETTE. (Fr.) *Asarum europæum;* also *Nepeta Glechoma.*

RONDOTTE. (Fr.) *Barbarea vulgaris.*

ROODPEER. An American name for *Phoberos Ecklonii.*

ROOGEE. *Megacarpæa polyandra.*

ROOM. A deep-blue dye obtained in Assam from a species of *Ruellia.*

ROOMAN. An Indian name for the Pomegranate.

ROOT. The same as *Radix.*

ROOT-OF-SCARCITY. The Mangel Wurzel, a variety of *Beta vulgaris.*

ROOTSTOCK. The same as Rhizome.

RÖPERA. This genus of *Zygophyllaceæ* is so called in honour of a German botanist. The species are New Holland shrubs, with binate stipulate leaves, and yellow stalked solitary flowers in the axils of the stipules. The calyx has four persistent sepals, as many petals, and eight stamens shorter than the petals, with awl-like filaments destitute of scales at their base. The ovary is sessile four-celled, with four little scales at the base: and the fruit capsular indehiscent four-celled, three of the cells generally empty, one containing a single seed. Externally the four angles of the capsule are elongated into four membranous-veined wings. [M. T. M.]

ROQUETTE. (Fr.) *Eruca.* — BÂTARDE. *Reseda Luteola.* — DE MER. *Cakile maritima.* — FAUSSE. *Brassica Erucastrum.* — SAUVAGE. *Diplotaxis tenuifolia.*

RORIDULA. A genus of *Droseraceæ,* comprising two South African shrubs or undershrubs, with long linear crowded leaves covered with glandular viscid hairs. The flowers are white in short terminal racemes, and are chiefly distinguished from those of *Drosera* by their entire style and three-celled ovary. One species, *R. dentata,* which is remarkably viscid, is often hung up in country houses of the Cape Colony to catch flies.

RORIDUS. Dewy; covered with little transparent elevations of the parenchyma, which have the appearance of fine drops of dew.

ROSACEÆ. (*Roseworts*). A natural order of dicotyledons which, taken in its most extended sense, includes all *Polypetalæ* with regular flowers, indefinite perigynous stamens, distinct or solitary carpels, and seeds without albumen. Many botanists, however, separate as distinct orders:—*Chrysobalanaceæ,* which are tropical trees or shrubs with solitary carpels, having the style at their base and the fruit usually dehiscent; *Drupaceæ,* or Plums and their allies, which have solitary carpels with a terminal style, and a drupaceous fruit; and *Pomaceæ,* or Pears and their allies, which have several carpels enclosed in the calyx-tube and adhering to it by their back. There remain in the *Rosaceæ* thus reduced a large number of genera and species, chiefly abundant in temperate regions, extending into the Arctic Zone as well as ascending to the highest elevations, and more sparingly dispersed within the tropics. They are herbs or shrubs, very rarely trees, with alternate often divided leaves accompanied by stipules, and flowers almost always terminal, solitary or in cymes or panicles; and are distinguished from the above-mentioned smaller orders by their carpels, which when ripe become achenes, or rarely berries follicles or capsules. They are divided into six distinct tribes—*Sanguisorbeæ* : Herbs or low shrubs, with small flowers without petals, and solitary one-seeded carpels, enclosed when ripe in the hardened tube of the calyx. These comprise eleven or twelve genera, including *Alchemilla, Poterium,* and *Sanguisorba* represented in Europe, the South American, and Antarctic *Acæna,* and the South African *Cliffortia. Roseæ* proper : with a fleshy calyx-tube closing over the one-seeded carpels, limited to the Linnæan genus *Rosa. Potentilleæ* : Herbs or weak shrubs, with a herbaceous calyx and numerous achenes in a head. They comprise about twenty genera, of which the most important are *Rubus, Potentilla, Fragaria, Geum, Dryas,* and *Agrimonia. Spiræeæ,* or *Spiræa* and a few small genera closely allied to it, with several-seeded carpels opening like follicles. *Quillaiæ* : Three or four South American genera with a capsular fruit. *Neuradeæ* : South European or African herbs having ten carpels in a ring, with a single pendulous seed in each.

ROSA. The genus which gives name to the large and important order *Rosaceæ* is distinguished by the following characters : —Leaves with stipules attached to the leaf-stalk ; petals five ; stamens and styles numerous ; seeds (achenes) numerous, enclosed within but not adhering to the fleshy calyx-tube, which is contracted at the orifice. Throughout the civilised world undisputed precedence among flowers has been conceded to the Rose in all ages and by universal consent. In the sacred writings, by classical authors, by the poets of all countries, including our own from Chaucer downwards, this Queen of Flowers is the epitome of beauty and fragrance, the emblem of refined sensual enjoyment. It has been the subject of scientific monographs and of floricultural disquisitions ; and its cultivation affords employment to hundreds of human beings, perhaps thousands, if there be taken into calculation the number of persons engaged in the manufacture of rosewater and attar. The species which has been cultivated from the highest antiquity is supposed to be *R. centifolia,* the Cabbage or Provence Rose, a flower which possesses in an eminent degree the admirable qualities of the tribe.

The patient skill of cultivators has for-

tunately been successful in depriving the Rose of one of its attributes—it has ceased to be an emblem of summer. By making careful selections of species and rearing hybrids, varieties deservedly called Perpetual have been obtained, and whoever will may now without difficulty crown himself with roses at any season. A bare enumeration of the groups in which cultivated roses are arranged by growers would occupy too much of our space; but the reader may be interested in knowing that the number of wild species described by botanists exceeds two hundred, to which may be added at least as many more subspecies or varieties; while the list of garden varieties, mostly with double flowers, numbers thousands, and is every year receiving fresh additions. The majority of these are raised on the Continent, though not a few held in high estimation are the production of home rosetums.

From the Burnet Rose, *R. spinosissima,* a native of Britain, as well as many parts of the Continent, all the numerous varieties of the Scotch Rose have been derived. *R. rubiginosa* and *R. micrantha,* indigenous species, are well known under the name of Sweet-brier. *R. canina,* with its varieties, is the common Dog-rose of our hedges. *R. arvensis* is the trailing white scentless rose so common in hedges and the borders of fields. *R. tomentosa* and *R. villosa* are the species, with downy leaves and large deep red blossoms, which love to find their way through hedge-bushes provokingly beyond the reach of the collector of wild flowers. The task of discriminating the species of this large genus is so difficult, even to the professed botanist, that an attempt to furnish the reader with a clue in an elementary work like the present, would be futile. The Rose is the national emblem of England.　　　[C. A. J.]

ROSACEOUS. Having the same arrangement as the petals of a single rose.

ROSADE. (Fr.) *Eugenia malaccensis.*

ROSA DEL MONTE. *Brownea Rosa.*

ROSAGE. (Fr.) *Rhododendron.* — DU CIEL. *Viscaria Cœli-rosa.*

ROSCOEA. A genus of Nepalese herbs belonging to the *Zingiberaceæ,* and named in honour of William Roscoe, the accomplished author of the *History of the Medici,* and who also published a magnificent volume on the plants of this order. The erect leafy stem springs from a cluster of tuberous roots, and bears at its upper part a spike of closely-packed large purple flowers. These flowers have a tubular calyx; a six-parted corolla whose segments are in two rows, the two outer lateral segments narrow and spreading, the intermediate one erect and arched, and the two inner lateral ones short, the intermediate one called the lip larger and two-lobed; the filament is very short, and bears a curved anther having two spurs at the base; the style is thread-like; and the stigma globular. Some of the species are in cultivation as stove-plants; their purple flowers are very handsome. (M. T. M.]

ROSE. *Rosa*. — of the Alps. *Rhododendron hirsutum*, and *R. ferrugineum*. — of Jericho. *Anastatica hierochuntina*; also said to be applied to *Mesembryanthemum Tripolium*. — of Heaven. *Viscaria Cœli-rosa*. — of May. *Narcissus poeticus*. —, AYRSHIRE. *Rosa arvensis*. —, BOURBON. A form of *Rosa indica*. —, BRIER. *Rosa canina*. —, BURNET. *Rosa spinosissima*. —, CABBAGE. *Rosa centifolia*. ' —, CHINESE. *Rosa indica*; also *Hibiscus Rosa sinensis*. —, CHANGEABLE. *Hibiscus mutabilis*. —, CHRISTMAS. *Helleborus niger*. —, CORN. *Papaver Rhœas*. —, COTTON. An American name for *Filago*. —, DAMASK. *Rosa damascena*. —, DOG. *Rosa canina*. —, ELDER. Gerarde's name for a variety of *Viburnum Opulus*. —, FAIRY. *Rosa Lawrenceana*. —, FRENCH. *Rosa gallica*. —, GUELDER, or GUELDRES. The sterile-flowered variety of *Viburnum Opulus*. —, HOLLY. *Helianthemum*. —, HUNDRED-LEAVED. *Rosa centifolia*. —, JAMAICA. *Meriana*; also *Blakea trinervis*, —, MACARTNEY. *Rosa bracteata*. —, MALABAR. *Hibiscus Rosa malabarica*. —, MALLOW. *Hibiscus Moscheutos*. —, MONTHLY. *Rosa indica*. —, MOSS. A garden variety of *Rosa centifolia*. —, NOISETTE. A hybrid rose of garden origin. —, OFFICINAL. *Rosa gallica*. —, PRAIRIE. *Rosa setigera*. — PROVENCE, or PROVINS. *Rosa centifolia*. —, ROCK. *Helianthemum*; also *Cistus*. —, SAGE. *Turnera ulmifolia*. —, SCOTCH. *Rosa spinosissima*. —, SOUTH SEA, of Jamaica. *Nerium Oleander*. —, SUN. *Helianthemum*. —, SWAMP. *Rosa carolina*. —, TEA-SCENTED. A variety of *Rosa indica*. —, WILD. *Blakea trinervis*.

ROSE. (Fr.) The flowers of the Rose. — DE CAYENNE. *Hibiscus mutabilis*. — DE CHIEN. *Rosa canina*. — DE CHINE. *Hibiscus Rosa sinensis*. — DE DAMAS. *Rosa damascena*. — DE GUELDRE. The sterile-flowered variety of *Viburnum Opulus*. — DE JÉRICHO. *Anastatica hierochuntina*. — DE MER. *Althœa rosea*. — DE NOËL. *Helleborus niger*. — DE SÉRANE. *Pæonia peregrina*. — D'INDE. *Tagetes erecta*. — D'OUTRE-MER. *Althœa rosea*. — DE LA CHINE. *Hibiscus Rosa sinensis*. — DES CHAMPS. *Dipladenia Rosa campestris*. — DU CIEL. *Viscaria Cœli-rosa*. — DU JAPON. *Hydrangea Hortensia*: also *Camellia japonica*. — MAUVE, or TRÉMIÈRE. *Althœa rosea*.

ROSEA. A genus of *Cinchonaceæ*, consisting of shrubs natives of Mozambique. The stipules are combined below into a membranous sheath, and above are prolonged into an awl-shaped point. The flowers are nearly sessile, in axillary clusters; the calyx supported by six overlapping bracts; the corolla salver-shaped, with the tube hairy within, and the limb divided into six or eight spreading lobes; the stamens six to eight, projecting from the corolla; the style cylindrical, twisted towards the top; the stigma cleft, protruding from the corolla; and the fruit somewhat fleshy two-celled few-seeded, surmounted by the calyx. The name has also been given to a plant synonymous with *Iresine*. (M. T. M.]

ROSE-A-RUBY. *Adonis autumnalis*.

ROSEAU. (Fr.) *Arundo*. — À FLÈCHES. *Alpinia Galanga*. —, À QUENOUILLE. *Arundo Donax*. — À SUCRE. *Saccharum officinarum*. — DE LA PASSION, or DES ETANGS. *Typha latifolia*. — DES INDES. *Bambusa*. — ÉPINEUX. *Calamus Rotang*. — ODORANT. *Acorus Calamus*. — PANACHE. *Digraphis arundinacea picta*; also *Arundo Donax variegata*.

ROSE-BAY. *Epilobium angustifolium*.

ROSELLE. *Hibiscus Sabdariffa*, the pleasantly acid ripened calyces of which are used both in the East and West Indies for making tarts and jellies, as well as a cool refreshing drink.

ROSE-MALOES. An Eastern name for the liquid storax obtained from *Liquidambar orientale*.

ROSEMARY. *Rosmarinus officinalis*. —, AUSTRALIAN. *Eurybia Dampieri*. —, MARSH. *Andromeda polifolia*; also an American name for *Statice caroliniana*. —, SEA. *Schoberia fruticosa*. — WILD. *Ledum palustre*; also *Andromeda polifolia*. —, —, of Jamaica. *Croton Cascarilla*.

ROSENIA. The generic name of two little-known South African bushes belonging to the groundsel tribe of *Compositæ*, and characterised by their many-flowered radiating heads, the ray-florets of which are fertile and strap-shaped, the disk tubular and perfect; by the receptacle, which has chaffy scales; and by the beakless achenes—those of the disk-florets crowned with a pappus of two series of bristles, the outer of which are shorter than the inner, and like those of the ray-florets which are in a single series. The twigs bear small prickles, and obovate one-nerved leaves, more or less clothed above and below with white down; the flower-heads are terminal and yellow. [A. A. B.]

ROSE-ROOT. *Rhodiola rosea*.

ROSETTA-WOOD. A handsomely veined East Indian wood of a lively orange-red colour, and close hard texture.

ROSEWOOD. A valuable South American timber, produced by several species of *Dalbergia*. That most esteemed, obtained from Rio Janeiro, is said to be chiefly produced by *D. nigra*; but inferior sorts are probably yielded by *Machærium firmum*, *incorruptibile*, and *legale*—trees which bear the name of Jacaranda in Brazil; and it is also attributed by Lindley to species of *Triptolemœa*. —, AFRICAN. The wood of *Pterocarpus erinaceus*. —, BURMESE. The wood of *Pterocarpus indicus*. —, CANARY. *Rhodorrhiza scoparia*. —,

DOMINICA. The wood of *Cordia Gerascanthus.* —, INDIAN. The timber of *Dalbergia latifolia* and *sissoides.* —, JAMAICA. The wood of *Amyris balsamifera,* and *Linociera ligustrina.* —, MOULMEIN. The timber of a species of *Milletia.* —, NEW SOUTH WALES. The wood of *Trichilia glandulosa.* —, TASMANIAN. The wood of one of the *Acacias.*

ROSEWORT. *Rhodiola rosea.*

ROSEWORTS. Lindley's name for the *Rosaceæ.*

ROSIER. (Fr.) *Rosa.* — À ODEUR DE REINETTE. *Rosa rubiginosa.*

ROSIN-WEED. *Silphium laciniatum.*

ROSMARINUS. The technical name of the plants more familiarly known under the name of Rosemary. The genus belongs to the *Labiatæ,* and consists of but one species, the Common Rosemary, *R. officinalis,* a bush, native of the South of Europe and Asia Minor, having narrow stalkless greyish leaves, the edges of which are rolled round on to the undersurface; and flowers with a purplish two-lipped calyx, a white or pale-blue corolla, from which protrude two stamens only, each stamen having a toothed filament and a two-celled anther.

Owing to its agreeable fragrance, Rosemary has been used from time immemorial. It was anciently employed in making garlands, and was considered useful in relieving headache and in stimulating the flagging mental powers: whence it was called Herb of Memory and Repentance. Thus in *Hamlet,* Ophelia says—

> There's rosemary, that's for remembrance;

and in *Romeo and Juliet* allusion is made to the use of Rosemary as a token of remembrance at funerals—

> Dry up your tears, and stick your rosemary
> On this fair corse.—Act iv. sc. 4.

This custom has not wholly disappeared from among us, though the employment of Rosemary in wedding-wreaths as a symbol of fidelity is now obsolete. Rosemary has slight stimulant properties, but is rarely used internally. It is employed in the form of lotion and wash for the hair, and is useful in cases of baldness. Its chief value, however, is as a perfume; it enters into the composition of Hungary Water, and other perfumes of a like nature. [M. T. M.]

There is a vulgar belief in Gloucestershire that the Rosemary will not grow well unless in the house where the mistress is 'master;' and so touchy are some of the lords of the creation upon this point, that we have more than once suspected them of privately injuring a growing rosemary in order to destroy this evidence of their want of authority.

The use of a decoction of rosemary-leaves in cider as a remedy for a cold, as also of oil of rosemary in hair-washes, no doubt depends upon the stimulating essential oil which the plant contains so abundantly. [J. B.]

ROSO DO CAMPO. A Brazilian name for *Kielmeyera.*

ROSSOLIS. (Fr.) *Drosera rotundifolia.*

ROSTELLATE, ROSTRATE. Terminating gradually in a hard long straight point—as the pod of radish.

ROSTELLUM. A narrow extension of the upper edge of the stigma of certain orchids.

ROSTRUM. Any beak-like extension; as in the stigma of some asclepiads.

ROSULA (adj. ROSULATE). A small rose; a rosette. A collection of spreading leaves or petals packed one over the other in many rows; as in double roses, or the offsets of house-leek.

ROSULÆ. Little warts on the thallus of lichens.

ROTALA. A genus of *Lythraceæ* from India, Australia, and Mexico, consisting of small herbs, with opposite or whorled sessile spreading leaves, and minute solitary axillary flowers with a tubular three-toothed (rarely five-toothed) calyx; three (rarely five) petals or none; three or five stamens; and a three-valved capsule, one-celled by the obliteration of the partitions, and many-seeded. [J. T. S.]

ROTATE, ROTÆFORM. Resembling a wheel; a monopetalous corolla with a spreading limb and very short tube.

ROTATION. A motion of circulation confined to the interior of the cells of plants.

ROTHIA *trifoliata* is a small prostrate hairy annual, with three leaflets to its leaves, and small yellow flowers on leaf-opposed pedicels. It is a common weed in many parts of India, and forms a genus of *Leguminosæ* of the suborder *Papilionaceæ* and tribe *Genisteæ.* It is allied to *Argyrolobium* and to *Lotonomis,* and much resembles some species in habit, but is readily distinguished by the keel-petals being almost or quite free, and by the narrow linear pod.

A few composite plants of the Mediterranean region and the Canary Isles, closely related to *Hieracium,* were also at one time ranked as a genus under this name, but they are now included in *Andryala.* They are biennial or perennial herbs, with entire toothed or pinnatifid leaves, often clothed with soft rusty down; and their yellow flower-heads, about the size of those of hawkweeds, are disposed in a corymbose manner at the ends of the branches. [A. A. B.]

ROTTBOELLIA. A genus of grasses belonging to the tribe *Rottboelliæ.* The inflorescence is in round jointed spikes, the spikelets inserted in notches on alternate sides of the spike, one to two-flowered, the lower male or neuter; pales membranaceous or shining; upper flower hermaphrodite; stamens three; stigmas feathery. There are twenty-seven species described under this genus by Steudel, and they are widely distributed over the surface of the globe, a large portion of them inhabiting salt-marshes. [D. M.]

ROTTLERA. A genus of *Euphorbiaceæ*, comprising about twenty species, of alternate (rarely opposite) leaved bushes or small trees, found in tropical Asia and the warmer parts of Australia. They are characterised by their two to five-parted calyx; by the total absence of corolla or disk; by the numerous stamens in the sterile flowers, with their filaments free or united near the base into a number of parcels; and by the female flowers having an ovary with two to four one-seeded cells crowned with a like number of undivided somewhat feathery styles. The leaves have rather long stalks, furnished with two glands at their point of union with the blades; the latter vary much in form, some few being peltate, others lobed or toothed, and both surfaces in many cases are clothed with soft starry hairs. The inconspicuous green or whitish flowers are sterile and fertile on the same or on different plants, and disposed in axillary or terminal spikes, racemes, or panicles.

R. tinctoria is a very common Indian bush or small tree, also found in the Indian Archipelago, tropical Australia, and, according to Mr. Hanbury, in South Arabia. The leaves are from four to eight inches long, smooth above, and minutely downy below. From the surface of the trilobed capsules of this plant, which are about the size of peas, a red mealy powder is obtained, well known in India as Kámalá, and much used by Hindoo silk-dyers, who obtain from it, according to Roxburgh, a deep bright durable orange or flame colour of great beauty. This is obtained by boiling the powder in a solution of carbonate of soda. 'The capsules are ripe in February or March, and the red powder is brushed off and collected for sale, no other preparation being necessary to preserve it.'

The root of the tree is also said to be used in dyeing. From a paper by Mr. Hanbury on this plant in the *Pharmaceutical Journal* for February 1858, to which the reader is referred for a full account of the Kámalá, it appears to be used in cutaneous complaints. 'Among the Arabs of Aden it is given internally in leprosy, and used in solution to remove freckles and pustules;' while in this country it has been used successfully in treating the eruption known as wildfire on children, by rubbing the powder over the affected part with moist lint. It appears, however, to be most valued as an anthelmintic, and has been extensively used with much success in India in cases of tapeworm; three drachms being sufficient for a robust person, and half that quantity for one of feeble habit. The genus is dedicated to Dr. Rottler, an eminent Dutch missionary and naturalist. [A. A. B.]

ROTUND. Orbicular, a little inclining to be oblong; as the leaf of *Lysimachia Nummularia, Mentha rotundifolia, &c.*

ROTUNDATE. Rounded off; a term usually applied to bodies which are not round themselves, but only at their ends.

ROUCOU, ROCOUYER. The Arnotto, *Bixa Orellana.*

ROUDON. (Fr.) *Coriaria.*

ROUGE-BE. (Fr.) *Camelina sativa.*

ROUGE-HERBE, or ROUGEOLE. (Fr.) *Melampyrum arvense.*

ROUGEOTTE. (Fr.) *Adonis æstivalis.*

ROUGE-PLANT. *Rivina tinctoria.*

ROUGETTE. (Fr.) A kind of olive.

ROUGH, ROUGHISH. Covered with little hard or sharp elevations, which produce the sensation of roughness; also applied to surfaces covered with coarse stiff hairs.

ROUILLE. (Fr.) *Uredo linearis*, and *U. Rubigo-vera*.

ROULINIA. A genus of *Asclepiadaceæ*, composed of about a dozen species, all of which are inhabitants of tropical America, and have a twining habit. Their leaves are cordate, and of a lively green colour; their flowers scented, pale-yellow or whitish, and arranged in racemes; their calyx is five-cleft; their corolla rotate and five-lobed; and their fruit smooth on the surface and ventricose. Nothing is known of their uses. The *Reulinia* of Brogniart is a totally different plant, synonymous with *Dasylirion*. [B. S.]

ROUM. A blue dye-stuff of Assam, obtained from a species of *Ruellia.*

ROUMA. (Fr.) *Ranunculus asiaticus.*

ROUMEA. *Xylosma.*

ROUPELLIA. A genus of *Apocynaceæ*, comprising a climbing plant, native of Sierra Leone. The calyx is five-parted, with a ring of small glands at the base; the corolla is creamy-white in colour, funnel-shaped, its limb divided into five broad twisted segments, while from its throat project ten flesh-coloured or brown processes united into a ring below; the filaments are very short, the anthers pointed; and the style is dilated into a fleshy five-furrowed mass, which is adherent to the anthers. This plant was supposed to yield the cream-fruit of Sierra Leone; but Dr. Thomson, who has had an opportunity of seeing the fruit of the present plant in the Calcutta Botanic Garden, states that it is follicular, and therefore does not correspond with the cream-fruit. *R. grata* is a showy stove-climber, whose flowers, however, scarcely realise in this country the expectations formed of them. [M. T. M.]

ROURE. (Fr.) *Quercus pedunculata.* — DES CORROYEURS. *Rhus Coriaria.*

ROUREA. A genus of *Connaraceæ*, comprising upwards of forty species, distributed chiefly in tropical Asia and tropical America, one occurring in Africa. It belongs with *Connarus* to the arillate-seeded group of the tribe *Connareæ*, and is distinguished from that genus by its sessile capsule, and by its calyx growing on after flowering. They are trees or shrubs, sometimes scandent, with alternate coriaceous imparipinnate leaves, and axillary panicles of small flowers.   [T. M.]

ROUREOPSIS. A name proposed by Planchon for two Malayan species of *Rourea*, which have since been reunited with the latter genus.

ROU-ROU. A Mexican furniture-wood resembling rosewood.

ROUSSEA (or ROUSSÆA) *simplex* is the sole representative of a genus of doubtful affinity, lately classed with *Brexiaceæ*. It is a scandent epiphytal shrub inhabiting the Mauritius, with opposite oblong leaves, and axillary flowers, which are white outside and purplish within. The calyx is deeply five-cleft; the corolla monopetalous five-lobed (or, as some would describe it, having five petals growing together); there are five stamens; and a fleshy five-celled berry, containing numerous seeds.   [B. S.]

ROUVET. (Fr.) *Osyris alba.*

ROUVRE. (Fr.) *Quercus sessiliflora.* — DES CORROYEURS. *Rhus Coriaria.*

ROWAN-TREE. A Scotch name for *Pyrus Aucuparia.*

ROXBURGHIA, ROXBURGHIACEÆ. A genus of monocotyledons presenting so many curious peculiarities in structure as to be generally admitted as a distinct order, the immediate affinities of which are not yet satisfactorily settled. It consists of three or four species from India and the Indian Archipelago. They are all tall twiners, with broad leaves, mostly opposite, and marked by several longitudinal ribs having transverse veins between them. The axillary peduncles bear one or very few green flowers, which are large and handsome but very fetid; the perianth has four divisions; there are four stamens, and the ovary and fruit consist of a simple carpel opening when ripe in two valves, numbers all very unusual among monocotyledons. The seeds are long, hanging from long funicles, covered towards the top with linear pellucid vesicles. The thick tuberous roots, after a previous preparation with lime-water, are candied with sugar and taken with tea, but are said to be insipid.

ROYENA. A Cape genus of shrubs or trees referred to the *Ebenaceæ*, numbering about twenty species, and differing from the true ebony (*Diospyros*), as well as others in the family, in the flowers being fertile and sterile on the same instead of on different plants. They have alternate simple entire smooth or downy leaves, either willow-like spathulate or ovate in form, bearing in their axils one to three-stalked white or yellow flowers not unlike those of some *Andromeda*. These have a five-lobed calyx, which in some continues to grow after the flower withers; a five-parted bell-shaped corolla with obtuse lobes; ten stamens, two opposite each corolla-lobe; and a hairy two to ten-celled ovary crowned with two to five styles. The fruits are globular or elliptical berries about the size of damsons, usually with five one-seeded cells.

R. lucida is a pretty white-flowered bush sometimes cultivated in greenhouses. Its ovate leaves are at first slightly downy, but glossy when mature; and the white flowers are stalked and solitary in the axils of the leaves. The wood of these plants is of a like nature with ebony; but the trees do not grow to a great size. It was named *Royena* by Linnæus after Adrien Van Royen, once Professor of Botany at Leyden.   [A. A. B.]

ROYLEA. The name of a genus belonging to the *Labiatæ*, distinguished from its congeners by having the border of the calyx in five equal divisions, and the lower lip of the corolla with its middle lobe entire. The only species is *R. elegans*, a native of India, an erect shrub having its branches clothed with fine down, the leaves hairy ovate or subcordate, and the flowers varying in colour from white to pale red. The genus is named in honour of the late Dr. Royle, a well-known botanist, author of *Illustrations of the Botany of the Himalaya*, &c.   [G. D.]

ROZELLE. *Hibiscus Sabdariffa*: see ROSELLE.

RUAY. Seeds used as weights in India and Burmah, the small Ruay being those of *Abrus precatorius*, and the large Ruay those of *Adenanthera pavonina.*

RUBAN D'EAU. (Fr.) *Sparganium ramosum.* —, DE BERGÈRE. *Digraphis arundinacea picta.* —, GRAND. *Arundo Donax.* —, PETIT. *Digraphis arundinacea.*

RUBANIER. (Fr.) *Sparganium.*

RUBELLUS, RUBENS, RUBER, RUBESCENS. The same as Red, Reddish.

RUBÉOLE. (Fr.) *Sherardia.*

RUBIACEÆ. Under this name those botanists who think that each whorl of leaves in *Galium* and its allies should be considered as two opposite leaves and two or more stipules, unite the two orders *Cinchonaceæ* and *Galiaceæ*. The large order thus formed would comprise all monopetalous plants with opposite leaves, interpetiolar stipules, stamens inserted in the tube of the corolla and alternating with its lobes, and an inferior compound ovary.

RUBIA. One of the genera of *Galiaceæ*, so named from the Latin *ruber* red, in allusion to the colour of the roots. The species are perennial herbs, occasionally somewhat shrubby at the base, and rough with stiff hairs. The flowers are axillary or terminal; the limb of the calyx entire or scarcely developed; the corolla rotate, five-parted; the stamens five, partially protruding from the tube of the corolla; and the styles two, confluent at the base, the stigmas button-like. Fruit somewhat globular juicy two-lobed, two or rarely one-celled, each cell containing a single seed.

The dye known as Madder consists of the dried roots of *R. tinctorum*. In the living roots the colouring-matter is yellow, but this becomes red on drying. The best madder is imported from the Levant, but some comes from Holland and France; the dye is much used in the latter country under the name of Garance. Some of the Indian species also yield a red dye.

Madder has sometimes been stated to possess medicinal virtues; these, however, are so slight as to be now disregarded. The bones of young animals fed on madder become tinged with a red colour, and phy-

Rubia tinctorum.

siologists avail themselves of this fact in their researches on the mode of growth of the bones. The stem and leaves of *R. tinctorum* are used in France for polishing metal-work, for which purpose their stiff hairs adapt them. The leaves and herbage also are used as fodder for animals.

One species, *R. peregrina*, is native in the South-west of England. It is a straggling herb, trailing over bushes by means of recurved prickles projecting from the edges of the leaves and stem. It greatly resembles the species of *Galium*, to which genus indeed the present is very closely allied; but from which it may be distinguished by the fleshy fruit, destitute of prickles or hairs, and by the five not four-parted flowers. [M. T. M.]

RUBICUND. Blushing; rosy red.

RUBIGINOSE. Brown-red; a term usually employed to denote a surface whose peculiar colour is owing to glandular hairs.

RUBOR, EDO. Redness of any sort.

RUBSEN-CAKE. An oilcake made on the Continent from the seeds of *Brassica præcox.*

RUBUS. The genus of the Bramble, Blackberry, Raspberry, Dewberry, and Cloudberry. The species are mostly shrubs (rarely herbs) trailing or erect, with prickly stems, pinnate quinate ternate or simply lobed leaves, and edible fruit. They belong to the *Rosaceæ*, among which they are sufficiently marked by the form of their fruit. The plants of this family, growing in all situations and in every kind of soil, vary greatly, and are consequently most perplexing to the botanist; and so little are authors agreed as to which are species and which varieties, that while Hooker and Arnott reckon but five species, Babington enumerates thirty-five. In a popular work it will be necessary to mention those only which may be considered typical species. Of *R. Idæus* no more need be said than that it is the original of the many varieties of Raspberry, and in its wild state differs from the cultivated kinds mainly in its smaller size. *R. rhamnifolius* and *R. corylifolius* furnish the Blackberries of the hedges, in which the calyx of the fruit is reflexed; *R. fruticosus* has also a reflexed calyx, but the leaves are hoary beneath. *R. cæsius* furnishes Dewberries, distinguished by the large size of the grains, which are covered with bloom and few in number, the whole being closely clasped by the calyx. *R. saxatilis*, the Roebuck-berry, and the badge of the M'Nabs, is an herbaceous species found in mountainous places in the North, and distinguished by its ternate leaves, and fruit of few red large grains. *R. Chamæmorus*, the Cloudberry, and badge of the M'Farlanes, is also herbaceous, with an erect stem six to eight inches high, lobed leaves, and a single flower which is succeeded by a large orange-red fruit of an agreeable flavour. The double-flowering *Rubus* of gardens is a variety of *R. fruticosus*. *R. laciniatus*, of which the native country is unknown, is a rampant species with deeply cut leaves, and large black fruit, which are highly ornamental during autumn. *R. odoratus*, the American Bramble, is an erect unbranched shrub, with large five-lobed leaves, and rose-coloured flowers. *R. occidentalis*, the Virginian Raspberry, has pinnate and ternate leaves, white flowers, and black fruit. Other species are grown in gardens, and two or three are deemed worthy of the conservatory. French: *Ronce*; German: *Brombeerstrauch.* [C. A. J.]

The Raspberry, *R. Idæus*, is a deciduous shrub with perennial creeping roots, biennial stems, which are round villose or prickly, and pinnate leaves which become trifoliate towards the upper part of the shoots. The stems are technically termed *canes*. The Raspberry is a native of Great Britain and of most countries in Europe. It grows wild as far north as Lat. 70°, and southward it appears to have been abundant on Mount Ida, in Asia Minor, Lat. 39° 40'. It was known to the ancients, and Linnæus retained the classic name of Ida, with which it was associated by Dioscorides. It was called in Greek *Batos Idaia*, and in Latin *Rubus Idæa*, the Bramble of Mount Ida. The generic name of *Rubus* is from the Celtic *rub*, red. The fruit is called in German *Hindbeer* or *Himbeer*, in Dutch *Braamboos*, and in Danish *Hindebär*. Gerarde calls it *Raspis* or *Hindberry*; in Scotland the plants and fruits are called *Rasps* very generally, doubtless from the roughness of the stems; but it is also known by the older Saxon or German name of *Hindbeer*, in some parts, and that is used by the Ettrick Shepherd :

> 'Twas only to hear the yorling sing,
> And pu' the crawflower round the spring,
> The scarlet hep and the hindberrie,
> And the nut that hang frae the hazel tree,
> Nor Kilmenie was pure as pure could be.

The Raspberry is much employed by cooks and confectioners in various ways, and also in the manufacture of liqueurs. It has a peculiarly rich aroma, and in this respect none of the many varieties exceeds the Red Antwerp ; some others are larger, but inversely in proportion to their size they are deficient in aroma.   [R. T.]

It is well known that the barren shoots of most of our British *Rubi*, from being too flexile to keep upright, bend downwards even from the hedges and thickets and root their ends in the soil, thus following that mode of increase which in the strawberry is effected by the scion. The loop thus formed was formerly an object of occasional search, being reputed in some counties (and we have known (t so in Gloucestershire) as capable of curing hernia or rupture when used aright, to which end the afflicted child is passed backwards and forwards through the arching bramble. The origin of this custom it is difficult to make out ; but, as is re-marked in *Notes and Queries*, the passing of children through holes in the earth, rocks, and trees, once an established rite, is still practised in various parts of Cornwall. Children affected with hernia are still passed through a slit in an ash sapling before sunrise, fasting ; after which the slit portions are bound up, and as they unite so the malady is cured.

It would appear that in Cornwall the bramble-cure is only employed for boils, the sufferer being either dragged or made to crawl beneath the rooted shoot.

We have heard of cows that were said to be mouse-crope, or to have been walked over by a shrew-mouse (an ancient way of accounting for paralysis), being dragged through the bramble-loop, in which case, if the creature could wait the time of finding a loop large enough and suffer the dragging process at the end, we should say the case would not be so hopeless as that of our friend's fat pig, who, when she was ailing, 'had a mind to kill her to make sure on her.'   [J. B.]

RUBY-WOOD. The Red Sanders wood of commerce, produced by *Pterocarpus santalinus*.

RUCKERIA. A genus of stemless Cape herbs belonging to the thistle group of the *Compositæ*, and somewhat intermediate in character between *Othonna* and *Euryops*, differing from the former in the ray and disk-florets, being alike in the ray and disk-florets, and from the latter in the sterile disk-florets having undivided stigmas. The leaves, which arise from the somewhat woody collar of the plant, are pinnately-parted with linear segments, and the rayed flower-head is single on the apex of a naked flower-stalk. *R. tagetoides* takes its name from its outward resemblance to some French marigolds. The cup-shaped involucre consists of a single series of oblong pointed scales ; the strap-shaped ray-florets are fertile ; the disk-florets tubular and sterile (rarely perfect) ; and the woolly pappus consists of many series of loosely-bearded white hairs. The three known species a e rather showy plants.   [A. A. B.]

RUDBECKIA. A well-known North American genus of herbaceous plants belonging to the *Compositæ*, and nearly related to *Helianthus*, from which they may be recognised by the cone-shaped instead of flat receptacle on which the florets are seated ; and from other of their allies by their four-sided achenes, which are either naked or furnished with a minute crown-shaped pappus, and embraced by the boat-shaped chaffy scales of the receptacle. From among the fifteen known species, at least seven have been cultivated in gardens. *R. laciniata*, very common in herbaceous borders, is a smooth branching plant four to eight feet high, the lower leaves pinnately parted, while those of the stem are three or five-parted, with ovate or lance-shaped toothed segments. The yellow-rayed flower-heads have drooping rays, neutral, and in a single series ; and the tubular and perfect disk-florets are of a greenish-yellow colour. *R. hirta* is clothed throughout with rough hairs, the stems slightly branched, one to three feet high, the lower leaves spathulate three-nerved, and the upper ones ovate or lance-shaped and sessile, while the handsome flower-heads with bright-yellow rays and a dark-purple disk are borne on the naked summits of the branches. Both are Canadian as well as United States plants. The species are desirable and suitable for planting in flower-borders. Linnæus named the genus after the Professors Rudbeck, father and son, who were his predecessors at Upsal.   [A. A. B.]

RUDDES. *Calendula officinalis* ; also *Chrysanthemum segetum*.

RUDERALIS. Growing among rubbish, or in waste places.

RUDGEA. A genus of *Cinchonaceæ*, consisting of trees or shrubs, natives of Guiana, with greyish hairy branches, large fringed deciduous stipules, and flowers in dense terminal panicles. The limb of the calyx is divided into five sharp segments ; corolla funnel-shaped, with an elongated tube, and a limb divided into five narrow segments abruptly bent downwards; stamens five, included within the corolla; style simple; stigma divided into two plates. Fruit succulent, two-celled, two-seeded. The flowers become black as they dry. [M. T. M.]

RUDIMENTARY. In an incomplete condition.

RUDOLPHIA. Three extremely handsome scarlet-flowered woody leguminous climbers, found in Mexico and San Domingo, form this genus, which is nearly allied to *Erythrina*, though readily distinguished by the simple instead of trifoliate leaves, as well as by the calyx, which is tubular, and rather deeply divided into four teeth, the upper and lower longer than the lateral ones. The glossy entire leaves are somewhat heart-shaped in form; and the handsome flowers—remarkable for their narrow pointed standard nearly an inch in length—are arranged in axillary stalked racemes, which are sometimes more than a foot long. The pods are compressed and many-seeded. None of the species are as yet known in gardens. [A. A. B.]

RUE. *Ruta.* —, COMMON. *Ruta graveolens.* —, FEN. *Thalictrum flavum.* —, GOAT'S. *Galega officinalis.* —, MEADOW. *Thalictrum flavum.* —, SYRIAN. *Peganum Harmala.* —, WALL. *Asplenium Ruta muraria.*

RUE. (Fr.) *Ruta.* — DE CHÈVRE. *Galega officinalis.* — DE MURAILLE. *Asplenium Ruta muraria.* — DES CHIENS. *Scrophularia canina.* — DES JARDINS. *Ruta graveolens.* — DES PRÉS. *Thalictrum flavum.*

RUELLIA. A large genus of *Acanthaceæ*, consisting of pilose herbs, natives of tropical Asia and Australia. They have opposite leaves, and flowers in axillary and terminal spikes, with leafy bracts. The calyx is five-parted; the corolla somewhat campanulate, with a limb composed of five equal spreading segments; the four didynamous stamens are included; the style is simple, with a subulate stigma; and the capsule is two-celled, with six to eight seeds. Some species are cultivated because of the beauty of their flowers. [W. G.]

Several species of this genus are used in the East in the preparation of a blue colouring-matter of the nature of indigo, but no precise information exists as to the particular species thus employed. One of the most important is a Chinese plant, temporarily named *R. indigotica* by Mr. Fortune. This is extensively cultivated in the neighbourhood of Ningpo and other parts of the province of Chekiang, and the indigo prepared from it is largely used by the country-people for dyeing their blue cloth. The pigment is prepared from the entire plant by a process somewhat resembling that employed in the preparation of the common indigo. The plant forms a bush a foot or a foot and a half high, and is cut down before the flowers appear. Large quantities of it are thrown into a circular tank about ten feet in diameter and two feet in depth, covered with water, and allowed to remain for about five days, when they become partially decomposed, and are removed by means of large flat-headed brooms made of bamboo twigs. The water is then well stirred with the brooms, and kept in a rapid circular motion for some time, and about forty pounds of lime thoroughly mixed with it, after which it is beaten with bamboo rakes for about half an hour, and then allowed to settle for three or four days, when the supernatant liquor is drawn off, and the thick paste of blue colouring-matter packed in baskets and exposed for sale—it being used for dyeing while in a wet state. The Chinese name Tien-ching is given to both the indigo of this plant, and to that of *Isatis indigotica*. In Assam a species of *Ruellia* called Room or Róum, which is probably identical with the Chinese, is used for the same purpose; and others in Pegu, Burmah, and Singapore. [A. S.]

RUEWORTS. Lindley's name for the *Rutaceæ*.

RUFESCENS, RUFUS. Pale red, mixed with brown.

RUGA. A wrinkle: hence *rugose*, covered with wrinkled lines, the spaces between which are convex; as the leaves of garden sage.

RUIZIA. The name given to a few shrubs of the *Sterculiaceæ* found in the Island of Bourbon, and closely related to *Dombeya* or *Astrapæa*, but differing in all the twenty stamens of the flowers being anther-bearing, as well as in their ten-celled ovary. The four species are named respectively *palmata*, *lobata*, *cordata*, and *dissecta*, from their palmate or maple-like, lobed heart-shaped or dissected leaves, which are stalked alternate and downy underneath. The white or rosy flowers, somewhat like miniature mallows, are disposed in axillary stalked cymes, each flower having a five-parted calyx with two bracts at its base; five oblong clawed petals; twenty stamens; and a ten-celled ovary crowned with ten short styles. The fruits are ten-celled globular capsules with two seeds in each cell. The name of Dr. Hippolite Ruiz, an eminent Spanish botanist and traveller in Peru and Chili, is perpetuated in this genus. [A. A. B.]

RULINGIA. Under this name are associated about a dozen species of Australian plants belonging to the *Byttneriaceæ*, and closely related to *Byttneria* itself, but readily recognised by the absence of the strap-like appendage seen on the back of the petals in that genus. They are small erect branching bushes, the stems and especially the leaves more or less clothed with soft starry hairs, like those seen on *Thomasia* and *Lasiopetalum*. The flowers are small, white, and disposed in axillary or terminal cymes. They have a five-parted calyx with triangular segments; five petals, concave at the base, with the sides incurved so as to form a little bag, and strap-shaped upwards; ten stamens slightly united at the base into a ring, the alternate ones only bearing anthers; and a five-celled ovary crowned with five more or less united styles. The fruits are smooth or rough five-celled capsules the size of peas, with one seed in each cell. *R. Drummondii*, a Swan River species, from the lobing of its leaves together with its habit resembling that of *Achillea*, has been called *achilleopsis*. *R. althæifolia* is in cultivation, so also are *R. corylifolia* and a few others, but none are remarkable for their beauty. The white starry flowers do not exceed a quarter of an inch in diameter.   [A. A. B.]

RUMBEH. A Malayan name for *Pierardia dulcis*.

RUMBIYA. A Malayan name for the Sago Palm.

RUMEX. The Dock and Sorrel genus— a large and widely distributed group of *Polygonaceæ*, occurring chiefly in the temperate zones of both hemispheres. They are herbs, more rarely undershrubs, with alternate leaves, sheathing stipules (ochreæ), and verticillate racemose flowers arranged in a. paniculate manner. These have a six-leaved perianth—the three outer leaves cohering at the base and herbaceous, the three inner larger, somewhat coloured, increasing much in size after flowering, when they often display a central tubercle; stamens six: styles three, with pencil-like stigmas; nut three-edged, enclosed in the three inner connivent enlarged leaves of the perianth. Many of the species are troublesome weeds. Some have been used as a substitute for Rhubarb-root, and others are cultivated for their pleasant acid foliage.

There are a good many British species belonging to this genus, which may be divided into three sections or subgenera:—
Lapathum: the Dock. In this the flowers are usually perfect, very rarely diœcious, the inner perianth-leaves usually tubercled; styles free, with multifid stigmas. They are insipid herbs, with pinnate-veined leaves, and many-flowered whorls; flowers in two three or five rows in each whorl; pedicels articulated at the base. The British species are *R. maritimus*, *palustris*, *pulcher*, *obtusifolius*, *conglomeratus*, *sanguineus*, *pratensis*, *crispus*, *aquaticus*, *Hydrolapathum*, and *alpinus*. This latter species is doubtless an introduced plant, but is well naturalised in the mid-counties of Scotland, where it is known as Monk's Rhubarb.
Acetosa: the Sorrel. In this group the flowers are often diœcious or polygamously monœcious; perianth-segments without tubercles; styles adhering to the angles of the ovary, with multifid stigmas. They are acid herbs or undershrubs, with usually hastate or sagittate leaves, and few-flowered whorls, the flowers in one or two rows in each whorl; pedicels articulated at the base in most of the species. Only two species of this section occur in Britain, *R.

Acetosa and *Acetosella*; but it includes also the French Sorrel, *R. scutatus*, which has polygamously monœcious flowers, and has escaped from cultivation in a few places.
Rumastrum, the third group, contains no British species. It occurs in Abyssinia and Arabia, and comprises insipid undershrubs with palmately-veined leaves, and few-flowered whorls, having the pedicels articulated at the middle. The flowers are usually perfect, rarely monœcious; the styles adhere to the angles of the ovary as in *R. Acetosa*, but the stigmas are not many-cleft.   [J. T. S.]

R. obtusifolius, the Common Dock, and several others are well-known as being among the greatest pests to agriculturists. A few species are cultivated for the supposed medicinal properties of their roots, and some as potherbs, the acidity in their leaves rendering them both wholesome and agreeable for such purposes.

The Common Sorrel, *R. Acetosa*, is a perennial, and is generally found in pastures where the soil is inclined to be irony. Formerly this plant was cultivated in gardens for its leaves, which were used as spinach or in salads, and in the time of Henry VIII. it was held in great repute. After the introduction of the French Sorrel, with large succulent leaves, it gradually lost its position as a salad and potherb, and for many years it has been entirely discarded from cultivation.

The Buckler-shaped or French Sorrel, *R. scutatus*, is a hardy perennial, a native of France and Italy, and is stated to have been introduced into this country in 1596. The leaves are blunt, somewhat halbert-shaped, glaucous smooth soft and fleshy. The stems are inclined to spread, but rise from a foot to eighteen inches high, and bear numerous greenish-white flowers disposed in terminal clustered panicles. The leaves are used for the same purposes as those of *R. Acetosa*, and are considered preferable on account of being more succulent, with rather less acidity.

The Sorrels are considered of great importance in French cookery, and are both agreeable to eat and very wholesome, although but little valued in this country, except at some of the most fashionable tables. On the Continent sorrel is extensively cultivated, and in the vegetable markets of Paris it is nearly as abundant during the season as peas are in those of London. It abounds in oxalic acid, and is regarded as a powerful antiscorbutic. The French have several varieties.   [W. B. B.]

RUMFORDIA. The only species of this genus, *R. floribunda*, is a handsome opposite-leaved Mexican bush of the *Compositæ*, related to the North American *Heliopsis*, and differing chiefly in habit. The whole plant is smooth, and the erect stems, furnished with ample glossy leaves, terminate in a panicle of very numerous bright-yellow flower-heads each about an inch across, and interspersed with oblong bracts. The leaves are ovate, narrowed to the base, shortly pointed, and three-nerved. Each head is stalked, and has an involucre of fifteen scales—the five outer leafy, the ten inner much smaller, pointed, and embracing by their bases the corresponding achenes of the strap-shaped ray-florets, which bear pistils only; while the central tubular florets are perfect, and have their achenes embraced by chaffy scales somewhat like those of the ray. [A. A. B.]

RUMINATED. Pierced by irregular passages, filled with colouring matter or minute dead cell-membranes, as the albumen of nutmeg.

RUMOHRA. *Polystichum.*

RUMPHIA. The name applied to a tree, native of Malabar, and considered to constitute a distinct genus of *Anacardiaceæ.* The leaves are simple, and the flowers in terminal racemes. The calyx is three-cleft, tubular; there are three petals and as many stamens; the ovary is solitary, and the fruit is fleshy, top-shaped, marked with three furrows, and containing a three-celled three-seeded stone. The generic name celebrates a botanist of the last century, known particularly by his work on the Botany of Amboyna. [M. T. M.]

RUNCH. *Raphanus Raphanistrum.*

RUNCINATE. Curved in a direction from the apex to the base; as the leaf of *Leontodon Taraxacum.*

RUNCINATO-LACINIATE. Both runcinate and laciniate.

RUNNER. A prostrate slender stem rooting at its extremity, as in the strawberry.

RUPESTRIS. Growing on rocks, or in rocky places.

RUPICOLA. Inhabiting rocks.

RUPPIA. A submersed aquatic belonging to the order *Naiadaceæ,* and distinguished from *Potamogeton* by having the four one-seeded capsules on long stalks. *R. maritima,* the only species, is an unattractive plant with the habit of the smaller pondweeds, remarkable only for the peculiarity of the stalk or spadix which bears the seed-vessels. This in its early stage is included within sheathing bracteas, but as the flowers approach maturity, their stalks become spiral and lengthen five or six inches, thus raising the flowers to the surface of the water. The plant is very widely diffused, being found in Britain and America, and also in the Sandwich Islands, and on the coasts of Southern India and Ceylon, constantly preserving the same appearance. [C. A. J.]

RUPRECHTIA. A genus of *Polygonaceæ,* inhabiting the West Indies, Brazil, and Guiana, distinguished from the closely allied genus *Triplaris* by having the fruit pyramidal with three furrows, and the nucleus three-lobed, runcinate. [J. T. S.]

RUPTILE. Bursting irregularly, not in the line of union of parts in cohesion.

RUPTINERVIS,　　RUPTINERVIUS.

When a straight-ribbed leaf has its ribs interrupted or swollen at intervals.

RUPTUREWORT. *Herniaria glabra;* also *Alternanthera polygonoides.*

RUPTURING. An irregular not definite mode of bursting.

RUSCUS. Evergreen shrubs belonging to the tribe *Asparageæ* of liliaceous plants. Its characters are:—Root not bulbous; flowers six-parted, persistent, imperfect; stamens connected at the base and forming a nectary; fruit a berry. *R. aculeatus,* the Butcher's Broom or Knee-Holly, is a singular plant, growing wild mostly in the South and West of England, but frequently planted in shrubberies. The stems, which are green erect rigid and branched above, grow to the height of about three feet, and bear numerous small coriaceous leaves, each terminating in a single spine. The flowers are small greenish-white, and solitary on the disk of the leaves; and the berry is about the size of a small cherry, and of a brilliant scarlet colour. The young shoots are sometimes eaten like those of

Ruscus aculeatus.

asparagus, and the mature plants made into brooms. *R. racemosus* or *Alexandrinus* is a favourite evergreen shrub with thick unarmed leaves and terminal racemes of small flowers. *R. androgynus,* a native of the Canaries, bears its flowers along the edges of the leaves. In *R. Hypophyllum,* from the South of Europe, they are borne beneath the leaves; and in *R. Hypoglossum,* also from the South of Europe, on the upperside under a leaflet. French: *Fragon piquant;* German: *Mausdorn.* [C. A. J.]

RUSH, POLISHING, or DUTCH RUSHES. The commercial name of *Equisetum hyemale,* which is imported principally from Holland, as a material for polishing wood, ivory, and brass, in consequence of the large quantity of silex it contains in its tissues, which is so abundant that the form may be retained when the plant is burnt. The greater number of the particles, according to Brewster, form simple straight lines; but the rest are grouped into oval forms, connected together like the pearls of a necklace by a chain of particles forming a sort of curvilinear quadrangle, these rows of oval combinations being arranged in pairs. In the straw and chaff of wheat, &c., which is also good when burnt for polishing, he noticed analogous phenomena, but the particles were arranged in a different manner, and displayed figures of singular beauty.   [M. J. B.]

RUSH. *Juncus.* —, BALD. *Psilocarya.* —, BOG. *Schœnus.* —, BULL. *Scirpus lacustris.* —, CLUB. *Scirpus.* —, DUTCH. *Equisetum hyemale.* —, FLOWERING. *Butomus umbellatus.* —, HARESTAIL. *Eriophorum vaginatum.* —, HORNED. *Ceratoschœnus.* —, MOSS. *Juncus squarrosus.* —, NUT. *Scleria.* —, PAPER. *Papyrus antiquorum.* —, SCOURING. *Equisetum hyemale.* —, SPIKE. *Eleocharis.* —, TWIG. *Cladium.* —, WOOD. *Luzula.*

RUSOT. A watery medicinal extract prepared in India from the sliced roots stem and branches of *Berberis Lycium,* and *B. aristata.*

RUSSELIA. A genus of *Scrophulariaceæ,* containing several herbs or shrubs, natives of Mexico and the Antilles. They have angular branches, with entire opposite ternate or whorled leaves, and scarlet flowers in axillary corymbs. The calyx is five-parted; the tube of the corolla dilated upwards, and the limb two-lipped; the four stamens are included, the anthers composed of two divaricate cells; the style is simple; the stigma obtuse; and the globular capsule has an attenuated beak, is two-celled, each of the cells containing several small seeds.   [W. C.]

RUSSIAN MATS. An article of commerce manufactured from the inner bark of *Tilia.*

RUSSULA. A genus of gill-bearing *Fungi* distinguished principally from *Lactarius* by the absence of milk. The species are numerous, but so variable in form and colour—which exhibits the brightest scarlet, pink, white, yellow, livid, &c., in one and the same species—that they are often very difficult to distinguish, though when once ascertained they are easy of recognition, even under considerable disguise. The gills are either white or of an apricot-yellow, according to the colour of the spores. Most of them are more or less depressed in age. The gills are mostly brittle and entire, with a peculiar character of their own, which, without inquiry as to the nature of the fluid they contain, at once indicates the genus. Some are extremely acrid, while others are mild and esculent. They are much esteemed on the Continent, though seldom used in England. Mrs. Hussey, however, was a great advocate for them, and speaks of one species as giving a daily and welcome supply to an invalid who could neither relish nor digest any other food.   [M. J. B.]

RUST. The common name of *Trichobasis Rubigo vera,* a parasitic fungus of the natural order *Pucciniæi,* which, with one or two other closely allied species confounded with it by the farmer, preys upon the leaves, glumes, stalks, &c. of cereals. They have been supposed to be mere conditions of *Puccinia graminis,* but this is not fully borne out by closer inquiry. Rust does not appear to be injurious to corn so long as it is confined to the flaggy leaves, as it seldom grows except when they are over-luxuriant, but it is a formidable adversary when it attacks the chaff or seed; and the more so because it is impossible to suggest any remedy. Every protospore is shed long before the grain is reaped, and therefore steeping the seed is useless. The application of any dressing to the soil is almost like breaking a butterfly upon a wheel. White wheat is more subject to have the chaff affected than red; indeed, some varieties are scarcely ever entirely free from the parasite.   [M. J. B.]

RUSTY. The same as Ferruginous.

RUTABAGA. The Swedish Turnip, *Brassica campestris rutabaga.*

RUTACEÆ (*Rutæ, Diosmeæ, Fraxinelleæ, Rueworts*). A large order of polypetalous dicotyledons, consisting of trees, shrubs, or rarely herbs, always more or less marked with glandular dots, especially on the foliage, and often strongly scented. The leaves are frequently opposite, simple or more generally compound, entire or rarely toothed, without stipules. The flowers are usually hermaphrodite and regular, sometimes showy and often sweet-scented; the sepals and petals are five each, with the same or double the number of stamens inserted on a hypogynous or somewhat perigynous disk; and the ovary has four or five cells, with two or rarely one ascending ovule in each. The fruit is a capsule or berry, rarely a drupe; and the seeds, whether with or without albumen, have always a large embryo. All the above characters are, however, liable to exceptions, and there is little beyond the glandular dots of the foliage to separate the order on the one hand from *Simarubaceæ,* and on the other from *Burseraceæ.* In its geographical range, the order extends over the tropical, subtropical, and temperate regions of the whole globe; it is, however, scarce in tropical Africa, and disappears entirely in cold climates and at great elevations. Taken in its most extended sense, the order is now divided into seven tribes, several of which, and not always those which are most distinct in character, are often considered as separate orders. They are—*Cuspariæ*: natives of tropical America, comprising nine genera of which the most important are *Almeidea, Galipea, Ticorea,* and *Monnieria. Ruteæ*: dispersed chiefly over the temperate regions of the Northern Hemisphere, with six genera, including *Ruta, Peganum,* and *Dictamnus. Diosmeæ*: eleven genera all South African, chiefly *Diosma* and small genera separated from it. *Boroniex* : eighteen genera, all Australian, including *Zieria, Boronia, Phebalium, Crowea, Correa,* &c. *Xanthoxylex* : dispersed over the tropical regions of both the New and the Old World, seventeen genera, including *Melicope, Evodia, Choisya, Xanthoxylon, Esenbeckia,* &c. *Toddaliex* : chiefly tropical in both the New and the Old World, comprising nine genera, of which the principal are *Toddalia, Hortia, Acronychia,* and *Skimmia. Aurantiex* : also tropical, but almost limited to Asia, thirteen genera, including *Glycosmis, Limonia, Murraya, Clausena, Atalantia, Citrus,* &c. The five first of the above tribes have their ovary usually lobed, and their fruit capsular or dividing into cocci ; whilst *Toddaliex* and *Aurantiex* differ in their undivided and indehiscent fruit, usually a berry or rarely a drupe. The *Aurantiex* have until lately been almost universally admitted as a distinct order : see AURANTIACEÆ and XANTHOXYLEÆ.

RUTA. This genus gives its name to the order *Rutacex.* The species are herbs or undershrubs, natives of the temperate regions of the Eastern Hemisphere. The leaves are beset with small glands, containing a powerfully smelling oil ; they are pinnate or much-divided. The flowers are yellowish or greenish, and arranged in terminal corymbs or racemes. The calyx has four persistent sepals ; the petals are four, concave ; stamens eight ; ovary four-lobed, on a short thick disk-like stalk, at the base of which is a ring of eight glandular pores ; style one ; fruit capsular, four-celled, with six to eight seeds in each cell.

The Common Rue, *R. graveolens,* a native of the South of Europe, is commonly cultivated in this country. It is a somewhat shrubby plant, two to three feet high, with pinnately divided bluish-green leaves, and yellowish flowers disposed in corymbs. The first flower that opens has usually ten stamens, the others eight only. These stamens are of unequal length ; each is bent inwards in its turn to touch the pistil, and after the pollen has been shed it bends back again. The powerful fetid odour and acrid taste of this plant depends on the presence of a volatile oil.

Rue is used medicinally as a stimulant and narcotic in flatulent colic, hysteria, &c. Its active properties are such as to admit of its much more general use, but practitioners have been perhaps deterred from employing it, by the symptoms of acrido-narcotic poisoning induced by an overdose. Locally applied, Rue is a powerful irritant. One species indeed, *R. montana,* is said to be so powerful that it is dangerous to handle the plant, even when the hands are protected by gloves. Rue was employed medicinally by the ancients; for ages it was considered potent to ward off contagion, and it is still employed to keep off noxious insects. Rue enters into the composition of the French perfume, entitled Vinegar of the Four Thieves. The Italians are stated to eat the leaves in salads. Shakspeare speaks of Rue as Herb

of Grace. Several species besides those mentioned in this notice are cultivated in gardens in this country. The name *Ruta* is from the Greek *ruo,* to preserve, in allusion to the effects of the plant on the health.   [M. T. M.]

RUTILANS, RUTILUS. Reddish, with a metallic lustre ; also brick-red.

RUTOSMA. This name has been applied to a herbaceous plant, *R. texana,* growing in New Mexico, Texas, &c., and constituting a genus of *Rutacex.* It is a low-growing plant, sending up many stems from a thick root, having linear entire strong-scented leaves, and flowers whose structure differs from that of *Ruta* and other adjacent genera in the petals being comparatively flat, and in having an eight-lobed disk without pores, a two-celled ovary, and rough seeds.   [M. T. M.]

RUTTON-ROOT. An Indian dye-root, *Maharanga Emodi.*

RUTTYA. A genus of *Acanthacex,* from South Africa, containing a single species. It has four stamens, the two barren ones being very short ; and the base of the anthers is mucronate. The capsule is four-seeded ; and the divisions of the calyx are very long and slender.   [W. C.]

RUYSCHIA. A genus of *Marcgraviacex,* containing about eight tropical American species, mostly forming epiphytal or scandent shrubs, which have thick quite entire leaves, and terminal often very long racemes of flowers. It is distinguished from the two allied genera *Marcgravia* and *Norantea,* by its petals being connate at their bases, and by having only five instead of an indefinite number of stamens. [A. S.]

RYANIA. A genus consisting of half-a-dozen species from tropical America, chiefly Guiana, properly belonging to *Flacourtiacex,* but on account of the cupular disk surrounding the ovary in some species, erroneously placed in *Passifloracex* by some writers. The *Ryanias* are trees with alternate almost entire leaves, axillary peduncles, no corolla, numerous stamens, a sessile ovary, and a capsule having three to five cells and valves. [B. S.]

RYE. *Secale cereale.* —, SPURRED. The grain of Rye, in an ergoted condition. —, WILD. *Elymus.*

RYHAN. The Egyptian name for Basil, *Ocimum Basilicum.*

RYKIA. A genus of *Pandanacex,* allied to *Pandanus.* Its distinguishing characteristics are : a one-celled fruit, with a columnar top, hollow internally, and separated from the rest of the fruit ; while the style grows out into a hard horny mass, and is after a time divided into two branches. *R. furcata,* a native of Java, is in cultivation under the old name of *Pandanus.* The present genus is named in compliment to a Dutch naval officer. [M. T. M.]

RYSSOPTERYS. A genus of *Malpighiacex,* consisting of shrubs of a climbing habit, natives of the Moluccas. The flowers are in branched clusters frequently unisexual, owing to the abortive condition of the ovaries, which are reduced to the condition of villous tubercles. The petals are five, entire; stamens ten, all fertile, united below into a cup by means of their filaments; ovaries three, one-celled, each with a single pendulous ovule; styles three; fruit in three divisions, or fewer by abortion, coherent in the axis of the flower, prolonged at the top into a wing-like process, which is thickened on its upper margin, while its sides are beset with tubercles, whence the name of the genus. [M. T. M.]

RYTIDEA. The name of a tropical African shrub of the family *Cinchonaceæ*. The flowers are tufted, in terminal spikes; the bracts and calyx hairy. The corolla is smooth, funnel-shaped, its limb divided into five oval spreading lobes; anthers five, sessile. Fruit somewhat fleshy, crowned by the limb of the calyx, one-celled, one-seeded. [M. T. M.]

RYTIDOPHYLLUM. A genus of *Gesneraceæ*, principally found in the West Indies, and consisting of shrubby or even arborescent plants. The leaves are alternate, and more or less of an ovate shape; and the flowers appear in axillary cymes, and are generally white, greenish, or pale yellow. The calyx is five-cleft, with ovate or oblong segments; the corolla cyathiform and oblique; the stamens scarcely projecting beyond the corolla; and the ovary immersed in the calyx is surrounded by a glandular ring. The different species constitute part of the undergrowth in virgin forests. [B. S.]

SABADILLA. The same as Cevadilla, the seeds of *Asagræa officinalis*.

SABAL. Next to *Chamærops*, this is the most northern genus of *Palmaceæ*, one of its representatives, *S. Palmetto*, reaching in Carolina as far north as latitude 34° 36'. Eight or nine species are described, but their botanical characters are very imperfectly known, and even the native country of the species so long cultivated in English gardens is uncertain; though, as all the other species are natives of the West Indies and the southern regions of North America, it is probable that it originally came from one of those countries. Some species have stout stems from twenty to thirty feet high, while others are either stemless or have short creeping stems. Their leaves are large, fan-shaped and plaited, and much cut at the edge, with fibrous threads hanging from between the segments; and their flower-spikes are irregularly branched and bear perfect flowers, possessing a cup-shaped three-cut calyx, three petals, six nearly distinct stamens, and three ovaries, which are at first distinct but at length coalesce and bear a three-sided style and round-headed stigma. They produce round or deeply two or three-lobed dark-green fruits, containing single horny seeds.

The soft interior of the very short stem of *S. Adansoni* is eaten in the Southern States of America, and its leaves are used for platting into hats resembling what are called 'chip-hats' in this country—as also are those of the Palmetto (*S. Palmetto*), a native of the same locality. In Mexico the leaves of *S. mexicana* are applied to the same use and are likewise made into mats, the trees being regularly cultivated for the purpose. [A. S.]

SABBATIA. A genus of North American herbs of the gentian family. The flowers are in terminal corymbs. The calyx is divided into from five to twelve narrow segments; the corolla is rotate and deciduous, its limb divided into as many lobes as the calyx; while to its tube are attached an equal number of stamens, which ultimately turn back; stigmas two, linear, ultimately twisted in a spiral manner. The fruit is a one-celled capsule, opening when ripe by two valves, and containing numerous very small seeds. The young stems of *S. angularis* are used in the North American States as a vermifuge. *S. stellaris* is in cultivation. [M. T. M.]

SABDARIFFA. *Hibiscus Sabdariffa*, called Red Sorrel in the West and Rozelle in the East Indies, where it is used in tarts, jellies, and salads, and to form a cooling drink.

SABIACEÆ. A small order of dicotyledons, nearly allied to *Sapindaceæ* and *Anacardiaceæ* in the structure of the ovary fruit and seeds, but differing essentially in the stamens being equal in number and opposite to the petals, two of the stamens being usually much larger than the others and perfect, the two or three others much smaller and often without anthers. The species are all tropical, and form trees shrubs or woody climbers, with alternate simple or pinnate leaves without stipules, and small flowers usually paniculate. They are not numerous, distributed into four genera, of which *Sabia* is Asiatic, *Phoxanthus* and *Ophiocaryon* American, and *Meliosma* common to both the New and the Old Worlds.

SABIA. A genus of *Sabiaceæ*, consisting of about ten species, from tropical and eastern temperate Asia. They are all shrubby, with weak or climbing branches, and alternate entire petiolate leaves. The flowers are small, usually greenish, in axillary cymes or panicles or rarely solitary; and are remarkable, in the small order, for their four or five stamens all nearly equal and perfect, and exactly opposite both to the sepals and petals.

SABICU-WOOD. Also called Savicu-wood, and Sayico-wood, a hard shipbuilding wood of Cuba, the produce of *Lysiloma Sabicu*.

SABINE, or SABINIER. (Fr.) *Juniperus Sabina*.

SABINEA. A genus of *Leguminosæ*, embracing three West Indian shrubs, having unequally pinnate leaves, somewhat like those of *Robinia*, but with smaller leaflets, and the pea-flowers as large as those of that plant, but instead of being arranged in many-flowered racemes, disposed in axillary fascicles of two to four flowers. These usually appear before the leaves, and have a shortly bell-shaped five-toothed calyx; a roundish standard the length of the free auricled wings, which are shorter than the blunt keel; and ten stamens, nine united and one free. The pods are compressed, about four inches long, and have a number of seeds. Excepting in the fascicled instead of racemed flowers the genus hardly differs from *Coursetia*, and it is nearly allied to *Tephrosia*, which has terminal racemes. The genus is named in compliment to Joseph Sabine, Esq., once secretary to the Horticultural Society of London.   [A. A. B.]

SABLIER. (Fr.) *Hura.*

SABLINE. (Fr.) *Arenaria.* — DE MAHON. *Arenaria balearica.*

SABOT. (Fr.) *Cypripedium.* — DE VÉNUS. *Cypripedium Calceolus.*

SABUDANA. An Indian name for Sago.

SABULOSE. Growing in sandy places.

SAC, SACCUS. A bag or cup; a term sometimes applied to the coronet of *Stapelia*, &c. *Sacculus* is a little bag.

SAC OF THE EMBRYO. The vesicle of the nucleus of an ovule, within which the embryo is formed.

SACCHARATE or SACCHARINE. Having a sweet taste.

SACCHARUM. A genus of grasses belonging to the tribe *Andropogoneæ*. It has the inflorescence in loose panicles, which are often very beautiful; spikelets more or less lanceolate; glumes two-valved two-flowered, enveloped in long wool; lower flower neuter with one pale, upper hermaphrodite with two pales; stamens one to three; stigmas woolly thick and generally violet-coloured. Steudel describes sixty-two species, which have a wide geographic range, though chiefly natives of tropical and subtropical countries.

The most important species is *Saccharum officinarum*, the Sugar Cane of commerce, respecting which Loudon has the following observations in the *Encyclopædia of Plants*:—'This grass or reed, though unknown to the ancients, has become of immense importance in modern times. There are many varieties or species, both wild and cultivated, natives of the banks of rivers and meadows in both the Indies, China, Africa, the South Sea Islands, and South America. It is cultivated in a zone extending from 35° to 40° on each side of the equator. Where it was first cultivated is unknown—in all probability in India, for the Venetians imported it from thence by the Red Sea prior to 1148. It is supposed to have been introduced into the islands of Sicily, Crete, Rhodes, and Cyprus by the Saracens, as abundance of

sugar was made in these islands previous to the discovery of the West Indies in 1492 by the Spaniards, and the East Indies and Brazil by the Portuguese in 1497 and 1560. It was cultivated afterwards in Spain, in Valentia, Granada, and Murcia by the Moors, and sugar is still made in these provinces. In the fifteenth century the Cane was introduced to the Canary Islands by the Spaniards, and to Madeira by the Portugese, and thence to the West India Islands and the Brazils. The Dutch began to make sugar in the island of St. Thomas in 1610, and in Jamaica in 1644. The culture of the Cane has since become general in warm climates, and the use of sugar universal; it forms one of the first articles of commerce throughout the world. It was in use in England in 1466, but chiefly in feasts and as a medicine, till it was brought from the Brazils about 1580 to Portugal, and imported from thence. The quantity consumed in Britain has always kept increasing. The consumption of England alone in 1790 amounted to 109,573,344 lbs., which, taking the inhabitants at eight millions, gives each individual at an average about 20 lbs. a year.' In 1863 there was imported into this country 11,731,979 cwts.   [D. M.]

Saccharum officinarum.

The Sugar Cane has been cultivated from time immemorial, and was known to many savage tribes of the Eastern Hemisphere, who grew it for the sake of sucking the stem or sweetening their food with the raw juice. The manufacture of sugar is supposed to have been derived from China. The native country of the Cane is doubtless the Eastern Hemisphere, but the exact locality whence it spread is unknown. India lays claim to it, and our name Sugar is a corruption of a Sanscrit word. New Caledonia, in the South Pacific, has also a peculiar claim to be regarded its native country. There the Sugar Cane not only grows with rapidity and attains an extraordinary size, but the barbarous natives of that large island possess an endless number of varieties. The consumption of sugar is largest proportionally in Australla, where the European population uses about 100 lbs. per head; while in England 36 lbs., and in Russia only 2 lbs. per head are consumed. Sugar is made into molasses and rum, and is also used medicinally. The leaves of *S. floridulum* are employed in the South Sea islands for thatching houses, and the stems for making arrows, &c. [B.S.]

SACCIFORM. Having the form of a bag.

SACCOCALYX. A low Algerian aromatic shrub, forming a genus of *Labiatæ*, with the habit, foliage, and most of the characters of *Satureia*, but distinguished chiefly by the calyx, which after flowering enlarges considerably, becoming inflated and globular. The flowers are very small and insignificant.

SACCOLABIUM. A very considerable genus of Indian and Madagascar vandeous orchids, some of the species of which are amongst the most beautiful of the orchid tribe. It was founded by Blume upon a small Javanese species, and named from *saccus* 'a bag,' and *labium* 'a lip,' in allusion to its flowers having a kind of pouch to the lip. The plants belonging to it are all epiphytes, with stems thickly clothed with two opposite ranks of long leathery leaves, from the axils of some of which the flower-spikes are produced. The flowers are not of large size, but are often extremely numerous and closely set on the spike; they have widely-spread nearly equal and similar sepals and petals, and an undivided spurred lip joined to the base of the erect semicylindrical column; and their partially two-celled anther contains two almost globular pollen-masses attached by a long caudicle to a minute gland. Several species are to be met with in the orchid-houses of this country; indeed one of the most beautiful of them, *S. guttatum*, was introduced and flowered nearly half a century ago, and is still a general favourite. Its flower-spikes are commonly from a foot to a foot and a half long, and very densely clothed with extremely numerous delicate waxy-white purple-spotted flowers on short stalks, the whole spike assuming a tail-like almost cylindrical form. There are several varieties differing merely in the depth of tint of their purple spots. It is a native of many parts of India, and also of Java. [A. S.]

SACCOLOMA. A small group of davallioid ferns, most of which are now referred to *Microlepia*. [T. M.]

SACCONIA. A West Indian tree forming a genus of *Cinchonaceæ*. It has leathery leaves, with white flowers arranged in a terminal cyme. The limb of the calyx is persistent wavy five-toothed; the corolla somewhat funnel-shaped, its limb divided into five obtuse lobes; stamens five, projecting beyond the corolla; ovary two-celled, surmounted by an epigynous fleshy disk; fruit succulent surmounted by the limb of the calyx and

containing a two-celled stone, in each cell of which there is a single seed. [M. T. M.]

SACCOPETALUM. A genus of Indian and Javanese trees of the family *Anonaceæ*. The flowers have a calyx with three sepals; a corolla of six petals, the three outer of which resemble the sepals, the three inner much larger, partially and temporarily united together, velvet-like in texture, and pouched at the base; very numerous overlapping stamens; and distinct ovaries containing several ovules. The parts of the flower are placed on a globular receptacle. [M. T. M.]

SACK-TREE. *Antiaris* or *Lepurazda saccidora*, the bark of which is formed into natural sacks in India, and used for carrying rice.

SADDLE-SHAPED. Oblong, with the sides hanging down like the flaps of a saddle.

SADDLE-TREE. *Liriodendron tulipifera*.

SADLERIA. A genus of polypodiaceous ferns of the section *Lomariea*, in which it is known by the veins anastomosing arcuately at the base so as to form costal areoles, as well as by its tree-like habit, elevated receptacle, and thick indusium. There are some three or four reputed species, all from the Sandwich Islands. [T. M.]

SADR. An Arabian name for *Zizyphus Lotus*.

SADRUS. An Indian name for the aromatic bark of *Cinnamomum malabathrum*.

SAD-TREE. *Nyctanthes Arbor tristis*.

SAFFLOWER. The Bastard Saffron, *Carthamus tinctorius*.

SAFFRON. A commercial name for the dried stigmas of *Crocus sativus*. —, BASTARD. The florets of *Carthamus tinctorius*. —, MEADOW. *Colchicum autumnale*. —, SICILIAN. *Crocus odorus*.

SAFFRON-COLOURED. Deep orange-coloured, with a dash of brown.

SAFFRON-WOOD. A South African name for *Elæodendron croceum*.

SAFRAN. (Fr.) *Crocus*. —, BÂTARD. *Carthamus tinctorius*. —, D'AUTOMNE. *Crocus sativus*. —, DES FLEURISTES. *Crocus vernus*. — DES INDES. *Curcuma*. — DES PRÉS. *Colchicum autumnale*. — DU GÂTINOIS. *Crocus sativus*, — FAUX. *Carthamus tinctorius*; also *Sternbergia lutea*.

SAFRANUM. (Fr.) *Carthamus tinctorius*.

SAFU. A name applied in the African island of St. Thomas to the fruit of *Pachylobus edulis*.

SAGA. A Siamese name for the seeds of *Abrus precatorius*.

SAGAPENUM. A fetid gum-resin supposed by some to be obtained from *Ferula persica*, and by others from *F. Szowitziana*.

SAGE. *Salvia*; also specially applied to

the culinary herbs, *Salvia officinalis* and *S. grandiflora.* —, BENGAL. *Meriandra bengalensis.* —, BLACK. *Cordia cylindrostachya.* —, JERUSALEM. *Phlomis fruticosa.* —, SEASIDE. *Croton balsamiferum.* —, WILD. A name in the Cape Colony for *Tarchonanthus camphoratus*; also *Lantana.* —, WOOD. *Teucrium Scorodonia.*

SAGENIA. A genus of coarse-habited aspidiaceous ferns, distinguished from the true species of *Aspidium*—that is, those with compoundly anastomosing veins and peltate indusia, by having the indusia distinctly reniform. There are several species found in the tropical parts of both worlds, one of the most familiar being the *S. macrophylla* of the West Indies. [T. M.]

SAGERÆA. A genus of *Anonaceæ*, consisting of three East Indian trees, very nearly allied to *Uvaria*, and differing chiefly in the small number of stamens, and in the carpels of the ovary being reduced to six or three.

SAGERETIA. A genus of *Rhamnaceæ*, the species of which were formerly referred to the Linnæan *Rhamnus*, which contained likewise the Jujubes and several other groups now regarded as distinct. The *Sageretias* are shrubs with slender sometimes half-climbing branches, commonly armed with thorns. Their leaves are short-stalked alternate or nearly opposite upon the lower parts of the branches, and of a leathery consistency, with small marginal teeth; and their little stalkless flowers are disposed in clusters along small simple or branched spikes produced either from the axils of the leaves or at the terminations of the branches. The species are confined to the tropical and subtropical countries of Asia and America. *S. theezans*, the Tia of the Chinese, is a thorny shrub, with slender angular branches and finely-toothed egg-shaped leaves, smooth and of a shining-green on the upper surface, somewhat resembling those of the tea-shrub. It is a native of Penang and the Philippine Islands, as well as of Southern China; and the poorer classes of the Chinese are said to employ its tea-like leaves as a substitute for true tea. [A. S.]

SAGESSE DES CHIRURGIENS. (Fr.) *Sisymbrium Sophia.*

SAGINA. The genus of Pearlworts, consisting of humble herbaceous plants belonging to the suborder *Alsineæ* of *Caryophyllaceæ*, and of which the characters are :—Styles, four or five; sepals and valves of the capsule equal in number to the styles; petals entire or wanting. *S. procumbens* is the minute perennial weed with slender spreading stems, and short bristle-like leaves, which infests the gravel-walks of gardens, and pertinaciously defies eradication. *S. erecta* forms little tufts on walls and dry banks, and differs from the last principally in *its* annual erect stems: the flowers in these and several allied species are inconspicuous. *S. nodosa* is

distinguished by bearing tufts of small leaves on the upper part of the stems, and rather large stalked white flowers. None of the species possess properties worthy of notice. French : *Sagine*; German : *Vierling.*   [C. A. J.]

SAGINA. A name for Broom corn in Italy.

SAGITTARIA. Handsome perennial aquatics deriving their name from the sagittate or arrow-headed form of their leaves. They belong to the order *Alismaceæ*, and are distinguished by having the barren and fertile flowers distinct but on the same plant (monœcious), and by bearing numerous stamens, and one-seeded carpels. *S. sagittifolia* bears directly from the root large glossy leaves which rise out of the water, and numerous delicate white flowers on a branched leafless stalk. This species, one of the last plants to linger on the banks of the Thames in the heart of London, is common in Siberia, China, Japan, and Virginia. The bulbs, which fix themselves in the solid earth below the mud, are said to constitute an article of food among the Chinese, who upon that account cultivate the plant extensively. Representations of it are frequent in Chinese drawings. Several other species are cultivated, mostly inhabitants of warm countries. French : *Sagittaire*; German : *Pfeilkraut.*   [C. A. J.]

SAGITTATE. Gradually enlarged at the base into two acute straight lobes, like the head of an arrow; as the leaf of *Rumex Acetosella.*

SAGO. A granulated form of starch obtained from the pith of the trunk of *Sagus lævis* and *S. Rumphii* in Singapore, the former furnishing most of the sago sent to Europe. In India it is obtained from *Phœnix farinifera*, in Java from *Corypha Gebanga*, and it is also produced by *Caryota urens*, and several other palms and *Cycadaceæ.* —, PORTLAND. A kind of arrowroot, manufactured from the corms of *Arum maculatum* in the island of Portland.

SAGUERUS. This genus of palms is almost entirely confined to the islands of the Indian Archipelago and the countries between Malacca and Burmah; only one species, *S. Wightii*, being indigenous to the Indian peninsula, though the common *S. saccharifer* occurs there in a cultivated state. Three of the five described species form handsome trees thirty or forty feet high, but the other two seldom exceed eight or ten feet. Their leaves are large terminal and pinnate, with narrow leaflets; and with the stalks, which are sometimes prickly, furnished at the base with a copious network of stiff black fibres, which remain for some time after the rest of the leaf has fallen away, but at last drops off and leaves a circular scar upon the trunk. Their separate male and female simply branched flower-spikes hang down from amongst the leaves, and somewhat resemble very large horse's-tails. Both sexes have three overlapping sepals and three not overlapping petals; the males containing an indefinite number of stamens, and the females a three-celled ovary bearing three stigmas. Their fruit is a large roundish usually three-seeded berry, rather flat and somewhat three cornered at the top, and possessing an acrid flesh.

S. *saccharifer*, the Areng, is a very common palm in the Indian islands, and on account of the variety of its products is of great value to the natives. The black horsehair-like fibre surrounding its leaf-stalks, called Ejoo or Gomuti by the Malays, is converted into cordage, employed for thatching, plaited into ornaments, &c.; a large supply of toddy or palm-wine is obtained by cutting off the flower-spikes, and this when inspissated affords an abundance of sugar, or when fermented a capital vinegar: considerable quantities of sago, of a rather inferior quality, is also derived from this palm, and several other products of minor importance. [A. S.]

SAGUS. A considerable number of species have from time to time been placed under this generic name, but Dr. Von Martius, in his celebrated work on the *Palmaceæ*, refers them all to *Metroxylon* and *Raphia*. The name *Sagus*, however, is retained for the largest and most important of the two well-marked sections into which the genus is divided. These are distinguished from each other by the manner in which they develope their flower-spikes, and also by the structure of their seeds. Thus, in the section called *Pigafetta*, the spikes are produced from the sides of the stem, and the seeds are homogeneous; while in *Sagus* the spikes are terminal, and the seeds have internal dark-coloured markings like nutmegs. These differences in the mode of flowering, although not regarded as of sufficient importance to warrant the establishment of two genera, exercise an important influence upon the relative duration of the trees: those of the *Pigafetta* section being capable of producing a long succession of flower-spikes, and consequently of living to an old age, while those of the *Sagus* section can only produce one spike of flowers; the flowering season being to them the sure precursor of their dissolution, the tree gradually withering and dying after the solitary flower-spike has produced its crop of scaly-coated fruits.

The word *Sagus* is derived from *Sago* or *Sagu*, which in the language of the Papuan race signifies bread, and is given by them to the two palms, S. *lævis* and S. *Rumphii*, from which the well-known sago of the shops is obtained. The former of these, S. *lævis* (alias *Metroxylon lœve*), the Spineless Sago Palm, from which the greatest part of the sago exported to Europe is derived, grows from twenty-five to fifty feet high, and has a rather thick trunk marked with the scars left by fallen leaves, and usually invested towards the summit with the withered remains of leafstalks; above these the large pinnate smooth-stalked

rather erect leaves form a graceful crown, from out of the centre of which the alternately-branched pyramidal flower-spikes arise, their bases being enveloped by smooth sheaths. S. *Rumphii* (alias *Metroxylon Rumphii*), the Prickly Sago Palm, resembles the former in general appearance, but is usually a much smaller tree, and has its leaf-stalks and the sheaths enveloping the lower

Sagus RumphiL

part of the flower-spikes armed with sharp spines from half an inch to about an inch long. These trees produce their flower-spikes when about fifteen years old, and the fruit is nearly three years in ripening, after which they die. In order to procure the greatest quantity of sago, the trees must be cut down immediately the flower-spike makes its appearance.

The Sago of commerce is prepared from the soft inner portion of the trunks of these two species, which are sociable palms, growing together in large masses, principally in swampy places. It is obtained by cutting the trunks into pieces about two feet long, the pieces being then split in half, and the soft substance scooped out and pounded in water till the starchy matter separates, when it is drained off with the water, allowed to settle, and afterwards purified by washing. It is then in the form of sago-meal, but before being sent to this country it is made into what is termed pearl-sago. This is a Chinese process, and is carried on principally at Singapore. The rough meal is first repeatedly washed and strained, then spread out to dry and broken into small pieces, which, when sufficiently hard, are pounded and sifted until they are of regular size. Small quantities are then placed in a large cloth or bag suspended from the ceiling, and shaken backwards and forwards for about ten minutes, when it becomes granulated or pearled, and is thoroughly dried and packed for exportation. [A. S.]

SAHEBA. An Indian name for a worm-seed, the produce of *Artemisia judaica*.

SAINBOIS. (Fr.) *Daphne Mezereum.*

SAINFOIN. (Fr.) *Onobrychis sativa.* — D'ESPAGNE. *Hedysarum coronarium.* — DU CANADA. *Desmodium canadense.*

ST. AGNES' FLOWER. *Erinosma.*

● ST. ANDREW'S CROSS. *Ascyrum Crux Andrea.*

ST. CATHERINE'S FLOWER. *Nigella damascena.*

ST. CHRISTOPHER'S HERB. *Osmunda regalis.*

SAINTFOIN. A fodder-plant, *Onobrychis sativa.*

ST. JAMES'S-WORT. *Senecio Jacobæa.*

ST. JOHN'S BREAD. *Ceratonia Siliqua.*

ST. JOHN'S-WORT. *Hypericum*, especially *H. perforatum.* —, MARSH. *Elodea.*

ST. MARTIN'S HERB. *Sauvagesia erecta.*

ST. PETER'S-WORT. *Ascyrum*; also *Symphoria*; also *Hypericum Ascyron* and *H. quadrangulum.* The St. Peter's-wort of the old herbals is *Primula veris.*

ST. THOMAS' TREE. *Bauhinia tomentosa.*

SAIRANTHUS. *Nicotiana.*

SAJNA, SUJNA. Indian names for *Moringa pterygosperma.*

SAKA. A colonial name for the Bastard Purpleheart, a timber-tree of Demerara.

SAKACHERA. A Sanscrit name for Henné.

SAKES. The Turkish name for gum mastic.

SAKUR. An Indian name for the small astringent galls formed on some species of *Tamarix.*

SÂL. *Shorea robusta* : see SAUL.

SALACIA. This genus, along with *Hippocratea*, forms the family *Hippocrateaceæ*, which is nearly related to *Celastraceæ*, differing mainly in having three instead of five stamens to the flowers. *Hippocratea* has fruits consisting of three samaroid carpels, while *Salacia* has a berried fruit. About sixty species are known, distributed over the tropics, though most numerous in India and the Eastern islands. They are smooth erect or trailing evergreen shrubs, with opposite shining often laurel-like leaves, and in their axils clusters or cymes of minute green or yellowish flowers. India, Africa, and America have each at least one species bearing edible fruit. Thus in Brazil, *S. dulcis* bears a depressed globular fruit, the size of a crab-apple, yellowish in colour, sweet and juicy, and (according to Dr. Spruce) much eaten by the Indians on the Rio Negro, who call it Waiatuma. In India *S. Roxburghii* bears a like-sized dull red fruit whose white pulp is eaten ; and in Sierra Leone *S. pyriformis* affords a sweet-tasted fruit the size of a bergamot pear. The name *Salacia* is that of the wife of

Neptune, in mythology. Among other synonyms of this genus are *Tontelea* and *Diplesthes.*   [A. A. B.]

SALADE DE CHANOINE. (Fr.) *Valerianella olitoria.* — DE PORC. *Hypochæris radicata.*

SALADELLE. (Fr.) *Statice Limonium.*

SALAGIT, or SALARAS. Indian names for the bitter stalks of *Ophelia elegans*, often confounded with Chiretta.

SALAL. *Gaultheria Shallon.*

SALANQUET. (Fr.) *Chenopodium maritimum.*

SALAXIS. A genus of heathworts, having a four-cleft calyx, the anterior division largest ; the stamens varying from six to eight, their filaments free or joined, the anthers connate or approximate ; the ovary of two or three cells, each one-seeded, and never opening. The species are shrubs, natives of the Mauritius, having their leaves in whorls of three or six together, their edges rolled back ; and the flowers in clusters at the ends of the branches.   [G. D.]

SALEP. The fecula of the tubers of *Orchis mascula, O. latifolia, O. Morio*, and other ophreous orchids, consisting almost wholly of bassorin. The tubers are dried and preserved for use. —, KASHMIR. The fecula of the tubers of a species of *Eulophia.* —, TAHITI. The fecula of *Tacca pinnatifida.* —, NORTH AMERICAN. The fecula of a species of *Habenaria.*

SALICACEÆ. An order of apetalous dicotyledons, considered by some botanists as a tribe of *Amentaceæ*, and by others distinguished from the two other tribes or orders, *Corylaceæ* and *Betulaceæ*, by their diœcious flowers, the ovaries of the females one-celled, with several ovules on two parietal placentas. They are trees or shrubs with alternate leaves. The seeds, in two-valved capsules, have always a tuft of long white silky hairs. The order only contains the two genera *Salix* and *Populus.*

SALICAIRE. (Fr.) *Lythrum Salicaria.*

SALICARIA. *Lythrum Salicaria.*

SALICOR, or SALICORNE. (Fr.) *Salicornia.* ●

SALICORNIA. Succulent marine plants belonging to the order *Chenopodiaceæ*, and well distinguished by their jointed stems. The genus is represented in Britain by *S. herbacea*, common in salt-marshes, a leafless plant six to ten inches high, much-branched and jointed. —, 'The articulations are thickened upwards, shrinking much when dry, in which state the upper extremity of each articulation forms a two-lobed membranous socket or short sheath, which receives the base of the articulation above it. Spikes of flowers dense, lateral and terminal, jointed like the stem, and bearing at the base of every short articulation, on two opposite sides, a cluster of three flowers, each composed of a single perianth, apparently quite closed at the top and pierced, as it were, by the bifid or trifid stigma, and the single or two stamens—when two they appear in succession. The various species of this genus, as well as others belonging to the same family, and growing abundantly on the coasts in the South of Europe and North of Africa, yield a vast quantity of soda, much employed in making both soap and glass, whence comes the English name, Glasswort.'—*Hooker and Arnott*. Large quantities of the ashes of these and allied plants were formerly imported under the name of *barilla*; but since the introduction of Le Blanc's process for obtaining soda from common salt, the importance of barilla as an article of commerce has much diminished. French: *Salicorne*; German, *Glasschmelz*. [C. A. J.]

SALIERNE. (Fr.) A kind of olive.

SALIGOT. (Fr.) *Trapa natans*; also *Tribulus*.

SALINE, SALSUS. Growing in salt places; having a salt taste.

SALIQUIER. (Fr.) *Cuphea*.

SALISBURIA. This name commemorates the botanical services of Mr. R. A. Salisbury, and is applied to a genus of *Taxaceæ*. The Maidenhair tree, or Ginkgo,

Salisburia adiantifolia.

S. adiantifolia, is a large Japanese tree of much botanical interest, and of singular appearance. It attains a height of sixty to eighty feet, and has a straight trunk with a pyramidal head. The small leaf-bearing twigs are thick and tubercled, and bear a tuft of four or five closely-packed stalked leaves, surrounding a terminal scaly bud. The leaves are fan-shaped, deciduous, leathery, notched, and have numerous closely-set forking veins like those of ferns. The flowers are diœcious. The male catkins are thread-like, stalked, borne at the end of the branches; the anther has two divergent lobes, beyond which the connective is prolonged in the form of a crest. The female flowers are borne on axillary stalks, and consist of an ovule, embedded partially in a shallow fleshy cup formed by the dila-

tation of the end of the flower-stalk. When ripe the seed has an outer fleshy covering, and a thin woody stone surrounding the fleshy albumen.

This tree is largely cultivated in China and Japan, and also in this country, as an ornamental object. As the leaves decay, they assume a yellow tint. The venation is thought to indicate a slight degree of affinity to ferns. The fruits are resinous and astringent; the kernels are thought by the Japanese to promote digestion; an oil is extracted from them.   [M. T. M.]

SALISIA. A genus of *Myrtaceæ*, so named in compliment to the Countess de Salis, a lover of horticulture. *S. pulchella* is a pretty shrub, native of the Swan River colony, with broad leathery hairy leaves, and rose-coloured flowers, arranged in loose corymbs. The tube of the calyx is prolonged beyond the ovary, the limb five-toothed; the petals five, slightly stalked; the stamens numerous, longer than the petals; the ovary five-celled, the cells opening by a longitudinal cleft even in the flower-bud, and containing numerous ovules.   [M. T. M.]

SALIX. The Willows form an important family of trees and shrubs, giving name to the order *Salicaceæ*. Both willows and poplars are amentaceous, and have their seeds invested with cottony down; but they are sufficiently distinct not only in the outline of the leaves, but in the form of the scales or bracts of the catkin, which in the poplars are jagged at the extremity, and in the willows are entire.

The Willows constitute so extensive a family that a perfect Salicetum or willow-plantation, in which every known species was represented, would assume the dimensions of a small wood; and they are so difficult of discrimination, that not even the experienced botanist ventures to assign individuals to their several species unless he has an opportunity of examining them in their various stages of growth. British botanists are not agreed as to the number of species into which the native willows should be distributed, for while Bentham reckons only fifteen, Babington extends the list to fifty-eight.

The Willows are natives of the temperate regions of the Northern Hemisphere, and are much more numerous in the Old World than in the New. The majority grow by the sides of watercourses, but a few high up in the mountains, and one is found nearer to the North Pole than any other shrubby plant. As far as it is possible to include under a general description so extensive an array of species, they may be characterised as trees or shrubs, varying in height from a few inches to sixty feet. They grow rapidly, and for the most part shoot readily from cuttings. The wood is white; the bark of the trunk rather smooth than otherwise, that of the branches either downy or smooth, in the latter case sometimes to such a degree as to appear varnished. In most species it is stringy and tough, and in all is of a bitter taste, owing to the presence of *salicine*. The leaves are undivided, either notched at the edges or even, stalked, often furnished with stipules, smooth silky downy or even cottony, and varying in shape from linear to round—some modification of the ellipse being, however, by far the commonest form.

The wood is soft smooth and light, and is applied to a great variety of purposes, especially for building fast-sailing sloops of war, and for making cricket-bats. Split into thin strips it is manufactured into hats. The twigs have from the earliest antiquity been employed in basket-work, and in Pliny's time (as they are indeed at present in the northern countries of Europe) were twisted into ropes. The leaves of several species are on the Continent used as fodder for cattle, being collected in summer, and stacked for winter consumption. In Sweden and Norway the bark is kiln-dried in seasons of scarcity, and is mixed with oatmeal.

Among the willows most worthy of notice is the Huntingdon or White Willow, *S. alba*, so called from the silky whiteness of the underside of the leaf; it grows rapidly, attains a large size, and is one of the most useful of the family as a timber-tree. The Bedford Willow, *S. Russelliana*, also attains a large size; its leaves are in shape very like those of the white willow, but differ in being larger and smooth on both sides. The timber is even more useful than that of the last, and the bark contains more tannin than the oak; it is in this species also that salicine is most abundant. The Crack Willow, *S. fragilis*, derives its name from the brittleness of the branches, which start from the trunk under the slightest blow. *S. babylonica*, the Weeping Willow, grows wild on the banks of the Euphrates and in other parts of Asia, and also in North America. In China it is a favourite tree, as appears from its frequent occurrence in drawings of Chinese ornamental scenery. The Goat Willow, *S. Caprea* (the badge of the Cummings), is the common hedge-willow, marked by its purplish-brown branches, which are covered with minute down when young; and by its large broad leaves, which are wavy at the edge, and densely clothed beneath with soft white cottony down.

The species used for basket-making are usually called Osiers. Several kinds are in common cultivation, all agreeing in bearing long flexible tough shoots, and narrow pointed leaves. The species best adapted for wickerwork are *S. viminalis* and *S. triandra*. Large quantities of osiers are now imported from Holland. *S. pentandra*, common in the North of England and Ireland, is remarkable for its large glossy leaves, more like those of the Portugal laurel than of the other willows; the foliage of this shrub is fragrant. The little willow which in some districts is so abundant on commons, trailing its wiry branches along the ground, is *S. fusca*. *S. herbacea*, the least of British trees, rarely exceeds the height of four inches. It is a native of many parts of Europe and North America, and in Great Britain is the last plant furnished with a woody stem which we meet with in ascending the mountains. French: *Saule*; German: *Weide*. [C. A. J.]

The medicinal properties of the Willow are common to all the species in greater or less degree. The bark is the part usually employed, especially that of *S. Russelliana*, *S. alba*, *S. Caprea*, and *S. fragilis*. It is valued for its tonic and astringent properties, and is used for the same purposes as cinchona-bark. The active properties depend upon the presence of an alkaloid called *salicine*, which is employed in ague, &c. in place of quinine. In case of a scarcity of the latter drug salicine might advantageously be used as a substitute, though it is scarcely so potent. *S. pentandra*, in addition to the bitter tonic principle, has slight aromatic properties. The sweet-scented male catkins of *S. ægyptiaca* are used in the preparation of Kalaf, a liquid which is used in the East as a stimulant and carminative. *S. chilensis* is said to furnish a kind of manna in Chili. A decoction of the roots of *S. nigra*, a North American species, is considered as purgative and febrifugal. [M. T. M.]

SALLOW. A name for *Salix cinerea*, *S. Caprea*, and the allied species, which are not flexible like the osier, but furnish the best charcoal for gunpowder. *S. Caprea* is called the Great Sallow.

SALMALIA. A genus of *Sterculiaceæ*, the two species of which were formerly included in *Bombax*, from which they are distinguished by their bell-shaped calyx being divided into three or five unequal blunt lobes; by their egg-shaped more erect petals; by the tube of the stamens being inflated or bulged out, and composed of numerous filaments in several series—the filaments being either simple or two-forked at the top, and the outer ones bearing one and the inner two anthers; and by the stigma being divided into five sharp-pointed spreading lobes. Both species are large trees, natives of tropical Asia, and have large hand-shaped leaves composed of from five to nine leaflets, and large red flowers either solitary or several together on the naked branches. Their fruits resemble those of *Bombax*, and are filled with seeds enveloped in silky cotton.

S. malabarica (alias *Bombax malabarica*), the Simool-tree of India, or Malabar Silk-cotton tree, attains a height of seventy or eighty feet, and has a prickly trunk and branches, leaves composed of five to seven leaflets, and clusters of flowers. The silk-cotton of the Simool, though very beautiful, is, like other silk-cottons, not adapted for spinning. It is chiefly used for stuffing cushions, and a kind of quilt or thick cloth is manufactured from it in Assam. The trunk yields a very pure gum and light porous wood, and its bark possesses emetic properties. *S. insigne* is distinguished from the last by its trunk and branches being unarmed, by its leaves being composed of nine leaflets, and by its solitary flowers. It is a native of Burmah. [A. S.]

SALMEA. A genus of trailing somewhat shrubby *Compositæ* peculiar to tropical America, and occurring most commonly in the West Indies. The stems are furnished with opposite stalked leaves, having ovate lance-shaped or heart-shaped blades; and the rayless somewhat pear-shaped white or yellow flower-heads are arranged in corymbs at the ends of the twigs. The florets are all tubular and perfect, with the involucral scales in two series, the receptacle conical and chaffy, and the vertically compressed achenes crowned with a pappus of two awns. These plants are related to *Bidens*, from which their shrubby habit at once distinguishes them, but more especially to *Verbesina*, of which again the habit is different, and the style-branches are blunt instead of cone-shaped at the apex. [A. A. D.]

SALOMONIA. Under this name are comprised about eight species of minute annual plants of the *Polygaleæ*, found in various parts of tropical Asia. In their habit and the appearance of their flowers they resemble *Polygalas*, but have four or five instead of eight stamens to the flowers. Four of the species are little branching plants one to four inches high, the stems furnished with ovate roundish or oblong entire leaves, and the minute white or lilac flowers arranged in spikes at the ends of the branchlets. The remaining four are leafless and parasitical on roots, whence they are separated as a distinct genus by Blume, with the name *Epirhizanthus*. The place of the leaves is supplied by minute brown scales. [A. A. B.]

SALOOP. The name given to sassafras-ten, flavoured with milk and sugar, sold to the working-classes in the early morning at the corners of London streets.

SALPIANTHUS. A seacoast plant from the western shores of tropical America, proposed by Kunth as a genus of *Nyctaginaceæ*, but which had been previously published by Lagasca under the name of *Boldoa.*

SALPICHLÆNA. A small group of polypodiaceous ferns nearly related to *Blechnum*, from which it differs chiefly in its scandent habit, and in having the parallel venules combined at the apex by a slight intramarginal veinlet. The only known species is *S. volubilis.* [T. M.]

SALPICHROA or SALPICHROMA. A genus of *Atropaceæ*, comprising Peruvian herbs heretofore included in *Atropa*, but distinguished from it in that the calyx does not increase in size as the fruit ripens, and is moreover divided into five linear erect segments. The corolla is narrow tubular fleshy, often contracted at the mouth, and becomes black in drying. The fruit when ripe is of a bright scarlet colour. The name is derived from the Greek words *salpinx* 'a tube,' and *chroma*

'colour,' in allusion to the colour of the trumpet-shaped flowers. [M. T. M.]

SALPIGLOSSIS. A genus of *Atropaceæ*, consisting of herbaceous viscid plants, natives of Chili. The leaves are pinnately lobed, and the flowers in terminal panicles. The calyx is bell-shaped, five-parted: the corolla funnel-shaped, its tube dilated above, its limb five-cleft spreading; the stamens five, four fertile, didynamous, with two-celled anthers opening by a single pore; the style thickened at the extremity with a somewhat two-lobed stigma; the fruit a two-celled two-valved capsule with numerous seeds. The flowers are showy, often with the veins coloured differently from the rest of the petal. Some of the species are cultivated as greenhouse plants, or as bedding plants in summer. The generic name is derived from the Greek words *salpinx* 'a tube' and *glossis* 'a tongue,' in allusion to the tongue-like style in the mouth of the corolla. [M. T. M.]

SALPIGOPHORA. *Campsidium.*

SALPINGA. A genus of one or two South American herbaceous melastomaceous plants allied to *Bertolonia*, but distinguished by the anthers having a tail-like appendage at their base, sometimes as long as the anther itself, and also by the three-sided capsules being invested with the eight or ten-nerved persistent calyx. The flowers are borne in a double scorpioid raceme. [A. S.]

SALPIXANTHA. A genus of *Acanthaceæ* containing a single species from Jamaica, now generally referred to *Geissomeria*, from which it differs only in the calyx being less deeply cut, and in the limb of the corolla being regular. [W. C.]

SALSA. An abbreviation for Sarsaparilla.

SALSAFY, or SALSIFY. *Tragopogon porrifolius.*

SALSEPARIELLE. (Fr.) *Smilax.* — D'ALLEMAGNE. *Carex arenaria.* — D'EUROPE. *Smilax aspera.*

SALSIFIS. (Fr.) *Tragopogon.* — D'ESPAGNE. *Scorzonera.*

SALSOLA. The Saltworts form a rather extensive genus of *Chenopodiaceæ*, and are most abundant in the temperate and warm regions of the Northern Hemisphere, principally in the Old World; occurring in the Southern Hemisphere only in Timor, Eastern Australia, New Zealand, Madagascar, and Chili. They are always confined to the seacoast or to salt-marshes, or other places where the soil is impregnated with salt: their generic name being thence derived from the Latin words *sal* 'salt,'and *solum* 'soil.' They are herbaceous or somewhat shrubby smooth or downy plants, with unjointed stems, and usually alternate but occasionally opposite stalkless more or less cylindrical fleshy or prickly leaves, bearing the small stalkless perfect flowers in their axils, together with two floral bracts resembling the leaves. Their fruit, called an utricle, has a loose thin shell, and contains a horizontal single-coated seed.

S. Kali, the Prickly Saltwort, is a common seashore plant in most European and many other countries. It is a brittle succulent annual of a pale bluish-green hue, with somewhat angular furrowed and striped bristly stems, very much branched, and spreading in all directions so as to form a bush from a foot to a foot and a half high; and has numerous awl-shaped nearly cylindrical spiny-pointed leaves, with broadened bases furnished with little prickles. *S. Soda,* a South European and North African species, is a succulent annual from one to two feet high, but not brittle like the last; and has smooth shining stems and somewhat flexuose branches, with soft nearly cylindrical short-pointed leaves of a bluish-green colour.

An impure carbonate of soda obtained from the ashes of these and several allied and other plants, known under the Spanish name *barilla,* was formerly an article of considerable commercial importance; and large quantities of it were annually imported into the United Kingdom from the Canary Islands, Spain, and other parts of the South of Europe, and employed in soap and glass-making; but since the introduction of soda manufactured from common salt as a commercial article, the imports have greatly decreased, though about a thousand tons of barilla and other alkalies are still annually imported, mostly from the Canary Islands and the Two Sicilies. For the preparation of barilla these plants are dried in heaps like hay, and afterwards burnt upon a rude grating constructed over a large hole, into which the semifluid alkaline matter flows, and is there left to cool and solidify. *Kali* is the Arabic name for the ashes of these soda-plants, and the term *alkali,* applied by chemists to soda, potassa, and similar substances, is derived either from *kali,* with the Arabic article *al* prefixed, or from a corruption of *sal* (salt) and *kali.*   .[A. S.]

SALSUGINOSE. Growing in places inundated with saltwater.

SALT-BUSH. The Australian *Atriplex nummularia.*

SALTIA. A genus of *Amaranthaceæ* from Arabia, consisting of a branched undershrub, with alternate leaves, and axillary and terminal spikes of bracteated flowers in threes—the central one perfect, the lateral sterile, and at length growing out into straight awns clothed with feathery wool. The perfect flowers have five hairy sepals, five stamens united at the base into a cup, with two-celled anthers and no staminodes; and the utricle is oblong with a vertical seed.   [J. T. S.]

SALT-TREE. *Halimodendron argenteum.*

SALTWORT. *Salicornia annua;* also *Salsola.* —, BLACK. *Glaux maritima.*

SALVADORACEÆ. A small order of monopetalous dicotyledons allied to *Oleaceæ* and *Jasminaceæ.* Like the former they are small trees or shrubs, with opposite entire leaves, and small paniculate flowers with a minute four-cleft calyx, and a four-cleft corolla; but there are four stamens, the ovary is one-celled with a single erect ovule and a sessile simple stigma, and the seed, as in *Jasminaceæ,* is erect without albumen. Only two genera, *Salvadora* and *Monetia,* have as yet been positively referred to the order.

SALVADORA. An unusual amount of interest is attached to this genus, on account of one of the species belonging to it being supposed to be the Mustard-tree of Scripture. It is the typical species of *Salvadoraceæ,* and was at one time the only genus referred to that order. The five described species are shrubs or small trees, and have a geographical range extending from Central Africa, Abyssinia, and Egypt through South-western Asia to India and Ceylon. They have stems with slightly swollen joints, opposite entire leathery leaves with scarcely any visible veins, and loose branching panicles of small flowers, which have a very minute four-leaved calyx, a thin four-parted corolla, with four stamens inserted between the lobes and connecting them together, and a one-celled ovary bearing an undivided stalkless stigma. Their little berry-like fruits contain solitary erect seeds.

The identification of the plants mentioned in the Bible is a task of great difficulty, and in almost all instances the result of the most learned investigations, whether by Biblical commentators or by botanists, is unsatisfactory and open to doubt. In our English version of the Bible the names of plants have been made to agree with those now in use, and the obvious inference among the unlearned is that the plants are the same. The researches of botanists, however, have shown that the tares, the aloes, the hyssop, and other Scriptural plants differ widely from those so called at the present day; and some writers have therefore thought it probable that the same is the case with the Mustard spoken of in the Gospels, the seed of which St. Matthew says 'is the least of all seeds; but when it is grown it is the greatest among herbs, and becometh a tree, so that the birds of the air come and lodge in the branches thereof.' (xiii. 82.) It is obvious that this description does not agree with the common mustard (*Sinapis*) as seen in this country, and consequently the assertion that the Scriptural plant belonged to a totally different genus has been readily believed. During their travels in the Holy Land, Captains Irby and Mangles met with a small tree (ascertained by Professor Don to be a *Salvadora*) with a small pungent mustard-like fruit, and they thought it might probably be the tree referred to by Christ. This supposition was afterwards strengthened by Dr. Royle, who found that the tree in question bore the same Arabic name (*Khardal*) as the common mustard, and that it was commonly regarded in Syria as the Mustard-tree of Scripture; though it is to be observed that the *Sinapis* grows to a much greater size in Syria than with us, and is frequently seen as high as twelve or fifteen feet, so that birds might easily lodge in its branches. The species of *Salvadora* growing in Syria is said by both Don and Royle

Salvadora indica.

to be *S. persica*, but that is a plant of small size, not a tree. *S. indica* however, a common Indian and Cingalese species, grows to a considerable height, and is probably the one meant. [A. S.]

SALVER-SHAPED. The same as Hypocrateriform, or Hypocraterimorphous.

SALVERTIA. A small genus of *Vochyaceæ* confined to Brazil. They are trees, with ovate leaves arranged in whorls, and white paniculate flowers, emitting a most delightful scent—in *S. convallariodora* resembling that of our lily of the valley. The calyx is five-lobed, one of the lobes being shaped into a spur, whilst two of the five petals are smaller than the rest. The ovary is free; and the capsule three-valved, triangular, and three-celled, each cell containing one seed. [B. S.]

SALVIA. A genus of *Labiatæ*, distinguished by its lipped calyx, and two forked stamens. The species are undershrubs or herbs, varying in general habit, and widely distributed over the earth. The name is from the Latin *salvo* 'I heal,' indicative of the supposed qualities of some of the species. Examples of this genus have been long and favourably known as objects of culture, and deservedly occupy a prominent place. It is only necessary to allude briefly to some of them. *S. splendens* is of interest on account of its period of flowering; *S. hians*, a native of Simla, is hardy, and also desirable on account of its showy violet-and-white flowers; *S. candelabrum* is a hardy perennial, a native of the South of Spain, the upper lip of its

flower greenish-yellow, the lower a rich violet, thus presenting a fine contrast; *S. pratensis* is a well-known ingredient of the hay-crop in some parts of Italy and the Ionian Islands, its blue flowers rendering it a great ornament in the meadows; *S. lyrata* and *S. urticifolia* are equally well known in North America. *S. officinalis* is the Common Sage, a familiar garden herb having aromatic and bitter properties. [G. D.]

SALVINIA. A genus of *Marsileaceæ* belonging to the same section as *Azolla*, and by some considered as a distinct natural order, *Salviniaceæ*. It has a floating thread-like rhizome containing a central bundle of vessels with several cavities around it, furnished above with fern-like subelliptic floating entire leaves, and below with long rootlets and fluted bladder-like fruit on short leafless branches. The fruit consists of globular bags composed of a double membrane, at length bursting irregularly. These bags are of two kinds: the one containing spherical antheridia upon branched stalks springing from a central placenta; the other short-stalked single-spored sporangia, seated like the former on a central column. The leaves are not curled up when young, and the upper surface is studded with warts, each of which bear a little crown of bristles. There is sometimes a central rib in the leaves, besides which there are reticulated veins more prominent below than above. The spermatozoids, according to Hofmeister, are furnished with a series of lash-like cilia, and the spores germinate by cell-division at their upper extremity, two or three archegonia being formed in the substance of the prothallus of which one only proves fertile. The young plant closely resembles that of *Selaginella*, apart from the two cotyledon-like processes. All the supposed species are reducible to one, which occurs in the South of Europe in stagnant pools, and is found in all the warmer parts of the world. [M. J. B.]

SALWOOD. *Shorea robusta.*

SALZMANNIA. The name of a Brazilian shrub, forming a genus of *Cinchonaceæ*. The leaves are smooth and shining; and the flowers are borne in axillary heads. The limb of the calyx is cup-shaped, slightly four-toothed; the tube of the corolla short, its limb divided into four oblong lobes; the stamens four; and the fruit dry, one-celled one-seeded, surmounted by the limb of the calyx. This genus is imperfectly known. [M. T. M.]

SAMA. The acrid Abyssinian *Urtica simensis*, which is, however, cooked as a vegetable.

SAMADERA. A genus of trees of the *Simarubaceæ*, natives of tropical Asia and Madagascar. The leaves are entire, and the flowers large pinkish, disposed in axillary umbels, surrounded by involucres of small bracts. The calyx is four-parted, its segments frequently provided externally with two glands at the base; petals four, much longer than the sepals; stamens eight, filaments attached below to a hairy scale; ovaries four or five on a short stalk, each one-celled, one-seeded; styles separate below, above confluent, longer than the petals. *S. indica*, a native of Travancore and Malabar, yields a bark which is employed as a febrifuge. From the seeds is procured an oil used in rheumatic affections. The bruised leaves are likewise employed in erysipelas.   [M. T. M.]

SAMANKA DES INDIENS, (Fr.) *Citrullus vulgaris*.

SAMARA. A genus of *Myrsinaceæ*, distinguished in the order by the petals being free and distinct as in *Embelia*, with the stamens inserted at their base, but always in fours, not in fives as in that genus; and by the stamens being always longer than the petals. The habit is also different. There are very few species, natives of Eastern Africa and tropical Asia, extending to Southern China. They are shrubs, often half-trailing, with entire evergreen leaves, and small flowers in very short axillary racemes.

SAMARA. An indehiscent fruit, producing a membranous expansion or wing, from its back or end.

SAMARIA-WOOD. *Icica altissima.*

SAMAROID. Resembling a Samara.

SAMBO. *Cleome.*

SAMBUCUS. A genus of small trees shrubs or more rarely herbs, belonging to the *Caprifoliaceæ*. The characters are: Corolla with a very short tube; berry three to four-seeded; leaves pinnate. *S. nigra*, the Common Elder, is a well-known tree of rapid growth when young, remarkable for the stoutness of its shoots, which when a year old are as large as those of many other trees at two or three years of age. They are covered with a smooth grey bark, and contain an unusual proportion of pith, which being easily removed, the branches may readily be formed into tubes, and on this account the Elder was formerly called Bore-tree. The wood is white and of a fine close grain, tough, fissile, and easily cut—hence it is used for making skewers and shoemakers' pegs. The leaves have an unpleasant odour when bruised, which is supposed to be offensive to most insects, and a decoction of them is sometimes employed by gardeners to keep off caterpillars from delicate plants. By village herbalists they are employed in making a kind of ointment, and the flowers serve for fomentations, or are made into a medicinal tea; while the berries are the principal ingredient in 'elderberry wine.' These are generally-purplish-black, but a variety occurs with berries of a greenish-white hue. *S. Ebulus*, or Danewort, is an herbaceous plant found in many parts of Britain as well as the Continent; it has a nauseous smell, and drastic properties. *S. racemosa*, a native of Central and Southern Europe, is a shrub which towards the end of summer is high-ly ornamental, with large oval clusters of bright scarlet berries. French: *Sureau*; German: *Hohlunder*.   [C. A. J.]

Evelyn says, speaking of the Common Elder:—' If the medicinal properties of the leaves, bark, berries, &c. were thoroughly known, I cannot tell what our countrymen could ail for which he might not fetch a remedy from every hedge, either for sickness or wound.' Aubray tells us that 'the apothecaries well know the use of the berries, and so do the vintners, who buy vast quantities of them in London, and some do make no inconsiderable profit by the sale of them.'

The Danewort, *S. Ebulus*, has purple flowers, but the berries are so much like those of the common elder as to be occasionally used for the same purposes. In accounting for its English name, Sir J. E. Smith says: 'Our ancestors evinced a just hatred of their brutal enemies the Danes, in supposing the nauseous, fetid, and noxious plant before us to have sprung from their blood.' But we cannot help thinking that both kinds of Elder were not only used medicinally, but were also held in great superstitious reverence. Mr. Jones, in his *Notes on Certain Superstitions in the Vale of Gloucester*, cites the following, which by the way is no unusual case: ' Some men were employed in removing an old hedgerow, partially formed of elder-trees. They had bound up all the other wood into faggots for burning, but had set apart the elder, and enquired of their master how it was to be disposed of. Upon his saying that he should of course burn it with the rest, and ordering it to be faggoted, one of the men said, with an air of undisguised alarm, that he never *heard* of such a thing as burning *Ellan Wood*; and, in fact, so strongly did he feel upon the subject, that he refused to participate in the act of tying it up.' The word Ellan (still common with us) indicates the origin of the superstition. In Low Saxon the *Sambucus nigra* is called *Ellhorn*. Arnkiel unsuspectingly relates, ' Our forefathers also held the Ellhorn holy, wherefore whoever need to hew it down (or cut its branches) has first to make request, " Lady Ellhorn, give me some of thy wood, and I will give thee some of mine when it grows in the forest,"—she which with partly bended knees, bare head, and folded arms was ordinarily done, as I myself have often seen and heard in my younger years.'

There exist many superstitions respecting elder-wands, elder-trees before stables, the shedding of water under them, and the elder-mother, a Danish superstition. The attributed curative effects of elder are well known. Its flowers are an eyewash and cosmetic, and its bark and leaves are used for various purposes, but the most curious use is that which has been recorded by Mr. Jones on the authority of Lord Ducie:—' A small piece cut from a young shoot just above and below a joint, so as to leave the bud projecting at each end of it after the fashion of a rude cross, borne constantly about the person, is a most certain and effectual cure for rheumatism. It appears, however, that the Elder to be thus efficient must grow in consecrated ground. In Tortworth churchyard (and others in the county of Gloucester) is such

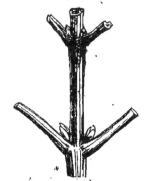

Cross of Elder-wood.

a tree, and we are told that application is frequently made for bits of it from a considerable distance, and that some of its recipients are not only willing but able to give it a good character of 'many years' standing.' We give a cut of a piece of elder of the orthodox form. [J. B.]

SAMOLUS. Small marsh plants with white flowers, possessing no attractive properties, belonging to the *Primulaceæ*, and distinguished by the half-superior capsule, and by five imperfect stamens alternating with the lobes of the corolla. *S. Valerandi*, the Brookweed or Water Pimpernel, is an erect plant eight to ten inches high, with bright green somewhat fleshy leaves, and terminal inconspicuous flowers. It is remarkable only for its wide geographical range, there being scarcely any country in which it does not abound where the soil is wet and gravelly. In Great Britain it is most frequent where small streams trickle over rocks on the seashore. *S. littoralis*, a native of Van Diemen's Land, is very similar in habit. French: *Samole*; German: *Samoskraut.* [C. A J.]

SAMP. A preparation of Indian corn largely used in the United States.

SAMPHIRE. *Crithmum maritimum*, the aromatic saline fleshy leaves of which are used in pickles; also *Borrichia arborescens.* —, GOLDEN. *Inula crithmoides.* —, JAMAICA. *Batis maritima.*

SAMSHOO. A spirituous liquor extracted, by fermentation and distillation, from rice, by the Chinese.

SAMYDACEÆ. An order of dicotyledons consisting of tropical trees or shrubs, with alternate leaves generally marked with pellucid dots; and hermaphrodite flowers, usually small in axillary clusters. The perianth is calyx-like, usually four or five-

lobed, without petals; the stamens are perigynous, often more numerous than the calyx-lobes, but in a single row alternating with small teeth or filaments without anthers; and the ovary is one-celled, with two three or more parietal placentas. The order contains one large genus, *Casearia*, and about half-a-dozen small ones allied to it. Some botanists unite with it *Homaliaceæ*, which have petals and a somewhat different arrangement of stamens, while others combine the whole with *Flacourtiaceæ.*

SAMYDA. The type of the *Samydaceæ*, and composed of shrubs or small trees inhabiting tropical America. The branches are often clad with thorns; and the leaves are more or less ovate serrate, and furnished with pellucid dots. The flowers are solitary or fasciculate in the axils of the leaves, and they are white or in some species purplish. The calyx is five-cleft; the corolla entirely wanting; the stamens are fertile (or, as Mr. Bentham expresses it, there are no staminodia or scales intermixed with the stamens), by which latter character *Samyda* is easily distinguished from its allies. *S. suaveolens*, an inhabitant of Brazilian forests, is remarkable for its white deliciously-scented flowers, strongly recalling to mind the odour of orange-blossoms. [B. S.]

SANA. A kind of Peruvian Tobacco.

SANDAL-TREE. *Sandoricum.*

SANDALWOOD. An odoriferous wood the produce of several species of *Santalum.* That of India is the *S. album*; that of the Sandwich Islands *S. Freycinetianum* and *S. paniculatum*; and that of Western Australia, *S. latifolium.* The name is given among the Russians to the red wood of *Rhamnus dahuricus*, used for dyeing leather. —, CITRON. *Santalum Freycinetianum.* —, QUEENSLAND. *Eremophila Mitchelli.* —, RED. *Adenanthera pavonina*; also *Pterocarpus Santalinus.* —, WHITE. *Santalum album.* —, YELLOW. *Santalum Freycinetianum.*

SANDALWORTS. Lindley's name for the *Santalaceæ.*

SANDARACH. A white resin not unlike mastic, but brittle, occurring in round or long tears, and obtained from *Callitris quadrivalvis.*

SANDBOX-TREE. A local West Indian name for *Hura crepitans*, the seeds of which are a drastic purgative, and contain a very limpid oil.

SANDERS-WOOD. An old name for Sandalwood. —, RED. The red Indian dyewood, obtained from *Pterocarpus Santalinus.* —, YELLOW. *Bucida capitata.*

SANDORICUM *indicum* is the sole representative of a genus of *Meliaceæ*, found in the Philippine Islands, the Moluccas, and the East Indies, and having an arboreous stem, trifoliolate leaves, axillary paniculate flowers, a short five-toothed calyx, five linear petals, ten stamens combined into a tube, a stigma divided into five lobes, and an apple-like berry containing five one-seeded nuts. Properties similar to those of *Melia* are attributed to the root, but the latter has a repulsive odour, whilst *Sandoricum* is aromatic: it is employed against leucorrhœa, combined with the bark of the root of *Carapa obovata*, which is bitter and astringent. [B. S.]

SANDPAPER-TREE. *Curatella americana.*

SANDWEED. *Arenaria.*

SANDWOOD. *Bremontiera Ammoxylon.*

SANDWORT. *Arenaria.* —, SEA. A common name for *Honkenya.* —, SPURREY. *Spergularia.*

SANFORDIA. A genus proposed by J. Drummond for a rutaceous shrub from Western Australia, allied to *Correa.* It has proved to be the same as *Geleznovia* previously published by Turczaninow.

SANG-DE-DRAGON. (Fr.) *Dracæna Draco*; also *Rumex sanguineus.*

SANGSORBE. (Fr.) *Sanguisorba,*

SANGUINAIRE. (Fr.) *Geranium sanguineum.* — D'ALLEMAGNE. *Scleranthus.*

SANGUINARIA. The Blood-root or Puccoon, *S. canadensis,* commonly found throughout the United States and Canada, is the sole representative of this genus of *Papaveraceæ.* It is an herbaceous plant about six inches high, and has a thick branching rootstock, which creeps along underground; and in early spring sends up from the ends of each of the little side-branches a single long-stalked leaf, and another stalk bearing a solitary flower. The leaf is wrapped round the flower-bud when it rises out of the ground, and is bluntly five to nine-lobed, roundish at first, but afterwards kidney-shaped. The flowers are large and conspicuous, and have two sepals, from eight to twelve white petals overlapping in two or three series, about twenty-four stamens with filaments shorter than the petals, and a short style with a broad two-lobed furrowed stigma. The fruit is an oblong pod-shaped two-valved capsule, containing numerous crested seeds attached to the frame or replum. The root has long been known to possess active medicinal properties, and various preparations of it are commonly prescribed by American doctors; but it has only recently come into use in this country, and that chiefly among the class of practitioners styling themselves 'eclectics.' Its principal use appears to be as an expectorant in diseases of the chest, or, in larger doses, as an emetic: and it would seem to owe its properties to the presence of an acrid alkaloid called *sanguinarina.* The American Indians formerly used the orange-coloured juice of the root for smearing their bodies, and for staining various domestic articles. The plant has also been successfully employed by American and French dyers. [A. S.]

SANGUINARY. *Achillea millefolium.*

SANGUINE, SANGUINEUS. Dull red passing into brownish-black.

SANGUINIÈRE. (Fr.) *Sanguinaria.*

SANGUISORBACEÆ. A small order which most botanists consider as a tribe of *Rosaceæ,* distinguished from *Roseæ* proper by the want of petals, and the solitary carpels. See ROSACEÆ.

SANGUISORBA. A genus of herbaceous plants giving name to the tribe *Sanguisorbeæ* of the order *Rosaceæ.* The genus is characterised by bearing its flowers, which contain both stamens and pistils, in heads or simple spikes; by the calyx of each flower being four-cleft, with two to three small bracts at its base; by the absence of petals, and by the presence of four stamens. *S. officinalis,* or Burnet, received its name from its supposed vulnerary properties. It is a slender plant one to three feet high, with pinnate smooth leaves, and terminal ovate heads of crowded dark-purple flowers. It grows in moist pastures and by watercourses, chiefly on a calcareous or magnesian soil, and is most frequent in the North of England and the extreme West. There are several other species, some of which are occasionally to be seen in gardens, especially *S. canadensis,* which in habit resembles the Common Burnet, but bears its flowers, rendered conspicuous by their white anthers, in long cylindrical spikes. French: *La grande pimprenelle des prés*; German: *Wiesenknopf.* [C. A. J.]

SANICLE. *Sanicula.* —, BEAR'S-EAR. *Cortusa Matthioli.* —, COMMON. *Sanicula europæa.*

SANICLE. (Fr.) *Sanicula*; also *Prunella.* — BÂTARDE D'AMÉRIQUE. *Mitella.* — FEMELLE. *Astrantia,* — DE MONTAGNE. *Geum.*

SANICULA. A small genus of umbelliferous plants represented in Britain by *S. europæa,* the Wood Sanicle, an herbaceous plant two to three feet high, frequent in thickets and woods. The root-leaves are palmate, with three-cleft serrated lobes, smooth and somewhat glossy; the minute whitish flowers grow in heads rather than umbels; the fruit is ovate and densely clothed with thick prickles, by means of which they attach themselves when ripe to the hair or wool of animals, and to the clothes of persons passing through woods where the plant is abundant. French: *Sanicle*; German: *Sanickel.* [C. A. J.]

SANSEVIELLA. A name formerly applied to the plant now called *Reineckia carnea,* the *Sansevieria carnea* of some writers.

SANSEVIERA. The Bowstring Hemps, —as the plants belonging to this genus of *Liliaceæ* are called, from the fibres of their leaves being used for bowstrings by the natives of the countries where they are indigenous—are stemless perennial plants, throwing out runners, and having only root-leaves which are thick fibrous and fleshy, and usually sword or lance-shaped with sheathing bases, either in two opposite rows or tufted; their simple flower-spikes rising from the centre, and bearing the whitish or yellowish-green flowers in clusters along them. In its technical characters the genus is very closely allied to *Dracæna*, the flowers differing only in the combined calyx and corolla not being divided further than the middle, and in the long slender erect style being terminated by an undivided round-headed stigma.

S. guineensis, the African Bowstring Hemp, has lance-shaped leaves from one to four feet long and three to four inches wide, flat in the middle, narrower and channelled or rolled in towards the base, and terminated upwards in a short blunt point; when young they are marked with pale-coloured cross-bands, but ultimately assume an uniform shining green.

S. Roxburghiana, the Moorva or Marool of the Indian peninsula, has leaves about the same length as the last, but very much narrower, and concave or channelled along the whole upper surface and convex or keeled below, somewhat approaching a cylindrical form, and terminated by a tapering spine-like point; they are also of a duller green, marked with alternate paler wavy cross-bands. The fibre of the Moorva is very strong and of fine quality, and is suitable for the manufacture of fine string and cordage. This latter plant is frequently confounded with *S. zeylanica*, a much smaller species. [A. S.]

SANTALACEÆ. (*Osyridaceæ*, *Sandalworts*). An order of apetalous dicotyledons, consisting of trees or more frequently shrubs or herbs, often parasitical on roots, with alternate or rarely opposite entire leaves without stipules, the flowers usually small and green in terminal or lateral heads cymes or spikes. The order is well characterised by the stamens being as many as and opposite to the lobes of the perianth; by the inferior one-celled ovary with three to five ovules, suspended from a free central placenta; by the indehiscent fruit with a single seed, and by the straight embryo in a fleshy albumen. The species are dispersed over the tropical and temperate regions of the globe, but are more abundant in the Old World than in America; they are distributed into about twenty genera of which the most important are *Quinchamalium*, *Pyrularia*, *Osyris*, *Thesium*, *Leptomeria*, and *Santalum*, to which some botanists add *Henslowia* and *Exocarpus*.

SANTALIN. The principle of the colouring-matter in *Pterocarpus Santalinus*.

SANTALUM. A genus of sandalworts, distinguished by having a superior calyx, which is four-cleft, furnished with four glands alternating with its divisions, and four stamens opposite to them. The species are trees or shrubs, natives of Asia, Australia, and the Pacific Isles. *S. album* yields the Sandalwood of India; that of the Sandwich Islands is derived from *S.*

Freycinetianum and *S. paniculatum*. The name of the genus is derived from the Persian. [G. D.]

SANTA-MARIA TREE. *Calophyllum Calaba*.

SANTOLINA. A genus of small twiggy undershrubs of the *Compositæ*, peculiar to the Mediterranean region. They have much in common with *Achillea*, from which they are distinguished by their quadrangular achenes being neither winged nor margined, as well as by the lower portion of their compressed corolla-tubes being prolonged into a sort of hood, enveloping the summit of the ovary. The common Lavender Cotton, *S. Chamæcyparissus*, is one of the widest-spread species, and has long been known in gardens, where it may be frequently met with planted along the margins of shrubbery borders. It is a neat erect branching bush one to two feet high, the stems and leaves clothed with a hoary pubescence. The small linear leaves, thickly set on the wiry twigs, are furnished with four to six rows of short obtuse teeth; and the yellow flower-heads, which resemble those of a chamomile divested of its white rays, are solitary, and stalked at the ends of the twigs. This plant was once esteemed for its vermifuge and stimulant properties, and the twigs have been used for placing in wardrobes to keep moths from clothes, as well as for their strong rather agreeable odour, which is common to all the species.

All the species have a strong resemblance to the foregoing, with the exception of *S. fragrantissima*, which differs in having the flower-heads in corymbs instead of singly at the apex of the twigs, which are furnished with ovate crenelled leaves. According to Forskal the Arabs use the juice of this plant for bathing the eyes. [A. A. B.]

SANTONINE. The vermifuge principle of the Semen Contra, a medicinal substance obtained from the flower-heads of some of the *Artemisias*, and a most powerful anthelmintic.

SANVITALIA. A genus of *Compositæ*, distinguished by the paleaceous receptacle of its flower-heads; by the achenes of the ray having three awns, those of the outer portions of the disk muricated, of the inner winged; and by the involucral scales being flat and imbricated in two or three series. *S. procumbens* is a common annual plant from Mexico, with a procumbent habit, ovate entire leaves, and flower-heads like those of a *Rudbeckia*, with a yellow ray and dark disk. [T. M.]

SANWUCK. An Indian name for *Panicum frumentaceum*.

SAOUARI or SOUARI-WOOD. An excellent timber for shipbuilding and other purposes, resembling Mora in its properties. It is obtained from *Caryocar nuciferum* and *C. tomentosum*, which yield also the delicious Souari-nuts.

SAP. The juice of a plant.

SAPALLO. A Spanish name for *Cucurbita Melopepo.*

SAPANWOOD. A dyewood obtained in Malabar and the islands of the Eastern seas, from *Cæsalpinia Sappan, C. coriaria,* and *C. pulcherrima.*

SAP-BALL. A local name for those *Polypori* which grow on trees, but applied more especially to *P. squamosus,* a species which abounds on decayed ash, and is found occasionally on other trees, the stems of which when large, after the juice has been squeezed out, is sometimes used by boys as their foundation for tennis-balls. The same species is sometimes used, when properly dried and shaped, to form razor-strops, but it is not so good for this purpose as *P. betulinus.* Specimens formed from the latter, received from Denmark, may be seen in the Museum of the Kew Gardens. [M. J. B.]

SAP-GREEN. A vegetable pigment composed of lime mixed with the colouring-matter of the berries of *Rhamnus catharticus.*

SAPID. Having a pleasant taste.

SAPIN. (Fr.) *Abies.* — À FEUILLES D'IF, or ARGENTÉ. *Abies pectinata.* — BAUMIER. *Abies balsamea.* — BLANC. *Abies pectinata.* — COMMUN. *Abies excelsa.* — DE NORMANDIE. *Abies pectinata.* — NORWÉGE. *Abies excelsa.* — PINSAPO. *Abies Pinsapo.*

SAPINDACEÆ. (*Æsculaceæ, Hippocastaneæ, Soapworts*). A large order of polypetalous dicotyledons, consisting of trees or shrubs, sometimes climbing, and very rarely almost herbaceous, with alternate or rarely opposite leaves, most frequently compound, and usually pinnate; the flowers usually small, paniculate or racemose, or rarely solitary. In the normal genera the sepals and petals are four or five each; the stamens either twice as many or of the same number, or more frequently eight whatever be the number of petals, and inserted within or upon or rarely around a more or less prominent hypogynous or almost perigynous disk. The ovary is several-celled, with one or two ascending ovules in each. The fruit is very various; the seeds usually without albumen, and with an inferior radicle. There are above seventy genera, chiefly tropical, but some are also found in temperate regions of the Northern Hemisphere. They are distributed into five tribes or suborders:—

1. SAPINDEÆ proper, with the stamens inside the disk, albuminous seeds, and leaves rarely opposite, including the large or wide-spread tropical genera *Serjania, Cardiospermum, Paullinia, Schmidelia, Cupania, Sapindus, Nephelium,* etc., as well as *Kölreuteria* and *Æsculus* from more temperate regions.

2. ACERINEÆ, scarcely differing from *Sapindeæ* proper, except that the stamens are less constantly within the disk, and the leaves more constantly opposite, although

generally considered as a distinct order. It is limited to *Acer* and two small genera separated from it: see ACERACEÆ.

3. DODONÉÆ, with the stamens outside of or on the margin of the disk, and the seeds without albumen. They comprise *Dodonæa* and five small genera.

4. MELIANTHEÆ, with the stamens inside the disk and seeds with albumen, containing only the two African genera *Melianthus* and *Bersama.*

5. STAPHYLEÆ, with the stamens outside the disk, seeds with albumen, and opposite leaves. The two last are often considered as distinct orders, and another separate order is frequently adopted for the genera *Æsculus* and *Ungnadia* of *Sapindeæ* proper, which have opposite and digitately compound leaves, but differ in no other respect whatever.

SAPINDUS. The typical genus of *Sapindaceæ,* found in both hemispheres, mostly within the limits of the tropics, and consisting of trees or shrubs, with alternate usually pinnate leaves without a terminal leaflet; and panicles of small white or greenish, perfect or unisexual, five or four-parted flowers. The fruits are fleshy, externally, and do not open when ripe. Those of several species are acrid, and are called Soap-berries, from their being used in the tropics as a substitute for soap, their outer covering or shell containing a saponaceous principle (*saponine*) in sufficient abundance to produce a lather with water; but the assertion of the old Jamaica historian, Patrick Browne, that 'a few of them will cleanse more linen than sixty times their weight of soap,' must be received with caution. Among the species thus used are *S. Saponaria* and *S. inæqualis* in the New World, and *S. Rarax* and *S. emarginatus* in the Old. Their excessively hard round black seeds are used for making rosaries, necklaces, bracelets, buttons, &c.; and a medicinal oil is extracted in India from those of *S. emarginatus.* The outer covering of the fruit of some species, such as *S. senegalensis* and *S. esculentus,* is eatable, but their seeds are poisonous. [A. S.]

SAPINETTE BLANCHE. (Fr.) *Abies alba.* — NOIRE. *Abies nigra.*

SAPIUM. A genus containing about a score of trees or shrubs of the order *Euphorbiaceæ,* found in the tropics of both hemispheres, and all of them yielding a milky juice, which in some is very acrid and even poisonous. The leaves resemble those of the willow, the poplar, or the laurel, and at their point of union with the stalk are furnished with two round glands; while the small greenish flowers are disposed in terminal spikes, the lower portion bearing the fertile, the upper the sterile flowers.

S. indicum, a widely distributed eastern species, is known under the name of Boroo in Borneo, where, according to Mr. Motley, the leaves are largely used for dyeing and staining rotang of a dark colour. The acrid milky juice produces a burning sensation like that from a capsicum. The young fruit is acid and eaten as a condiment, while at the same time the fruit is one of the ingredients used for poisoning alligators. The ripe fruits are woody trilobed capsules, about an inch across, with three cells, and one oily seed in each.

The Milkwood of Jamaica, *S. laurifolium*, receives its name from the milky juice which abounds in the stem, and is a source of annoyance to sawyers and others when the wood is green. *S. salicifolium* affords in Paraguay a bark which is used instead of that of oak for tanning. Most modern authors unite this genus with *Stillingia*, from which there are no reliable characters to distinguish it. [A. A. B.]

SAPODILLA. *Sapota Achras.* The West Indian Sapodilla-wood, yielded by this tree, is a fancy wood used for furniture.

SAPONAIRE. (Fr.) *Saponaria officinalis.* — **FAUX-BASILIC.** *Saponaria ocymoides.*

SAPONARIA. A genus of herbaceous plants belonging to the order *Caryophyllaceæ*, and allied to *Dianthus*, from which they are distinguished by the absence of bracts at the base of the calyx, and by the seeds not being flattened. *S. officinalis*, or Soapwort, is admitted into the British Flora, but is never found except in the neighbourhood of human dwellings, and is not considered to be a native. In its foliage this plant resembles the sweetwilliam, but the flowering stalks are stouter and taller; the flowers are of a delicate rose-colour and fragrant, and are collected into a dense terminal panicle. A variety with double flowers is common both in waste places and gardens. The plant takes its name from the peculiarity that its leaves bruised in water may be worked into a lather. French: *Savonniere*; German: *Seisenkraut.* [C. A. J.]

SAPOR. The taste which a thing has.

SAPOTACEÆ. An order of monopetalous dicotyledons, consisting of trees and shrubs chiefly tropical or subtropical, with the juice frequently milky, alternate undivided leaves without stipules, and small flowers, solitary or clustered in the axils of the leaves. It is distinguished from all other *Monopetalæ* by the perfect stamens, either opposite to the lobes of the corolla or twice as many; by a superior ovary divided into two or more cells, with one ovule in each; and by the fruit, which is either a berry or a drupe. There are about twenty genera, of which the most important are *Chrysophyllum, Lucuma, Sapota, Sideroxylon, Isonandra, Bumelia, Bassia*, and *Mimusops.*

SAPOTA. A genus that gives its name to the order *Sapotaceæ*, and which consists of trees, natives of tropical America and extratropical Australia. The flowers have a calyx of five or six overlapping segments; a somewhat bell-shaped corolla, with an erect five to six-parted limb; twelve stamens, six fertile, six with-

out anthers, the filaments flattened awlshaped, the anthers extrorse; ovary six to twelve-celled, with a single ovule in each cell; fruit succulent, frequently one-celled, by the suppression of the other cavities. *S. mammosa* [now LUCUMA] yields the Marmalade fruit sometimes called the Vegetable Egg. The milky juice of this tree has emetic properties, and is used as a caustic to destroy warts; it is said also to be used to form a kind of sympathetic ink. *S. Achras* yields an edible fruit called in the West Indies the Sapodilla plum. The bark of this tree is astringent and febrifugal; the seeds also are aperient and diuretic. The fruits of the species mentioned are highly esteemed in the West Indies, but those that have ripened in this country have been little esteemed. [M. T. M.]

SAPOTE NEGRO. (Fr.) *Diospyros.*

SAPPADILLE. (Fr.) *Anona.*

SAPPANWOOD. A wood of commerce obtained from *Cæsalpinia Sappan.*

SAPROLEGNIEÆ. A natural order of doubtful affinity, forming a peculiar group, consisting of *Saprolegnia, Achlya,* and one or two other more or less perfectly defined genera, with the habit of moulds and the fructification of *Algæ.* They grow for the most part on dead or living animals, and are nearly colourless. The fruit is contained in swollen parts of the threads, which sometimes produce a succession of sporangia by the repeated protrusion of the inner membrane into the cavity, or sometimes by the formation of lateral cysts. In *Pythium* one sporangia only is produced. Impregnation takes place by conjugation between the sporangia and the swollen tips of the lateral branchlets. The reproductive bodies are zoospores, which move by means of lash-like appendages. The cell-walls consist of nearly pure cellulose, exhibiting a brilliant blue when treated with iodine. These plants differ from all known *Algæ* in growing principally on animal substances, though their mode of reproduction in some respects strongly resembles that of *Vaucheria.* It is curious that the same animal has been observed, when immersed, to produce a *Saprolegnia*, and when surrounded merely with air to produce a *Mucor.* Were zoospores of the same type known amongst *Fungi*, these productions would doubtless be referred to them; but in the present state of our knowledge, they stand on the confines of both. There is some reason however to believe, from the observations of Hofmeister, that impregnation is effected in truffles much in the same way as it is in *Saprolegnieæ.* They are great enemies to fish and other animals preserved in aquaria, which are frequently infested with them when living. It is said that doses of carbonate of soda prevent their growth, and if so it is probable that bisulphate of potash may be more effectual from its known effects on obscure cryptogamic growths. [M. J. B.]

SAPROSMA. A genus of cinchonaceous trees, natives of Java, having numerous crowded sessile axillary or terminal flowers, which have a four-toothed persistent calyx; a hairy four-cleft corolla, to the throat of which are attached four stamens; a cleft stigma; and oval smooth fruit, crowned by the limb of the calyx, one-celled, and one-seeded. The fruits and the wood of these trees are said to have a filthy smell, whence the name of the genus, from the Greek words *sapros* 'putrid,' and *osme* 'smell.' [M. T. M.]

SAPUCAYA. *Lecythis Ollaria.*

SAPUTÁ. A Brazilian name for *Tontelea.*

SARACEN'S CONSOUD. *Senecio sarracenicus.*

SARACHA. *Witheringia.*

SARAZINE. (Fr.) *Aristolochia Clematitis.*

SARCANDRA. A genus of *Chloranthaceæ*, consisting of Chinalese shrubs, with the appearance of that of the species of *Chloranthus*. The flowers are perfect, in loose spikes, concealed within a concave bract; stamen solitary, with a thick fleshy filament, which adheres partially to the ovary; anther two-celled, the cells opening lengthwise, approximate above but diverging below; fruit fleshy, one-seeded. The name is from the Greek, and alludes to the fleshy stamen. [M. T. M.]

SARCANTHUS. Originally this genus of orchids consisted of two or three Chinese species split off the older genus *Vanda*, but several East Indian and Philippine plants have since at various times been added. They are epiphytes, with flat or sometimes terete leaves on opposite sides of the stems, and racemes of small but rather showy flowers growing opposite the leaves. Their flowers have nearly equal spreading sepals and petals, a short three-lobed fleshy lip jointed with the column and spurred, the spur being divided inside, and an erect half-cylindrical column. The anther is two-celled; and the two pollen-masses are lobed or channelled behind. [A. S.]

SARCINA. A very curious production of a somewhat doubtful nature, but of some importance in consequence of its connection with one of the most serious diseases to which the human frame is subject. In cancerous affections of the stomach, which are almost always accompanied by distressing vomiting, the matter thrown up very frequently contains minute quadrilateral bodies connected together in patches consisting of four, or some multiple of four. The mode of multiplication is not uncommon amongst the lower *Algæ*, but it is not without example amongst *Fungi*, or even amongst lichens. As however true *Algæ* are, as far as we know, never developed in animal substances, the first presumption is that *Sarcina*, a name derived from the masses resembling little woolpacks, is some form of fungus analogous to the yeast-form of *Penicillium* and other thread-moulds. Attempts, however, at making these bodies germinate have failed entirely, possibly from not placing them in a fluid favourable to their growth. In diluted syrup they remain perfect for many months, without showing the slightest tendency to increase. *Sarcina* is not, however, confined to affections of the stomach, but has been found in urine—whether of patients or animals suffering from cancer of the bladder or kidneys we cannot say. A circumstance, however, occurred a few years since which tends greatly to confirm our notion that the matter is of fungous origin. Dr. H. O. Stephens, on examining at Bristol a cargo of bones just imported from South America, observed that many of them were covered with an orange-coloured gelatinous mass, looking like some *Fusisporium*. On examination, however, it had exactly the structure of *Sarcina*, and on this as well as on other accounts we believe *Sarcina* to be a fungus and not an alga. [M. J. B.]

SARCINANTHUS. A genus of the order *Pandanaceæ*. The species have a scandent or twining stem, with two-lobed stalked leaves crowded together at the ends of the branches. The spadix is stalked and axillary. The genus differs from its near allies *Carludovica* and *Evodianthus* in the thick fleshy perianth of the male flowers; its limb is divided into a number of lobes arranged in one row. There are also differences in the insertion of the stamens and the form of the lobes of the perianth in the female flower. The species inhabit Central America. [M. T. M.]

SARCOBASIS. The same kind of fruit as the Carcerulus.

SARCOCAPNOS. A genus of *Fumariaceæ*, differing from *Corydalis* in the short indehiscent pod, with three-nerved valves, and only two seeds. They are perennial herbs, occuring in the western portion of the Mediterranean region, and have branched diffuse stems, often somewhat shrubby at the base; with alternate long-stalked leaves, usually tripartite or ternate, thick and fleshy, and short few-flowered terminal racemes of rather large yellowish flowers with purple blotches at the tip, upper petal with an obtuse spur. [J. T. S.]

SARCOCARP. The fleshy part of the pericarp lying between the epicarp and endocarp.

SARCOCEPHALUS. The name of a climbing shrub, native of Western Tropical Africa, and constituting a genus of *Cinchonaceæ*. The flowers are grouped in terminal heads, and are fused together, and with the receptacle, into one large fleshy mass. The free margins of the calyx are very short; the corollas funnel-shaped, five to six-cleft; anthers five or six, sessile within the throat of the corolla; ovaries fused together; styles distinct; stigmas button-like; fruits succulent, combined into a one-celled berry, surmounted by the limb of the calyx. *S. esculentus* has pink flowers and an edible fruit, of the size of a peach, whence it has been called the Sierra Leone Peach. The generic name is derived from the Greek, and is significant of the fleshy heads of flowers. [M. T. M.]

SARCOCHILUS. As originally constituted this genus consists of a small number of subtropical Australian Feejean and Malayan orchids, but a German orchidologist has recently combined with them numerous Eastern species referred by other botanists to the genera *Aërides, Dendrocolla, &c.* It is here restricted to the few original species, which are small epiphytal plants, with short stems, narrow distichous coriaceous leaves, and bracteated spikes or racemes of fleshy open sometimes showy flowers. These have nearly equal blunt sepals, the lateral ones adnate to the base of the lip, and similar but smaller petals, a concave fleshy spurless lip continuous with the short erect column, and a terminal anther containing four pollen-masses cohering in globose pairs, and attached to a broad strap-shaped caudicle. [A. S.]

SARCOCLINIUM. A genus of *Euphorbiaceæ* of that group in which the cells of the fruit contain but one seed. The three known species, found in Ceylon and the Malayan peninsula, are trees of medium growth, the ends of their branches furnished with a tuft of large glossy simple leaves, accompanied by stipules, and bearing in their axils long racemes of minute flowers, the sterile and fertile on different plants. The leaves, which are of the same form as the leaflets of a horse-chestnut, are in *S. Hookeri* two to three feet long. Of those of *S. longifolium*, which are not so large, Mr. Thwaites remarks: 'As they are of a firm consistence, and do not rapidly decay, they are used by the Cingalese for thatching.' [A. A. B.]

SARCOCOCCA. Small branching evergreen shrubs of the order *Euphorbiaceæ*, found in the temperate parts of India Ceylon and Java. They have glossy lance-shaped or elliptical entire three-nerved leaves; and in their axils short spikes of small white or yellowish unisexual flowers not unlike those of the box, followed by black berries a little larger than cherry-stones. These plants are closely related to the common box of our gardens, but differ in the berried fruit, and the position of the fertile flowers, which are at the base instead of the apex of the spikes, as well as in their trinerved leaves. The generic name refers to the fleshy nature of the fruit, a circumstance uncommon in the family. [A. A. B.]

SARCOCOLLA. One of the few genera composing the small order of *Penæaceæ*, and, like its congeners, found only in the neighbourhood of the Cape of Good Hope. The four described species are little shrubs, with opposite entire overlapping leaves, furnished with little blackish wart-like

bodies in their axils. The flowers have two small bractlets at their base, and are produced in clusters at the points of the branches in the axils of large leaf-like coloured bracts, which are frequently covered with a greasy resinous exudation. The gum-resin called Sarcocool, now but seldom met with, is generally said to be the produce of *S. squamosa* (alias *Penæa Sarcocolla*) and of *Penæa mucronata*, but there is no evidence that such is the case. The Sarcocolla of the ancients, so named from the Greek words *sarx* 'flesh' and *kolla* 'glue,' in consequence of its being supposed to possess the property of agglutinating wounds, is said by Dioscorides to have been obtained from a Persian tree, and consequently not from any species of the present genus, which is confined to Southern Africa. Sarcocool occurs in the form of little gravel-like grains, and has a bitter-sweet taste. It contains *sarcocolline*, a peculiar principle convertible into oxalic acid by the action of nitric acid. [A. S.]

SARCODERM. An intermediate fleshy layer in the testa of some seeds; a layer of either the primine or secondine.

SARCODES. A genus of *Ericaceæ* of the tribe *Monotropeæ*, allied to *Pterospora*, but with much larger flowers, an elongated style, and wingless seeds. It consists of a single species, an erect herbaceous parasitical plant from California, with a fleshy stem, succulent scale-like leaves, and a long raceme of pendulous flowers, the whole plant of a blood-red colour.

SARCOGLOTTIS. Under this name are grouped a few West Indian and tropical American terrestrial orchids, which some authors regard as a section of *Spiranthes*, and others as entitled to rank as a distinct genus, characterised mainly by the erect flowers having the lateral sepals decurrent the whole length of the ovary and forming a sort of sac, and by the pollen-masses being stalked. [A. S.]

SARCOGONUM. A section of the polygonaceous genus *Mühlenbeckia*, consisting of those Australian species which have fringed stigmas. [J. T. S.]

SARCOLÆNA. A genus of *Chlenaceæ* peculiar to Madagascar, and comprising a few species, having a shrubby habit, decumbent branches, ovate leaves (more or less plicate when young), paniculate flowers, a fleshy involucre surrounding the calyx, five petals, an indefinite number of stamens, and a three-celled capsule, each cell containing two seeds. [B. S.]

SARCOLOBUS. A genus of *Asclepiadaceæ*, containing three species of glabrous twining shrubs from India and Java. They have opposite oval fleshy or coriaceous leaves, and few-flowered interpetiolar umbels. The calyx is five-leaved; the corolla rotate and five-cleft, with a naked throat, and no staminal corona; the gynostegium is somewhat hemispherical; the pollen-masses are erect, clavate with long stalks; the stigma is five-sided and mamillose;

and the follicles are fleshy, and contain margined seeds without hairs.   [W. C.]

SARCOMA. One of the names of the disk.

SARCOPHYSA. A genus of *Atropaceæ*, comprising a climbing shrub, native of New Grenada. The leaves are alternate and leathery, and the flowers handsome, in pendulous clusters. The calyx is large and brightly coloured, fleshy and distended, tubular and contracted at the throat, the limb divided into five erect persistent segments; the corolla has a long tube, somewhat dilated in the middle, and a shortly five-lobed limb; and the fruit is included within the fleshy calyx. The name of the genus is expressive of the peculiarities of the calyx, from *sarx* 'flesh' and *phusa* 'a bladder.'   [M. T. M.]

SARCOPHYTE. This is one of those curious parasitical plants of the family *Balanophoraceæ*, which have been so elaborately described by Dr. Hooker in the *Transactions of the Linnæan Society.* It comprises a single species, a fleshy fungus-like plant, found growing in South Africa on the roots of species of *Mimosa.* The inflorescence is branched, with small bracts at the base of the pedicels. The flowers are diœcious, the males panicled, each with a three-lobed perianth, concealing three free stamens, with many-celled anthers; and the females in globose heads, without a perianth. The name, derived from the Greek, signifies 'flesh-plant.'   [M. T. M.]

SARCOPODIUM. A genus of tropical Asiatic orchids of the *Dendrobideæ* group, allied both to *Dendrobium* and *Bolbophyllum*, to one or other of which most of the known species, about twenty in number, were at one time referred. The plants belonging to it are creeping epiphytes, with leathery leaves, borne singly upon the pseudobulbs, from the base of which the single or few-flowered peduncles arise. Their flowers are of a thick leathery nature, rather showy, with ringent sepals (the lateral ones enlarged at the base and adnate with the foot of the column), smaller petals, and a short fleshy lip enlarged at its base and moveably jointed with the base of the column, which is short hornless and furnished with a prolonged foot; the two-celled anther contains four nearly equal free pollen-masses.   [A. S.]

SARCOSTEMMA (including *Philibertia*). A genus of *Asclepiadaceæ*, composed of about forty species indigenous to the tropics of both hemispheres, and consisting of climbing or erect often epiphytal shrubs, which are either leafless or furnished with linear or cordate leaves, and umbellate white yellow or purplish flowers, often emitting a powerful scent. The calyx is five-cleft; the corolla either rotate or urceolate-rotate; the staminal corona double; the pollen-masses in club-shaped cylinders; the follicles smooth; and the seeds furnished with a hairy appendix. *S. glaucum* yields the Ipecacuanha of Venezuela, and is

used as a sudorific and in cases of humoral asthma. The young shoots of *S. Forskalianum* and those of *S. stiptaceum* of Arabia are eaten. The pith of *S. pyrotechnicum* is used as tinder. The milky juice of *S. viminale* is slightly and agreeably acid, and used by travellers to allay thirst.   [B. S.]

SARCOSTIGMA. This genus consists of two species, natives of Southern India and Java, both climbing or twining shrubs, with alternate simple entire thickish leaves without stipules, and flowers of separate sexes on distinct plants; the long flower-spikes being produced usually in pairs from the sides of the branches, and having the stalkless flowers in little clusters along them. The genus was first referred to the *Thymelaceæ*, afterwards to *Phytocrenaceæ*, but is now placed in the order *Icacinaceæ*. *S. Kleinii*, a native of Courtallum and Cochin on the Malabar coast of India, produces oval somewhat flattened fruits about an inch long and half an inch broad, containing a large seed, from which a thick semifluid oil called Odal or Adul is expressed.   [A. S.]

SARCOTHECA. A genus of *Oxalidaceæ*, comprising a shrub, native of the Indian Archipelago, with square branches, entire thick leaves, and elongated axillary or terminal racemes of flowers, occurring either singly or in pairs. The calyx consists of five persistent overlapping sepals; the corolla of five stalked oblong petals, convolute in æstivation; stamens ten, five long, five short, the filaments awl-shaped, connected at the base into a cup; ovary sessile, five-celled, with two ovules in each cell; styles five, filiform; capsule globose, five-celled.   [M. T. M.]

SARGASSUM. A genus of dark-spored *Algæ* belonging to the natural order *Fucaceæ*, characterised by the fruit-bearing

Sargassum bacciferum.

receptacles being collected in little bundles in the axils of the leaves; the air-vessels, which are merely transformed leaves, with or without a terminal point, being stalked and separate. The species are extremely numerous, and chiefly tropical or subtropical. The great interest of the genus to the general reader consists in the far-famed Sargasso-sea owing its origin to one of the species, *S. bacciferum*. We have no species inhabiting our shores, but *S. vulgare* and

S. bacciferum are occasionally brought to us by the waves.   [M. J. B.]

SARIBUS. This genus of palms, originally established by Blume, is now combined with *Livistona*, the characters by which it was said to be distinguished from that genus being very slight. Among the species referred to it were *Livistona rotundifolia*, called *Saribus* by Rumphius; and *L. chinensis*, and a species from Cochin China, now called *Livistona cochinchinensis*. Two Javanese species, *S. olivæformis* and *S. subglobosa*, were afterwards added.   [A. S.]

SARMENTACEÆ. See VITACEÆ.

SARMENTIDIUM. A group of cymes or spikes arranged centrifugally, as the flowers are in the cyme itself.

SARMENTUM. A runner, such as that of the strawberry: hence *sarmentose*, bearing runners.

SARMIENTA *repens* is the sole representative of a Chilian genus of *Gesneraceæ*, easily distinguished from its allies by having two fertile and three sterile stamens, whilst all other *Gesneraceæ* have one sterile and four fertile stamens. *S. repens* is herbaceous, and climbs by means of its rooting *stems* over forest-trees. Its leaves are fleshy ovate and dotted; its peduncles are terminal, and bear from one to two scarlet flowers. The calyx is four and five-cleft; and the corolla tubular, ventricose towards the apex, and five-lobed; whilst the capsule is ovate.   [B. S.]

SAROTHAMNUS. The generic name now generally adapted for the Common Broom, *S. scoparius*, better known as *Spartium* or *Genista scoparia*, and separated from *Genista* chiefly because the lips of the bell-shaped calyx are minutely instead of deeply toothed. From *Cytisus* the genus differs in the very long curved style and minute stigma.

The Broom grows naturally in the Canary Isles, Western Europe, and Scandinavia, as well as in Britain, and is applied to various economic purposes. Neat little baskets are made from the twigs divested of their bark in Madeira; and in some parts of Europe the green tops are used as winter food for sheep, preventing (according to Withering) the disease called rot, and salutary in dropsy, to which sheep are liable. The Broom has a place in our 'Materia Medica.' Pereira says:—' Broomtops in large doses are emetic and purgative, in small doses diuretic and laxative. They are used almost entirely in dropsies, sometimes with great benefit, and are administered in the form of infusion or decoction. The seeds, which keep better than the tops, are given in the form of a powder, in doses of from ten to fifteen grains, in mint-water. There are other species of the genus, natives of Western Europe, most of them bearing great resemblance to the Common Broom, which is the badge of the Forbes'. Thus, according to Sandford, it was the bonny Broom which the Scottish clan of Forbes wore in their bonnets when they wished to arouse the heroism of their chieftains, and which in their Gaelic dialect they called *bealadh* in token of its beauty.

The *Ordre de la Geneste* was the denomination of an order of knighthood instituted by Louis of France in 1234, and continued till the death of Charles V. The collar of this order consisted of a chain of broom-flowers interlaced with lozenges of gold and fleur-de-lis, with a pendent cross having the inscription 'Exaltat Humiles,'—the founder considering the broom as the emblem of humility. 'This humble shrub,' writes Baines, ' was not less distinguished than the rose herself during the civil wars of the fourteenth century; for a sprig of the *Planta Genista* was the adopted badge of Geoffrey Duke of Anjou, father of our Henry II.; and from this cognizance he acquired the name of Plantagenet, by him transmitted to his princely descendants, who all bore it from Henry, who has been called the first royal sprig of Genista, down to the tyrant Richard, the last degenerate scion of the plant of Anjou.'   [A. A. B.]

SARRACENIACEÆ. A small order of polypetalous dicotyledons, consisting of herbs from Northern or tropical America, remarkable for their pitcher-shaped radical leaves. They are characterised by five imbricate sepals; petals also five and imbricate, or sometimes more; numerous hypogynous stamens; a three or five-celled ovary with numerous ovules; a loculicidal capsule, and seeds with a copious albumen and minute embryo. Some of these characters are, technically considered, nearly those of *Ternstrœmiaceæ*, whilst the herbaceous stem and the seeds indicate a greater affinity with *Papaveraceæ* and *Nymphæaceæ*. There are only three small genera known — *Sarracenia, Darlingtonia*, and *Heliamphora*.

SARRACENIA. A genus of *Sarraceniaceæ*, distinguished in the order by having

Sarracenia purpurea.

five petals always present; a five-celled ovary and capsule; and by the style being expanded into a large umbrella-shaped disk, bearing the five minute stigmas underneath at the edge—this peculiar conformation having given rise to the name of Side-saddle-flower popularly given to the plants. There are half a dozen species, natives of the marshes of North America. The pitcher-shaped petioles of their radical leaves have a small lamina at the top which has been called a lid, although it never closes over the pitcher. The pitcher itself in the older leaves is usually full of water. It has not yet been ascertained whether this water is derived from rain or dew, or is secreted by the leaf itself; but, however derived, it serves to drown the flies and other insects which these leaves are admirably adapted to catch and retain. At the mouth of the pitcher there is in most species a saccharine exudation which attracts them: the surface immediately below is smooth and polished, and still lower it is beset with sharp,reflexed hairs, which allow the insects to descend but effectually obstruct their return. The flowers are large yellowish or purple, on radical leafless scapes. *S. purpurea* is frequently imported; and some of the other species are in cultivation.

SARRASIN. (Fr.) *Fagopyrum esculentum.* — DE TARTARIE. *Fagopyrum tataricum.*

SARRETTE. (Fr.) *Serratula.*

SARRIETTE. (Fr.) *Satureia.*

SARRON. (Fr.) *Chenopodium* (or *Blitum*) *Bonus Henricus.*

SARSAPARILLA. The rhizome of several species of *Smilax*, chiefly imported from South America and Mexico, and employed in medicine. —, AMERICAN. *Aralia nudicaulis.* —, AUSTRALIAN. *Hardenbergia monophylla.* —, BRAZILIAN. *Smilax papyracea (siphilitica*, Mart.). —, COUNTRY. *Hemidesmus indicus.* —, FALSE. *Aralia nudicaulis.* —, GERMAN. *Carex arenaria, C. disticha,* and *C. hirta.* —, GUATEMALA. *Smilax papyracea.* —, HONDURAS. Probably *Smilax papyracea.* —, INDIAN. *Hemidesmus indicus.* —, ITALIAN. *Smilax aspera* and *S. excelsa.* —, JAMAICA. *Smilax officinalis.* —, LIMA. *Smilax officinalis.* —, LISBON. *Smilax papyracea.* —, NEW HOLLAND. *Smilax glycyphylla.* —, NEW ZEALAND. *Ripogonum parviflorum.* —, PERUVIAN. *Smilax obliquata.* —, RIO NEGRO. *Smilax papyracea.* —, VERA CRUZ. *Smilax medica.* —, WILD. *Aralia nudicaulis.*

SARSHAPA. A Sanscrit name for Mustard-seed.

SARTORIA. A perennial herb from the chain of the Isaurian Taurus in Asia Minor, having the habit foliage and flowers of *Onobrychis* and *Hedysarum*, but differing from both of these genera in the pod, which is oblong-linear, very flat thin and indehiscent, but not jointed, although it usually contains two seeds. It has therefore been established as a distinct genus of *Leguminosæ* of the tribe *Hedysareæ.*

SARTWELLIA. The only species of this genus of *Compositæ* of the tribe *Flaveriæ*, called *S. Flaveria,* and peculiar to Southern Texas, is a many-stemmed erect smooth herb, about a foot high, having opposite linear-filiform leaves, and corymbs of numerous shortly-stalked small yellow flower-heads terminating the twigs. The plant differs from its allies in the presence of a cup-shaped nearly entire pappus, crowning the ten-ribbed achenes. There are three to five strap-shaped pistil-bearing ray-florets, and about a dozen tubular and perfect florets of the disk, all surrounded by an involucre of four or five ovate scales. It is dedicated to H. P. Sartwell, an American botanist. [A. A. B.]

SASA. An Indian name for the oil of Cucumber-seeds.

SASSAFRAS. A genus of *Lauraceæ*, consisting of trees, natives of North America and the East Indies. The leaves are deciduous and veiny; the flowers yellowish, dioecious, and appearing before the leaves. The perianth is six-parted; fertile stamens nine, in three rows, the anthers all opening inwardly, four-celled, the three innermost stamens with two glands at the base. In the female flowers there are nine sterile stamens, the innermost often confluent. Fruit fleshy, placed on the thick fleshy top of the flower-stalk.

S. officinale, formerly called *Laurus Sassafras,* is a native of North America, extending from Canada to Florida. The root, wood,

Sassafras officinale.

and bark have stimulant and sudorific properties, which depend partly on the presence of a volatile oil. In medicine various preparations of Sassafras are used in rheumatic and skin affections, generally however in combination with other more potent drugs. Sassafras-tea mixed with milk and sugar forms the drink known as Saloop, which is still sold to the working-classes in the early morning at the corners of the London streets. In Virginia the young shoots are made into a kind of beer; in Louisiana the leaves are used as a condiment in sauces, while their mucilaginous properties render them useful for thickening soups. The fruits have an agreeable perfume, and with the oil extracted from them are made use of by perfumers. The wood and bark furnish a yellow dye. In Sumatra *S. Parthenoxylon* answers the same purposes. *S. officinale* is frequently grown in this country as an ornamental tree. It is remarkable for the variety it presents in the size and shape of its leaves.

What is known as Orinoco Sassafras is the produce of *Nectandra cymbarum*, while Cayenne Sassafras is derived from *Licaria guianensis*. Sassafras-nuts, which were formerly used as astringents and tonics, are the seeds of one or two species of *Nectandra*. The name Sassafras is said to be a corruption of the Spanish word for saxifrage. [M. T. M.]

SASSAFRAS. *Sassafras officinale.* — AUSTRALIAN. *Atherosperma moschata.* —, BRAZILIAN. *Nectandra cymbarum.* —, CAYENNE. *Licaria guianensis,* which yields an excellent timber. —, NEW HOLLAND. *Doryphora Sassafras.* —, ORIENTAL. *Sassafras Parthenoxylon.* —, ORINOCO. *Nectandra cymbarum.* —, SWAMP. *Magnolia glauca.* —, TASMANIAN. *Atherosperma moschata.*

SATINE. A cabinet-wood of French Guiana, the produce of *Ferolia guianensis.*

SATINÉE. (Fr.) *Lunaria biennis* and *L. rediviva.*

SATINWOOD. A beautiful veneering wood of India, obtained from *Chloroxylon Swietenia.* —, BAHAMAS. A timber supposed to be the produce of *Maba guineensis.*

SATIRE. (Fr.) *Phallus.*

SATUREIA. A genus of the *Labiatæ,* and the type of the suborder *Satureæ.* There are several species, of which the most important are *S. hortensis* and *S. montana,* both well known under the more familiar names of Summer and Winter Savory, and highly esteemed in cookery for their powerful aromatic flavour.

The Summer Savory, *S. hortensis,* is a hardy annual, a native of the South of Europe, and supposed to have been introduced into this country in 1562, as both the Winter and Summer Savory were known to Gerard in 1597. The stem is erect branching pubescent, and of a reddish-green colour. The leaves are opposite linear-lanceolate smooth, and of a pale-green. The flowers are small axillary pale lilac, and generally in twos on each footstalk. The leaves are used for the same purposes as those of the Winter Savory. Both species were noticed by Virgil as being among the most fragrant of herbs, and on this account were recommended to be grown near beehives. Vinegar flavoured with savory and other aromatic herbs

was as much used by the ancient Romans as mint-sauce is at the present day with us.

The Winter Savory, *S. montana,* is a hardy and very dwarf suffrutescent evergreen, a native of the South of France and other parts of Europe, and known in this country since 1562. The leaves are sessile linear-lanceolate entire, abruptly terminated by a short sharp point. The flowers are axillary small, pale purple almost white, borne two or three together on the same footstalk. The whole plant is highly aromatic, and is employed like other sweet herbs for seasoning in cookery. To preserve a supply, it may be cut just before the flowers expand, and dried in the same manner as directed for basil. [W. B. B.]

SATYRIA. A genus of American shrubs belonging to the *Vacciniaceæ.* The flowers are purple, and may be discriminated from those of adjacent genera by their filaments being combined into a tube; by the anthers being alternately long and short, opening by two pores at the top; and by the cells of the ovary containing but one ovule. The fruit is inferior and fleshy. The name is from *saturos,* 'a satyr.' [M. T. M.]

SATYRIDIUM *rostratum.* A little terrestrial Cape orchid, allied to *Satyrium,* from which it differs in the parts of its flower being more flatly spread out, in its pollen-masses having only one gland, and in its minute one-lipped stigma. [A. S.]

SATYRIUM. An extensive genus of ophrydeous orchids found principally in Southern Africa, the Mascaren Islands, and Northern India, and consisting of testiculate-rooted terrestrial plants in habit resembling some of our common species of *Orchis.* The flowers are what is called pirgent or two-lipped, the sepals and petals being all directed downwards and connate at the base, forming a kind of lower lip; while the hooded double-spurred or saccate labellum is erect at the back, and forms the upper lip. They have a reversed anther, pollen-masses with naked glands, and a two-lipped stigma with the upper much larger than the under lip. [A. S.]

SAUCE-ALONE. *Sisymbrium Alliaria.*

SAUGE. (Fr.) *Salvia.* — D'AMÉRIQUE *Turchonanthus.* — DE BÉTHLÉEM. *Pulmonaria.* — DE JÉRUSALEM. *Pulmonaria.* — DES BOIS. *Teucrium Scorodonia.* — EN ARBRE. *Phlomis fruticosa.* — GRANDE. *Salvia officinalis.* — PETITE. *Salvia hispanorum.* — SAUVAGE. *Teucrium Scorodonia.*

SAUGH. The Sallow, *Salix caprea.*

SAUL. The Sál, one of the most useful known Indian timbers for building and engineering purposes. It is the produce of *Shorea robusta,* and yields in abundance the resin called Dammar.

SAULE. (Fr.) *Salix.* — À BOIS GLAUQUE. *Salix daphnoides.* — AMANDIER. *Salix triandra.* — LAURIER. *Salix pentandra.* — MARCEAU. *Salix caprea.*

NOIR. *Salix daphnoides.* — PLEUREUR. *Salix babylonica.*

SAUMAY, or SAWMAY. An Indian name for *Panicum miliaceum.*

SAUNDERS-WOOD. Sanders-wood.

SAURAUJA. One of those genera respecting which considerable diversity of opinion exists as to its position in the Natural System. It was formerly referred to *Ternströmiaceæ,* and is still retained thereby some; though it differs from other genera of that order in having a great number of minute seeds with copious albumen and a very small embryo, resembling those of *Dilleniaceæ,* to which order other botanists refer it, but from which it is distinguished by its seeds being destitute of the fleshy appendage or aril characteristic of that order. Between thirty and forty species are described, mostly natives of the Indian Archipelago and other parts of tropical Asia, a few only belonging to tropical America. They are trees or shrubs, with the young branches clothed with stiff hairs, and have alternate mostly sharp-toothed thick leaves with strongly marked veins running from the midrib to the margin; and white or yellow flowers, disposed in panicles or several together upon stalks growing from the angles of the leaves. Their five sepals, and also their five petals overlap each other, the petals being usually united together at the bottom, and having the numerous stamens adhering to them, the latter having loosely-swinging anthers opening by pores or slits at the top. The ovary is from three to five-celled, with numerous ovules in each cell; and bears from three to five styles, which are free, or more or less united. The fruits are succulent, and very seldom open naturally at maturity. [A. S.]

SAURINE. (Fr.) A kind of olive.

SAUROGLOSSUM *elatum.* A South Brazilian terrestrial orchid with a very tall spike of densely-set green flowers. It belongs to the *Spiranthidæ* group, and is, according to Dr. Lindley, nearly allied to *Pelexia,* from which it is distinguished by its lateral sepals being incurved, its very long column, triangular undivided stigma, and its narrow free not cucullate lip. [A. S.]

SAUROMATUM. A genus of Indian herbs, of the order *Araceæ.* From a globular fleshy rootstock proceeds first a spadix on a short stalk, with scales at the base, the spathe being tubular below and spreading above, marked with purple spots. The spadix bears a quantity of club-shaped rudimentary stamens below the fertile ones, the anthers being distinct, their cells opening by an oblique chink. The ovaries are numerous distinct and one-celled, with two ovules from the base of the cavity. The fruits are succulent and one-seeded. The pedately-divided leaf, on a tall stout often mottled stalk, appears after the spadix. *S. guttatum* is an interesting stove-plant, and its handsome foliage and spotted

stem together render it an ornamental object. [M. T. M.]

SAUROPUS. This genus of *Euphorbiaceæ* contains about eight species, found in tropical India and the Eastern islands. They are small twiggy shrubs having altogether the habit of *Phyllanthus,* their pale-green entire oblong or ovate leaves being arranged in a two-ranked manner, and bearing in their axils clusters of small green or yellow flowers, which are fertile and sterile on the same plant. The calyx consists of six divisions, which are often united nearly to the apex, forming a flat circular flower; in some the calyx is reflexed and umbrella-like, but what is characteristic of the genus is the disk, which consists of six glands arising from near the base of the calyx-segments immediately surrounding the three stamens in the sterile flower, and the three-celled ovary crowned with its three reflexed styles in the fertile flower. The fruits are three-celled capsules sometimes a little fleshy, with one or two seeds in each cell. *S. trinervia,* called also *Phyllanthus trinervia,* is notable in the genus from its three-nerved leaves, which are ovate-lanceolate in form. [A. A. B.]

SAURURACEÆ. A small order of apetalous dicotyledons allied in some respects to *Piperaceæ,* consisting of herbs usually simple or little branched, with alternate stipulate entire leaves, and small flowers in dense terminal spikes or racemes. There is no perianth, although sometimes the coloured bracts at the base of the spike assume the appearance of petals. There are from three to six or seven stamens usually united with the base of each ovary, which is three or four-lobed, and consists of as many carpels, with two or more ovules to each. The fruit is a small capsule or a berry. There are very few species, natives of North America or of Central or Eastern Asia, distributed in four or five genera, which, however, might perhaps all be reduced to the two original ones, *Saururus* and *Houttuynia.*

SAURUROPSIS. A name proposed by Turczaninow for the *Saururus Loureiri* from Northern China, which he considers sufficiently distinct to form a separate genus. It is, however, scarcely adopted by other botanists.

SAURURUS. An herbaceous perennial, a native of the marshes of North America, constituting the genus which gives its name to the small order *Saururaceæ.* It has alternate broad heart-shaped leaves, and small white flowers, nearly sessile in a slender naked terminal spike, from which the plant has derived the popular name of Lizard's-tail. Each flower consists of six or seven stamens, with rather long distinct filaments round the base of the ovary. The fruit is somewhat fleshy, consisting of three or four carpels united at the base, each with a single seed. A second species from North-eastern Asia is by some considered as a distinct genus.

SAUSSUREA. A genus of herbaceous alpine plants belonging to the thistle group of compound flowers, and distinguished by the pappus being of several rows, the inner feathery and much the longest, and by the anthers being furnished with two bristles at the base. There are several species. *S. alpina* is found on Snowdon, and in the highlands of Scotland. It is a well-marked plant eight to twelve inches high, with oblong root-leaves which are cottony below, a simple erect woolly stem almost bare of leaves, and terminating in a crowded tuft of rather large purple flowers. [C. A. J.]

SAUTELLUS. A deciduous bulb formed in the axils of leaves, or round the summit of a root.

SAUVAGESIACEÆ, or SAUVAGEÆ. A tribe of *Violaceæ*, considered by some botanists as a separate order, distinguished by the presence of staminodia in the shape of a ring of filaments or a tube or cup round the five perfect stamens. The group has also considerable affinity with some *Ochnaceæ*.

SAUVAGESIA. The type of the order *Sauvagesiaceæ*, by some botanists classed with *Violaceæ*. It is a genus confined to the tropics, and composed of small annual or biennial herbs found on roadsides and amongst the grass of tropical meadows. Their leaves are alternate lanceolate, and their flowers regular, white or pink, and either axillary or in terminal racemes. The calyx consists of five sepals, and the corolla of five petals, opposite to which latter are five fertile stamens alternating with five scales. The style and stigmas are simple, the capsule ovate three-cornered, one-celled, and three-valved. Some of them are scarcely an inch high when beginning to flower. *S. erecta*, the Herb of St. Martin, is very mucilaginous: it has been used in Brazil for complaints in the eyes, in Peru for disorders of the bowels, and in the West Indies as a diuretic. [B. S.]

SAUVE-VIE. (Fr.) *Asplenium Ruta-muraria*.

SAVANNAH FLOWERS. A West Indian name for various species of *Echites*.

SAVIA. A genus of the group of *Euphorbiaceæ*, in which the cells of the fruit are two-seeded. The eight or ten known species found in the East and West Indies and Madagascar are evergreen shrubs, with somewhat laurel-like leaves, bearing in their axils a few stalked or sessile inconspicuous flowers, which are either sterile and fertile on the same or on different plants. [A. A. B.]

SAVIGNYA. A genus of *Cruciferæ*, consisting of a small annual Egyptian herb, with thickish leaves, the lower ones stalked oval and bluntly toothed, and the upper sessile narrow and entire; the racemes of small pale-purple flowers are opposite the leaves; stamens all free; pouches divaricate, the lower ones often deflexed ob-

long or elliptical, with flattish valves, and a septum of two laminæ, crowned by the short four-sided style; seeds numerous, compressed, with broad margins. [J. T. S.]

SAVIN. *Juniperus Sabina.*

SAVIN-TREE. *Cæsalpinia bijuga*; also *Fagara lentiscifolia.*

SAVONETTE-TREE. *Pithecolobium micradenium.*

SAVONIER. (Fr.) *Sapindus.* — PANICULÉ. *Kölreuteria paniculata.*

SAVONNIÈRE. (Fr.) *Saponaria.*

SAVORY. *Satureja.* —, GARDEN or SUMMER. *Satureja hortensis.* —, MOUNTAIN or WINTER. *Satureja montana.*

SAVOY. *Brassica oleracea bullata major*, a rough-leaved hardy winter cabbage.

SAWWORT. *Serratula.*

SAXATILIS, OSUS, ICOLUS. Living on rocks or stones.

SAXE-GOTHÆA. This coniferous genus takes its name from a German title of the late Prince Consort of England. The only species, *S. conspicua*, is a native of Patagonia, where it forms a small tree having the appearance of a yew; though its botanical relationship is with the juniper, its fruit being what is called a galbulus, consisting of the scales of the female cone consolidated into a fleshy irregular mass, enclosing a single nut-like seed. Its male inflorescence consists of a short spike or catkin of two-celled anthers furnished with a reflexed appendage at their apices. [A. S.]

SAXIFRAGACEÆ. An order of polypetalous dicotyledons, whose limits are as yet far from being settled. Many botanists would include in it all *Calycifloræ* with definite stamens, a partially inferior ovary with two or more distinct cells, and as many distinct styles, many ovules, and albuminous seeds; but several genera have at various times been associated with it which have exceptionally indefinite stamens, consolidated styles, or seeds without albumen. Taken, however, in the abovementioned general sense, it would include the three following suborders:—

1. *Saxifrageæ* proper: Herbs inhabiting chiefly temperate or cold regions, with alternate or rarely opposite leaves, without stipules, containing besides the large genus *Saxifraga* about twenty others, including *Chrysosplenium*, *Vahlia*, *Heuchera*, &c.

2. *Hydrangeæ*: Shrubs chiefly extratropical, from Asia or America, with opposite undivided leaves without stipules, comprising *Hydrangea*, *Adamia*, and about six other genera.

3. *Cunoniaceæ*: Tropical or Southern trees or shrubs, with opposite leaves and interpetiolar stipules, containing about twenty genera, of which the best known are *Weinmannia*, *Ceratopetalum*, *Acrophyllum*, *Callicoma*, *Cunonia*, &c. Besides these *Brexiaceæ*, *Escalloniaceæ*, *Philadelphaceæ*, and some others with consolidated

styles are often added as suborders to *Saxifragaceæ*. See CUNONIACEÆ and HYDRANGEACEÆ.

SAXIFRAGA. Under this name are included those plants of the order *Saxifragaceæ* which have five petals, and a two-celled two-beaked many-seeded capsule. The genus is a large one, containing upwards of 150 species, most of which are dwarf herbs with tufted foliage, and panicles of white yellow or red flowers. Of these twelve or more are natives of Britain, and numerous others are cultivated either as border plants or to decorate rockeries. *S. granulata*, frequent in meadows and pastures, is well marked by its clustered tubers, glandular stems about a foot high, and showy pure white flowers. *S. umbrosa*, well known under the name of London Pride, is abundant on the Irish mountains, as is also *S. Geum*, an allied species. *S. stellaris*, a small species with white flowers, is common on the margins of mountain-streams in the North. *S. aizoides* grows in similar localities, and is distinguished by its panicled yellow flowers spotted with orange. *S. tridactylites* is a small plant with viscid stems, and leaves which are generally tinged with red, and small white flowers; it is common on dry ground and wall-tops, and rarely exceeds the height of three inches. *S. hypnoides*, frequent in rocky mountainous situations and a very common garden plant, may be considered as the type of a group which agree in having moss-like tufted foliage and panicled white flowers; as is *S. oppositifolia* of another group of alpine species with purple flowers. Other kinds, more or less resembling the above, abound in the alpine districts of both hemispheres. French : *Saxifrage* ; German: *Steinbrech*.   [C. A. J.]

SAXIFRAGE. *Saxifraga*. —, BURNET. *Pimpinella Saxifraga*. —, GOLDEN. *Chrysosplenium*. —, MEADOW. *Seseli*. —, PEPPER. *Silaus pratensis*.

SAXIFRAGE DORÉE. (Fr.) *Chrysosplenium*. — TUBÉREUSE. *Septas capensis*.

SAXO-FRIDERICIA. A handsome reed-like plant from the marshes of the Savannah, about Mount Roraima on the borders of British Guiana, described by Schomburgk as a genus of *Juncaceæ* allied to *Rapatea*. It has long linear radical leaves, and a tall scape, flattened and terminating in a dense head of flowers as in *Rapatea* ; and the flowers have a nearly similar structure, except that each cell of the ovary and capsule has several ovules or seeds instead of a single one. The flowers are also more closely sessile in the head, and the leafy bracts form a close spathe bursting laterally as the head protrudes.

SAYAVER. (Fr.) *Oldenlandia umbellata*.

SAYERNE. (Fr.) A kind of Olive.

SCAB. A noxious disease in potatoes, in consequence of which the tubers are deeply pitted, the pits often producing an olive-green dust, the spores of a species of *Tu-*

burcinia. The quality of the potato does not always suffer much injury, as by a curious process a new growth is formed beneath the scab, so that when boiled and peeled the scabby appearance in great measure vanishes. The saleable value is, however, in all cases much diminished. It is certainly more frequent where cinder-dust has been used as manure, but it occurs in poor scaly ground where no manure has been applied. See TUBURCINIA. [M. J. B.]

SCABER, SCABROUS. Rough to the touch.

SCABIEUSE. (Fr.) *Scabiosa arvensis*. — VEUVE. *Scabiosa atropurpurea*.

SCABIOSA. A genus of herbaceous plants with slender erect stalks, and terminal heads of flowers which are often radiated like those of the *Compositæ*, with which they are indeed allied. They belong to the *Dipsaceæ*, and are distinguished by having a common scaly receptacle, and a bristly calyx, which is permanent and crowns the fruit. The most familiarly known species perhaps is *S. atropurpurea*, called Mournful Widow in cottage gardens, where it is a favourite, and where it has been so long in cultivation that its native country is unknown. The Devil's Bit, *S. succisa*, is common on heathy pastures, growing to the height of two feet or more, and distinguished by its præmorse fleshy roots, ovate undivided leaves, and button-like heads of purple flowers. Many of the foreign species are ornamental. German: *Skabiose*.   [C. A. J.]

SCABIOUS. *Scabiosa*. —, SHEEP'S. *Jasione*.

SCABRID, SCABRIUSCULOUS. Slightly rough to the touch.

SCABRIDÆ. One of the Linnæan natural orders, comprising the figs, &c.

SCABWORT. *Inula Helenium*.

SCÆVOLACEÆ. A name by which the genus *Scævola*, and some others with only one ovule in each cell of the ovary, have been distinguished from other *Goodeniaceæ*, but they are not generally adopted as a distinct order.

SCÆVOLA. The greater number of the species of this the most extensive genus of *Goodeniaceæ* are peculiar to Australia and the Sandwich Islands. Two, however, have a very wide geographical range, being found growing on the seashores of Tropical Asia, Western Africa from Senegal to the Cape of Good Hope, Mauritius and Madagascar, the West Indies, Mexico, and the Pacific Islands. All are herbaceous plants or small shrubs, with nearly always alternate leaves, bearing in their axils usually white or blue flowers, either solitary or in racemes or cymes. They have a superior five-lobed calyx ; a corolla split open to the base on the upper side ; stamens with unconnected anthers ; a one to four-celled ovary with solitary ovules ; and a stigma surrounded by a fringed cup. The fruit is dry or fleshy, not opening at maturity.

S. Lobelia (alias S. Königii and S. Taccada), the Taccada of India and Ceylon, is one of the widely dispersed species, being commonly found on the seashores of tropical Asia and the islands of the Indian and Pacific Oceans. It is an erect shrub from two to five feet high, with a thick succulent stem, full of pith when young but ultimately becoming hard and woody, as also do the branches. The pith of the young stems and branches is beautifully fine and white, and resembles that of the Rice-paper plant, with which it has been confounded; but it is seldom obtainable in pieces exceeding three-quarters of an inch in thickness. It is much used by the Malays and Siamese for making artificial flowers, small figures, and other articles used as decorations at feasts and on festivals. The young leaves are eaten as pot-herbs.　　　　　[A. S.]

SCALARIFORM. Ladder-shaped; the name of the tubes of vascular tissue found in ferns.

SCALD-BERRY. Rubus fruticosus.

SCALDWEED. A name for Dodder.

SCALES (adj. SCALY). Small rudimentary close-pressed leaves, resembling minute scales.

SCALLION. Allium ascalonicum majus.

SCALPELLIFORM. Having the form of a common penknife-blade, but planted vertically on a branch.

SCAMMONÉE. (Fr.) Convolvulus Scammonia. — D'ALLEMAGNE. Calystegia sepium. — D'AMÉRIQUE. Batatas Jalapa. — DE MONTPELLIER. Cynanchum monspeliacum.

SCAMMONY. A cathartic gum-resin obtained from the root of Convolvulus Scammonia. — MONTPELLIER. A drug obtained from Cynanchum monspeliacum and its ally C. acutum.

SCANDENS. Climbing—by whatever means, except by twisting.

SCANDIX. A genus of Umbelliferæ, known by its laterally compressed fruit with a long beak, each half of it having five equal blunt ridges, without vittæ or oil-vessels. The species are annual herbs, natives of Europe and Eastern Asia. The name is adopted from the Scandix of the ancients, the designation of an unknown edible plant.　　　　　[G. D.]

SCAPE. A long naked or nearly naked peduncle, which rises up from the crown of a root.

SCAPEL. The caulicle, or neck formed between the root and cotyledon at the time of germination.

SCAPHIDIUM. A hollow case containing spores in algals.

SCAPHIUM. The carina or keel of papilionaceous flowers.

SCAPHIUM. The generic name given to a tree of Malacca previously known as Sterculia Scaphium, but differing from most species of Sterculia in the fifteen stamens of the sterile flowers, and especially in the singular boat-shaped follicular fruits, which are papery in texture, and marked with parallel nerves running from base to apex. The follicle bursts early, leaving fully exposed the solitary erect seed which is attached to its base, and when fully matured and dry is of an elliptical form and deeply wrinkled. Mr. Hanbury, writing of the seeds of this plant in the Pharmaceutical Journal for July 1861, observes that they have been imported into France as a certain specific against diarrhœa and dysentery; they have been tested, but no good results have been obtained. When macerated in water they swell enormously in volume, forming a large gelatinous mass; and this mucilaginous property gives a value to the fruit in the eyes of the Siamese and Chinese, in both which countries the jelly is sweetened and used as a delicacy. The Siamese names of the fruit are Boatam-paijang and Bungtalai. The leaves of the tree are smooth entire, oblong or ovate, pointed at the apex, and rounded or heart-shaped at the base. The flowers are imperfectly known.　　　　　[A. A. B.]

SCAPHYGLOTTIS. A small genus of Peruvian and Brazilian vandeous orchids remarkable for their peculiar habit, the greater number of the species having slender straggling stems bearing narrow pseudobulbs in the axils of the leaves. Its little axillary flowers have connivent sepals, the lateral ones prolonged at the base and connate with the foot of the column; similar but smaller petals; a narrow lip continuous with the column but turned up so as to be parallel with it; a slightly prolonged thin-edged column; and four rounded pollen-masses cohering in pairs, and attached by narrow caudicles to a broad gland.　　　　　[A. S.]

SCARIOUS. Having a thin dry shrivelled appearance, as the involucral leaves of many species of Centaurea.

SCARLET. The same as Coccineus.

SCARLET-RUNNER. Phaseolus multiflorus.

SCARLET-SEED. Ternströmia obovalis, and Lætia Thamnia.

SCAROLE? or ESCAROLE. Cichorium Endivia latifolia.

SCARRED. Marked by the scars left by bodies that have fallen off. The stem, for instance, is scarred at the points whence leaves have fallen.

SCATTERED. Dispersed: used in opposition to whorled, opposite, ternate, or similar terms.

SCEAU DE NOTRE DAME, or DE LA VIERGE. (Fr.) Tamus communis. — DE SALOMON. Polygonatum officinale and P. multiflorum.

SCENTWOOD of Tasmania. *Alyxia buxifolia.*

SCEPACEÆ. An order founded by Lindley on the genus *Scepa* or *Aporosa*, from tropical Asia, which has, however, since been united with the large order *Euphorbiaceæ.*

SCEPA. This genus, long considered as the type of a distinct family to which it gave the name, is now generally placed in the *Euphorbiaceæ*, among the genera of which it is readily known by its sterile flowers being disposed in axillary drooping catkins, somewhat like those of the birch, and the fertile flowers (borne on different plants) arranged in short axillary racemes or fascicles, each flower having a two-celled four-ovuled ovary crowned with two entire or forked styles. The name *Scepa* should, however, give place to that of *Aporosa*, which has the precedence. About a dozen species are known, all from the eastern hemisphere, and mostly from India and Java. They are trees or bushes with laurel-like leaves placed alternately on the stem, and accompanied by minute stipules. *Aporosa* (or *Scepa*, or *Lepidostachys*) *Roxburghii*, known in India as Kokra, affords, according to Dr. Roxburgh, a hard wood, which is useful for various purposes.   [A. A. B.]

SCEPTRE-FLOWER. *Sceptranthus.*

SCHÆFFERIA. A genus of *Celastraceæ*, comprising two rigid glabrous shrubs from the West Indies, Texas, and New Mexico. The leaves are alternate or clustered, small obovate or spathulate, and entire; the flowers are small and insignificant, diœcious solitary, or in clusters in the axils of the leaves. They have four sepals, petals, and stamens, a small disk, a free two-celled ovary with two ovules in each cell, and a small pea-shaped drupe containing two one-seeded nuts.

SCHAFFNERIA. A curious fern of Mexico, considered by Fée as the representative of a distinct genus of scolopendrioid ferns, characterised by its reticulated veins and radiately disposed short double sori. The fronds are simple, with a black stipes, rotundly flabellate or obovate, the veins radiately forked, with the venules anastomosing in several series of unequal elongated areoles.   [T. M.]

SCHAKAR. A Persian name for *Saccharum officinarum.*

SCHANGINIA. A small genus of *Chenopodiaceæ*, consisting of about four species, natives of Egypt, Arabia, and Northwestern Asia. These are herbaceous or rarely shrubby plants from six to eighteen inches high, smooth, and having narrow alternate rather fleshy leaves, bearing in their axils solitary or clusters of small stalkless flowers, with minute scale-like bracts at their bases. The flowers are either perfect or of the female sex only, and have the calyx cut at the top into five lobes. The fruit is half enclosed in the fleshy or berry-like tube of the calyx; and the seeds are vertical, double-coated, having a flat spiral embryo without albumen.   [A. S.]

SCHAPZIGER, SCHABZEIGER. A kind of Swiss cheese, flavoured with the leaves of *Melilotus cœruleus.*

SCHARKARA. A Sanscrit name signifying hard, stony: from which, according to Humboldt, the generic name *Saccharum* is derived.

SCHAUERIA. *Hyptis.*

SCHEELEA. A few tropical American palms have recently been formed into a genus under this name, but the characters by which it is distinguished from the older and better-known genera *Attalea* and *Maximiliana*, to which two at least of the so-called species of *Scheelea* were formerly referred, are very slight even if constant, which is doubtful. With the exception of one dwarf stemless species, they are lofty palms with thick cylindrical trunks from forty to eighty feet high, crowned with magnificent pinnate leaves composed of numerous narrow sharp-pointed leathery leaflets. Their large flower-spikes are enclosed in single thick woody spathes tapering to both ends and eventually splitting open along the back; some species have both sexes of flowers on the same spike, while others produce them on separate trees. The flowers are distinguished from those of *Attalea* by the petals being tapered instead of flat, and by the stamens being only six in number instead of ten or more; and from those of *Maximiliana* by the shape of the petals, and by the shorter stamens. Their fruits contain a single hard bony stone, surrounded by a fibrous and often oily husk.   [A. S.]

SCHEERIA. A genus of *Gesneraceæ* named in honour of F. Scheer, who introduced the two species composing it from Mexico, where they are diminutive herbs, with perennial catkin-like rhizomes and small flowers, giving little promise that under cultivation they would become the ornamental plants we find them in our hothouses. Of *S. mexicana* we possess two varieties, one having purple, the other blue flowers; it is perhaps handsomer than its congener, *S. lanata. Scheeria* belongs to the *Achimenes* tribe, and has a five-cleft calyx, a funnel-shaped corolla, a mouth-shaped (stomatomorphous) stigma, and a dehiscent capsule. The leaves are opposite, more or less heart-shaped and serrated, whilst the flowers appear in the axils of the leaves.   [B. S.]

SCHEIDWEILERIA. One of the forty-two genera into which Klotzsch has attempted to separate the 350 or more species of the extremely natural genus *Begonia*. It is much better regarded as a section of the latter than as a distinct genus. [A. S.]

SCHELHAMMERA. This not very euphonious name commemorates Professor Schelhammer of Jena, and is applied to a genus of *Melanthaceæ*. The species are perennial herbs, natives of eastern extra-tropical Australia. The roots are fibrous; the leaves broad, amplexicaul; and the flowers purple, terminal, solitary, stalked, without bracts. The bell-shaped perianth consists of six stalked segments, each with a shallow pit at the base; style central; stigmas three, central spreading; fruit a three-valved capsule containing a few seeds. One or two species are in cultivation, and are pretty purple-flowered greenhouse plants. [M. T. M.]

SCHELLOLEPIS. *Goniophlebium.*

SCHENKIA. The name of a genus of *Gentianaceæ*, comprising an herbaceous species, with rose-coloured flowers in spike-like cymes. In the structure of the flowers the genus resembles *Sebæa*, but the anthers are not bent downwards, and are unprovided with glands at their tips. The capsule also differs in being partially four-celled. The species is a native of the Cape of Good Hope. [M. T. M.]

SCHERBET, or **SHERBET.** An Eastern beverage consisting of water in which jelly or syrup has been dissolved. It is also made with honey and various flavouring ingredients, and is coloured by the juice of the berries of *Phytolacca decandra* and of *Cornus mascula*, the latter of which are an esteemed fruit in Asia Minor.

SCHEUCHZERIA. A curious rush-like marsh-plant belonging to the order *Juncaginaceæ*, of which the characters are: Perianth of six reflexed leaves, the inner ones narrower: filaments slender; ovaries three; capsules three, singularly inflated; flowers greenish, in a flexuose bracteated raceme. *S. palustris* grows in marshes, but is rare in Britain. [C. A. J.]

SCHIAKA. A Caroline Island name for *Macropiper methysticum.*

SCHIEDEA. A genus of *Caryophyllaceæ*, consisting of a small shrub from the Sandwich Islands, with knotted forked branches, the younger ones four-sided; leaves small opposite connate lanceolate; flowers small white in paniculate cymes; parts of the flower in fives, the stamens twice as many as the small bifid scale-like petals; capsule ovoid, three or four-valved, with numerous black globose tuberculated seeds without a strophiole at the hilum. [J. T. S.]

SCHILLERA. *Eriolæna.*

SCHIMPERA. A genus of *Cruciferæ* from Arabia. It is a small herb with the habit of *Vella annua*, having runcinate leaves, flowers with entire petals, and a one-celled indehiscent pouch crowned by the oblique leaf-like style, and containing a solitary pendulous seed. [J. T. S.]

SCHINUS. The Greek name for the mastick-tree, *Pistacia Lentiscus*, but now applied to a genus of *Anacardiaceæ*, consisting of trees and shrubs, natives of tropical America, &c. The leaves are unequally pinnate, the terminal leaflet very long. The flowers are small white, in terminal or axillary panicles, diœcious; calyx five-parted, persistent; stamens ten, inserted beneath a wavy fleshy disk; ovary solitary; styles three or four, terminal, very short; fruit succulent round, the stone one-celled one-seeded, its outer surface traversed by six longitudinal channels filled with oil.

'The leaves of some of the species are so filled with a resinous fluid, that the least degree of unusual repletion of the tissue causes it to be discharged; thus some of them fill the air with fragrance after rain; and *S. Molle* and some others expel their resin with such violence when immersed in water as to have the appearance of spontaneous motion, in consequence of the recoil.'—*Botanical Register*, t. 1580.

S. Areira is said to cause swellings in those who sleep under its shade. The fresh juicy bark of this shrub is used in Brazil for rubbing newly-made ropes, which it covers with a bright dark-brown varnish. The juice of this plant is used in diseases of the eyes. The root of *S. Molle* is used medicinally in Peru, while the resin that exudes from the tree is employed to astringe the gums. From the fruits is prepared a kind of wine in Chili. The small twigs serve for toothpicks. The specific name *Mollé* or *Mulli* is an adaptation of the Peruvian name for the shrub. [M. T. M.]

SCHISMATOPERA. The plant bearing this name, *S. distichophylla*, only differs from *Pera* in the four to eight stamens of its sterile flowers being supported on the end of a column formed by the union of the filaments, which are nearly free in *Pera*. The latter genus is remarkable among *Euphorbiaceæ* for its minute flowers, which are sterile and fertile on different plants, being enclosed in a small round involucre, that in the young state might readily be mistaken for a leaf-bud, arising as it does from the axil of the leaf. *S. distichophylla* is a small tree of Brazil and Guiana, having alternate two-ranked glossy leaves in size and form like those of the Portugal laurel, and bearing in their axils round involucres the size of small peas, containing three or four minute greenish-white sweet-scented blossoms. [A. A. B.]

SCHISMATOPTERIDES. A group of ferns proposed by Willdenow, for those genera in which the spore-cases are pseudo-gyrate dehiscing by a cleft, or the fructification is disposed in spikes or panicles instead of on the under-surface of the frond. It included such genera as *Gleichenia*, *Todea*, *Schizæa*, and *Osmunda*. [T. M.]

SCHISMUS. A genus of grasses belonging to the *Festuceæ*, the inflorescence of which is in simple panicles, the spikelets of which contain from five to seven florets; outer glumes two; flowering glumes the length of the florets or longer; lower pale emarginate, with a short awn at the point; upper pale entire; stamens three; style lengthened out. This genus contains only a few species, all annuals save one, *S. pa-*

tens, which is a native of Chili, the others being African and Persian. [D. M.]

SCHISTACEUS. Slate-grey.

SCHISTANTHE. A genus of *Scrophulariaceæ*, containing a single species, an imperfectly known herb from South Africa, which in habit and general structure resembles the South American genus *Alfonsoa*, except that the posterior lobes of the corolla are separated to the base. [W. C.]

SCHISTOGYNE. A genus of *Asclepiadaceæ*, containing a single species, a twining shrub from Southern Brazil. It has velvety cordate leaves, and few-flowered extra-axillary peduncles. The calyx is five-parted. The corolla is rotate-campanulate, clothed with a white villous covering on the inside, and the limb is divided into five spreading linear-lanceolate segments. The five-leaved staminal corona is inserted at the base of the included gynostegium; the anthers are terminated by a membrane; the ovoid pollen-masses attached below the apex; and the enlarged stigma divided into subulate segments. [W. C.]

SCHISTOSTEGA. A beautiful genus of acrocarpous annual mosses, consisting of a single species, with minute often frond-like stems springing from a mass of green threads, and bearing a small capsule without any peristome, containing spores radiating in lines from the columella as in *Splachnum*. The only species, *S. osmundacea*, occurs in several parts of England in caverns, which are illuminated by a golden-green light from the refractive property of its conferva-like shoots. The leaves are reduced at the base of the stems to mere threads; above they are vertical, two-ranked, and more or less confluent with each other or the stems, or leafy only at the tip, where they form a rose-like tuft, so that in the same species there are transitions from the more simple to the usual horizontal eight-ranked insertion. The name alludes to a supposed splitting of the lid, but this is not a constant character. [M. J. B.]

SCHIVERECKIA. A genus of *Cruciferæ* from Russia, with the habit of *Draba*, but the longer stamens having dilated and toothed filaments; pouch elliptical, with convex valves, depressed longitudinally in the middle; seeds numerous, compressed not margined; seed-stalks free. [J. T. S.]

SCHIZÆINEÆ. A tribe of polypodiaceous ferns, distinguished by having the horizontal ring apical on the spore-cases, so that they appear to be crowned by its convergent striæ, and thus become radiate-striate at the apex. It consists of two subtribes—the *Lygodieæ*, scandent plants in which the striæ are united at the apex so as to leave no vacant space; and the *Schizæe*, dwarf herbaceous plants, in which the striæ are disjoined so as to form an orbicular apical vacuity. [T. M.]

SCHIZÆA. The typical genus of the *Schizæineæ* of the group *Schizæe*, and distinguished by having its fructifications

seated on special contracted converging pinnæform appendages. They are very curious plants, with dichotomously-branched wiry-looking fronds; and are widely dispersed, occurring in North and South America, the West Indies, India, New Holland, the Pacific Islands, and the Cape of

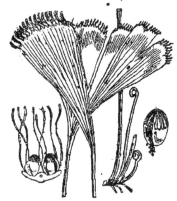

Schizæa flabellum.

Good Hope. In some cases (as in *S. flabellum* of Brazil) they form very handsome fan-shaped fronds, with a fringe of the fertile appendages on the upper margin. The segments of these appendages are beautiful objects under a magnifier. [T. M.]

SCHIZANDRACEÆ, or **SCHIZANDREÆ.** A tribe of *Magnoliaceæ*, considered by some botanists as a distinct order, distinguished from true *Magnolieæ* chiefly by their usually climbing habit, want of stipules, and unisexual flowers. They extend over tropical and Eastern Asia and North America, and only comprise two genera, *Schizandra* and *Kadsura*.

SCHIZANDRA. A genus of *Schizandraceæ* (or, according to some authorities, of *Magnoliaceæ*, tribe *Schizandreæ*), consisting of weak or climbing shrubs, with alternate entire leaves marked with transparent dots and without stipules, and solitary one-flowered axillary or lateral pedicels. The flowers are unisexual, red white or yellowish. The sepals and petals, varying in number from nine to twelve altogether, pass gradually the one into the other. The stamens in the males are more or less united in a globe or a ring. The carpels of the females are in a head when in flower, which as the fruit ripens becomes a long loose spike. There are six species known, one from North America with red flowers. The others, from tropical Asia, the Indian Archipelago, North-eastern Asia or Japan, have been distinguished, from differences in their stamens, into two or three genera, or united into one under the name of *Sphærostema*. One, the *S. grandiflora* from

Nepal, is handsome, with rather large white sweet-scented flowers, and all are more or less aromatic.

SCHIZANTHUS. A genus of *Scrophulariaceæ*, containing a few annual more or less viscid herbs, natives of Chili. The leaves are mostly pinnatisect, and the handsome flowers are borne on one-sided terminal cymes. The calyx is deeply five-cleft; the spreading limb of the corolla is elegantly divided into numerous segments; the two fertile stamens have two-celled anthers; the style has an obtuse apex; and the capsule is membranaceous. [W. C.]

SCHIZOCÆNA. A name proposed for a few Indian ferns now referred to *Cyathea*, in which the involucre or cup is split into a few broad lobes.

SCHIZOCHITON (*Chisocheton* of Blume). A small genus of *Meliaceæ*, confined to Java, and consisting of trees with paripinnate leaves, oblong and at the base oblique leaflets, paniculate flowers, an almost entire and urn-shaped calyx, five linear petals, from six to eight anthers, a club-shaped style, and a three or by abortion one or two-celled capsule, each cell containing a solitary seed. [B. S.]

SCHIZOCODON. A genus of *Polemoniaceæ*, founded on a single species, whose native locality is on the mountains of Japan. It is a perennial herb, with coriaceous evergreen leaves, all radical on long petioles, and simple scapes, somewhat longer than the leaves. The calyx and corolla are chiefly five-parted; the five stamens alternate, with as many linear ciliate scales; the style simple terminal and persistent; and the stigma three-toothed. [W. C.]

SCHIZOGRAMMA. *Gymnogramma*.

SCHIZOGYNE. The only species of this genus of *Compositæ*, *S. sericea*, is a much-branched little bush about a foot high, found growing on maritime rocks in the Canary Islands. The stems are furnished with alternate linear leaves about an inch in length, and terminate in corymbs of numerous small yellow flower-heads. There are two varieties, one in which the stems and leaves are covered with a white tomentum, and another in which they are quite smooth. The genus differs chiefly from *Inula* in the entire instead of fringed or lacerated anther-tails. [A. A. B.]

SCHIZOLÆNA. A genus of *Chlenaceæ* peculiar to Madagascar, and composed of elegant small trees, with ovate glabrous leaves, and paniculate or racemose flowers, either terminal or growing out of the old wood of the trunk. The involucre is not fleshy as in *Sarcolæna*; there are three sepals, five petals, an indefinite number of stamens, a three-celled capsule, and numerous seeds in each cell. [B. S.]

SCHIZOLEPTON. A small genus of ferns sometimes referred to *Schizoloma*, but differing in not having a membranaceous indusium, and hence proposed as one of the *Tænitideæ*, ranking near *Tænitis*,

which it resembles in its uniform veins without free veinlets, but from which it differs in the sori being immersed in a groove, the exterior margin of which is thickened. *S. cordatum*, the typical species, is a Molucca plant. [T. M.]

SCHIZOLOBIUM. A genus of the *Leguminosæ* closely related to *Cæsalpinia*, of which it has the flowers, but differing in the pods, which are described as obovate compressed one-seeded, each of the two valves readily splitting into two portions, the outer coriaceous in texture, and the inner, which encloses the seed, membranaceous. The only known species, *S. excelsum*, is a noble tree of Brazil and Panama, attaining a height of 130 feet, the branches furnished towards the apex with large and handsome twice-pinnate leaves like the fronds of some large fern, and terminating in great panicles of pale-yellow flowers. The leaves vary from two to five feet in length, and are made up of about eighteen pairs of pinnæ, each bearing about twenty pairs of oblong leaflets clothed beneath with a white or yellowish pubescence. The individual flowers have a shortly tubular calyx, with a five-parted reflexed border, five-clawed notched petals, ten perfect stamens, and a shortly stalked many-ovuled ovary crowned with a simple style. [A. A. B.]

SCHIZOLOMA. This genus of ferns differs from *Lindsæa* only in having the veins netted instead of free; the fructification is in all respects the same. It contains a few species found in India, Malacca, New Holland, and South Africa, but does not occur in America. [T. M.]

SCHIZOMERIA. A genus of *Cunoniaceæ* from Eastern Australia. It forms a tree, with simple stalked oblong-elliptical acute serrate leaves, undivided caducous stipules, and small white flowers in terminal panicles; petals five, laciniate; stamens ten, with head-shaped anthers; ovary free, two-celled, with numerous ovules. [J. T. S.]

SCHIZONEMA. A curious genus of diatomaceous *Algæ*, which, from the abundance of the gelatinous element, is characterised by its forming variously fissured branched threads containing several chains, or in the ultimate divisions a single chain of frustules. The species are, with one or two exceptions, confined to salt water. [M. J. B.]

SCHIZOPETALON. A genus of *Cruciferæ*, consisting of Chilian annual herbs with pinnatifid leaves, and long bracteated racemes of white flowers, which are remarkable for their pinnatifid petals. The embryo has four green cotyledons, which are spirally twisted; the pod is narrowly linear, beaded. [J. T. S.]

SCHIZOPHRAGMA. A Japanese shrub forming a genus of *Saxifragaceæ*, of the tribe or suborder *Hydrangeæ*. It has the habit and almost all the characters of *Hydrangea* itself, with similar small flowers in a broad compound cyme or corymb, the outer ones much enlarged and barren; and only appears to differ from that genus in the ovary and fruit having four or five cells instead of two only.

SCHIZOPHYLLUM. A remarkable genus of gill-bearing *Fungi*, in which the coriaceous gills are split through their whole length along the central substance or trama, the two divisions turning back and becoming involute. The pileus is white, or slightly tinged with red or amber, and is more or less rough with little bundles of short threads, the margin variously lobed, and the surface zoned. The species are few in number and essentially tropical, *S. commune*, the most universal of tropical fungi, extending, though rarely, into temperate regions. It is one of the fungi which frequently make their appearance on imported wood in hothouses, and is always in such situations a pleasing object. In a natural situation it is one of our rarest fungi, and has been seen by very few mycologists. [M. J. B.]

SCHIZOPLEURA. The name of a genus of shrubs of the family *Myrtaceæ*. The species are natives of Swan River, and are closely allied to *Beaufortia*, the points of distinction being these:—Flowers in terminal heads; calyx detached from the ovary; anthers opening horizontally; ovary free; capsule parchment-like, included within the thickened calyx-tube. [M. T. M.]

SCHKUHRIA. A genus belonging to the *Compositæ* and the subtribe *Heleneæ*, and comprising about a dozen species, which are spread over Mexico and South America. All are much-branched slender annual weeds of little beauty, having pinnately cut or tripartite leaves, and solitary yellow flower-heads arising from the axils of the leaves or the ends of the branchlets. The involucre of about five obtuse scales encloses from four to ten florets, from one to five of which are strap-shaped and pistil-bearing, the others tubular and perfect. The achenes are three to four-angled, and crowned with a pappus of six or eight broad membranaceous scales, which are either all rounded at the apex, or all bristle-pointed, or the alternate pointed and the others blunt. *Achyropappus* and *Hopkirkia* are synonyms of the genus, which bears the name of Ch. Schkuhr, a German botanist. [A. A. B.]

SCHLAGINTWEITIA. The *Hieracium albidum*, a well-known hawkweed of the Alps of Southern Europe, has been separated under the above name, mainly, as it would appear, from its having a few foliaceous bracts surrounding the flower-heads. It is a herb about six inches high, all its parts clothed more or less with dark glandular hairs; the stems are simple or slightly branched, furnished with lanceolate distantly toothed leaves, and terminating in solitary pale-yellow flower-heads about an inch across. It was named in honour of the brothers Schlagintweit, who travelled in North-western India and Central Asia,

where one of them met a cruel and untimely fate. [A. A. B.]

SCHLECHTENDALIA. A rather handsome erect perennial herb of Montevideo, remarkable in the tribe *Mutisieæ* of the *Compositæ* for its peculiar habit. Its unbranched rather robust stems, from six inches to two feet high, are more or less clothed with soft rusty hairs, and furnished (chiefly at the base) with rigid grassy leaves like those of *Luzula alba*, whence the plants receive the specific name of *luzulæfolia*. The stems terminate in from one to five stalked flower-heads, each furnished with an involucre of numerous straw-coloured narrow slender-pointed scales, enclosing a goodly number of yellow florets: these are all tubular, perfect, and deeply divided into five equal narrow portions, clothed outside with short silky down. The top-shaped achenes are clothed with soft hairs, and crowned with a pappus of broad slender-pointed unequal pales. It has been named after Dr. F. L. Schlechtendal, an eminent German botanist. [A. A. B.]

SCHLEGELIA. A name given to some plants now referred to *Tanæcium*. [B. S.]

SCHLEICHERA *trijuga*, the tropical Asiatic plant upon which this genus of *Sapindaceæ* is founded, was formerly combined with the closely allied American *Melicocca*, from which, however, it is distinguished by its flowers having a five-toothed calyx, no petals, from six to ten stamens inserted between the ovary and the disk, and occupying the centre of the flower, a three-celled ovary terminated by a style, and a three-cleft stigma. It is a large tree, and has abruptly pinnate leaves composed usually of three pairs of leaflets, and spike-like racemes of small flowers, succeeded by round one two or rarely three-celled fruits, with a solitary seed covered with a pulpy arillus in each cell. It is common in the peninsula of India (where it is called Koosumbia), in Ceylon, and also in Burmah, where its timber is employed for purposes requiring great strength and solidity. In India and Ceylon the lac-insect (*Coccus*) frequents this tree; and considerable quantities of stick-lac, from which part of the shellac and lac-dye of commerce is prepared, are collected from its young branches. An oil also is expressed from the seeds, and used both for burning in lamps, and also as a cure for the itch. [A. S.]

SCHLEIDENIA. A genus of *Boraginaceæ*, consisting of small prostrate Brazilian herbs, with alternate narrow entire leaves, and small axillary white or yellow flowers, solitary or in spikes. The genus is closely allied to *Heliotropium*, and has the habit of some of its smaller tropical species, and indeed scarcely differs except in its fruit, which is a small drupe enclosing four nuts, instead of separating into two or four distinct dry nuts. There are four species, all of a very weedy aspect.

SCHLIMMIA *jasminodora.* An extremely fragrant Central American orchid forming a genus of the vandeous suborder. It is an epiphyte with long slender single-leaved pseudobulbs, and radical bracteated flower-stalks about a foot high, bearing on one side and towards the summit three pure white flowers. These have fleshy unequal sepals, the upper one being narrow straight and free, and the two lower much larger and completely combined into a deep sack, beyond the mouth of, which the two narrow reflexed petals project; the very minute lip is fleshy and warted at its base, and thin and trowel-shaped above, and is articulated with the column, which is eared on each side of its apex, and has its prolonged base connate with the lateral sepals; the two pollen-masses are attached by a long wedge-shaped caudicle to a minute moon-shaped gland. [A. S.]

SCHMIDELIA. A genus of *Sapindaceæ* distributed through the tropics of both hemispheres, and consisting of a considerable number of species, either trees or shrubs, with leaves composed of three leaflets, or rarely of only one; and producing from their axils, simple or divided racemes of small white flowers, having four sepals, as many petals (one of them always abortive), and four glands opposite the petals; the ovary is two or sometimes three-lobed. In most cases only one of the lobes ripens, and forms a globose fleshy or dry fruit, containing a single thin-shelled seed.

The fruits of *S. africana* form one of the many remedies employed in Abyssinia against the tapeworm, which in that country is a common complaint. The dried fruits are pounded and mixed with flour, and then made into cakes. The species is a native of both East and West tropical Africa, and forms a tree of from twenty to thirty feet high. The sweet pulpy part of the fruit of *S. edulis* is eaten in Brazil, where the fruits are called Fruta de Paraó; but the seeds of most of the genus possess unwholesome properties, and those of *S. Cobbe,* a Cingalese species, are reputed to be poisonous. [A. S.]

SCHOBERIA. A genus of marine plants belonging to the *Chenopodiaceæ,* and closely allied to *Chenopodium,* from which they are most obviously distinguished by their small fleshy semicylindrical leaves. *S. fruticosa,* the Shrubby Sea-Blite, abundant on the muddy coast of Norfolk, is an erect shrub two to three feet high, locally known by the name of Sea Rosemary. It grows also on other parts of the eastern coast of England, but is rare. *S. maritima* is a procumbent annual species with a branched diffuse stem, and is of frequent occurrence on most parts of the coast. All the species abound in soda, and in all the flowers are inconspicuous. [C. A. J.]

SCHŒNIA. A genus of *Compositæ,* nearly allied to *Helichrysum, Helipterum,* and *Pteropogon,* from which it is described as differing, in the inner scales of the invo-lucre being appendaged and radiant, in the many-flowered heads, and in the central florets being truly male. The flowers are always tubular, but they are surrounded by a scarious involucre in many series, the inner of which have petaloid appendages, which spread out so as to appear like ray-florets. The receptacle is without scales, and the achenes are obovate with a setose pappus in a single series. They are Swan River annuals. [T. M.]

SCHŒNOCAULON. *Asagræa.*

SCHŒNOPRASUM. *Allium Schœnoprasum.*

SCHŒNORCHIS *juncifolia* is a Javanese epiphytal orchid, with fleshy subulate leaves, allied to *Saccolabium,* from which it is distinguished chiefly by its column being furnished with a couple of long slender erect horn-like processes at its base. Two other Javanese species were originally placed in the genus by Blume, but they are now removed to *Saccolabium.* [A. S.]

SCHŒNUS. A genus of sedge-grass belonging to the tribe *Rhynchosporeæ.* It has the inflorescence in heads or crowded panicles, the spikelets of which are one or many-flowered; glumes in two rows, the lowest three or four empty, the upper having flowers in their axils; flowers hermaphrodite, with bristles round the ovary. There are upwards of thirty species described in Steudel's *Synopsis;* these have a wide geographical range. *S. nigricans* is the only European species. [D. M.]

SCHŒNUS, WHOLE. *Scirpus Holoschœnus.*

SCHOMBURGKIA. A small tropical American genus of epidendreous orchids of the tribe *Bletideæ,* named in honour of the late Sir Robert Schomburgk, the well-known scientific explorer of Guiana. The plants belonging to it have generally very large long pseudobulbs rising from naked ring-scarred creeping rootstocks, and each furnished with two or three leathery leaves. They are also remarkable for the great length of their slender terminal flower-stems, which are clothed with great dry spathaceous sheaths, and bear at their extremity a short roundish raceme of long-stalked showy flowers. Generically it is nearly allied to *Epidendrum,* from which, however, its eight pollen-masses at once distinguish it. The flowers have quite similar spreading free sepals and petals, and a membranous three-lobed half-cucullate lip, connate at its base with the edge of the winged column.

In one species, *S. tibicinis,* a native of Honduras, the pseudobulbs are between one and two feet long and quite hollow and smooth inside, and are commonly used by the native children as trumpets, whence it is called the Cowhorn orchid. At their base too there is always a small hole, and masses of ants and other insects take advantage of it in constructing their nests. [A. S.]

SCHÖPFIA. A genus of *Olacaceæ*, consisting of tropical American or Asiatic shrubs, or small trees, with alternate entire leaves, and white flowers, often large for the order, in short axillary racemes or clusters. Their structure is in some respects curious, and has given rise to differences of opinion. A small outer cup is considered by some as an involucre, by others as a calyx, whilst the disk adnate to the base of the ovary which bears the corolla is thought by some to be the true calyx. The petals are united into a campanulate or tubular corolla as in the true *Monopetalæ*, and the lower part of the ovary to which the above-mentioned disk is adnate is the only portion which enlarges after flowering; and its margin shows a ring round the top of the ripe drupe, thus offering the anomaly of a superior ovary and an inferior fruit. There are about ten species known, of which rather more than half are Asiatic.

SCHOTIA. A South African genus belonging to the *Cæsalpineæ* section of *Leguminosæ*, in which the flowers are regular instead of papilionaceous. The genus is related to *Cassia*, but may at once be recognised by the ten perfect stamens of the flowers, which do not open by pores at the apex but by slits along their whole length. *S. tamarindifolia* (or *speciosa*) is a scrubby bush of eight to ten feet, having simply pinnate leaves, and terminal panicles of deep crimson blossoms; and from the calyx being slightly tubular, and coloured like the petals, the flower bears some resemblance to that of a short-tubed *Fuchsia*. According to Dr. Atherstone, the beans from the pods of this plant are roasted and eaten in the Albany districts, where they are called Boerboom, and the powerfully astringent bark is used medicinally as well as in tanning. The genus was named in honour of Richard Van der Schot, the travelling companion and friend of Jacquin.   [A. A. B.]

SCHOUWIA. A genus of *Cruciferæ* from Arabia, distinguished from *Psychine* by their oval pouches with a narrow ring at the back of each valve.   [J. T. S.]

SCHRADERA. A genus of *Cinchonaceæ*, consisting of tropical American pseudo-parasitical shrubs, bearing their flowers in terminal stalked heads encircled by an involucre. The limb of the calyx is slightly five-toothed; the corolla funnel-shaped, with a slender tube, a hairy throat, and a limb divided into five to eight spreading lobes, which have a thickened keel-like ridge on the outside, and sometimes a small thick hook-like process within; anthers sessile, partially projecting from the tube of the corolla; fruit succulent pea-shaped, two to four-celled; seeds numerous, small, embedded in pulp. [M. T. M.]

SCHRANKIA. A genus of *Leguminosæ*, with flowers like those of *Mimosa*; but the pods, instead of being flat as in that genus and jointed between the seeds, are four-sided with continuous valves, linear in form, and covered with slender recurved prickles. There are about a dozen species, all American, and ranging from the Southern States to Brazil. Most are straggling perennial herbs, with slender angular stems, covered with numerous recurved prickles like those on some roses, and bearing twice-pinnate leaves, which are much like those of *Mimosa pudica*, and have the same singular property of closing when touched. The pink flowers are borne in round balls or spikes in the axils of the leaves. The genus was named in honour of F. Schrank, an eminent German botanist.   [A. A. B.]

SCHREBERA. A genus of doubtful affinity, placed by some with *Bignoniaceæ*, by others with *Jasminaceæ*, but with neither of which natural orders it seems intimately connected. There is only one species, *S. swietenoides*, the Muccaady or Mogalinga-marum of India. It is a tall tree, deriving its specific name from a certain resemblance to *Swietenia Mahagoni*. The leaves are pinnate; the flowers dirty-white, and arranged in panicles; the calyx tubular, and irregularly divided into three or five lobes; the corolla hypocraterimorphous, and divided into from five to seven lobes; the stamens two in number; and the fruit, a pear-shaped capsule, two-celled, and enclosing in each cell four winged seeds. The tree is found in valleys in various parts of India.   [B. S.]

SCHUBERTIA. A genus of *Asclepiadaceæ*, containing several species of twining hairy and milky shrubs from tropical South America. They have opposite leaves, and fleshy flowers in handsome umbels. The calyx is deeply five-parted; the corolla funnel-shaped, the tube swollen below, and the limb divided into five linear spreading lobes; the anthers terminated by a short membrane; the pollen-masses obovate compressed and pendulous; and the stigma turbinate.   [W. C.]

SCHUERMANNIA. This genus comprises an Australian myrtaceous shrub, with solitary axillary flowers, each provided with two opposite membranous bracts. The five-ribbed tube of the calyx is somewhat fleshy, adherent to the ovary; its limb divided into five petaloid membranous lance-shaped segments; petals five, roundish concave; stamens nine or ten, alternating with an equal number of barren stamens; anthers opening by pores; style thread-like protruding, twisted spirally at the end; ovary one-celled, enclosed within the calyx.   [M. T. M.]

SCHULTZIA. The name of a genus belonging to the order of umbellifers, and distinguished from its congeners by its fruit being cylindrically prismatic, compressed laterally, each half of it with five narrow ridges; and by having a single oil-vessel in each groove, and two at the line of junction. The only species is *S. crinita*, a native of the Altai mountain range. The genus was named in honour of John Henry Schultz, a German botanist. [G. D.]

SCHUURMANSIA. A genus of *Violaceæ* of the tribe *Sauvagesiæ*, distinguished in the tribe by all the staminodia being free and linear or subulate, and by the winged seeds. There are two species known, trees or shrubs from the Indian Archipelago, with alternate entire or serrate leaves, and yellow flowers in a terminal panicle.

SCHWÆGRICHENIA. *Cleistes.*

SCHWANNIA. A genus of Brazilian climbing shrubs, belonging to the *Malpighiaceæ*. The flowers are red, placed in panicles on the ends of the branches; the calyx is deeply five-cleft, four of the segments having at their base two glands; petals five, stalked fringed; stamens six, all fertile, the filaments combined at the base, the anthers hairy at the back; ovaries three, style single. The fruit consists of three winged carpels, each with a single seed. [M. T. M.]

SCHWEIGGERIA. A genus of *Violaceæ*, so named in compliment to Professor Schweigger, author of a *Flora of Erlangen*. The species are Brazilian shrubs, with narrow finely-toothed leaves, and solitary stalked axillary flowers. The calyx is divided into five unequal segments, the three hinder ones hastate, and much larger than the two narrow anterior segments; petals five unequal, the uppermost or hindermost very large, and spurred at the base; stamens partially attached to the calyx, unequal in size, the anthers crested, the crest of the two anterior ones larger than that of the others, and concealed within the spur of the petal. The fruit is capsular, surrounded by the withered remnants of the flower. *S. pauciflora*, a species with white flowers, is in cultivation. [M. T. M.]

SCHWEINITZIA. The name of a genus of fir-rapes, distinguished by the following characters:—The corolla is bell-shaped, five-lobed, with five dilatations at the base, and as long as the concave pieces of the calyx; and the bag-like cells of the anthers open by a pore. The only species is *S. odorata*, a native of North America, and parasitical on the roots of different plants. The name was given in honour of L. D. von Schweinitz. [G. D.]

SCHWENKIA. A curious genus referred to *Scrophulariaceæ*. The species are tropical American herbs with panicled flowers; calyx tubular; corolla tubular, its limb five-toothed, with two to five club-shaped glands placed between the teeth; stamens five, inserted at the base of the tube of the corolla, opposite to its segments, two only fertile, the remainder antherless; ovary two-celled, the placentæ and ovules attached to the partition between the two cavities; fruit capsular, two-valved. *S. americana*, a species with lilac flowers, is in cultivation. Dr. Schwenk was Professor of Medicine at Jena. [M. T. M.]

SCHWERINIA. This genus, founded upon an erroneous observation, is absolutely identical with *Meriania*. [B. S.]

SCIADOCALYX. A gesneraceous genus consisting of only one species, *S. Warszewiczii*, a native of New Granada, and cultivated in hothouses on account of its ornamental qualities, and flowering during the winter months. Its rhizome is catkin-like; its stem densely covered with hairs, as are also its ovato crenate leaves and axillary flower-stalks; its calyx is proportionally large and bell-shaped, whilst the tubular corolla is somewhat inflated towards the top, and of a bright pinkish-scarlet colour. [B. S.]

SCIADOPHYLLUM. A genus of ivyworts, distinguished by a peculiarity of the corolla, the petals of which cohere at the apex; in other respects it is nearly allied to *Aralia*. The species are trees or climbing shrubs, natives of Asia and tropical America. The name is from the Greek words signifying 'shade' and 'leaf,' in allusion to the great size of the leaves in some species. [G. D.]

SCIADOPITYS *verticillata* is the representative of a singular genus of *Coniferæ* peculiar to Japan, and closely allied to the North American *Sequoia*. It has recently been introduced to our gardens, and has been cultivated from time immemorial by the Japanese around their temples. It belongs to the tribe *Cunninghamieæ*, and chiefly differs from its nearest ally, with which it shares the free seeds, in having cones with bracteate scales and five to eight seeds. The trunk is erect, from a hundred to a hundred and fifty feet high, and of pyramidal habit; the branches verticillate; and the leaves linear, from thirty to forty sessile and crowded at the ends of the branches. The flowers are probably diœcious, the stamens numerous, and the cones are nearly globose, and ripen in the second year. [B. S.]

SCIADOSERIS. The generic name given by Kunze to a perennial herb belonging to the *Compositæ*, cultivated in the Berlin Botanic Garden, and supposed to be of Chilian origin. Its stems are one to two feet high, irregularly branched above, and terminating in corymbs of white flower-heads; the lower leaves thrice pinnatifid, with sheathing bases, and upwards of a foot long, the sheathing portion only of the upper leaves developed; involucre of two series of lance-shaped scales, enclosing twenty to thirty tubular and perfect five-parted florets, which are seated on a frilled receptacle; achenes four or five-angular, and crowned with a uniserial pappus of unequal rough white hairs. The specific name, *vaginata*, refers to the sheathing bases of the leaves. The plant is said to be related to *Vernonia*. [A. A. B.]

SCIAPHILA. A genus of *Triuridaceæ*, consisting of small slender leafless herbs, usually erect and simple, of a white or reddish colour, which are found in tropical countries growing on moist decaying vegetable matter or leaf-mould. The small flowers, in a terminal raceme, are monœcious, with a perianth of six divisions and three stamens; the ovary consists of several distinct carpels with lateral styles, and one ovule in each, and the fruit is a little head of small seed-like nuts like that of some *Alismas*. There are eight species known—four from tropical America, four from Ceylon, Java, or the Philippine Islands.

SCILLA. A genus of bulbous plants giving name to the suborder *Scilleæ* of liliaceous plants, distinguished from *Allium* by having the flowers inserted one above the other on the scape, and from *Ornithogalum* by having the petals deciduous. Two species are indigenous to Britain: *S. verna*, a beautiful little plant four to six inches high, with long narrow leaves, and dense corymbs of bright-blue fragrant flowers, very abundant on the cliffs of Cornwall, and frequent also in the Orkney and Shetland Isles ; and *S. autumnalis*, which grows also in Cornwall and in other parts of England, not being exclusively confined to the seashore. In this species the corymbs of flowers, which are of a dull purplish-blue, are elongated, and the leaves and flowers do not appear simultaneously. Of the cultivated species, *S. præcox*, *S. sibirica*, and *S. bifolia* are most prized, as they put forth their brilliant blue flowers at the very beginning of spring. *S. italica* and *S. peruviana* are far more pretentious plants, but they bloom later in the season, when flowers are more abundant; the former is a native of Switzerland and Italy, the latter of the Spanish peninsula, from whence it was introduced to South America by the early colonists, and naturalised in various parts of Chili and Peru. French : *Scille* ; German : *Meerzwiebel.* [C. A. J.]

SCIMITAR-SHAPED. The same as Acinaciform.

SCINDAPSUS. A genus of Indian herbs belonging to the *Orontiaceæ*. The species have a scrambling stem, and perforated or pinnately-divided leaves on long channelled stalks. The spadix is sessile or nearly so, with female flowers at the lower part and perfect flowers above, encircled by a spreading spathe, which soon falls off ; ovaries one-celled, with one or two erect ovules. *S. officinalis* is cultivated at Midnapore, in Bengal, for the sake of its fruit, which is cut into pieces, dried, and employed medicinally. The fruit of *S. pertusus* is likewise employed as a remedy in skin-diseases, rheumatism, &c. Several species, known for the most part under the name of *Pothos*, are in cultivation. The holes in the leaves of some of these plants have been taken as the indications of future lobes, but Trécul, who has examined them carefully as to this point, says that the perforations depend upon the distention of certain portions of the tissue of the leaf with gas, and upon the subsequent bursting of the skin of the leaf. As the leaves increase in size and age, so the gaps grow larger. [M. T. M.]

SCIPOULE. (Fr.) *Urginea Scilla.*

SCIRPUS. A genus of sedge-grasses belonging to the tribe *Scirpeæ*. It has the inflorescence in solitary spikes or several together, clustered and forming heads; glumes imbricated on every side, none of the scales empty ; style jointed at the base, and deciduous ; the flowers furnished with bristles beneath the ovary. This genus, as adopted by some authors, is extensive, and contains many species, which have a wide geographical distribution. Steudel has described them under different genera, and only retained a few under the original. There are fourteen of them natives of the British Isles, nearly all growing in situations where they are frequently covered by water during the winter. *S. lacustris*, the well-known Bulrush, is extensively used for making bottoms of chairs, floor-mats, &c., in most parts of Europe. [D. M.]

SCITAMINEÆ. A large order of monocotyledons, which, taken in a comprehensive view, corresponds with the anomal alliance of Lindley. It is almost entirely tropical, and includes many plants of considerable size, and all remarkable among monocotyledons for their leaves (which are often large, and have pinnate or diverging veins), and for their unsymmetrical flowers: their perfect stamens being always reduced to five or fewer, whilst the perianth divisions are of the normal number, six. The ovary is usually three-celled, and the seeds albuminous. The whole group comprises three tribes or orders—*Musaceæ*, with more perfect anthers than one ; *Zingiberaceæ*, with only one perfect two-celled anther ; and *Marantaceæ*, with only one perfect one-celled anther—the other stamens (if present) being always converted into barren mostly petal-like staminodia.

SCLAREA. *Salvia Sclarea.*

SCLARÉE. (Fr.) *Salvia Sclarea.*

SCLERACHNE. A genus of grasses belonging to the tribe *Agrostideæ*. The inflorescence is in contracted shining panicles, the spikelets of which are linear and one-flowered ; glumes two equal, or the lower a little the smaller ; pale with a short awn at the apex. This small genus contains only two species, which are annuals, and natives of the Southern States of America. [D. M.]

SCLERANTHACEÆ. The genus *Scleranthus* and two or three others belonging to the *Paronychiaceæ* have been proposed as a separate order under the above name, on account of their deep calyx-tube bearing the stamens at the top, and hardening round the nut when in fruit; but the separation is not generally adopted.

SCLERANTHUS. Unimportant weeds giving name to the order *Scleranthaceæ*. They rarely exceed a few inches in length, and have much-branched diffuse stems. opposite linear leaves (which are united at the base by a membrane), and inconspicuous green flowers, of which the calyx is contracted at the mouth, and becomes rigid when in fruit. The segments of the calyx are edged by a narrow white membrane, which gives the flowers a variegated appearance. There are two British species—*S. annuus*, the annual Knawel, a common weed in cornfields; and *S. perennis*, which scarcely differs except in having perennial roots. French: *Gnavelle*; German: *Wilde Knauel.* [C. A. J.]

SCLERIA. A genus of sedge-grasses belonging to the tribe *Sclerineæ.* The inflorescence is in spikes; male female or androgynous; scales imbricated on every side, the lower subdistichous and empty; stamens three, rarely one to two; female spikelets one-flowered; styles three-cleft; androgynous spikelets with the lowest flower female, the others male. Steudel describes 149 species, which have a wide geographical distribution, chiefly within or bordering on the tropics of the southern hemisphere. [D. M.]

SCLEROCHITON. A genus of *Acanthaceæ*, containing a single species from the Cape of Good Hope. It is an erect undershrub, with small rigid suboval leaves, and solitary axillary flowers. The persistent calyx is five-parted; the corolla has a single lip with an incurved tube and five-lobed limb; the four stamens are exserted, and the anthers consist of a single semiovate cell which has a dilated margin; the style is persistent; the stigma is bidentate; and the capsule is two-celled, the lower half compressed, the two seeds being borne above the middle. [W. C.]

SCLEROCHLOA. A genus of grasses belonging to the tribe *Festuceæ*, the species of which are arranged by Steudel under *Glyceria*, and by Bentham under *Poa.* [D. M.]

SCLERODERMA. A genus of puffballs with a hard coriaceous coat, which contains a mass of spores here and there divided by thin filmy partitions. In an early stage the component threads produce swollen sporophores, which bear about four rugged spores on as many papillæ. The threads except in the partitions soon vanish, and the spores seem to acquire their full size and structure when free. In general the peridium bursts irregularly at the summit, but in *S. Geaster* it opens in a stellate manner, exposing a globular mass of seeds. *S. vulgare*, which is neat subglobose and about the size of an onion, is common in woods and on lawns, the surface being variously cracked or warty. Some of the species, when growing in sand, and assuming a subterraneous habit, are occasionally mistaken for truffles, but they are too tough to be good articles of food in any condition. One of them is subject to be infested by *Boletus parasiticus*, which is abundant in the pleasure-grounds at Kew, though rare elsewhere. [M. J. B.]

SCLEROGEN. The hard matter deposited by some plants in the interior of their cells, as in those forming the shell of the walnut.

SOLEROGENEA. A condition in cultivated plants, consisting in a tendency to revert to their natural condition, which is indicated by a hardening of the tissues, accompanied frequently by a diminution of cellular development and of the nutritious matters of which it is the object of the cultivator to promote the formation. It is in fact exactly analogous to what is called grittiness in pears, which is exhibited exactly in proportion to the approach of any especial variety to the wild condition. It is the vascular bundles more especially which are affected, and in consequence such roots as carrots, beet, turnips, &c., become almost uneatable, potatos are stringy, and even fruits like apricots (especially the variety called Breda) become more or less disagreeable. This condition may either belong to particular individuals produced from seed, or it may be dependent on peculiarly dry seasons or other conditions unfavourable to rapid growth. The cellular tissue or its richness in fecula is not always affected. Stringy potatos, for example, are sometimes more mealy than others. This affection is totally different from one in which the tissues are hardened from an alteration in the structure of the walls due to some chemical change, or from the condensation of the contents of the cells from some similar cause. Good cultivation and well-selected seed are the only remedies, and even these are not always efficient. [M. J. B.]

SOLEROID. Having a hard texture.

SCLEROLOBIUM. A genus of *Leguminosæ* of the tribe *Cæsalpineæ*, comprising eight species of forest-trees peculiar to Brazil and Guiana. They have alternate equally pinnate leaves, and small yellow odoriferous flowers, disposed in great profusion in large terminal racemed panicles. The essential characters of the genus are: a shortly tubular five-parted persistent calyx; five very narrow petals; ten perfect stamens, their filaments free and bearded at the base; and a sessile ovary which, when ripe, is a compressed elliptical woody pod with a few seeds. *S. tinctorium* has, according to Mr. Spruce, a rough bark which abounds in tannin, and is used as a dye about Caripí, in Brazil. *S. chrysophyllum*, so called from the golden-yellow silky hairs on the under-surface of the leaflets, is a North Brazilian species, growing to a height of sixty or a hundred feet. Its white wood is used for making charcoal and for other purposes. The name of the genus alludes to the hard woody nature of the pod, which does not open when ripe like most others. [A. A. B.]

SCLEROÖN. A genus of *Verbenaceæ*, containing a single species from Mexico. It is a shrub with opposite entire leaves, and flowers in axillary few-flowered cymes. The calyx is campanulate and four-toothed; the corolla funnel-shaped, with a quadrifid limb; there are four stamens; the ovary is four-celled, with one ovule in each cell: the short style has an obtuse stigma; and the indehiscent drupe is covered by the persistent calyx.* [W. C.]

SCLEROPHYLAX. A curious genus of small Chilian plants having affinities with *Nolanaceæ*, *Ehretiaceæ*, and *Myoporaceæ*. The stems are branched, bearing spathulate geminate leaves, and axillary sessile flowers in pairs; calyx five-parted, with a very short tube, two or three of the segments being elongated into triquetrous spines or leaf-like expansions; corolla funnel-shaped, contracted at the mouth with a bell-shaped five-parted limb, somewhat two-lipped, resembling that of the small-flowered *Petunias*. [J. T. S.]

SCLEROSCIADIUM. A genus of umbellifers, distinguished by having the tips of the petals two or three-toothed; the fruit roundish ovate, each half with five thick equal ribs; and one oil-vessel in each of the narrow grooves, and two at the line of junction. The only species is *S. humile*, a native of Mogador. The name is derived from two Greek words signifying 'hard' and 'umbel,' in allusion to the habit of the plant. [G. D.]

SCLEROSTYLIS. This genus of *Aurantiaceæ* consists of trees or shrubs natives of India, Java, &c. Professor Oliver, the most recent investigator of the order, is of opinion that the genus should be cancelled, and its species referred to *Glycosmis* and *Atalantia*. [M. T. M.]

SCLEROTHAMNUS. The generic name of a small much-branched wiry-stemmed bush of West Australia belonging to the *Leguminosæ*, and closely related to *Pultenæa*, differing chiefly in the minute two-seeded pods being stalked instead of sessile. The specific name, *microphyllus*, alludes to the minute heath-like leaves, which are closely set, and bear in their axils the solitary inconspicuous pale-yellow pea-flowers. It is of little beauty. [A. A. B.]

SCLEROTIUM. A spurious genus of *Fungi*, but not without interest, so far as it shows the strange forms which under particular circumstances may be assumed by various species. The productions referred to *Sclerotium*, as the name implies, consist of a mass of cells compacted into a solid body, attached occasionally at the base by a few delicate threads. Sometimes the outline of the external cells is waved, as in the cuticle of many phænogams. These productions are either entirely free, or more or less imbedded in the substances on which they grow—sometimes being merely covered by the cuticle, sometimes slightly immersed, but occasionally deeply imbedded in the pith or other soft structures. They occur on decaying agarics, on herbaceous stems, rotten wood, amongst moss or dung, on putrefying roots or fruit, or even on decomposed animal matter. A few—as the *Sclerotium of Peziza tuberosa*, *Agaricus tuberosus*, &c.—are mere dormant

winter states of more perfect plants. Some, on the contrary, as the *Sclerotia* of onions, peas, &c., are peculiar conditions of filamentous moulds, induced by too great moisture, or a too liberal supply of nutriment. Such assertions, however evident, are difficult of proof, and therefore subject to contradiction; but by placing thin slices in closed cells containing a proper fluid they may sometimes be induced to fructify, as was done in the case of a *Sclerotium* abounding frequently on onions by Mr. Hoffman and Mr. Berkeley. The rose-coloured *Sclerotium* of rush-pith when placed in a moist situation uniformly produces *Peziza Curreyi*, exactly as ergot develops different species of *Cordiceps*. A few authors still consider these productions true species, but no fruit has ever been found in them, and indeed the development of mere conidia would not be decisive on this point. [M. J. B.]

SCOBIFORM. Having the appearance of fine sawdust.

SCOBINA. The zigzag rachis of the spikelets of grasses.

SCOKE. *Phytolacca decandra.*

SCOLIOSORUS. A Mexican fern formerly referred to *Antrophyum*, but having neither netted veins nor netted sori as in that genus. The fronds are simple, and the veins reduced to an obscure midrib. It has been referred to the *Tænitideæ*, in consequence of having non-indusiate linear interrupted flexuose sori lying between the midrib and margin. [T. M.]

SCOLOPENDRE. (Fr.) *Scolopendrium.*

SCOLOPENDRIUM. A genus of polypodiaceous ferns, typical of that group of *Aspleniæ* in which the sori are double, opening face to face. The veins are free and parallel-forked, terminating in club-shaped apices. The typical species is *S. vulgare*, the Common Hartstongue fern, which has normally long strap-shaped simple fronds, but occurs in a monstrous state in almost every conceivable form. A few other species are recorded, some of them pinnate, but these are sometimes regarded as abnormal forms of other totally distinct plants. [T. M.]

SCOLOPIA (including *Phoberos*). A genus of *Flacourtiaceæ* inhabiting tropical Asia and Australia, and composed of spiny shrubs and trees, with alternate leathery simple glabrous leaves, and bearing inconspicuous racemose hermaphrodite flowers. The calyx is from eight to ten-lobed, the corolla wanting, the stamens indefinite, the style simple, and the fruit a leathery berry filled with a jelly-like pulp. We know nothing of the properties of the half-dozen species composing this genus. *Scolopia* being the older name, it has been adopted in preference to *Phoberos* by leading botanists. [B. S.]

SCOLYMUS. A genus of *Compositæ* numbering four species, natives of Southern Europe and Northern Africa. These plants, having all the florets of the flower-head strap-shaped, belong to the *Cichoraceæ*, and from all others of that group are at once distinguished by their thistle-like appearance. The leaves are lance-shaped in outline and deeply toothed, the teeth again divided, and all the divisions ending in rigid spiny points, while the nerves are white in some of the species, as in milk-thistles, and give the leaves a handsome appearance. The flower-heads are solitary, at the ends of the branches or the short axillary shoots, small for the size of the plants, surrounded by leafy bracts, and of a rich saffron colour. *S. maculatus* is sometimes cultivated for the sake of its spotted variegated leaves. [A. A. B.]

SCOPARIACEÆ. A name under which Link proposed to establish a distinct order for *Scoparia* and a few other *Scrophulariaceæ* allied to it, but which has not been adopted.

SCOPARIA. A genus of *Scrophulariaceæ*, containing several branching herbs or shrubs from South America, one of them having, however, established itself in all the temperate regions of the globe. The leaves are opposite or verticillate, and the single-flowered pedicels rise generally in pairs from the axils. The calyx is four to five-parted; the rotate corolla is quadrifid; there are four stamens; the two cells of the anthers are united above but diverging below; the capsule dehisces septicidally, with entire valves; and the seeds are numerous and reticulated. [W. O.]

SCOPOLIA. Scopoli was a distinguished Austrian naturalist, who died towards the end of the last century. The genus named in compliment to him comprises a perennial plant, native of the mountains of Eastern Europe. The leaves are in pairs, one larger than the other. The flowers are solitary, placed on axillary pendulous stalks: in their structure they resemble those of *Hyoscyamus*, but may be distinguished by the following characters:—Corolla funnel-shaped, traversed by fifteen nerves, the limb divided into five very short lobes; stamens equal in length, the filaments short dilated and hairy at the base, cylindrical above; ovary surrounded by a five-lobed fleshy disk; fruit similar to that of henbane. *S. carniolica* is a pretty spring-flowering plant, with dull purple flowers. The name has been at various times given to other genera. [M. T. M.]

SCORDIUM. *Teucrium Scordium.*

SCORIAS. A most curious genus of *Fungi* which has hitherto occurred only in the United States of America, where it forms large spongy cinder-like masses (whence the name) amongst fallen leaves, consisting of intricate necklace-like dark threads, which here and there produce cysts containing asci and sporidia. It is nearly allied to *Capnodium*, of which it seems to be an exaggerated form, with

the mycelium more gelatinous and more highly developed. [M. J. B.]

SCORODONIA. *Teucrium Scorodonia.*

SCORODOSMA. *S. fœtidum*, the only known species of this genus of *Umbelliferæ*, is, as its names imply, a powerfully smelling plant. Its leaves are deeply cut, its umbels very large, and its flowers unisexual; the males with an indistinct calyx, five yellow petals, as many stamens, and two rudimentary styles; and the females with white petals, five small glands occupying the position of the stamens, and styles bent downwards and terminated by large stigmas. The fruit is circular in outline, compressed from back to front, each of its halves marked by three ridges, the lateral ones being expanded into wings; there are no vittæ. From its near allies, *Ferula* and *Dorema*, it is distinguished by the inconspicuous calyx, the petals, and the want of vittæ.

It is a native of the desert region of Central Asia, from which circumstance, conjoined with its odour and a resemblance to Kæmpfer's figure of the plant yielding assafœtida, it was surmised that it might be the plant producing that drug, a surmise now known to be incorrect. It was first introduced to the notice of botanists by Prof. Bunge of Dorpat. [M. T. M.]

SCORPIOID. An inflorescence which is rolled up towards one side in the manner of a crozier, unrolling as the flowers expand.

SCORPIONE. (Fr.) *Myosotis.*

SCORPION-PLANT. *Renanthera arachnitis*; also *Genista scorpius.*

SCORPIURUS. A small genus of herbaceous plants belonging to the *Leguminosæ*, and distinguished by bearing their fruit in the form of a jointed pod, each division containing a seed, which as it approaches maturity becomes revolute, and has a fancied resemblance to the tail of some reptile—whence its name, Scorpion's-tail. Unlike most of the plants with which they are associated, they have simple leaves, and they bear axillary one to four-flowered peduncles, which are longer than the leaves, with yellow rarely purple flowers. The species are mainly distinguished by the number of flowers seated on the same stalk, and by the external condition of the pod, whether scaly tuberculated or prickly. They are natives of the Mediterranean regions. [C. A. J.]

SCORSONÈRE. (Fr.) *Scorzonera.*

SCORZONERA. A genus of *Compositæ* indigenous to the south of Europe and temperate parts of Asia, consisting of perennial herbs, with undivided lanceolate leaves, simple or branched stems, and distinct terminal heads of flowers of a yellow or purple colour. The heads are many-flowered, the florets being all perfect, containing both stamens and ovary; the involucre is many-leaved, the leaves being much imbricated on each other, and the receptacle is naked. The corolla of all the florets is ligulate ; the achenes are all of the same form, beakless, smooth or slightly hairy, having a lateral areolë ; and the pappus is in many rows, feathery, and in part interwoven.

Among the species of this genus, which are very numerous, is one the properties of which, although it is much esteemed as an esculent vegetable, should be more generally known. This plant, *S. hispanica*, is distinguished by its branching stem terminating in single heads of flowers, its lanceolate-smooth or very slightly pubescent leaves, and its involucre, which encloses the heads of flowers, being oblong and smooth, and the scales of which it consists acuminated. It is a native of Spain, but is cultivated in this country ; and its root is sold in the markets as corzonera, a name derived from *escorza*, the Spanish name for a serpent, in allusion to its cooling antifebrile effects, it having formerly been employed in Spain on account of these properties for the cure of serpent-bites. It has also sometimes been called Viper's-grass. It is perennial, standing five or six years, and is very easy of cultivation, growing vigorously in good ground, and bearing the hardest winters of this country without injury. Unless, however, the ground is good and favourably situated, the root is likely to be small, the first year. It will also bear transplanting without any apparent injury, and will grow with its usual vigour after it has been exposed in the market or lain out of the ground for some weeks, or even months. The root is nearly the shape of a carrot, but smaller and dark-coloured, while internally it is pure white. The taste is sweetish and agreeable, something like that of the roots of certain umbelliferous plants or the common hazel-nut, and a variety with a paler skin has a still more agreeable flavour.

Its effects on the digestive organs are to increase the flow of gastric juice and bile, and as it acts as a deobstruent generally, it is slightly aperient. Its antibilious power is scarcely inferior to that of dandelion, if at all so, being, it is believed, superior in this property to any other esculent in use in this country ; and it is on this account one of the best remedies in many (if not in most) cases of indigestion, and especially for that state of the digestive organs called bilious.

These good effects, however, cannot be insured unless the vegetable is properly cooked, as its medicinal qualities may be quickly destroyed. It should be cut as little as possible, and washed not scraped, as the abundant milky juice on which its salutary properties depend then escapes. After boiling for about twenty or twenty-five minutes, or till it is quite soft (rather more salt being added to the water than usual in cooking vegetables), it is to be taken out and peeled, as the dark skin then comes off as readily as that of a boiled potato. When fresh from the garden a quarter of an hour may be sufficient, which

it is of some importance to the invalid to know, because after it has become quite soft all further boiling is injurious to its medicinal qualities, and soon destroys them ; but when it has lain out of the ground for a long time and become hardened, it may require twice the time boiling, the rule then being to boil it till it is soft. It is usually eaten in the same way as asparagus, which is the preferable mode for the invalid. As it is one of the most agreeable of vegetables in point of flavour, it undoubtedly deserves to be much more cultivated.

S. hispanica is not the only species in use as an esculent vegetable, *S. deliciosa*, a native of Sicily, being much valued in its native country. It is there in most extensive cultivation on account of its sweet, very grateful flavour, and its cooling effects.   [B. C.]

SCOTCH ATTORNEY. *Clusia.*

SCOTCH BONNETS. The name in some districts for *Marasmius Oreades*, or the true Champignon ; also applied to the Bonnet-pepper, *Capsicum tetragonum.*

SCOTINO. An Italian name for *Rhus Cotinus.*

SCOTTIA. A West Australian genus belonging to the tribe *Genisteæ* of the *Leguminosæ*. The two species, *S. dentata* and *S. angustifolia*, are branching diffuse bushes, with slender stems bearing simple opposite leaves, which are heart-shaped and toothed or almost linear in form. The flowers are brick-red tinged with green, and nearly an inch long, sessile and solitary in the leaf axils ; they have a five-toothed bell-shaped calyx with five bracts at its base ; and the upper petal or standard is shorter than the side-petals or wings, which are as long as the lower petal or keel ; the stamens are united into one parcel, and the flat pods contain a number of seeds. The name commemorates Dr. R. Scott, once Professor of Botany at Dublin. [A. A. B.]

SCRATCHWEED. The Cleavers, *Galium Aparine.*

SCREW-TREE. *Helicteres.*

SCRIPTUREWORTS. A name applied to the species of *Opegrapha*, or Letter Lichen.

SCROBICULATE. Marked by little depressions : the same as Pitted.

SCROPHULAIRE. (Fr.) *Scrophularia.*

SCROPHULARIACEÆ (*Scrophularineæ, Personatæ, Rhinanthaceæ, Linariads*). A large order of monopetalous dicotyledons, generally distributed over the world, consisting of herbs or rarely shrubs, with opposite or alternate leaves without stipules, and irregular flowers either axillary or in terminal racemes or panicles. They are distinguished from other irregular *Monopetalæ* by the free calyx of five or rarely four parts or lobes ; the corolla of five or four lobes ; two or four perfect stamens ; a superior two-celled ovary, with several usually numerous ovules in each cell; and by albuminous seeds. The latter character is the most positive to separate them from *Bignoniaceæ* and *Acanthaceæ*, which often closely resemble some of their genera. From some *Solanaceæ* with slightly irregular flowers, the *Salpiglossidæ*, a tribe of *Scrophulariaceæ*, can only be separated by a fine-drawn arbitrary line. The æstivation or arrangement of the lobes of the corolla has suggested the division of the order into three suborders, which have been sometimes considered as distinct groups, viz.: 1. *Salpiglossidæ*, with a centrifugal inflorescence, the æstivation of the corolla either altogether plaited or partially imbricate, with the two upper lobes *outside*. These include *Browallia, Brunsfelsia, Salpiglossis, Schizanthus*, and a few others.— 2. *Antirrhineæ* (or *Personatæ* proper of some authors), with an inflorescence either centripetal or compound, and the corolla bilabiate, in æstivation with the upper two lobes *outside*. To these belong above ninety genera, among the most important of which are *Calceolaria, Verbascum, Antirrhinum, Scrophularia, Pentstemon, Mimulus, Herpestis, Gratiola, Torenia, &c.*—3. *Rhinanthideæ*, with the inflorescence of *Antirrhineæ*, but the corolla imbricate, with the upper two lobes (sometimes united into one) always *inside*. There are nearly seventy genera, including *Sibthorpia, Scoparia, Veronica, Buchnera, Gerardia, Bartsia, Euphrasia, Rhinanthus, Pedicularis, Melampyrum, &c. Buddleia* (which see) and its allies, formerly included in *Scrophulariaceæ*, are now referred to *Loganiaceæ*.

SCROPHULARIA. A genus of *Scrophulariaceæ*, containing nearly one hundred species of herbs or undershrubs found scattered over the extratropical regions of the Old World, one species only having been found in the New World, probably carried thither from Europe. The leaves are opposite, or alternate above; the calyx is five-lobed or five-cleft; the corolla subglobose, its limb minute with two short lips—the upper with two straight lobes and frequently a small scale or abortive stamen within it, the lower with three lobes, the two lateral straight, the middle one decurved; the style simple, thickened at the apex, the stigma emarginate; and the capsule two-celled, dehiscing septicidally by two valves with their margins turned inwards.

The plants of this genus have generally an unpleasant smell. The generic name is derived from the property which the roots were supposed to have of curing scrofula. A decoction of one of the common British species, *S. nodosa*, is sometimes used by farmers to cure the scab in swine. [W. C.]

SCROTIFORM. The same as Pouch-shaped.

SCROTUM. A pouch; the volva of some fungals.

SCURF. The loose scaly matter that is found on some leaves, &c. See LEPIDOTE.

SCUTATE, or SCUTIFORM. The same as Buckler-shaped.

SCUTATI'PILI. The same as what are generally called LEPIDES: which see.

SCUTELLARIA. Herbaceous or rarely shrubby labiate plants, well marked by their ovate calyx, furnished at the back with a concave scale, which finally assumes the appearance of a hinge, on which the upper lip of the calyx closes on the fruit. The genus is represented in Britain by *S. galericulata*, the common Skullcap, an herbaceous perennial with branched stems, oblong leaves, and long-tubed axillary blue flowers, all turned one way; it is tolerably abundant on the banks of rivers, lakes, and canals. *S. minor* is a smaller tufted plant with pale-purplish flowers, of which the lower lip is spotted; it is abundant in marshy places in the west of England, and is found also in some of the midland counties. Among the cultivated species are *S. micrantha*, from Siberia and the north of China, a handsome species with spiked racemes of blue flowers; *S. coccinea* from Mexico, with scarlet flowers, &c. French: *Toque*; German: *Schildkraut*. [C. A. J.]

SCUTELLIFORM. The same as Patelliform, but oval not round, as the embryo of grasses.

SCUTELLUM. Among lichenals such a shield as that of *Parmelia*, formed with an elevated rim which is derived from the thallus.

SCUTICARIA *Steelii*. A common epiphytal orchid from Demerara, with long thong-like pendulous leaves rising from short ring-scarred pseudobulbs, and large solitary dingy-yellow purple-spotted flowers, which grow on very short stalks. It forms a genus by itself, belonging to the *Maxillarideæ*, distinguished by its marked habit and by the shape of the gland on which its two pairs of pollen-masses are seated. The gland is transverse to the pollen-masses, broad and somewhat lunate in the middle, and with the sides extended into long taper-points. [A. S.]

SCUTIGERA. *Platycerium.*

SCUTUM. The broad dilated stigma of some asclepiads, as *Stapelia.*

SCYPHA. The cup-like dilatation of the podetium of lichenals, having shields on its edge.

SCYPHANTHUS. *Grammatocarpus.*

SCYPHIPHORA. The name of a shrub from the shores of the Molucca Isles, constituting a genus of *Cinchonaceæ*. The flowers are in axillary corymbs, and have an undivided calyx; corolla funnel-shaped, its limb divided into four lance-shaped spreading segments; stamens four, projecting from the corolla; fruit succulent, marked with eight grooves, surmounted by the tubular calyx, and containing two one-seeded stones. The name is derived from the Greek, and implies 'cupbearer,' in allusion probably to the calyx. [M. T. M.]

SCYPHOCORONIS. The generic name of a minute annual weed of Western Australia belonging to the *Compositæ* and related to *Helichrysum*. The branching stems, not more than one or two inches high, are furnished with small spathulate leaves; and each twig terminates in a single head of yellow flowers, with the florets all tubular and perfect, enclosed by an involucre of five narrow scales. The narrow cylindrical achenes are crowned with an entire cup-shaped pappus-ring. All the parts of the plant are more or less clothed with clammy pubescence. [A. A. B.]

SCYPHOFILIX. *Microlepia.*

SCYPHOGYNE. A genus of *Ericaceæ*, distinguished by its calyx being four-cleft, the anterior division largest, and by the style ending in a broad and cup-like point. The species are small shrubs, natives of the Cape of Good Hope; they are usually much branched, with small leaves arranged in whorls of three; the flowers are small, and nearly sessile. The name is from the Greek, and indicates the cup-like form of the stigma. [G. D.]

SCYPHULARIA. *Davallia.*

SCYPHULUS. The bag or cup out of which the seta of scale-mosses proceeds.

SCYPHUS. The coronet of such plants as *Narcissus.*

SCYTHIAN LAMB. *Cibotium Barometz.*

SEA-BELLS. *Convolvulus Soldanella.*

SEA-COLANDER. The American name in the North-eastern States of *Agarum Turneri.*

SEAFORTHIA A genus of palms originally established upon a tropical Australian species, *S. elegans*; but upwards of twenty-five other species (chiefly inhabitants of Sumatra, Java, Borneo, and other islands of the Indian Archipelago), have since been added to it, including those formerly placed in the genera *Pinanga*, *Ptychosperma*, and *Drymophlœus*. All these are spineless, and either with thick ringed trunks from ten to forty feet high, or dwarf reed-like stems. They have large pinnate leaves, with leaflets divided or irregularly torn at the apex; the lower ones standing out almost horizontally, and their stalks forming a long cylindrical sheath round the upper part of the stem, below which the flower-spikes make their appearance. These are at first enclosed in spathes varying from one to four in number, and have numerous tail-like branches, along which the flowers are arranged either in straight lines or in spirals, the lower portions having them in threes, one female between two males, and the upper in pairs of males only. The one-seeded fruit has a granular fibrous rind, the seed being in most species marked like a nutmeg. [A. S.]

SEA-GIRDLES. *Laminaria digitata.*

SEAGREEN The same as Glaucescent.

SEA-HANGERS. *Laminaria bulbosa.*

SEAKALE. *Crambe maritima.*

SEA-LACES. *Chorda filum.*

SEALWORT. *Polygonatum officinale.*

SEA-OTTER'S CABBAGE. The English name of *Nereocystis Lutkeana.*

SEA-THONGS. The common name of *Himanthalia lorea.*

SEA-TRUMPET. *Ecklonia buccinalis.*

SEAVES. *Juncus.*

SEA-WAND. *Laminaria digitata.*

SEAWARE. A synonym of Seaweed.

SEAWEEDS. Lindley's name for the *Fucaceæ*. See ALGÆ.

SEAWRACK. A name given to seaweeds thrown up by the tide and carried into the neighbouring country for manure. Also *Zostera marina*, which, during the height of the distress in Lancashire, in 1863, was proposed as a substitute for cotton, though no practical result followed the suggestion.

SEAWRACKS. Lindley's name for the *Zosteraceæ.*

SEBÆA. A genus of herbs belonging to the *Gentianaceæ*, natives of the Cape of Good Hope and of New South Wales. The flowers are in corymbs, and have a four to five-parted calyx, whose segments have on their outer surface a prominent ridge; a funnel-shaped corolla, withering on the plant; four to five stamens, projecting from the tube of the corolla, the anthers glandular at the top, and ultimately bent downwards; a thread-like style, with two globular stigmas; and a capsular fruit. Some of the species are known in this country as elegant greenhouse or bedding-out plants. [M. T. M.]

SEBASTIANIA. A genus of *Euphorbiaceæ*, numbering eight species, milky-juiced trees or shrubs of Brazil and Peru, having smooth alternate ovate or elliptical leaves, and minute green flowers disposed in slender axillary or terminal bracteate spikes, the sterile and fertile usually on different plants. The genus is united with *Stillingia* by modern authors. [A. A. B.]

SEBÉ. (Fr.) *Allium Cepa.*

SEBESTANS, or SEBESTENS. The name under which the dried fruits of *Cordia Myxa* and *C latifolia* have long been used as a medicine in India.

SEBESTENA. A name applied by Gærtner to a group of plants now referred to *Cordia.*

SÉBESTIER. (Fr.) *Cordia.*

SECALE. A genus of grasses related to *Triticum*, distinguished by its spiked inflorescence, which bears two-flowered spikelets, having a long-stalked rudiment of a third floret; glumes subulate. To the genus belongs the Rye, *S. cereale*, a corn-plant commonly cultivated for its nutritious grain, the flour of which forms an inferior kind of bread. According to Karl Koch, it is found undoubtedly wild on the mountains of the Crimea, especially around the village of Dshimil, on granite, at the elevation of from 5,000 to 6,000 feet. In such places its ears are not more than one to two and a half inches long. Its native country explains the reason why it is so much hardier than any variety of wheat. As a corn-crop in this country it is probably the most limited in its growth of any grain, and this is gradually decreasing by the substitution of wheat.

The name of *S. cornutum* is sometimes given to Ergot of Rye, which is a black horn-like spur, into which the seeds or grains of rye and other grasses are changed as the result of disease. In rye some of these spurs are as much as an inch in length, whilst in *Lolium* or Ray-grass they seldom attain to half the length or size of the former, and in smaller grasses the ergot is in proportion to the size of the seed. The Ergot of Rye has long been known as prevailing to a considerable extent in countries where *rye* is grown for bread, and some dreadful maladies are reported to have arisen when the ergot has been ground with the flour. Among other effects incidental to its long use is said to be the production of gangrene. Ergot is frequently employed by the medical practitioner in cases of difficult parturition. Its more immediate effect upon gravid animals appears to be the procuring of abortion; and as one of the commoner grasses, in which it occurs probably to a greater extent than in any other of our native species, is the *Lolium perenne*, which is always found to be largely mixed with all good pastures, it often becomes a matter of importance to look well to a meadow in autumn before turning in cows, as there is too much reason to believe that abortion is somewhat frequent from a want of care in this respect.

Some years since the late Earl Ducie suffered considerably from the 'dropping of calves' in the case of some of his most valuable stock. At this time a quantity of ergotised *Lolium* was gathered in the field where these occurrences took place. This was sent for our examination, and from this, and the report given us of the general state of the meadow, we have little doubt but that this diseased grass was the cause of the calamity.

The quantity of ergot in almost any native species of grass in some low damp meadows is quite astonishing; however, it is lessened by draining. Uplands are not without a quantity of ergotised grass if they have sufficient altitude to attract atmospheric vapours. Where and when it prevails, there is much evidence to show that it is not advisable to depasture; but, if needs must, then the skimming over the bents with the scythe before the admission of cattle, is a plan that might obviously be had recourse to with advantage. [J. B.]

SECAMONE. A genus of *Asclepiadaceæ* containing nearly thirty species of climbing or decumbent shrubs, natives of South Africa, India, and Australia. They have opposite leaves and minute flowers in dichotomous cymes arising from between the petioles. The small calyx is five-cleft, as is also the rotate corolla; the staminal crown consists of five laterally compressed leaflets; there are twenty erect pollen-masses; the short stigma is contracted at the apex or slightly bilobed; and the follicles are smooth, with numerous comose seeds. Some of the species contain an acrid principle, which makes them useful as medicines. Smyrna Scammony is obtained from an Egyptian species. [W. C.]

SECHIUM *edule* is the Chocho of the West Indies, a cucurbitaceous plant, native of and commonly cultivated in all the West Indian islands for the sake of its fruit, which is reckoned extremely wholesome, and commonly used there as an article of food by all classes. The generic name is derived from a Greek word, signifying 'to fatten in a stall,' the fruit, besides its utility as food for man, having the reputation of being a very fattening food for hogs and other animals. It is a climbing plant furnished with three to five-cleft tendrils, and has smooth stems rising from a very large fleshy root, which sometimes weighs as much as twenty pounds, and resembles a yam both in appearance and in its eatable qualities when cooked. It has cordate five-angled scabrous leaves, and yellow separate male and female flowers on the same plant. These latter have a rotate corolla, with ten nectar-bearing glands in the tube; united stamens, with distinct zigzag anthers; and a one-celled ovary containing a single pendulous ovule. The fruit is about four inches in length, oblong, between fleshy and succulent, sometimes furnished with small innocuous prickles, and either green or cream-coloured. The plant has been introduced into Madeira and other Atlantic islands, and from this source its fruits are sometimes sent to this country in a fresh state, and sold in Covent Garden Market under the name of Chayotes. [A. S.]

SECOTIUM. A fine genus of gasteromycetous *Fungi* belonging to the natural order *Podaxinei*. The hymenium is sinuous like that of a young puffball, and forms a mass round the top of the stem as in *Boletus*, or extends above it. The outer coat of the pileus, though intimately connected with the underlying substance which sometimes entirely encloses the hymenium, occasionally breaks away so as to leave a sort of valve enclosing the base of the stem. The spores are either dark or light-coloured. A small species occurs in the south of France, but the finer forms are found in Australia, New Zealand, &c. A large Swan River species, of which only imperfect specimens have at present been received, is said to be a most delicious fungus. [M. J. B.]

SECRETION. Any organic but unorganised substance produced in the interior of plants.

SECTILE. Cut into small pieces, as the pollen-masses of some orchids.

SECTUS. Divided down to the base.

SECUND. Having all the flowers or leaves or other organs turned towards the same side.

SECUNDINE. The second integument of an ovule, within the primine and lying over the nucleus.

SECURIDACA. A genus of trailing shrubs of the milkwort family, numbering about thirty species, which are mostly natives of tropical America. They have alternate ovate or elliptical leaves; and axillary or terminal racemes or panicles of white violet or rose-coloured flowers, in form and structure resembling those of some species of *Polygala*, except that the ovary is one instead of two-celled. The fruits, which are remarkable in the family, are very much like one of the two-winged carpels which make up the fruit of a maple (*Acer*). The Buaze fibre plant, *S. pallida*, spoken of by Dr. Livingstone in his *Travels*, belongs here, and has been described and figured in the botany of *Peters' Travels in Mozambique*, by Dr. Klotzsch, under the name of *Lophostylis pallida*. It is a bush of four to eighteen feet high, the twigs furnished with smooth pale-green oblong leaves, and the small dingy-purple flowers disposed in axillary racemes. It grows in rocky places at the foot of hills near the Zambesi and Shire Rivers, as well as in Mozambique. The twigs are cut by the natives in January and February for the sake of the fibre, of which they make cord, fishing-nets, &c. The fibre resembles flax, and some of it brought home by Dr. Livingstone, and tested by Messrs. Marshall of Leeds, was pronounced equal to flax worth 50*l.* or 60*l.* per ton. Cross-sections of the stem of this and other species are singular from the absence of medullary rays and the presence of layers of bark between the layers of wood. Such a specimen may be seen in the Museum of the Kew Gardens, sent by Dr Welwitsch from Western Africa. Many of the South American species ramble to a great height over other trees, and are beautiful objects when in flower. The generic name alludes to the hatchet-like wing of the fruit. [A. A. B.]

SÉCURIDACA DES JARDINIERS. (Fr.) *Coronilla Emerus.*

SEDGE. *Carex*; also *Cladium.* —, **SWEET** *Acorus Calamus.*

SEDGES. Lindley's name for the *Cyperaceæ.*

SEDGWICKIA. A genus proposed by Griffith for an Assamese tree which has proved to be the *Liquidambar Altingia* of Blume.

SEDUM. A genus of herbaceous or somewhat shrubby plants, branched mostly from the root, and bearing at the same time elongated stems, which terminate in cymes of yellow white or purple flowers, and other shorter flowerlessstems crowded with fleshy leaves, which are either flat or more frequently about equal in breadth and thickness. They belong to the order *Crassulaceæ*, the characters being :—Stamens twice as many as the petals ; petals not united ; glands at the base of the ovaries not laciniated.

The structure of *Sedums* being such as to enable them to vegetate for a long time without absorbing moisture from the earth, they flourish in most arid soils, and are to be found clothing the surface of rocks, or the sides of walls and quarries. Of the British species belonging to the group, with leaves cylindrical or nearly so, the most frequent are *S. acre*, the Stonecrop, common in such localities as those described, as well as on dry sandhills near the seashore—a low plant with tangled stems, short fleshy leaves (which are produced into a kind of spur at the base), and golden-yellow flowers: and *S. anglicum*, similar to the last in habit, with white flowers speckled with crimson. *S. Telephium*, Orpine or Livelong, the *Herbe aux Charpentiers* of the French, is a more robust plant, twelve to sixteen inches high, with large flat leaves and dense corymbs of dull purple flowers, resembling in habit *Rhodiola rosea.* Several foreign species are cultivated, principally for covering old walls or ornamenting rockeries. French : *Joubarbe.* [C. A. J.]

SEDUM À ODEUR DE ROSE. (Fr.) *Rhodiola rosea.* — **FAUX-OIGNON.** *Sedum Cepœa.* — **PYRAMIDAL DES JARDINIERS.** *Saxifraga Cotyledon.* — **REPRISE.** *Sedum Telephium.*

SEEBRIGHT. *Salvia Sclarea.*

SEED-BOX. *Ludwigia alternifolia* and *L. hirtella.*

SEEDRA. An Arabian name for *Zizyphus Lotus.*

SEEKAKAI. An Indian name for a kind of soapnut obtained from *Mimosa abstergens (Acacia concinna)*, a decoction of the pods of which is used as a hair-wash in India.

SEEMANNIA. A gesneraceous genus named by Regel in honour of Dr. Berthold Seemann, discovered in the Andes of Peru and Bolivia by Ruiz and Pavon, but only of late years introduced to Europe by the Polish traveller Warscewicz. It has quite the habit of *Gesnera*, attains a height of three to four feet, and is chiefly valued by gardeners on account of its bright scarlet blossoms, which throughout the winter enliven our hothouses, and appear in numbers in the axils of the lanceolate leaves or in terminal racemes. The only known species is *S. sylvatica (S. ternifolia* or *Gesnera sylvatica).* The five-cleft calyx has linear lance-shaped segments, the corolla is tubular, the glandular disk surrounding the ovary is five-lobed, the stigma two-lobed, and the fruit a capsule. [B. S.]

SELT. A name in Burmah for the wood of several species of *Acacia.*

SEG. An East Anglian name for rushes reeds and sedges. —, SEA. *Carex arenaria.*

SEGG. The Flag, *Iris Pseudacorus.*

SEGGRUM. *Senecio Jacobæa.*

SEGRA-SEED. *Feuillea cordifolia.*

SEGUIERIA. A genus of *Petiveriaceæ,* comprising a few species of South American shrubs with alternate entire ovate or elliptical leaves, and terminal panicles of white or greenish-yellow flowers. The whole of the plant smells more or less of garlic; the stipules often become hardened, and hooked like prickles. The flowers have a five-parted coloured calyx, no petals, numerous stamens, and a one-celled ovary with one ovule. The fruit resembles one of the two portions which make up the fruit of a maple. The nearly allied genus *Gallesia* has a like fruit, but the calyx is four instead of five-parted. 'The root, wood, and all the herbaceous parts of *S. alliacea* have a powerful odour of garlic or assafœtida ; baths impregnated with them are in repute in Brazil in cases of rheumatism, dropsy, and hæmorrhoidal affections. The wood abounds in potash, and the ashes are employed in clarifying sugar, and in soapmaking in Brazil.'—*Lindley's Vegetable Kingdom.*　　　[A. A. B.]

SÉHU. (Fr.) *Sambucus.*

SEIGLE. (Fr.) *Secale.* — BÂTARDE. *Bromus secalinus.*

SELAGINACEÆ. A small order of monopetalous dicotyledons, agreeing with *Verbenaceæ* in their irregular flowers, two or four stamens, and free two-celled ovary not lobed, with one ovule in each cell; but differing from that order, as well as from the closely allied *Myoporaceæ,* in the anthers being always one-celled only. They are herbs or small shrubs, with alternate leaves, and blue white or rarely yellow flowers in terminal heads or spikes. There are about a dozen genera, of which *Globularia* is European, *Gymnandra* from temperate or Northern Asia or North-western America, and all the others, including *Selago* itself, from Southern Africa.

SÉLAGINE. (Fr.) *Selago.*

SELAGINELLA. A genus of clubmosses distinguished from *Lycopodium* by the flat two-ranked stem, and double two to three-valved fruit, one of which contains the large pallid spores, the other the free spore-like orange or scarlet antheridia, which at length produce the spiral spermatozoids. Both sometimes occur together in the axil of the same leaf, but they are sometimes separate. The species vary greatly in stature and habit, some being small and like the larger *Jungermanniaceæ,* while others attain a considerable height. The leaves, which sometimes assume a bluish tint, are generally of different sizes, as in *Hypopterygium* or *Cyathophorum* amongst mosses. Germi-

nation takes place by cellular division of a portion of the spores, and the young plant when produced from the archegonium has two opposite leaves like

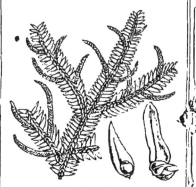

Selaginella Sprucei.

cotyledons, looking very much like the embryo of some exogens. The species are numerous, and are inhabitants of warm regions. They are frequently extremely elegant, and are in consequence favourite objects of cultivation. *S. convoluta* has the fronds curiously curled in and contracted when dry, so as to form a ball like the rose of Jericho, which expands when moistened. *S. mutabilis* has the remarkable property of changing its colour every day : in the morning it is of a bright green, but as the day advances it gradually becomes pale, and at night resumes its deeper tint. Dr. Hooker has observed that this arises from a daily contraction of the green contents of the cells under the influence of light. Several of the smaller species have a creeping habit, but many of them are erect variously branched and forked, while others are partially supported by bushes. Several send down long straight roots into the soil, which serve both as organs of nutrition and as props. *S. Sprucei* is a good representative species. [M. J. B.]

SELAGO. A genus of *Selaginaceæ,* containing upwards of seventy species of herbs or undershrubs from the Cape of Good Hope. They have small entire and alternate leaves, and sessile spiked flowers with large bracts ; the calyx is ovate or campanulate, and more or less deeply three to five-lobed ; the tube of the corolla is short, and the limb four to five-lobed, sometimes somewhat two-lipped ; there are four stamens. The single style has an acute stigma ; and the ovary breaks up into two one-seeded achenes.　　　[W. C.]

SELENIA. A genus of *Cruciferæ,* resembling those of the tribe *Cremolobidæ* in the inverted seeds, but differing in the pouch having a broad and not a narrow septum. It consists of an annual herb from Arkansas and Texas, with the habit of *Brassica*; the stems three-edged; the leaves pinnatifid; the flowers golden-yellow, at first corymbose, but at length elongating into a leafy raceme. The pouch resembles that of *Lunaria*, but has inflated valves.   [J. T. S.]

SELENIDIUM. *Microlepia.*

SELENIPEDIUM. According to the younger Reichenbach, the author of this genus, it agrees in all its characters with *Cypripedium*, except that the ovary is three-celled and three-furrowed or three-lobed. He refers to it ten species, all of which had previously belonged to *Cypripedium*.   [A. S.]

SELFHEAL. *Prunella vulgaris*; also *Sanicula vulgaris.*

SELINUM. A genus belonging to the order *Umbelliferæ*, distinguished from its allies by the following characters:—The petals are obovate and notched at the end; the fruit is compressed, each half having five wing-like ribs, the two lateral of which are the most prominent; each furrow has a single oil-vessel, and there are two at the line of junction. The species are smooth perennial herbs, with leaves much subdivided; and the flowers are white. They are found in Europe, Nepal, and North-western America. The name is from the Greek *selinon* 'parsley,' in allusion to its general aspect.   [G. D.]

SELK. A name in Egypt for *Beta vulgaris.*

SELLÆFORM. Saddle-shaped.

SELLIGUEA. A genus of polypodiaceous ferns of the tribe *Gymnogrammeæ*, in which it is known by its pinnate veins, with reticulated venules having free included veinlets. The fronds are simple,

Selliguea Feei.

rarely pinnatifid or palmately-lobed, and the sori are oblong or linear-oblique, *lying* between and parallel with the primary veins. A few species, all of them Eastern,

are known. One of the larger ones is represented in Plate 14 *d*, and a figure of *S. Feei* is subjoined.   [T. M.]

SELLOA. A perennial herb of the *Compositæ*, peculiar to Mexico. It has a short rootstock, furnished with a few opposite elliptical three-nerved leaves resembling those of a plantain (whence it is called *S. plantaginea*); and the peduncle or flower-stem, which is nearly a foot high and furnished with two or three bracts, terminates in from one to three rather large rayed flower-heads, the ray florets strap-shaped, pistil-bearing, and three-toothed at the apex; those of the disk tubular and perfect, and all seated on a cone-shaped chaffy receptacle enclosed by an involucre of three series of scales, those of the outer row being broader than the others. The five-angled smooth achenes are crowned by two or three hispid awns, but are not winged as in the nearly related *Verbesina*. It is named after C. Sello, a German botanical traveller in Brazil.   [A. A. B.]

SEM. *Phaseolus trilobus.*

SEMECARPUS. A genus of Indian trees of the *Anacardiaceæ*, nearly allied to *Anacardium*. The flowers are in terminal panicles, and are distinguished from those of adjacent genera by the presence of five separate equal stamens, and a one-celled sessile ovary with a single ovule suspended from its upper part. *S. Anacardium* is the Marking-nut tree of India. The thick fleshy receptacle bearing the fruit is of a yellow colour when ripe, and is roasted and eaten by the natives. The unripe fruit is employed for making a kind of ink, and when pounded serves in the formation of a kind of birdlime. The hard shell of the fruit is permeated by a corrosive juice, which is employed externally in sprains and rheumatic affections, in scrofulous eruptions, and for destroying warts. From its acrid nature great care is required in its employment, as it is likely to cause a great deal of inflammatory swelling. This juice, when mixed with quicklime, is employed to mark cotton or linen with an indelible mark. When dry it forms a black varnish much used in India, and amongst other purposes it is employed, mixed with pitch and tar, in the caulking of ships. The seeds, called Malacca-beans or Marsh-nuts, are eaten, and are said to stimulate the mental powers, and especially the memory. From them an oil is procured which is used in painting. The generic name is derived from the Greek word *semeion* 'a mark,' and *karpos* 'fruit,' in allusion to the dyeing property of the juice of the fruit.   [M. T. M.]

SEMEIANDRA. A genus of *Onagraceæ*, distinguished by the following characters:—Calyx subglobose at the base, its border four-cleft, the posterior piece shortest; petals four, very narrow, and shorter than the limb of the calyx; stamens two, adherent below, free above, one ending in a petal-like expansion, the other with two perfect cells. The only species is a Mexican shrub, the leaves of which vary in form and position, being opposite or alternate, ovate or oblong, and hairy on both sides, with red flowers in terminal clusters. The name is from the Greek, and indicates the presence of one perfect stamen. [G. D.]

SEMELE. A genus of *Liliaceæ* of the tribe *Asparagineæ* found in the Canaries, closely allied to *Ruscus*, of which it has very much the habit, but differing in having perfect flowers intermixed with male ones, and in the perianth-segments being united into a short turbinate tube. *S. androgyna*, formerly *Ruscus androgynus*, is a climbing shrub, with scale-like leaves and cladodia (branches taking the form of leaves), from the side of which the flowers are produced. [J. T. S.]

SEMELLE DU PAPE. (Fr.) *Opuntia vulgaris.*

SEMEN. The seed of flowering plants. —CINÆ, or SEMENCINE. A drug analogous to Semen Contra, and obtained from several species of *Artemisia*. — CONTRA. The name of *Artemisia Siebieri* and some allied species, the leaves and flower-heads of which form a celebrated vermifuge. — CORNICULATUM. The receptacle of certain Fungals. — SERIPHU. A drug obtained from *Artemisia cœrulescens.*

SEMI. In composition = half, or one side only. Thus—*semi-amplectens* or *semi-amplexicaul*, half-clasping a stem; *semi-cordate*, heart-shaped on one side only; *semi-hastate*, hastate on one side only; *semi-lunate*, crescent-shaped; *semi-ovate*, ovate on one side only; *semi-pollicaris*, half an inch long; *semi-reniform*, reniform on one side only; *semi-sagittate*, arrow-headed on one side only; *semi-teres*, half-terete—and so on.

SEMI-ANATROPOUS. The same as Hemianatropus.

SEMI-FLOSCULOSE. Having the corolla split and turned to one side, as in the ligule of composites.

SEMINATIO. The act of dispersing seeds naturally.

SEMINULUM. A spore.

SEMIRAMISIA. A genus of South American shrubs belonging to the *Vacciniaceæ*. They have stiff five to seven-nerved leaves, and extra-axillary flower-stalks thickened at the base, and bearing very large solitary flowers. The calyx is top-shaped, marked with five ridges, its free border five-toothed; and the limb of the corolla folded in the bud. [M. T. M.]

SEMI-SEPTATE. Half-partitioned; having a dissepiment which does not project into the cavity to which it belongs sufficiently to cut it off into two separate cells.

SEM-KE-GOND. An Indian name for the gum of *Bauhinia emarginata.*

SEMOLINA. A granular preparation of wheat.

SEMPERVIRENS. Evergreen; retaining greenness during winter as well as summer.

SEMPERVIVUM. A genus of shrubby or herbaceous plants belonging to the *Crassulaceæ*, and allied to *Sedum*, from which they are distinguished by having about twelve petals, and the glands at the base of the ovaries lacinlated if present. *S. tectorum*, the Common Houseleek, is a well-known plant with thick fleshy leaves arranged in the form of a double rose, from among which rise succulent stalks bearing cymes of purple flowers, which on close examination prove no less beautiful than singular. It is commonly to be met with on the tops of outhouses and cottages, but is not believed to be a native of Britain. Of the foreign species, those with shrubby stems have yellow rarely white flowers, and are all natives of the Canaries. See ÆONIUM. One species, *S. cæspitosum*, has been known to remain alive in an herbarium for eighteen months, and to grow when subsequently planted. Other species which are herbaceous approach *S. tectorum* or some of the stone-crops in habit. French: *Joubarbe* ; German : *Hauswurz.* [C. A. J.]

SÉNÉ. (Fr.) *Senna.* — BÂTARDE. *Coronilla Emerus.* — FAUX. *Colutea arborescens.* — DES PROVENÇAUX. *Globularia Alypum.*

SENEBIERA. Insignificant weeds with prostrate diffuse stems, and finely-divided leaves, belonging to the order *Cruciferæ*, distinguished by their two-celled two-seeded seed-vessels, which are broader than long, and either wrinkled or crested with sharp points. *S. didyma*, the Lesser Wartcress, is most abundant in the west of England, where it frequently covers waste ground to the exclusion of every other weed, and may be distinguished by its acrid smell alone, resembling that of peppercress; its flavour is most nauseous. The Swine's Cress, *S. Coronopus*, resembles it in habit, but is destitute of the pungent smell: it is said to have been formerly used as a salad. Both species have minute white flowers, and the latter is remarkable for its large seed-vessels, which have the appearance of being carved. [C. A. J.]

SENECILLIS. Of this genus of *Compositæ* there are three species—*glauca*, *carpatica*, and *Jacquemontiana*, natives respectively of Central Russia, the Carpathian mountains, and Kashmir. Excepting in the pappus, which consists of one row of rough hairs much shorter than the ribbed achenes, these plants have altogether the characters of *Ligularia*, and might be passed over as belonging to that genus. They are perennial herbs, with stalked root-leaves of the consistence of those of the cabbage, sessile stem-leaves, and nodding yellow-rayed flower-heads disposed in terminal panicles. The plant usually cultivated as *S. glauca* is *Ligularia macrophylla*, which greatly resembles the former, but has a different pappus. [A. A. B.]

SENECIO. This genus of *Compositæ*, represented in Britain by the well-known Groundsel and Ragweed, is perhaps the most extensive in point of species in the vegetable kingdom. Nearly 900 different kinds are known to botanists; they are spread over all parts of the globe, but are found in greatest profusion in temperate regions. They are either annuals, perennials, shrubs or undershrubs, with entire pinnatifid or variously toothed or lobed leaves placed alternately on the stem; and solitary panicled or corymbose flower-heads, the florets of which are either all tubular, or more commonly the central tubular and the marginal strap-shaped. The prevailing colour is yellow—purple, dingy white, or blue being comparatively rare. The essential character of the genus is to have an involucre consisting of a single series of scales of equal length, which are often surrounded at the base by a number of narrow bracts to which the name calycule is given.

There are 596 species described in Decandolle's *Prodromus*. Of these, South Africa claims 200; Europe, North Africa, and Western Asia, 115; South America, 103; North America and Mexico, 55; the East Indies, 43; Australia and the Pacific Isles, 35; Mauritius and Madagascar, 28; Canary Isles, 10; and China and Japan, 5. Since the publication of the *Prodromus* more than 300 species have been made known from different countries, but the proportion to each is nearly the same.

The Groundsel, *S. vulgaris*, the Ragwort or Ragweed, *S. Jacobæa*, and our other native sorts afford a good idea of the appearance of the European species, the most noteworthy of which is perhaps the well-known *S. Cineraria*, better known in gardens as *Cineraria maritima*, extensively used for planting in flower-beds for the sake of contrast with scarlet and other colours, its beautiful foliage being clothed with short white down. It is a half-hardy perennial, propagated by cuttings layers or seeds, and is found wild on the shores of the Mediterranean. South Africa is the native country of *S. elegans*, a pretty autumn-flowering annual, having the habit of the common groundsel, but with brilliant purple flower-heads. Many fine varieties of this plant exist.

The generic name *Cineraria* is restricted to a few Cape plants which differ from *Senecio* in the achenes of the ray-florets being winged. The beautiful early spring-flowering plants cultivated in greenhouses as *Cinerarias* belong however to *Senecio*, and have been obtained by horticulturists, by intercrossing with each other a number of the Canary Island species, such as *S. populifolius*, *S. Tussilaginis*, &c. The deep blue colour of some of the garden varieties of these plants is singular in the genus, and not at all common in the family.

As South Africa is the richest in species in the Old World, so is the Andean region in the New; and the species are there remarkable for their shrubby habit. M. Weddell remarks that the proportion without strap-shaped florets to those with such, is as three to one in the Andes, while in most other countries the reverse is the case. In his Flora of the alpine regions of the Cordilleras, M. Weddell describes 120 species of this genus, and it is curious to remark the large proportion of these which have the leaves quite glossy or glutinous on the upper surface and clothed with warm wool underneath, as if the better to protect them from the excessive cold, for many grow quite close to the perpetual snow-line. The name Tola is given by the Bolivians to some of the gummy-leaved species of this genus, which they use as firewood. The name of the genus is taken from the Latin *senex* 'an old man,' in allusion to the white pappus-hairs which crown the achenes. [A. A. B.]

SENECIONIDÆ. One of the large tribes into which the *Compositæ* of the suborder *Tubuliflorœ* have been divided, and characterised chiefly by the form of the style. The most typical genera of its principal subdivisions are *Helianthus, Tagetes, Anthemis, Artemisia, Gnaphalium*, and *Senecio*.

SÉNEÇON (Fr.) *Senecio vulgaris*. — EN ARBRE. *Baccharis halimifolia*.

SENECTUS. Old age is the most formidable of all diseases, and one which all the contents of Medea's cauldron cannot arrest. Every organised being has its appointed limits, and whether its period of existence be a day or a century, no earthly power can prolong it. Exogenous trees, however, seem at first sight to contradict this; but we must remember that the new growth of each year, dependent on the evolution of the buds, must be regarded in some measure separately from the whole, to which it bears some such sort of relation as that of seed to a plant. As, however, each new layer is in close connection with those which went before, and since these after a time are subject to decay, after the lapse of years the first-formed wood perishes, the tree becomes hollow, and the sound wood is ultimately more or less affected by the decayed matter within. The effect is in many instances so slow, that a thousand years or more may pass before the general health is so affected as to induce complete destruction. Even in trees, however, the constitution after a time begins to fail, the sap is not carried to the extremities, and in consequence they die—indicating most surely that the tree is past its prime, and that the central wood, if not actually decayed, no longer performs its functions.

In annual or biennial plants life is occasionally prolonged to the second or third year if anything has prevented the formation of seed; and amongst cryptogams, which multiply by cell-division as well as by spores, a portion of the original cell may exist for a long time in the absence of fruit, but no sooner is this formed than death ensues as a necessary consequence. [M. J. B.]

SENEGAL-ROOT. The diuretic and very bitter root of *Oocculus Bakis*.

SENÈGRE. (Fr.) *Trigonella fœnum graecum.*

SENEKA-ROOT. The root of *Polygala Senega.*

SÉNEVÉ. (Fr.) *Sinapis.*

SENGREEN. *Sempervivum tectorum.*

SENI, SENARIUS. In sixes.

SENNA. The leaflets of several species of *Cassia* used in medicine for their purgative properties; it is often adulterated with the leaves of *Solenostemma Arghel, Tephrosia Apollinea, Coriaria myrtifolia,* &c. —, of the Chilenos. *Myoschilos oblongus.* —, ALEPPO. *Cassia obovata.* —, ALEXANDRIAN. *Cassia acutifolia* and *C. obovata.* —, AMERICAN. *Cassia marilandica.* —, BLADDER. *Colutea arborescens*; that of the Cape is *Sutherlandia frutescens.* —, INDIAN. *Cassia elongata.* —, MECCA. *Cassia elongata.* —, NUBIAN. *Cassia œthiopica.* —, SCORPION. *Coronilla Emerus.* —, SENEGAL. *Cassia obovata,* —, TINNEVELLY. *Cassia elongata.* —, TRIPOLI. *Cassia œthiopica.* —, WILD. *Poinciana pulcherrima*; also an American name for *Cassia marilandica.*

SENNA-TREE. *Cassia emarginata.*

SENSITIVE PLANT. *Mimosa sensitiva;* also *M. pudica, Oxalis sensitiva,* and others. —, BASTARD. *Æschynomene americana.* —, WILD. *Cassia nictitans.*

SENUS. The sixth.

SENVY. *Sinapis nigra.*

SEPALS. The divisions of the calyx. Hence *sepaline,* belonging to a sepal; and *sepaloid,* resembling a sepal in appearance.

SEPAWN, SEPON. Maize-meal boiled in water, used as food in the North American States.

SEPEDONIUM. Almost everyone who is accustomed to observe *Fungi* in our woods has been at times struck with a peculiar condition of *Boleti,* in which they become mouldy, and when broken are filled with a yellow powder, and have frequently a nasty fishy smell. This arises from their being attacked by a naked-spored mould, *S. chrysospermum,* which consists of loosebranched threads, bearing at their tips rather large echinulate spores. Other species occur on *Helvellae, Pezizae, Geoglosseae,* &c., varying in colour and in the structure of the spores, which are interesting microscopical objects. A rose-coloured species, which occurs occasionally on *Pezizae,* is worth attentive examination. [M. J. B.]

SEPICOLOUS. Inhabiting hedgerows.

SEPTAL. Of or belonging to a septum.

SEPTAS. A genus of *Crassulaceae,* consisting of two species inhabiting the Cape of Good Hope, and having the habit of some species of *Saxifraga.* They are herbaceous, and have tuberous roots, simple stems, opposite or verticillate leaves, and white almost umbellate flowers. The calyx is from five to nine-cleft; and the petals stamens scales and carpels are from five to nine in number. They are old inmates of our gardens; but their uses are entirely unknown. [B. S.]

SEPTATE. Partitioned off by septa.

SEPTENATE, SEPTENOUS. Growing in sevens.

SEPTFOIL. *Tormentilla officinalis.*

SEPTICIDAL. A mode of dehiscing, in which the fruit is resolved into its component carpels, which split asunder through the dissepiments.

SEPTIFORM. Having the appearance of a dissepiment, as is the case with the placenta of some plants, as *Plantago.*

SEPTIFRAGAL. A mode of dehiscing, in which the backs of the carpels separate from the dissepiments, whether formed by their sides, or by expansions of the placenta.

SEPTILE. Of or belonging to dissepiments.

SEPTORIA. A genus of coniomycetous *Fungi,* resembling externally minute species of *Sphaeria,* but producing naked spores instead of asci and sporidia. The spores are frequently filiform and curved, and are either continuous or septate. Many of the species occur only on living leaves, on which they are true parasites; but others are as constantly found on white or discoloured spots which have lost their vitality, and are separated from the living portion more or less definitely by a coloured ring, and are then only distinguished from *Depazea* by their structure. In these cases possibly they may be mere secondary forms of other plants, but in the true parasites the same supposition is not so well founded. It is indeed conjectured that many analogous productions are mere sexual forms of larger *Fungi,* but this is mere conjecture, however suggestive of further inquiries. [M. J. B.]

SEPTULUM. A little partition of any kind.

SEPTUM. The partition of an ovary or fruit produced by the sides of the carpels brought together and consolidated; also a partition of any kind.

SEQUAMETL. A Mexican name for *Agave americana.*

SEQUOIA (including *Wellingtonia*). A genus of the *Abietinae* tribe of *Coniferae* from North-western America, closely allied to *Sciadopitys,* and distinguished from it principally by its peltate scales without bracts, and five to seven seeds. Only two species are known with certainty, *S. sempervirens* and *S. Wellingtonia* (*Wellingtonia gigantea* of Lindley), both trees of extraordinary height. *S. gigantea* of Endlicher is a nonentity, being founded upon a sterile branch of *Pinus bracteata,* coupled with Douglas's account of *S. sempervirens.*

The claims of *S. Lawsoniana*, recently introduced to our gardens, have not yet been critically examined.

S. sempervirens is the Redwood of the timber trade, and extends from Upper California to Nutka Sound. It attains gigantic dimensions, being frequently more than 300 feet high, and imparting to the woods of its native country a peculiar character—'something,' Douglas tells us, 'which plainly shows that we are *not* in Europe.' The Redwood has long been an inmate of our gardens, and principally differs from the *Wellingtonia* in having linear rather obtuse and beneath whitish leaves.

S. Wellingtonia (the *Wellingtonia* of our gardens, and the Big or Mammoth-tree of the Americans) was at first thought to be confined to a single spot, the so-called Mammoth Grove of Calaveras in Upper California; but it has since been found in the Mariposa and Frezno Groves, and in various other parts of the Sierra Nevada, though nowhere attaining such a height as in the spot where it was first discovered, in June 1850, by an American hunting-party. The tallest tree of the Mammoth Grove, stripped of its bark for tho purpose of being exhibited, was 327 feet high, and at the base was 90 feet in circumference. The greatest dimensions seems to have been attained by a tree which was found

Sequoia Wellingtonia.

broken at a height of 300 feet, and which measured at that place 18 feet in diameter. Considering that it was 112 feet in circumference at the base, and tapered regularly to the point where broken, it is calculated to have been when in the fullness of its growth 450 feet high. It was at first thought that these trees might be 3,000 years old, but that estimate has since been reduced by actual counting of the concentric rings to about 1,100 years. A specimen of this gigantic tree, showing its enormous rela-

tive proportions, may be seen at the Crystal Palace, Sydenham.

The *Wellingtonia* was introduced into Europe by Mr. W. Lobb in 1853, and stands our climate remarkably well. The wood when first cut is white, but ultimately turns to a mahogany colour. The young branches are not unlike those of some cypress or juniper; and like many other *Coniferæ*, including the Redwood, they have two kinds of leaves. The ordinary leaves are evergreen, alternate subulate, or ovate lance-shaped. In seedling plants they are more compact than in fully-grown trees. The cones are ovate, and rather larger than those of the Redwood. [B. S.]

SERAPIAS. A small South European genus of terrestrial orchids belonging to the ophrydeous suborder. Its flowers have the lateral sepals agglutinated to the upper one, forming a kind of hood open in front, and out of which the lip protrudes. The lip has a couple of plates at its base, and is three-lobed, with the lateral lobes rounded and embracing the column, and the middle one long and pendulous. The anther is erect beaked, and has its cells parallel and contiguous; and the caudicle of the two masses of pollen are fixed to a single gland included within the stigmatic hood. [A. S.]

SÉRENTE. *Abies Picea*.

SÉRÈQUE. (Fr.) *Genista saxatilis.*

SERIAL. Arranged in rows.

SERICEOUS. Silky; covered with very fine close-pressed hairs, silky to the touch.

SERICOCARPUS. A genus of *Compositæ* peculiar to North America, closely related to *Aster*, and characterised by the simple unequal pappus, few ray and disk-florets, and oblong imbricated involucres with cartilaginous scales. They are perennial herbs one to three feet high, with sessile leaves, and corymbose flower-heads, having the ray-florets white, those of the disk pale-yellow. The generic name alludes to the silky hairs on the achenes. There are five species known. [A. A. B.]

SERICOCOMA. A genus of *Amaranthaceæ* inhabiting the Cape of Good Hope. They are annuals or perennials with alternate leaves (except the lowest and sometimes those of the branches), and bear large flowers in solitary terminal compact spikes or heads. These flowers are solitary or two or three together, the middle one three-bracted, the other with two bracts. They have a perigone of five sepals, woolly on the outside, nearly equal, or if unequal the longer ones spinescent; stamens five, united at the base into a cup, with scale-like intermediate staminodes; utricle very woolly, one-seeded. [J. T. S.]

SERICOGRAPHIS. A genus of *Acanthaceæ* containing several species of herbs or undershrubs, natives of tropical America. The stem is jointed, and the flowers are arranged in secund spicate racemes, with small bracts and bractlets. The calyx is five-parted; the two stamens have many parallel anther-cells; and the capsule is seed-bearing below, and contains four seeds.   [W. C.]

SERINGA. The Portuguese name for the India-rubber tree.

SÉRINGA, or SÉRINGAT. (Fr.) *Philadelphus.*

SERINGIA. An East Australian genus of *Byttneriaceæ*, the two known species of which are shrubs with alternate ovate or lance-shaped leaves, clothed underneath with rusty down, as are also the small white starry flowers, which are arranged in axillary cymes. The calyx is bell-shaped, deeply five-toothed; corolla none; stamens ten, five of them anther-bearing; ovary five to seven-lobed, the lobes or carpels becoming distinct when ripe, and not uniting to form a capsule as in *Thomasia* and other allied genera. It was named after N. C. Seringe, a well-known Swiss botanist.   [A. A. B.]

SERINGUE. A South American name for the caoutchouc-yielding *Siphonia.*

SERIOLA. A small genus of the chicory group of *Compositæ*, comprising three species from the Mediterranean region, and one from Southern Brazil. The latter is a smooth perennial herb with the aspect of a sowthistle, and is sometimes used like endive as a salad in Brazil. The others are perennial yellow-flowered weeds resembling *Hypochæris*, and only to be distinguished by the achenes, which are not dissimilar, but all alike, terminating in a long slender beak, tipped with a single series of feathery pappus-hairs. [A. A. B.]

SERIPHIUM. A South African genus of *Compositæ* ranking near to *Gnaphalium*, and characterised by the crowded one-flowered heads, and beakless achenes crowned with a single series of pappus-hairs, which are feathery towards the apex—not a biserial pappus, as in the closely-allied genus *Stœbe* from the same country. About a dozen species are known—much-branched undershrubs, with numerous linear heath-like leaves, often spirally twisted, and small white flower-heads arranged in close terminal spikes or round heads.   [A. A. B.]

SERISSA. An Indian shrub forming a genus of *Cinchonaceæ*. The flowers are white, in terminal tufts; the calyx-limb divided into four or five segments, with occasionally little teeth between them; the corolla funnel-shaped, its tube hairy, its limb four or five-lobed; the stamens four or five, with very short filaments, and anthers projecting beyond the tube of the corolla, the ovary two-celled, surmounted by a fleshy disk, with a simple style, and a stigma divided into two linear branches; and the fruit succulent two-celled, each cell containing a single seed. *S. fœtida*, a native of India, Japan, China, &c., has astringent properties. Its root is employed in cases of diarrhœa, also in ophthalmia and certain forms of ulcers. This plant is cultivated as a pretty stove-shrub. There is a variety with double flowers, which is the more interesting inasmuch as double flowers are rare in the order.   [M. T. M.]

SERJANIA. A genus of *Sapindaceæ* closely allied to *Paullinia*, and not distinguishable from it by its flowers, the distinctions between these and some other genera of the order residing solely in the structure of their fruit. In the present genus the fruit consists of three thin pieces or carpels firmly joined together in the centre, and not separating from each other nor opening spontaneously at maturity, each piece being drawn out into a thin wing at the base, and containing a single seed in the upper part—the seed having a thin brittle shell, and usually a minute two-lobed arillus. Like the *Paullinias*, the species of *Serjania*, of which there are a considerable number, are confined to the tropics of the Western Hemisphere, and are climbing shrubs furnished with tendrils for their support. Their leaves are usually composed of one two or three sets of leaflets in threes, or are rarely unequally pinnate, and have minute stipules at their base; and their flowers are borne in racemes produced near the leaf-axils, the stalk of the raceme generally having two tendrils close to its base. All the species possess narcotic poisonous qualities of more or less intensity. *S. lethalis* is supposed to be one of the plants from which the wasp called 'Lecheguana de mel vermelho' in Brazil collects its poisonous honey. M. St Hilaire has recorded the exceedingly violent effect of this honey upon his own person. In most cases it produces a sort of drunkenness or delirium only to be removed by emetics, but it sometimes occasions death. The plant forms one of the fish-poisons called Timboe by the Brazilians.   [A. S.]

SERMONTAISE. (Fr.) *Levisticum officinale.*

SEROTINOUS. Appearing late in a season, or later than some other part or species allied to it.

SERPÆA. A Brazilian genus of the tribe *Heliantheæ* of *Compositæ*. There are two species, both branching perennial herbs, with opposite stalked rough leaves, and long-stalked yellow flower-heads, either two or three together, or solitary at the ends of the branches. The ray-florets are strap-shaped and neutral; the disk-florets tubular and perfect; the outer achenes three sided, and crowned with three pappus-awns, the inner compressed and two-awned, and all of them seated on a conical chaffy receptacle. It is named after Dr. Serpa, once Professor of Botany at Pernambuco.   [A. A. B.]

SERPENTAIRE. (Fr.) *Dracunculus.*

SERPENTARY-ROOT. The root of *Aristolochia Serpentaria.*

SERPENT-WITHE. *Aristolochia odoratissima.*

SERPICULA. A small genus of *Haloragaceæ* inhabiting the tropical and subtropical regions of both hemispheres, most of the species being natives of the Cape of Good Hope. They are branched creeping herbs, with alternate or opposite leaves, and axillary usually monœcious flowers, the males on long pedicels, the female perfect ones subsessile. [J T S.]

SERPOLET. An essential perfumery oil obtained from *Thymus Serpyllum.*

SERRA, SERRATURES. The sawtoothings at the edge of leaves and similar bodies.

SERRADELLE. (Fr.) The Serradilla, *Ornithopus sativus.*

SERRADILLA. (Port.) *Ornithopus sativus,* a kind of green fodder.

SERRÆA. An Arabian shrub belonging to the *Malvaceæ.* The flowers have an outer calyx of three membranous heart-shaped entire leaves, concealing the inner five-cleft calyx; petals five, yellow with a purple spot; ovary five-celled, with two ovules in each compartment, fruit a five-celled five-valved capsule. [M. T. M.]

SERRAFALCUS. A genus of grasses belonging to the tribe *Festuceæ,* now included in *Bromus.*

SERRATE. Having sharp straight-edged teeth pointing to the apex. When these teeth are themselves serrate, they are *biserrate* or *duplicato-serrate.*

SERRATULA. A genus of herbaceous plants belonging to the tribe *Cynarocephalæ* of compound flowers, distinguished by having a hairy (not feathery) pappus of several conspicuously unequal rows, the inner row longest; and by the scales of the involucre, which are neither hooked nor spinous. The genus is represented in England by *S. tinctoria,* the Common Sawwort, a slender erect plant one to two feet high, growing on commons and in bushy places. The leaves are entire or pinnatifid, serrated but not prickly; and the flowers grow in terminal heads, small and shaped like those of a thistle; but the oblong scales of the involucre are blunt, and nearly destitute of any cottony appendage. The herbage yields a yellow dye. Other species have been introduced from various temperate countries of the Eastern Hemisphere. French: *Sarrette*; German: *Färberscharte.* [C. A. J.]

SERRON. (Fr.) *Chenopodium* (or *Blitum*) *Bonus Henricus.*

SERRONIA. *Ottonia.*

SERSALISIA. This genus of *Sapotaceæ* is closely allied to *Sideroxylon,* and its flowers agree with those of that genus in having their calyx and corolla five-parted, with five fertile stamens opposite the lobes of the latter, and five sterile scale-like ones, and also, in their five-celled ovary and un-

divided stigma; but they are well distinguished by their very different seeds, those of the present genus having a thin brittle shell marked with a long scar or hilum, and being destitute of albumen, while those of *Sideroxylon* are hard and bony, and furnished with copious albumen. The three species of *Sersalisia* are small hard-wooded trees, natives of the eastern coast of tropical Australia. [A. S.]

SERTULUM. A simple umbel.

SERVICE-BERRY. *Amelanchier canadensis.*

SERVICE-TREE. *Pyrus Sorbus* alias P *domestica.* —, WILD. *Pyrus torminalis.*

SESAME. *Sesamum orientale* and *S. indicum.*

SESAMUM. A genus of *Pedaliaceæ,* consisting of annual herbs indigenous to the East Indies, but cultivated in various other tropical and subtropical countries. The leaves are opposite or alternate, quite entire or variously lobed; the flowers axillary, and of a yellow or pinkish colour. The calyx is five-cleft, the corolla two-lipped, the stamens four with the rudiment of a fifth, and the capsule oblong quadrangular, two-valved and two-celled, each cell containing numerous oily seeds. It is especially on

Sesamum indicum.

account of the latter peculiarity that *S. indicum* is extensively cultivated. Its seeds contain an abundance of a fixed oil, as tasteless as that of the olive, for which it might be substituted, and which is expressed in Egypt in great quantities. It is sometimes called Gingelly oil, and, if of very good quality, is employed for adulterating oil of almonds. It is, however, apt to become rancid. The leaves of *Sesamum* are emollient. [B. S.]

SESBAN. *Sesbania ægyptiaca.*

SESBANIA. Twiggy shrubs or shrubby annuals dispersed over the tropics of both hemispheres, belonging to the *Leguminosæ,* and formerly combined with *Æschynomene*. They have pinnate leaves, composed of numerous pairs of leaflets without a terminal one, but having a bristly point in place of it, the leaflets often possessing the irritable nature of the well-known sensitive plant. Their flowers, usually of a yellow colour, are produced few or several together on stalks rising from the leaf-axils, and are succeeded by long narrow cylindrical or flattened pods containing many seeds, between which they are so much constricted that the seeds appear to lie in separate cells, but they are not truly jointed like those of *Æschynomene*.

S. *aculeata*, the Danchi of India, is an erect slightly branched annual, with the stems and leafstalks armed with minute prickles, leaves composed of from twenty to fifty pairs of narrow leaflets, and racemes with few rather large flowers on slender stalks, producing erect almost cylindrical or tapered sharp-pointed pods. It is cultivated in India for its fibre, which, though coarse, is of great strength and very durable in water or when repeatedly wetted, and is consequently valuable for the ropes of fishing-nets, &c.; but it is not suitable for ships' cordage, as it contracts very much when wet. It is found also in the West Indies, and in Tropical Africa.   [A. S.]

SESELI. A genus of *Umbelliferæ* having the following characters :—The calyx has five short teeth ; and the fruit is oval or oblong, each half of it having five prominent ribs, the two lateral of which are broadest : in each furrow there is usually one rarely two oil-vessels, and two rarely four at the line of junction. The species are biennial or perennial herbs, with much-divided leaves, and white rarely yellow flowers. They are natives of Europe, Central Asia, and North America.   [G. D.]

SESELI. (Fr.) *Seseli.* — COMMUN *Sium Sisarum.* — DE CRÈTE. *Tordylium officinale.* — DE MONTPELLIER. *Silaus pratensis.*

SÉSES. (Fr.) *Cicer arietinum.*

SESLERIA. A genus of grasses belonging to the tribe *Festuceæ.* The inflorescence is in simple spikes ; spikelets two to six-flowered ; glumes two membranaceous, nearly equal and pointed or mucronate ; flowering glumes three to five-toothed, the central tooth longest ; stamens three ; styles two, short. This genus contains twenty species, most of which are natives of alpine or subalpine countries, where they reach to great elevations on the mountains. In Britain it is represented by S. *cærulea*, which is not a common grass though generally plentiful where it grows. French : *Seslère.*   [D. M.]

SESQUI. This term, prefixed to the Latin name of a measure, shows that such measure exceeds its due length by one half ; thus, *sesquipedalis* means a foot and a half.

SESSEA. A genus of Peruvian shrubs or trees belonging to the *Solanaceæ.* The

flowers are in terminal panicles ; calyx tubular, five-toothed ; corolla funnel-shaped, its limb with five spreading segments ; anthers opening longitudinally ; ovary two-celled ; fruit capsular, surrounded by the calyx, two-celled two-valved, each valve splitting into two halves ; seeds numerous, winged.   [M. T. M.]

SESSILE. Sitting close upon the body that supports it, without any sensible stalk.

SESUVIACEÆ. A name given by Wight to the *Tetragonieæ*, a tribe of *Ficoideæ* or *Mesembryaceæ.* Other botanists limit *Sesuvieæ* to a tribe of *Tetragoniaceæ*, considering the latter as a distinct order.

SESUVIUM. This genus of *Tetragoniaceæ*, or *Mesembryaceæ*, consists of half a dozen species found on the shores of most tropical countries, consisting of smooth herbaceous plants, with succulent opposite entire nearly veinless leaves, and usually solitary flowers. The latter have a five-parted persistent calyx coloured inside, and no petals ; and the fruit is a three to five-celled capsule, opening crosswise through the middle when ripe, the upper or lid-like half falling away and leaving the lower, which contains the numerous seeds, attached to the plant.

S. *Portulacastrum* is common on the sandy shores of the tropical and warm regions of the Western Hemisphere. It is a prostrate plant, with more or less lance-shaped leaves and stalked flowers, having the calyx green outside and purple or white within. S. *repens*, the Eastern species, has rooting stems ; leaves which vary in form from round or oval to long spatula-shaped ; and stalked flowers, with the calyx purplish outside and rosy within. Both are eatable as potherbs, but have a rather saltish taste. The large tufts of S. *repens* are frequently buried in the loose sand, and then become blanched and tender, and are greedily sought after by hogs. French : *Sésuve.*   [A. S.]

SETA. A bristle of any sort ; a stiff hair ; a slender straight prickle ; also the stalk which bears the spore-case of plants of the muscal alliance.

SETACEO, SERRATE. Having the serratures ending in bristle-like points.

SETARIA. A genus of grasses belonging to the tribe *Paniceæ.* The species are now included under *Panicum.* French : *Sétaire.*   [D. M.]

SETHIA. By some this genus is combined with *Erythroxylon*, which then forms the sole genus of *Erythroxylaceæ* ; while others separate it, and characterise it by the calyx being five-lobed, and by the styles being united together, and bearing three distinct stigmas at the top. The three described species are confined to the Indian Peninsula and Ceylon. S. *indica* is a small tree, with inversely egg-shaped or oblong feather-veined leaves, pale-coloured on the under-surface ; and with yellow flowers borne singly or two or three together in the leaf-axils. An empyreumatic oil or wood-tar obtained from this tree is used by the natives of Ceylon and Southern India as a preservative application to the timber employed by them in the construction of boats. [A. S.]

SETIFORM. Having the form of a seta.

SETOSE. Covered with stiff hairs or setæ.

SETTERWORT. *Helleborus fœtidus.*

SETULA. The stipe of certain fungals.

SETWALL. *Valeriana pyrenaica.*

SEUBEL. An Algerian name for the flowers of *Andropogon Nardus.*

SEUBERTIA. The native Daisy of the Azores, *Bellis azorica,* has been separated from the others by Mr. Watson under the above generic name, mainly on account of the glandular achenes, and the flat instead of conical receptacle of the flower-head. The leaves are like those of the common daisy in form, but the heads are smaller, and it has branching stems. It is named after Dr. M. Seubert, author of a *Flora of the Azores.* [A. A. B.]

SEUILLET, or SEUR. (Fr.) *Sambucus nigra.*

SEUTERA. A genus of *Asclepiadaceæ,* consisting of a single species from North America. It is a slender climbing littoral herb, with linear fleshy leaves, and minute glabrous flowers in few-flowered extra-axillary umbels. The calyx is composed of five lanceolate sepals; the corolla is rotate, with a short tube and five acute limb-segments; the staminal corona consists of five erect fleshy leaflets united to the base of the sessile gynostegium; the ovoid pollen-masses are pendulous, and affixed by the apex; the conical stigma is obscurely bifid; and the smooth follicles contain many comose seeds. [W. C.]

SEVERINIA. The name applied to an imperfectly known tree, referred to the *Aurantiaceæ.* The tree is described as bearing spines and ovate sessile leaves, and having axillary flowers in fascicles or solitary, with a five-lobed calyx, five petals, ten stamens in five parcels, curved anthers, and a two-seeded fruit. [M. T. M.]

SEVOEJA. *Stenanthium frigidum.*

SÉVOLE. (Fr.) *Scævola.*

SEXTUPLICI. Six times.

SHADBUSH. *Amelanchier canadensis.*

SHADDOCK. *Citrus decumana.*

SHAG. A Scotch name for the refuse of barley. Also a preparation of tobacco sold in shops.

SHAGGY. The same as Hirtus.

SHAKER. *Briza media*

SHALDANEH, SHEADANA. Persian names for the seeds of the Hemp plant.

SHALLON. *Gaultheria Shallon,* the berries of which are much eaten in North-west America.

SHALLOT. *Allium ascalonicum.*

SHALOO. An Indian name for *Sorghum saccharatum.*

SHAMOOLA. An Indian name for *Panicum frumentaceum.*

SHAMROCK. *Trifolium repens;* or according to others *Oxalis Acetosella.* The Shamrock is the national emblem of Ireland.

SHAREWORT. *Aster Tripolium.*

SHAWIA. A name formerly given to two New Zealand shrubs of the *Compositæ* now placed in *Eurybia,* where they are notable for their few-flowered heads. See EURYBIA. [A. A. B.]

SHEA-BUTTER. A solid fat obtained in Africa from the seeds of *Bassia Parkii.*

SHEADENDRON. A name given by Bertolini to a tree of which specimens were sent to him from Mozambique as the Butter-tree of the natives. It has since been shown by Klotzsch that this tree, with two other allied species or varieties from the same country, belong to the order *Combretaceæ,* and indeed only differ from *Combretum* itself by the unimportant character of the fruit being four-angled instead of four-winged; they will therefore probably be considered as species of *Combretum.* It is still however far from being proved that either of them is really the tree called Shea by the natives, as furnishing the fatty substance which has been compared with butter, more especially as the tree so designated in other parts of Tropical Africa is known to belong to a totally different natural order.

SHEATH. A part which is rolled round a stem or other body. The same as Vagina.

SHEEPSBANE. *Hydrocotyle vulgaris.*

SHEEP'S-BEARD. *Arnopogon.*

SHEEP'S-BIT. *Jasione montana.*

SHEPHERDIA. The generic name of plants belonging to the order of oleasters. The stamens and pistils are on separate plants; the barren flowers have the calyx shortly tubular and four-cleft, with eight stamens; and the fertile flowers have a tubular four-cleft calyx. The species are small shrubs, natives of North America, with opposite deciduous leaves, and small sessile flowers in their axils.

S. canadensis is a small shrub, clothed with rusty scales. *S. argentea,* which has an edible scarlet fruit, is the Buffalo-berry of the United States. The genus was named in honour of Mr. J. Shepherd, once curator of the Liverpool Botanic Garden. [G. D.]

SHEPHERD'S-CLUB. *Verbascum Thapsus.*

SHEPHERD'S-KNOT. *Tormentilla officinalis.*

SHEPHERD'S-NEEDLE. *Scandix Pecten Veneris.*

SHEPHERD'S-PURSE. *Thlaspi*; also *Capsella Bursa pastoris.*

SHEPHERD'S-ROD, or SHEPHERD'S-STAFF. *Dipsacus pilosus.*

SHEPHERD'S WEATHERGLASS. *Anagallis arvensis.*

SHERARDIA. Humble annuals belonging to the order *Galiaceæ*, distinguished by having a funnel-shaped corolla, and fruit crowned with the calyx. *S. arvensis*, or Field Madder, the only British species, is a common weed in pastures and cornfields, and has trailing branched stems a few inches long, narrow acute leaves with rough margins, about six in a whorl, and terminal umbellate heads of minute pinkish-hue flowers, at the base of which is a whorl of seven or eight leaves. German: *Ackerröthe.* [C. A. J.]

SHERBET. See SCHERBET.

SHIELDS. The reproductive bodies of lichenals. The same as Apothecia.

SHIELD-SHAPED. The same as Clypeate.

SHINGLE-WOOD. *Nectandra leucantha.*

SHIN-LEAF. *Pyrola elliptica.*

SHIVE. *Allium Schœnoprasum.*

SHOEBLACK PLANT, or SHOE-FLOWER. *Hibiscus Rosa sinensis.*

SHOLA. An Indian name for the pithlike cellular substance obtained from the stem of *Æschynomene aspera*, used for making hats, bottle and glass covers, toys, &c.

SHOOTHEE. An Indian name for the roots of *Curcuma Zerumbet.*

SHOREA. Large resinous tropical Asiatic trees forming a genus of few species, belonging to the order *Dipteraceæ*, and characterised by the flowers having five sepals overlapping each other in the bud, and ultimately enlarging into erect equal or unequal leafy wings surmounting the fruit; five sepals; twenty-five or an indefinite number of stamens in two or three series, with the filaments widened and cohering at the base, and the anthers two-celled with the connecting portion prolonged into a coloured bristle; and a short thick style, with a bluntish or three-toothed stigma. They have entire or wavy-edged leaves, and axillary and terminal panicles of very sweet-smelling yellow flowers, producing one-seeded fruits enclosed in the closely overlapping lower portion of the sepals.

S. robusta, the Saul or Sál, is a native of India, from the provinces of Bengal and Behar to the foot of the Himalaya mountains within the limits of the tropics. It is a most magnificent timber-tree, frequently attaining a height of upwards of a hundred feet. Its wood is of a light-brown colour, close-grained strong and durable, and is very extensively employed in India, both by the natives and by Europeans, for shipbuilding engineering and other purposes where great strength and toughness are requisite. It is considerably stronger but at the same time much heavier than Indian teak. An oil is obtained from the seeds. Part of the resin known as Dammar is likewise obtained from this and other species of *Shorea*, particularly from *S. Selanica*, a native of the Eastern Archipelago. [A. S.]

SHOREWEED. *Littorella.*

SHORTIA. A North American genus of *Pyrolaceæ*, comprising a single species, distinguished from *Pyrola* by having a three instead of a five-valved capsule. It is a little nearly stemless glabrous perennial plant, with long-stalked roundish somewhat cordate toothed leaves, and single-flowered scapes. [A. S.]

SHREETALY. An Indian name for *Corypha umbraculifera.*

SHUBIT. An Arabic name for the aromatic fruit of *Anethum Sowa.*

SHUMAC. The dried and chopped leaves and shoots of *Rhus Coriaria.*

SHUNUM. *Crotalaria juncea.*

SHUPRAK. An Indian name for the root of *Thalictrum foliolosum*, used as a febrifuge and a tonic aperient.

SHURIFA. The Persian name for the Custard Apple.

SHUTTLECOCK. *Periptera punicea.*

SHUTURKHAR. An Indian name for the Camel's-thorn, *Alhagi Maurorum.*

SIALITE. (Fr.) *Dillenia.*

SIBBALDIA. Dwarf evergreen alpine plants belonging to the tribe *Potentilldæ* of *Rosaceæ*, and distinguished from *Potentilla* by having five to ten instead of numerous styles. *S. procumbens* is found near the summits of the Highland mountains of Scotland as well as in similar localities on the European continent and in America. The leaves are trifoliate almost destitute of hairs, the leaflets being wedge-shaped and coarsely-toothed at the apex; and the flowers are small yellowish, and collected into heads. There are two or three foreign species closely allied to the above. [C. A. J.]

SIBTHORPIACEÆ. A name under which Don proposed to establish a distinct order for *Sibthorpia* and a few small genera of *Scrophulariaceæ* allied to it, but which has not been adopted.

SIBTHORPIA. A genus of *Scrophulariaceæ*, containing a few species of prostrate hairy herbs of Europe, Northern Africa, and the Andes in South America. They have alternate or fasciculate reniform leaves, and one-flowered pedicels rising singly or in fascicles from the axils of the leaves. The calyx is divided into four to eight deep spreading segments; the corolla is subrotate, with as many divisions as the calyx, or with an additional one; the stamens are as numerous as the segments of the corolla, or are fewer, and have two-celled sagittate anthers; the style is entire, with a capitate stigma; and the capsule is membranaceous compressed two-celled two-valved, and dehisces in a loculicidal manner.   [W. C.]

SICIOTE. (Fr.) *Sicyos.*

SICKLE-POD. *Arabis canadensis.*

SICKLEWORT. *Prunella vulgaris.*

SICYOS, or **SYCIOS.** · A genus of climbing plants belonging to *Cucurbitaceæ,* and inhabiting tropical and temperate parts of the globe. Their stems are angular, and furnished with tendrils for climbing; their leaves are simple and lobed; their flowers monœcious, the males being arranged in racemes, and the females solitary; the calyx is five-toothed, and the corolla monopetalous whitish and five-cleft; there are five stamens, and a dry one-seeded fruit. *S. angulatus* of North America has a root and seeds which are bitter and diuretic.   [B. S.]

SICYOSPERMA *gracile* is the only known representative of a genus of *Cucurbitaceæ* inhabiting Sonora, one of the states of Western Mexico. It is an annual, which has a slender climbing stem, two-cleft tendrils, cordate leaves more or less lobed, white monœcious flowers arranged in racemes, a five-toothed calyx, a monopetalous corolla, five monadelphous stamens, and an ovate lenticular brown or blackish seed-like fruit, containing only a single pendulous seed. The genus is closely allied to *Sicyos.*   [B. S.]

SIDA. An extensive genus of *Malvaceæ,* comprising herbs and shrubs, natives of the tropical and subtropical zones both of the Eastern and Western Hemispheres. The calyx is cup-shaped and five-cleft; petals five, their stalks sometimes intertwined so as to form a tube; column of the stamens dilated at the base, forming a sort of vault over the ovary; styles five or more; fruit of five or more indehiscent carpels, each containing a single pendulous seed.

Many of the species are used medicinally. Thus the root of *S. acuta* is esteemed by the Hindoos as a valuable stomachic, and is administered in ague, dysentery, and as a remedy for snake-bites. The leaves are used as a poultice, as likewise are those of *S. retusa, S. stipulata,* and *S. mauritiana.* Others are used in rheumatic affections, and as an application in cases of the stings of wasps and other insects. The wood of these trees is very light; that of *S. micrantha* is used to make rocket-sticks in Brazil, where large quantities are employed on fête-days at the doors of the churches. The bark of some of the species contains an abundance of fibrous tissue,

available for cordage, etc. The Chinese cultivate *S. tiliæfolia* for the sake of its fibre, which they prefer to hemp. The seeds of several kinds are said to be aperient.   [M. T. M.]

SIDALCEA. A genus of herbs belonging to the mallow family, and natives of North-western America. The lower leaves are entire, the upper ones palmately divided, and the flowers red purple or white, arranged in racemes; the calyx is not provided with an involucel; the tube of the stamens divides above into five outer parcels of anthers opposite the petals, and ten inner parcels; and the fruit consists of five to nine membranous carpels, each containing a single seed.   [M. T. M.]

SIDERITIS. A genus of *Labiatæ,* distinguished from its congeners by the following characters:—The tube of the corolla is included in the calyx, and its upper lip is erect entire or notched, while the lower has the middle lobe broadest; the two upper stamens are short and perfect, the two lower longer but imperfect. The species are either herbs shrubs or undershrubs, natives of Southern Europe, temperate Asia, and the Canary Islands. Their flowers are small and usually yellow, in the axils of leaf-like bracts. The name comes from the Greek *sideros* 'iron,' given to a plant supposed to have the power of healing sword-wounds. [G. D.]

SIDEROXYLON. So named from the Greek *sideros* 'iron' and *xulon* 'wood,' on account of the very hard wood afforded by the various species. The woods of many widely different trees, however, are likewise called Ironwood, almost every country producing a hardwood to which that name is given. The present genus belongs to the *Sapotaceæ,* and is composed of between thirty and forty species, distributed through both hemispheres, but very rarely extending beyond the limits of the tropics. The majority are trees, some attaining a large size, with alternate generally veiny leaves, and axillary clusters of usually whitish flowers, succeeded by roundish berries about the size of cherries, in which are from one to three seeds. The flowers have both the calyx and corolla more or less deeply five-lobed or parted; five fertile stamens rising from the tube of the corolla opposite its lobes, and five sterile scale-like ones alternate with them; and a five (or rarely two or four) celled ovary.

The fruits of *S. dulcificum,* as the specific name denotes, have an exceedingly sweet taste, and are one of the kinds known to the English residents in Western tropical Africa, where the plant is indigenous, under the name of Miraculous-berry, from their being eaten in order to counteract the acidity of any article of food or drink—their sweet flavour being retained by the palate for a considerable length of time. They are rather more than half the size of olives, and somewhat of the same shape.

Among the natives they form an article of trade. [A. S.]

SIDESADDLE-FLOWER. *Sarracenia.*
—, CALIFORNIAN. *Darlingtonia californica.*

SIDHEE. An Indian name for the dried leaves and capsules of *Cannabis sativus.*

SIDR. An Arab name for Lotus-wood.

SIEBERA. A genus of the thistle tribe of *Compositæ*, only differing from *Xeranthemum* in the apices of the involucral scales being produced into slender spines. *S. pungens*, the only species, is a native of Asia Minor and Persia. It is a slightly-branched annual, the twigs furnished with lance-shaped hoary leaves, and terminating in solitary flower-heads with cone-shaped involucres. [A. A. B.]

SIEGESBECKIA. This genus comprises a few coarse annual weeds of the *Compositæ*, widely spread over the warmer regions of the globe. The readiest mark of recognition is found in the involucral scales, which are in two rows, those of the outer row being linear-spathulate in form, twice the length of the others, and clothed with glandular pubescence. The most common species, *S. orientalis*, ranges from Persia eastwards to Japan, and thence south to Australia. It is a much-branched erect herb one to three feet high, with opposite broadly triangular or ovate coarsely-toothed leaves, and leafy panicles of small yellow flower-heads. The ray-florets shortly strap-shaped and pistil-bearing, those of the disk tubular and perfect; the achenes are without pappus, and are half enclosed by the chaffy scales of the receptacle. [A. A. B.]

SIEMPRE VIVA. *Triptilion spinosum.*

SILTHES. *Allium ascale.*

SIEVERSIA. A genus of *Rosaceæ* having the habit nearly of *Geum*, but differing in the styles being jointed, the upper joint dissimilar to the lower, and usually deciduous. *S. montana* from Austria and *S. reptans* from Switzerland are cultivated; they are herbaceous plants about six inches high, with leaves like those of a *Geum*, and large solitary handsome yellow flowers. [O. A. J.]

SIGMOID. Having a form somewhat resembling the letter S.

SILAUS. A genus of *Umbelliferæ*, distinguished by each half of the fruit having five sharp-edged equal ribs with numerous vittæ in each furrow, and four to six at the line of junction. The species are perennial herbs, natives of Europe and Asia. Their leaves are usually in numerous narrow or linear subdivisions. The name was used by Pliny to indicate some umbelliferous plant. [G. D.]

SILBADANI. A furniture wood of Demerara.

SILENE. An extensive genus of herbaceous plants belonging to the tribe *Sileneæ*

of *Caryophyllaceæ*. The species agree in the following characters:—Sepals united; stamens ten; capsule stalked, dry, opening at the top with six teeth; styles three to four. Of the British species the most frequent is *S. inflata*, or Bladder Campion, common in cornfields and meadows, a perennial herbaceous plant one to two feet high, with ovate leaves, which, as well as the stems, are glaucous, and with numerous panicled white flowers, which are remarkable for their greyish-green inflated calyces. The Sea Campion, *S. maritima*, scarcely differs from the preceding except in having smaller leaves, shorter stems, and larger flowers. *S. acaulis*, the Moss Campion, is a humble tufted plant with numerous bright purple flowers, and is abundant on the Scottish mountains, of which in June and July it is one of the greatest ornaments. It is found also on some of the mountains in Wales and the North of England. Species indigenous to various temperate countries of the Eastern and Western Hemispheres are occasionally cultivated, some of the most ornamental being *S. pendula*, *integripetala*, *Atocion*, and *Armeria*, all annuals; and *S. Schafta* and *Elizabethæ*, dwarf perennials. [C. A. J.]

SILER. The generic name of an umbelliferous plant, the calyx of which has a five-toothed border; and each half of the fruit has nine blunt ribs, five of which are more prominent than the others, while the remaining four have each a vitta under them. *S. trilobum* is a native of Europe and Asia, with triternate leaves, and large umbels of white flowers. [G. D.]

SILICLE, SILICULE. A silique about as broad as long, or broader.

SILIQUASTRUM. *Cercis Siliquastrum.*

SILIQUE. The long pod-like fruit of crucifers, consisting of a pair of valves applied to a frame on which the seeds grow.

SILIQUOSÆ. A Linnæan order synonymous with *Cruciferæ*.

SILK-COTTON TREE. *Bombax*; also *Eriodendron.*

SILK-FLOWER. *Calliandra trinervia.*

SILK-TREE. *Acacia Julibrissin.*

SILKWEED. *Asclepias Cornuti*, formerly called *A. syriaca*; also a name sometimes given to *Confervæ.*

SILKY. The same as Sericeous.

SILPHIUM. A genus of stout perennial herbs belonging to the *Compositæ*, natives of the United States, Oregon, and Texas. They have opposite whorled or alternate leaves, and large yellow flower-heads, either solitary at the ends of the branches, or disposed in panicles or corymbs. The chief features of the genus are the monœcious radiate heads; the ray-florets strap-shaped and pistil-bearing, the disk-florets tubular and sterile; and the broad flat perfect achenes surrounded by a wing which is notched at the summit, and usually (but not always) terminates in two short awn-like teeth, which represent the pappus.

The most interesting species is the Compass-plant, *S. laciniatum*, of which Dr. Asa Gray writes :—'On the wide open prairies the leaves are said to present their faces uniformly north and south, whence it is called the Compass-plant.' In a paper relating to this plant, communicated to the Botanical Society of Edinburgh in January 1862 by Mr. Gorrie, there are various notices of the plant by different travellers; but Mr. Gorrie states that he is unable to determine the correctness of their observations, and until a competent botanist shall assert that the 'broad flat leaves of this plant point due north and south with an accuracy as unvarying as that of the magnetic needle,' we shall be slow to believe that such is the case—the more so when we find such a note as the following of Lieut. J. W. Albert of the United States Army: 'It is said that the planes of the leaves of this plant (*S. laciniatum*) are coincident with the planes of the meridian, but those I have noticed must have been influenced by some local attraction that deranged their polarity.' The plant is also known as Pilot-weed, Polar-plant, Rosin-weed, and Turpentine-weed—the latter names from the abundant resin exuded by its stems, which grow to a height of three to six feet, as well as by the leaves, which are ovate in outline, and deeply pinnatifid, the segments being again divided. The tuberous roots of *S. læve*, a plant with smooth dock-like leaves, are eaten by the natives of the Columbia River valley. *S. terebinthaceum* is sometimes called the Prairie Burdock, from its rough heart-shaped root-leaves, about two feet in length, resembling those of the burdock ; and *S. perfoliatum* gets the name of Cup-plant, because the winged stalks of its opposite leaves are united together so as to form a cup with the stem in its centre. These two last, with the Compass-plant and others, have been cultivated in English gardens. [A. A. B.]

SILPHIUM. A gum-resin supposed by some to be obtained from *Thapsia Silphion*, and by others from *Prangos pabularia.*

SILVER-BUSH. *Anthyllis Barba-jovis.*

SILVER-GRAIN. The glittering plates observed in the wood of many exogens, and caused by the division of the medullary plates.

SILVER-TREE. *Leucadendron argenteum.*

SILVER-WEED. *Potentilla anserina*; also *Argyreia.*

SILVER-WOOD. *Mouriria*; also *Guettarda argentea* and *Quelania lætioides.*

SILVERY. Having a whitish metallic lustre.

SILVIA. A genus of *Scrophulariaceæ*, containing two small prostrate under shrubs from Mexico, with opposite leaves, and large yellow flowers. The calyx is tubular-campanulate, with the apex divided into five imbricate lobes; the tube of the corolla is long, and the spreading limb is deeply cut; the stamens are included, and the parallel cells of the anthers are nearly equal, and slightly mucronate at their base; the capsule is ovate and acute. [W. C.]

SILYBUM. Robust herbaceous plants belonging to the thistle group of *Compositæ*, among which they are distinguished by having the filaments united, and the pappus in many rows. *S. Marianum*, the Milk Thistle, grows to the height of three to four feet or more, with a furrowed stem, and large spreading wavy spinous leaves, of which those next the root are pinnatifid, and variegated with green and milk-white. The involucre is subglobose and spinous, and the florets purple with long tubes. The specific name *Marianum* was given to this plant to preserve the legend that the white stain on the leaves was caused by the falling of a drop of the Virgin Mary's milk. It was formerly cultivated, the young leaves being used as a spring salad, the root boiled as a potherb, and the heads treated like the heads of the artichoke. It grows wild in waste places in many parts of England, and still retains its place in old-fashioned gardens. French : *Chardon Marie; Carthame maculé.* [C. A. J.]

SIMABA.. A genus of *Simarubaceæ*, consisting of trees and shrubs, natives of Tropical America, having the leaves alternate, and either simple or ternate or pinnate, and the flowers in axillary masses or racemes. The calyx is small; the petals four or five, long and spreading ; and the stamens eight or ten, each filament having a scale adherent to it. The ovary consists of four or five carpels, the styles of which are distinct, but become united above into one having a five-lobed stigma. The fruit is a drupe but often dry, usually having the same number of carpels as the ovary.

Among the species *S. Cedron* is very remarkable for the properties of its seed. It is distinguished by its large pinnated leaves with twenty or more narrow elliptical leaflets, and its large panicles of flowers, which are three or four feet long. It is a small tree, native of New Grenada, and bears a fruit about the size of a swan's egg, containing only one seed, four of the cells being barren.

The Cedron of commerce, which looks like a blanched almond but is larger, is the kernel of the fruit. As a remedy for the bites of serpents it appears to have been known to the inhabitants from time immemorial, and was first reported in this country as deserving of notice in 1699, but it was not till very recently that anything certain was known either of the seed or its uses. Part of its reputation is owing to its febrifugal powers in intermittent fever, it being successfully prescribed in that disease by the physicians of New Grenada, a country abounding in forests of quina-trees ; but it principally rests upon its efficacy as an antidote for the bites of snakes scorpions and other noxious animals, it being universally believed that its application will neutralise the poison even of the most dangerous among them. On the latter account it is so much valued, that there are scarcely any persons in New Grenada or the adjacent countries who have not a piece of this seed, which they always carry with them, and a single seed will sell for four shillings. When a bite has been received a small quantity mixed with water is applied to the wound, and about two grains scraped into brandy (or, if it cannot be obtained, into water) is given internally. The active principle on which the medicinal qualities of the Cedron depend has been separated by M. Lecoy, who has named it *cedrine*. Every part of the plant but especially the seed is, owing to its presence, intensely bitter. Dr. Seemann has given a full account of the Cedron in the *Botany of H. M. S. Herald*.　　[B. C.]

SIMARUBACEÆ. An order of polypetalous dicotyledons, consisting of trees or shrubs remarkable for the bitter taste of their bark, and natives of hot countries, a very few only being found without the tropics. They have generally alternate compound leaves without transparent dots; no stipules; small unisexual regular flowers in axillary panicles or racemes; three to five sepals and petals; as many or twice as many stamens inserted round the base of a disk; a free lobed ovary with as many styles and cells as lobes; and one ovule laterally attached in each cell. The fruit is various, the seeds solitary pendulous, with or without albumen, and having a superior radicle. All the above characters have, however, exceptions in individual genera, and it is only by various combinations of the majority of characters that the order can be distinguished from *Rutaceæ*, and some others which are closely allied. Thirty genera are referred to it, including *Quassia, Simaruba, Ailantus, Cneorum, Brucea, Suriana, Brunellia, Picramnia*, and *Balanites*.

SIMARUBA. The natives of Guiana apply this name to a tree, some parts of which they use with great success in dysentery. Botanically it is applied to a genus of *Simarubaceæ*, consisting of tropical American trees, with unisexual flowers; calyx small cup-shaped, five-toothed; petals five, longer than the calyx, spreading; stamens five, surrounding as many rudimentary ovaries. In the female flowers are five ovaries, placed on a disk surrounded by ten scales or rudimentary stamens; styles five, separate below, above conjoined into one, and terminated by a broader five-lobed stigma; fruit of five drupes.

S. amara, a native of the West Indies and Guiana, yields the drug known as Simaruba-bark, which is, strictly speaking, the rind of the root. It is employed as a bitter tonic in diarrhœa and dysentery, as well as in various forms of indigestion. In large doses it is said to act as an emetic purgative and diaphoretic. *S. versicolor*, a Bra-

zilian species, has similar properties. The fruits and bark are used as anthelmintics, and an infusion of the latter is employed in cases of snake-bite. The plant is so bitter that insects will not attack it, on which account the powdered bark has been

Simaruba amara.

employed to kill vermin. *S. glauca*, a native of Cuba, furnishes a glutinous juice, which is employed in certain cases of skin-disease. *S. amara* (*officinalis*), the Mountain Damson, is occasionally to be met with in hothouses in this country.　　[M. T. M.]

SIMBI. *Phaseolus trilobus*.

SIMETHIS. A genus of *Liliaceæ* allied to *Anthericum*, but differing in the segments of the perianth being combined at the base, the filaments being woolly on the lower part, and the seeds only two (or one) in each cell of the capsule, furnished with an arillus. It contains a single species, *S. bicolor*, common in Western Europe, but in the British Isles only found in Dorset Devon and Kerry. It is a small herb with a slender rootstock, emitting a tuft of thick and fleshy fibres. The leaves are all radical, grass-like; the scape branched at the top, with a paniculate corymbose cyme of rather small rose-coloured flowers, with a spreading perianth.　　[J. T. S.]

SIMILARY PARTS. The elementary organs or tissues of plants—such as cellular tissue, woody tissue, spiral vessels, &c.

SIMMONDSIA. The name of a genus of *Euphorbiaceæ*, in which it is remarkable from there being no albumen to the seed. There is but one species, *S. californica*, a small evergreen much-branched bush, regularly forked and furnished with opposite oblong-lanceolate entire leaves, and inconspicuous green flowers borne in their axils. The males are clustered, the females solitary and nodding—the former with a five-parted calyx and ten or twelve stamens, and the latter with a five-parted calyx enclosing a three-celled ovary tipped with three short styles. The mature nuts resemble an ordinary acorn in size and shape. They are said to have a flavour like filberts, but the after-taste is nauseous, and they are apt to cause purging. The plant is cultivated in some botanic gardens under the name *Brocchia dichotoma*. The genus commemorates T. W. Simmonds, a naturalist who accompanied Lord Seaforth to the West Indies.   [A. A. B.]

SIMOCHILUS. A genus belonging to the order of heathworts. Its calyx is coloured four-angled and fleshy in its nature, and furnished with eight ribs; the border of the corolla is four-cleft, and the seed-vessel two or four-celled, very rarely one-celled. The only species is a Cape shrub, resembling a heath, whose leaves are in whorls of three or four together, and the flowers in terminal heads.   [G. D.]

SIMPLE. Not consisting of several distinct parts.

SIMPLER'S JOY. *Verbena officinalis.*

SIMPLICISSIMUS. Not divided or branched at all.

SIMSIA. A genus of *Compositæ*, natives of Texas and Mexico, closely related to *Helianthus*. They are perennial herbs one to three feet high, the lower leaves opposite trilobed and toothed, the upper usually alternate and entire. The uniserial strap-shaped yellow ray-florets are neuter, the disk-florets tubular and perfect; and the compressed two-awned achenes are seated on a chaffy receptacle, enclosed by an involucre of two or three series of narrow scales. *Geræa* belongs to this genus, and a plant which has been called *Barrattia* only differs in the absence of pappus-awns. Its name commemorates Dr. John Sims, for many years editor of Curtis's *Botanical Magazine.*   [A. A. B.]

SIMSON. *Senecio vulgaris.*

SINAPIDENDRON A genus of *Cruciferæ* of the tribe *Brassiceæ*. They are undershrubs from Madeira, with the habit of *Brassica nigra* or *Sinapis arvensis*, differing from both genera in the more beaded pods, and especially in the subangular seeds partly imbedded in the somewhat spongy dissepiment.   [J. T. S.]

SINAPIS. An adaptation of the Greek word for 'mustard' applied to a genus of *Cruciferæ*. In the opinion of most modern botanists this genus is inseparable by any save arbitrary characters from *Brassica*. The features especially assigned to *Sinapis* are the following:—Calyx of four spreading sepals; style small short acute; fruit cylindrical, its valves traversed by one or more prominent nerves; seeds in one row. The species are herbaceous plants found in most quarters of the globe, but especially in the Mediterranean region.

The Black Mustard, *S. nigra*, yields the greater portion of the condiment so generally used in this country. The plant is indigenous, but is nevertheless largely cultivated in Yorkshire and Durham. The seeds are of a reddish-brown colour. Mixed with those of *S. alba* they are crushed between rollers, and subsequently pounded and sifted twice or oftener. From the residue left on the sieve a fixed oil is obtained by pressure. The powdered mustard is usually mixed with a considerable quantity of wheaten flour and a small quantity of turmeric powder—admixtures which are readily detected by the microscope. The term 'flour of mustard' is not quite accurate, as the mustard-seeds themselves contain little or no starchy material. The chemical ingredients of mustard-seeds are somewhat complex. Among them are a peculiar acid called myronic acid, noticeable as containing a proportion of sulphur, and which, when mixed with water and a peculiar substance called myrosine (analogous to albumen), also found in mustard-seeds, yields Volatile Oil of Mustard, which has no separate existence in the seeds, but is formed artificially in the manner just stated. This oil is very acrid, and has been employed as a rubefacient. The fixed oil before mentioned as existing in the seed itself has little or no acridity, and has been used as a purgative and vermifuge.

Hippocrates is said to have employed mustard medicinally, while Columella speaks of its irritant action on the eyes—

Seque lacessenti fletum factura sinapis.

In modern medicine mustard is most frequently employed in the well-known form of poultice. If its effects be properly watched, this application is safe and most valuable where a speedy result is desired; but if allowed to remain on too long, especially in persons who from disease or other causes are not sensitive to pain, it may produce ulceration and gangrene. Internally mustard is employed as an emetic in narcotic poisoning, &c. As a condiment mustard is valuable for its stimulant effects, which render it useful in cases of weak digestion, or as an adjunct to fatty and other indigestible articles of food.

The White Mustard, *S. alba*, is also indigenous in this country. Its seeds are larger than those of the Black Mustard, and of a yellow colour externally. Chemically they differ in containing a crystalline substance known as sulpho-sinapisin. Moreover, its myrosine yields with water a pungent oil of a different character from the Volatile Oil of Mustard previously mentioned. The seeds have similar properties to those of *S. nigra*. They have been recommended to be swallowed whole as stomachics and laxatives, a process by no means free from danger. The seed-leaves or cotyledons of this plant, together with those of *Lepidium sativum*, form the well-known agreeable salad known as 'mustard and cress.' The facility and speed with which this salad may be grown at all seasons and in all places, together with its wholesome properties, are great advantages. It is, moreover, both interesting and instructive to watch the germination of these seeds, and the peculiar shape of their seed-leaves.

The seeds of *S. arvensis*, the Common Charlock, yield an oil that is good for burning. In France the leaves are used as forage for cattle. It is a pity that in this country no use is made of so common and troublesome a weed. The leaves of *S. cernua* are eaten in Japan, while the seeds furnish an oil. *S. juncea* is cultivated for its oil, called in India Soorsa; it is used for burning, and also for rubbing the body in illness. Various other species are cultivated for their leaves or for the oil derived from the seeds. Among them are— *S. chinensis, S. dichotoma, S. pekinensis, S. ramosa,* and *S. glauca. S. nigra* may be discriminated by its lyrate leaves, the upper ones entire; and the pods on short stalks, smooth and pressed against the stem; while in *S. alba* the pods are spreading, very hairy, and terminated by a long beak containing a single seed. The microscopical structure of the skin of these seeds is very curious, and has been described by Dr. Hassall in his work on *The Adulteration of Food.* Among the six-sided cells constituting the outer skin of the seed may be seen, according to this observer, funnel-shaped cells penetrating into the interior of the seed. *S. nigra,* which grows some ten or twelve feet high in Palestine, is regarded by some as the Mustard of Scripture, in preference to *Salvadora.* See BRASSICA and DIPLOTAXIS.　　　[M. T. M.]

SINCLAIRIA. A trailing Mexican bush belonging to the *Vernonia* tribe of *Compositæ,* and closely related to *Andromachia,* from which the naked instead of frilled receptacle serves to distinguish it. It has opposite stalked elliptical leaves, and the twigs terminate in panicles of numerous yellow flower-heads; the ray-florets are strap-shaped and pistil-bearing; the disk-florets tubular and perfect, and the cylindrical-ribbed achenes are crowned with a biserial pappus of tawny rough hairs. It is named after Dr. A. Sinclair, R.N., a botanist who collected largely in New Zealand, and died there in 1861.　　　[A. A, B.]

SINDHOOKÁ, SINDUYA, Indian names for *Vitex Negundo.*

SINDOC. An Indian name for Culilawan-bark.

SINDUVARA. A Sanscrit name for *Vitex trifolia.*

SINISTRORSE. Twining to the left hand; a term usually confined to the stems of plants.

SINKFIELD. *Potentilla.*

SINNINGIA. A small genus of *Gesneraceæ* inhabiting South America, and named by Nees von Esenbeck in honour of the curator of the Botanic Garden at Bonn, M. Sinning. The *Sinningias* are suffruticose plants with rather large fleshy more or less ovate leaves, a bell-shaped generally five-winged calyx, a five-lobed corolla the tube of which is variously inflated, five distinct glands surrounding the ovary, and a mouth-shaped stigma. They are closely allied to the *Ligerias* (of

which the old *Gloxinia speciosa* of the gardens is the type), and are frequently met with in hothouses. *S. velutina* may be regarded as the type of the genus. [B. S.]

SINUATED. Having the margin alternately uneven with deep concavities and convexities. *Sinuato-dentate* is sinuated and dentate at the same time.

SINUS. The recesses formed when the edge of any part is lobed.

SIPHOCAMPYLUS. This name, derived from the Greek *siphon* 'a tube' and *campulos* 'curved,' in allusion to the corolla, is usually applied to a genus of tropical American undershrubs of the family *Lobeliaceæ.* The flowers in some of the species are placed on solitary axillary stalks, while in others they are aggregated into a dense raceme or corymb. The corolla is tubular, with an undivided tube which is dilated or curved, rarely straight, its limb five-cleft and two-lipped, the segments being of nearly equal size; stamens five, inserted with the corolla on to the upper part of the calyx-tube, two or all of the anthers hairy or pointed at the top; ovary partly inferior, two-celled; style within the corolla; stigma divided into two rounded lobes; capsule two-valved. The flowers are showy, of a scarlet or yellowish hue. Several species are in cultivation, *S. microstoma* being one of the handsomest; it has closely-packed corymbs of rich crimson flowers. *S. Caoutchouc* is said to be so named from the abundance of viscid juice which it contains. [M. T. M.]

SIPHONACANTHUS. A genus of *Acanthaceæ,* containing a few herbs, natives of Brazil. It differs from *Ruellia* in having a slightly swollen tubular corolla with a short limb, a more fleshy fruit with fewer seeds, and in the flowers being without bracts, and arranged in a spicate manner at the apex of the stem. [W. C.]

SIPHONANDRACEÆ. An order of monopetalous dicotyledons proposed by Klotzsch to include the *Vacciniaceæ* and the tribes *Arbuteæ* and *Andromedeæ* of *Ericaceæ,* a rearrangement which has not been generally adopted.

SIPHONANDRA. A genus of *Vacciniaceæ* comprising a Peruvian shrub, with elliptic spine-pointed leaves, and clustered flowers, whose diagnostic characters reside in the anthers and filaments being all of equal length, and especially in the long tubular anthers, which equal the corolla in length and open by two pores. The name of the genus is expressive of this peculiarity, being derived from *siphon* 'a tube.' [M. T. M.]

SIPHONANTHUS. A genus of *Verbenaceæ,* by some considered as only a section of *Clerodendron,* containing those species with a funnel-shaped corolla, very long tube, and almost equal limb. [W. C.]

SIPHONEÆ. A natural order of green-spored *Algæ,* rooting or merely attached by the base, with a simple or compound frond formed of a single thread-shaped branched cell, or of a number of such cells united together into a spongy frond. It is divisible into two distinct suborders: in one of which, *Caulerpeæ*, the main cell is filled with a network of branching fibrils, amidst which the minute zoospores are dispersed; in the other, *Codieæ*, the filaments, which may be either free or closely united into a common frond, are filled with green endochrome, and give rise here and there to capsules which ultimately contain one or more zoospores. The *Caulerpeæ* are all inhabitants of warm coasts, but the *Codieæ* are often found in colder climates. In either division we have species which are truly aquatic or terrestrial, or at the least amphibious. In the second division there are many species, as for example those of *Halimeda*, which resemble corallines from the quantity of carbonate of lime which enters into their composition. In *Vaucheria* and *Bryopsis* we have the threads whether branched or single perfectly free, and in *Botrydium* the vegetative part is reduced to a minimum, and all that is visible is a mass of bladdery capsules.   [M. J. B.]

SIPHONIA. To this genus we are indebted for the greater part of our supply of Caoutchouc or India-rubber. It belongs to the *Euphorbiaceæ*, and consists of some half-dozen species, one of which, *S. elastica*, is a native of French Guiana, and the remainder of the Amazon and Rio Negro districts of Brazil. They are called Seringa-trees by the Brazilians, from the Portuguese word *seringa*, signifying a syringe or clyster-pipe, the caoutchouc having first been used for making those articles; and

Siphonia elastica.

the generic name, derived from the Greek *siphon*, has reference to the same use. The species are trees varying from twenty-five to seventy or upwards of a hundred feet in height, and all contain a milky juice in more or less abundance, though they do not all yield caoutchouc of good quality, that from some of the species being brittle. Their leaves consist of three en-

tire leaflets radiating from the top of a long stalk, and are clustered towards the ends of the branches; and their flowers are borne in loosely-branched panicles, with numerous little branchlets consisting of a few male flowers and a female at the top. Both sexes have a bell-shaped five-toothed or five-parted calyx, and no corolla; the males containing a central stamen-column bearing five or ten anthers in one or two series or whorls some distance below the apex; and the females a three-celled ovary bearing a more or less three-lobed stigma with or without a short style. Their fruit is a rather large capsule composed of three one-seeded pieces, which split in halves when ripe. The raw seeds are poisonous to man and to quadrupeds, but macaws eat them greedily, and they are an excellent bait for fish; long boiling, however, deprives them of their poison, and renders them very palatable.

The bulk of the Caoutchouc exported from Pará, whence our chief supply is derived, is obtained from *S. brasiliensis*, which is the one common in the forests of the province of Pará; but that brought down to Pará from the Upper Amazon and Rio Negro is derived from *S. lutea* and *S. brevifolia*. These three species are all slender smooth-stemmed trees averaging one hundred feet in height: the Pará species, however, yields the greatest abundance of caoutchouc. Europeans first became acquainted with caoutchouc in the early part of last century, and its botanical history was made known by M. de la Condamine in 1736, but it is only within the last forty or fifty years that it has become such an important article in our manufactures and commerce. It exists in the tree in the form of a thin white milk, and is obtained by making incisions in the trunk, from which it exudes and is collected in little earthen vessels, and afterwards converted into the black homogeneous elastic mass familiar to us as india-rubber, by pouring the milk upon moulds and immediately holding them over the dense smoke caused by burning the nuts of the Urucuri palms (*Attalea excelsa* and *Cocos coronata*) until it is sufficiently hard to bear another coating, when the process is repeated until the requisite thickness is obtained, and the mould is then removed. Formerly these moulds were always in the form of shoes or bottles, and hence one of the kinds of caoutchouc is known commercially as bottle-rubber; but they are now frequently shaped something like battledores for folding linen, only thinner. In 1863 65,649 cwts. of caoutchouc were imported into the United Kingdom. [A. S.]

SIPHONODON. A name given by Griffith to a tree from the Indian Archipelago, which constitutes a genus agreeing in most respects with the order *Celastraceæ*, but very peculiar in the structure of its pistil. The ovary, half immersed in the calyx, has numerous uniovulate cells arranged in two or four series; and the conical upper portion has a cavity at the top, stigmatic inside, from the centre of which arises a style-like column, the homology of which is not well understood. The only species known has alternate crenate coriaceous leaves, and axillary peduncles bearing an umbel of three or four small greenish-yellow flowers.

SIPIRI-TREE. *Nectandra Rodiæi.*

SIPO-DÉ-CHUMBO. *Cuscuta racemosa.*

SIRABALLI. A fragrant valuable timber of Demerara, supposed to be the produce of a *Nectandra* or *Oreodaphne.*

SIRI, or **SIRIH.** *Chavica Siriboa.*

SIRIEHOUT. A South African name for *Tarchonanthus camphoratus.*

SIRITCH. An Arab name for the sweet oil of the seeds of *Sesamum orientale.*

SIRKI. An Indian grass, *Saccharum Munja.*

SISARUM. *Sium.*

SISON. A genus of *Umbelliferæ,* in which each half of the fruit has five narrow equal ribs, and one club-shaped vitta in each groove. The species are perennial herbs, natives of Europe and Asia, with the uppermost leaves narrower and more deeply divided than the lower. *S. Amomum* is a species well known in some parts of Britain, with cream-coloured flowers and aromatic seeds. The name is said to be from the Celtic *'sium* 'running stream,' some of the species formerly included growing in moist localities.　　　[G. D.]

SISSOO. *Dalbergia Sissoo,* a valuable timber-tree of India.

SISYMBRIUM. A genus of uninteresting herbaceous plants belonging to the *Cruciferæ,* not easily to be distinguished from several allied genera. There are numerous species, of which the most frequent in Britain are: *S. Alliaria,* or Garlic Mustard, sometimes called Sauce-alone, a tallish hedge-weed with heart-shaped leaves, white flowers, and erect pods; *S. officinale,* an erect branched plant, with rough stems and leaves, the latter jagged with the points turned backwards (runcinate), minute pale-yellow flowers, and rough pods, which are pressed close to the stem—a common hedge-weed; and *S. Thalianum,* another hedge-weed six to eight inches high, with oblong toothed leaves, and slender stems bearing a few inconspicuous white flowers. The other species are of less common occurrence, but possess no interest.　　　[C. A. J.]

SISYRINCHIUM. A genus of *Iridaceæ,* the species of which are indigenous to the tropical and temperate parts of America and New Holland. They are herbs having fibrous roots leaves arranged in two rows, a stem frequently branched, a two-valved general spathe, inconspicuous flowers, a perianth consisting of six parts, three stamens, an inferior three-celled many-seeded capsule, and round seeds. *S. ga-*

laxoides is a mild purgative, and used as such in South America.　　　[B. S.]

SITAL-PATI. An Indian name for mats made from *Maranta dichotoma.*

SITOBOLIUM. *Dennstædtia.*

SITUS. The position occupied by an organ.

SIUM. A genus of *Umbelliferæ,* in which the fruit is compressed laterally, and crowned by the head-shaped styles; each half of it has five equal blunt ribs, and numerous oil-cells in the furrows, as well as at the line of junction. The species are terrestrial or aquatic herbs, chiefly found in the temperate parts of the Northern Hemisphere. Their leaves vary greatly in subdivision and outline. The name is from the Celtic *siu* 'water,' in allusion to their habitat.　　　[G. D.]

Of the several species of strong-smelling weedy-looking plants belonging to this genus only one is grown for culinary purposes—*S. Sisarum,* better known by its common name of Skirret. This plant, although usually treated as an annual, is a hardy perennial, a native of China, and has been cultivated in this country since A.D. 1548. The lower leaves are pinnated, having from five to nine oval oblong leaflets finely toothed; at the base they are sheathing and of a reddish colour; the stem, which rises about a foot high, is channelled, and terminated by an umbel of small white flowers. The roots, for which this plant is cultivated, are composed of small fleshy tubers about the size of the little finger, joined together at the crown. When boiled and served with butter they form a nice dish, declared by Worlidge, when writing in 1682, to be 'the sweetest, whitest, and most pleasant of roots.'　　　[W. B. B.]

SKIMMIA. The name of a genus of evergreen shrubs, with oblong entire stalked leathery dotted leaves, and flowers in terminal panicles. The flowers are polygamous, with a four-parted persistent calyx; four petals; four deciduous stamens attached to the receptacle alternate with the petals; a fleshy four-lobed disk and a free ovary, with a solitary pendulous ovule in each of its four cells. The fruit is fleshy and drupe-like, with four cartilaginous one-seeded stones, containing an albuminous embryo.

The true position of the genus is doubtful, it having been referred to *Celastraceæ* and *Aurantiaceæ.* Professor Oliver, in his memoir on the latter group, says that the present genus differs from citronworts in its albuminous seeds, stamens in one row, and abortion or tendency to abortion of one sex. In other respects it is exceedingly like *Aurantiaceæ* in structure, especially agreeing in the form of the pistil, and in the succulent fruit. *S. japonica* is a pretty dwarf-growing holly-like shrub, with dark shining evergreen entire flat leaves, and clusters of bright red berries, which give the plant a very handsome appearance. It is now frequent in cultivation. Other species are natives of Northern India and Japan.   [M. T. M.]

SKINNERA. A genus of *Onagraceæ*, distinguished by the tube of the calyx being dilated above the seed-vessel, the petals small and scale-like, and the fruit a many-seeded berry. *S. excorticata*, alias *Fuchsia excorticata*, is a New Zealand shrub, with the leaves alternate acute slightly toothed, and whitish beneath; the calyx purple and yellow-green, the petals violet. The genus was named in honour of Mr. Skinner, an English botanist.   [G. D.]

SKINNERIA. A genus of *Convolvulaceæ*, containing a single species, a cæspitose herb from India. The calyx consists of five sepals; the corolla is small and somewhat urceolate; the single style has a two-lobed capitate stigma; and the ovary is one-celled, and has four ovules. [W. C.]

SKIRRET. *Sium Sisarum.*

SKULLCAP. *Scutellaria.*

SKUNKWEED. *Symplocarpus fœtidus.*

SLASHED. The same as Laciniate.

SLATE-GREY. Grey bordering on blue.

SLAVEWOOD. *Simaruba officinalis.*

SLEEP-AT-NOON. *Tragopogon pratensis.*

SLEEPWORT. *Lactuca sativa.*

SLIMY. The same as Mucous.

SLIPPER-PLANT. *Pedilanthus.*

SLIPPERWORT. *Calceolaria.*

SLOAK, SLOKE, or SLOUKAWN. Synonyms partly of the common *Porphyræ*, partly of *Ulvæ*, but more especially of the former, the latter being usually called Green Sloke.   [M. J. B.]

SLOANEA. A tropical American genus of *Tiliaceæ*, comprising upwards of thirty species, some of which on slight differences have been separated as distinct genera with the names *Ablania*, *Dasynema*, and *Dasycarpus*. They are trees, often upwards of a hundred feet high, with alternate feather-veined leaves; either evergreen or deciduous, and varying in length from a few inches to upwards of a foot and a half, with the inconspicuous white or greenish-yellow flowers disposed in racemes panicles or clusters in the axils. The stamens are very numerous, inserted on a broad flat and not conical disk, as in *Elæocarpus*. The fruits vary from the size of a hazel-nut to that of an orange, of a woody consistence, clothed outside with stout bristles like those on the husk of a Spanish chestnut, and when ripe split into four or five pieces, with a few seeds in each. The wood of many species is extremely hard and difficult to work; that of *S. jamaicensis* is known in Jamaica as Breakaxe and Ironwood. The genus bears the name of Sir Hans Sloane, the founder of the British Museum.   [A. A. B.]

SLOE. The fruit of *Prunus spinosa.*

SLOGWOOD. *Hufelandia pendula.*

SLOKE. The edible *Porphyræ*; also called Laver. —, GREEN. A name given to several species of *Ulva*, also called Oystergreen. See SLOAK.

SMALLAGE. The Wild Celery, *Apium graveolens.*

SMARAGDINUS. Grass-green.

SMARTWEED. *Polygonum Hydropiper.*

SMEATHMANNIA. A genus of *Passifloraceæ* from tropical Africa, remarkable for its erect habit, in a natural order including so many creepers and twiners. The three or four species comprising the genus have alternate oblong or obovate often serrated leaves, and axillary white flowers. Both calyx and corolla (or perigone, as some writers call them) are five-lobed; the corona is urn-shaped, the stamens twenty, and the styles five in number; whilst the fruit is an inflated one-celled five-valved capsule, enclosing numerous seeds. *S. lævigata* has for some years been an inmate of our hothouses, being one of the numerous introductions of the late Mr. Whitfield from Sierra Leone.   [B. S.]

SMILACEÆ. An order of monocotyledons, with the six petal-like divisions of the perianth, six stamens, and three-celled free ovary of *Liliaceæ*, but differing from that order in their netted veined leaves, and in their fruit being a small berry instead of a capsule. They are for the most part climbers with small flowers, and are distributed over the tropical and temperate parts of the world. The order is restricted to the large genus *Smilax*, with one or two lately separated from it, and *Ripogonum*. Many botanists unite it with *Liliaceæ* as a tribe or suborder.

SMILACINA. A genus of herbaceous plants, principally inhabiting North America, belonging to the *Smilaceæ*. *S. bifolia* is a small plant, having the stem furnished with two alternate triangular leaves; the flowers, which are small white and four-parted, grow in the form of a spiked raceme; stamens four; fruit a two-celled berry, yellow with brown spots. It is a native of the North of Europe. Several American species are cultivated.   [C. A. J.]

SMILAX. An extensive genus, giving its name to the order *Smilaceæ*. The species are climbing shrubs, natives of the warmer temperate and tropical regions of both hemispheres. The rootstocks are tuberous or fibrous; the stems usually prickly; the leaves stalked net-veined, and bearing on either side of the leafstalk a tendril; and the flowers are in globular heads, sessile or stalked in the axils of the leaves, rarely clustered, still more rarely solitary. The latter are polygamous, and have a six-parted spreading perianth, the three outer segments of which are rather larger than the three inner; stamens six; filaments thread-like; fruit baccate, one to three-seeded.

Some of the species of this genus furnish the drug known as Sarsaparilla, so called from the Spanish *sarza* 'a bramble,' and *parilla* 'a vine,' in allusion to the thorny stems of the plants. The Sarsaparilla of the shops consists of the roots, to which are attached portions of the rootstocks, of various species of this genus. It is by no means clearly ascertained what are the exact species yielding the varieties of this drug met with in commerce. That imported from Columbia and Guatemala is supposed to be the produce of *S. officinalis*. Mexican Sarsaparilla is yielded by *S. medica*,

Smilax medica.

Brazilian or Rio Negro Sarsaparilla is furnished by *S. papyracea*. Other species are mentioned as occasionally used, but much doubt prevails on this subject. The species named *S. Sarsaparilla*, which is common in the United States, does not appear to be used medicinally, notwithstanding its name.

In commerce the various kinds of Sarsaparilla are divided into two principal groups, according to the quantity of starchy material they contain. The mealy Sarsaparillas contain an abundance of farinaceous matter in the inner part of the rind. To this group belong Caraccas Sarsaparilla, the produce probably of *S. officinalis* or *S. siphilitica*; Brazilian Sarsaparilla, which is imported in cylindrical bundles, and is considered to consist of the roots of *S. papyracea* and *S. officinalis*; and Honduras Sarsaparilla, the botanical origin of which is not known. The non-mealy Sarsaparillas are known as Jamaica or Red-bearded Sarsaparilla, which is imported into Jamaica from Columbia, and is probably the produce of *S. officinalis*; what is known as Lima Sarsaparilla, which belongs to this division, consists of roots, imported not only from Lima, but also from Costa Rica. *S. officinalis* is supposed likewise to be the source whence these kinds are derived; Vera Cruz Sarsaparilla is the produce of *S. medica*.

Of these several kinds, the Jamaica and Lima sorts are most esteemed; the more acrid the taste, the higher the value set on the drug. The immediate effects of Sarsaparilla are those of a diaphoretic; in large doses it creates nausea and vomiting. Its more remote effects appear to be those of a tonic; it is considered a valuable remedy in those weakened and depraved conditions ascribed to a poisoned state of the blood—hence it is administered in old syphilitic cases, in chronic rheumatism, and in certain skin-diseases. Practitioners, however, differ in opinion as to the value of the drug, as much as botanists do as to the proper species to be employed. Much of this uncertainty no doubt depends upon the employment of an inert kind.

Pereira, from whose work on *Materia Medica* these remarks have been condensed, also alludes to the China root, the produce of *S. China*, which was first introduced from China in A.D. 1535 as an infallible remedy for gout. It has shared the fate of many so-called infallible remedies, and has fallen into disuse. *S. aspera*, a native of the South of France, Italy, &c., yields Italian Sarsaparilla, which has the same properties as the American kinds. *S. ovalifolia* is used medicinally in India, as are also the large tuberous rootstocks of *S. lanceæfolia*. Australia also supplies a medicinal species, *S. glyciphylla*; of this species the leaves also are used as tea. *S. Macabucha* is employed in the Philippines in dysentery and other complaints. *S. anceps* is employed medicinally in the Mauritius. The fact that so many species are employed medicinally, in so many quarters of the globe, is strong evidence of their value.

Other species furnish articles of food; such are *S. China*, the rootstocks of which are eaten by the Chinese. The rootstocks of *S. Pseudo-China* are manufactured into a kind of beer in South Carolina; they are also used to fatten hogs. The young shoots of some of the species are employed as asparagus in Persia, &c. The rootstocks of *S. China* yield a yellow dye with alum, a brown one with sulphate of iron. The pliant stems of *S. Pseudo-China* and other species are employed for the manufacture of baskets, &c. Several of the species are in cultivation, more as objects of botanical interest than for any beauty. The name *Smilax* was employed by the Greeks to designate some poisonous tree; others derive the name from *smile*, a cutting or scratching implement, in allusion to the rough prickles on the stem. [M. T. M.]

SMITHIA. A genus of *Leguminosæ* of the suborder *Papilionaceæ*, consisting of herbs or undershrubs from tropical Asia and Africa, with pinnate leaves, small leaflets, and yellow purple or blue flowers in axillary racemes. The genus is exceedingly well defined by its deeply two-cleft striate calyx, by the stamens united in two parcels, and the jointed pod folded back into the calyx as in *Uraria* and *Lourea*. It consists of about eighteen species, some of them handsome, but chiefly to be reckoned among tropical weeds. Some are said to have sensitive leaves.

SMOKE-PLANT. *Rhus Cotinus.*

SMOKEWOOD. *Clematis Vitalba.*

SMOKY. Having a dull greyish-black colour.

SMOOTH. Free from asperities or hairs, or any sort of unevenness.

SMUT. An affection of wheat, barley, oats, and other plants of the same natural order, deriving its name from the black sooty mass into which the receptacle of the germen and the base of the glumes are converted, the pistil and stamens being completely abortive. It commences its growth long before the sheath opens to give liberty to the inflorescence. Smut is produced by a fungus of the genus *Ustilago*, belonging to the division *Coniomycetes*, and characterised by its simple spores springing at first from delicate threads or produced in the form of closely-packed cells, which ultimately break up into a powdery mass. It is far more common in oats and barley than in wheat, and sometimes does considerable damage, affecting the ultimate produce; but as the spores are blown away at an early stage, and there is no appearance of the malady, like bunt, at harvest, it is not much regarded by agriculturists. It is a common notion indeed amongst them that it may be prevented by proper dressing, and several preparations are sold for the purpose, which make great promise, but it is quite clear from the nature of the fungus that they must be wholly inoperative. The spores are dispersed over the whole face of the country, and do not adhere to the grain itself. As soon as the seed is sown, they are ready in the soil to contaminate the young plant. We have in vain attempted to impregnate grain with smut, though rubbing healthy seeds with bunt-spores seldom or never fails. The probability is that the smut-spores require a long season of rest before their germination takes place, whereas bunt-spores develope their peculiar spawn a few hours after being sown. Smut occurs in all parts of the world where cereals are cultivated, as, for example, on the hot banks of the Indian River Soane and is subject to slight variations according to the different plants upon which it is developed, but not such as to justify the separation of several species. On Indian corn it attains an enormous size, measuring frequently some inches in diameter. The Smut fungus is described under the name of *Ustilago segetum.* [M. J. B.]

SMUT-BALLS. The same as Bunt.

SMYRNIUM. The name of a genus of *Umbelliferæ*, known by each half of the fruit having five ribs, three of which are prominent and sharp, and the two marginal ones indistinct; there is a single vitta in each furrow. The species are biennial herbs, natives of Middle and Eastern Europe, with umbels of yellow or yellow-green flowers. One species, *S. Olusatrum*, is not uncommon in some parts of Britain; its flavour is strong, resembling that of celery, and it is used as a potherb. The name is derived from the Greek *smurna*, one of the names of myrrh, in allusion to the odour. [G, D.]

The Alisander or Alexanders, *S. Olusatrum*, is a biennial, a native of Britain, and usually met with near the sea, as well as in the vicinity of old residences, where it might have been formerly cultivated. The plant grows from two to three feet high, the stem-leaves being ternate stalked serrate, and of a pale-green colour. Before the introduction of celery, the leafstalks, which are the parts that are edible, were blanched and used either as a salad or potherb. The flavour somewhat resembles that of celery, but is stronger and not so agreeable, on which account it has been neglected, and we believe is almost entirely gone out of cultivation. [W. B. B.]

SNAG. *Prunus spinosa.*

SNAIL-FLOWER. *Phaseolus Caracalla.*

SNAIL-PLANT. *Medicago scutellata*, and also *M. Helix*; the pods of these are called snails from their resemblance to those mollusks.

SNAKE-ROOT. The root of *Polygala Senega.* —, BLACK. *Botrophis actæoides*; also *Sanicula marilandica.* —, BUTTON. *Eryngium aquaticum*; also *Liatris.* —, CANADA. *Asarum canadense.* —, CEYLON. The tubers of *Arisæma papillosum.* —, VIRGINIAN. *Aristolochia Serpentaria.* —, WHITE. *Eupatorium ageratoides.*

SNAKE'S-BEARD. *Ophiopogon.*

SNAKE'S-HEAD. *Fritillaria Meleagris*; also an American name for *Chelone.*

SNAKE'S-TAIL. *Lepturus incurvus.*

SNAKE'S-TONGUE. *Lygodium.*

SNAKEWEED. *Polygonum Bistorta.*

SNAKEWOOD. *Brosimum Aubletii*, sometimes called *Piratinera guianensis.*

SNAPDRAGON. *Antirrhinum majus*; also *Silene Antirrhina.* —, JAMAICA. *Ruellia tuberosa*, now called *Cryphiacanthus barbadensis.*

SNAP-TREE. *Justicia hyssopifolia.*

SNAPWEED. *Impatiens.*

SNEEZEWEED. *Helenium autumnale.*

SNEEZEWOOD. *Pteroxylon utile.*

SNEEZEWORT. *Achillea Ptarmica.*

SNOWBALL TREE. The sterile-flowered variety of *Viburnum Opulus*, commonly known as the Gueldres Rose.

SNOWBERRY. *Chiococca racemosa.* —, CREEPING. *Chiogenes.*

SNOWDROP. *Galanthus nivalis.*

SNOWDROP TREE. *Chionanthus virginica*; also *Halesia.*

SNOWFLAKE. *Leucojum.* —, SPRING. *Erinosma.*

SNOWFLOWER. *Chionanthus virginica.*

SNOW-MOULD. *Lanosa nivalis.*

SNOW-PLANT. *Protococcus.*

SOAPBERRY. The seed of *Sapindus Saponaria, S. emarginatus,* and other species.

SOAPNUT. The fruit of *Acacia concinna* (alias *Mimosa abstergens*).

SOAP-PODS. The Chinese name of the pods of several species of *Cæsalpinia.*

SOAP-ROOT, EGYPTIAN. *Gypsophila Struthium.*

SOAPWOOD. *Clethra tinifolia.*

SOAPWORT. *Saponaria,* especially *S. officinalis ;* also *Vaccaria vulgaris.*

SOBOLE. A creeping rooting stem.

SOBOLEWSKIA. A genus of *Cruciferæ* from Southern Russia. The plants have stalked cordate-reniform toothed leaves, elongated racemes of white flowers, and an indehiscent wingless oblong-compressed one-celled one-seeded pouch. [J. T. S.]

SOBRALIA. One of the genera of orchids of the tribe *Vanillidæ,* comprising about twenty-five tropical American species, all terrestrial plants with slender tall reedy stems, clothed with leaves which are often plicate, and bearing upon their summits several often very large and extremely showy flowers, which in some species are of a thin almost transparent nature. It has nearly equal sepals joined at their bases, similar or very slightly different petals, an undivided or three-lobed cucullate lip rolled round the long column, which is thin-edged and thickened upwards, with a trifid anther-bed, having the anther attached to the central of the three fleshy segments. The original and finest species of the genus is the Peruvian *S. dichotoma,* which Pöppig describes as having bamboo-like stems from twelve to twenty feet high forming impenetrable thickets, and flowers two inches long, white externally and violet internally. Other species, however, far exceed this in the size and beauty of their flowers—such, for example, as the *S. macrautha* of Mexico and Guatemala, the very fugitive flower of which measures eight inches across, and varies from rich purple to very pale rose-colour or nearly white. [A. S.]

SOCRATEA. A small genus of palms inhabiting the forests of tropical America, and formerly associated with the old genus *Iriartea (Deckeria),* from which it may, however, at once be distinguished by being very bitter in every part. This property disqualifies the leaves from being eaten as 'cabbage,' and in Central America has obtained for these palms the name of Palmas amargas, in contradistinction to the different species of *Iriartea,* which are termed there Palmas dulces, and are used as food. The *Socrateas* are fine unarmed trees, bearing a crown of pinnatifid leaves, with generally sinuate-dentate segments, below which the spadices appear. The spadix is enveloped in five to eight spathes, and one and the same spadix bears monœcious flowers. The male flowers have a three-leaved calyx and corolla, both valvate, twenty-four or more stamens, and a small rudimentary germen ; the female flowers have the same kind of calyx and corolla, but the latter is imbricate ; there are no stamens or staminodes, and the germen is three-celled, developing into an elliptical or oblong-obovate one or two-seeded berry of an orange or yellow colour. [B. S.]

SOCRATESIA. A genus of *Vacciniaceæ,* comprising a Central American shrub with five-nerved leaves, and pendulous flowers, in terminal racemes, protected by scarlet bracts ; the calyx is short, tubular, with five radiating tubular processes at the base ; the filaments are of unequal length, and the anthers open by two pores at the top. [M. T. M.]

SODA. An alkaline product of several species of *Salsola, Suæda,* and *Salicornia.*

SOFTWOOD, BLACK. *Myrsine læta.*

SOGALGINA. A genus of *Compositæ,* comprising two Mexican weeds furnished with opposite lance-shaped three-nerved leaves, and solitary stalked yellow flower-heads. The generic name is an anagram of *Galinsoga,* a genus with which these plants were formerly confounded. They differ in the involucral scales being in more than one series, and in the two-lipped ray-florets, the outer lip larger and toothed, the inner of two linear lobes either separate or grown together. [A. A. B.]

SOJA (or SOYA) *hispida* is the only representative of a genus of *Leguminosæ* of the tribe *Papilionaceæ,* and much cultivated in tropical Asia on account of its beans, which are used for preparing a well-known brown and slightly salt sauce (Soy), used both in Asia and Europe for flavouring certain dishes, especially beef, and supposed to favour digestion. Of late it has been cultivated as an oil-plant. *S. hispida* is an erect hairy herb, with trifoliolate leaves, and axillary racemose flowers, which have a five-cleft calyx, a papilionaceous corolla, ten diadelphous stamens, and an oblong pod which contains from two to five ovate compressed seeds. Modern botanists generally refer the plant to GLYCINE: which see. [B. S.]

SOLA, or SOLAH. The light Indian Spongewood of Bengal, *Æschynomene aspera.*

SOLANACEÆ (*Cestraceæ, Nightshades*) An order of perigynous monopetalous dicotyledons, characterised by regular or nearly regular flowers ; the stamens inserted in the tube of the corolla, equal in number to and alternate with its lobes ; a free two-celled ovary with several ovules in each cell ; and albuminous seeds in a berry or capsule. It is thus easily distinguished from all others, except *Scrophulariaceæ,* from which it is only separated by the more regular flowers ; while some genera are quite intermediate. The *Solanaceæ* generally are herbs or shrubs, very rarely trees, with alternate leaves often in pairs, one smaller than the other ; the inflorescence terminal, or more frequently axillary or a little above the axil. They are natives of all tropical countries, more especially America, and a few are found in more temperate climates. Many are remarkable for their strong narcotic poisonous qualities.

There are above sixty genera, variously distributed into tribes by different botanists. The most important are *Solanum, Capsicum, Physalis, Nicotiana, Datura, Solandra, Petunia, Hyoscyamus, Atropa, Mandragora, Lycium,* and *Cestrum.* A few genera forming the groups called *Nolanaceæ* and *Retziaceæ* are by many botanists included among *Solanaceæ.*

SOLANDRA. The name of Dr. Solander, still well remembered as the fellow-traveller of Sir Joseph Banks and Captain Cook, and for the importance of his botanical observations, has been attached to, a genus of tropical American shrubs belonging to the *Solanaceæ* (*Atropaceæ*). The species have large somewhat fleshy leaves clustered near the ends of the branches, and large terminal solitary flowers ; the calyx is tubular ; the corolla funnel-shaped distended, its limb five-lobed ; the stamens five, with versatile anthers opening lengthwise : the ovary partially four-celled ; and the fruit fleshy, four-celled, surrounded by the calyx. Four or five species having yellowish or greenish flowers are in cultivation. In their flowers and leaves they resemble the old *Datura arborea.*   [M. T., M.]

SOLANUM. Few genera of plants are more important than this, which includes among its species the Potato, and serves as the type of the order *Solanaceæ.* The species are very numerous, distributed widely over the globe, but especially frequent in South America. They reckon among them herbs shrubs or small trees, with lateral or terminal inflorescence. The inflorescence, indeed, in the first instance is always terminal, but in course of growth it becomes *bent* downwards to give place to a shoot, which is given off from the side of the stem lower down, so that there is a reciprocal change in the direction of the shoot and of the inflorescence. In this way the seeming anomaly of an inflorescence placed on the side of the main stem, and not axillary to a leaf (frequently not even opposite to one), may be explained. The calyx consists of five or more segments ; the corolla is rotate or bell-shaped, with a short tube ; the stamens are generally five in number, with short filaments, and anthers converging into a cone round the style, each anther opening by two pores at the top. The fruit is a berry containing many seeds.

The most important of the many species is *S. tuberosum,* more familiar under the name of the Potato. Of this plant the underground stems or tubers are in common use as an esculent. These tubers are frequently considered roots, but erroneously so, their true nature being revealed by the little 'eyes' or rudimentary buds, which under favourable circumstances become developed into shoots. A true root, it may be remarked, does not (except in certain very exceptional cases) bear buds or shoots. Another proof that these tubers are really dilated branches is, that occasionally small leaf-bearing tubers are met with in the axils of the ordinary leaves of the plant.

The introduction of the Potato into Europe is ascribed to certain colonists sent from this country to Virginia under the auspices of Sir Walter Raleigh. The plant is indigenous in Chili and Peru. The varieties cultivated in this country are very numerous. The Potato consists of a mass of cells, enclosing starch-granules and an albuminous juice. The chemical composition of the Potato is probably subject to great variations, as the analyses of different chemists vary considerably. In general terms, it may be stated that Potatos contain water in quantity amounting to three-fourths of their weight, the remaining fourth part being made up of starch, gum, sugar, albumen, vegetable fibre, and a very small proportion of fatty material.

Potatos in cultivation are subject to various diseases, the most important and disastrous of which is one which first made its appearance (at least as a widely-spread malady) in 1845. This potato-murrain appears, from the researches of the Rev. M. J. Berkeley and others, to be due to the presence of a fungus, *Botrytis* (or *Peronospora*) *infestans,* which first attacks the leaves, causing discoloration, and thence rapidly spreads down the stems to the tubers. The principal effects of the disease consist in the increased quantity of water, the diminished quantity of starch, and the conversion of the albumen into casein. [See POTATO MURRAIN.] Owing to the almost entire dependence of the Irish peasantry on this vegetable for food, the most disastrous consequences ensued from the failure of this crop ; and it is still heartily to be wished that something of a less precarious nature should be grown, which would furnish a larger percentage of nutritious matter than the potato. Numerous substitutes have been proposed and tried, but time is required to combat the prejudice in favour of the potato, and to develope sufficiently the capabilities of the proposed substitutes.

In addition to their use as a vegetable, Potatos furnish a large quantity of starch, employed for various purposes in the arts. It forms the basis of certain farinaceous foods, as Bright's Nutritious Farina, &c., and is mixed with wheaten flour in the manufacture of bread. This adulteration can readily be detected by the microscope, especially on the addition of a solution of potash, which causes the starch-granules of the potato to swell up, while no effect is produced on the starch-grains of wheat,

From potato-starch is also procured a substance analogous to gum, called Dextrine, which is employed as a substitute for gum, size, and paste.

The pulp of the Potato, after the extraction of the starch, becomes hard and horny when dried, and is used in the manufacture of snuffboxes, &c. Raw potatos scraped are used as a popular cooling application to burns and scalds. From Potatos a coarse-tasting brandy is prepared in large quantities on the Continent. The stem and leaves have slightly narcotic properties, on which account the extract from them has been employed as a narcotic to allay pain, in cough and rheumatism, &c. Potatos when decaying have been stated to emit a phosphorescent light, but this requires confirmation.

S. Dulcamara, the Woody Nightshade or Bitter-sweet, is a well-known British plant scrambling over hedges, with more or less cordate leaves, the upper ones hastate ; and the flowers in drooping cymes, of a purple colour, with a yellow or green spot at the base of each petal ; the fruits oval fleshy and of a bright-red colour. The young stems are collected in the autumn, for medicinal purposes; they have at first a bitter taste, which is succeeded by an agreeable sweetness. A decoction of this plant has been considered useful in rheumatic and skin complaints, but its efficacy is very doubtful. In large doses it might act as an acrid narcotic. The berries are poisonous, and are stated to furnish green and violet dyes.

Another common species, *S. nigrum*, is often met with as a weed in waste places. It attains the height of a foot or more, has ovate wavy leaves, white flowers, and black berries—whence the name. Like most of its congeners, this species possesses slight narcotic properties, on which account in Bohemia the leaves are placed in the cradles of infants to promote sleep. The leaves likewise are used as soothing poultices. In the islands of Bourbon and Mauritius, however, the leaves are eaten in place of spinach ; and the fruit is said to be eaten without inconvenience by the soldiers stationed in British Kaffraria.

Besides the above-mentioned species, others are used for medicinal, alimentary, and other purposes. Some of them seem to be employed, in most parts of the world, as narcotics to allay pain, &c. ; others are sudorific and purgative. The parts employed are the roots, leaves, seeds, and juices of the fruits. *S. toxicarium* is used as a poison by the natives of Cayenne. *S. pseudo-quina* is esteemed as a valuable febrifuge in Brazil.

Among those used for food, of which mention has not hitherto been made, are *S. album* and *S. æthiopicum*, the fruits of which are used in China and Japan. Those of *S. Anguivi* are eaten in Madagascar. *S. esculentum* and its varieties furnish the fruits known as Aubergines or Brinjals, which are highly esteemed in France, and may occasionally be met with in Covent Garden Market ; they are of the size and form of a goose's egg, and usually of a rich purple colour. The Egg-plant, which has white berries, is only a variety of this. The Peruvians eat the fruits of *S. muricatum* and *S. quitense*; those of *S. ramosum* are eaten as a vegetable in the West Indies. The Tasmanian Kangaroo Apple is the fruit of *S. laciniatum* ; unless fully ripe, this is said to be acrid. In Gipps' Land, Australia, the natives eat the fruits of *S. vescum*, which like the preceding is not agreeable till fully ripe, when it is said to resemble in form and flavour the fruits of *Physalis peruviana*. Of other species the leaves are eaten : as those of *S. oleraceum* in the West Indies and Feejee Islands, of *S. sessiliflorum* in Brazil, &c.

Other species are employed as dyes. Such is *S. indigoferum*, cultivated in Brazil for the sake of its indigo. The juice of the fruit of *S. gnaphalioides* is said to be used to tint the cheeks of the Peruvian ladies, while their sisters of the Canary Isles employ for a similar purpose the fruits of *S. Vespertilio*. The fruits of *S. saponaceum* are used in Peru to whiten linen in place of soap. *S. marginatum* is employed in Abyssinia for tanning leather. The Tomato, once included here, is now referred to Ly-COPERSICUM : which see.   [M. T. M.]

The native country of the Potato, *S. tuberosum*, and the date of its introduction into Britain, have been subjects of much discussion. There can be no doubt of its being indigenous in various parts of South America—plants in a wild state having been found on the Peruvian coast, as well as on the sterile mountains of Central Chili and Buenos Ayres. The Spaniards are believed to have first brought it to Europe, from Quito, in the early part of the sixteenth century. It afterwards found its way into Italy, and from thence it was carried to Mons in Belgium by one of the attendants of the Pope's legate. In 1598 it was sent from Mons to the celebrated botanist Clusius at Vienna, who states that in a short time it spread rapidly throughout Germany. The first potatos that reached this country were brought from Virginia by the colonists sent out by Sir Walter Raleigh in A.D. 1584, and who returned in 1586. They were planted on Sir Walter's estate near Cork, and were used for food in Ireland long before they were even known or cultivated in England. Gerarde had a plant in his garden in Holborn, and has given a figure of it in his *Herbal*, published in 1597, under the name of *Batata virginiana*. He recommends the roots to be eaten as a delicate dish, and not as common food. In the time of James the First they were so rare as to cost two shillings a pound, and are mentioned in 1619 among the articles provided for the royal household. In 1633, when their valuable properties had become more generally known, they were deemed worthy of notice by the Royal Society, which took measures to encourage their cultivation with the view of preventing famine : but it was not until nearly a century after the above date that they were grown to any great extent in England.

In 1725 they were introduced into Scotland and cultivated with much success, first in gardens, and af.erwards (about 1760), when they had become plentiful, in the open fields. Since that period the prejudices which so long existed against their use both in England and Scotland have gradually vanished, and for many years past the Potato-crop has been regarded throughout the British Dominions as a most valuable addition to the staple commodities of life, only second in importance to cereals.

The varieties of the Potato are innumerable—some early, others late; and these again differing considerably, not only in size form and colour, but in their quality, being either waxy, or dry and floury. It has also been found that when a particular variety has been grown in the same soil for any length of time it degenerates, and requires to be renewed either by seed, but more frequently by resorting to sets or sorts which have been grown in a different soil and locality. In this way varieties are continually changing, and every town or district has its particular favourite.

As a vegetable, the Potato is excellent in whatever way it may be dressed—whether plain boiled, steamed, fried, or roasted. With the flour of potatos puddings and cakes have been made; starch has also been obtained, which for purity and nutritive properties is very little inferior to arrowroot. By distillation a powerful spirit is produced, and even a strong wine by the fermentative process. The most remarkable instance of the utility of the potato is probably that of M. Parmentier, who did so much in France to promote its cultivation towards the end of the last century, and who gave a grand entertainment at Paris, at which Benjamin Franklin, Lavoisier, and many other celebrated men of that day were present. Every dish consisted of potatos dressed in an endless variety of form and fashion; even the liquors were the produce of this precious root; and it is only to be regretted that the bill of fare, and the recipes of the cooks, have not been preserved.

The mysterious disease which made its appearance amongst Potatos in this country in 1845, soon after the introduction of guano as a manure, threatened the entire destruction of the crop; and we are still without any known preventive, the disease being regarded as an epidemic, to which the plant has become liable at some period of its growth according to the conditions of the atmosphere.   [W. B. B.]

SOLDANELLA. A genus of *Primulaceæ*, principally distinguished by the corolla, which is somewhat bell-shaped, with the border five-cleft, and each division fringed at the margin. The species are small herbs of graceful habit, natives of alpine districts of Continental Europe. One of them, *S. alpina*, a native of Switzerland, is well-known as an object of culture. The generic name is from the Latin *solidus* 'a piece of money,' the leaves of the species being in shape like coin.   [G. D.]

SOLDANELLE. (Fr.) *Convolvulus Soldanella*.

SOLDIER-WOOD. *Calliandra purpurea*.

SOLEA. *Viola*.

SOLEIL, or S. À GRANDES FLEURS. (Fr.) *Helianthus annuus*. — D'OR. *Narcissus aureus*. — VIVACE. *Helianthus multiflorus*.

SOLEIROLIA *corsica* is a delicate little weed of the family *Urticaceæ*, found in Corsica and Sardinia, and nearly related to *Parietaria*, but readily recognised by the minute green flowers being single instead of three or more together in the axils of the leaves. *Helixine* is the generic name adopted by some authors.   [A. A. B.]

SOLE-LEATHER, or SOLE-LEATHER KELP. A name given to the thicker *Laminariæ*, as *L. digitata*, *bulbosa*, &c., without particular reference to any individual species.   [M. J. B.]

SOLENANTHA. A genus of *Violaceæ*, proposed by Don, which has proved to be the same as *Hymenanthera* of Brown.

SOLENANTHUS. A genus of *Boraginaceæ* allied to *Cynoglossum*, from which it differs chiefly in the corolla being tubular and cylindrical. It is a native of Siberia, the Caucasus, Taurus, Northern Persia, and the Mediterranean region. The stem and foliage resemble those of *Cynoglossum*, and are often covered with white down or wool; the flowers are also arranged in scorpioid racemes, as in that genus, but they are tubular, five-lobed at the apex, with five very short scales in the throat; the stamens are more or less exserted; the nuts depressed prickly immarginate.   [J. T. S.]

SOLENIDIUM *racemosum*. An epiphytal orchid from Tropical America, bearing pseudobulbs, and having the habit of *Oncidium*, from which it is generically distinguished by the column in its early stage being bordered by a membrane terminating upwards on each side in a thin triangular tooth; by the presence of a pair of minute glands at the lower end of the column; and by the crest on its lip consisting of a pair of long feathery raised plates.   [A. S.]

SOLENOCARPUS. An Indian tree supposed to form a distinct genus of *Anacardiaceæ*. The leaves are unequally pinnate, and the flowers are arranged in panicles at the ends of the branches. These are perfect, and have a five-cleft deciduous calyx, five petals inserted with the ten stamens on the outside of the disk surrounding the one-celled ovary, a short style with oblique stigma, and an oblique fruit containing a single pendulous seed. The rind of the fruit is traversed by a number of channels containing oil—whence the name of the genus, from *sôlēn* 'a tube,' and *carpos* 'a fruit.'   [M. T. M.]

SOLENOGYNE. A little perennial herb of the *Compositæ* peculiar to South-eastern Australia, where it grows in pasture-land.

In aspect it is very like our own daisy—whence the specific name, *bellidioides*, given to it; but the much smaller flower-heads are different in structure. There are no white ray-florets; all are tubular and yellow, the outer three-toothed and pistil-bearing, the inner four or five-toothed and with stamens only. The achenes are oblong compressed beakless, and without pappus. [A. A. B.]

SOLENOPHORA *coccinea* is the sole representative of a Mexican genus of *Gesneraceæ*, with a long and large obconical five-cleft calyx, an obliquely funnel-shaped corolla, and an ovary totally submersed in the calyx. *S. coccinea* is a shrub of four to six feet high, with pubescent branches, opposite ovate duplicato-serrate leaves, one of each pair being always of smaller size than its companion; the flowers are scarlet, and appear in the axils of the leaves. [B. S.]

SOLENOSTEMMA. A genus of *Asclepiadaceæ*, containing a single species from Arabia and Egypt. It is an erect branching hoary undershrub, with white fleshy leaves, and white umbellate flowers. The calyx and corolla are five-parted: the staminal corona is cup-shaped and five-lobed, surrounding the base of the stipitate gynostegium; the clavate-compressed pollen-masses are pendulous, and the follicles ovoid and smooth, with many comose seeds. [W. C.]

SOLID. Not hollow or furnished with internal cavities of any kind.

SOLIDAGO. Perennial herbaceous plants belonging to the tribe *Corymbiferæ* of compound flowers, distinguished by the following characters:—Florets of the ray about five, yellow, furnished with a hair-like pappus; anthers without bristles at the base; involucre much imbricated; fruit nearly cylindrical. Numerous species are described; most of them have erect rod-like scarcely-branched stems, with alternate serrated leaves, and terminal spikes or racemes (often one-sided and paniculate) of numerous small yellow flowers. *S. Virgaurea*, the common Golden Rod, the only British species, is common in woods and heathy thickets, where it grows to the height of one to two feet, while on sea-cliffs it scarcely exceeds a few inches. The American species are frequently cultivated, but owing to their coarse habit are mostly confined to shrubberies and old-fashioned borders, where their bright yellow flowers contrast well with Michaelmas daisies. The leaves of *S. odora* are fragrant, and the essential oil distilled from them has been employed in medicine. French: *Verge d' Or*; German: *Goldruthe*. [C. A. J.]

SOLITARY. Growing singly.

SOLLYA. A genus of *Pittosporaceæ* found in South-western Australia and Tasmania, and consisting of climbing shrubs, with simple leaves, and blue flowers in cymes opposite the leaves. They have a small five-parted calyx, five ovate campanulate spreading petals, five stamens with arrowheaded anthers cohering into a cone and emitting the pollen by pores, a short style with a partially two-lobed stigma, and a thin many-seeded papery berry. [R. H.]

SOLOMON'S SEAL *Polygonatum.* —, FALSE. *Smilacina.*

SOLUTE. Completely separate from neighbouring parts.

SOM. The Arabic name for Garlic.

SONALI. An Indian name for the pods of *Cathartocarpus Fistula.*

SONCHUS. A genus of herbaceous rarely shrubby plants belonging to the tribe *Cichoraceæ* of compound flowers. The principal characters are:—Head composed of many florets; fruit much compressed, destitute of a beak; pappus soft hair-like, not feathery. The most common British species are—*S. arvensis*, Corn Sowthistle, a perennial herbaceous plant growing among corn, with much-toothed clasping leaves, and large yellow terminal flowers, of which the stalks and involucre are thickly clothed with glandular hairs; and *S. oleraceus* and *S. asper*, or Milk Thistle, annuals too common as weeds in cultivated ground, with hollow milky stems, glossy leaves, which are so sharply toothed as to be almost prickly, and yellow flowers. Some of the shrubby species, natives of Madeira and the Canaries, are sometimes admitted into the conservatory for the sake of their elegant foliage. *S. tenerrimus* is eaten in Italy as a salad, as was formerly the case with *S. oleraceus*, though it has long given place to more palatable herbs. French: *Laiteron*; German: *Saudistel.* [C. A. J.]

SONDERA. A name proposed by Lehmann for two Australian *Droseras*, which have the parts of the flower in fours instead of being in fives. As there is no other difference between these and other species, the genus has not been adopted.

SONERILA. A very extensive genus of East Indian melastomaceous plants, remarkable in the order for having all the several parts of their flowers in whorls of three, or trimerous, as it is technically called. The plants belonging to it are mostly herbaceous, though sometimes subshrubby, and of variable habit—some with and others without stems, some glabrous and others hirsute, and some with different kinds of leaves on the same plant. Their flowers are mostly purple or violet, borne in scorpioid racemes. [A. S.]

SONF. An Indian name for Aniseed.

SONNERATIA. A genus of *Myrtaceæ*, comprising eight species, all trees of moderate size inhabiting the coast-regions of India and the islands of the Eastern Archipelago. It has been referred to the loosestrife order, but appears rather to belong to the myrtleblooms, its fruit being an unopening berry divided internally by thin partitions into from ten to fifteen cells, filled with seeds which nestle in granular pulp, and which have a curved embryo. Its flowers have a bell-shaped four to eight-cleft calyx cohering with the ovary at the very base; from four to eight petals rising from the throat of the calyx and between its lobes, or rarely none at all; numerous stamens rising in several series along with the petals, and having the slender free filaments curved inward before flowering; and a long style and roundish stigma. All the species have opposite entire thickish almost veinless leaves, without dots, and large usually solitary terminal flowers.

Dr. M'Clelland, in his *Report on the Teak Forests of Peru*, states that the Kambala, *S. apetala*, is found throughout the Sunderbunds at the mouths of the Ganges, and to as far south as Rangoon, and that its strong hard close-grained wood is used at Calcutta for making packing-cases for beer and wine. *S. acida* is widely dispersed throughout Tropical Asia, occurring abundantly in most of the islands of the Indian Archipelago; but it is almost exclusively confined to the seacoasts, where it grows together in large masses, being what is called a littoral and sociable plant. A kind of silkworm feeds upon its leaves. Its acid slightly bitter fruits are eaten as a condiment by the Malays.   [A. S.]

SOOJEE. Indian wheat ground but not pulverised; a kind of semolina.

SOONTOOL. The fruit of *Sandoricum indicum*.

SOOPAREE, SOOPARI. Indian names for the fruit of the Areca or Betelnut Palm.

SOORSA. The Indian name for an oil obtained from *Sinapis juncea*.

SOOTY. As if smeared with soot. The same as Fuliginous.

SOPHOOLESIA. A genus of Central American vacciniaceous shrubs that grow upon the trunks of old trees, and have slender branches. The flowers are axillary, solitary on long stalks, thickened towards the base. The tube of the calyx is hairy; the corolla purple; the filaments distinct one from the other, and of unequal length; and the fruit dry and papery, containing two to four compartments.   [M. T. M.]

SOPHORA. A genus of *Leguminosæ*, widely spread through the tropical and temperate regions of both the Old and New Worlds, one of its species (*S. tomentosa*, a shrub of variable height) being found on the seashores of Tropical Asia, Africa, America, and Australasia. The species are not numerous, but they differ greatly in general appearance, some growing into trees of large size, while others are shrubs, and one or two herbaceous plants. All, however, agree in having pinnate leaves, with usually opposite leaflets and an odd one at the end; and terminal simple racemes or branching panicles of flowers, succeeded by cylindrical or slightly flattened but never winged fleshy or hard woody pods, containing many seeds, between which they are constricted, and not usually opening at maturity. The flowers are pea-like, with a rather broad standard.

S. japonica is a very handsome tree, long ago introduced into the gardens of this country from China; but it is not so frequently grown as, from its ornamental character and hardiness, it deserves to be. It is of quick growth, and forms a large round-headed tree forty feet high or more, with smooth dark-green young branches, graceful deep-bluish-green pinnate leaves, and in the autumn producing at the points of the branches large loosely-branching panicles of small whitish or cream-coloured flowers, which give it a beautiful and conspicuous appearance, though the flowers themselves are small. In China the flowers are used for dyeing a yellow colour. They are called Wai-fa or Wai-hwa by the Chinese, and are employed to give the fine yellow colour to the silk used for the garments of the mandarins, and also for dyeing blue cloth green. Large quantities of them are thus consumed, the tree being cultivated on this account in the provinces of Fokien, Honan, and Shantung, from whence sacks full of these little flowers are despatched to other parts of the empire. All parts of the tree possess purgative properties, and it is said that even those who merely prune it are affected, as also are turners when employed upon its fine-grained hard wood. The tree is only known in a cultivated state, and its native country is therefore uncertain, though it is most probably indigenous to either China or Japan.   [A. S.]

SOPHOROCAPNOS. A genus of *Fumariaceæ* from China, founded on the *Corydalis pallida*, which differs from the other species of that genus in having the pod with membranous transverse partitions between the seeds. It is a weak branched herb, with bipinnate leaves, and spicate pale-yellow flowers having a longish spur. The capsules are six or eight-seeded, linear beaded and beaked.   [J. T. S.]

SOPHRONIE. (Fr.) *Witsenia.*

SOPHRONITIS. The four known species of this genus of orchids are all Brazilian, and are little epiphytes with one-leaved pseudobulbs, and loose axillary few-flowered racemes of brilliant scarlet or violet flowers. Though of small size, the brilliancy of their tints causes them to be much sought after by cultivators. Their flowers have spreading, nearly equal, free sepals and petals; an entire cucullate tongue-shaped lip connate with the base of the column, which is free and furnished with a wing on each side of its apex, the wings being entire and conniving in front; and a terminal eight-celled anther containing eight pollen-masses.   [A. S.]

SOPS-IN-WINE. *Dianthus Caryophyllus.*

SORB. The Service-tree, *Pyrus domestica.*

SORBIER, or S. DES OISEAUX. (Fr.) *Pyrus Aucuparia.* — DES BOIS. *Pyrus torminalis.*

SORBINE. A saccharine matter obtained from the berries of the Mountain Ash, *Pyrus Aucuparia.*

SORBUS. The generic name given by Linnæus to the Mountain Ash or Rowan-tree, the cultivated Service-tree, and a few others which, by their pinnate leaves more than anything else, appear to differ from *Pyrus.* Modern botanists are, however, unanimous in referring these trees to the same genus as the apple and pear. See PYRUS. [A. A. B.]

SORDIDUS. Any dirty or muddy colour: thus *sordidè luteus* = dirty yellow.

SOREDIA. A name given to the little mealy patches which are so common on the thallus of lichens, and which arise from the rupture of the outer surface, and the protrusion of the gonidia by which the lichen is multiplied. [M. J. B.]

SOREMA. A genus of *Nolanaceæ* from Chili, consisting of prostrate annuals, having convolvulaceous blue flowers, and twenty free ovaries heaped about the base of the style. The drupes are one-celled, one-seeded, open at the base. [J. T. S.]

SORGHO. (Fr.) *Sorghum.*

SORGHUM. A genus of grasses belonging to the tribe *Andropogoneæ.* The inflorescence is in panicles; glumes two-flowered, one neuter, the other hermaphrodite; pales of the hermaphrodite flowers bearded, of the neuter beardless. The species of *Sorghum* are extensively cultivated for food, particularly *S. vulgare.* In Spain, Italy, and other parts of the South of Europe, as well as in Arabia and Asia Minor, the Millet or Guinea Corn occupies a place similar to that which oats and barley hold in the field-culture of the northern parts of Europe. The flour which the round hard seeds yield is very white, and makes good bread when properly manufactured. It is called Dana in India, and is said to be used chiefly by the lower classes of the population. It is also employed for feeding horses, swine, poultry, &c., where it is extensively grown. It is frequently cultivated in Botanical Gardens in England, where it has been tried also as a general crop, but the climate has been found too cold and damp for ripening its seeds properly. [D. M.]

SORI. The patches of spore-cases found on ferns.

SORIDIUM. A little slender leafless annual from Brazil, forming a genus of *Triuridaceæ,* only differing from *Sciaphila* in the number of divisions of the perianth and of the stamens, these being four and two respectively, instead of six and three.

SOROCEA. A Brazilian tree, forming a genus of *Artocarpaceæ.* The leaves are serrated; the flowers diœcious, the female ones borne in axillary clusters. Surrounding the ovary is a tubular five-toothed perianth, which becomes incorporated with the succulent fruit. There is a single pendulous seed. [M. T. M.]

SOROMANES. One of the genera of acrostichoid ferns, consisting of robust scandent or creeping plants, with large pinnate fronds, dimorphous as usually occurs in this group. The veins are pinnate, the venules connivent, all anastomosing at an acute angle and without free included veinlets. The fertile fronds are contracted. *S. serratifolium,* the only species, is a native of Mexico and Columbia. [T. M.]

SOROSIS, SOROSUS. The fleshy mass formed by a consolidation of many flowers, seed-vessels, and their receptacles—as the Pineapple, the Bread-fruit, &c.

SORREL. *Rumex Acetosa.* —, CLIMBING. *Begonia scandens.* —, GARDEN. *Rumex Acetosa.* —, INDIAN. *Hibiscus Sabdariffa.* —, MOUNTAIN. *Oxyria.* —, RED. *Hibiscus Sabdariffa.* —, SHEEP'S. *Rumex Acetosella.* —, SWITCH. *Dodonæa viscosa.* —, TREE. *Rumex Lunaria.* —, WOOD. *Oxalis Acetosella;* also *Begonia acutifolia.*

SORREL-TREE. *Eubotrys* or *Lyonia arborea.*

SOTOR. A name given by Fenzl to *Kigelia pinnata.*

SOUARI-WOOD. A durable timber of Demerara, obtained from *Caryocar tomentosum.*

SOUCHET. (Fr.) *Cyperus.* — A PAPIER. *Papyrus antiquorum.* — SULTAN. *Cyperus esculentus.*

SOUCI. (Fr.) *Calendula.* — D'EAU. *Caltha palustris.* — DES JARDINS. *Calendula officinalis.* — HYGROMÈTRE, or PLUVIAL. *Dimorphotheca pluvialis.*

SOUDE. (Fr.) *Salsola.* — COMMUNE. *Salsola Soda.* — COUCHÉE. *Salsola Kali.*

SOUFRE VÉGÉTAL. (Fr.) *Lycopodium clavatum.*

SOULAMEA. A genus of the *Simarubaceæ* peculiar to the Moluccas and the Feejee Islands, and represented by a single species, *S. amara,* a tree with simple alternate stalked obovate leaves, and small green flowers disposed in short axillary spikes. The fruits are singular, being very markedly heart-shaped, whence the plant has been called *Cardiophora* and *Cardiocarpus.* They are compressed, coriaceous in texture, and about an inch in length; and in their absence the plant may be known from its allies by the flowers, which have three sepals, six stamens, and a two-celled and two-ovuled ovary tipped with two short styles. Like the *Quassia* and most others of the family, this plant is excessively bitter in all its parts. The root and bark, bruised and macerated in water, are used in India, Java, the Moluccas, &c., as an emetic and tonic, in pleurisy, asthma, cholera, snake-bites, epilepsy, &c. These plants were formerly placed in the order Polygalaceæ. [A..A. B.]

SOULANGIA. A name under which Brongniart proposed to separate some species of *Phylica* as a distinct genus, but the characters given have not proved sufficiently constant for its adoption by subsequent botanists.

SOULIER. (Fr.) *Cypripedium.*

SOUM. A negro name for *Balanites ægyptiaca.*

SOURING. A country name for the Crab apple.

SOURSOP. The fruit of *Anona muricata.*

SOURWOOD. *Lyonia arborea.*

SOUSHUMBER. *Solanum mammosum.*

SOUTHERNWOOD. *Artemisia Abrotanum.*

SOUVIENS-TOI DE MOI. (Fr.) *Myosotis palustris.*

SOWA. *Anethum Sowa.*

SOWBANE. *Chenopodium rubrum.*

SOWBREAD. *Cyclamen europæum.*

SOWDWORT. *Salsola Kali.*

SOWERBÆA. A genus of *Liliaceæ* consisting of two Australian species, with much of the appearance of *Allium*, but without the odour of garlic or the bulb of that genus. The root consists of a cluster of fibres, emitting long narrow radical leaves, and erect scapes bearing each a dense head or umbel of pink flowers surrounded by a few short bracts. They are at once distinguished from those of *Allium* by the stamens, of which three only bear anthers, the other three being reduced to short scales. Both species, *S. juncea* and *S. laxiflora*, are occasionally to be found in cultivation in our greenhouses.

SOWTHISTLE. *Sonchus.*

SOY. A sauce originally prepared in the East, and said to be produced from the beans of *Soja hispida.*

SOYEUSE. (Fr.) *Asclepias syriaca.*

SOYMIDA *febrifuga*, the Rohuna of Hindostan, is the sole representative of a genus of *Cedrelaceæ*, peculiar to the East Indies. It is a useful tonic in intermittent fevers; but Ainslie found that it deranged the nervous system, occasioning vertigo and subsequent stupor, if given beyond the extent of four or five drachms in twenty-four hours. It has been employed successfully in India in bad cases of gangrene, and in Great Britain in typhus-fever, and as an astringent. It forms a tall tree, with wood resembling mahogany, and a very bitter astringent bark. On the Coromandel coast of India it is known as the Redwood-tree. The leaves are paripinnate, the panicles large, and either axillary or terminal. Both calyx and corolla are composed of five leaves, and the capsule is woody, and five-valved

five-celled, each cell containing several winged seeds. [B. S.]

SPACHEA. A genus of tropical American trees or shrubs of the family *Malpighiaceæ.* The flowers are in terminal racemes, and have a five-parted calyx, whose segments are provided at the base with two glands; petals five, larger than the calyx, bent backwards; stamens ten, some of them abortive, the filaments combined at the base into a hairy ring adnate to the calyx; fruit a woody drupe, with a two-celled stone, and one seed in each stone. [M. T. M.]

SPADICEUS. Bright brown; pure and very clear brown.

SPADIX. A branch or axis bearing numerous closely-packed sessile flowers, and inclosed in a spathe or spathes; a spike inclosed in a spathe.

SPÆTLUM. A North-west American name for *Lewisia rediviva.*

SPAIRELLE. (Fr.) *Spiræa.*

SPALANTHUS *confertus.* The sole representative of a genus of *Combretaceæ*, confined to the Malayan Islands. It is a glabrous shrub, with ovate oblong leaves without stipules, and terminal spikes of sessile white flowers. The calyx has a long tube, the corolla five petals; the stamens are ten in number, and the capsule is large, and has five wings, and five one-seeded cells. [B. S.]

SPALLANZANIA. A Madagascar tree forming a genus of *Cinchonaceæ.* The flowers are in terminal corymbs; the five lobes into which the limb of the calyx is divided are leafy; the corolla is funnel-shaped, with a long slender tube and spreading five-lobed limb; there are five stamens attached to and projecting from the throat of the corolla; and the capsule is crowned by the calyx-limb, two-celled, dividing from above downwards into two valves. The same name is synonymous with *Gustavia* and *Aremonia*, two widely different genera. [M. T. M.]

SPAN. Nine inches, or the space between the thumb and little finger when spread out.

SPANISH DAGGER. A West Indian name for *Yucca aloifolia.*

SPANISH JUICE. The extract of the root of the Liquorice, *Glycyrrhiza glabra.*

SPANISH NEEDLES. A name given in the West Indies to the fruits of a species of *Bidens.*

SPARASSIS. A fine genus of hymenomycetous *Fungi*, exactly intermediate as regards form between the club-shaped natural order *Clavati* on the one hand, and the ear-shaped *Auricularini* on the other, but in substance and natural affinity really belonging to the former. It forms large subhemispherical masses a foot or more in diameter, consisting of numerous plates, which fructify all round and resemble a particular form of macaroni. Two species at least afford a most excellent and abundant food. They are found in the pine and mixed woods of. Sweden and Germany, and both are said to be equally delicious. Neither appears in a considerable collection made in Hungary, nor do their esculent properties appear to be recognised there. _S. crispa_ has recently been found in Britain.　　[M. J. B.]

SPARATTOSPERMA. _Tecoma._

SPARAXIS. The species composing this genus of _Iridaceæ_ inhabit the Cape of Good Hope, and are herbs with bulbous tubers, simple or paniculate stems, serrate narrow leaves, and large showy flowers arranged in spikes. Both calyx and corolla are composed of three parts; there are three stamens, and a three-celled capsule enclosing numerous round seeds. The bulbous tubers of _S. bulbifera_ are edible.　　[B. S.]

SPARGANIUM. A genus of water-plants belonging to _Typhaceæ_, and found in almost every part of the world, including the British Islands. The leaves are linear, and the flowers are monœcious and arranged in globular heads, the upper ones containing the male flowers. There is no perianth; the stamens are numerous; and there are several ovaries, each containing one pendulous ovule. The fruit is drupaceous, and one to two-celled. The root of _S. ramosum_ and of _S. simplex_ was formerly used medicinally under the name of Radix Sparganii, and was supposed to cure snake-bites. The stem has been used for making paper.　　[B. S.]

SPARGELLE. (Fr.) _Genista sagittalis._

SPARGOULE, or **SPARGOUTE.** (Fr.) _Spergula._

SPARMANNIA. A genus of _Tiliaceæ_, known from among its allies by the outer series of the very numerous stamens being destitute of anthers, and by the globular or ovoid capsular fruits (the size of a marble or larger) being covered with prickles or tubercles. The four known species, natives of Eastern and Southern Africa, are shrubs or trees, with heart-shaped toothed or lobed leaves, and terminal cymes of white flowers.

The genus bears the name of Dr. A. Sparmann, a Swedish botanist, who went with Captain Cook on his second voyage round the world, and introduced the well-known _S. africana_, which is commonly met with in greenhouses. It is a shrub of three to twelve feet, with long-stalked heart-shaped leaves, clothed with soft downy and pretty white flowers produced in stalked umbels; and consisting of four narrow sepals, four petals, many stamens with yellow filaments and purple anthers, and a five-celled ovary tipped with a simple style.　　[A. A. B.]

SPARROWGRASS. A corruption of _Asparagus._

SPARROWTONGUE. _Polygonum aviculare._

SPARROWWORT. _Passerina._

SPARSE. Scattered, irregularly distributed.

SPARSETTE. (Fr.) _Nardus stricta._

SPART. The Esparto, _Machrochloa tenacissima._

SPARTIANTHUS. _Spartium._

SPARTINA. A genus of grasses belonging to the tribe _Chlorideæ_. It has the inflorescence in raceme-like spikes; spikelets one-sided, inserted in a double row; glumes keeled membranaceous, pointed or shortly awned; pales two awnless, cleft and toothed, shorter than the glumes; stamens three; styles two, very long; seed compressed and smooth. Steudel describes twenty species under this genus, the greater part of which are American. The British representatives, _S. stricta_ and _S. alternifolia_, are among the rarest of British grasses.　　[D. M.]

SPARTIUM. The generic name of the well-known Spanish Broom, which differs from our native broom, _Sarothamnus scoparius_, in the calyx being split above, and thus one instead of two-lipped. The plant is widely spread over the Mediterranean region, and has been cultivated in British gardens for upwards of 300 years. The growth is like that of the common broom, but the green polished twigs are terete and rush-like, instead of angular; while they are usually devoid of leaves, the latter when present being lance-shaped or linear. The handsome yellow pea-flowers, arranged in racemes at the ends of the twigs, are highly perfumed, and very attractive to bees. A double-flowered variety is in cultivation.

By macerating the twigs a good fibre is obtained, which is made into thread in Languedoc, and into cord and a coarse sort of cloth in Dalmatia. The flowers are said to afford a yellow dye, and the seeds in large doses are emetic and purgative, and sometimes used in dropsy like those of the common broom. Besides its name of _S. junceum_, the plant is known by those of _Spartianthus junceus_ and _Genista hispanica_. The name _Spartium_ is from the Greek word denoting 'cordage,' in allusion to the use of the plant.　　[A. A. B.]

SPARTOTHAMNUS. A genus of _Myoporaceæ_, containing a single species from Australia. It is a branching shrub, having the habit of some species of _Spartium_. The branches are tetragonous opposite and rigid, and bear a few small deciduous and opposite leaves; while the white flowers are borne on short pedicels in the axils of the uppermost leaves. The calyx is five parted, the corolla campanulate and subregular, the four stamens are somewhat unequal, the style is bifid at the apex, and the ovary is four-celled, with a single ovule in each cell.　　[W. C.]

SPATHACEÆ. A Linnæan order equivalent to *Amaryllidaceæ*.

SPATHACEOUS. Having the appearance of a spathe, or being furnished with one.

SPATHE. A large bract rolling over an inflorescence and guarding it while young.

SPATHELIA. A genus of *Simarubaceæ*, comprising trees, natives of mountainous regions in the West Indies. They are lofty and handsome, with large pinnate leaves, and terminal panicles of small reddish flowers. The calyx is five-parted; the petals five, overlapping; stamens of the male flower five, flattened, generally but not always having a cleft scale at their base; ovary rudimentary, on a short stalk. In the perfect flowers are five stamens and a three-celled ovary, surmounted by a short three-cleft style; fruit dry three-cornered winged, three-celled. *S. simplex* is a very handsome stove-plant, with large spreading panicles of red flowers. [M. T. M.]

SPATHELLÆ. The pales and glumes of grasses.

SPATHICARPA. This name has been given to an herbaceous plant forming a genus of *Araceæ*. The species is a native of La Plata, and throws up a single hastate leaf, a slender erect stalk longer than the leaf, and terminated by the inflorescence, which consists of a spathe adherent to the spadix. The flowers are arranged in three rows; the central one consists of male flowers, the lateral ones of female flowers; the anthers open by pores; the ovaries are free one-celled, with a single ovule; and the fruit fleshy. [M. T. M.]

SPATHILLA. A secondary spathe in a spathaceous inflorescence, as in Palms.

SPATHIUM. One of the subdivisions of the genus *Epidendrum*, including those species (between forty and fifty in number) with slender leafy erect stems, and flowers on a long peduncle proceeding from a spathe consisting of one or more equitant bracts. The flowers have the lip wholly attached to the column. [A. S.]

SPATHODEA. A genus of *Bignoniaceæ*, composed of tall trees inhabiting Tropical Asia and Africa, having imparipinnate leaves, paniculate flowers, a spathaceous calyx, a more or less bell or funnel-shaped corolla of a bright-yellow orange or purplish colour, and a capsular fruit divided into two cells by a partition placed contrary to the direction of the valves. *S. lævis* is an inmate of our hothouses, and is like all the other species highly ornamental on account of its foliage and blossoms. All the climbing species (natives of America formerly classed with this genus have been referred to *Dolichandra* and *Macfadyena*: whilst all the white flowering kinds (including the New Holland ones) constitute the genus *Dolichandrone*. [B. S.]

SPATHOGLOTTIS. One of the genera of the *Bletieæ* tribe of epidendreous orchids, distinguished from *Bletia* itself by the middle segment of its deeply three-parted lip having a claw or stalk, with two tubercles or plates at its base, and by its two-celled anther. All its species are Asiatic, and terrestrial plants, with subterranean corms, plicate sword-shaped leaves, and generally yellow flowers. [A. S.]

SPATHULATE. Oblong, with the lower end very much attenuated, so that the whole resembles a druggist's spatula.

SPATHULEA, or SPATHULARIA. A genus of *Fungi* allied to *Helvella*, and distinguished by the compressed receptacle running down the stem on either side, and confluent with it. The only species, *S. flavida*, which has the hymenium of a beautiful buff, contrasting well with the whitish stem, is not uncommon in firwood, and is very beautiful. [M. J. B.]

SPATULE. (Fr.) *Iris fœtidissima.*

SPATULUM. A North-west American name for *Lewisia rediviva.*

SPAWN. The same as Mycelium.

SPEARMINT. *Mentha viridis.*

SPEARWOOD. *Acacia doratoxylon.*

SPEARWORT. *Ranunculus Lingua* and *R. Flammula.*

SPEAUTRE. (Fr.) *Triticum Spelta.*

SPECIFIC CHARACTERS. The short descriptions by which botanists endeavour to distinguish one species from another.

SPECULARIA. A genus of *Campanulaceæ* having the tube of the calyx long, the corolla wheel-shaped and five-lobed, five stamens with flat hairy filaments, a short style with ten lines of hairs, and a long seed-vessel opening by valves above the middle or near the apex. The species are small herbs, natives of Middle Asia (one found in America), having the leaves alternate, the lower differing in form from the others, and the flowers varying in colour—blue purple or white. The name is from the Latin *speculum* 'a mirror,' to indicate the brightness of the flowers in sunshine. [G. D.]

SPEEDWELL. *Veronica.*

SPELT. An inferior kind of wheat grown in France and Flanders, *Triticum Spelta.*

SPERAGE. *Asparagus officinalis.*

SPERGULA. Herbaceous plants of humble growth, with slender stems and very narrow leaves belonging to the order *Illecebraceæ*. The characters are:—Calyx five-parted; petals five, entire; stamens five or ten, inserted on a perigynous ring; styles five, distinct; seeds numerous, keeled or winged round the edge. *S. arvensis*, the Corn Spurrey, a common weed in cornfields and cultivated ground generally, especially where the soil is light or sandy, is a straggling plant about a foot high, with somewhat downy stems and leaves, the latter awl-shaped and nearly cylindrical—the longest an inch long or more, disposed in opposite tufts at the knots of the stems which are swollen. The flowers, which are white, grow in loose terminal panicles; and their stalks, when the fruit is approaching maturity, become reflexed so as to form an acute angle with the stem. According to Don, this plant is grown on the Continent to serve as pasture for cattle, imparting a fine flavour to mutton, and enriching the milk of cows. *S. pilifera* has of late years been grown in English gardens as a substitute for grass on lawns. Its foliage is of a pleasant green colour and delicate texture; it soon establishes itself, and possesses the recommendation of retaining its verdure in the dryest and hottest seasons. The latter advantage it owes to the fact that it belongs to a class of plants which evaporate their moisture slowly, while its long fibrous roots descend to a sufficient depth to be little affected by drought. French: *Spergule*; German: *Ackerspergel*.   [C. A. J.]

SPERGULARIA. A genus of *Illecebraceæ* often called *Lepigonum*, and consisting of small weedy herbs, occurring in the temperate zones chiefly on the seacoast, with opposite or fasciculate-whorled setaceous or more or less cylindrical fleshy leaves, scarious stipules, and lilac or pink flowers in dichotomous or racemose cymes, the pedicels reflexed after flowering. The calyx is five-parted; the petals five, rarely absent; stamens five or ten (sometimes fewer), situated on an obsolete perigynous ring; style three or five (rarely two) cleft; capsule three or five-valved; seeds often margined or membranously winged. There are several British species.   [J. T. S.]

SPERMACOCE. Tropical weeds of the family *Cinchonaceæ*. The flowers are axillary sessile or somewhat whorled, white or blue, the corolla salver-shaped. When ripe the fruit splits into two valves from above downwards, one valve remaining attached to the partition, and therefore the cavity formed by those parts remains, for a time at least, closed; the other valve becomes detached from the partition, so that the second cell of the fruit is thus opened. Both cells contain a single seed. *S. ferruginea* is employed instead of Ipecacuanha in Brazil; so also is *S. Poaya*. In the West Indies *S. verticillata* is used for the same purpose. The root of *S. hispida* is employed in India as a sudorific; it is stated to possess similar properties to Sarsaparilla. The generic name is derived from *sperma* 'seed' and *ake* 'point,' said to be in allusion to the point-like calyx-teeth surmounting the seed-vessel.   [M. T. M.]

SPERMANGIUM. The case containing the spores of Algals.

SPERMATIA. See SPERMOGONIA.

SPERMATOCYSTIDIUM. The supposed male organs of the muscal alliance. See ANTHERIDIA.

SPERMATOZOIDS. It is now as certain that impregnation takes place in many cryptogams as in phænogams, but the mode in the two is very different, and that in cryptogams follows rather the type of the animal than that of the vegetable kingdom. As however there was some doubt on the subject when the structure of the male organs was at first well ascertained, the spiral bodies by which impregnation is accomplished in acrogens were called Spermatozoids, to distinguish them from the spermatozoa of animals. In acrogens they appear always to be more or less spiral, though the spire is sometimes much expanded; and the bodies in this case, with their two lash-like appendages, approach the type which is usual amongst *Algæ*, in which class they are sometimes with difficulty distinguished from the really reproductive zoospores. In *Fungi*, unless *Saprolegnia* and its allies be included, the impregnating bodies or Spermatia are more like minute pollen-grains, though there is no evidence at present that they perform their functions by a kind of germination. In ferns, *Equiseta*, and *Salvinia*, instead of the two long appendages there are a multitude of shorter ones. Their motion when immersed in water is very lively and various. They are produced in a peculiar cellular tissue from the endochrome, and not, as has been supposed, partly from that and partly from the walls of the cells. It was once believed, in consequence of the faith reposed in Schleiden's theory of reproduction in phænogams, that the Spermatozoids of ferns when entering the archegonia did not perform the office of impregnation, but themselves by cellular division became the new plant. This notion, however, is now exploded.   [M. J. B.]

SPERMIDIUM. One of the names of the Achene.

SPERMODERM. The skin or testa of a seed.

SPERMODON. A genus of sedge-grasses, belonging to the tribe *Rhynchosporeæ*. Spikelets of inflorescence one or few-flowered; flowers hermaphrodite or polygamous; scales subdistichous, without bristles; stamens one to three; styles two to three-cleft. The few species described under this genus are natives of Brazil and New Holland.   [D. M.]

SPERMOGONIA. Almost all Lichens exhibit in different parts of their thallus black or brownish specks, whose nature has been variously interpreted by authors. Some have considered them as transformations of the shields by which *Lecidea* or other shield-bearing genera are transformed into *Endocarpa* or *Verrucarieæ*; while others like Hedwig, with more probability, have regarded them as male organs. With the older microscopes it was impossible to ascertain their structure. It now however appears that they all produce, either on simple or branched threads, naked extremely minute bodies, which are mostly short and linear and straight or curved, but in some cases elliptic or irregular like the stylospores of *Fungi*. These bodies were at first asserted by Itzigsohn to have active motion, but this has not been confirmed by the generality of observers, who regard whatever motion may appear as simply molecular or (as it is sometimes called) Brownian. Certain it is that they have no whip-like appendages, such as are so commonly found in the spermatozoids of *Algæ*, or even in their zoospores. As these bodies are so general in Lichens, as appears from the admirable memoirs of the Tulasnes and Dr. Lindsay, it is highly probable that they are of sexual importance. The case scarcely admits of direct proof, but the absence of motile threads or active motion, however produced, is of little consequence, as it does not follow, because they exist in some Cryptogams, that they should exist in all. Since there is some difference of structure, and doubts may exist as to their real nature, the Messrs. Tulasne have thought it best to propose for the cysts the name Spermogonia, and for the spore-like bodies that of Spermatia. In a few cases, as in *Peltidea*, the spermatia, as said above, resemble stylospores, but on the contrary in several *Fungi* there are bodies exactly resembling spermatia as well as stylospores. [M. J. B.]

SPERMOPHORUM. A cord which bears the seeds of some plants ; also the placenta itself.

SPERMOTHECA. The seed-vessel ; the case in which seeds are contained.

SPERMUM. In Greek compounds a seed, or any seed-like part.

SPHACELE. A genus of *Labiatæ*, distinguished from its congeners by the following characters :—Corolla having a wide tube, the upper lip slightly bifid, the lower longest and notched ; filaments of the stamens smooth. The species are undershrubs, natives of Western America from California to Chili, with wrinkled and opposite leaves, which are hoary beneath, the flowers in loose whorls. The name is from the Greek word `sphakos` 'sage,' indicating some resemblance to that plant. [G. D.]

SPHÆRALCEA. Closely allied to *Malva*, and belonging to the *Malvaceæ*, this genus is principally distinguished by the presence of three ovules in each compartment of the ovary ; the upper one ascending, the two lower ones pendulous. The fruit is globular, consisting of several carpels containing three seeds, or by abortion one only. The carpels open along one edge, and ultimately separate one from the other. The species are natives of Tropical America. Some of them are employed medicinally for their demulcent properties, as marshmallow is with us. [M. T. M.]

SPHÆRANTHUS. A genus of the *Compositæ* containing about a dozen species of much-branched glutinous smooth or downy annual weeds, found in tropical or subtropical parts of Asia, Africa, and Australasia. They have winged stems furnished with oblong or lance-shaped decurrent leaves, and the flower-heads are borne in dense spherical clusters, so that without examination a cluster of flower-heads might be readily mistaken for a single one. The florets are pink, all tubular, the outer ones fertile and three-toothed, the inner sterile and five-toothed ; the achenes are smooth or downy, and without pappus. *S. mollis*, a common Indian weed on dry cultivated land, is remarkable when fresh for the strong honey-like odour secreted by the innumerable soft glandular hairs which clothe the whole plant. [A. A. B.]

SPHÆRENCHYMA. Spherical or spheroidal cellular tissue, such as is found in the pulp of fruits.

SPHÆRIACEI. A large and interesting order of sporidiferous *Fungi*, but more important in a botanical than an economical point of view. They are characterised by carbonaceous or membranaceous cysts, or perithecia composed of cells or very rarely of interwoven threads pierced at the tip with a pore or narrow slit, and often ending in a distinct short or elongated nipple or crest-like process. The walls are lined within with a diffluent gelatinous mass of asci and barren threads (paraphyses). The cysts are either free from any stroma, whether naked or exposed, or variously seated on or within a filamentous fleshy or corky cellular mass called, according to the prevalence of a floccose or cellular structure, a subiculum or stroma. Though the normal form of fruit is ascigerous, there is reason to believe that many of them produce a second form of fruit, consisting of naked spores contained like the asci within a perithecium. In the highest genus, the sporiferous state, if we may judge from *Cordiceps purpurea* and its allies, is a mere thin stratum of exposed cells, while in some true *Sphæriæ* and *Hypoxyla* it assumes the form of different genera of moulds. The subject is, however, still in its infancy, and the whole theory of secondary fruit requires many repeated observations before it can be considered as decisive, though the analogy of the red-spored *Algæ* and some others, is in its favour.

Sphæriacei are abundantly produced upon decayed wood, herbaceous stems, &c. ; they affect also more fugacious organs, and appear sometimes when there is some degree of vitality left in the matrix. They occur also on dung, on the naked soil, and on animal substances, as caterpillars, chrysalises, &c. They are not uncommon on cryptogams, and occur even on marine *Algæ*, while one at least in every stage of growth is covered by the sea. One or two curious species are found on truffles while still in their native place of growth. They are found in all parts of the world which are not subject to such extremes of temperature as are hostile to all vegetation, save that of the lowest *Algæ*. [M. J. B.]

SPHÆRIA. The typical genus of the natural order of Fungi *Sphæriacei*, formerly almost coextensive with the order, and consisting of at least 1500 species, but still containing numerous representatives, after repeated reduction by the separation of distinct genera. *Sphæria* as now defined consists of those *Sphæriacei* which have carbonaceous perithecia which are not immersed in a distinct stroma, but are either quite exposed, partially sunk into their matrix, or covered by the cuticle, and accompanied by a more or less decided growth of threads constituting the mycelium. A few genera are separated in consequence of slight modifications of the perithecia and their contents which it is not necessary to indicate here. After every reduction we have still above 200 species in Great Britain, and there are probably at least 500 good species. The characters depend on the mode of growth, on the form, clothing and sculpture of the perithecia, on the comparative abundance of mycelium or subiculum, but above all on the structure of the sporidia, which exhibit a marvellous variety of colour, outline, division, &c., which makes them admirable subjects for the microscope. Though the whole development of each sporidium must be taken into account, together with the variations to which it may be subject, and species must not be proposed on slight or untenable grounds, there are certain limits within which change can take place, and with proper caution the fruit affords the most certain distinctive characters. Though, however, the sporidia afford good specific characters, they are not in general to be depended upon for generic distinctions—an observation which applies to other *Sphæriacei*, and to the great mass of lichens. [M. J. B.]

SPHÆRINE. A genus of *Amaryllidaceæ*, consisting of perennial herbs, with erect or adscendent stems, scattered leaves, and umbellate terminal flowers. It is closely related to *Alstrœmeria*, but the ovary is but little superior, and the capsule is indehiscent. They are natives of Peru. [T. M.]

SPHÆROBLASTUS. A cotyledon which rises above-ground, bearing at its end a spheroid tumour.

SPHÆROBOLUS. A curious genus of *Nidulariacei*, distinguished by the sporangium being solitary, and at length ejected by the eversion of the lining-membrane of the common peridium, which splits in a stellate manner, and remains attached by the points of the rays like a little bladder. *S. stellatus* is the most common species, and is found occasionally on rotten sticks in woods, though in such situations seldom abundantly. On the contrary, it occurs in the greatest profusion on a heaps of sawdust, or in hothouses. The sporangia are thrown like a shell out of a mortar to a considerable distance considering the size of the plant, which scarcely exceeds that of a hemp-seed, and adhere closely to whatever substance they may chance to meet with in their course,

A year or two since this little plant excited considerable alarm in a large establishment in Scotland, especially from its prevalence in an orchid-house. The very walls of the houses, the leaves of the orchids, and, in short, every substance in the conservatories were studded with little brown pellets, which adhered with great tenacity. The gardener, ignorant of the cause, fancied that it must be some new disease, which might possibly prove as fatal as the vine and potato murrain. He was, however, requested to send some of the *Sphagnum* which surrounded the orchid-roots, which was suspected to be the seat of the mischief; and when a portion of this was placed under a bell-glass the inside was soon in the same condition as the orchid-leaf, and the origin of the supposed mischief was clear, to the great delight of the gardener. All lovers of curious plants should look out for this singular fungus, which will amply repay a close observation. [M. J. B.]

SPHÆROCARPUS. A genus of Liverworts allied to *Riccia*, and distinguished by the superficial fruit being collected in clusters on the filmy frond, surrounded by a sessile or pedicellate undivided pitcher-shaped or ovate proper involucre. The spores have their surface divided into little areæ, each of which has a minute wart in the centre. The cells of the walls of the capsule are filled with starch-grains. *S. terrestris* is found on the ground in clover-fields or fallows, but appears to be more common in the eastern counties, than in the rest of England. [M. J. B.]

SPHÆROCARYA. A genus of sandalworts, distinguished by having the calyx persistent and five-cleft, the tube club-shaped; ten glands in the throat of the calyx, five of which (alternate with its divisions) are small and petaloid; and five stamens opposite the divisions of the calyx. The species are Indian trees, with alternate oblong leaves, and clusters of small green flowers. *S. edulis*, indigenous to Nepal, bears a fruit which is used by the natives. The name is derived from Greek words signifying 'sphere' and 'nut,' in allusion to the shape of the fruit. [G. D.]

SPHÆROCEPHALUS. Having flowers growing in close spherical heads.

SPHÆROCIONIUM. *Hymenophyllum.*

SPHÆROCOCCOIDEÆ. A natural order of rose-spored *Algæ* belonging to the series with spores contained in necklace-like strings, the nucleus lodged in an external conceptacle, which is hollow, and has a placenta at the base; all the cells of the fertile threads being gradually changed into spores, and at length separating. The substance of the frond is cartilaginous or membranaceous. It contains many of our most beautiful *Algæ* belonging to the genera *Delesseria* and *Nitophyllum*, and has representatives in most parts of the habitable world. *Delesseria Leprieurii* occurs in the Hudson River at Westpoint, sixty miles from the sea, and in the estuaries of several rivers in the Southern States of America. The same species is found also in New Zealand.   [M. J. B.]

SPHÆROCOCCUS. A genus of rosespored *Algæ*, the type of the natural order *Sphærococcoideæ*. It once embraced many species now referred to other genera, and is now nearly restricted to the European *S. coronopifolius* and *S. crinitus.* The characters of the genus, as given by Dr. Harvey, are :—Frond cartilaginous, compressed, two-edged, linear, with two-ranked branches and an internal rib, cellular ; central cells fibrous ; medial many-sided, those of the surface minute and disposed in filaments. Fruit spherical tubercles, having a thick fibro-cellular pericarp, and containing a mass of minute spores on a central placenta. *S. coronopifolius* is common on the Irish shores, but rare in Great Britain, except on the southern coasts. [M. J. B.]

SPHÆROCOMA. A dwarf much branched shrub or undershrub, with small opposite linear fleshy leaves, and small flowers in dense clusters, which after flowering become globular heads, hispid with the numerous abortive sepals. It is a native of the deserts about Aden, and forms an exceptional genus of *Caryophyllaceæ*, allied to *Polycarpæa*, but having only two ovules to the ovary, and a single seed in the small utricular fruit.

SPHÆROLOBIUM. A genus of a small group of *Leguminosæ*, exclusively Australian, in which the ten stamens are free, and the minute pods contain but two seeds. It differs from its near allies in the distinctly two-lipped calyx, the upper lip the larger and bifid, the lower three-parted. The species are small bushes, with wiry terete rush-like stems usually devoid of leaves, and abundantly clothed near the apex with small red or yellow pea-flowers. *S. alatum* is exceptional in having winged stems; and *S. vimineum*—cultivated in England—is peculiar to Tasmania and South-eastern Australia, while all the others are natives of Western Australia.   [A. A. B.]

SPHÆROPTERIS. *Peranema.*

SPHÆROSPORE. The quadruple spore of some algals.

SPHÆROSTEMA. A name under which the Asiatic species of *Schizandra* have been distinguished as a genus.

SPHÆROSTEPHANOS. *Mesochlæna.*

SPHÆROSTIGMA. About a dozen species of *Œnothera*, having spherical instead of four-lobed stigmas, have been on this account separated as a distinct genus by some botanists with the above name. The most desirable species is *Œ. bistorta,* a large-flowered variety of which, called *Veitchiana,* is in cultivation. It is a pretty annual, with stems about a foot high, furnished with linear or lance-shaped and sessile sharply-toothed leaves, and axillary solitary bright-yellow flowers about an inch

across. It is a native of California, as are most of the species, and was introduced into England in 1858. The flowers of most of the species are diurnal.   [A. A. B.]

SPHÆROTHALAMUS. Under this name Dr. Hooker has described a new genus of *Anonaceæ,* comprising a shrub, native of Borneo, with lance-shaped nearly sessile leaves, handsome orange-coloured flowers, having three roundish leafy erect sepals, six thick petals in two rows, placed with the numerous stamens on a globular thalamus, and numerous carpels, each with a short style and two ovules. The only species, *S. pulcherrimus,* is stated to be a very handsome plant.   [M. T. M.]

SPHÆROZYGA. A genus of green-spored *Algæ* containing many beautiful microscopical objects, allied to *Oscillatoria,* and distinguished by the free threads, which are not immersed in a dense jelly, as in *Nostoc,* exhibiting at intervals large swollen connecting joints, either solitary or in chains, which are sometimes furnished with cilia; and ultimately contain zoospores. *S. spiralis* is remarkable for its spiral threads, which occur in such quantities as to tinge the water in which they grow of a delicate green. The species occur in various parts of the world, and though many of them affect comparatively high latitudes, they are also abundant in some hot springs, where they are used *en masse* as an application to diseased glands, to which they may possibly do good from containing in minute quantities an alkaline iodide.   [M. J. B.]

SPHAGNEI. A natural order of mosses distinguishable at once by their habit, but technically characterised by their apparent perfectly sessile globose capsule, supported upon the elongated swollen sheath (vaginula), within which is a very short stem, the spore-sac passing over the top of the short columella, their pale tint often changing to lilac, their fasciculate branchlets, the absence of proper roots, and the peculiar structure of the leaves, which consist of large cells with orbicular perforations in their walls, between which runs a spiral thread, and surrounded by narrow elongated cells derived from the stem. The veil does not burst till the lid flies off. When this is ruptured, according to some authorities, a slight but distinct detonation takes place. The female flowers occupy the place of a branch, while the male flowers (which are globose and stalked like those of *Jungermanniaceæ*) are seated at the tips of the branches—not in the axils but at the side of the leaves, as in *Fontinalis.* The branches, moreover, have a similar origin.

Sphagnei are essentially aquatic plants, and though sometimes left dry by the subsiding of the water, they cannot flourish without considerable moisture. Few plants more rapidly form turf-beds, but unless mixed with other plants the turf which arises from them is useless for economical purposes on account of its spongy nature. No plant affords a better material for packing than dry *Sphagnum* on account of its great elasticity, and when slightly moistened it is the best of all substances for enveloping the roots of plants which have a long distance to travel before planting. They afford also a useful material in the cultivation of orchids and some other plants in the conservatory. There is but one genus, *Sphagnum*, which occurs in all parts of the world in temperate climates. The species are difficult of definition, and are probably far less numerous than is supposed. [M. J. B.]

SPHAGNUM. See SPHAGNEÏ.

SPHAIGNÉ. (Fr.) *Sphagnum.*

SPHALEROCARPIUM. A bony oneseeded seed-vessel, inclosed in a fleshy cup, not belonging to the pericarp.

SPHENOCLEA. A genus of bellworts, having the following characters :—The calyx has five deep-keeled lobes; the corolla is shortly tubular, its five divisions with inflexed margins concealing the anthers; the style is very short, ending in two obscure points; and the capsule is two-celled, opening by a lid at the top. The only species is an Indian herb inhabiting marshy places, having alternate narrow and entire leaves, and flowers in close terminal heads. [G. D.]

SPHENOGYNE. A genus of Cape *Compositæ*, some of which form handsome annuals in our flower-gardens. They have an imbricated involucre, the inner scales of which or all have a dilated scarious termination; the receptacle is paleaceous, and the pappus simple in a single row of obovate or wedge-shaped blunt scales, which become opaque-white when mature. The stigmas have a dilated truncate apex. They are herbs or subshrubs, with the aspect of *Anthemis*; and have large spreading rayed flower-heads, of an orange colour barred with black. [T. M.]

SPHENOTOMA. A small genus of *Epacrideæ* distinguished by its calyx of five sepals, with two bracts at the base; its salver-shaped corolla, with a slender tube and beardless limb divided into five obtuse spreading wedge-shaped segments; its included stamens, and its five-celled seedvessel. It comprises shrubs, natives of the southern coast of Australia, having the branches annulated when naked; imbricated sharp-pointed leaves, cucullate and half-sheathing at the base; and white flowers, in simple terminal spikes. [R. H.]

SPHEROIDAL. Any solid with a figure approaching to that of a sphere.

SPHERULA. A globose peridium through whose opening sporidia buried in pulp are emitted.

SPHINCTOLOBIUM. A name given by Vogel to three Brazilian trees of the *Leguminosæ*, with unequally pinnate leaves, and panicles of rose-coloured flowers. These plants are now placed in *Lon-*

chocarpus, of which they have all the characters. [A. A. B.]

SPHONDYLIUM. *Heracleum.*

SPHRIGOSIS. We have already under the article RANKNESS noticed one form of this disease, which may be either constitutional or the effect of over-nutriment. Fruit-trees are not however the only members of the vegetable kingdom which suffer from this evil, which is notorious in many of our cultivated crops, and no less deceptive than injurious. Here, however, over-luxuriance may arise from constitutional defects rather than from injudicious manuring. Those persons who undertake to supply good turnip-seed check the luxuriance of the root by repeated transplanting, as it is found that seed raised from the finest roots produce plants which have a tendency to make a luxuriant head rather than a large and sound root. Where crops are to be consumed in the green state, it is always a question whether increased weight may not be attained at the expense of nutritious quality; and in the case of potatoes, though a large crop of tubers may be obtained, their keeping properties will in proportion be diminished. —a circumstance which may not be of much consequence where an immediate sale is the object, except indeed to the purchaser, but which would prove disastrous where the crop is to be stored.

Fungi seem occasionally to exercise some influence on the apparent luxuriance of a crop by their action on chlorophyll. No crops look better than those of the potato which will ultimately fall a prey to the murrain, and the peculiar green hue of bunted wheat foretells the disease to the practised eye months before the ear bursts through the sheath. The bright green of fairy rings is perhaps due merely to the manure from the fungi of the previous year, but we could quote other instances in which the presence of the spawn of fungi in tissues increases the green tint of the leaves. [M. J. B.]

SPIC. (Fr.) *Lavandula Spica.*

SPICA. See SPIKE.

SPICANARD FAUX. (Fr.) *Allium Victorialis.*

SPICANTA. *Blechnum.*

SPICE-BUSH. *Oreodaphne californica*; also *Benzoin odoriferum.*

SPICEWOOD. A North American name for *Benzoin odoriferum.*

SPICKNEL. *Athamanta.*

SPICULA (adj. SPICULATE). A fine fleshy erect point.

SPICULÆ, or SPICULES. The points of the basidia of fungals; also their aciculæ.

SPICULÆA. A terrestrial genus of orchids, belonging to the tribe *Neotteæ.* The only described species is from Southwestern Australia, and is a small glabrous brown herb, the stems provided with one thick cordate leaf, and the flowers brown numerous, minute and racemose. The scape has one bract about the middle. It differs from *Drakæa* in the claw of the lip not being jointed, and in some other particulars. The flowers are very irritable, and in their outline resemble the body of a spider. [W. B. H.]

SPIDERWORT. *Tradescantia.* — **MOUNTAIN.** *Lloydia serotina.*

SPIELMANNIA *africana*, which is the only known species of a genus of *Verbenaceæ*, is a Cape shrub with opposite slightly hairy leaves, from the axils of which arise singly sessile white flowers. The distinguishing characteristics of the genus are to be sought in the calyx, which is split into five linear segments; while the salver-shaped corolla has a nearly regular limb, the throat or aperture of which is closed with fine hairs. There are two ovules in each of the two cavities of the ovary; the style is short, surmounted by a hooked stigma; and the fruit when ripe forms a kind of drupe. [M. T. M.]

SPIGELIA. A well-known genus of *Loganiaceæ*, readily known among the others by the style being jointed above the base, and especially by the two-lobed capsular fruits, which when ripe open at the apex and fall away, leaving their cup-shaped hardened base attached to the calyx.

There are about thirty known species, natives of tropical or subtropical America, annual or perennial herbs, with opposite or whorled ovate or lance-shaped leaves, and purple or blue flowers (with funnel-shaped corollas) arranged in terminal one-sided spikes. The Pink-root, Worm-grass, or Indian-pink of the shops is the produce of *S. marilandica*, a native of the Southern States of America, a herb of from six to eighteen inches high, with perennial fibrous roots, rather large ovate leaves, and beautiful carmine funnel-shaped corollas contracted at the apex, and not unlike those of the scarlet honeysuckle. Both roots and leaves of this and of *S. Anthelmia*, a common South American weed, 'are active anthelmintics, but their efficacy is much impaired by keeping. They are also purgative and slightly narcotic, and are apt to produce very unpleasant symptoms after being exhibited: dimness of sight, giddiness, dilated pupil, spasms of the muscles of the eye, and even convulsions are reported by Barton to have been brought on by them. *S. glabrata* is reckoned by Martius among poisons; and Mr. Hartweg reports that a species of the same genus kills dogs in Equatorial America.' (*Lindl. Veg. Kingd.*) The Pink-root and some of the other species have been in cultivation; but being difficult to keep, they are not often seen in gardens, though extremely pretty plants. The genus is named after Dr. Spigelius, a surgeon and anatomist of Brussels, who died at Padua in A.D. 1625. [A. A. B.]

SPIGNEL. *Meum Athamanticum.*

SPIKE, SPICA. An inflorescence consisting of flowers sessile on a long axis. A *compound spike* is a collection of spikes arranged in a racemose manner.

SPIKELET. The small terminal collection of florets among grasses. The same as Locusta.

SPIKENARD. *Nardostachys Jatamansi*; also *Valeriana celtica.* — of Crete. *Valeriana Phu.* —, AMERICAN. *Aralia racemosa.* —, FALSE. *Aralia nudicaulis*; also *Smilacina racemosa.* — PLOUGHMAN'S. *Baccharis*; also *Conyza squarrosa.* —, SMALL, or WILD. *Aralia nudicaulis.* —, WEST INDIAN. *Hyptis suaveolens.*

SPIKENEL, or **SPICKNEL.** *Meum Athamanticum.*

SPIKE-RUSH. *Eleocharis.*

SPILANTHES. Of this genus of *Compositæ* upwards of forty species are enumerated, natives of the tropics of both hemispheres, mostly smooth annual branching weeds, with opposite lance-shaped or ovate leaves, and stalked terminal solitary yellow flower-heads, with or without short strap-shaped ray-florets. The latter when present are pistil-bearing, the others tubular and perfect. Achenes of the disk compressed without pappus, those of the ray with two short awns; receptacle conical and chaffy; involucre of two series of scales, the outer foliaceous. The leaves of many of the species have a singularly pungent taste, which is especially noticeable in the Pará Cress, *S. oleracea.* This plant is cultivated as a salad and potherb in tropical countries, and like many cultivated plants its native country is uncertain. It is a smooth erect branching annual, about a foot high, with stalked elliptical or heart-shaped blades, and inconspicuous yellow flower-heads, solitary at the ends of the branches. The Japanese call the plant Hoko So. [A. A. B.]

SPILOCÆA. A spurious genus of *Fungi*, arising from the obscure growth of certain species of *Cladosporium*, which is worthy of notice here, because the greater part of the round black patches which are common upon apples, and take so much from their market value, are referable to this genus. The fungus which produces these spots, or a closely-allied species, is common also on pears and pear-trees, and is extremely mischievous. Unfortunately, its attacks are so insidious as to give very little hope of remedy. The same measures which are so efficacious against the white mildew of peaches and vines seem useless here. [M. J. B.]

SPINACH, or **SPINAGE.** *Spinacia oleracea*, the leaves of which are a common and esteemed potherb. —, NEW ZEALAND. *Tetragonia expansa.* —, PRICKLY, and ROUND. Garden varieties of *Spinacia oleracea.* —, STRAWBERRY. *Blitum capitatum.*

SPINACIA. A genus of *Chenopodiaceæ*, composed almost entirely of uninteresting weedy-looking plants, with small flowers of no beauty. Of this genus, which is bisexual, the male flowers being borne on one plant and the female flowers on another, there is only one species, the *S. oleracea*, well known as a favourite pot-herb during the early spring and summer months.

The Common Spinach is a hardy annual whose native country is unknown, though generally supposed to be Western Asia. It has been cultivated in this country for more than 300 years, and is noticed in Turner's *Herbal* of 1568 as 'an herb lately found,' and not much in use.' The plant has large thick succulent deep-green leaves, of a somewhat triangular form, produced on long footstalks. The stem is erect large round and hollow, about two feet high. The male plants are distinguished by their green uninteresting flowers, growing in long terminal spikes; while those of the females are axillary sessile and clustered. The seeds are prickly in some varieties, and smooth in others.

Spinach is solely cultivated for its large fleshy leaves, which, although rather insipid, are considered wholesome; and when properly dressed, and thoroughly deprived of all moisture before being mashed with butter or rich gravy and a few sorrel leaves, they make an excellent dish, which may be eaten with any kind of meat. It is a singular fact that the water drained from Spinach after being boiled is capable of making as good match-paper as that made by a solution of nitre. [W. B. B.]

SPINDLE-SHAPED. The same as Fusiform.

SPINDLE-TREE. *Euonymus europæus.*

SPINE. A stiff sharp-pointed body, consisting of woody tissue covered with cellular tissue. A hardened leafstalk, stipule, abortive branch, or any other process into the composition of which woody tissue enters. *Spines of the leaves* are the hardened extremities of lobes, or in some cases superficial spiny elevations.

SPINESCENS, SPINIGER, SPINOSUS. Covered with spines.

SPINIFEX. A genus of grasses belonging to the tribe *Paniceæ*, and having the heads or bundles of inflorescence terminal and axillary, with the male and fruiting plants distinct: glumes thin and membranaceous, seven to nine-nerved, those of the male plant unequal, the inner the shortest, those of the fruiting plant equal and acuminate; flowers two, sessile; anthers three; lowest flower neuter, upper hermaphrodite. The few species belonging to this small genus are mostly natives of New Holland. [D. M.]

SPINKS. *Cardamine pratensis.*

SPINOSO-DENTATE. Having teeth tipped with spines.

SPINULOSO-CILIATE. Ciliated with fine spines.

SPIRÆA. An extensive genus of shrubby or herbaceous plants belonging to the tribe *Spiræidæ* of rosaceous plants, and thus characterised :—Petals five ; seed-vessels oblong, opening at the side (follicles), and containing one to six seeds suspended from the inner edges of the follicle. The best-known British species is *S. Ulmaria*, the Meadow-sweet, or Queen of the Meadows, an herbaceous plant with pinnate leaves having a large terminal lobe, erect slender rigid stems about two feet high, and terminal dense corymbs of white highly fragrant flowers. It is common near watercourses and in damp meadows. *S. Filipendula*, or Dropwort, also a British species, is a plant of similar habit; but the leaves are pinnate, with all the leaflets jagged and deeply serrated. The white scentless flowers while in bud are tinged with crimson externally. This species grows in dry pastures and on heaths ; a pretty variety of it with double flowers is frequent in gardens. *S. salicifolia*, a shrub with terminal compound clusters of dull rose-coloured flowers, is found in woody places in Scotland and the North of England, and in some parts of North Wales is very abundant.

Of the foreign shrubby kinds of *Spiræa* some are very handsome : for example, *S. prunifolia*, with double flowers, a native of Japan, a beautiful shrub, with leaves like those of the plum, silky beneath, and pure white flowers ; *S. hypericifolia* and *S. chamædrifolia*, with white flowers; *S. bella* from Nepal, with rose-coloured flowers growing in lateral and terminal corymbs ; *S. tomentosa* from Canada, with cottony leaves and pyramidal panicles of rose-coloured flowers ; *S. Fortunei* from China, with ovate smooth toothed leaves, often tinged with purple, and rose-coloured flowers—and many others. Some are valued from the rapidity of their growth, and others for their remaining in flower during many months. French : *Reine des prés* ; German : *Wiesenkönigen.* [C. A. J.]

SPIRÆANTHEMUM. A genus referred to *Saxifragaceæ* by A. Gray, comprising Polynesian plants, with opposite or verticillate leaves, interpetiolar deciduous stipules, and small paniculate perfect or polygamo-diœcious flowers. The calyx is eight or five-cleft ; petals nine ; stamens four or ten : follicles four or five, compressed dehiscent, one or two-seeded. [J. T. S.]

SPIRALTHREAD. *Spironema.*

SPIRANTHES. A terrestrial genus of orchids forming the type of a tribe called the *Spiranthideæ*, consisting of about fifty species, for the most part inhabitants of the New World. One species, *S. australis*, is common to Australia, New Zealand, and tropical and subtropical Asia. They are herbs with tuberous or thick fibrous roots, numerous linear grass-like leaves growing from the root and stem (occasionally wanting, or represented by small brown scales), and small flowers in a spirally-twisted spike, by which the genus is easily recognised. The name is derived from *speira* a 'spiral' and *anthos* a 'flower,' in allusion to the spiral arrangement of the flowers. The tuberous roots of *S. autumnalis* were formerly esteemed as an aphrodisiac. *S. uretica* is administered in Chili in cases of ischury. Three species are found in the British Isles.   [W. B. H.]

SPIRÉE. (Fr.) *Spiræa.*

SPIRES. *Phragmites communis*; also applied to Rushes and Sedges.

SPIRIDENS. A genus of mosses remarkable both as regards size and structure. The peristome is double, the outer composed of sixteen long teeth, which when free curl up from within into a spiral, while the inner consists of a membrane divided into as many cilia, in part free, in part combined above. The capsule is lateral and unequal. Though the genus is pleurocarpous, it has rather the habit of a gigantic *Bartramia* than of a *Hypnum*. *S. Reinwardtii* occurs in Java, Tahiti, and the Philippine Isles, attaining a length of more than a foot. It belongs to a small natural order, *Cryptothecei*, distinguished by the cylindrical stem, imbricated leaves, and nitriform veil. The order is represented in this country by *Cryphæa heteromalla*, which is common on trees, and by the rare *Daltonia splachnoides*, which has not been found out of Ireland. A species of *Dendropogon*, which belongs to the same order, hangs down in great masses from trees in Mexico, and is an admirable substance for packing.   [M. J. B.]

SPIRIT-LEAF, or **SPIRIT-WEED.** *Ruellia tuberosa*, now called *Cryphiacanthus barbadensis.*

SPIROCHÆTA. A genus of *Compositæ*, comprising an annual herb of Columbia. The stem is decumbent; the involucre is of two rows of bracts; the flowers equal, each with a slender tube, dilated above into a five-cleft throat; and the style divided into two linear awl-shaped branches. Fruits multicostate, oblong, covered with glandular hairs; pappus in one row, consisting of four smooth hairs twisted spirally at the points, whence the name of the genus.   [M. T. M.]

SPIRODELA differs from *Lemna* in the presence of spiral vessels in all its parts, as well as in some points of less cardinal importance. The genus is represented in this country by the Greater Duckweed, *S. polyrhiza*, the largest of our British species. Its fronds are roundish fleshy, nearly half an inch in length, green above, purple below, the roots numerous and clustered. The flowers are very rarely observed, and the fruit is unknown.   [M. T. M.]

SPIROLOBEÆ. One of the divisions of the *Cruciferæ*, distinguished by having the cotyledons incumbent and spirally twisted.

SPIRONEMA. A genus of *Commelyna-*

ceæ, established by Lindley for a Mexican plant, more curious than handsome, with large oblong-lanceolate acute radical leaves, and erect leafless almost rush-like flowering stems, having the small fragrant flowers clustered along its rigid branches, in the axils of chaffy scales. The three rigid sepals and three extremely delicate petals are the same as in many other *Commelynaceæ*, but the structure of the stamens is peculiar: the very slender filaments contain spirally-twisted bundles of vessels, and the anthers are placed transversely at the base of a large delicate heart-shaped connective.

SPIROSTACHYS. A South African tree constituting a genus of *Euphorbiaceæ*. The leaves are entire stalked smooth; the flowers monœcious; the males in crowded catkins, with spirally arranged bracts, their calyx enclosed within the bract; and the females solitary at the base of the male catkin, or in pairs, with a three-celled ovary, and thick style supporting three thick recurved stigmas. The generic name is given in allusion to the spirally arranged bracts of the catkin.   [M. T. M.]

SPITHAMA (adj. SPITHAMÆUS). Seven inches, or the space between the tip of the thumb and the forefinger separated as widely as possible.

SPIXIA. A genus of Brazilian trees of the family *Euphorbiaceæ*. The leaves are large and leathery; the flowers are axillary diœcious, surrounded by an involucre of somewhat globular form, studded by star-shaped hairs; the calyx is small, two to three-parted; stamens two to three, longer than the calyx, surrounding four rudimentary ovaries. In the female flowers there is a two-leaved calyx surrounding an oblong hairy three-celled ovary; stigma entire; fruit capsular.   [M. T. M.]

SPLACHNEI. A natural order of acrocarpous mosses, characterised by a straight capsule with a well-marked and often large swelling (apophysis) at the base, diaphanous large-celled leaves, the spores radiating in lines from the columella, and the plants growing on decayed wood or the dung of animals. They are amongst the most remarkable of mosses, especially those which occur in the Northern Hemisphere. The peristome is generally well-marked, and in *Tayloria splachnoides* the teeth are remarkably long, and singularly curled after the lid has fallen. In *Œdipodium*, however, there is no peristome. It is singular that the species of the Northern Hemisphere grow on dung, while those of the Southern Hemisphere (with one exception) only occur on decayed wood.   [M. J. B.]

SPLACHNUM. A beautiful genus of mosses remarkable for the immense development of the apophysis in several species, which gives them a very striking appearance. In *S. rubrum* and *luteum* (the former of which is European, and the latter extends to America) it is shaped like an umbrella, and is of a red or yellowish hue; while in *S. vasculorum*, which occurs in the

Scottish Highlands, it is rugged, and of a deep purple. In *S. Gunnii*, a fine Tasmanian species, it resembles a Turk's-cap gourd; while in *S. ampullaceum*, which occurs in marshy places on a level with the sea or on the dung of animals, it is pitcher-shaped, and of a reddish or golden-yellow colour. The swelling is hollow, the central portion (a continuation of the axis) being connected with the outer by delicate threads. Several genera have been separated from it, but most of them rest on insufficient grounds. French : *Splanc.*   [M. J. B.]

SPLEENWORT. *Asplenium.*

SPLENDENS. The same as polished, but having the lustre a little broken from slight irregularity of surface.

SPLITGERBERA. A Japanese shrub forming a genus of *Urticaceæ*. The leaves are opposite or in threes, entire or two-lobed, membranous; and the flowers in axillary spikes, with four-leaved unequal involucre; perianth of the male flowers four-parted, with four stamens opposite its segments; filaments flattened petaloid, at first infolded, afterwards spreading. The female flowers are placed above the males in the upper part of the stem; they have an ovate perianth closely applied to the ovary, and nearly adnate to it. The ovary is one-celled, with a single ovule, and a cylindrical style terminated by an elongated hairy stigma.   [M. T. M.]

SPODO. In Greek compounds = ash-grey.

SPONDIACEÆ, or SPONDIEÆ. A tribe of *Anacardiaceæ*, considered by some botanists as a distinct order, but only differing from the other tribes by the ovary being completely two to five-celled instead of being reduced by abortion to a single cell. Besides *Spondias* itself, it only includes nine species distributed into six genera.

SPONDIAS. By some authors this genus is considered as the type of a distinct natural order, while others refer it to *Anacardiaceæ*. The points of distinction are to be sought in the alternate dotless leaves, and in the cup-like disk surrounding the five distinct carpels, each of which contains a single pendulous seed.

The species are natives of the tropics of both hemispheres, and the fruits of some of them are edible. Thus in Brazil and the West Indies, *S. lutea, S. Mombin, S. tuberosa*, &c. yield fruits eaten under the name of Hog Plum, the taste of which is said to be peculiar, and not agreeable to strangers. These fruits are chiefly used to fatten swine. *S. dulcis*, a native of the Society Isles, yields a fruit compared in flavour to that of the pine-apple. *S. mangifera* yields a yellowish-green fruit, which is eaten in India, and is used as a pickle in the unripe state.

Some of the species are employed medicinally. Thus the bark leaves and wood of *S. mangifera* are used in various complaints in India. An insipid gum also

exudes from the bark of this tree. *S. Mombin* has astringent leaves, while its fruits are laxative, and its seeds are said to be poisonous. The bark of *S. venulosa* has aromatic astringent properties. *S. tuberosa* is also employed in fevers; the fruit is the part used. *S. Birrea* affords to the natives of Abyssinia an edible kernel, while its fruits are employed in Senegal in the preparation of an alcoholic drink.

The flower-buds of *S. Mombin* are used as a sweetmeat with sugar. One or two species are in cultivation in this country. The generic name is said to be derived from the Greek name for a kind of plum; it may also be derived from *sponde* ' a cup,' in allusion to the peculiar cup-like disk in the flowers.   [M. T. M.]

SPONÉE. (Fr.) *Spergula.*

SPONGELET, SPONGIOLE. The young tender extremity of a root, by which fluid food is absorbed from the earth.

SPONGE-TREE. *Acacia Farnesiana.*

SPONGEWOOD. *Æschynomene aspera.*

SPONGIOCARPEÆ. A natural order of rose-spored *Algæ*, consisting of a solitary genus, POLYIDES : which see. [M. J. B.]

SPONGY. Having the texture of a sponge, that is to say, very cellular, with the cellules filled with air : as the coats of many seeds.

SPONTANEOUS GENERATION. In the days of Aristotle, and to a late date in the last century, the notion that corruption is the source of life was almost universal, and it is a common popular opinion even in the present day. In the scientific world indeed, except amongst a few philosophers of the German school, the opinion has been all but exploded, that organised beings can arise without pre-existent germs. It has, however, of late been revived by Pouchet and others in France; and if their facts could be implicitly depended upon, the doctrine would certainly be in a condition less exposed to doubt than it has of late been considered. Its opponents, however, in France—amongst whom may be reckoned men of no mean pretensions, as Payen, Quatrefages, Bernard, and Dumas—have met the subject with counter-statements which appear quite irresistible.

Wherever due attention has been paid to prevent the possibility of access of atmospheric air, no vegetation has ever appeared, provided proper precautions have been taken to place all possibly pre-existent germs in such a condition that their reproductive powers must be destroyed. If the residue of rain or snow-flakes or the dust of tradewinds is carefully examined, numerous animal and vegetable productions may always be detected; and the lower forms of either kingdom are propagated with such extreme rapidity, that the swarming of animals or vegetables in infusions seems almost magical. Some of these will bear a heat equal or even much superior to that of boiling-water for some time without losing their vitality.; therefore the simple boiling of water is not sufficient, even should care be taken to exclude the outward air, or to prevent its containing reproductive germs by passing it through a furnace. Concentrated sulphuric acid has sometimes been used for the same purpose, but this plan is subject to error, as, whatever may be the case with germs which may be present on the outside of a bubble passing through the acid, it does not follow that those in the middle of the bubble should be killed. The existence of intestinal worms even in infants in the womb, and that in situations in which it seemed impossible that there could be any access from without, was once regarded as decisive on the question; but the discoveries of Van Beneden and others have set this at rest, except with the sworn advocates of Heterogenesis, who deny their doctrine with a sneer at their small pretensions to credit, inasmuch as they are not Frenchmen. No observations, indeed, require greater caution and nicety than those which are requisite to establish or disprove the doctrine, and there is no subject which has less excuse for anything like dogmatism. In trustworthy hands the proof of Heterogenesis has always failed, and true philosophy will not readily adopt a theory which is *à priori* opposed by such a multitude of facts.

A parting observation may be offered respecting organisable lymph in animals, or protoplasm in plants. Undoubtedly new living cells and structures seem to be generated in such substances without any immediate connection with the contiguous tissues. It must, however, be remembered that such matters can only generate new tissues or organs when still endowed with life and in contact with living tissues. The serum of blood, for instance, when removed from its fountain (though kept at the proper temperature), will never generate blood-globules, and other similar examples might be adduced.   [M. J. B.]

SPOONWORT. *Cochlearia officinalis.*

SPORANGIOLUM. A case containing sporidia.

SPORANGIOPHORUM. The axis or columella on which are borne the spore-cases of some ferns.

SPORANGIUM. A word used in cryptogams to denote the case in which the spores are formed. In ferns it is applied to the little cysts with their elastic ring; in pseudoferns to the organs immediately containing the spores, whether naked or contained in a common receptacle; in mosses to the urn-shaped bodies which are often called capsules and thecæ. Amongst algæ lichens and fungi it is seldom used in a general sense. In the latter it is sometimes applied to asci when large and pear-shaped as in truffles, to the spore-bearing vesicles of moulds, or to the lens-shaped bodies contained in the receptacles of plants like *Nidularia*, though they are certainly not of the same nature as (or in scientific language homologous with) the organs just mentioned.   [M. J. B.]

SPORE. As the reproductive bodies of cryptogams do not contain an embryo, but are merely cellular, consisting of one or more cells variously combined together, they are called spores to distinguish them from true seeds. Amongst *Fungi* the name is restricted to those reproductive bodies which are produced either singly, or in little chains at the tips of the fruit-bearing threads. In many cases, however, these bodies are generated within cells or asci, and they are then for distinction's sake termed sporidia. It is however desirable that the word spore should be used in the more general sense as opposed to seed, the grand distinction between cryptogams and phænogams consisting in the different nature of their mode of reproduction. The spores of acrogens are produced mostly in mother-cells four together, after the manner of pollen-grains —often however retaining their original form, so that when mature they have one spherical and three plain sides. In a few genera, however, there is only a single spore in each sporangium. In *Algæ* the spores are sometimes, as in *Desmiospermeæ*, nothing more than the transformed joints of certain threads; sometimes they appear, as in most if not all *Gongylospermeæ*, to be formed from the contents of a cell, as in the ascigerous *Fungi*, sometimes they are endowed with active motion like animals, and are then called Zoospores. In lichens they are of the same nature as the sporidia of *Fungi*. The word sporules is sometimes used generally in the sense of spores, sometimes to denote distinct granules within spores. These are occasionally called sporidiola.

Spores germinate either by elongation of some particular part, and subsequent cell-division, or by cell-division without any protrusion of a thread or membranous expansion. In *Myxogastres* they germinate sometimes after the fashion of other *Fungi*, but sometimes the outer case is ruptured, and a body appears with the attributes of some of the lower *Infusoria*, which, apparently without any cellular division, produces the semigelatinous mycelium peculiar to those *Fungi*. [M. J. B.]

SPORE-CASE. The immediate covering of the spores of cryptogams.

SPORENDONEMA. A genus of *Fungi* proposed at first on erroneous characters, of which one supposed species, which forms scarlet masses on decayed cheese, differs from *Torula* only in its bright colour. *S. Muscæ* occurs in flies in autumn, oozing out between the rings of the abdomen, and at length killing them. The species requires further study, and will probably be traced to some higher stage of development. The flies which are attacked by it before death fasten themselves by their proboscis to leaves or other substances, where they remain attached for some time. *See* SAPROLEGNIÆ. [M. J. B.]

SPORIDESMIUM. An obscure genus of naked-spored *Fungi* (*Coniomycetes*), consisting of a multitude of species forming conspicuous black soot-like patches on rails, decayed wood, &c. Many of them are probably merely conditions of *Fungi* and lichens. There is scarcely any mycelium, and the whole plant consists of nothing more than cellular spores of various shapes. The genus is worthy of notice, here only as explaining the origin of the above-mentioned patches, which must attract every eye the least attentive, and whose nature it may be desirable to ascertain. [M. J. B.]

SPORIDIA. A name given to the spores of *Fungi* and lichens when they are contained in asci. Sporidia like spores may consist of one or more cells, and these may be covered with a distinctly organised cuticle as in many truffles. They have frequently a thick gelatinous coat, which is usually absorbed as the contents of the cells become fully organised. They germinate by the protrusion of the inner membrane, the outer being ruptured or perforated, or in some cases by the elongation of both. In compound sporidia a distinct germinating thread is often produced by each cell. Sporidia often contain one or more oil-globules, and occasionally distinct cytoblasts, which are sometimes confounded with the oil-globules. Like other organs they are subject to disease, and may be either wholly effete, or so distorted and altered in chemical composition as to be incapable of germination. It is a mistake to suppose that they are constant in size and form. Great differences of dimensions and outline may exist in the same ascus. Microscopical measurements are therefore valuable only within certain limits, and the same may be said of form. Sporidia have sometimes a very different outline when seen from the back or side; and in some cases, like the spores of so many agarics, they are hollowed out on one side like the seed of a *Veronica* or a fragment of a bombshell. In many cases the ascus in which they were generated is absorbed, so that they appear naked; and it is probable that occasionally they undergo further development when free, as is certainly the case with some spores or protospores of *Fungi*. [M. J. B.]

SPORIDIIFEROUS. Bearing sporidia.

SPORIDIOLA. The spores or sporules of thallogens and acrogens.

SPOROBOLUS. A genus of grasses belonging to the tribe *Agrostideæ*, the species of which are now placed in *Vilfa*, &c. by Steudel. [D. M.]

SPOROCARP. The involucre of pepperworts: the spore-cases of lycopods; any spore case.

SPOROCLADIUM. A branch on which

the reproductive bodies of some algals are found.

SPOROCYST. The spore-case of algals.

SPORODERM. The skin of a spore.

SPOROPHORE. A name given to the fertile cells in the naked-spored *Fungi*, and synonymous with the basidia of French authors. In such *Fungi* as agarics the sporophores are clavate or swollen above, and bear generally four little points called spicules, or by the French sterigmata, on which the spores are seated. In *Tremella* the sporophores are globular or quadripartite, the spicules being drawn out into long threads. In *Coniomycetes* they are often very short and obtuse, or thread-shaped, and occasionally branched. [M. J. B.]

SPOROPHYLLA. A name given to the little leaflets which, as in *Plocamium*, bear the tetraspores. [M. J. B.]

SPORULE. *See* SPORE.

SPRAGUEA. A Californian herb forming a genus of *Portulaceæ* allied to *Claytonia*, but differing in the petals being reduced to four, the stamens to three, and the styles and valves of the capsule to two, and by the remarkable large orbicular cordate thin and transparent sepals. The leaves are all radical, and somewhat succulent; the flowers are densely imbricate in spikes, several of which form a dense umbel on a leafless scape, the large sepals giving it an elegant and singular aspect.

SPREADING. Having a gradually outward direction, as petals from the ovary.

SPREKELIA. The genus of the Jacobean Lily, *S. formosissima*, and one or two other species. It is remarkable for its declinate perianth, with scarcely any tube, and a limb of which the upper segments are reflexed, and the lower sloped downwards and convolute at the base. The filaments are inserted equally with a connecting membrane, and are fasciculate declinate and recurved like the style; the leaves are linear-lorate, produced after the flowers, and the scape somewhat two-edged hollow and one-flowered. [T. M.]

SPRENGELIA. A small genus of *Epacrideæ*, natives of South and Eastern Australia and Tasmania, distinguished by having a five-parted slightly-coloured calyx, surrounded by numerous bracts; a five-parted beardless corolla; stamens free, the anthers occasionally united; and the seed-vessel five-celled. They are upright branching shrubs; the leaves sharp-pointed cucullate and half-sheathing at the base; and the flowers terminal, on short lateral branchlets. [R. H.]

SPRING-BEAUTY. An American name for the *Claytonias*.

SPRINGERS. A local name applied to the variety of *Agaricus arvensis* figured by Bulliard, and distinguished by its elongated pileus, tall stem, and thinner ring.

They grow in very large rings, and sometimes (as in 1860) occur in thousands, yielding excellent buttons for pickling where it is not thought essential to retain a pale colour, as in the buttons of *A. campestris*. This, however, is next to impossible, as the plant when bruised at once turns yellow, and unless thrown at once into water acquires soon a brown tint which is indelible. When full-grown they are very good for stewing, though not so delicate in flavour as the true mushroom, neither do they yield such good ketchup as that species. [M. J. B.]

SPRIT *Juncus articulatus*.

SPRUCE. *Abies*. *A. nigra* is the Black Spruce, *A. alba* White Spruce, and *A. rubra* Red Spruce. —, HEMLOCK. *Abies canadensis*. —, NORWAY. *Abies excelsa*.

SPRUCE. A fermented liquor made from molasses or treacle, and a decoction of the twigs of the Spruce Fir.

SPRUCEA. A handsome tall bushy shrub discovered by Mr. Spruce on the shores of the Amazon near the mouth of the Rio Negro, and named after him as a genus of *Cinchonaceæ*. The flowers, of a yellowish cream-colour and with a fine scent of *Vanilla*, are in dense terminal corymbs. The almost globular tube of the corolla with minute broad lobes, and the long projecting stamens, distinguish it from all allied genera; the two-celled ovary, with numerous imbricate ovules, and the evidently capsular fruit, show that it belongs either to the tribe *Cinchoneæ* or to that of *Rondeletieæ*, but the ripe seeds being as yet unknown it cannot at present be determined to which of these groups it should be referred.

SPUMARIA. One of the most conspicuous genera of the semigelatinous puffballs, occurring in the form of frothy and at length lobed masses, white without and dusty within, on the stems of grasses, amongst dead leaves, &c. The peridia are at length completely confluent. There is no beauty to recommend the two or three species of the genus. [M. J. B.]

SPUNK. *Polyporus igniarius*.

SPUR. A hollow terete extension of some part of the flower. The same as Calcar.

SPURGE. *Euphorbia*. —, BRANCHED. *Ernodea littoralis*. —, CAPER. *Euphorbia Lathyris*. —, CYPRESS. *Euphorbia Cyparissias*. —, PETTY. *Euphorbia Peplus*. —, SUN. *Euphorbia helioscopia*.

SPURGEWORTS. Lindley's name for the *Euphorbiaceæ*.

SPURRY. *Spergula*. —, CORN. *Spergula arvensis*. —, KNOTTED. *Sagina nodosa*. —, SAND. *Spergularia*.

SPUR-TREE. *Petitia domingensis*.

SPURWORT. *Sherardia arvensis*.

SPYRIDIUM. A genus of *Rhamnaceæ*, comprising a considerable number of Australian species very nearly allied to *Trymalium* and to *Cryptandra*, and many of them have been described under one or other or both of these genera. They agree also with both genera in their more or less inferior three-celled ovary, and in their capsule enclosing three membranous or crustaceous cocci; but differ from *Trymalium* chiefly in their flowers being closely sessile in little heads, surrounded by small brown bracts; and from *Cryptandra* in their stamens being inserted immediately round the disk, not adnate to the calyx-tube above the disk. They are all small procumbent or heath-like shrubs, more or less hoary with a close tomentum, with small entire leaves, and very small flowers, the heads usually collected into axillary or terminal cymes or compound heads. Few, if any, out of nearly thirty species known, are likely to be ornamental enough for cultivation.

SQUAMA. A scale-like rudimentary leaf, such as coats and guards the leaf-bud.

SQUAMATE. Covered with small scale-like leaves.

SQUAMATIO. A disease, consisting in a preternatural formation of rosettes of scale-shaped leaves, such as occasionally appears on the rose-willow.

SQUAMELLA. A scale-like membranous bract, such as is found very commonly on the receptacle of composites.

SQUAMOSE. Scale-like.

SQUAMULÆ. The hypogynous scales of grasses.

SQUARROSE. Covered with bodies which spread at right angles, or at a greater angle, from the surface which bears them, or being so arranged.

SQUARROSO-DENTATE. Having teeth which do not lie in the plane of the leaf, but form an angle with it.

SQUARROSO-LACINIATE. Lacerated in a squarrose way.

SQUARROSO-PINNATIPARTITE. Deeply pinnatifid with squarrose divisions, as the leaf of *Achillea Millefolium*.

SQUARROSO-PINNATISECT. Pinnatifid, with the segments so straggling as to appear on different planes.

SQUASH. A variety of *Cucurbita Melopepo*. —, LONG. An American name for *Cucumis verrucosa*.

SQUAW-ROOT. *Conopholis*.

SQUAW-WEED. *Senecio aureus*.

SQUILL. *Urginea maritima*; also the genus *Scilla*. —, CHINESE. *Barnardia*. —, ROMAN. *Bellevalia*.

SQUILLE. (Fr.) *Urginea maritima*.

SQUINANCY-BERRY. *Ribes nigrum*.

SQUINANCYWORT. *Asperula cynanchica*.

SQUINE. (Fr.) *Smilax China.*

SQUIRREL-CORN. An American name for *Dicentra canadensis.*

SQUIRREL-TAIL. *Hordeum maritimum.*

SQUITCH. *Triticum repens;* also *Agrostis stolonifera.*

SRIGUNDA. An Indian name for Sandal-wood.

STAAVIA. A genus of *Bruniaceæ,* distinguished by the corolla being of five lanceolate petals, thick and fleshy below; and the seed-vessel half-inferior and two-horned. The species are Cape shrubs, with linear leaves hard at the end; and flowers intermixed with chaffy scales, arranged in heads with numerous white bracts. The genus was named after Martin Staaf, a correspondent of Linnæus.　　　[G. D.]

STACHIDE. (Fr.) *Stachys.*

STACHYANTHUS. A genus of *Compositæ,* comprising a Brazilian herbaceous plant of somewhat shrubby habit, covered with closely-pressed white hairs, and having partially-toothed leaves, globular flower-heads surrounded by an involucre of oblong scales; the achenes hairy, surmounted by a pappus of many rows of hairs, the outer ones shorter than the inner.　　　[M. T. M.]

STACHYS. In Greek compounds = a spike.

STACHYS. The generic name of plants belonging to the order *Labiatæ,* and distinguished from their congeners by the following characters:—The calyx is somewhat bell-shaped, with five nearly equal teeth; the tube of the corolla is about as long as the calyx, its upper lip arched and entire, the lower three-lobed, the two lateral lobes bent down; and the two anterior stamens are longest. The species are herbs shrubs or undershrubs, widely distributed, and varying greatly in habit. The flowers are two or more in a whorl, usually in terminal masses. The name is from *stachys,* the Greek for 'spike,' in allusion to the aspect of the inflorescence.　　[G. D.]

STACHYTARPHA, or STACHYTARPHETA. A genus of *Verbenaceæ,* generally considered as a section of *Verbena.* It differs from the true *Verbenas* in having a two-celled fruit, splitting into two seed-like nutlets, and having the two upper stamens without anthers. The species are aromatic herbs or shrubs, natives for the most part of tropical or subtropical America. The flowers are densely packed upon somewhat fleshy spikes. *S. jamaicensis* is possessed of remarkable medicinal virtues according to the Brazilians; its leaves are sometimes used to adulterate tea, and in Austria they are sold under the name of Brazilian tea.　　　[W. O.]

STACKHOUSIA, STACKHOUSIACEÆ. A genus of polypetalous dicotyledons allied to *Celastraceæ,* but differing in so many points that it is universally adopted as a distinct order. It consists of about twenty species, all Australian excepting two, one from New Zealand, the other from the Philippine Islands. They are all herbs, with a perennial often woody stock, and simple or little branched erect stems; the leaves are alternate narrow or small, the flowers white or yellow in a terminal raceme. The calyx is small five-lobed, the tube lined with the disk, on which the stamens are inserted alternately with the petals as in *Celastraceæ;* but the petals are more or less combined in a tubular corolla, the stamens are unequal, and the ovary and fruit are divided into two to five (usually three) lobes or cocci, all which characters are as different from those of *Celastraceæ* as is the habit. None of the species present any interest beyond their botanical structure. The genera *Tripterococcus* and *Plokiostigma,* proposed to be separated from *Stackhousia,* have not been generally adopted.

STÆHELINA. A genus of *Compositæ,* so named in honour of a Swiss physician and botanist. The species are shrubs, natives of the Mediterranean regions, with narrow leaves, downy on the under-surface, and terminal flower-heads, surrounded by a cylindrical involucre of overlapping scales; receptacle flat, scaly; corollas all tubular, five-cleft; style tumid, and hairy at its upper part; achenes oblong, surmounted by a pappus of one row of hairs, combined at the base into four or six bundles.　　　[M. T. M.]

STAFF-TREE. *Celastrus.*

STAGGER-BUSH. *Lyonia mariana.*

STAGGERWORT. *Senecio Jacobæa.*

STAG'S-HORN. *Rhus typhina;* also *Cenomyce cervicornis,* and *Lycopodium clavatum.*

STALK. The stem or support to an organ; as the petiole of a leaf, the peduncle or pedicel of a flower, &c.

STALKLESS. See SESSILE.

STALKLETS. Secondary petioles; petiolules; the stalks of leaflets.

STAMEN. That organ of the flower to which the pollen belongs. —, STERILE. A body belonging to the series of the stamens, but without pollen.

STAMINAL. Consisting of stamens.

STAMINIDIA. The antheridia of cryptogamic plants.

STAMINIGEROUS. Bearing stamens.

STAMINODE, STAMINODIUM. A rudimentary stamen, or what appears to be so.

STANDARD. The fifth petal of a papilionaceous flower.

STANDERWORT. *Orchis mascula.*

STANE-RAW, or STANEY-RAG. A name of the *omphalodes* variety of *Parmelia saxatilis,* which is also called Black

Orottles. It is employed by the Highland peasants to prepare a brown dye which is much used for domestic purposes. Both the dye and the lichen are called by the Shetlanders Scrottyle. [M. J. B.]

STANGERIA. A very remarkable genus of *Cycadeaceæ*, quite distinct from any other of the order in its fern-like foliage. It is a Natal plant, with a thick napiform trunk, a few coarse pinnate leaves, the pinnæ of which are oblong-lanceolate spinuloso-serrate, and traversed by parallel forked veins like those of a *Lomaria.*

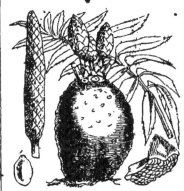

Stangeria paradoxa.

The fructification is in cones, the male cylindrical, with numerous stamens inserted on the under-side of its compound scales; the females on separate plants, ovoid, with two inverse ovules in the base of each scale. The genus, of which only one species (*S. paradoxa*, figured above) is known, is closely related to *Encephalartos* in structural characters, but differs remarkably in habit and foliage. [T. M.]

STANHOPEA. A most beautiful though not very extensive genus of epiphytal orchids belonging to the *Vanda* tribe. About twenty-six species have been described, natives of South and Central America: one, *S. grandiflora*, being found in Trinidad. They are pseudobulbous herbs, with broad membranaceous plicate leaves, radical sheathing often pendulous scapes, and large spotted fragrant flowers. The species may generally be recognised by the lip being divided into hypochil or lower cavity, mesochil or middle part (from which the horns proceed), and epichil or front moveable lobe; and by the pendulous flowers, with a spreading or reflexed perianth. The genus is named in honour of Earl Stanhope, who was at one time President of the Medico-Botanical Society of London. *S. tigrina*, of which a figure is subjoined, together with *S. Barkeriana, Wardii*, and *Bucepha-*

lus, are amongst the finest species of this genus. [W. B. H.]

Stanhopea tigrina.

STANHOPEASTRUM. An epiphytal genus of orchids belonging to the *Vandeæ*. The only species at present known is highly curious, and until lately has been referred to *Stanhopea*; but it differs from that genus in having a lip quite free from horns, and not divided into separate parts. The lip is described as being ovate, obsoletely triangular at the end, short, in form resembling a slipper, very fleshy, of a bright-yellow orange colour passing towards the point into pure white, and mottled on its sides with handsome purple blotches. The remaining parts of the flower are white, with purple spots near the base of the petals. The flowers, which grow in pairs, are large and showy. It is a native of Central America. [W. B. H.]

STANLEYA. A genus of *Cruciferæ* from North-western America, consisting of smooth glaucous perennials, with lyrate-pinnatifid or entire leaves, and long racemes of yellow flowers. The pod is slender cylindrical on a long stipe. [J. T. S.]

STANMARCH. *Smyrnium Olusatrum.*

STANNIA. A genus of *Cinchonaceæ*, differing little from *Posoqueria*, save in the one-celled berry. The corolla is funnel-shaped, with a very long tube; its limb divided into five lobes, opposite to which are five scaly prominences; and the stamens are of unequal length, and project beyond the mouth of the corolla. *S. formosa*, a native of the Caraccas, is a fine tree with lance-shaped laurel-like leaves, and white fragrant flowers three to four inches in length. It is in cultivation as a highly ornamental stove-plant. [M. T. M.]

STAPELIA. An extensive genus of *Asclepiadaceæ*, containing upwards of 100 species of succulent branching plants without leaves, natives of the Cape of

Good Hope. The branches are generally four-sided and toothed, and covered over with dark tubercles, giving the plants a very grotesque appearance; the calyx is five-parted; the corolla rotate five-cleft and fleshy; the staminal corona double, the outer series of leaves or lobes entire or cleft, the inner subulate and entire or bifid; the gynostegium is generally exserted; the anthers are simple at the top, the pollen-masses being fixed by their base, and having one edge cartilaginous and

Stapelia Asterias.

pellucid; and there are two subcylindrical follicles containing numerous comose seeds. The singular and beautiful large flowers spring from uncertain points of the succulent stems. They exhibit a variety of colours, forming exquisite marbled or dotted patterns; and notwithstanding the repulsive odour (like carrion) which almost all the flowers possess, they are extensively cultivated because of their beauty. One of the finest of the species is *S. Asterias*, figured above.   [W. C.]

STAPHISAGRIA. *Delphinium Staphisagria.*

STAPHYLEACEÆ. (*Bladder-nuts.*) A small group of polypetalous *Thalamifloræ*, formerly united with *Celastraceæ*, but now recognised as having the essential characters of *Sapindaceæ*, and added by many botanists to that order as a tribe, distinguished by the stamens being inserted outside instead of inside the disk, and by albuminous seeds. They consist of trees or shrubs, with opposite pinnate leaves furnished with stipules, and white usually small flowers in racemes or panicles. They are natives of Europe, Asia, and Tropical and North America, and comprise three genera, *Staphylea*, *Euscaphis*, and *Turpinia*. By some they are made a separate order.

STAPHYLEA. A genus of *Staphyleaceæ*, distinguished in that order (or suborder) chiefly by the large inflated capsule. There are four species known, dispersed over the temperate regions of the northern hemisphere. They are all shrubs, with opposite pinnate leaves, consisting of three five or more leaflets, and white

pendulous flowers in axillary racemes or panicles. *S. pinnata* from Central and Eastern Europe, and sometimes also *S. trifoliata* from North America, are cultivated in our shrubberies under the name of Bladder-nuts.

STARCH-CORN. *Triticum Spelta.*

STARCHWORT. *Arum maculatum.*

STARE, or STARR. *Ammophila arundinacea, Carex arenaria;* and other coarse seaside sedges and grasses.

STAR-FLOWER. *Trientalis americana.*

STAR-FRUIT. *Damasonium stellatum* alias *Actinocarpus Damasonium.*

STAR-HEAD. *Asterocephalus.*

STAR-JELLY. *Nostoc commune.*

STAR OF BETHLEHEM. *Ornithogalum umbellatum;* also *Hypoxis decumbens.*

STAR OF JERUSALEM. *Tragopogon porrifolius.*

STAR OF NIGHT. *Clusia rosea.*

STAR OF THE EARTH. *Plantago Coronopus.*

STARRY. Arranged in rays like the points of a star. The same as Stellate.

STARRY PUFFBALL. *Geastrum.*

STAR-SHAPED. The same as Stellate.

STAR-SLOUGH. A name which is applied in some districts to the common *Nostoc*, supposing it to be the remains of fallen stars.   [M. J. B.]

STARWORT. *Stellaria;* also *Aster Tripolium* and *Helonias dioica.* —, ITALIAN. *Aster Amellus.* —, WATER. *Callitriche.*

STATICE. A very extensive genus of herbaceous or subshrubby plants of the order *Plumbaginaceæ*, characterised by their flowers being spiked or panicled: the calyx funnel-shaped, of one piece, plaited and somewhat scarious; the petals five, slightly connate; the stamens attached to the base of the petals, and the nut one-seeded, enclosed in the calyx. They are amongst the most interesting ornaments of our greenhouses and flower-gardens, and are found in the south and east of Europe, in the Canary group, and in Central Asia.   [T. M.]

STATICE. (Fr.) *Armeria vulgaris.*

STAUNTONIA. Now that the Indian plants formerly referred to *Stauntonia* have been separated and formed into distinct genera under the names *Parvatia* and *Holbœllia*, the present genus is reduced to two species, one of which (*S. chinensis*) is a native of China, and the other (*S. hexaphylla*) of Japan. These are woody climbing shrubs, with compound leaves composed of from three to seven (usually five) radiating leaflets, and few-flowered racemes of largish unisexual flowers produced from the axils of the leaves. Both sexes of flowers have six fleshy sepals, but neither possess any petals; and the genus is thus distinguished from the two allied genera above mentioned, both of which have petals. The males contain six stamens, with the filaments united instead of free, as in *Holbœllia*; and the females six sterile stamens and three distinct ovaries, containing several ovules intermixed with hairs. The generic name is given in honour of Sir George Staunton, who accompanied Lord Macartney to China in A.D. 1792, and afterwards wrote the account of the embassy. It belongs to the *Lardizabalaceæ*. The Japanese species has leaves composed of five or six lance-shaped leaflets terminating in short bristly points. It is called Nibe Kadsura or Tuso So by the Japanese, who eat its roundish watery berries, and use their juice as a remedy for ophthalmia.   [A S.]

STAURACANTHUS. A genus of *Leguminosæ*, including a Portuguese shrub, destitute of leaves, and with the habit of *Ulex nana*; the branches being spiny, each of the spines branching into two smaller spines at the sides, and the flowers yellow; calyx two-lipped, the upper lip deeply divided into two segments, the lower three-toothed: vexillum folded, longer than the lance-shaped wings; keel blunt; stamens ten, monadelphous; pod compressed hairy many-seeded. *S. aphyllus*, a dwarf shrub, is a handsome plant, but only half-hardy. The generic name is derived from the Greek *stauros* a 'cross' and *akantha* 'a thorn,' in reference to the cross-like spines.   [M. T. M.]

STAURANTHERA *grandifolia* is the only known representative of a genus of cyrtandreous *Gesneraceæ*, peculiar to Pulo Penang, and having very much the habit of *Glossanthus*. It is a herb with rather large leaves; the flowers are paniculate, the calyx subrotate bell-shaped and almost ten-cleft; the corolla is large, furnished with a short tube having a spur at the base, and a border divided into five lobes. There are four fertile stamens, and the anthers are coherent, whilst the capsule is dehiscent.   [B. S.]

STAURANTHUS. The name of a Mexican evergreen tree, with alternate leathery dotted leaves, and greenish flowers arranged in racemes. Calyx persistent, with four small teeth; petals four, longer than the calyx, bent downwards, and having thickened margins; stamens four, inserted on the receptacle, alternate with the petals; ovary sessile one-celled, with a single pendulous ovule; stigma sessile, four-lobed; fruit fleshy olive-shaped red, covered with small glands like an orange. This tree is doubtfully referred to *Celastraceæ* or *Aurantiaceæ*, with neither of which however does it agree well. The name is derived from the Greek *stauros* 'a cross' and *anthos* 'flower,' in allusion probably to the four petals.   [M. T. M.]

STAUROGLOTTIS. *Phalænopsis.*

STAUROPHRAGMA. A genus of *Scrophulariaceæ*, having the calyx deeply divided into five segments, the capsule cylindrical indehiscent, and the valves involute at the margin. *S. natolicum*, a native of Natolia, has the leaves covered with grey down, and the flowers yellow and scented. The name, from the Greek *stauros* 'a cross,' refers to the appearance presented by a transverse section of the capsule.   [G. D.]

STAVERWORT. *Senecio Jacobæa.*

STAVESACRE. The acrid emetic purgative seeds of *Delphinium Staphisagria.*

STAVEWOOD. *Simaruba amara.*

STAY-PLOUGH. The Restharrow, *Ononis arvensis.*

STÉBÉ. (Fr.) *Stœbe.*

STEENHAMMARIA (often written **STEENHAMMERA**). A genus of *Boraginaceæ*, usually called *Mertensia*, included in *Pulmonaria* by Linnæus, from which it differs by the short open five-parted calyx and longer stamens, as well as by the nuts being slightly fleshy on the outside. It has also been referred to *Lithospermum*, but the limb of the corolla is not spreading, and the nuts have not the hard and stony pericarp of that genus. The species have blue or red flowers, in paniculately or corymbosely arranged scorpioid racemes, and smooth glaucous leaves.

S. maritima, which is not uncommon on the northern coasts of Britain, is a trailing glaucous plant with fleshy ovate leaves, tasting like oysters (whence it is sometimes called the Oyster-plant); and pretty blue flowers, red while in bud. The other species are from Siberia, Kamtschatka, and North America.   [J. T. S.]

STEEPLE-BUSH. *Spiræa tomentosa.*

STEGANIA. *Lomaria.*

STEGNOGRAMMA. A genus of polypodiaceous ferns related to *Gymnogramma*, and having the veins connivently anastomosing as in *Nephrodium*. They are herbaceous pinnately or pinnato-pinnatifidly divided ferns, with a stoutish caudex, sometimes subarborescent, and linear or oblong oblique parallel sori. There are two or three species, from India and the Eastern Archipelago.   [T. M.]

STEIRODISCUS. A Cape annual plant, forming a genus of *Compositæ*. The leaves are pinnately divided; and the flower-heads terminal, surrounded by a ventricose many-leaved involucre; receptacle naked; florets yellow—those of the ray strap-shaped, of the disk tubular; stigmas conical; fruits linear smooth, with no pappus, the inner ones always sterile—whence the name of the genus, from the Greek *steiros* 'sterile.'   [M. T. M.]

STELIS. A genus of orchids belonging to the tribe *Malaxideæ*, consisting of about 130 species, inhabiting South and Central America and the West Indian Islands. They are small herbs, from two or three inches to two feet high, generally found growing on the trunks and branches of trees. The stems are simple, with one sheathing leaf, and ochreate bracts; and the flowers are in terminal spikes or racemes, usually very minute, green yellow or purple. *Stelis* is distinguished from *Pleurothallis*, to which genus it is closely allied, by having a short truncate three-lobed column, the front angles of whose anthers are uniformly mucilaginous. The flowers of some species are irritable, closing suddenly when moved or touched. In one species, *S. purpurascens,* eight pollen-masses have been found, the only case at present known.　　　[W. B. H.]

STELLARIA. A genus of herbaceous plants belonging to the tribe *Alsineæ* of the order *Caryophyllaceæ*, and distinguished by the following characters:— Sepals five; petals two-cleft; stamens ten; styles three; capsule opening by six valves. Several species are indigenous to Great Britain. *S. Holostea*, the Greater Stitchwort, called also Satin-flower and Adder's-meat, is one of our early hedge-flowers, with long straggling quadrangular stems, narrow grass-like leaves, and large panicled lustrous white flowers with deeply-cloven petals. *S. media* is the common Chickweed, sufficiently marked by a line of hairs on one side of the stem, changing to the opposite side whenever it reaches a pair of leaves. French: *Stellaire*; German: *Augentrostgras*.　　　[C. A. J.]

STELLATÆ, or STELLATES. A group of monopetalous, dicotyledons, scarcely differing from *Cinchonaceæ*, but sometimes distinguished as a separate order under the name of GALIACEÆ: which see.

STELLATE, STELLIFORM. Having a number of narrow divisions placed round the stem like the rays of a star.

STELLATO-PILOSE. Having hairs formed in a stellate manner.

STEM. That part of a plant which bears or has borne leaves or their rudiments; the ascending axis of growth. It may be either subterranean, or exposed to the air and light.

STEM-CLASPING. When the base of a leaf surrounds a stem. The same as Amplexicaul.

STEMLESS. Having no visible or obvious stem. See ACAULIS.

STEMONACANTHUS. A genus of *Acanthaceæ* from tropical America, containing a few species of shrubs or herbs, with the flowers in paniculate or contracted cymes. The calyx is five-cleft or five-parted; the corolla-tube slightly curved and clavate, with the subequal lobes spreading or reflexed; the didynamous stamens exserted; the anther-cells parallel, and often produced beyond the connective; and the capsule four to eight-seeded.　　　[W. C.]

STEMONITIS. A genus of myxogastrous *Fungi*, with a more or less elongated delicate single deciduous peridium, filled with a network of threads connected with the stem, which penetrates more or less completely the whole mass. *S. fusca* is one of those species which occasionally occur in great profusion in hothouses, and is common in woods amongst fallen leaves, &c.; forming large tufts of cylindrical peridia supported on dark bristle-shaped stems, which are often more persistent than the network. This species is found in all parts of the world with slight modifications.　　　[M. J. B.]

STEMONOPORUS. A name proposed by Thwaites for a genus of *Dipteraceæ*, which other botanists consider as a section only of *Vateria*, as it has the fruit of that genus, and only differs from the original type in the stamens not numbering more than fifteen, with obtuse hot acuminate anthers. It consists of several species, tall resiniferous trees, with alternate entire coriaceous leaves, and white flowers either axillary or in terminal panicles. There are several species known, natives of Tropical Asia, but chiefly of Ceylon.

STEMONURUS. A genus of *Olacaceæ*, established by Blume for three or four trees from the Indian Archipelago. In the species which suggested the name the anthers have at their back a curious long tuft of hairs, which is turned inwards over their face. This species, however, proves to be strictly a congener of the previously published *Lasianthera* from Tropical Africa; and the other species, for which Blume's name is no longer applicable, belong to Wallich's genus *Gomphandra*. The name *Stemonurus* is therefore now suppressed.

STENACTIS. A genus of erect branched herbs, natives of North America, Northern India, &c. The leaves are toothed; the flower-heads solitary at the ends of the branches, surrounded by an involucre of two or three rows of narrow overlapping scales; receptacle flat, naked; florets of the ray strap-shaped, white or violet,— those of the disk yellow, tubular; achenes compressed; pappus of the outer ones hairy deciduous, arranged in one row, that of the inner in two rows.　　　[M. T. M.]

STENANDRIUM. A genus of *Acanthaceæ*, containing several small plants from South America. It is allied to *Crossandra*, differing chiefly in its more lowly habit, and in having more slender anthers.　　　[W. C.]

STENANTHERA. A genus of *Epacridaceæ* containing a single species, *S. pinifolia*, which has a five-parted calyx surrounded by numerous bracts; a tubular corolla twice the length of the calyx, with a short-spreading half-bearded limb; stamens included within the throat of the corolla; and a one-seeded drupe. The flowers are axillary erect, with a slightly swollen scarlet tube and greenish-yellow limb; and the leaves needle-shaped, and much crowded on the branches.　　　[R. H.]

STENANTHIUM. A North American genus of *Melanthaceæ* allied to *Veratrum*, from which it differs in the perianth-segments being united at the base, and there adhering to the ovary. It is a smooth perennial, with a rod-like leafy stem from a somewhat bulbous base; the leaves are long and grass-like; and the flowers small white, in a long terminal panicle. [J. T. S.]

STENIA. An epiphytal genus of orchids belonging to the tribe *Vandeæ*. The only species, *S. pallida*, is from Demerara, and is a stemless herb without pseudobulbs, having oblong leaves narrowed at the base, recurved at the apex: and solitary radical yellow flowers about two inches in diameter. In habit it very much resembles *Maxillaria*, but it may easily be distinguished from that genus by the labellum not being articulated with the foot of the column. [W. B. H.]

STENOCARPUS. A genus of *Proteaceæ*, having a tubular calyx, cleft at the back; the four sepals bear each a sessile anther; the style is filiform, with an oblique stigma; and the seed-vessel a linear or cylindrical follicle containing several seeds

Stenocarpus Cunninghami.

having a wing at their base. They are mostly large shrubs, one species however, *S. Cunninghami*, being a lofty tree, its flowers dark-yellow or orange, in axillary or terminal umbels, and its leaves leathery, entire or sinuate. The species are natives of New South Wales, Tropical Australia, and New Caledonia. [R. H.]

STENOCHILUS. A genus of *Myoporaceæ*, containing several species, natives of Australia. They are shrubs with alternate leaves, and solitary sometimes double axillary pedicels; the calyx is five-parted, and the lobes are imbricate at the base; the corolla is irregular and funnel-shaped; the four didynamous stamens are exserted; the style has a simple apex; and the two-celled ovary has two pendent ovules in each cell. [W. C.]

STENOCHLÆNA. An acrostichaceous genus of ferns having dimorphous fronds (the sterile ones pinnate, the fertile contracted and either pinnate or bipinnate) borne on scandent rhizomes. The pinnæ have a marginal gland near the base on the upper edge, and the veins form narrow costal areoles (sometimes hardly distinguishable), from which parallel forked veins run out to the margin. One tropical species abounds in India and the Pacific Islands; another is met with in South Africa and Madagascar. The costal areoles are often apparent near the apex of the pinnæ when they are not evident near the base. [T. M.]

STENOCORYNE. A genus of orchids belonging to the tribe *Vandeæ*. It is an epiphytal herb, with elongated quadrangular pseudobulbs, solitary cartilaginous leaves, and the flowers in a close raceme, orange spotted with brown. The scape is produced from below the pseudobulbs. The genus is nearly related to *Bifrenaria*, but differs in having two distinct glands at the base of the caudicles. The only known species is from Demerara. [W. B. H.]

STENOGASTRA. A small genus of *Gesneraceæ* confined to Tropical America, of which *S. hirsuta* (*Gloxinia hirsuta* of the gardens) is the type. The calyx is small and obliquely bell-shaped, the tube of the corolla very narrow and cylindrical, the ovary surrounded by five distinct glands, and the stigma mouth-shaped. *S. hirsuta* is a stemless perennial, with almost radical leaves, several clothed with long hairs, ovate or oblong in shape; whilst the pedicels are one-flowered, and bear pale blue flowers. [B. S.]

STENOGYNE. The name of a genus of *Labiatæ*, in which the calyx has the three upper teeth smaller than the others; the corolla is about as long as the calyx, curved, hairy inside, the upper lip erect and notched, the lower of three nearly equal and entire divisions: and the style ends in two equal lobes. The species are herbaceous, natives of the Sandwich Islands, with hard crenate leaves, and flowers in the axils of small awl-shaped bracts. The name, derived from the Greek, alludes to the narrow lobes of the style. [G. D.]

STENOLOBIUM. A small genus of *Bignoniaceæ*, not to be confounded with the *Stenolobium* of Bentham, a leguminous type noticed below. It is peculiar to Tropical America, but *S. stans* (*Bignonia* or *Tecoma stans* of botanical writers) has become naturalised in many parts of the Old World, and has for many years been an inmate of our hothouses. It is reported to be diuretic. The *Stenolobiums* are erect bushes, somewhat resembling the ash in foliage. When young the leaves are often unifoliolate, but in older plants they are generally pinnate, and the leaflets deeply-serrated at the margin. The flowers are placed in rich clusters at the ends of the branches, and they are invariably yellow, more or less deep in colour. The calyx is regular, and has five ribs terminating in five pointed teeth; the corolla is funnel or bell-shaped; the stamens (four with the rudiment of a fifth) have divergent anthers, which are either glabrous or covered with long hairs, and afford excellent characters for distinguishing the different otherwise very similar-looking species; the capsule is linear and flat, its partition placed contrary to the direction of the valves; and its numerous winged seeds are in single rows. [B. S.]

The same name has been applied to a genus of papilionaceous *Leguminosæ*, consisting of climbing shrubs, with trifoliolate leaves, and axillary flowerstalks bearing numerous tufts of blue flowers. The calyx is bell-shaped, two-lipped; the vexillum erect, provided with a membranous appendage on each side at the base; stamens ten, diadelphous; ovary sessile; style filiform; pod sessile, linear compressed, thickened at the sutures, many-seeded—the seeds separated one from the other by transverse cellular partitions.

The generic name is derived from the Greek *stenos* 'narrow,' in allusion to the structure of the pods. The species are natives of Tropical America. [M. T. M.]

STENOMESSON. An amaryllidaceous genus of bulbs, chiefly from Peru. They produce linear or lanceolate leaves, and a solid terete scape, bearing a few or many-flowered umbel of erect or drooping blossoms, which have a slender cylindraceous tube constricted in the middle, and subventricose in the upper part; and with a six-cleft regular limb, and a six-toothed coronet bearing stamens between the teeth. The style is filiform, with a clavate dilated apex. The flowers are yellow orange-coloured or scarlet, and very handsome. [T. M.]

STENOPETALUM. A genus of *Cruciferæ* from Australia, consisting of herbs with linear leaves, entire or the lower ones lyrately pinnatifid, and terminal racemes. The pouch is obovate or elliptical, slightly compressed, parallel to the septum, the valves slightly concave; the seeds numerous, with short seed-stalks. [J. T. S.]

STENORHYNCHUS. A terrestrial genus of orchids belonging to the *Neotteæ*. About ten species have been described, inhabitants of Tropical America and the West Indian Islands. They are herbs with fascicled roots, broad radical leaves, spikes densely imbricated with large coloured bracts, and the flowers generally hairy and showy. It differs from *Spiranthes*, to which it is closely allied, in its large showy flowers and coloured bracts, and the want of calli at the base of the lip; while from *Pelexia* it differs in its large flowers and bracts, and in the rostellum being hard and horny, remaining as a rigid spine upon the apex of the stigma after the pollen-masses have fallen away. The name is derived from *stenos* 'narrow' and *rhynchos* 'a beak.' [W. B. H.]

STENOSEMIA. A genus of acrostichoid

ferns of the reticulated series. The two or three known species are dwarf plants with ternately divided fronds, having the two pinnæ very oblique and bipinnatifid, and bulbiferous in their axils. The fertile fronds are cut up into many irregular narrow segments. The lowermost venules anastomose, so as to form costal areoles, while the ultimate or marginal ones are free. The plants are natives of the Indian Archipelago. [T. M.]

STENOSIPHON. A genus of *Onagraceæ*, in which the tube of the calyx is narrow and long; the corolla is of four petals, the two posterior largest; and the stamens eight in number, the four opposite the petals being longest. The only species is a native of Texas, of herbaceous habit, with slender branches; the leaves alternate, very narrow, and rigid; and the flowers white, in dense spikes. The name is from the Greek *stenos* 'narrow' and *siphon* 'a tube,' and refers to the narrow tube of the calyx. [G. D.]

STENOSIPHONIUM. A genus of *Acanthaceæ*, containing four species of shrubs from India. They have toothed leaves, and axillary and terminal spikes. They differ from *Ruellia* in having the calyx divided to the middle, and in the slender tube of the corolla opening upwards into a campanulate limb. [W. C.]

STENOSTOMUM. A small West Indian genus of *Cinchonaceæ*, consisting for the most part of low trees, with elliptical or oblong leaves furnished with deciduous or persistent stipules, and sometimes covered with a sticky resinous exudation on the upper surface; and bearing axillary two-branched flower-spikes, having the flowers (which are small whitish and stalkless) arranged along the inner sides of the branches, with one also in the fork. It is characterised by the flowers having the short free part or limb of the calyx four or five-toothed or almost entire, and persistent on the mature fruit; by the salver-shaped corolla, with four or five overlapping lobes, and with the stamens (which have narrow anthers and very short filaments) inserted below its throat, and either entirely included within the tube or half protruded; and by the two to six-celled ovary with a simple style and round-headed stigma, the ovary ultimately forming an unopening fruit, containing a two to six-celled stone, with as many cylindrical seeds. [A. S.]

STEPHANANDRA. A Japanese shrub, with alternate broadly ovate lobed or cut leaves, and small flowers in loose terminal cymes, forming a genus of *Rosaceæ* allied to *Spiræa*, and resembling some of its species in habit. It differs essentially, however, in the ovary being reduced to a single carpel with two pendulous ovules; and in the fruit, which is a small follicle, with one or two globular albuminous seeds.

STEPHANOPHYSUM. A genus of

Acanthaceæ containing several species of herbs, from Tropical America. The calyx has five equal divisions; the tube and limb of the corolla are small, but the throat is more or less inflated; and the stamens are just included, and have slender anthers. The flowers are in axillary cymes, which have an umbellate arrangement in most of the species.   [W. C.]

STEPHANOPODIUM. The name of a Peruvian tree, constituting a genus of *Chailletiaceæ*. The leaves are entire bistipulate, and the flowers placed in heads on the swollen tops of the flower-stalks. The calyx is five-cleft, the tube of the corolla equalling the calyx, its limb five-lobed and bilabiate; stamens five; ovary two-celled, with two ovules in each compartment, surrounded at the base by five glands; style simple, stigma two-lobed; fruit drupaceous, two-celled.   [M. T. M.]

STEPHANOTIS. A genus of *Asclepiadaceæ*, containing a few species, from Madagascar. They are sinistrorse climbing shrubs, with smooth coriaceous leaves, and beautiful fragrant pedicellate flowers in interpetiolar umbels. The calyx is five-leaved; the corolla salve-shaped, with a tube somewhat swollen at the base, and a limb with five oblique segments; the staminal corona composed of five erect simple short acuminate leaves; the anthers terminated by a membrane; the stigma conical and entire or obscurely two-lobed; and the two follicles thick horizontal and acuminate, containing many comose seeds. The species are generally cultivated for the great beauty of their flowers.   [W. C.]

STEPHENSONIA. A garden name of *Verschaffeltia*: more correctly *Stevensonia*.

STERCULIACEÆ. (*Bombaceæ, Sterculiads*.) An order of polypetalous dicotyledons, with the valvate calyx, contorted petals (sometimes wanting), and monadelphous stamens of *Malvaceæ*, but differing from them in their anthers being always two-celled. They consist of tropical South African or Australian herbs shrubs or trees, with alternate entire lobed or digitately compound leaves, furnished with stipules; and axillary or rarely terminal flowers, often large and handsome. The order has been variously extended or broken up into smaller ones by different botanists. By the most recent arrangement the *Bombaceæ* have been referred to *Malvaceæ*, as having always one-celled anthers; and *Sterculiaceæ*, including *Byttneriaceæ*, have been divided into seven tribes, comprising forty-one genera:—1. *Sterculieæ* proper, with unisexual flowers, no petals, five to fifteen anthers, adnate to the top of the column, and carpels distinct when in fruit. They are all trees or shrubs, including *Sterculia, Heritiera*, and three other genera. 2. *Helictereæ*: trees or shrubs, with hermaphrodite flowers, five petals, five to fifteen anthers, singly or by twos or threes alternating with the teeth or lobes of the staminal column, comprising six genera,

of which *Helicteres* and *Pterospermum* are the largest. 3. *Eriolæneæ*, or the genus *Eriolæna*, with numerous anthers covering the upper half of the staminal column. 4. *Dombeyeæ*: consisting of herbs shrubs or rarely trees, with ten to twenty stamens on a short column, two to four together, alternating with the barren lobes of the column or staminodia. They include *Dombeya, Pentapetes, Melhania*, and four other genera, all African or Asiatic. 5. *Hermannieæ*: herbs or shrubs, with only five stamens, including the large African genus *Hermannia*, the tropical genera *Melochia* and *Waltheria*, and three others. 6. *Byttnerieæ*: mostly shrubs or trees remarkable for their petals being concave or hood-shaped at the base, and often terminating in a long appendage. The principal genera are *Theobroma, Guazuma, Byttneria*, and *Commersonia*. 7. *Lasiopetaleæ*: shrubs almost exclusively Australian, with five stamens almost free, and petals reduced to small scales or entirely wanting; eight genera, including *Lasiopetalum* and *Thomasia*. See BYTTNERIACEÆ.

STERCULIA. Although much reduced by the separation of numerous groups under the names *Cola, Firmiana, Brachychiton, &c.*, *Sterculia* (which gives its name to the order *Sterculiaceæ*) is still one of considerable extent; and its species are widely dispersed through the tropics of both hemispheres, occurring most abundantly, however, in Asia and the Asiatic Islands, more sparingly in America and Africa, and rarely in Australia. Nearly all the species are trees, sometimes of considerable size; and by far the greater number have simple undivided feather-veined leaves, comparatively few having their leaves lobed so as to resemble a hand, or divided into several distinct leaflets radiating from a common centre. Their flowers are borne in usually somewhat drooping panicles, and are most commonly of one sex only. They have a coloured bell-shaped calyx, and no petals; and their fruits consist of five or fewer more or less woody pieces called follicles, radiating from a common centre and opening along their inner or top edge, each follicle containing several albuminous seeds.

S. carthaginensis, a fine tree forty feet high or upwards, native of America from Mexico to Brazil, has large roundish three to five-lobed leaves, covered with velvety hairs underneath but smooth above; and its yellowish flowers are scurfy outside and spotted with purple inside. It is called Chicha by the Brazilians, and Panama by the Panamians; and its seeds, which are about the size of pigeon's eggs, are, like those of many other species, commonly eaten by the inhabitants as nuts.

S. urens, an Indian and Cingalese species, has five-lobed hand-shaped leaves velvety underneath, erect panicles of flowers covered with sticky yellow down, and fruits clothed with stiff bristly stinging hairs. All the *Sterculias* contain mucilage, and the trunks of some exude large quantities of mucilaginous gum, resembling tragacanth both in appearance and in its property of not dissolving in cold water, but merely swelling and becoming jelly-like, owing to the presence of *bassorin*. The present species yields part of the gum known in India as Gum Kateera, a quantity of which was some years ago sent to this country as a substitute for tragacanth, but was found unsuitable, although Dr. Thomson states that it has been used by calico-printers. Another kind from Sierra Leone is the produce of *S. Tragacantha*.

S. villosa, a native of Peninsular India, has five to seven-lobed leaves velvety underneath, with the lobes either again three-lobed or deeply toothed, pendulous panicles of flowers, and fruits clothed with star-like hairs. The inner bark of the *Sterculias* is composed of very tough fibres. That of the present species is called Oadal or Oo'dhall in India, where very strong pliable ropes which are not affected by wet are made of it, and are commonly used by the elephant-hunters. In Goa and Canara capital bags, used for the conveyance of rice and other merchandise, are made by soaking logs of the trunk or large branches for a few days in water, and then stripping off the bark entire and sewing up the bottom. The bark of another species (*S. guttata*) is used on the Malabar Coast for making articles of clothing. French : *Sterculier*. [A. S.]

STEREOSPERMUM (including *Dipterospermum*). A genus of *Bignoniaceæ*, embracing about a dozen species, all of which are confined to tropical parts of Africa and Asia. They are all trees, with imparipinnate leaves, and terminal panicles bearing white often highly fragrant flowers. The almost bony scarcely winged seeds, attached to the very corky septum of a cylindrical or almost square capsule, together with a cup-shaped calyx and almost bell-shaped corolla, at once distinguish the genus from all others of the order to which it belongs. [B. S.]

STEREUM. A genus of hymenomycetous *Fungi* belonging to the division in which the hymenium is perfectly even, without gills spines folds or other prominences. The substance is coriaceous, and the fruit-bearing surface free from bristles, and neither soft nor fleshy. Many of the species are extremely common on dead trunks or timber. *S. purpureum*, with purplish and lilac tints, is to be found on every fallen poplar, the hairy orange-yellow *S. hirsutum* on oak, and the pallid cinereous *S. sanguinolentum*, which bleeds when scratched, on fallen conifers. The species are too tough for food, and they have, as far as we know, no available economical properties. Some of the exotic species attain a large size, and are extremely handsome. *S. lobatum*, than which there are few handsomer *Fungi*

when well grown, occurs in every tropical or subtropical collection. [M. J. B.]

STERIGMATA. The elevated lines or plates upon stems produced by the bases of decurrent leaves.

STERIGMUM. An indehiscent superior many-celled dry fruit, such as that of *Tropæolum*.

STERILITAS, or **STERILITY** (adj. **STERILE**). Barrenness in the vegetable as in the animal world may be either constitutional or accidental. In Italy it is observed that those Stone Pines which are of a more vivid green than usual do not produce fruit, and the effect of constitutional rankness in this respect is known to every cultivator. Again, there may be constitutional peculiarities which prevent the formation of fruit where all the necessary organs seem properly developed. It frequently happens, however, that all these organs are not present, or, if they are, it is in such a metamorphosed condition that they cannot perform their proper functions. The sepals may be multiplied to the total suppression of the other parts of the flower; the stamens may be turned into leaves or petals, and the pistil into leaves. The suppression of petals does not, however, seem to be so disastrous as their multiplication, and even stamens may be wanting without destroying fertility, as in *Cælebogyne*, not to mention violets and other plants. Far more frequently, however, sterility arises from outward agents, from the effect of long-continued drought or moisture, from frost or cutting winds or other atmospheric conditions, or again from outward injuries. Even when impregnation has taken place, the ovules in the same pistil will not in every case attain perfection; and where fruit has been set abundantly, the demands of all may be so urgent that every one may fail. The fruit indeed may increase to a considerable size, or even approach maturity; but in most cases, if the ovules have proved abortive, it will fall off. In a few varieties, however, when the fruit has once swelled from the stimulus of impregnation, it may arrive at perfection even though no seeds are present, which is however, except in the gardener's view, no less a case of sterility, strictly speaking, than the other. Parasites mostly induce or promote sterility; but in the grape-mildew, where the development of the berry is so much checked, the growth of the seeds on the contrary seems actually to be promoted. [M. J. B.]

STERIPHOMA. A genus of *Capparidaceæ*, comprising a shrub whose branches are invested with star-shaped brownish hairs, stalked leaves, with a prominent swelling at the end of the stalk next to the blade of the leaf, and solitary flowers on axillary stalks. The calyx is hairy, two-lobed; petals four, yellowish, sessile, the two anterior ones larger than the others; stamens six, protruding beyond the corolla; ovary on a long stalk, two-celled; stigma sessile; fruit with a thick rind, inter-hally fleshy. *S. cleomoides*, a native of Caraccas, is in cultivation as a hothouse shrub. [M. T. M.]

STERNBERGIA. A genus of *Amaryllidaceæ*, consisting of dwarf bulbous plants found in Eastern and Central Europe, and having linear-lorate leaves, often later than the flowers, and solid scapes bearing a single erect flower of a funnel-like form, with a straight tube widened upwards, and a six-parted semipatent limb; the six stamens are inserted unequally in the throat; and the style is filiform, with a three-lobed stigma. *S. lutea* is a well-known garden flower, blooming at the end of summer, and looking like a large yellow autumnal crocus. [T. M.]

STEUDELIA. A genus of *Paronychiaceæ*, the same as *Adenogramma*, which is the name more generally adopted.

STEVENIA. A genus of *Cruciferæ* from Siberia, an annual covered with grey stellate pubescence, having an ascending branched stem, with oblong linear entire leaves, and corymbose racemes of white flowers; calyx with the two outer sepals bulging at the base; pod oblong, constricted between the seeds, with plane valves; seeds two to four in each cell, ovate-compressed, immarginate. [J. T. S.]

STEVENSONIA. *Verschaffeltia.*

STEVIA. Esteve was a professor of botany at Valencia. The present genus of plants named in honour of him, consists of numerous species of herbaceous or somewhat shrubby *Compositæ*, natives for the most part of Tropical America. The leaves are entire or three-cleft, occasionally whorled, but usually opposite; and the heads of flowers are arranged in dense corymbs; the involucre is cylindrical, and consists of a few acuminate scales; receptacle naked; corollas all tubular, white pink or purple; stigmas cylindrical, club-shaped; achenes striated; pappus scaly, the scales sometimes awned. Numerous species are cultivated as bedding or border plants in this country. [M. T. M.]

STICHIDIA. A name given to the pod-like processes containing tetraspores in some of the rose-spored *Algæ*, as in *Dasya* and *Odonthalia.* [M. J. B.]

STICHUS. In Greek compounds = a row of anything.

STICKADORE. *Lavandula Stæchas.*

STICKSEED. *Echinospermum.*

STICTA. A fine genus of foliaceous coriaceous or membranaceous, velvety tomentose or more rarely smooth lichens, belonging to the same group as *Parmelia*, with the habit of the ground liverworts (*Peltideæ*), and remarkable for the round white or yellow pits on the under-side, which extend to the medullary stratum, and have been called cyphellæ. Several of the species are very large, and even our own *S. glomulifera* is sometimes three

feet across. The genus is by no means confined to temperate regions, some of the finest occurring in warm countries. *S. pulmonaria* is a popular remedy in diseases

Sticta pulmonaria.

of the lungs, under the names of Lungwort, Hazel Rag, Hazel Crottles, or Rags. *S. sylvatica* and *fuliginosa* are remarkable for their fetid fish-like smell. [M. J. B.]

STICTOPHYLLUM. A genus of *Compositæ*, comprising an herbaceous plant, native of Northern India, with linear-oblong sessile leaves, revolute at the margins, and with a thick midrib. The flowers are like those of a *Serratula*, from which and other allied genera the present one may be distinguished by its persistent feathery pappus of distinct hairs; and by the scales of the involucre, which are destitute of any appendage. [M. T. M.]

STIFFTIA. A genus of Brazilian arborescent *Compositæ*, of the mutisiaceous group, distinguished by its closely-imbricated involucre, of which the outer scales are roundish ovate, and the inner linear; its naked alveolate receptacle; its glabrous regular florets, with five circinately recurved lobes; its much exserted caudate anthers; its short-armed bifid style; and its glabrous elongated achenes, and multiserial pappus of linear serrated hairs. *S. chrysantha* is a handsome species, with lanceolate acuminate leaves, and terminal heads of showy orange-coloured flowers, issuing from amongst the long coloured pappus-hairs. It is now more commonly referred to *Augusta.* [T. M.]

STIGMA (pl. STIGMATA). That surface of a style, usually at its extremity, to which the pollen adheres when it fertilises the ovules.

STIGMAPHYLLON (sometimes written STIGMATOPHYLLON). This name is expressive of the leafy nature of the stigmas in the flowers of the genus of *Malpighiaceæ* to which it is applied. The species are tropical American shrubs, for the most part of climbing habit, the root usually tuberous; inflorescence umbel-like, the pedicels usually thickened at the top; calyx five-parted, the four outer segments with two glands at the base, externally ; petals five, stalked, longer than the sepals, unequal ; stamens ten, unequal in size—the four opposite to the glands of the calyx sterile, the remainder fertile ; styles three, dilated at the top into a leafy stigmatic expansion ; fruit of three or fewer winged carpels. Some of the species are in cultivation, and have handsome yellow flowers. [M. T. M.]

STIGMATIC. Of the nature of a stigma.

STIGMATOPHORUS. That part of the style of composites which bears the stigmata.

STIGMATOSTEMON. A body formed by the union of anthers with the stigma.

STILAGINACEÆ. (Antidesmads.) A name originally proposed by Agardh for a small group of genera, including Antidesma, whose affinities had been little understood ; but they have recently been included in the large order Euphorbiaceæ, an arrangement which appears to be generally adopted.

STILAGINELLA. A genus of Euphorbiaceæ of the tribe Antidesmeæ, established by Tulasne for a few trees or shrubs from Tropical America, nearly allied to the Asiatic Antidesmas, but differing from them chiefly in their ovary being two-celled with two ovules in each cell, instead of being reduced to a single carpel. Eight species have been described, all remarkable for the minute peltate scales, which give a hoary appearance to the branches and foliage, and for the numerous small flowers in axillary racemes or panicles. It has since been ascertained that the genus had been a short time previously published by Allemäo at Rio Janeiro under the name of Hieronyma.

STILAGO. A genus originally proposed by Linnæus, but which has proved not to be distinct from Antidesma.

STILBACEÆ. (Stilbids.) A small order of monopetalous dicotyledons whose immediate affinities are very uncertain. It consists of South African shrubs, with small crowded entire leaves like those of a Phylica or of some heaths ; the flowers sessile, in dense terminal spikes. The calyx is five-cleft, the corolla also five-cleft, with four perfect stamens inserted between its lobes, the place of the fifth being occupied by a small rudimentary stamen or empty ; the ovary is free two-celled, with one erect ovule in each, and the style simple. The fruit is a small nut, or rarely a two-valved capsule, with a single erect seed, containing a minute embryo in firm albumen. The order is usually placed near Verbenaceæ and Selaginaceæ, but Lindley regards it as more nearly allied to Diapensiaceæ. To the original genus, Stilbe, have been added three others, separated from it upon rather trifling characters.

STILBE. The principal genus of Stilbaceæ, distinguished from the others by straight flowering spikes, narrow corolla-lobes, parallel anther-cells, and an indehis-

cent fruit. It only contains four species, all from the Cape Colony, and offering very little if any interest.

STILLINGIA. The Tallow-tree of China is the best-known representative of this genus of Euphorbiaceæ; but there are two or three other Chinese and Japanese species, and as many more natives of the Southern States of America. With the exception of the tallow-tree and one herbaceous species, they are shrubs ; and all have alternate entire leaves, and terminal catkin-like spikes of flowers. The fruit is a capsule composed of three one-seeded opening pieces, and is girded at the base by an enlarged bract.

S. sebifera, the Tallow-tree, is a native of China and the adjacent islands, but it has been introduced into and partly naturalised in India and the warm parts of America. It has rhomboid-shaped sharply taper-pointed leaves about two inches broad, on slender stalks with two prominent glands at the point of attachment between the stalk and leaf ; and its flower-catkins are from two to four inches long. Its fruits are about half an inch in diameter, and contain three seeds thickly coated with a fatty substance which yields the tallow. This is obtained by steaming the seeds in large cauldrons, then bruising them sufficiently to loosen the fat without breaking the seeds, which are removed by sifting ; and the fat is afterwards made into flat circular cakes and pressed in a wedge-press, when the pure tallow exudes in a liquid state, and soon hardens into a white brittle mass. This tallow is very extensively used for candle-making in China; but, as they get soft in hot weather, the candles generally receive a coating of insect-wax. A liquid oil is obtained from the seeds by pressing. The tree yields a hard wood, used by the Chinese for printing blocks, and its leaves are employed for dyeing black. [A. S.]

STIMULI (adj. STIMULANS). Stings; sharp stiff hairs, containing an acrid fluid which when they pierce the skin produces pain.

STIMULOSE. Covered with stings.

STINKHORN. Phallus impudicus.

STINKING-WEED, or STINKING-WOOD. Cassia occidentalis.

STINKWEED. A local South of England name for Diplotaxis muralis.

STINKWOOD. The useful wood of Oreodaphne bullata, which has a most unpleasant odour lasting for a long time. Also that of Fœtidia mauritiana and Zieria macrophylla.

STIPA. A genus of grasses belonging to the tribe Stipeæ. The inflorescence is in nearly simple lax panicles, the spikelets of which are one-flowered ; glumes two, membranous, longer than the two cartilaginous pales, of which the lower is convolute, with a long beard at the apex, and the upper entire; beard jointed at the base, and deciduous. Steudel describes 104 species under this remarkable genus, which has a wide geographical distribution, obtaining its maximum in the warm temperate zones. The well-known Feather Grass of gardens, *S. pennata*, is a very ornamental species, and is frequently planted in flower-borders on that account. It is, when dry, dyed of various bright colours to make household ornaments. [D. M.]

STIPAGROSTIS. A genus of grasses belonging to the tribe *Stipeæ*, and now placed as one of the sections of the genus *Aristida*. [D. M.]

STIPELS. Secondary stipules, such as are found at the base of the leaflets of compound leaves.

STIPES. The petiole of the leaves of ferns. The stem which carries the pileus of such fungals as agarics.

STIPIFORM. Having the appearance of the trunk of an endogenous tree; as the papaw and other simple-stemmed exogens.

STIPITATE. Elevated on a stalk which is neither a petiole nor a peduncle; as, for example, some kinds of carpels.

STIPULAR. Of or belonging to or standing in the place of stipules.

STIPULES. Processes of various kinds arising from the base of a leaf, usually from its sides. *See* OCHREA and RETICULUM.

STIRLINGIA. A genus of *Proteaceæ*, having a regular four-cleft calyx, with plane reflexed spreading lobes; four stamens longer than the tube, inserted in the upper part of it, the anthers cohering at first, but finally free; a smooth filiform style, with a dilated stigma; and a seed-vessel, or nut containing a single obconical hairy seed. They are small shrubs, natives of South-western Australia, with repeatedly cut leaves, and small yellow flowers in racemes or panicles. [R. B.]

STIRPS. A race or permanent variety: as the Red Cabbage.

STITCHWORT. *Stellaria*, especially *S. Holostea*.

STOCK. *Matthiola.* —, TEN WEEKS. *Matthiola annua.* —, VIRGINIAN. *Malcolmia maritima.*

STOCKSIA. A rigid branching glaucous and thorny shrub from the mountains of Beloochistan, forming a genus of *Sapindaceæ*, remarkable chiefly for its few simple linear and entire leaves. The flowers are rather small, clustered along the branches. The fruit is unknown.

STŒBE. A genus of *Compositæ*, including a number of small Cape shrubs, having awl-shaped crowded leaves, frequently spirally twisted, the younger ones hairy, the older smooth. The flower-heads are aggregated into roundish or spike-like masses, each surrounded by an involucre

of overlapping dry membranous scales; corolla solitary, tubular; anthers provided with two little hairs at the base; stigmas feathery at the top; achenes oblong; pappus of one row of scales, membranous below, feathery above. Three or four species are in cultivation as greenhouse plants. The Greeks had a plant known to them as *stoibe*, and this word has furnished a name for the present genus. [M. T. M.]

STŒCHAS. (Fr.) *Lavandula Stœchas.* — CITRIN. *Gnaphalium Stœchas.*

STOKESIA. A genus of *Compositæ*, including a perennial erect-branched glaucescent herbaceous plant, having the upper part of the stem very hairy, some of the leaves spiny at the margins, and the flower-heads solitary at the ends of the branches; each surrounded by a somewhat globular involucre, the outer scales of which are prolonged into a leafy spiny-margined appendage, the inner ones ciliated; the receptacle is fleshy and naked; corollas blue, palmately divided, sprinkled over with glands; stigmas somewhat awl-shaped; achenes short, quadrangular; pappus of one row of deciduous membranous scales. *S. cyanea* is cultivated in open borders, in summer, for the sake of its handsome blue flowers. [M. T. M.]

STOLE, STOLON. A sucker which at first appears at the surface of the earth, and then turns downwards, piercing the soil or rooting into it.

STOMA, STOMIUM. The opening provided on the side of the spore-cases of ferns, through which dehiscence takes place. Also the ostiolum of certain fungals.

STOMATE, STOMATIUM. An organic aperture in the skin of a plant, by means of which respiration is maintained, to provide for which it is always placed over a cavity in the parenchyma, beneath it.

STOMATECHIUM. A genus of *Boraginaceæ* from the Cape of Good Hope, with the habit of *Echium*, having the calyx pentagonal five-cleft; the corolla tubular, with a five-cleft limb, the segments of which are obtuse, closed at the throat by five roundish fleshy scales, muricate externally; the stamens included; and the nuts four, subrotund rugose. [J. T. S.]

STOMATIFEROUS. Bearing stomates.

STOMATOMORPHOUS. Mouth-shaped.

STONE. A hard body found in certain fruits, and produced by the ossification of the endocarp or lining of the fruit.

STONEBREAK. *Saxifraga.*

STONECROP. *Sedum.* —, COMMON. *Sedum acre.* —, DITCH. *Penthorum.* — VIRGINIAN. *Penthorum sedoides.*

STONE-FRUIT. A drupe, such as the plum, peach, cherry, &c.

STONE-HORE. *Sedum reflexum*, the Stone Orpine.

STONEWORT. *Chara.*

STOOL. A stemless mother-plant used for propagation by annually bending its branches or 'layers' into the soil.

STORAX. A gum-resin obtained from *Styrax officinale*; also from several species of *Liquidambar*.

STORAXWORTS. Lindley's name for the *Styracaceæ*.

STORK'S-BILL. *Pelargonium.*

STRACHEYA. A Himalayan herbaceous plant forming a genus of *Leguminosæ* of the suborder *Papilionaceæ*. The very short stem, with almost radical pinnate leaves, and leafless scapes bearing one to four red flowers, as well as the shape and structure of those flowers, render it difficult to distinguish the plant in that state from the smaller species of *Hedysarum*; but the fruit is very different, and places *Stracheya* in the tribe *Galegeæ*. The pod is oblong-linear, flat and thin, indehiscent, with the faces often covered with prickly tubercles, as in *Hedysarum*; but it has no trace of transverse joints between the seeds, and is bordered by prickly teeth. The nearest affinity of the genus is with the Siberian *Eversmannia*.

STRAKÆA. A genus of *Aristolochiaceæ*, comprising a tree or shrub, native of the Molucca Isles. The branches are jointed; the leaves stalked leathery and palmately nerved; and the flowers sessile on a branched spike. The tube of the perianth is elongated four-cornered, and its limb divided into three or four ovate concave segments; stamens nine to twelve; ovary four-celled; style short, stigma peltate; fruit pod-like four-celled, four inches in length, and tapering at the base. [M. T. M.]

STRAMINEUS. Straw-coloured; dull-yellow mixed with white.

STRAMOINE. (Fr.) *Datura.*

STRAMONIUM. The Thorn Apple, *Datura Stramonium.*

STRANGLE-TARE. *Vicia lathyroides*; also *Cuscuta europæa*.

STRANGULATE. Contracted and expanded in an irregular manner.

STRANVÆSIA. An interesting genus of *Pomaceæ*, inasmuch as its fruits are intermediate between true capsules and pomes. The species is a native of Nepal, and has evergreen lance-shaped saw-toothed leaves, and white flowers in woolly corymbs. The tube of the calyx is top-shaped, not adherent to the ovary, its limb five-toothed; stamens twenty, alternately long and short; ovary free five-celled, each cell with two collateral ascending ovules; style five-cleft at the top; fruit capsular, enclosed within the orange-coloured calyx-tube, dividing into five valves. *S. glaucescens*, better known under the old name of *Cratægus glauca*, is grown in sheltered spots as an ornamental tree. The generic name commemorates the botanical services of the Hon. W. Fox-Strangways. [M. T. M.]

STRAP-SHAPED. The same as Ligulate.

STRAPWORT. *Corrigiola.*

STRATIOTES. The Water Soldier, a plant of singular appearance, belonging to the order *Hydrocharidaceæ*. The barren and fertile flowers grow on separate plants, and are contained in two-leaved spathes; the former numerous, with twelve to thirteen stamens, and twice as many imperfect ones; the latter solitary, with six stigmas, and numerous sterile stamens, which however sometimes become perfect. The plant, which resembles an American aloe in miniature (hence its name, *S. aloides*), is attached to the mud by a cord-like runner, or is suspended free in the water, elevating only its flowers and a portion of its leaves above the surface. The leaves are of a highly cellular structure, and pellucid. The Water Soldier is a dangerous plant to introduce into artificial water, as it increases with great rapidity, and is more curious than ornamental. French: *Aloïdes*; German: *Wasserfeder*. [C. A. J.]

STRATUM. A layer of tissue. *Str. cellulosum* is a cellular layer forming the exterior of bark, immediately below the epidermis; *Str. corticale* is any layer belonging to bark; and *Str. ligneum* is one of the woody layers in the stem of exogens. *Str. sporidiiferum* is the flesh, and *Str. sporophorum* the hymenium, of certain fungals.

STRAVADIUM. A Latinised version of a Malabar name applied to certain Indian trees of the family *Barringtoniaceæ*. The genus is nearly allied to *Barringtonia*, but is distinguished from it by its four-parted calyx, two-celled ovary, and ribbed four-sided fruit. The root of *S. racemosum* has aperient qualities, and its bark has a bitter taste, and is employed in fevers. [M. T. M.]

STRAW. The above-ground stem of Grasses, especially of the cereals.

STRAWBERRY. *Fragaria.* —, ALPINE. *Fragaria vesca.* —, BARREN. *Potentilla Fragariastrum*; also *Waldsteinia fragarioides.* —, DALMATIAN. *Arbutus Unedo.* —, HAUTBOIS. *Fragaria elatior.* —, PINE. *Fragaria grandiflora.* —, SCARLET. *Fragaria virginiana.* —, WOOD. *Fragaria vesca.*

STRAWBERRY-BUSH. *Euonymus americanus.*

STRAWBERRY-TREE. *Arbutus Unedo.*

STREAMWORTS. A name sometimes given to the *Haloragaceæ*.

STREBLORHIZA. *Clianthus.*

STRELESKIA. A Tasmanian genus of *Lobeliaceæ*, comprising a small herbaceous species with a rosette of leaves, from the midst of which springs a flower-stalk bearing a single flower; calyx four or five-lobed; corolla bell-shaped, its tube entire not split, its limb four or five-cleft, the segments being unequal in size; filaments short, dilated at the base, and hairy; anthers within the corolla, detached, two of them hairy; capsule leathery. [M. T. M.]

STRELITZIA. This gorgeous-flowered genus of *Musaceæ* was so named in honour of Charlotte of Mecklenburg-Strelitz, the Queen of George III. The species are large herbaceous plants, natives of the Cape of Good Hope. Their foliage is handsome, consisting of long-stalked glaucous leaves arising from a contracted stem, the base of the leafstalk sheathing. The common flower-stalk is encircled below by the sheath of the leafstalk; while its upper portion gives origin to a large bract or spathe placed obliquely, within which are the flowers. The perianth consists of six segments, in two rows; the three outer ones (sepals) are ovate lance-shaped, nearly equal, usually of a bright orange-colour; the three inner ones (petals) are unequal in size; the two lower or front ones are bright purple, united together, each one lobed on the outer side towards the upper part, so that the two united petals are distinctly halbert-shaped, and conceal within a fold the five perfect and one sterile stamen; the third or posterior petal is much smaller than the other two, somewhat hooded. The style is thread-like, and the stigma divided into three linear branches; fruit capsular three-celled, bursting through the cells into three valves; seeds numerous, with an orange-coloured tuft of hairs attached to them.

The seeds of *S. reginæ* are eaten by the Kaffirs. The fine leaves and large orange and purple flowers render this one of the most splendid of plants. Four or five species are in cultivation. *S. reginæ* is the most magnificent of all, the other species being in some instances smaller. *S. humilis* is, as it were, a reduced copy of the larger kind.

S. juncea is remarkable for the general absence of a blade to the leaf, so that the leafstalks resemble the stems of large rushes. The writer has, however, occasionally observed a small ovate-acute blade on the top of these stalks. [M. T. M.]

STREPTACHNE. A genus of grasses belonging to the tribe *Stipeæ*. Spikelets one-flowered; florets stalked; glumes lax, with short awns; lowest pale cylindrical, upper terminating in a simple awn, not jointed at the base; stamens three; styles two, the stigmas feathery. The three species are all natives of New Holland. [D. M.]

STREPTOCARPUS. A genus of *Gesneraceæ* of the tribe *Cyrtandreæ*, inhabiting Southern Africa, and consisting of herbs furnished with a stem, or being altogether without it. The leaves are opposite, one of the pair being usually smaller than its companion. From their axils arises a scape bearing one (rarely two) or a panicle of bluish or purplish flowers, and being coiled up before the unfolding of the blossoms. The calyx is five-cleft; the corolla tubulose funnel-shaped; the stamens five in number, only two of them fertile; and the capsule pod-like, and towards the point spirally twisted. [B. S.]

STREPTOCAULON A genus of *Asclepiadaceæ*, containing six species of twining plants, generally pubescent or tomentose, natives of India and the Eastern Archipelago. They have opposite leaves, and small flowers in interpetiolar cymes. The calyx is five-parted; the corolla rotate and five-parted, with five scales in the throat alternate with the segments; the filaments are distinct, and the anthers are united to the lower margin of the stigma; the pollen-masses are granular; the stigma is pentagonal; and the follicles are cylindrical spreading and smooth, and contain many comose seeds. [W. C.]

STREPTODESMA. A low scrubby rigid and thorny shrub from the deserts of Patagonia, forming a genus of *Leguminosæ* of the tribe *Hedysareæ*, scarcely to be distinguished from *Adesmia*, except by the pods consisting of globular joints, and more or less spirally twisted within the calyx and persistent corolla.

STREPTOLIRION. A genus referred to *Commelynaceæ* by some authors, and to *Trilliaceæ* by others. They are Indian plants, with the characters very nearly the same as in *Tradescantia*, only differing in the petals being small (shorter than the sepals), and the anthers, which are all perfect as in that genus, shaped like the sterile ones of *Aneilema*. The habit, however, is very different, resembling that of *Smilax*; as it has a twining stem, and ovate cordate-acuminate leaves. The flowers are in axillary and terminal racemes, containing from two to six blossoms; the filaments bearded with yellow hairs. [J. T. S.]

STREPTOPUS. A genus of *Melanthaceæ*, consisting of perennial herbaceous plants, with creeping rootstocks, from which are thrown up ovate net-veined leaves, which embrace the stem, and whose under-surface is woolly. The flowers are usually solitary, stalked, the stalks curiously bent in the middle; the perianth is six-parted deciduous bell-shaped; ovary three-celled; ovules numerous; style thread-shaped; fruit succulent; seeds numerous, whitish, with a loose coating. Three or four species are in cultivation in English gardens, having been originally imported from North America Hungary and Nepal. The generic name is derived from *streptos* 'twisted,' and *pous* 'a foot,' in allusion to the bent flower-stalks. [M. T. M.]

STREPTOSTIGMA. A name given by Thwaites to a sapindaceous tree from Ceylon, which proves to be a congener of *Harpulia* of Roxburgh. Presl gave the same name to the *Thinogeton*, a seacoast herb from Western Tropical America belonging to *Solanaceæ*.

STRIÆ (adj. STRIATE). Streaks; any

sort of longitudinal lines, whether arising from veins, or fine streaks of colour, or long channellings.

STRICTUS. Very upright, or very straight.

STRIGA. A genus of Scrophulariaceæ, containing several scabrous herbs, which are parasitic on the roots of plants. They are natives of Asia Africa and Australia. The lower leaves are opposite, and the upper alternate; they are linear, or sometimes reduced to mere scales. The flowers spring singly from the axils, forming a terminal spike; the calyx is tubular and costate; the corolla-tube is incurved, and the spreading limb two-lipped.   [W. C.]

STRIGÆ. Sharp close-pressed rigid hairs.

STRIGOSE. Covered with strigæ. Linnæus considered this word synonymous with Hispid.

STRIGULA. A genus of lichens belonging to the section with cyst-like fruit, occurring on the leaves of trees principally in tropical countries. The thallus is produced beneath the true cuticle, whence it has usually a bright shining appearance, which, in connection with the pure white or green tint and jet-black fruit, makes the species (though small) very conspicuous. The European species are doubtful, and perhaps S. Babingtoni, which occurs on box and laurel-leaves in this country, might be referred to the fungal genus Asterina: at any rate, it differs greatly in its dingy hue and partly filamentous thallus from the tropical species.

Strigulæ are subject to a curious change, in which the filaments of the thallus are predominant and become erect, bearing gonidia at their tips. In this state they have been described as species of Cephaleurus.   [M. J. B.]

STRINGWOOD. Acalypha rubra.

STRIPED. Marked with longitudinal stripes of colour.

STROBILACEOUS, STROBILIFORM. Having the appearance of a strobilus.

STROBILANTHES. A large genus of Acanthaceæ, comprising many herbs and shrubs scattered over Tropical Asia and Africa. The flowers are in axillary or terminal heads, or spikes that are sessile or pedunculate: the calyx is divided to the base into five sepals; the five lobes of the corolla are nearly equal, and spreading; the four stamens have parallel and equal anther-cells; the two cells of the ovary have each two ovules; the style is subulate and entire, or with a very minute upper tooth; and the capsule generally has the seeds towards its middle.   [W. C.]

STROBILORHACHIS. A genus of Acanthaceæ, containing two handsome species from Tropical America. They are shrubs or herbs, with four-sided spikes, which are covered with the broad limbs of the bright-coloured corolla; the corolla is

two-lipped, with a slender incurved tube opening upwards into a broad limb, the upper lip of which is two-lobed, and the lower three-lobed; the stamens are included; and the stigma is two-lipped and compressed, funnel-shaped.   [W. C.]

STROBILUS. A fir-cone; also any fruit which resembles a fir-cone; an imbricated scaly inflorescence; a collection of hard scales, representing distinct flowers arranged spirally, but closely imbricated.

STROMA. A word synonymous with Thallus, but applied especially to the substance in which the perithecia are immersed in such genera as Hypoxylon, or which contains the fructifying cells as in Dothidea.   [M. J. B.]

STROMANTHE. A genus of Marantaceæ, comprising an East Indian species, with large stalked variegated leaves, and flowers in a branched spike arranged in pairs between two coloured bracts. The distinguishing characteristics reside in the inner segments of the corolla, of which there are two of unequal size, while the third (or lip) is absent. The staminode is petal-like, very large, roundish concave at the top; the two stamens are petaloid, united at the base with the staminode; the sterile one concave at the top, the concavity concealing the deflected stigma; the fertile stamen bears a one-celled anther on its outer surface; the ovary is two-celled.   [M. T. M.]

STROMBOCARPA. A section of Prosopis, distinguished by the pod being spirally twisted like a corkscrew, and which some botanists have proposed to adopt as a distinct genus of Mimoseæ. There are several species, chiefly bushy shrubs, some of them abundant in the plains of Buenos Ayres and Patagonia, as well as in New Mexico, and known by the names of Retorquillo and some others, expressive of the singular shape of their fruits.

STROMBOSIA. A genus of Olacaceæ, consisting of trees with alternate entire coriaceous leaves, and very small flowers in axillary clusters or small cymes. It is distinguished in the order by having five stamens opposite the petals, and the ovary almost completely superior, divided nearly to the top into three four or five cells; whilst the fruit, a one-seeded drupe as in other genera, is almost completely inferior. There are six species known, one from Tropical Africa, the remainder from Tropical Asia.

STROMBUS-SHAPED, STROMBULIFORM. Twisted in a long spire, so as to resemble the convolutions of the shell called a Strombus—as the pod of Acacia strombulifera or Medicago polymorpha.

STRONG-MAN'S-WEED. Petiveria alliacea.

STROPHANTHUS. This name, derived from the Greek strophos 'a twisted cord or rope,' and anthos 'a flower,' is expressive of the chief peculiarity of the flowers

In this genus of *Apocyneæ*, the species referred to which are shrubs, natives of Tropical Africa and Asia. The flowers are in terminal heads; the corolla funnel-shaped, its throat partly closed by ten scales, its limb divided into five long tail-like segments, whence the name of the genus; the style thread-like, dilated at the top, with a cylindrical stigma; the fruit a double follicle. Two or three Indian and West African species are grown in this country for the pretty appearance and singularity of their flowers. The wood of *S. dichotomus* is used for planks, &c. in India.   (M. T. M.)

STROPHE. A term applied to the spirals formed in the development of leaves.

STROPHIOLE. A tubercle found surrounding the hilum of some kinds of seeds.

STRUMA. A cushion-like swelling; a goitre. A protuberance at the base of the spore-cases of some urn-mosses.

STRUMARIA. A genus of *Amaryllidaceæ*, consisting of Cape bulbous herbs, with lorate linear leaves, and solid scapes bearing many-flowered umbels of erect blossoms, which have a regular six-parted perianth with a short tube and stellated patent limb, six stamens, the filaments connected at the base, and an erect filiform angular columnar style, thickened or strumous below, with a trifid stigma. The flowers are white lined with red or green, or wholly red.   [T. M.]

STRUMIFORM. Having the appearance of a struma.

STRUMULOSE. Furnished with a small struma.

STRUTHIOLA. A genus of *Thymelaceæ*, consisting of South African shrubs, with the heath-like habit and foliage and almost all the characters of *Gnidia*, but differing from that genus essentially in their stamens, which are always four instead of eight; and generally in their flowers, which are axillary along the upper branches, and not in terminal heads. Nineteen species have been described, amongst which *S. virgata* with pink flowers, *S. erecta*, and some others have occasionally been grown in our greenhouses amongst Cape shrubs.

STRUTHIOPTERIS. A genus of hardy ferns of the polypodiaceous division, remarkable for their handsome growth. The fronds grow erect around a short upright caudex: the sterile ones in an outer series pinnato-pinnatifid; the fertile in the centre pinnate, with the pinnæ contracted moniliform, the margins rolled inwards so as to cover the sori. The veins are free. They are easily recognised by their dissimilar fronds, though technically very little different from *Polypodium* beyond the contraction and revolution of the fertile fronds. One species is European, another (or perhaps a variety) North American, and a third is found in India and Japan.   [T. M.]

STRYCHNIN. The poisonous principle obtained from *Strychnos nux vomica*.

STRYCHNOS. Certain solanaceous plants were known to the ancient Greeks by this name, which is now applied to a genus of *Loganiaceæ*. The species consist of trees or climbing shrubs, natives of the tropics of Asia and America. The leaves are entire strongly-nerved opposite, one of them, however, being frequently abortive, and developing from its axil a tendril-like branch. The flowers are in terminal or axillary corymbs or panicles, greenish-white and generally fragrant; the calyx has four or five overlapping segments; the corolla is tubular, its limb divided into four or five valvate segments; there are four or five stamens; and the fruit is a kind of berry, enclosing a single cavity, and generally many-seeded; the seeds being flattened disk-like and silky, surrounded by pulp. The valvate æstivation of the corolla and the succulent indehiscent fruit are the distinguishing characteristics.

The species to which the greatest interest is attached is that yielding the seeds known under the name of Nux-vomica.

Strychnos nux vomica.

This is a moderate-sized tree, destitute of spines or tendrils, native of the Coromandel Coast and Cochin China. The fruit is very like an orange in appearance, and contains numerous seeds of a flattened circular outline, about the size of a halfpenny, rather thicker near the circumference than elsewhere, the exterior of an ash-grey colour, covered with fine silky hairs, and the interior consisting of very hard grey albumen, in which, near the circumference, the embryo is embedded. The seeds have an intensely bitter taste, owing to the presence of two most energetic poisons, *strychnin* and *brucin*, which exist in the seeds conjoined with certain peculiar acids; but the pulp is innocuous, and is said to be greedily eaten by birds. If nitric acid be added to the powdered seeds a deep orange-yellow colour is produced.

Nux-vomica acts as a poison on man and animals, producing stiffness of the muscles, great distress, tetanic convulsions, and ultimately death. Strychnin and brucin produce precisely similar effects, but are far more powerful; insomuch that Dr. Christison reports that he has seen a dog killed in two minutes, when not more than the sixth part of a grain had been injected into the animal's chest. These substances act for the most part on the spinal cord. In cases of poisoning by these formidable drugs, but little can be done beyond emptying the stomach immediately, as no antidote has yet been discovered. Astringents and narcotics are recommended, and also the use of artificial respiration. It is also said that the fruit of the cucurbitaceous *Feuillœa cordifolia* is an antidote against this and other poisons, but this statement requires confirmation. Medicinally nux-vomica is used, in the shape of extract or tincture, in certain forms of paralysis and indigestion; and in small doses it acts as a tonic and diuretic. The bark of the tree possesses similar properties to the seeds, but in a less degree.

Serious consequences ensued in the early part of the present century from this bark having been imported and used as Angostura bark (see GALIPEA); and in Calcutta it is still said to be sold for the harmless bark of *Soymida febrifuga*, or Rohun-bark. Owing to the timely interposition of Dr. O'Shaughnessy, an error was rectified which otherwise might have had frightful consequences. It appears that a chemist procured, as he thought, a new alkaloid from the Rohun-bark, analogous to quinine, and which was therefore manufactured for the purpose of being employed in the Indian Army as a substitute for that drug. Dr. O'Shaughnessy, however, detected that the alkaloid in question was brucin, and that it had been derived from nux-vomica bark sold under the name of the harmless Rohun-bark.

The wood of the nux-vomica tree is hard and very bitter; it is said to be used in India in cases of intermittent fever and in snake-bites. A decoction of the leaves is used externally in rheumatism.

S. Tieuté, a climbing shrub, growing in Java, yields a juice which is used by the natives for poisoning their arrows. Its effects are precisely similar to those of nux-vomica, being dependent on the same ingredients. This poison is called Upas Tieute, but must not be confounded with the true Upas: see ANTIARIS. *S. toxifera* also yields a frightful poison called Ourari or Wourali, employed by the natives of Guiana. It has been tried in cases of hydrophobia, but with no good result. *S. colubrina*, a native of Malabar, furnishes one kind of *lignum colubrinum*, or Snakewood; it is considered by the natives as an infallible remedy in cases of snake-bite, and is also given in fevers and other complaints. *S. ligustrina* and other species are said to yield in Java various kinds of Snakewood, used for similar purposes to the one last mentioned. *S. Pseudo-Quina*, a native of Brazil, yields Colpache-bark, which is largely used in

that country in cases of fever, and is considered to equal quinine in value; its fruit is edible. It is stated that this species does not contain strychnin in spite of its bitter taste, and hence it is not considered to be poisonous.

From *S. potatorum*, a tree found in the mountains and forests of India, are obtained the seeds known in that country as Clearing Nuts. The fruit is black, of the size of a cherry, and contains only a single seed. These seeds are employed to clear muddy water; they are simply rubbed round the inside of the vessel for a minute or two, and then the water is allowed to settle. Their efficacy for this purpose depends, according to Dr. Pereira, on their albumen and casein, which act as fining agents, like those employed for wine or beer. Many other seeds might be used for the same purpose. The fruits and seeds are also used medicinally in India.

The pulp of the fruit of several species is harmless and edible: thus in Egypt and Senegal the natives eat the fruit of *S. innocua*; the Indians do not scruple to eat the fruits of *S. potatorum*; and the pulp of the Tieute even is said to be edible. The plant yielding St. Ignatius-beans is not known with certainty: it is, however, surmised to be a species of *Strychnos* from the quantity, of strychnin contained in the seeds: see IGNATIA. [M. T. M]

STRYPHNODENDRON. A genus of *Leguminosœ*, closely allied to *Inga*, but distinguished by the following characteristics:—Stamens ten; pod linear compressed, indehiscent leathery, pulpy within, and becoming baccate as it ripens; seeds numerous, pendulous. These trees are mostly natives of Brazil, and possess astringent properties, whence the name of the genus, from *struphnos* 'astringent' and *dendron* 'a tree.' [M. T. M.]

STUARTIA. A genus of *Ternströmiacræ*, consisting of North American shrubs, with membranous serrate leaves, white on the under-surface; and large white flowers, on solitary or double axillary stalks. The calyx is persistent, divided into five lanceolate segments; petals five, somewhat coherent at the base, crenulate at the margin; stamens numerous, in many rows, adherent to the petals; ovary free five-celled, with two ovules in each compartment; styles five, distinct or connate; fruit capsular, five-valved; seeds winged. *S. virginica* and *S. Malachodendron* are grown in this country; they are somewhat tender, but the beauty of their flowers renders them very desirable inmates of a garden; they flower in autumn. [M. T. M.]

STUBWORT. *Oxalis acetosella.*

STUPA (adj. STUPPEUS, STUPOSE). Tow; a tuft of long hairs.

STURMIA. A terrestrial genus of orchids, belonging to the *Malaxideæ*, generally included in the genus *Liparis*, consisting of one species, which is found in bogs and wet places in Europe and North

America. It grows about six inches in height, and has a tuberous root, and two leaves about half the length of the stem; the flowers are few small and racemose. It is a native of some of the south-eastern counties of England. [W. B. H.]

STURTIA. A genus of *Malvaceæ*, named in compliment to an Australian explorer, and founded upon a somewhat shrubby species, with smooth stalked leaves, and solitary stalked flowers, the outer calyx of which consists of three entire leaves, the inner being five-toothed, the petals wedge-shaped, the ovaries five many-seeded, the styles united, and the stigmas linear. The plant is a native of Central tropical Australia. [M. T. M.]

STYLAPTERUS. A genus of *Penæaceæ*, comprising a small number of heath-like small-flowered undershrubs from Southern Africa, chiefly distinguished from *Penæa* by the want of the large persistent coloured bracts of that genus.

STYLATE. Having a persistent style.

STYLE. The narrowed upper end of a carpellary leaf; the part which bears the stigma.

STYLEWORT. *Stylidium.*

STYLEWORTS. Lindley's name for the *Stylidiaceæ.*

STYLIDIACEÆ. A small order of monopetalous dicotyledons, nearly allied to the irregular-flowered *Campanulaceæ* or *Lobeliaceæ*, of which it has the inferior two-celled ovary and capsular fruit, with numerous albuminous seeds; but it is remarkable for the stamens, two in number, being united with the style in a highly irritable column of curious structure, the stigma lying in a cavity at the apex, surrounded and concealed by the anthers. It consists of small herbs or undershrubs, chiefly Australian, with a few species from New Zealand, the Straits of Magelhaens, or Tropical Asia; and is divided into three four or five genera, of which *Stylidium* itself contains the great majority of the species.

STYLIDIUM. A genus of *Stylidiaceæ*, having an adherent two-lipped calyx of from two to five divisions; a monopetalous corolla, with an irregular limb and a twisted tube; two stamens, united with the style into a column longer than the limb of the corolla; the stigma lying in a cavity at the apex of the column, surrounded and concealed by the anthers. This column is extremely irritable; it hangs down on one side of the flower until it is touched, when it instantly springs up, and shifts at once to the opposite side with great force. The seed-vessel is two-celled, and contains numerous small seeds, which are sometimes stalked. The species are herbaceous plants or small shrubs, with scattered entire leaves, sometimes in whorls, and pink white or violaceous (rarely yellow) flowers. They are natives of most parts of Australia, particularly the south-western por-

tion, and also of Tasmania. Two species, *S. Kunthii* and *S. tenellum*, are found in India; and *S. uliginosum* is a native of Ceylon. [R. H.]

STYLINE. Of or belonging to the style.

STYLISCUS. The channel which passes from the stigma through the style into the ovary.

STYLOBASIUM. The name of an Australian shrub, with entire smooth leaves, and polygamous flowers, in the axils of the upper leaves; the calyx is five-lobed, coloured; the corolla absent; stamens ten, hypogynous; ovary one-celled, with two ovules; style lateral or basal; fruit drupaceous. The genus is included in the order *Chrysobalanaceæ*. [M. T. M.]

STYLOCERAS. A genus of American trees of the *Euphorbiaceæ*. The leaves resemble those of the cherry-laurel, *Cerasus Laurocerasus*; and the flowers are either monœcious or diœcious: when monœcious, arranged in solitary or double axillary spikes, the lower flowers of which are male, the terminal female; when diœcious, the males in spikes, and the females solitary, stalked. The fruit is capsular globose, surmounted by the persistent horn-like styles, from which latter organs the genus derives its name. The fruit is said to be edible. [M. T. M.]

STYLOCORYNE. One of the genera of *Cinchonaceæ*, consisting of trees, with flowers on axillary stalks. The limb of the calyx is short tubular five-toothed; the corolla salver or funnel-shaped, its limb five-parted; stamens five, inserted on to the throat of the corolla; the anthers linear and very long; the style projecting beyond the corolla, and terminated by a club-like stigma; the fruit succulent, surmounted by the limb of the calyx. The name is expressive of the club-like stigma surmounting the style. [M. T. M.]

STYLODISCUS. A genus of *Euphorbiaceæ*, represented by a large tree, native of India, the leaves of which are pinnate, and the flowers diœcious, very numerous, small, and arranged in axillary panicles. The calyx has five concave sepals, encircling as many stamens, which are united below into a column; ovary rudimentary; in the female flowers there is a five-parted calyx, with five glands opposite to the segments, and representing the stamens. Fruit baccate three-celled, each cell with two seeds. [M. T. M.]

STYLOGYNE. A genus of *Myrsinaceæ*, including a Brazilian shrub, whose leaves are entire, marked by pellucid spots; and whose flowers are in terminal panicles. The calyx is five-parted, its segments convolute; corolla five-parted, twisted in the bud like the calyx, ultimately reflected; stamens five, the anthers nearly as long as the filaments; style as long as the corolla; fruit drupaceous. The unusual length of the style probably suggested the name of the genus. [M. T. M.]

STYLOPHORUM. Certain North American herbs of the family *Papaveraceæ* have been comprised in a genus of this name. They are described as having a yellow juice, divided leaves, and yellow somewhat corymbose flowers. The calyx is of two hairy caducous sepals; petals four; stamens numerous; ovary one-celled, with three to four parietal placentæ; style column-like; stigma three to four-lobed; fruit a capsule, bursting by three or four valves. The genus derives its name from the presence of a style surmounting the ovary, a rare circumstance in the plants of the poppy family. [M. T. M.]

STYLOPODIUM. The double fleshy disk from which the styles of umbellifers arise.

STYLOSANTHES. A genus of papilionaceous *Leguminosæ*, consisting of herbs or undershrubs, usually covered with sticky hairs, and natives of the tropics of both hemispheres. The leaves have three leaflets, and the flowers are grouped in a dense terminal or axillary spike, bearing a number of bracts, in the axils of which the flowers are placed either singly or in pairs—if in pairs one of them frequently imperfect. The flowers are polygamous: the hermaphrodite ones are sterile, and have a calyx with a long tube surmounted by a two-lipped limb, a papilionaceous corolla, and ten monadelphous stamens, while the female flowers are fertile, and have no calyx or corolla, but an erect ovary with two ovules, a short hooked style, and a thick stigma. The pod is jointed, the lower joint occasionally empty, the upper terminated by the persistent style, whence the name of the genus. The dimorphism of the flowers is curious. Some of the species with yellow blossoms are grown in this country. [M. T. M.]

STYLOSPORE. A name proposed by the Tulasnes for the naked spores in such genera as *Diplodia, Hendersonia, &c.*, in consequence of their being produced at the tips of short thread-like cells, or more rarely on branched threads. If the distinction of spores and sporidia hold good there is no necessity for the name, except in connection with the theory that these genera are mere conditions of true acigerous *Fungi* belonging to the genus *Sphæria* and its allies. This theory is founded on the fact that supposed species of these genera often grow on the same matrix with *Sphæria*, and are not distinguishable without microscopical examination; that, as in the case of *Sphæria inquinans*, the naked and inclosed spores are produced on different parts of the same thallus; and that in some genera, as in *Tympanis*, naked spores and asci are produced from the same hymenium. These stylospores are regarded therefore as a secondary kind of fruit, comparable with the conidia of other *Fungi*, or the oïdioid spores of *Erysiphe*, though in that genus stylospores of two kinds (or possibly stylospores and spermatia) are produced as well as conidia. It is not supposed that these stylospores have sexual functions, as they are sometimes observed to germinate, and in several *Fungi* spermatia have been observed very similar to those of lichens—as, for instance, in *Valsa hypodermia*. The cysts which inclose the stylospores are called Pycnidia. [M. J. B.]

STYLOSTEMON. An epigynous stamen.

STYLOTEGIUM. The coronal or orbicular mass which forms part of the androeceum of such asclepiads as *Stapelia*.

STYPANDRA. A genus of *Liliaceæ* from Southern Australia, consisting of perennial herbs, with creeping rhizomes, and linear-ensiform leaves. The flowers are blue or whitish, on pedicels articulated with the perianth, paniculate-corymbose; the perianth is six-parted, with equal spreading segments; the stamens six, with curved filaments, bearded at the apex; the capsule subglobose, three-celled; the seeds few oval smooth, without a strophiole at the hilum. [J. T. S.]

STYPHELIA. A genus of *Epacridaceæ*, distinguished by having a five-parted calyx, surrounded by a few bracts; an elongated tubular corolla, the segments of the limb bearded and revolute; stamens longer than the tube, with oblong-linear anthers; and a five-celled nearly dry seedvessel containing a single seed. They are harsh erect shrubby plants, natives of New South Wales and Tasmania, with scattered oblong or lanceolate sharp-pointed leaves on short footstalks; and the flowers generally axillary, drooping, red or green. [R. H.]

STYPHNOLOBIUM. A genus of papilionaceous *Leguminosæ*, represented by a tree, with unequally pinnate leaves, and flowers in terminal racemes or panicles; calyx five-toothed; vexillum rounded reflected, scarcely larger than the wings; keel blunt, as long as the wings; stamens ten, monadelphous or distinct; ovary stalked; style filiform, curved; pod moniliform fleshy indehiscent many-seeded, the seeds encircled by austere pulp, whence the name of the genus, from the Greek *stuphnos* 'astringent.' The pulp of the fruit of *S. japonica* yields a yellow dye. This tree, which is better known as *Sophora japonica*, thrives well in this country. A fine example of it may be seen growing in the Oxford Botanic Garden. [M. T. M.]

STYPTIC. Astringent.

STYRACACEÆ. (*Symplocaceæ, Symplocineæ, Halesiaceæ, Storaxworts*.) An order of dicotyledons connecting in some measure *Monopetalæ* with *Polypetalæ*, but usually classed with the former. It consists of trees or shrubs, chiefly tropical, a very few being found in North America. They have alternate undivided leaves without stipules, and solitary clustered or paniculate flowers, often white and usually axillary. The calyx is free or more or less adherent, with four or five teeth; the corolla consists of as many divisions or petals, often only cohering by their adhesion to the staminal ring; stamens definite or indefinite, inserted on or adhering to the base of the corolla; ovary superior or more or less inferior, with two or more ovules in each cell; fruit drupaceous, with one or few seeds containing a slender embryo in the midst of albumen. The two principal genera, *Symplocos* and *Styrax*, are considered by some botanists as types of two distinct orders, but are more generally regarded as tribes only of *Styracaceæ*. Among the smaller genera *Halesia*, or the American Snowdrop-tree, is the only one of general interest.

STYRAX. The typical genus of the *Styracaceæ*, consisting of trees and shrubs, natives of Asia and North America. The leaves are entire, frequently covered with star-shaped hairs; and the flowers are white, in racemes. The calyx is bell-shaped, five-toothed; corolla five-parted, longer than the calyx; stamens ten, adherent to the base of the petals, filaments cohering below, distinct above; ovary partially three-celled; fruit globose, adnate to the base of the persistent calyx, one-celled one-seeded.

S. officinale, a native of the Levant, &c., yields a balsamic resinous substance known as Storax, and which is obtained by stripping off pieces of the bark of the shrub, and submitting them to pressure. In this way liquid storax is obtained: solid storax appears to be the same substance mixed with fine sawdust and dried. Storax is used by perfumers on account of its agreeable odour, and it is employed in medicine as a stimulating expectorant.

S. Benzoin, a native of Sumatra, Borneo, &c., yields the resin called Benzoin. Incisions are made into the tree, the juice exudes, dries, and the dried mass is removed by a knife or chisel. Each tree yields annually about three pounds of benzoin, that which is formed during the first three years being of better quality than that which exudes subsequently. Benzoin is employed medicinally in chronic pulmonary disorders, and also by perfumers for various purposes. It is used in Roman Catholic churches in the composition of incense. Other species, besides those just mentioned, yield a fragrant resin. Some of the kinds are grown in this country, their pure white flowers rendering them very ornamental in shrubberies.   [M. T. M.]

SUÆDA. The plants belonging to this genus of *Chenopodiaceæ* grow only on seashores, or in saline plains and other places where the soil is impregnated with salt. They are almost exclusively confined to the temperate and tropical regions of the Northern Hemisphere, very few being found in the Southern. They are smooth or downy herbaceous or more frequently shrubby plants, with alternate somewhat tapering fleshy stalkless leaves, bearing solitary or clustered stalkless or short-stalked usually perfect flowers in their axils. Their fruits, called utricles, are enclosed in the slightly enlarged or inflated berry-like calyx, but do not adhere to it. *S. fruticosa* alias *Chenopodium fruticosum*, or *Salsola fruticosa*, is one of our rarer British species; but it is very common in the warmer parts of Europe, and also in Northern Africa and Western Asia. It is a shrubby erect branching evergreen perennial plant, from two to three feet high, with thick and succulent semicylindrical bluntish pale green leaves, and small stalkless flowers, either solitary or two or three together. In England it is found only on some parts of the eastern and southern coasts. It is one of the plants burned in Southern Europe for the manufacture of barilla.   [A. S.]

SUB. In composition usually = somewhat; as *sub-rotund*, somewhat round; or, *sub-globose*, approaching the globular form. Also nearly; as *sub-insipidus*, nearly insipid.

SUBARBORESCENT. Having a somewhat tree-like aspect.

SUBER (adj. SUBEROSE). Cork. The epiphlœum of bark, when it acquires an elastic soft texture, and is preternaturally enlarged.

SUBER. *Quercus Suber*, the Cork-tree.

SUBJEE. An Indian name for the leaves or capsules of the Indian Hemp.

SUBMERSED. Buried beneath water.

SUBMARGINAL. Situated near the margin.

SUBORDER. One of the minor groups into which Natural Orders are divided; as the *Papilionaceæ* and *Mimoseæ* of the order *Leguminosæ*.

SUBRAMEAL. Growing on a branch below a leaf.

SUBRAMOSE. Having a slight tendency to branch.

SUBROSEUS. Having something of a rose-colour.

SUBULARIA. A minute stemless aquatic annual belonging to the order *Cruciferæ*, common in ditches lakes and streams which have a sandy or gravelly bottom; in most of the colder countries of Europe. The whole plant consists merely of a tuft of white fibrous roots, a few very narrow awl-shaped leaves about an inch long, and a leafless stalk two inches high, bearing a few scattered small white flowers which expand and ripen their seeds under water. *S. aquatica*, or Awlwort, the only species, is indigenous to Scotland and the North of England and Ireland. French: *Subulaire*; German: *Wasserpfriemen*.   [C. A. J.]

SUBULATE, SUBULIFORM. Awl-shaped; linear, very narrow, tapering to a very fine point from a broadish base.

SUBULI. The aciculæ or sharp processes formed by some fungals.

SUCCISE. (Fr.) *Scabiosa succisa*.

SUCCISUS. Abruptly broken off, or appearing to be so.

SUCCORY. *Cichorium Intybus.* —, GUM. *Chondrilla.* —, HOG or SWINE'S. *Hyoseris.* —, LAMB. *Arnoseris.* —, POISONOUS. *Apogeris fœtida.*

SUCCOSE. Full of juice.

SUCCOWIA. A genus of *Cruciferæ*, comprising an annual inhabiting Northern Africa, the Mediterranean, and the Canary Islands; and having pinnatipartite leaves, and erect elongated racemes opposite them. The pouch is two-valved ovate-globose, with the valves concave, prickly, with a four-sided subulate style. [J. T. S.]

SUCCUBOUS. A term used in the description of *Jungermanniaceæ*, intimating that the anterior margin of each leaf as set on the branches passes beneath the posterior margin of that which succeeds it. See INCUBOUS. [M. J. B.]

SUCCULENT. Very cellular and juicy, as the stems of *Stapelia.*

SUCE-PIN. (Fr.) *Hypopithys multiflora.*

SUCKER. A shoot thrown up by a plant from beneath the surface of the ground, as is common with roses, &c.

SUCKLING. *Trifolium filiforme.*

SUCRION. (Fr.) A kind of barley.

SUDORIFIC. Having the power of causing perspiration.

SUERCE. (Fr.) *Swertia.*

SUÉRIN DE TOURS. (Fr.) *Cucumis Melo.*

SUFFIS. (Fr.) *Pinus Pumilio.*

SUFFRUTEX. An undershrub or shrub of small size, herbaceous at the ends of the shoots, though woody at their base.

SUFFRUTICOSE. Having a somewhat shrubby habit.

SUGAR. The saccharine constituent of organised bodies, that of commerce being obtained from the juice or sap of certain plants, and especially of the Sugar-cane. —, BEET. The product of different varieties of beet-root, of which the Silesian is the most prolific. —, CANE. The product of the sugar-cane, *Saccharum officinarum*, and its varieties. —, DATE. The product of the date, *Phœnix sylvestris*, and other palms, as *Saguerus saccharifer*; this is less sweetening than cane-sugar. —, GRAPE. A granular kind of sugar obtainable from grapes, less sweetening than cane-sugar. —, LIQUORICE. An uncrystallisable extract obtained from the root of *Glycyrrhiza glabra.* —, MAPLE. The product of the sugar-maple, *Acer saccharinum.*

SUGAR-BERRY. The fruit of *Celtis occidentalis.*

SUGAR-CANE. *Saccharum officinarum.* —, CHINESE. *Sorghum saccharatum.*

SUGAR-TREE. *Myoporum platycarpum.*

SUIN. (Fr.) *Sambucus nigra.*

SUJNA. An Indian name for *Moringa pterygosperma.*

SUKHIANG. A Chinese name for *Aloexylon Agallochum.*

SUKON. The Malayan name for the Bread-fruit.

SULCATE. Furrowed.

SULCATO-RIMOSE. Furrowed and cracked like the cotyledons of a Spanish chestnut.

SULCI. The lamellæ of certain fungals.

SULEEKHE. An Indian name for the aromatic bark of *Cinnamomum Culilawan.*

SULIA. (Fr.) *Hedysarum coronarium.*

SULION. (Fr.) *Sambucus nigra.*

SULLIVANTIA. A genus of *Saxifragaceæ*, containing a single species from Ohio, a low spreading perennial with rounded and cut toothed or slightly lobed leaves, and small white flowers, in a branched loosely cymose panicle on a nearly leafless scape. The calyx is bell-shaped, cohering below only, with the base of the ovary five-cleft; petals five, entire, acute; stamens five; capsule two-celled, two-beaked, with numerous wing-margined seeds. [J. T. S.]

SULPHUREUS. Sulphur-colour; a pale bright-yellow, with a mixture of white.

SULPHUR-WEED or SULPHURWORT. *Peucedanum.*

SULTAN, SWEET. *Amberboa moschata.* —, YELLOW. *Amberboa odorata.*

SULTAN DOUX. (Fr.) *Amberboa moschata.*

SUMAC. (Fr.) *Rhus.* — À LA GALE or À LA PUCE. *Rhus radicans.* — AMARANTE or DE VIRGINIE. *Rhus typhina.* — À FEUILLES DE MYRTE. *Coriaria myrtifolia.* — DE CEYLAN. *Connarus.* — FUSTET. *Rhus Cotinus.*

SUMACH, SHUMAC. The dried and chopped leaves and shoots of *Rhus Coriaria.* —, AMERICAN. *Rhus typhina.* —, JAMAICA. *Rhus Metopium.* —, STAGSHORN. *Rhus typhina.* —, SWAMP. *Rhus venenata.* —, TANNER'S. *Coriaria myrtifolia.* —, VENICE. *Rhus Cotinus.* —, VIRGINIAN. *Rhus typhina.* —, WEST INDIAN. *Brunellia comocladifolia.*

SUMBUL. An Eastern name for the root of *Nardostachys Jatamansi*; also the root of an umbelliferous plant supposed to be allied to *Angelica.*

SUN. *Crotalaria juncea.*

SUNBURN. See HELIOSIS.

SUNDEW. *Drosera.*

SUNDROPS. An American name for *Œnothera fruticosa* and *Œ. riparia.*

SUNFLOWER. *Helianthus*; also *Helianthemum* and *Calendula officinalis.* —,

COMMON. *Helianthus annuus.* —, FALSE. *Helenium.* —, TICKSEED. *Coreopsis trichosperma.*

SUNIPIA. An epiphytal genus of orchids belonging to the tribe *Malaxideæ.* The leaves are solitary, leathery; the spike radical or from beneath the base of the pseudobulb; and the flowers small white, stained with pink, nearly hidden by the large spathaceous bracts. It differs from all other genera in the anther opening vertically with two pairs of equal pollen-masses, adhering to as many tough round elastic legs or caudicles meeting at the rostellum, which has no gland. In habit it approaches *Bolbophyllum.* The name is derived from the Indian word Sunipiang. The only species, *S. scariosa,* is found in the Khasya Hills, the Sikkim Himalaya, &c., at an elevation of 5,000 to 6,000 feet above the sea-level.   [W. B. H.]

SUNN. *Crotalaria juncea.*

SUNSTROKE. See HELIOSIS.

SUPERBE DU MALABAR. (Fr.) *Methonica superba.*

SUPERFICIAL, SUPERFICIARIUS. Found at the surface.

SUPERIOR. Growing above anything. A calyx is *half-superior* when it appears to grow from above the base of an ovary; and absolutely superior when it appears to grow from the top of the ovary. On the contrary, the ovary is superior when it grows above the origin of the calyx.

SUPERPOSED, SUPERPOSITUS. Stationed above anything; placed one above another, as ovules in an ovary.

SUPERVOLUTE. When one edge is rolled inwards and is enveloped by the opposite edge, also rolled inwards, as the leaves of an apricot-tree.

SUPERVOLUTIVE. An æstivation in which leaves are supervolute.

SUPPLE-JACK. *Paullinia curassavica, polyphylla,* and *barbadensis;* also *Cardiospermum grandiflorum.* Also a Virginian name for *Berchemia volubilis.*

SUPRA. Above or upon anything.

SUPRA-AXILLARY. Growing above an axil.

SUPRADECOMPOUND. Divided into a multitude of pieces; so much divided that the number and mode of division cannot be precisely ascertained; as the leaves of the carrot, fennel, &c.

SUPRAFOLIACEOUS. Growing above a leaf.

SUPRAFOLIAR. Growing upon a leaf.

SURCULUS. The same as Sucker; also the young prostrate stem of a moss.

SURCURRENT. The opposite of decurrent; when a leafy expansion runs up the stem.

SUREAU. (Fr.) *Sambucus nigra.* — D'EAU. *Viburnum Opulus.*

SURELLE. (Fr.) *Oxalis acetosella.*

SURETTE. (Fr.) *Byrsonima spicata.*

SURIANACEÆ. *Suriana,* a branching pubescent maritime shrub, found on most tropical coasts, with narrow entire rather thick leaves, and terminal yellow flowers, has so many peculiarities of structure that, after having been successively added on to various orders, it has been proposed to consider it as forming an order by itself under the above name, or at most to associate with it *Rigiostachys,* a Mexican shrub of a very dissimilar aspect. *Suriana* has now, however, been referred with very little hesitation to *Simarubaceæ,* whilst the place of *Rigiostachys* still remains very doubtful.

SURINAM-POISON. *Tephrosia toxicaria.*

SURINGEE. An Indian name for the flower-buds of *Calysaccion longifolium.*

SURISHA. An Indian name of *Sinapis nigra* and *S. dichotoma.*

SURON. (Fr.) *Bunium Bulbocastanum.*

SURRE. (Fr.) The acorns of *Quercus Suber.*

SURRIER. (Fr.) *Quercus Suber.*

SURSAH, SURSEE, SURSON. Indian names of *Sinapis nigra* and *S. dichotoma.*

SURSUM. Upwards; as *sursum hamulosus* = bordered with hooks directed upwards, i.e. towards the point of the leaf.

SUSPENDED. Hanging up by the side; as many seeds.

SUSPENSOR. A cellular cord by which the embryo of some seeds is suspended from the foramen.

SUSUM. A tall reed-like herb from Java, with lanceolate radical leaves, and numerous flowers in a large terminal panicle, forming a genus of *Juncaceæ,* closely allied to the Australian *Xerotes,* but differing in the three connate thick and undivided stigmas which crown the ovary.

SUTHERLANDIA. Several species of this genus of *Leguminosæ (Papilionaceæ)* have been described, but it is probable they all belong to one variable species, *S. frutescens,* a showy shrub of moderate size, with unequally pinnate leaves, and large scarlet flowers succeeded by dry bladdery thin-shelled pods containing numerous seeds. The flowers have a hoary nearly equally five-toothed calyx; a pea-like corolla, with the sides of the upper petal folded back, very short wing or side petals, and rather longer boat-shaped lower petals; one free and nine combined stamens; a slender style, bearded lengthways along the back, and transversely at the apex in front; and a terminal stigma. It is a native of the Cape of Good Hope, and in English gardens is called the Cape

Bladder Senna, from the resemblance of its pods to those of *Colutea*, with which in fact it was formerly combined. According to Thunberg, the dried and pulverised roots and leaves are useful in diseases of the eye. [A. S.]

SUTTONIA. *Myrsine.*

SUTURAL. Of or belonging to the suture; thus *sutural dehiscence* is the act of splitting along the line of junction of two valves.

SUTURE. The line of junction of two different parts.

SUZELLE. (Fr.) *Rumex acetosa.*

SWAINSONA. This genus of *Leguminosæ* differs from *Colutea* in the stigma being terminal not lateral; and also in the legume, which is not so much inflated as in *Colutea*, and more pointed from the persistence of the style. The flowers have nearly equal calyx-teeth; the standard is almost orbicular, the wings oblong falcate or twisted, and the keel broad obtuse or produced into a twisted beak; the upper stamen free; and the pod inflated or turgid, with the upper suture compressed, or the pod divided by a longitudinal partition. The species are Australian herbs or undershrubs, with unequally pinnate leaves, and flowers in axillary racemes, either purple blue red or white. Some of the species, as *S. Greyana*, *S. procumbens* also known as *S. violacea*, and *S. galegifolia*, are very handsome plants. [M. T. M.]

SWALLOWWORT. *Asclepias*; also *Chelidonium majus* and *Thapsia Asclepium*.

SWAMMERDAMIA. A genus of *Compositæ*, represented by a Tasmanian undershrub, whose leaves are wedge-shaped entire leathery, whitish on the under-surface; and which bears pale flowers, arranged in paniculate heads, each head surrounded by an involucre of overlapping linear scales. The receptacle is naked, the outer florets three-toothed female, the central florets hermaphrodite five-cleft; the achenes cylindrical, surmounted by a pappus of one row of hairs, each with a little knob at the extremity. [M. T. M.]

SWAN-NECK, or SWANWORT. *Cycnoches.*

SWARTZIA. This genus was formerly regarded as the type of a distinct suborder of *Leguminosæ*; but it now forms, in combination with a few allied genera, a tribe of the suborder *Cæsalpinieæ*. Its flowers are thus characterised:—The calyx is at first globular or egg-shaped and firmly closed, but ultimately splits irregularly into valves or sepals, which curve backwards; the corolla is frequently altogether wanting, and when present consists of only one petal, or rarely of two or three; the stamens are indefinite in number, and rise from beneath the ovary, some of them being longer than the rest, and barren; and the ovary is usually stalked, and tapers gradually at the top into a style of greater or less length. It is an exclusively tropical American genus, and consists of about forty species, most of which are large forest-trees, and yield hard durable timber. They have simple or more frequently unequally pinnate leaves, and axillary racemes of flowers, succeeded usually by small splitting pods containing several seeds.

S. tomentosa, a native of French Guiana, is one of the American trees named Palo Santo by the Portuguese. It is of very large size, with a trunk sixty or more feet high, and upwards of three feet in diameter, supported at the base by six or eight narrow buttresses. The heartwood is of a reddish colour, or blackish in old trees, very hard and close-grained, and extremely durable. A red juice exudes from cracks in the bark, and becomes hardened into a blackish resin. [A. S.]

SWEDE. A kind of Turnip, so called from having been introduced from Sweden. It is the *Brassica campestris rutabaga*.

SWEET-GALE. *Myrica Gale.*

SWEET-JOHN. The narrow-leaved varieties of *Dianthus barbatus.*

SWEETLEAF. *Symplocos tinctoria.*

SWEETSOP. The fruit of *Anona squamosa* and *A. sericea.*

SWEETWATER. A variety of white grape.

SWEETWILLIAM. *Dianthus barbatus*; also *Silene Armeria*. —, BARBADOS. *Ipomœa Quamoclit.*

SWEETWOOD. A timber obtained in Jamaica from *Oreodaphne exaltata*. —, BLACK. *Strychnodaphne floribunda*. —, LOBLOLLY. *Oreodaphne Leucoxylon.* —, LOWLAND. *Nectandra sanguinea.* —, MOUNTAIN. *Acrodiclidium jamaicense.* —, PEPPER. *Nectandra sanguinea.* —, RIO GRANDE. *Oreodaphne Leucoxylon.* —, SHRUBBY. *Amyris.* —, TIMBER. *Acrodiclidium jamaicense*, *Nectandra exaltata*, and *N. leucantha.* —, WHITE. *Nectandra sanguinea* and *N. leucantha.* —, YELLOW. *Nectandra sanguinea.*

, SWERTIA. A genus of perennial herbs of the order *Gentianaceæ*. The species are distributed through Central Europe and Asia, and occur also in Northern India. The flowers have a five-parted calyx; a rotate five-cleft corolla, whose segments have at the base two little glandular pits surrounded by fine hairs; stamens inserted on to the throat of the corolla; anthers unchanged; fruit one-celled two-valved; seeds membranous, winged. *S. perennis* is said to have been found formerly in Wales. The Russians drink the infusion of the leaves as a medicine, and the Tartars apply the leaves to wounds. [M. T. M.]

SWETH. *Allium Schœnoprasum.*

SWIETENIA *Mahagoni* is the sole representative of a genus of *Cedrelaceæ*, peculiar to the warmer parts of America, and yielding the timber known as the Mahogany of commerce. It is a stately tree, principally met with in Central America and Mexico, growing upon rocky soil. The leaves are imparipinnate, and the flowers axillary. The calyx is-five-cleft, short; the corolla has five petals, and the stamens are united into a tube bearing ten anthers; the fruit is a five-celled woody capsule, each cell containing numerous winged seeds. The bark is considered a febrifuge, and the seeds prepared with oil were used by the ancient Aztecs as they are by the modern Mexicans as a cosmetic, under the names of Pepitos del Sopilote, Zopilotl, or Tzontecomatl. The timber is largely employed in making household furniture in this country.   [B. S.]

SWINE'SBANE. *Chenopodium rubrum.*

SWINE'S-SNOUT. *Taraxacum dens leonis.*

SWORD-SHAPED. The same as Ensiform.

SYAGRUS. A genus of palms resembling the cocoa-nut tree in appearance, and indeed closely allied to it in botanical characters, most of them having, in fact, been formerly referred to *Cocos.* The principal points of difference between them consist in the flower-spike being enveloped in a single spathe in *Cocos* and a double one in *Syagrus* ; and in the hard bony shell of the fruit of the latter having a broad smooth band or channel running from each of the three pores, and meeting at the top. Like the cocoa-nuts, the fruits of the different species of *Syagrus* contain a single oily sometimes hollow seed enclosed in a hard bony shell surrounded by a fibrous rind, the shell also having three pores or holes near the base, as in the well-known cocoa-nut. Of the five or six known species, one, *S. amara,* is a native of the West Indian island of Martinique, and the rest are indigenous to Brazil.   [A. S.]

SYCAMINE. The Sycamore.

SYCAMORE. *Acer Pseudo-Platanus.* — AMERICAN. *Platanus occidentalis.* —, NEW SOUTH WALES. *Brachychiton luridum.*

SYCHNOCARPOUS. Having the power of producing fruit many times without perishing, as is the case with all trees and herbaceous perennials.

SYCIOS. *Sicyos.*

SYCOMORE. (Fr.) *Acer Pseudo-Platanus;* also *Ficus Sycomorus* alias *Sycomorus antiquorum.* — FAUX. *Melia Azedarach.*

SYCOMORPHE of Miquel, the same as *Covellia* of Gasparrini, is the name of a genus proposed for some species of *Ficus* from Tropical Asia.

SYCOMORUS. A name under which Gasparrini proposed to separate from *Ficus* as a distinct genus the *F. Sycomorus* (*S. antiquorum*), and some other African species.

SYCONIUM, SYCONUS. Such fruits as

that of the fig, consisting of a fleshy receptacle loaded with flowers, each producing its own proper seed-vessel.

SYCOPSIS. An East Indian tree or shrub, with alternate undivided leaves, and small dioecious flowers in their axils, which forms a distinct genus of *Hamamelidaceæ.*

SYGWAM. An Indian name for Teak-wood.

SYLVAN, SYLVATICUS, SYLVESTRIS. Growing in woods.

SYLVIE. (Fr.) *Anemone nemorosa.* — JAUNE. *Anemone ranunculoides.*

SYLVULA. A plantation.

SYMBOLANTHUS. A shrubby plant native of the mountains of Peru, and constituting a genus of *Gentianaceæ.* It may be known by the following characters :— Calyx five-parted, pentangular; corolla rose-coloured, salver-shaped, the tube three inches in length, the limb divided into five segments; stamens within the tube of the corolla, united at the base by a circular membrane. The one-celled ovary is girt by a glandular disk; and surmounted by a stigma divided into two linear plates. So showy a plant should not long remain absent from our greenhouses. [M. T. M.]

SYMMETRY (adj. SYMMETRICAL). That kind of arrangement in which the number of parts of one series corresponds with that of the other series; as, for example, when a flower with five sepals has five petals, and five ten or fifteen stamens.

SYMPETALOUS. A growing of the stamens to the petals, so as to produce the appearance of a monopetalous corolla ; as in the mallow.

SYMPHORIA. *Symphoricarpus.*

SYMPHORICARPUS. The generic name of plants belonging to the order of caprifolis. The ovary is four-celled, two of the cells being abortive, while the other two produce each one hard seed. The species are shrubs, natives of North America and Mexico. One of them, *S. racemosus,* is the well-known Snowberry, cultivated in gardens, producing large white berries. The name is from the Greek *symphoreo* 'to bear together' and *carpos* 'fruit,' in allusion to the clusters of berries.   [G. D.]

SYMPHYANDRA. A genus of *Campanulaceæ,* known by the five stamens having the filaments dilated at the base, fringed with hairs and free, and the anthers adhering so as to form a long cylindrical tube. The species are perennial herbs, natives of Crete and the Caucasus, with alternate cordate and crenato-dentate leaves, the lowest of which are largest. The name is from the Greek, and indicates the union of the anthers.   [G. D.]

SYMPHYANTHEROUS. The same as Syngenesious.

SYMPHYOGLOSSUM. A genus of *Asclepiadaceæ,* comprising two herbaceous twiners from Northern China, closely allied to *Cynanchum*, but differing in the arrangement of the scales of the staminal corona, which are scarcely connected into a ring at the base, but the outer ones are closely united with the corresponding inner ones.

SYMPHYOGYNA. One of the finest genera of the frondose *Jungermanniaceæ*, distinguished by the want of a perianth, and a calyptra springing from the back of the frond, which is mostly erect and stipitate. It belongs to the division *Haplolæneæ*. The species have the habit of *Hymenophylla*, for which they may be mistaken

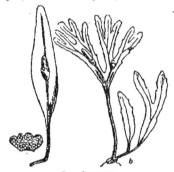

Symphyogyna.
a. subsimplex.　　*b.* hymenophylla.

when out of fruit. They would probably not be difficult of cultivation, and would undoubtedly be acceptable objects amongst the more minute inmates of the fern-house. The species are almost confined to the Southern Hemisphere. Five are found in New Zealand, and about half that number in New Holland and Tasmania, whereas a single doubtful species only occurs in North America. [M. J. B.]

SYMPHYOMYRTUS. An Australian genus of *Myrtaceæ* of very curious structure has received this name. It constitutes a shrub, bearing heads of flowers at the base of the previous year's branches; these heads consisting of twelve or fourteen flowers, closely packed, and being fused together upon a fleshy receptacle. The calyx, before the expansion of the flower, is closed by a little circular lid, which subsequently separates and falls off; there is no corolla; the stamens are numerous, attached to the inner margin of the receptacle; and the fruit is a woody globular mass, from the upper part of which project the true fruits or capsules, which are three-celled, and burst partially by three valves. The name of the genus is indicative of the very singular fusion of the flowers above described, and is derived from the Greek *sumphyo* 'to unite or grow together.' [M. T. M.]

SYMPHYONEMA. A small proteaceous genus, having a deeply four-parted calyx; stamens inserted on the middle of the segments, cohering towards the upper part of the filament, but with free anthers; a filiform style with a bluntish stigma; and a single-seeded nut. They are herbaceous plants or small shrubs, having much-divided leaves, with linear segments, and yellow flowers in terminal or axillary spikes; and are all natives of New South Wales. [R. H.]

SYMPHYOPETALUM. A low shrub with small leaves, silvery underneath, and red flowers on short axillary peduncles. It is a native of Western Australia, and was described by Drummond as a genus of *Rutaceæ* of the tribe *Boronieæ*. It proves, however, to be the same as the one previously published by Turczaninow under the name of *Nematolepis*.

SYMPHYOSTEMON. The union of stamens by their filaments. The same as Monadelphous.

SYMPHYSIS. A growing together.

SYMPHYTUM. A genus of *Boraginaceæ*, inhabiting Europe and Central Asia. It consists of roughish perennials, with sessile often decurrent or stalked leaves, and terminal solitary or twin scorpioid racemes of rather large pale-yellow purple or blue flowers. The calyx is five-parted; the corolla cylindrico-tubular, enlarged above the middle, where it is closed by five narrow scales, and shortly five-toothed at the apex; the stamens are included; and the nuts ovate rugose, perforated at the base, and adhering to the receptacle by their base.

Two species occur in Britain, the most common of which, *S. officinale*, is a coarse branched plant with a thick rootstock, a stem strongly winged by the decurrent bases of the leaves, and pale-yellow or reddish-purple flowers. *S. tuberosum* is smaller, with nearly simple stems, a tuberous rootstock somewhat resembling the tuber of a Jerusalem artichoke, leaves more or less stalked except the uppermost, and the flowers pale-yellow. [J. T. S.]

Of this genus our native species, *S. officinale*, the Comfrey, is a well-known plant of watercourses, having much the taste and properties of borage, for which it was not unfrequently substituted in the old English cool tankard, and amongst herbalists it was highly extolled as a ' cooler of the blood.'

In 1811 *S. asperrimum* was introduced from the Caucasus; its graceful pendent light-blue flowers and bold foliage recommended it as an ornamental plant in spacious flower-gardens or the front of the shrubbery, in which it has to a greater or less extent kept a place in old gardens. Some few years ago it was recommended as a green ' soiling' plant, and our trials of it certainly show that it is capable of producing large crops, two in the season, perhaps amounting to from forty to fifty tons of green food per acre. The following is the result of an analysis of *S. asperrimum* by Professor Voelcker:—

	Leaves		Stem	
	In Natural State	Calculated Dry	In Natural State	Calculated Dry
Water	88·400	.	94·74	.
Flesh-forming substances . .	2·712	23·37	·09	13·00
Non-nitrogenised substances :—				
Heat and fat-producing matters .	6·898	59·49	3·81	72·49
Inorganic matters (ash) . .	1·990	17·14	·76	14·45
	100·000	100·00	100·00	100·00

On comparison the above figures will show this plant to be almost equal to some of our more important green-food crops ; and certainly, if we take into consideration the quantity of its produce, there are few plants capable of yielding so much of green food as the Comfrey. Dr. Voelcker says that 'the amount of flesh-forming substances is considerable. The juice of this plant contains much gum and mucilage, and but little sugar.'

The cultivation of Comfrey is easy ; even a moist clay soil will not be unsuitable. Divisions of its suckers may be planted in rows two feet apart, and fully a foot between each of the plants in the rows. It may be cut twice and will yield largely, especially if some rotten dung be dug in between the rows when the plantation is dressed up for winter.   [J. B.]

SYMPLOCACEÆ, or SYMPLOCINEÆ. See STYRACACEÆ.

SYMPLOCARPUS. A genus of *Orontiaceæ*, comprising a few herbaceous species found growing in wet places in North America and Northern Asia. The leaves are large, stalked ; the spathe nearly sessile hooded, and tapering to a point ; the spadix globular, covered with perfect flowers ; perianth four-parted, ultimately becoming fleshy ; stamens four, the filaments linear, flattened ; ovary one-celled ; the style four-cornered, the stigma minute ; fruits confluent, one-celled, one-seeded.

S. fœtidus, so called from its disgusting garlic-like odour, is employed medicinally in North America—the roots in cases of asthma, the leaves as an application to ulcers. The seeds are also considered to be antispasmodic, and useful in coughs. The plant may be occasionally met with in cultivation.   [M. T. M.]

SYMPLOCIUM. The spore-case of a fern.

SYMPLOCOS. A very large genus, regarded by some botanists as typical of a distinct natural order, *Symplocaceæ*, while others refer it to *Styracaceæ*. It is confined to the tropical and subtropical countries of Asia and America, and consists of trees and shrubs, with simple usually toothed leaves, and small flowers disposed in axillary clusters or racemes ; the flowers having a five-lobed calyx, a five to ten-lobed corolla, an indefinite number of stamens, and a two to five-celled ovary.

The fruits, which vary from globular to ellipsoid, are fleshy and crowned by the calyx-lobes, and usually contain only one or two seeds.

S. Alstonia, alias *Alstonia theæformis*, is a branching shrub growing ten or twelve feet high, with shining evergreen leaves resembling those of the tea—so much so, indeed, that when first discovered in New Grenada it was erroneously supposed to be that shrub. According to Humboldt, the infusion of the leaves of this plant, though not so palatable as tea, owing to its astringency, possesses valuable medicinal properties. Gardner, however, states that the Brazilians drink an infusion of one of the species, previously scorching the leaves. The leaves of nearly all the species of *Symplocos* turn yellow in drying. Those of *S. tinctoria*, which is called Sweetleaf in Georgia and Carolina, are used for dyeing yellow ; and the leaves of other species are employed for the same purpose in Nepal. In India the bark of *S. racemosa*, called Lodh, is used both as a dyeing material and as a mordant for other dyes ; when employed alone it gives various shades of brown and chocolate-colour.   [A. S.]

SYN. In Greek compounds = union, adhesion, or growing together.

SYNALYSSA. A genus of gelatinous lichens, nearly allied to *Lichina*, with fastigiate fronds, and remarkable for the peculiar mode of growth of its gonidia, resembling the structure of some *Palmella*, and in this agreeing with *Paulia*. The species are few in number ; two occur in this country.   [M. J. B.]

SYNAMMIA. *Goniophlebium*.

SYNANDRA. A genus of *Labiatæ*, distinguished by the following characters :— Calyx thin, bell-shaped, with four nearly equal teeth ; corolla with a long tube, the upper lip entire, the lower three-cleft, the middle lobe broadest and notched at the end ; stamens four, approaching in pairs, the two upper with one barren and one fertile cell, the barren cells of each pair coherent to each other. The only species is *S. grandiflora*, an herbaceous plant resembling a *Lamium*, native of some of the Southern States of America. Its leaves are ovate heart-shaped ; and the flowers yellowish white, in pairs. The name is derived from the Greek words *sun* 'together' and *aner* 'stamen,' in allusion to the union of the anthers.　　[G. D.]

SYNANTHERÆ. Another name for the *Compositæ.*

SYNANTHEROUS. Having the anthers growing together.

SYNAPHEA. A proteaceous genus of a remarkably rigid character, distinguished by having a four-cleft gaping tubular calyx; four stamens, one of which is sterile, shorter than the tube, inserted on the lower part of each of the segments of the calyx; a style, which is curved, thickened at the upper part, with an oblique dilated stigma united to the sterile stamen; and an obovate downy nut. It consists of South-west Australian stemless shrubs, with lobed coarse leathery leaves, and yellow flowers in axillary or terminal spikes.　　[R. H.]

SYNAPISMA. A genus of *Euphorbiaceæ,* represented by a shrub, native of New Caledonia. The leaves are entire and acuminate; the male flowers in axillary and terminal catkins, the females in loose pendulous racemes. The calyx has five convolute leaves, surrounding a column consisting of ten to fifteen stamens united together, and having at the base five glands. In the female flowers the calyx is small, the ovary three-celled, surmounted by a short three-cleft style; and the fruit is divided when ripe into three carpels, each two-valved and one-seeded.　　[M. T. M.]

SYNCARPIUM. A fruit consisting of many carpels consolidated and adhering to a central receptacle or growing point, as in *Magnolia.*

SYNCARPOUS. Having a fruit whose carpels are consolidated.

SYNCLADEI. A section of mosses containing only the natural order *Sphagnei,* in which the branches are fasciculate; and the female flower, like that of pleurocarpous mosses, occupies the place of a branch, or is inserted in the axis of two or more branches. As the fructification advances—to use the words of Dr. Hooker, who has admirably illustrated the genus in his *Antarctic Flora*—the receptacle elongates, and the perichætial leaves becoming separated from one another, it presents the appearance of a lateral branch. The antheridia are found at the clavate and usually discoloured extremities of short deflexed ramuli inserted singly amongst the leaves. The bunches of branches, which consist of three five or seven, are spirally inserted, five fascicles constituting a spiral.　　[M. J. B.]

SYNDAW. *Alchemilla vulgaris.*

SYNDESMIS. A small shrub constituting a genus of *Anacardiaceæ.* The leaves are entire; and the flowers in terminal corymbs, with the calyx coloured, the petals four to five, linear-lanceolate, and four to five stamens, inserted with the petals in the stalk-like thalamus supporting the ovary, their anthers cleft below. The ovary is stalked, somewhat globose, with one erect ovule; the style is lateral thread-like, and the stigma simple.　　[M. T. M.]

SYNEDRELLA. A small genus of *Compositæ,* native of Tropical America; *S. nodiflora,* which is a common weed of cultivation, being also found sparingly in India, though not indigenous there. It is an annual, with opposite nettle-like tri-nerved leaves, rough above and having notched margins; and sessile flower-heads, in clusters of four to five together in the axils of the leaves, each head with an involucre of chaff-like scales enclosing a number of yellow florets—those of the ray strap-shaped, with lacerate winged achenes, and a pappus of two awns; those of the disk tubular, with triangular wingless achenes, and a like pappus. [A. A. B.]

SYNEDROUS. Growing on the angle of a stem.

SYNEMA. That part of the column of an orchid which represents the filament of the stamens.

SYNGENESIOUS. Having the anthers united at their edges, so as to form a tube.

SYNGONIUM. A genus of tropical American herbs, of the family *Araceæ.* The rootstock is scandent, and sends up pedately-divided leaves, and short flowerstalks terminated by a greenish-yellow spathe encircling the spadix, which is wholly covered with flowers. Above are four or five two-celled anthers opening by pores; and below them several ovaries fused together, each having a single cavity with a single seed. *S. auritum* is in cultivation.　　[M. T. M.]

SYNGRAMMA. A genus of hemionitoid ferns, distinguished in the group with netted naked sori, by having the primary veins parallel forked, and the venules sparingly reticulated towards the margin. The species have simple or pinnate fronds, and are entirely Eastern and tropical. [T. M.]

SYNNEMA. A genus of *Scrophulariaceæ,* containing a single species, a lowly-branching pilose herb from Burmah. It has opposite sessile lanceolate leaves, semipinnatifid below, but becoming more simple upwards. The calyx is five parted; the galea of the corolla falcate; the didynamous stamens placed under the galea, the filaments having dilated membranaceous bases; and the anthers sagittate, with two nearly equal cells; the entire style with a minute stigmatic surface; and the seeds numerous.　　[W. C.]

SYNNOTIA. A group of Iridaceous plants now usually referred to *Gladiolus.* The perianth is six-parted and somewhat two-lipped, gaping; the spathes two-valved membranaceous torn; the stigmas three, dilated at the apex, fimbriate spreading and recurved; the seeds globose and shining.　　[T. M.]

SYNOCHLAMYS. *Cheilanthes.*

SYNOCHORION. The same kind of fruit as the Carcerulus.

SYNŒCIA. A genus proposed by Miquel for the *Ficus macrocarpa* and *F. diversifolia*, two Javanese species, in which the usually minute perianth is entirely abortive.

SYNONYMS. Names which have the same meaning; a synonym is what lawyers call an alias.

SYNORHIZOUS. Having a radicle whose point is united to the albumen.

SYNŌUM. A genus of *Meliaceæ* peculiar to New Holland, with alternate imparipinnate leaves, and quite entire leaflets, barbate in the axils of the veins on the underside, and axillary racemes of flowers. The calyx is five-cleft, the corolla has four ovate petals; there are eight anthers, and a three-celled capsule, with two seeds in each cell. [B. S.]

SYNPHLEBIUM. *Schizoloma.*

SYNTHLIPSIS. A genus of *Cruciferæ* from New Mexico, consisting of a branched diffuse canescent herb, with sinuato-pinnatifid leaves, and lax racemes of rose-coloured flowers. The fruit is a pouch, of an oblong elliptical shape, slightly notched at the tip, and compressed contrary to the partition; the valves boat-shaped, strongly keeled but wingless at the back, though slightly produced at the apex. [J. T. S.]

SYNZYGANTHERA. A small genus of *Lacistemaceæ* confined to South America, and consisting of a couple of shrubby species, with alternate oblong-lanceolate leaves, catkin-like flowers (by abortion monœcious), four bracts surrounding each perigone, without a glandular disk around the ovary, and a three-celled berry-like capsule. [B. S.]

SYNZYGIA. The point of junction of opposite cotyledons.

SYRENIA. A genus of *Cruciferæ* from Eastern Europe and Central Asia, consisting of biennials, with the habit of *Erysimum*, having rather large pale-yellow flowers, and elongated four-sided compressed pods, with keeled one-nerved valves; the seeds in two rows with incumbent cotyledons contrary to the partition of the pod, not parallel with it as in *Erysimum*, which also has but one row of seeds in each cell. [J. T. S.]

SYRINGA. The Lilacs of our gardens are familiar representatives of this genus of *Oleaceæ*, of which about six species and a number of varieties are known. The native country of some of these plants is not well ascertained, although the genus appears to be confined to South-eastern Europe and Central and Eastern Asia, but some of the so-called species are supposed to have originated in gardens. They are shrubs of from four to fifteen feet or more in height, with entire leaves, and terminal more or less pyramidal panicles of usually sweet-smelling flowers, characterised by having a short four-toothed persistent calyx, a salver-shaped corolla with a long tube and four-parted limb, two enclosed stamens, and a short two-pronged enclosed style. Their fruit is an egg-shaped or lance-shaped somewhat flattened two-celled capsule, splitting when ripe into two boat-shaped pieces, with a partition in the middle, each piece containing two narrow-winged seeds.

The Common Lilac, *S. vulgaris*, is generally supposed to be a native of Persia, from whence it is said to have been introduced into Europe; but it does not appear to be certainly known in a wild state, and some botanists have therefore supposed it to be merely a luxuriant cultivated variety of the Persian Lilac, *S. persica*. It is, however, said to occur wild in Transylvania, Wallachia, and Bulgaria. It is the largest species of the genus, and also one of the commonest and most beautiful of our spring-flowering ornamental shrubs. The several varieties differ principally in the size and colour of their flowers.

The Persian Lilac, *S. persica*, is also supposed to have originally come from Persia, but nothing is known with certainty as to its native country. It is a smaller species than the last, seldom growing more than six or eight feet high, and has smallish lance-shaped leaves, sometimes cut in a pinnatifid manner. There are both a white and a purple-flowered variety.

S. Josikœa is so named in honour of the Countess von Josika, who, about thirty years ago, first discovered this species at Clausenburg in Transylvania. It is a tall shrub, with pointed elliptic lance-shaped wrinkled leaves, and has bluish-purple flowers, which, unlike those of the other species, are scentless.

In addition to the above there is a plant known as the Rouen Lilac, *S. rothamagensis*, the Lilas Varin of the French, said to have been raised by M. Varin in the Botanic Garden at Rouen from seeds of the Persian Lilac; but it agrees with the species called *S. dubia* or *S. chinensis*, said to be from China, though known there only in a cultivated state. The Rouen Lilac is intermediate between the common and Persian sorts, and strengthens the supposition of those two being varieties of one species. [A. S.]

SYRINGA DES JARDINS. *Philadelphus coronarius.*

SYRINGODEA. *Erica.*

SYZYGITES. A most curious genus of vesicular moulds, consisting of a single species, which is not uncommon in woods on decaying agarics. The threads are much-branched above, and on some of the branches little swellings occur which unite with each other two together, like the threads of *Conjugatæ*. A sporangium is ultimately formed at the point of junction, which is filled with a mass of elliptic spores.

This mode of fructification is without any parallel amongst *Fungi.*   [M. J. B.]

SYZYGIUM. A genus of *Myrtaceæ*, consisting of trees or shrubs, natives of Asia and Tropical Africa. The flowers are in cymes or corymbs, the limb of the calyx undivided; the petals four or five, inserted on to the throat of the calyx, united together into a hood and soon falling off; the stamens numerous, inserted *with the* petals; the style simple; and the fruit baccate, one-celled by abortion, and containing only one or two seeds. *S. guineense* is an object of worship to the natives of the Gambia district, and they also eat the ripe fruits; in Senegal the plant is used in rheumatism. *S. Jambolanum,* a native of India, has an edible fruit; its bark, which is astringent, is used medicinally, and also in dyeing; the timber is hard and durable. Two or three of the Indian species are in cultivation in this country.   [M. T. M.]

SZOVITSIA. A genus of *Umbelliferæ,* the fruit of which is oblong-elliptical, each half with five primary ribs, which are narrow and hairy, and four secondary thick ribs having transverse folds. The only species is a smooth annual plant, with repeatedly divided leaves, the divisions long and narrow; the flowers are white. [G. D.]

TAAG. The Bengal or Sunn Hemp, *Crotalaria juncea.*

TABAC. (Fr.) *Nicotiana Tabacum.* — DES PAYSANS *Nicotiana rustica.* — DES VOSGES. *Arnica montana.*

TABACHIR, or **TABASHEER.** A substance secreted in the joints of bamboos, in bluish-white masses with a pearly lustre. It is mainly composed of siliceous matter which the plant is unable to incorporate in its tissues, and is reputed to possess tonic properties.

TABACINUS. Tobacco-coloured; a pale brown, like common kanaster.

TABEBUIA. *Tecoma.*

TABERNÆMONTANA. An extensive and wide-spread tropical genus of *Apocynaceæ,* characterised by its flowers having a five-parted (in *T. coronaria* five-cleft) calyx, furnished with from four to seven narrow glands near the bottom of each lobe on the inside; a salver-shaped corolla, usually with the tube inflated at the insertion of the stamens; the latter having very short filaments or none, and generally long taper-pointed anthers shaped like arrow-heads; and a double ovary, with a long style bearing a two-lobed stigma supported by a broad ring. The numerous species are either shrubs or trees, sometimes attaining a great height. They have opposite entire mostly smooth leaves, on short stalks dilated at the base and forming false stipules; and cymes of fragrant yellow or white flowers, generally in pairs at the points of the branches, each flower producing a double or, by abortion, single more or less fleshy fruit, containing few or many seeds marked with a longitudinal groove, and angular by mutual pressure. Like most other dogbanes, the *Tabernæmontanas* possess a milky juice; but the milk, instead of being exceedingly acrid and drastic like that of many allied genera, is, in some species at least, perfectly bland and wholesome. This is particularly the case with the Hya-Hya or Cow-tree of British Guiana, *T. utilis,* which when tapped yields a copious supply of thick sweet milk, resembling that of the cow in appearance, but rather sticky from the presence of caoutchouc. The tree yields a soft white wood; and its bark is used medicinally by the Indians. French : *Taberne.*   [A. S.]

TABES. A wasting : a disease which consists in a gradual decay of the power of growth.

TABLA. A Peruvian name for Cinchona-bark peeled from the trunk of the tree, which is of a higher value than that taken from the branches.

TABOURET. (Fr.) *Thlaspi.*

TABULA. The pileus of certain fungals.

TACAMAHAC, or **TACAMAHACA.** A balsamic bitter resin attributed to *Icica Tacamahaca,* to *Calophyllum Inophyllum,* and to *Elaphrium tomentosum;* also an American name for the resin obtained from the buds of the Tacamahac Poplar, *Populus balsamifera.* —, EAST INDIAN. The resin of *Calophyllum Calaba.*

TACAMAQUE. (Fr.) *Populus balsamifera.* —, DE BOURBON. *Calophyllum Inophyllum.*

TACAZZEA. A genus of *Asclepiadaceæ,* chiefly differing from *Periploca* in the corolla and stamens being smooth, not hairy ; in the anthers not cohering together at the apex ; and in the stigma having a little notched point at the summit. *T. venosa,* the only species, is an erect twiggy-branched shrub, native of Abyssinia, where it is found growing on the banks of the River Tacazze, and hence the generic name. It has narrow oblong taper-pointed leaves, marked on both sides with netted veins, smooth on the upper surface and hoary underneath ; flowers disposed in loose somewhat forking panicles; and smooth woody thin fruits, in pairs spreading widely apart, containing smooth brown-skinned seeds furnished with hair-tufts.   [A. S.]

TACCA, TACCACEÆ. The tropical genus *Tacca,* belonging to the regular-flowered monocotyledons with an inferior ovary, has been considered sufficiently distinct in organisation to form an order of itself, under the name of *Taccaceæ.* It would appear, however, that it might very well be included in *Burmanniaceæ,* of which it has the one-celled ovary with three parietal placentas, and the stamens inserted on the six-cleft perianth ; while the differences in the structure of the seed are not so great as had been supposed. It consists of perennial herbs, sometimes large, with a tuberous root. The leaves are all radical, entire or divided; the flowers are greenish brown, in an umbel on the top of a simple leafless scape, surrounded by an involucre of simple bracts. There are six or seven species known, two from Tropical America, the remainder African or more especially Asiatic, extending over the Indian Archipelago and the Pacific Islands.

The various species grow in the open country. *T. pinnatifida* is generally found in sandy places near the sea. The leaf-stalks of this species are plaited into bonnets by the Society Islanders, but the principal use made of all the species is that of their tubers, which, resembling new potatoes, contain a great deal of starch known as South-sea Arrowroot, and far preferable to any other arrowroot in cases of dysentery. The tubers are dug up after the leaves have died away, and are rasped and macerated four or five days in water, when the fecula separates in the same manner as sago does. It is largely employed as an article of diet throughout the Tropics, and is a favourite ingredient for puddings and cakes in the South Seas. *Tacca* chiefly differs from its ally *Ataccia* in having a one-celled instead of a three-celled fruit. The perigone is six-cleft, the stamens six in number, and the fruit a berry. All the leaves are radical, and palmate or bipinnatifid. The flowers are arranged in umbels at the end of a scape, green tinged with purple—the umbels being surrounded by large bracts. [B. S.]

TACHIADENUS. A genus of *Gentianaceæ*, comprising some herbaceous or somewhat shrubby species, natives of Madagascar. The flowers are white, with a five-parted calyx, the segments of which are frequently dilated towards the top; the corolla has a slender elongated tube, terminating in a bell-shaped five-lobed limb; the anthers are erect; the ovary is one-celled, surrounded by a disk; and the fruit is capsular two-valved. [M. T. M.]

TACHIBOTA. A genus of doubtful affinity, referred by some to *Bixaceæ*, from which, however, it differs chiefly in its three-celled ovary. The genus is peculiar to Guiana, and only represented by one species, a shrub with alternate simple leaves, small axillary racemose flowers of a white colour, and a black capsular fruit. The calyx is five-cleft, and the corolla composed of five petals; the stamens are six in number, and the stigmas three, while the capsule is three-cornered three-celled and three-valved, and includes numerous minute seeds. [B. S.]

TACSONIA. A genus of shrubby *Passifloraceæ*, having the general appearance of *Passiflora*, and the same structure of stamens pistil and fruit, but differing in the usually long cylindrical tube of the calyx, which is furnished with two crowns, one at the throat and the other near its base. In *T. manicata*, however, a very handsome species, the tube scarcely exceeds in length

that of a passion-flower. The species are natives of Central America and the West Indies. The fruits of several of them, as *T. mollissima*, *tripartita*, and *speciosa*, are eaten. They are of a very ornamental character. [W C.]

TACUARI. The South American name of certain species of *Mabea*, whose hollow shoots are used as tobacco-pipes.

TÆNIOPSIS. A genus of polypodiaceous ferns of the tribe *Tænitideæ*, and consisting of species having a strong resemblance to *Vittaria*, from which they differ in not having the sori placed in an extrorse-marginal furrow, but in a furrow at the back of the frond. The fronds are simple or lobate, coriaceous, with the veins simple or forked and obscure, and the sori linear continuous submarginal, and either superficial or immersed. They are found plentifully in the tropical parts both of the Old and New World. [T. M.]

TÆNIOPTERIS. *Tæniopsis.*

TÆNIOSTEMA. The name of a Mexican herb, constituting a genus of *Cistaceæ*. The leaves are entire, covered with somewhat woolly star-shaped pubescence; the flowers are very small, borne on tufted flower-stalks, and have a three-parted calyx, no corolla, and three stamens standing opposite the sepals, the filaments flattened, somewhat spoon-shaped, and bearing very small roundish anthers. The ovary is one-celled, with three parietal placentas, each with two ascending straight ovules near the base. Fruit capsular. The generic name is derived from the Greek *tainia* 'a band,' in allusion to the flattened filaments of the stamens. [M. T. M.]

TÆNITIS. A net-veined genus of *Tænitideæ*, one of the tribes of polypodiaceous ferns, and consisting of a few tropical Asiatic and American species, having simple or pinnate fronds; from a creeping caudex, uniformly reticulated veins forming long oblique or longitudinal areoles without free included veinlets, and non-indusiate linear submarginal or medial sori, which are superficial or somewhat immersed. *T. blechnoides* is the type. [T. M.]

TAFÉ. A fermented liquor prepared from rice in Java.

TAFFIA. A spirit distilled from the fermented juice of the sugar-cane.

TAFGA. The fragrant North African *Rhaponticum acaule*, which has the odour of *Acacia Farnesiana*.

TAGETES. Showy annuals much cultivated under the names of African and French Marigolds. The characters of the genus are:—Flowers compound; involucre simple, composed of five bracts, which are united into a tube; florets of the ray five (in *T. lucida* three to four), persistent; pappus of five erect bristles. The species are natives of Mexico Peru and Chili, but are also grown in China and India, and in some parts of the latter country are considered sacred flowers. *T. patula*, the French Marigold, is in France known by the name of *Petit Œillet d'Inde*. Of this many varieties are cultivated, some with double flowers variegated with gold and orange-brown. *T. erecta*, the African Marigold, (Fr. *Grand Œillet d'Inde* or *Rose d'Inde*) is a larger plant, with double yellow flowers. The scent of both these plants is strong and offensive, but the more finely-cut continuous-flowering *T. tenuifolia* has a more agreeable smell. *T. lucida*; a much smaller plant, is a perennial, with simple lanceolate finely-serrated leaves, and corymbs of small yellow fragrant flowers. German: *Sammetblume*. [C. A. J.]

TAIL-POINTED. Excessively acuminated, so that the point is long and weak. The same as Caudate.

TAILWORTS. A name formerly given by Lindley to the order *Triuridaceæ*.

TAL, or **TALA**. An Indian name for the Palmyra Palm, *Borassus flabelliformis*.

TALARÆ. The wings of a papilionaceous corolla.

TALAUMA. One of the genera of *Magnoliaceæ*, so called from the native name applied to some of the South American kinds. The species are trees or shrubs, of tropical and subtropical regions of the Old and New World; and are remarkable for their fine fragrant flowers. The floral structure is much like that of *Magnolia*, but the fruit differs in the fusion of its constituent carpels, and in the irregularly circular mode of splitting. The seeds adhere to the axis after the separation of the carpels by means of a long elastic cord, as in *Magnolia* and *Michelia*. [M. T. M.]

TALEA. A cutting; a small branch employed to propagate a plant.

TALESFUR. An Indian name for the highly fragrant leaves of *Rhododendron Anthopogon*, used as a medicinal snuff in India.

TALICTRON. (Fr.) *Sisymbrium Sophia*.

TALINOPSIS. A genus of *Portulacaceæ* from New Mexico, allied to the South African *Anacampseros*, and the Chilian *Grahamia*. It has much the habit of the latter, from which it is distinguished by the bractless flowers, leathery epicarp of the three-valved capsule separating from the papery three-valved endocarp, and wingless seeds. From *Anacampseros* it differs in habit, in the persistent equal sepals, the short style, and the coriaceous valves of the capsule, which do not separate at the base and fall away. It is an undershrub, with five purple petals, and about twenty stamens in five bundles. [J. T. S.]

TALINUM. A genus of *Portulacaceæ*, inhabiting the warmer parts of both hemispheres, but most abundant in Tropical and Subtropical America. The genus is distinguished by its deciduous sepals, ten or twenty stamens, and three-valved capsule with numerous wingless seeds. It

consists of smooth fleshy herbs or undershrubs, with alternate or subopposite entire exstipulate leaves, and cymose racemose or solitary flowers on axillary peduncles, bearing white purple or yellow very fugacious petals. *T. patens*, a native of Brazil, is there used in the same way as the common purslane. [J. T. S.]

TALIPAT, TALIPOT. Indian names for *Corypha umbraculifera* and *C. Taliera*.

TALISPATHREE, TALISPUTRIE. Indian names for *Flacourtia cataphracta*, a plant used as a gentle astringent.

TALLEH. An Arabic name for the Abyssinian Myrrh, produced by *Acacia Sassa* and *A. gummifera*.

TALLICOONAH. A medicinal oil made in Sierra Leone from the seeds of *Carapa Touloucouna* or *C. guineensis*.

TALLOW-SHRUB. *Myrica cerifera*.

TALLOW-TREE. *Stillingia sebifera*, the seeds of which are covered with a waxy substance, used in China for making candles.

TAMALT. A Mexican name for *Lycopersicum esculentum*.

TAMANU. A green heavy resin from the Society Islands, obtained from *Calophyllum Inophyllum*.

TAMARA. A Hindoo name for *Nelumbium speciosum*.

TAMARACK. A North American name for the Hackmatack or American Larch, *Abies pendula*.

TAMARA-TONGA. A Malabar name for *Averrhoa Carambola*.

TAMARICACEÆ. An order of polypetalous dicotyledons, consisting of shrubs or undershrubs, rarely trees or hard prostrate herbs, found chiefly in maritime sands, or in sandy or gravelly places along torrents in mountainous districts. Their leaves are usually small entire and alternate, often fleshy or reduced to scales; the flowers white or pink, sometimes solitary, but more frequently in terminal spikes racemes or panicles. Allied in many respects to *Portulacaceæ*, *Elatinaceæ*, and *Hypericaceæ*, they are at once known by the structure of the ovary, which is not completely divided into cells, but contains three placentas erect from the base of the cavity, these being either quite free or cohering variously with each other or with the walls of the cavity, so as to form three imperfect cells; and by the erect seeds bearing long hairs, either in a terminal tuft or all over the testa, or slightly united in a marginal wing. The two principal Asiatic and European genera, *Tamarix* and *Reaumuria*, are regarded by some botanists as types of distinct orders; and the splendid Mexican genus *Fouquiera*, differing chiefly in the large petals united into a tubular corolla, has only recently been associated with the *Tamaricaceæ* as a third tribe.

TAMARIND. The pleasant acid fruit of *Tamarindus indica.* —, BASTARD. *Acacia Julibrissin.* —, —, of Jamaica. *Acacia lebbek lichophylloides.* —, BLACK. *Codarium acutifolium.* —, BROWN. *Codarium.* —, MANILLA. The fruit of *Pithecolobium dulce.* —, NATIVE, of New South Wales. *Ompania australis.* —, VELVET. The African name for the fruits of *Codarium acutifolium.* —, WILD. *Codarium;* also *Pithecolobium filicifolium.* —, —, of Jamaica. *Acacia arborea.* —, —, of Trinidad. *Pentaclethra filamentosa.* —, YELLOW. *Acacia villosa.*

TAMARINDUS. This name is supposed to be derived from the Arabic *Tamar* signifying 'dates,' and *Indus* in allusion to the country whence the tree was originally derived. Botanically it is applied to a genus of *Leguminosæ*, characterised by a calyx which is tubular at the lower part, but above has a two-lipped limb—the upper lip of three reflexed segments, the lower of two segments; petals three, the central one hood-like; stamens nine to ten, of which seven are short and sterile; pod many-seeded, filled with pulp.

The Tamarind-tree, *T. indica*, is the only species, but it has two varieties, charac-

Tamarindus indica.

terised by the varying length of the pod. The East Indian variety has long pods, with six to twelve seeds, whereas the variety cultivated in the West Indies has much shorter pods, containing one to four seeds. The tree has an elegant appearance, from its graceful pinnated foliage and its racemes of sweet-smelling flowers, the calyx of which is yellow, the petals yellow streaked with red, the filaments purple, and the anthers brown. The tamarind-pods imported from the East Indies vary in length from three to six inches, and are slightly curved. They consist of a brittle brown shell, within which is a soft acid brown pulp, traversed by strong woody fibres; the seeds are again immediately invested by a thin membranous covering. West Indian tamarinds are usually im-

ported preserved in syrup, the outer shell having been removed.

Tamarinds owe their grateful acidity to the presence of citric tartaric and other vegetable acids. In addition to their cooling qualities they act as gentle laxatives, and are useful in some forms of sore-throat. The pulp mixed with salt is used as a liniment in rheumatism by the

Tamarindus indica (fruit).

Creoles of the Mauritius. The seeds are employed medicinally by the natives of Bengal in dysentery, and they are also used by the Cingalese as food in times of scarcity, the dark outer skin being removed by maceration. Powdered, the seeds are employed as a poultice to boils; this powder also is mixed with thin glue to form a very strong cement for wood. The flowers of the tree are used in Ceylon in cases of liver-disease. Medicinal virtues are also ascribed to the leaves, which are used internally in jaundice, and externally as an application to sore eyes or ulcers. An infusion of the leaves is employed to furnish a yellow dye. In the Mauritius a decoction of the bark is used in asthma, and as a tonic and astringent in dysentery. The timber is valuable for building purposes, and furnishes excellent charcoal for the manufacture of gunpowder. Tamarinds form an important ingredient in Indian cookery, especially in curries; and they are also used in Western India in preserving or pickling fish, which under the name of tamarind-fish is considered a delicacy.

It is said that no plants will grow under the shade of the Tamarind—hence it is considered unsafe to sleep under the trees. It is also said that the acid moisture they exhale, does really affect the cloth of tents, if they are allowed to remain under the trees for any length of time. The Tamarind-tree has long been cultivated in English stoves, but rarely perfects its flowers and fruit in this country. [M. T. M.]

TAMARINIER. (Fr.) *Tamarindus.* — DES HAUTS. *Acacia heterophylla.*

TAMARISK. *Tamarix.* —, GERMAN. *Myricaria germanica.*

TAMARIX. Shrubs or small trees giving name to the order *Tamaricaceæ*, well marked by their twiggy branches, minute scale-like leaves, and small spiked flowers.

T. anglica or *T. gallica* is a native of most of the countries of Southern Europe, Asia Minor, Tartary, Japan, Barbary, and Arabia, especially in a saline soil. It was known to the Greeks and Romans under the name of *Myrica*, and frequent mention of it occurs in the writings of the ancients. It is to be found, apparently wild, on various parts of the sea-coast of England, but is not believed to be indigenous. The Tamarisk grows freely from cuttings, and will bear exposure to any degree of wind. The stems and leaves abound in sulphate of soda, and a species either closely allied to or identical with the common Tamarisk produces in Arabia a substance considered by the Bedouins a great dainty, and called by them *mann* or *manna*, from its outward resemblance to the 'manna' of Scripture. In the month of June it drops from the branches upon the fallen twigs and leaves, which always cover the ground beneath the tree, and being collected and cleaned is eaten with bread. Some travellers suppose this substance to be not an exudation from the tree, but the produce of an insect which infests the Tamarisk. It is said to be most abundant in rainy seasons. French: *Tamarise*; German: *Tamarisken*. [C. A. J.]

TAMARIX DE NARBONNE. (Fr.) *Tamarix gallica.*

TAMATTE. A Malayan name for *Lycopersicum esculentum.*

TAMBOOKIE-WOOD. A hard handsome wood, which when powdered is used by the South African Zulus as an emetic.

TAMBULI. An Indian name for the leaf of the Betel-pepper.

TAMIER. (Fr.) *Tamus.*

TAMKAI. An Indian name for *Terminalia Bellerica*, the kernels of whose seeds are eaten.

TAMPUI. The edible fruit of *Hedycarpus malayanus.*

TAMUS. The only European representative of the order *Dioscoreaceæ*, and distinguished from other genera by its fruit being a roundish three-celled berry crowned with the remains of the flower, and containing one or two seeds in each cell, the cell-partitions becoming obsolete in the ripe fruits. There are two well-known species, *T. communis*, the Black Bryony of our hedges, and *T. cretica*, a native of Greece and the Greek Archipelago. They are both climbing plants, and have thick tuberous roots, sending up annual twining stems, which grow to a great length, and climb over bushes and hedges. The former has entire heart-shaped taper-pointed leaves; and the latter trilobed leaves, heart-shaped at the base, with the side-lobes large and rounded, and the middle one lance-shaped. Their flowers are of separate sexes, borne on different plants, and are produced in the leaf-axils— the males in slender branched racemes, the females in shorter racemes.

The large fleshy roots of the Black Bryony contain an abundance of acrid clammy juice, and were formerly used in the preparation of stimulating plaisters. Rustic practitioners employ them for removing the discoloration of the skin from bruises. The fruits steeped in gin are a popular remedy for chilblains; while the Greeks use the young suckers of both species like *Asparagus*, which they much resemble. [A. S.]

TAN. The bark of oak and other trees used for tanning leather. Half-spent tan is used by gardeners for making hotbeds.

TANACETUM. A genus of perennials belonging to the tribe *Corymbiferæ* of compound flowers, and allied both in characters and properties to *Artemisia*. *T. vulgare*, the Common Tansy, is an erect herbaceous plant one to two feet high, with repeatedly-divided deeply-cut leaves, and terminal corymbs of button-like flower-heads, of which all the florets are yellow. All parts of the plant have a strong aromatic scent, and an exceedingly bitter taste. Tansy was formerly much employed in medicine, and still retains its place in some cookery-books as an ingredient in puddings cakes and omelets, viands which now rarely appear at table. Tansy-wine also still enjoys some reputation among rustic practitioners as a stomachic. A variety with curled leaves is cultivated as an ornamental plant for garnishing dishes. None of the foreign species are worthy of particular notice. French: *Tanaisie*; German: *Rheinfarrn.* [C. A. J.]

TANÆCIUM (including *Schlegelia*). A genus of climbing shrubs belonging to the *Crescentiaceæ*, and confined to the West Indies and the tropical parts of South America. Their branches are often rooting, their leaves either simple or trifoliolate; their flowers white pink scarlet or violet in colour, arranged in axillary or terminal racemes or panicles; and their fruit is an indehiscent oblong berry, either black or grey, in some species scarcely larger than a coffee-berry, and in others assuming the dimensions of a large shaddock. The calyx is cup-shaped five-ribbed persistent, and obscurely five-toothed; the corolla tubular, and towards the top becoming funnel-shaped; the stamens are four in number, with the rudiment of a fifth; and the fruit is two-celled. *T. parasiticum* of Jamaica is an inmate of our hot-houses, and climbs over walls or trees like ivy. *T. lilacinum* (or *Schlegelia lilacina*) has an edible berry called in Guiana Emossé beroy, and used by the natives for dyeing their cotton cloth and straw furniture. The fruit of *T. albiflorum* of Jamaica is employed for poultices. [B. S.]

TANDONIA. A genus of *Basellaceæ* from Peru and New Grenada. The stem is often twining, with alternate entire leaves, and fleshy blossoms in long slender many-flowered simple or branched spikes. The outer calyx is two-cleft, the inner five-parted; the stamens five, united at the base; the style elongated, with a capitate somewhat trilobed stigma; and the fruit ovate-compressed, enclosed within the unchanged calyx. [J. T. S.]

TANG, or TANGLE. The common name of *Laminaria digitata*. The Orkney kelpmen give this name exclusively to the narrow-fronded variety, while the ordinary form is called Cuvy. —, BLACK. *Fucus vesiculosus*. [M. J. B.]

TANGHADI. *Cassia auriculata*, the bark of which is used for tanning in India.

TANGHIN. *Tanghinia*.

TANGHINIA. The custom of trial by ordeal, in the unerring efficacy of which our own ancestors were strong believers, is now confined to a few of the most savage nations of the world, though even among them it is gradually dying away before the

Tanghinia venenifera.

advancing steps of civilisation. In Madagascar the natives formerly placed the most unlimited confidence in the poisonous seed of the Tanghin as an infallible detector of guilt, its use having descended to them from the remotest antiquity. This Tanghin or Tanquen is the only plant belonging to a genus which botanists have named *Tanghinia*, one of the *Apocynaceæ*, and confined to Madagascar. The species, *T. venenifera*, is a tree, with smooth alternate lance-shaped thickish leaves, about six inches in length, clustered towards the points of the branches and directed upwards; it bears large terminal cymes of flowers, each supported by a couple of bracts, and having a spreading five-parted calyx without glands, a salver-shaped corolla with rose-coloured lobes, and a green funnel-shaped tube hairy inside and closed at the mouth by five green ish scales; the stamens being inserted into the upper or wide part of the tube, with a roundish tubercle under each; and a double ovary with a long style and thick stigma bearing two tubercles at the top. In general only one of the ovaries comes to perfection,

forming an ellipsoid fruit between two and three inches long, somewhat pointed at the ends, and having a smooth purplish skin tinged with green, containing a hard stone surrounded by a thick fibrous flesh. The portion used as an ordeal is the seed, which is pounded, and a small piece is swallowed by each person to be tried: those in whom it causes vomiting escape, but to those whose stomachs retain it it is quickly fatal, and their guilt is then held to be proven. [A. S.]

TANGLE. *Laminaria digitata* and *L. saccharina*. —, BLUE. An American name for *Gaylussacia frondosa*.

TANIERS. The Blue Eddos or Nut Eddos, *Caladium sagittæfolium*.

TANNIN. The astringent tanning principle or impure tannic acid of the bark or galls of the oak and other trees, and of other vegetable substances.

TANQUEN. *Tanghinia*.

TANROUGE. (Fr.) *Weinmannia*.

TANSY. *Tanacetum vulgare*. —, GOOSE. *Potentilla Anserina*. —, WILD. *Potentilla Anserina*; also *Ambrosia artemisiæfolia*.

TAPEINANTHUS *humilis* constitutes a small pancratiform genus of *Amaryllidaceæ*. It was formerly known as *Pancratium humile*, and is a native of Spain. It has a short scape rising in autumn before the leaves, and bearing two yellow flowers with ovate-oblong segments, a short cup, long diverging filaments, an erect style, and an obtuse stigma. [T. M.]

TAPEINOSTEMON (sometimes but erroneously spelt *Topeinostemon*) is the name given to a genus of Brazilian herbs of the family *Gentianaceæ*. The species are branched annuals, with many-flowered cymes; calyx small, five-parted; corolla somewhat funnel-shaped; stamens five, inserted into the base of the tube of the corolla, the anthers unchanging, concealed within the corolla; ovary partly two-celled; stigma short, divided into two plates. The fruit is a capsule much longer than the calyx, and partially four-celled. [M. T. M.]

TAPEINOTES. The few species of Brazilian *Gesneraceæ* which form this genus are little soft fleshy herbaceous plants, with simple or branched stems rising from small underground tubers; their leaves are on stalks opposite each other; and their small whitish flowers are borne singly, or sometimes two together, on solitary or twin flower-stalks springing from the leaf-axils. The genus is closely allied to *Nematanthus*, the principal distinction between the two genera residing in the shape of the corolla; that of the present having the tube narrow at the base, but suddenly enlarged, particularly on the lower side, into a nearly globose shape, and again drawn in towards the orifice, the limb being erect and two-lipped. The calyx is free and unequally five-parted, with egg-shaped segments. *T. pusilla* scarcely attains an inch in height. [A. S.]

TAPENIER. (Fr.) *Capparis spinosa.*

TAPER. The opposite of angular; usually employed in contradistinction to that term, when speaking of long bodies. The same as Terete.

TAPERING. Gradually diminishing in diameter.

TAPER-POINTED. Terminating very gradually in a point, as the leaf of *Salix alba.* The same as Acuminate.

TAPIA. The Garlic Pear, *Crataeva Tapia.*

TAPIER. (Fr.) *Crataeva.*

TAPINA. The name originally given by Dr. Von Martius to a Brazilian genus of *Gesneraceae,* but which was afterwards altered by M. Decandolle to *Tapeinotes,* in order to prevent its being confounded with two other genera possessing names of nearly the same orthography—viz., *Tapinia* among fungi, and *Tapeinia* among Irids. It is derived from the Greek word *tapeinos* 'humble,' the plants belonging to it being of very dwarf habit. [A. S.]

TAPINANTHUS. Professor Oliver, the most recent writer on *Loranthaceae,* considers this to be a mere section of *Loranthus,* and not worth constituting a distinct genus. The species so named are natives of Africa, and have pentamerous flowers arranged in axillary clusters, each flower provided with a bract. [M. T. M.]

TAPINOCARPUS. A genus of *Araceae,* founded on an herbaceous species, growing in damp grassy places in the Concan districts of Western India. The rootstock is fleshy and perennial, and sends up heart-shaped entire leaves. Generically it approaches *Arum* and *Dracunculus,* but differs especially in the position of the ovules, of which there are six in each ovary, two or three erect, attached to the base of the ovary, the remainder pendulous from the top. The generic name is derived from the Greek *tapeinos* 'lowly' and *karpos* 'fruit,' in allusion to the position of the fruit. [M T M.]

TAPIOCA. An agglomerated kind of starch prepared from the root of *Manihot utilissima,* and generally employed as diet for invalids. —, PEARL. A fictitious kind of Tapioca, formed of prepared grain.

TAPIRIA. The name applied to a tree, native of Guiana, and supposed to constitute a genus of *Amyridaceae,* but which is imperfectly known. The calyx has five deciduous segments; the corolla as many petals, inserted on to a disk surrounding the ovary and bearing ten stamens; stigmas five; capsule one-celled five-valved, with five seeds. [M. T. M.]

TAP-ROOTED. Having a large simple conical root, which forms a centre round which the divisions are arranged.

TAPURA. The name of a genus of *Chail-*

letraceae, comprising a shrub native of Guiana. The flowers are small, and have an irregularly five-lobed calyx; a somewhat two-lipped corolla, to the base of which the five stamens are attached; of these the two lateral ones are much shorter than the rest; ovary sessile three-celled, with two pendulous ovules in each compartment. The wood of *T. guianensis* is employed by the Creoles of Guiana for constructive purposes. [M. T. M.]

TAQUARUSSA. A Brazilian reed.

TAR. A thick viscid oleo-resin obtained by heat from the wood of the pine-tree, and chiefly employed as a preservative of timber, especially among shipping.

TARA. An Indian name for *Corypha Talicra,* the Talipot Palm. Also a Tahiti name for *Colocasia macrorhiza;* and a Sandwich Island name for *Caladium esculentum* and others.

TARACHIA. *Asplenium.*

TARASPIC. (Fr.) *Iberis.*

TARATOUF. (Fr.) *Helianthus tuberosus.*

TARAXACUM. The technical name of the genus of *Compositae* to which the familiar Dandelion belongs. The species are herbs, with a perennial rootstock, terminated by a tuft of leaves, from the centre of which emerge smooth hollow leafless unbranched stalks, surmounted by a single head of bright-yellow flowers. The involucre consists of an outer row of bracts, which are spreading or reflexed, and an inner row which are erect. The receptacle on which the flowers are placed is flat and smooth, the corollas all strap-shaped and yellow; and the pappus of many simple hairs. The fruit is surmounted by a long beak, like a little column, on the top of which the pappus is placed. If the flowers be examined previous to maturity, this beak is seen to be very short, but it rapidly lengthens as the fruit ripens. The genus is known from *Leontodon* by the simple not feathery pappus; and from *Crepis* by the unbranched flower-stalks.

By many botanists it is considered that there is only one species, *T. dens leonis,* which admits of many varieties. The plant is universally found in Europe, Central Asia, North America, and the Arctic regions. The most common variety in this country has broad runcinate leaves, and the outer bracts of its involucre are bent downwards. This well-known plant varies much in stature and appearance according to the locality in which it grows. That found in boggy places, sometimes considered to constitute a distinct species under the name of *T palustre,* has nearly entire leaves, and the outer scales of the involucre are ovate and pressed upwards.

The rootstock of the Dandelion (*dent du lion*) is extensively used in medicine as an aperient and tonic, especially in liver-complaints; it has also diuretic properties. When blanched the leaves may be used as a salad, but are too bitter to be agreeable.

They are eaten by cattle with advantage, also by rabbits. Schoolboys collect the leaves as a food for silkworms, when mulberry-leaves cannot be obtained; both contain a milky juice. The rhizomes may be used in the same manner as chicory.

The bright-yellow flowers of this plant open in the morning between five and six o'clock, and close in the evening between eight and nine—hence this was one of the plants selected by Linnæus to form his floral clock. Is there any connection between this fact and the childish trick of guessing the hour by the number of tufts left on the receptacle after a vigorous attempt to remove them by blowing them off? The generic name is possibly derived from the Greek taraxo, 'I have excited' or 'caused,' and achos 'pain,' in allusion to the medicinal effects of the plant.

The genus is included among the cichoraceous group of the composite family, on account of its strap-shaped flowers, and of the milky juice by which the whole plant is permeated. [M. T. M.]

TARCHONANTHUS. The name of a genus of *Compositæ*, consisting of Cape shrubs, with the flower-heads disposed in terminal panicles, or solitary in the axils of the leaves. The flowers are unisexual and diœcious, surrounded by an involucre of five scales, arranged in one row. The corollas are tubular, somewhat bell-shaped five-toothed, hairy outside and smooth within. In the male flowers the anthers are provided with two hairs at the base, while in the centre of the flower is a glandular nectary simulating the ovary; the females are surrounded by an involucre having a double row of bracts, many in number, and not combined together in any degree, as is the case with the bracts of the male flowers; there is no nectary; the fruit is very hairy and destitute of pappus. One or two species with purple flowers are grown in this country [M. T. M.]

TARE. The Common Vetch, *Vicia sativa*; also *Ervum*. —, TINE. *Lathyrus tuberosus*.

TARFA. An Arab name for *Tamarix orientalis*.

TARGIONIACEÆ. One of the suborders of *Marchantiaceæ*.

TARGIONIA. A genus of liverworts belonging to the suborder *Targioniaceæ*, of the natural order *Marchantiaceæ*, in which the capsule is solitary and sessile. The frond resembles that of *Marchantia*, is porous above, and has a central rib, and is clothed below, where it is generally of a dark-purple, with scales and rootlets. There is a bivalvate general involucre, without any proper perianth, containing about four archegonia, of which one only is impregnated, the membrane of the archegonium adhering closely to the capsule. The species belong chiefly to warm countries. One only occurs in Great Britain, and this principally in the eastern counties on mossy banks; it is very abundant in the South of Europe, where it is generally accompanied by *Lunularia*. [M. J. B.]

TARGOLA. An Indian name for the fruit of the Palmyra Palm, *Borassus flabelliformis*.

TARI. The sap of *Phœnix sylvestris*, which is drunk in India either fresh or fermented.

TARO. The tuberous roots of *Caladium esculentum*.

TARRA. The name in Lima for the pods of *Coulteria tinctoria*.

TARRAGON. *Artemisia Dracunculus*.

TARTAR-BREAD. *Crambe tatarica*.

TARTAREOUS. Having a rough crumbling surface, like the thallus of some lichens.

TARTARIAN LAMB. *Cibotium Barometz*.

TARTON-RAIRE. (Fr.) *Daphne Tartonraira*.

TARUMA. A South Brazilian name for the bark of *Vitex Taruma*.

TASCO. A Spanish name for the refuse of flax; the toppings of hemp.

TASMANNIA. A genus of *Magnoliaceæ*, consisting of one Tasmanian and two Australian species, named in honour of the Dutch navigator Tasmann, the discoverer of the island now called Tasmania, or Van Diemen's Land, an important British colony. The genus is closely allied to *Drimys*, but distinguished from it by a portion of its flowers being unisexual, the two sexes being borne on different plants, and by the ovary consisting of a single carpel. All three are shrubs, and have simple entire smooth and leathery evergreen dotted leaves, scattered on the branches; and inconspicuous flowers crowded together in the axils of the upper leaves, or terminal, producing little unopening

Tasmannia aromatica.

fruits containing several shining black seeds. The flowers have two sepals and two to five petals, all deciduous; numerous stamens, with their anthers directed outwards; and a free ovary, containing numerous ovules in two rows, and ending in a stigma which runs down its inner angle.

T. aromatica, the Tasmanian species, possesses, as its specific name implies, aromatic qualities, particularly its bark, which so closely resembles the Winter's Bark of Magelhaen's Straits (*Drimys Winteri*), that it is substituted for it by colonial doctors. The colonists call it the Pepper-plant, and use its little black pungent fruits as a substitute for pepper. It grows in large masses, and in favourable situations attains a height of twelve feet, with a trunk sometimes as much as nine inches in diameter; the branches being somewhat whorled, and when young clothed with red bark. Under the microscope the wood exhibits a structure resembling that of many coniferous plants, the fibres being marked with similar circular disks. [A. S.]

TAT. An Indian name for cloth made from the fibre of *Corchorus olitorius*.

TATABA. A large tree of Guiana, yielding a hard tough wood, adapted for shipbuilding, gun-carriages, &c.

TATTIE. An Indian name for window or door-screens made from split bamboo.

TAUSCHERIA. A genus of *Cruciferæ* from Siberia, comprising smooth erect annuals, with small whitish flowers on racemes opposite the leaves, and oval almost boat-shaped indehiscent pouches beaked at the apex, surrounded by a leathery inflexed wing, and containing a single seed. [J. T. S.]

TAUSCHIA. A genus of *Umbelliferæ*, containing a single Mexican species. It is a perennial herb with much-divided leaves, and a very short stem which lengthens in fruiting. The calyx-limb is obsolete; the petals are entire, with a long inflexed apex; the fruit is contracted at the side; the carpels have five filiform obtuse ridges, the interstices furnished with a single vitta. The carpophore is undivided, and is indicated by a furrow in the middle of the deep furrow of the commissure. [W C.]

TAUZIN. (Fr.) *Quercus Toza.*

TAVOLA. *Terminalia Catappa.*

TAWNY. The same as Fulvous.

TAXACEÆ. A suborder of *Coniferæ*, often considered as a distinct order, distinguished chiefly by their fruits not being collected in cones, each ovule growing singly, unprotected by hardened scales. See CONIFERÆ.

TAXANTHEMA. *Statice.*

TAXODIUM. A genus of *Coniferæ*, of the tribe *Cupressineæ*, consisting of lofty trees, inhabiting for the most part the rich swampy soil of Florida and other southern states of North America. The branches are slender straight or drooping, and clothed with fine linear deciduous leaves arranged in two rows. The male

catkins are in loose panicles; the females are roundish, and are composed of peltate two-seeded scales, the seeds being destitute of wings.

T. distichum, the Deciduous Cypress, is commonly seen in this country as an ornamental tree on lawns and in similar situations, where its feathery foliage renders it an attractive object. In its native country its bark and wood are much used for covering houses, for thin planks, ribs of ships, water-conduits, and other purposes. The roots sometimes bear large hollow excrescences, which are made use of by the negroes for beehives. The root is also applied to suppurating wounds. [M. T. M.]

TAXOLOGY, TAXONOMY. That part of Botany which relates to the laws of classification.

TAXUS. A well-known evergreen tree, placed by some authors among the conifers, from which, however, it is separated by others, in consequence of the fruit not being collected in cones, each ovule growing singly, unprotected by hardened scales; so that this is a degree of organisation yet lower than that of conifers themselves.

T. baccata, the Common Yew, is characterised by a trunk peculiarly suggestive of massiveness and solidity, not being covered, like the trunks of most other trees, with a splitting bark, but seemingly composed of a number of smooth stems fused together. The bark itself is of a reddish-brown hue, and scales off in thin plates. At the height of a few feet from the ground it sends out numerous horizontal branches, which spread in all directions, and are densely clothed with tough twigs, leafy throughout their whole extent or nearly so. The leaves are thickly set on two opposite sides of the stem, narrow, slightly recurved, dark-green and shining above, but paler below. The flowers, which are of two kinds, and grow on separate trees, appear among the leaves, and on the underside of the twigs. The barren flowers are the most numerous, appearing in the form of membranous scaly buds, from the centre of each of which protrudes a slender column, terminating in a tuft of stamens. The fertile flower resembles a minute acorn, the cup of which swells, and when ripe has the appearance of red cornelian, enclosing an oval brown nut, the summit of which is uncovered. These berries, if berries they may be called, drop when ripe, and contain a sweet glutinous juice. They are of a mawkish disagreeable taste, but are eaten with impunity by children, and greedily devoured by wasps, caterpillars, and several kinds of birds. The nut contains a kernel, which has an agreeable flavour like that of the stone-pine. The leaves are poisonous, though to what extent is a disputed question; but of this there can be no doubt, that their effects on the human frame are deadly, and that to give them to cattle is a perilous experiment. It appears from all accounts that the poison is more virulent in the young shoots than in any other part of the tree, but that it exists, in greater or less quantities, both in the leaves and in the green bark. The leaves are more dangerous in a half-dry state than when fresh.

The wood is hard, compact, of a fine and close grain, flexible, elastic, splitting readily, and incorruptible. It is of a fine orange-red or deep-brown; and the sapwood, which does not extend to a very great depth, is white and also very hard. The fineness of its grain is owing to the thinness of its annual layers (for the yew is a tree of exceedingly slow growth)—250 of these being sometimes found in a piece not more than twenty inches in diameter. The yew is a native of most of the temperate parts of Europe and Asia, growing in its wild state in situations little exposed to the direct rays of the sun, and generally in a clayey loamy or calcareous soil.

Yew-trees of great antiquity and large size are often to be met with growing in churchyards, but from what motive they were planted in such situations is not positively known. The reason assigned by some is, that the poisonous foliage of the yew typefied death,—others that its durability and slowly-altering features symbolised the Resurrection—others, in order that it might afford a supply of twigs to be worn on Palm Sunday—and others again, taking a still more utilitarian view, that there might be always at hand a supply of wood for making bows. Yews are in existence which are supposed to be above a thousand years old. The dimensions of the largest range from thirty to fifty feet in circumference. The yew is the badge of the Frasers. French : *If.* [C. A. J.]

The succulent fruit of the yew has a sweet sickly taste, and is not unwholesome, though it is stated that the contained seed is noxious. The leaves are poisonous to some animals, especially to cows and horses. On the human subject yew-leaves have an effect similar to that of *Digitalis,* but do not produce the remarkable and dangerous cumulative effects which are to be dreaded from the incautious use of that plant. Medicinally, yew-leaves might be used as a sedative. In poisonous doses the following effects have been remarked —giddiness, irregular and depressed action of the heart, convulsions, and insensibility. Yew-leaves or preparations therefrom have been used in calculous complaints, in epilepsy and convulsions, and also in gouty disorders. 'Yew-tree tea,' an infusion of the leaves, is, according to Dr. Taylor, sometimes used by the poor and ignorant for the same purposes as savin, but with equal danger. [M. T. M.]

TAYA. *Xanthosoma peregrinum.*

TAYLORIA. A remarkable genus of splachnoid mosses, with acute leaves, a mitriform veil, a capsule with a long neck, and sixteen or thirty-two entire or bifid teeth, disposed in pairs, springing far below its mouth and highly hygroscopic, especially in *T. splachnoides.* There are but three European species, of which *T. serrata* occurs in this country. *T. splach-*

noides, one of the most beautiful of mosses, figured in Hooker's *Musci Exotici,* occurs in North America. The species are perennial, and grow on decayed animal or vegetable substances in alpine situations. The genus was named after Dr. Taylor, Sir W. J. Hooker's associate in the preparation of the *Muscologia Britannica.* [M. J. B.]

TAYOVE. (Fr.) *Calocasia macrorhiza* and *Caladium esculentum.*

TCHOUMA. A Chinese name for the fibre of *Böhmeria nivea.*

TE. A Panama name for an infusion of the leaves of *Corchorus siliquosus.*

TEA. *Thea.* Also a name applied to the dried leaves of various plants, and to the infusions prepared from them and used either as beverages or medicinally. ABYSSINIAN. *Catha edulis.* —, APPALACHIAN. *Viburnum cassinoides,* and *Prinos glaber.* —, ARABIAN. *Catha edulis.* —, ASSAM. *Thea assamica*; in commerce the cultivated tea-plant grown in Assam. —, AUSTRALIAN. The name of several species of *Leptospermum* and *Melaleuca.* —, BENCOOLEN. *Glaphyria nitida.* —, BLACK. *Thea Bohea*; also commercially applied to the leaves of the Tea-plant when prepared by fermentation. —, BOTANY BAY. *Smilax glycyphylla.* —, BOURBON. *Angræcum fragrans.* —, BRAZILIAN. *Stachytarpha jamaicensis.* —, BUSH, of Africa. *Cyclopia genistoides.* —, CANARY. *Sida canariensis.* —, CAROLINA. *Ilex vomitoria.* —, COFFEE. An infusion of the leaves of *Coffea arabica,* drunk by the natives of Sumatra. —, FAHAM. *Angræcum fragrans,* an infusion of which is drunk to promote digestion ; its odour is owing to the presence of coumarin. —, GREEN. *Thea viridis* ; also commercially applied to tea-leaves prepared in a particular manner, and often imitated by artificial colouring. —, HIMALAYA. The tea cultivated in the mountainous districts of Northern India is imported under this name. —, JESUITS. *Psoralea glandulosa.* —, LABRADOR. *Ledum latifolium.* —, LEMON-GRASS. An infusion of the leaves of *Andropogon Schœnanthus,* substituted for tea in many of the interior districts of India. —, MALAY. *Glaphyria nitida*; also *Eugenia variabilis.* —, MEXICAN. *Ambrina ambrosioides*; also *Psoralea glandulosa.* —, MOUNTAIN. *Gaultheria procumbens.* —, NEW JERSEY. *Ceanothus americanus.* —, NEW ZEALAND. *Leptospermum scoparium.* — OF HEAVEN. A Japanese name for the leaves of *Hydrangea Thunbergii.* —, OSWEGO. *Monarda didyma.* —, PAIGLE. An infusion of the dried blossoms of the Cowslip, which is drunk in some counties of England. —, PARAGUAY. *Ilex paraguayensis.* —, SASSAFRAS. Saloop. —, SOUTH-SEA. *Ilex vomitoria.* —, SWEET. An Australian name for *Smilax glycyphylla.* —, THEEZAN. *Sageretia theezans.* —, WEST INDIAN. *Capraria biflora.* —, WILD. *Amorpha canescens.*

TEA-BERRY. *Gaultheria procumbens.*

TEAK, or TEAKWOOD. A hard heavy durable timber obtained from *Tectona grandis,* and extensively employed for ship-building purposes. —, AFRICAN. The timber of *Oldfieldia africana.* —, BEN. The wood of *Lagerströmia microcarpa* ; also applied to inferior Teak. —, NEW SOUTH WALES. *Eudiandra glauca.*

TEARS OF ST. PETER. *Anthacanthus microphyllus.*

TEAR-THUMB. An American name for *Polygonum arifolium* and *sagittatum.*

TEASEL, or TEAZEL. *Dipsacus.* —, FULLER'S. *Dipsacus Fullonum.* —, WILD. *Dipsacus sylvestris.*

TEA-TREE, CEYLON. *Elæodendron glaucum.* —, NEW JERSEY. *Ceanothus americanus.* —, NEW SOUTH WALES. *Melaleuca uncinata* ; also *Callistemon pallidum* and *C. salignum.* —, NEW ZEALAND. *Leptospermum scoparium.* —, SWAMP, of Australia. *Melaleuca squarrosa.* —, WHITE. *Melaleuca genistifolia.*

TEAZELWORTS. Lindley's name for the *Dipsaceæ.*

TECLEA. An Abyssinian tree, constituting a genus of *Xanthoxylaceæ.* The leaves have three lance-shaped smooth leaflets ; the flowers are placed on spikes or panicles—the males having a four to five-toothed calyx, four or five concave erect petals, and as many stamens inserted at the base of a fleshy coloured three-cornered rudimentary ovary ; and the females having a cup-shaped four-toothed calyx, four yellowish-green petals, four abortive stamens, a one-celled ovary surrounded by a disk, and containing a single ovule ; the stigma is peltate.   [M. T. M.]

TECOMA (including *Sparattosperma* and *Tabebuia).* A genus of *Bignoniaceæ,* composed of about fifty species, tall trees inhabiting the tropical parts of America, and valued chiefly on account of their hard almost indestructible timber, which has procured for several species the name of Roble = Oak. The White Wood of the West Indies (*T. leucoxylon* or *Bignonia pallida),* the Guayacan of Panama (*T. Guayacan),* the Porrier de la Martinique of the Caribbean Islands (*T. pentaphylla),* and several Brazilian species might be particularly pointed out as yielding firstrate timber for house and ship-building, or wood for making bows for savages. Several species are of importance in medicine. *T. impetiginosa* abounds in tannin ; its bark is bitter and mucilaginous, and it is used in lotions baths &c., in inflammation of the joints and in cases of debility. *T. Ipe* has similar qualities, and is prescribed by the Brazilians as a gargle in ulcers of the mouth ; the leaves are milder, and are sometimes used in ophthalmic affections. The leaves of *T. subvernicosa* (*Sparattosperma lithotriptica)* are bitter acrid and diuretic, and have in Brazil a reputation in cases of calculus.

When young the *Tecomas* often have simple or unifoliolate leaves, but as they grow up the leaflets increase in number, so that they become digitate. The flowers are arranged in terminal bunches, and in many species appear after the leaves have fallen off. They are large, very numerous, and of bright tint—golden-yellow purple pink or pure white. The calyx is cup-shaped, and splits into irregular segments, rendering it either bilabiate or five or three-lobed ; the corolla is funnel-shaped ; the stamens didynamous, with a fifth sterile one, the anthers glabrous and divergent. The fruit is a linear flat capsule, the valves of which are placed contrary to the direction of the partition, dividing the fruit into two cells, whilst the winged seeds are numerous, and arranged in single rows.

The name Tecoma is derived from the Mexican Tecomaxochitl (i. e. Tecomatl = an earthen war-vessel of peculiar shape, and xochitl = a flower), which Jussieu, the founder of the genus, believed to be the native name of a Mexican species of *Tecoma* ; but the Tecomaxochitl of the Aztec language is in fact *Solandra guttata.* For other species formerly classed with *Tecoma,* see CAMPSIS, TECOMARIA, STENOLOBIUM, and PANDOREA   [B. S.]

TECOMARIA. A genus of *Bignoniaceæ,* consisting of about half a dozen species indigenous to South America. But one species, *T. capensis* (*Bignonia* or *Tecoma capensis),* though originally confined to Brazil, has become widely spread over various parts of the Old World, including the East Indies, the Mediterranean region, and various parts of Africa. It was first brought to Europe from the Cape of Good Hope—hence its specific name ; and it has for more than a century been an inmate of our greenhouses. More recently two other species (*T. fulva* and *T. roseifolia)* have also found their way thither. The calyx of *Tecomaria* is regular five-ribbed and five-toothed ; the corolla tubular ; and the stamens five in number, one of which is sterile. The fruit is a linear flat capsule, smooth on the surface, and divided by a partition, running contrary to the direction of the valves, into two cells, on each side of which is a single row of numerous winged seeds. All the species are erect shrubs, with pinnate leaves the leaflets of which are acutely serrated, and terminal orange or yellow-coloured flowers arranged in panicles. They recommend themselves by their beauty, but seem to have no known uses.   [B. S.]

TECOMATE. The Mexican name of *Crescentia alata.*

TECOMAXOCHITL. The Aztec name of *Solandra guttata.*

TECTARIA. *Polystichum.*

TECTONA. The genus of the Teak-tree, belonging to the order *Verbenaceæ.* Its flowers have a bell-shaped five-cleft calyx ; a funnel-shaped corolla, with a nearly equally five-cleft spreading limb, and a tube hairy in the throat; five or six nearly equal stamens rising from the corolla-tube and protruding from it; and a two-pronged stigma. Its fruits contain a hard four-celled stone, with a fleshy oily seed in each cell. There are two species, both enormous timber trees, with large entire egg-shaped or elliptical deciduous leaves, hoary with star-shaped hairs underneath, and covered with rough points on the upper surface, which renders them useful for polishing wood.

The Common Teak, *T. grandis*, is a native of Southern and Central India, extending

Tectona grandis.

as far north as the province of Bundel-cund, and also of Burmah, Pegu, and some of the islands of the Indian Archipelago. It has quadrangular young branches, opposite leaves, terminal panicles of white flowers, and round fruits about the size of cherries, covered with spongy wool, and enclosed in a kind of bladder formed of the enlarged calyx. *T. Hamiltoniana* is found on the banks of the Irrawaddy River in Pegu and Ava, and also in the Philippine Islands. It differs from the last by its young branches being six or eight-angled, with leaves in whorls of three or four, by its blue flowers, and by its hard nut-like fruits being destitute of woolly covering, and having the enlarged calyx adhering to it, not inflated.

Teakwood is an invaluable wood to ship-builders, and is very largely employed in the construction of both merchant vessels and ships of war; its great strength and durability, added to the facility with which it can be worked, and its non-liability to be injured by the attacks of *Fungi*, rendering it peculiarly suitable for these purposes.   [A. S.]

TECUM, or TUCUM. A Brazilian name for *Astrocaryum vulgare*.

TEEL, TIL. Indian names for *Sesamum orientale*.

TEESDALIA. A genus of humble annuals belonging to the tribe *Thlaspideæ* of cruciferous plants, and distinguished by the following characters:—Pouch notched; cells two-seeded; filaments having a little scale at the base within. There are only two species. *T. nudicaulis* is an unimportant weed two to three inches high, with a few spreading radical lyrate leaves, and several generally leafless stalks, bearing at the summit close corymbs of white flowers, in which two of the petals are much larger than the others; it grows on dry banks, but is not a common plant. *T. regularis*, a native of Southern Europe, a plant of similar habit, has the petals equal.   [C A. J.]

TEESOO. A yellow dye obtained in India from the flowers of *Butea frondosa*.

TEETA. The roots of *Picrorhiza Kurroa*.

TEETH. Any kind of small marginal divisions.

TEFF. An African corn-plant, *Poa abyssinica*.

TEGMEN. The inner skin which covers the seed; the glumes of grasses.

TEGMENTA. The scales of a leaf-bud: they are *tegmenta foliacea* when modifications of leaves, *t. fulcracea* when of stipules and petioles, *t. petiolacea* when of petioles only, and *t. stipulacea* when of stipules only.

TEGULARIA. *Didymochlæna*.

TEIL-TREE, or TIL-TREE. *Tilia europæa*.

TEINIER. (Fr.) *Pinus Cembra*.

TEJ-BUL. A North Indian name for the warm spicy capsules and seeds of *Xanthoxylon hastile*.

TEJ-PAT. The leaves of *Cinnamomum Tamala* or *C. malabathrum*.

TELA. The elementary tissue.

TELAKAL. A vernacular name in India for Cullilawan-bark.

TELEKIA. A genus of *Compositæ*, comprising a tall herbaceous plant, having the habit of *Inula Helenium*. The ray-florets are ligulate, the ligulæ long and narrow; the disk-florets are tubular; the anthers are provided at the base with elongated appendages; and the fruits are linear-elongated many-ribbed triangular, and surmounted by a crown-like toothed somewhat cartilaginous pappus. *T. speciosa*, a native of Hungary, is sometimes met with in gardens in this country; its flower-heads are yellow.   [M. T. M.]

TELEPHIUM. A genus of *Illecebraceæ*, inhabiting the Mediterranean region, and also found at the Cape of Good Hope. This genus has the leaves usually alternate, a remarkable exception in the natural order to which it belongs. It is distinguished by having five persistent petals, five stamens, three spreading recurved styles, and an incompletely three or four-celled capsule containing numerous seeds. They are smooth glaucous herbs or undershrubs, with many nearly simple procumbent stems, clothed with oblong or oval leaves, furnished with small stipules, and terminated by cymose clusters of small white or greenish flowers, disposed in a racemose manner.   [J. T. S.]

TELFAIRIA. A genus of *Cucurbitaceæ*, of which there is only one species at present known—*T. pedata*, a tall climbing plant, native of the coast of Zanzibar. This has slender woody stems, fifty to a hundred feet long, climbing to the tops of the highest trees, and supporting themselves by means of very long two-parted tendrils. The leaves are large long-stalked pedate, of a shining green, paler and spotted with white underneath; and the flowers are of separate sexes, borne on different plants—the males growing six or eight together upon stalks produced from the leaf-axils, and the females singly. They have a deeply five-cut calyx with sharply-serrated segments, and a corolla of five purple petals spotted with white, marked with a broad bright-green band towards the base inside, and beautifully fringed at the top; the males containing five stamens, with wedge-shaped filaments, and distinct straight anthers; and the females a ten or more furrowed ovary ending in a short style, and a three to five-lobed stigma. The fruit, like that of many cucurbits, is of a very large size, frequently two or three feet in length, and eight or ten inches thick; it is green, and has ten or twelve deep longitudinal furrows outside; the inside being divided into from three to six cells, each of which contains a large number of flat almost circular seeds about an inch and a half across, a single fruit frequently containing upwards of 250. By pressure these seeds yield an excellent bland oil; and they are, moreover, as palatable as almonds.   [A. S.]

TELIPOGON. A genus of orchids from South America, belonging to the tribe *Vandeæ*. Eleven species have been described. Perianth spreading; sepals narrow, acute; petals broadly ovate: lip of the same form as the petals, but larger; column hairy. They are epiphytal herbs, with leafy few-flowered stems, and terminal yellow or yellow-and-purple flowers of no great beauty.   [W. B. H.]

TELLIMA. A genus of *Saxifragaceæ* from North-western America, comprising a few perennial or annual herbs, with few usually alternate stem-leaves, and numerous root-leaves; the flowers racemose, with greenish or rose-coloured petals; the calyx bell-shaped, usually adhering to the ovary at its base; the petals five; stamens ten; styles two or three, distinct; capsule one-celled. This genus is restricted to *T. grandiflora* by Professor A. Gray, the others being placed in *Lithophragma* on account of having the top of the calyx-

tube not enlarged, and the styles three in number instead of two.   [J. T. S.]

TELMISSA sedoides. The only known representative of *Crassulaceæ*, found near Aleppo; a small herb, with alternate terete fleshy leaves, and minute white flowers. The calyx is from three to five-cleft; the petals from three to five; and there are as many ovaries and capsules.   [B. S.]

TELOPEA. Few if any genera of *Proteaceæ* excel the plants of this genus in the splendour of their flowers. The species are large shrubs, natives of New South Wales and Tasmania, with entire or slightly-toothed leaves, and scarlet flowers in terminal clusters, surrounded by a deciduous involucre. The flowers are somewhat irregular and four-toothed, and conceal within them four stamens, a semicircular gland at the base, and a many-seeded ovary. Each seed has a delicate wing surrounding it. *T. speciosissima*, the Waratah, is grown in this country as a greenhouse shrub.   [M. T. M.]

TELOXYS. A genus of *Chenopodiaceæ*, founded upon the Siberian and North American *Chenopodium aristatum*, which has a distinct annular disk round the base of the ovary. It is a branched annual, with lanceolate or linear entire leaves, and small flowers in axillary dichotomous cymes; the uppermost branches sterile, awn-like.   [J. T. S.]

TEMBOUL. (Fr.)   *Chavica Betel*.

TEMPLETONIA. Robert Brown applied this name to a genus of New Holland shrubs of the family *Leguminosæ*, in honour of an Irish botanist. The leaves are wedge-shaped mucronate, and the flowers large solitary axillary crimson. The calyx is five-toothed, the lowest tooth being longer than the rest; the corolla is papilionaceous, with a spreading standard, straight wings shorter than the keel; the stamens are partially diadelphous; the style awl-shaped; and the pod stalked compressed many-seeded. Two or three species are grown in greenhouses for the sake of their flowers.   [M. T. M.]

TENCHWEED. *Potamogeton*.

TENDRIL. A twisting thread-like process by which one plant clings to another.

TENGA. An Indian name for the Cocoa-nut.

TENNEY. The Tamil name for *Setaria italica*.

TENORIA. A name given by Sprengel to some species of *Bupleurum*.

TENTWORT. *Asplenium Ruta-muraria*.

TENUIS. Thin.

TEORA. An Indian name for *Lathyrus sativus*.

TEPAL. Another name for petal. Also the pieces of a perianth, being of an ambiguous nature, between calyx and corolla.

TEPEJILOTE. A Central American name for the flowers of a species of *Chamædorea*, which while still enclosed in the spathes, are highly esteemed as a culinary vegetable.

TEPESIA. A genus of *Cinchonaceæ*, comprising a shrub, native of Chili, of which little is yet known. The calyx has a four-toothed limb, two segments of which are larger than the other two. The fruit is a four-celled berry, surmounted by the limb of the calyx.   [M. T. M.]

TEPHRO. In Greek compounds = ash-grey.

TEPHROSIA. A widely distributed genus of *Leguminosæ*, containing many species, some trees, some shrubs, some even herbaceous, growing for the most part in the tropical or subtropical regions of both hemispheres. The leaves are unequally pinnate, covered with a grey silky down. The flowers are usually in terminal clusters, but occasionally stalked in the axils of the leaves; they are either white flesh-coloured or purple; the calyx is somewhat bell-shaped, five-cleft, the two upper segments longer than the rest; the vexillum or standard of the corolla is somewhat circular in outline, bent backward, hairy externally, scarcely exceeding in size the side-petals or wings, which latter are adherent to the keel formed by the two lower petals; stamens monadelphous or diadelphous. The legume or pod

Tephrosia apollinea.

is linear compressed, straight or curved, sessile or on a short stalk, sometimes transversely jointed; seeds numerous.

Some of the species require notice, as they possess medicinal and other useful properties. Thus *T. apollinea*, a native of Egypt and Nubia, furnishes a kind of indigo. The seeds moreover are made into an ointment, used to heal the wounds of camels. The leaves and seed-vessels of this plant are occasionally found mixed with Alexandrian senna. The leaves may be recognised by their silky hairs, and by the lamina on two sides of the midrib being very nearly equal in size and shape, not larger on one side at the base as is the case with all samples of senna-leaves. The linear pods of the present plant are very different from any description of true senna-pod. See CASSIA.

T. cinerea is employed in the West Indies to stupefy fish. The leaves and stems of *T. toxicaria* are used for the same purpose in the West Indies, the Feejee Islands, and elsewhere. The stems and leaves are pounded and thrown into the river or pond, when the fish speedily become stupefied; the larger fish are stated to recover if placed in fresh water, but the smaller ones perish. The roots of this plant are employed as an application in certain skin-diseases in the Mauritius and Surinam.

T. purpurea is used medicinally in various ways by the natives of India. Thus the roots, pounded and mixed with arrack, are used as a wash for the mouth. In the form of ointment they are applied in cases of elephantiasis; they are also given, in the state of infusion or decoction, in certain cases of indigestion and to check vomiting. The juice of the plant mixed with honey is used as an application to pustular eruptions on the face. Several species are in cultivation. The generic name is derived from the Greek *tephros* 'ash-coloured,' in allusion to the colour of the leaves.   [M. T. M.]

TERAMNUS. *Glycine.*

TERASPIC. (Fr.) *Iberis umbellata.*

TERATOLOGY. The same as Morphology.

TERCINE. A supposed third integument of an ovule, but in reality a layer of the primine or secundine, or the secundine itself.

TÉRÉBENTHINE DE BOSTON. (Fr.) *Pinus palustris.*

TEREBINTHACEÆ. An order of polypetalous dicotyledons established by Jussieu, and adopted by all botanists who unite *Anacardiaceæ* with *Burseraceæ*; but as these are now definitively separated, Jussieu's common name has been abandoned.

TÉRÉBINTHE. (Fr.) *Pistacia Terebinthus.*

TEREDO. Any disease in plants produced by the boring of insects.

TERES, TERETE. Tapering; free from angles; cylindrical or nearly so.

TERGEMINATE. When each of two secondary petioles bears towards its summit one pair of leaflets, and the common petiole bears a third pair at the origin of the two secondary petioles; as in *Mimosa tergemina*.

TERMINAL. Proceeding from the end.

TERMINALIACEÆ. *Combretaceæ.*

TERMINALIA. The typical genus of the division of *Combretaceæ* characterised by the flowers having no petals, and the cotyledons being rolled round each other. It contains a considerable number of species, large trees or shrubs, dispersed over the tropics of both hemispheres. Most of the species have the leaves, which are alternate and entire, clustered towards the points of the branches, the slender flower-spikes growing from their axils and bearing perfect flowers at the bottom and male ones above, the former producing one-seeded hard-stoned fruits called drupes, which are either flattened and have the two edges attenuated or winged, or are egg-shaped without wings or obscurely angled, not surrounded by five or more longitudinal wings like those of the very closely allied genus *Pentaptera.* Their flowers have a five-cut bell-shaped calyx-limb, no petals, ten stamens in a double row, and a slender style ending in a sharpish stigma.

The astringent fruits of several species of this genus have long been employed for tanning and dyeing purposes by the natives of India; and are now brought to this country in considerable quantities, under the name of Myrobalans, and used chiefly by calico-printers for the production of a permanent black. The principal kinds of Myrobalan are the Chebulic, the produce of *T. Chebula,* which are smooth and oval; and the Belleric, *T. Bellerica,* obscurely five-angled, and covered with greyish silky down. The seeds of *T. Catappa* are like almonds in shape and whiteness, but though palatable they have none of their peculiar flavour.   [A. S.]

TERMINOLOGY. That part of Botany which teaches the meaning of technical terms.

TERNARY, TERNATE. When three things are in opposition round a common axis; a whorl of three.

TERNATO-PINNATE. When the secondary petioles, on the sides of which the leaflets are attached, proceed in threes from the summit of a common petiole.

TERNIOLA. A genus of *Podostemaceæ,* consisting of small plants resembling the species of *Jungermannia.* They are natives of India and Ceylon, and have a leaf-like rootstock, whence proceed a number of linear entire sessile leaves—those on the flower-stalk united together into a tube around the flower, which has three stamens, and as many carpels. [M. T. M.]

TERNSTRÖMIACEÆ. An order of polypetalous dicotyledons, consisting of trees or shrubs, chiefly tropical, and many of them of great beauty, which, like the *Clusiaceæ (Guttiferæ),* have imbricated sepals and petals, indefinite hypogynous stamens, and a free ovary divided into cells with the placentas in the axis; but differ from that order generally in their alternate leaves, hermaphrodite flowers, and usually curved embryo, much less fleshy, and often enveloped in albumen. These characters have, however, several exceptions, and the precise line between *Ternströmiaceæ* and *Clusiaceæ* is difficult to trace.

The order has been divided by Choisy into two sections, *Ternströmiaceæ* and *Camelliaceæ,* upon characters which have not proved sufficiently correct; and, on the other hand, it has been recently enlarged by the addition of *Rhizobolaceæ* and *Marcgraviaceæ.* It is now divided into the following six tribes:—1. *Rhizoboleæ,* with digitately compound leaves, and the embryo either folded lengthways or spirally twisted, comprising the two American genera *Caryocar* and *Anthodiscus*: see RHIZOBOLACEÆ. 2. *Marcgravieæ*: climbers or epiphytes, with the flowers in racemes, usually intermixed with hood-shaped or variously deformed bracts, and numerous small seeds without albumen. They consist of the three American genera, *Marcgravia, Norantea,* and *Ruyschia*: see MARCGRAVIACEÆ. 3. *Ternströmieæ*: erect trees or shrubs, with entire leaves, indehiscent fruit, and few albuminous seeds, with a curved embryo. They include eight genera from both the New and the Old World, of which *Ternströmia, Freziera,* and *Eurya* are the most important. 4. *Sauraujeæ*: differing from *Ternströmieæ* chiefly in their numerous small seeds, with a more abundant albumen. To these belong *Saurauja,* from the New and the Old World, and two small Asiatic genera. 5. *Gordonieæ*: differing from *Ternströmieæ* in their anthers being versatile and not erect, and usually in their capsule opening loculicidally, their straighter embryo, and rarer albumen. They include *Stuartia, Camellia, Gordonia,* and six other genera. And 6. *Bonnetieæ*: distinguished by the septicidal dehiscence of their capsule, as well as by the petals being contorted in the bud, not imbricate as in the other tribes. They are all American, with the exception of one species, and comprise *Bonnetia, Kielmeyera,* and five other genera.

TERNSTRÖMIA. The representative of the natural order *Ternströmiaceæ,* and a genus comprising about twenty-five species, inhabiting Tropical Asia and America, where they form evergreen ornamental shrubs or trees. Their leaves are coriaceous entire or serrato-crenate; their flowers are axillary nodding, generally solitary, and either white or more or less pink; the calyx consists of five sepals, highly imbricate; the corolla of five petals; the stamens are numerous; the stigma is sessile or on a short style, and either two to three-lobed or entire. The fruit is indehiscent, and contains largish seeds. Their uses are unknown. [B. S.]

TERPNOPHYLLUM. This name, signifying 'beautiful leaf,' is applied to a tree forming a genus of *Clusiaceæ.* The young leaves are of a beautiful red colour, while the flowers are yellowish diœcious, in axillary tufts. The calyx has four overlapping deciduous segments; there are four petals; numerous stamens united into a kind of disk, which adheres also to the petals, and is surmounted by a number of small tubercles, each of which bears three or four anthers. In the female flower there are eighteen scale-like triangular sterile stamens; and a free two-celled ovary, with a single ovule; the stigma almost sessile, peltate. The fruit is fleshy, containing a balsamic juice.   [M. T. M.]

TERRA JAPONICA. A trade name for Gambir. — MERITA. The Turmeric, *Curcuma longa.*

TERRANEOUS, TERRESTRIAL. Growing on land.

TERRE CRÊPIE. (Fr.) *Picridium vulgare.* — NOIX. *Carum Bulbocastanum.* — NUE. A kind of *Agrostis.*

TERRETTE. (Fr.) *Glechoma.*

TERSONIA. A Swan River shrub, with small alternate thick fleshy leaves, and axillary pedicellate flowers, forming a genus of *Phytolaccaceæ* closely allied to *Gyrostemon*, but distinguished by its seeds having no albumen.

TERTIANAIRE. (Fr.) *Scutellaria galericulata.*

TESSELATED. When colour is arranged in small squares, so as to have some resemblance to a tesselated pavement.

TESSÉRANDRA. A genus of Brazilian shrubs of the *Oleaceæ*, having sessile leaves, and axillary panicles of flowers. The calyx is small cup-shaped, with four blunt teeth; the petals four, linear; the stamens four, of equal length, with dilated filaments; and the ovary oblong, on a fleshy receptacle, two-celled, each compartment having two ovules. The fruit is a purplish-coloured drupe.   [M. T. M.]

TESSULARIS. When the three dimensions of a body, thickness breadth and length, are equal.

TESTA. The skin of a seed.

TESTACEUS. Brownish-yellow, like unglazed earthenware.

TESTA DI QUAGLIA. The Italian name for *Martynia proboscidea.*

TESTICULAR, TESTICULATE. Having the figure of two oblong bodies, as the roots of *Orchis mascula.*

TESTUDINARIA. The distinction between this genus and *Dioscorea*, the type of the order of yams (*Dioscoreaceæ*), depends more upon the general habit of the plants than upon characters derived from the flowers or fruit; for, with the exception of the seeds being winged at the top only, instead of all round, their technical peculiarities are almost identical. In habit, however, they differ widely. True yams produce large underground thin-skinned tubers; but in the two species of *Testudi-*

naria, the corresponding portion, called the rootstock or rhizome, is wholly above ground, and is coated with a bark-like corky or woody substance, which in time becomes deeply cracked and forms large angular protuberances; this has been compared to the shell of a tortoise; whence its generic name. These rootstocks are usually more or less globular, and frequently of a large size, some of them measuring four feet in diameter. Several slender climbing stems rise from their summit and grow to the length of thirty or forty feet, bearing small entire smooth more or less heart-shaped leaves, in the axils of which the short racemes of little inconspicuous greenish-yellow flowers are produced. Both species are natives of the Cape of Good Hope. The best-known, *T. elephantipes*, is occasionally seen in greenhouses in this country, where it is commonly called the Elephant's-foot, in reference to its unwieldy rootstock. At the Cape it is known as Hottentot's Bread: the fleshy inside of its rootstocks having at one time afforded part of the food of the Hottentots, though now it is only eaten by baboons and other animals.   [A. S.]

TETA DE CAPRA. A Chilian name for *Tetilla hydrocotylæfolia.*

TÊTE CORNUE. (Fr.) *Bidens tripartita.* — DE COQ. *Hedysarum caput galli.* — DE DRAGON. *Dracocephalum austriacum.* — D'OR. *Ranunculus auricomus.* — DE MÉDUSE. *Euphorbia Medusæ.* — DE MOINEAU. *Centaurea Scabiosa.* — DE MORT or DE NOIRE. *Antirrhinum Orontium.* — DE SERPENT. *Iris tuberosa.* — DE SOURIS. *Sedum sexangulare.*

TETER. Having a very bad smell.

TETILLA. The natural order *Francoaceæ* contains, as at present constituted, only two genera, *Francoa* and *Tetilla*; the latter comprising certain Chilian annuals, with stalked roundish palmately-nerved leaves, from among which rises a naked stalk supporting a raceme of flowers. Each flower is slightly irregular as to its calyx and corolla, which circumstance affords the main distinction between the genus and *Francoa*. The leaves are slightly astringent, and are used for medicinal purposes in Chili.   [M. T. M.]

TETRA. In Greek compounds = four; as *tetraphyllous*, four-leaved; *tetrapterous*, four-winged; *tetrapyrenous*, four-stoned, &c.

TETRACARPÆA. A genus of *Dilleniaceæ*, including a Tasmanian shrub of low stature. The flowers are white, and borne in terminal racemes. The calyx has four persistent sepals; the corolla four roundish stalked petals, within which are eight stamens, with two-celled anthers, each of which has a thickened connective; fruit of four many-seeded follicles.   [M. T. M.]

TETRACERA. The plants belonging to this genus of *Dilleniaceæ* are mostly climbing shrubs, rarely erect small trees; and have alternate, entire or toothed, thick evergreen leaves, and terminal or lateral panicles of flowers, which by abortion often become unisexual. They are widely spread over the tropics of Asia, Africa, and America. The flowers have four to six sepals, and as many petals; numerous stamens, with the filaments dilated at the top; and three to five ovaries cohering at the bottom, and each containing numerous ovules in two rows, ultimately ripening into one to five-seeded capsules or follicles, which split open along their inner edge.

Few of the species possess much interest beyond their botanical characters, nor are any of them remarkable for beauty. Like the rest of the order they contain some degree of astringency. *T. potatoria* is called the Water-tree at Sierra Leone, on account of its climbing stems yielding a good supply of clear water when cut across—hence also the specific name adopted by botanists. In Brazil a decoction of *T. Breyniana* and *T. oblongata* is applied to swellings of the legs, prevalent in that country; while in Guiana an infusion of the Tigarea *(T. Tigarea*, called Liane rouge by the French in Cayenne, from the red colour of its infusion) is employed in venereal complaints. [A. S.]

TETRACHÆNIUM. A fruit formed by the adhesion of four achenes.

TETRACME. A genus of *Cruciferæ*, allied to *Erysimum*, but with the pod short, and furnished with four horns at the tip. It is a small annual from the Caspian desert, and is the *Notoceras quadricorne* of Decandolle. [J. T. S.]

TETRACOCCOUS. Having four cells elastically dehiscing and separating.

TETRADENIA. A genus of *Labiatæ*, founded on a small undershrub from Madagascar, with petiolate ovate crenate leaves. The campanulate calyx is five-toothed; the corolla is divided into five nearly equal lobes; the four equal stamens have naked filaments, the cells of the anthers being confluent; and the style is slightly bifid. [W. C.]

TETRADYMOUS. Having four cells or cases.

TETRADYNAMOUS. Having six stamens, of which two are longer than the four others, which stand in pairs on opposite sides of an ovary; as in crucifers.

TETRAGLOCHIN. The name applied to a genus of *Sanguisorbaceæ*, comprising a shrub, native of the Andes of Chili. Some of the leafstalks are destitute of blade, but are spiny and provided with sheathing stipules; the true leaves are tufted and linear. Flowers on solitary axillary stalks, diœcious: the males having a four-leaved calyx, no corolla, and two stamens; and the females an ovate calyx-tube, with four broad wings, surmounted by a four-parted limb, and a one-celled ovary, with a single pendulous ovule, and three or four short styles, with fringed

stigmas. The fruit is adherent to the winged calyx-tube. The generic name is derived from the Greek *tetra* 'fourfold' and *glochin* 'an angle.' [M. T. M.]

TETRAGONELLA. A genus belonging to the order *Tetragoniaceæ*, founded upon a single species, *T. amplexicoma*, the Iceplant of the Tasmanian colonists, so called from its being covered with watery pustules which give it a crystalline appearance. It is a decumbent or erect and climbing plant, common on the seashores of Tasmania and Southern Australia, having lance-shaped or oblong-rhomboid leaves, and small long-stalked yellow flowers. The character by which this genus is sought to be distinguished from *Tetragonia* consists in the ovary being free, not adhering to the calyx; but Dr. Hooker, who combines the two genera, states that he has never found any fruits upon his numerous specimens, and consequently thinks that it has no title to rank even as a distinct species, much less as a separate genus, and that it is in reality the male plant of the common New Zealand Spinach (*Tetragonia expansa*). Its flowers have twelve stamens, two opposite each of the four lobes of the calyx and one between each pair of lobes; while those of *T. expansa* have sixteen, in four bundles between the lobes. [A. S.]

TETRAGONIACEÆ. A small order of dicotyledons united by Fenzl with *Portulacaceæ*, but differing from them essentially in their several-celled ovary. They are much more closely connected with *Ficoideæ* (or *Mesembryaceæ*) and are often united with them as a suborder, only differing in the usual absence of petals. They are succulent-leaved herbaceous plants, chiefly maritime, and are found generally within the tropics, in the South Sea Islands, in Southern Africa, and in the Mediterranean region. The principal genera are *Tetragonia, Aizoon, Trianthema,* and *Sesuvium.*

TETRAGONIA. With the exception of the New Zealand Spinach, which is found in Japan as well as in New Zealand, this genus, the type of the *Tetragoniaceæ*, is confined to the Southern Hemisphere, and is most abundant at the Cape of Good Hope; but it is also found in the temperate regions of South America, and in Australia, Tasmania, and New Zealand. Most of the species are what are called littoral plants, being found growing upon seashores. They are usually of decumbent herbaceous habit, but are occasionally erect and somewhat shrubby. They have alternate stalked fleshy leaves, and flowers on stalks growing from the leaf-axils. The flowers, which are destitute of petals, have a four-lobed calyx, with the tube adherent to the quadrangular ovary, four to twelve stamens, and from three to eight short styles. The fruits are usually four-cornered, with the corners frequently produced into tubercles or horns, and contain a hard unopening three to eight-celled stone covered with a thin green flesh, each cell containing a single seed. [A. S.]

The New Zealand Spinach, *T. expansa*, is found in Tasmania, Australia, Norfolk Island, and on both sides of South America, as well as in New Zealand and Japan. It is a half-hardy annual under cultivation, and was introduced to this country from New Zealand in 1772 by Sir Joseph Banks, on his return from accompanying Captain Cook in his first voyage round the world. It is of trailing habit, with many branches, which are furnished with numerous ovate or rhomboid alternate thick succulent deep-green leaves. As a substitute for summer spinach, this plant has been grown in private gardens for many years past; and it yields a large produce, which in the hands of a skilful cook may be made an excellent vegetable dish, although inferior to spinach. In dry warm seasons it has been found very useful for culinary purposes when there has been a scarcity of the true spinach. The chief objection to it as a cooked vegetable, is the abundance of mucilage, which gives it a somewhat slimy consistence. [W. B. B.]

TETRAGONOLOBUS. A genus of leguminous plants allied to *Lotus*, from which they are well distinguished by their quadrangular winged pods. *T. edulis* or *purpureus*, the Winged Pea, a native of Sicily, is an herbaceous annual with diffuse hairy stems, ovate leafy stipules, trifoliolate leaves, and axillary one to two-flowered peduncles, each furnished with a bract; the flowers are deep red, and the legume is smooth and broadly winged. The pods were formerly employed by the poor of Sicily and Spain as an esculent vegetable; and the plant is cultivated as a popular border annual on account of its curious pods. Two or three other species are grown, which have yellow flowers. Of these *T. maritimus* and *T. siliquosus* are perennials; *T. conjugatus* is an annual, distinguished by having its pods always in pairs. See LOTUS. [C. A. J.]

TETRAGONOUS. Four-cornered or quadrangular.

TETRAMELES. A genus of the small order *Datiscaceæ*, in which it is remarkable as being the only large-growing tree. The branches are flexuose; the leaves acute or acuminate, sometimes lobed; and the flowers small and very numerous, diœcious, appearing before the leaves, spicate—those of the males panicled and erect, and those of the females nearly simple elongated and pendulous. They have a four-cleft calyx and no corolla; the males having also four stamens, and the females a one-celled ovary with numerous ovules, and four styles. This tree is the Jungle-bendy of India, and the Weenong of Java. [T. M.]

TETRANEMA. A genus of *Scrophulariaceæ*, containing a single species from Mexico, a small herb with the habit of a *Gloxinia*, having opposite thick leaves. The calyx is five-cleft; the tubular corolla bilabiate, with the upper lip blunt and the lower trifid; and there are four fertile stamens, the fifth being altogether absent. The genus is separated from *Pentstemon* by this latter character alone. [W. C.]

TETRANTHERA. An extensive genus of *Lauraceæ*, chiefly found in the tropics and warm parts of the Eastern Hemisphere, one species, however, extending to as far north as Japan, and another as far south as New Zealand, but very few being American. The majority are trees, frequently of large size, having evergreen or rarely deciduous feather-veined leaves, and little heads or umbels consisting of numerous flowers, surrounded by an involucre formed of four to six broad concave overlapping bracts, the two sexes being usually produced by distinct trees.

T. laurifolia is widely dispersed over Tropical Asia and the islands of the Eastern Archipelago to as far south as New Guinea. Its leaves and young branches abound in a viscid juice, and in Cochin China the natives bruise and macerate them until this becomes glutinous, when it is used for mixing with plaster to thicken and render it more adhesive and durable. Its fruits yield a solid fat, commonly used in the same country for making candles, notwithstanding its disagreeable odour. [A. S.]

TETRAPATHÆA. A genus of New Zealand climbing plants belonging to the order *Passifloraceæ*, and differing little from *Passiflora*, except in the tendency of the flowers to become diœcious, and in the parts of the flower being arranged in fours. The flower-stalks usually bear three flowers. [M. T. M.]

TETRAPHIS. A genus of acrocarpous mosses belonging to the natural order *Tetraphidei*, which is distinguished by the peristome having but four teeth. It consists of a single species only, which has somewhat the habit of a *Mnium*, and occurs in shady rocky places, at the decaying roots of trees, and on banks in a peaty soil. The stems grow from a common base as in *Schistostega*, and some of them bear a little cup-shaped cluster of gems at the top. The veil is mitriform, and is irregularly plicate, resembling somewhat that of *Orthotrichum*. The genus *Tetradontium* (of which one species, *T. Brownianum*, is of rare occurrence in Great Britain) is separated from it on account of habit, the long linear but minute leaves at the base being very peculiar. A form, sometimes separated as a species, however occurs, in which the leaves are broader. *T. repandum* differs in having lash-shaped branchlets, and the mouth of the capsule notched or wavy at the interstices of the peristome. Mr. Wilson believes that he has found this in a barren state in Cheshire. [M. J. B.]

TETRAPHYLLOUS. Four-leaved.

TETRAPLASANDRA. Under this name is described a genus of *Araliaceæ*, comprising a lofty tree, with pinnate leaves, and umbellate inflorescence, native of the Sandwich Isles. The flowers are polygamous; the calyx-tube is hemispherical, connate with the ovary, its limb truncate or slightly five-toothed; petals seven to eight, epigynous, slightly coherent, caducous; stamens inserted with the petals, and four times as numerous (twenty-eight to thirty-two), the filaments short; ovary seven to ten-celled, style none; stigma obscurely radiated; fruit baccate, with eight to ten one-seeded stones. The generic name is derived from the Greek *tetraplasios* 'fourfold' and *andra* 'a stamen.' 　　[M. T. M.]

TETRAPLEURA. A genus of leguminous plants, consisting of one species, *T. Thonningii*, a large tropical West African tree, with opposite ,bipinnate leaves, and spikes of flowers agreeing in their technical characters with those of *Adenanthera*, to which genus, in fact, the plant was formerly referred under the name of *Adenanthera tetraptera*. It is, however, distinguished by the singular form of its pods, which are hard and woody, of a deep mahogany-colour, and beautifully polished. They are blunt at the ends, flattened, slightly curved, with thin sharpish edges; and have an elevated ridge of the same form and structure as the edges of the pod, running along the middle of both flat sides throughout their entire length, so that at first sight they appear like four-winged pods. Inside they are transversely divided into a number of distant one-seeded cells, the seeds being egg-shaped, flattened, about the size of tamarind-seeds, and surrounded by a pulpy substance, which the natives of the Zambezi River in Eastern Africa employ as a detergent. 　　[A. S.]

TETRAPOMA. A genus of *Cruciferæ* founded on the *Camelina barbariæfolia*. The genus, however, is more nearly allied to *Cochlearia*, from which it differs chiefly by the pouch being four-valved, one-celled, with four rows of seeds. They are annuals or biennials, inhabiting Siberia and North-western America, having the habit of *Nasturtium amphibium*. 　　[J. T. S.]

TETRAPTEROUS. Four-winged.

TETRAPTERYGIUM. A genus of *Cruciferæ*, consisting of a smooth glaucous herb, growing in Armenia. It differs from *Isatis* in the cordate pouch, which has also two narrow wings on the disk, so that it is four-winged. 　　[J. T. S.]

TETRAPYRENOUS. Four-stoned.

TETRAQUETER. Having four very sharp and almost winged corners.

TETRASPORE. In the rose-spored *Algæ* two forms of fructification are uniformly found—the one capsular, in which spores are fertilised by impregnation; the other consisting of little clusters of spores, in most cases four in number, but very rarely eight. This form of fruit does not seem to be a mere modification of the capsule, but rather to be of the nature of gemmæ, multiplying the in-

dividual without impregnation. It is called tetrasporic, and the separate bodies tetraspores. They are usually formed by the division (often unequal) of one globose endochrome, three of the four divisions only being in general visible, in which case the fruit is sometimes erroneously called trisporic. When all four are visible at once the division is said to be crucial. In some genera, however, the oblong or elliptic endochrome is divided transversely, when the division is called zonate or annular. The tetraspores may be simply immersed in the frond, when they are called sori; or contained in external warts or excrescences (hemathecia), or in proper leaflets (sporophylla), or, lastly, in elongated pod-like processes (stichidia). In the genus *Seirospora* they are disposed in necklace-like branched strings. Decaisne was inclined to consider the tetrasporic fruit as the normal fruit, and the conceptacular as gemmate; but in this he has not been followed by algologists. 　　[M. J. B.]

TETRASPORIC. Composed of tetraspores.

TETRASTICHOUS. Having a four-cornered spike.

TETRATHECA. A genus of *Tremandraceæ*, inhabiting Tasmania and the southern parts of the Australian Continent, and composed of twenty species of heath-like shrubs, having small linear lanceolate or ovate leaves, generally arranged in whorls; axillary solitary flowers, of a purple yellow or white colour, and possessing the peculiarity of only opening in a bright sun or on fine days, but closing when it is going to rain and on the approach of evening; whilst those of the allied genus *Platytheca* are not affected by any meteorological or astronomical changes. The calyx is four to five-cleft; the corolla composed of four or five petals; the stamens are from eight to ten in number, the anthers two or four-celled; and the capsule obovate and two-celled. Several species have been introduced in our greenhouses. 　　[B. S.]

TETRATOME. A genus of *Monimiaceæ*, consisting of trees or shrubs, with unisexual diœcious flowers. The males have a somewhat bell-shaped perianth, dilated at the throat, while the limb is divided into four segments, two of which are provided with a jagged appendage; and the stamens are numerous, inserted on the perianth in four rows. The females have a bell-shaped perianth, equally four-cleft above, adherent below to the ovaries, which are numerous, attached to the interior of the perianth, each having one cell containing a single pendulous ovule. The fruits are drupe-like, and very small. The generic name is derived from the Greek *tetra* 'fourfold' and *tome* 'a segment,' in allusion to the four-parted perianth. The species are natives of Tropical America. 　　[M. T. M.]

TETTER-BERRY. *Bryonia dioica*.

TETTERWORT. *Chelidonium majus.*

TETTIGAHA, or TETTIGASS. Cingalese names for *Trichadenia zeylanica.*

TEUCRIDIUM. A genus founded on a single plant from New Zealand, which resembles a *Teucrium*, though it belongs to *Verbenaceæ*. It is an erect branching herb, with a slender stem, opposite petiolate entire leaves, and solitary axillary flowers. The calyx is bell-shaped, with five sharp teeth; the corolla is hairy, bell-shaped, and divided into obovate marginal lobes; the four stamens are exserted, and have one-celled anthers; the ovary is four-lobed and two-celled; and the fruit is a small four-lobed hispid nut buried in the persistent calyx, and consisting of four one-seeded achenes. [W. C.]

TEUCRIUM. The Germanders and their allies form a most extensive genus of herbs and shrubs belonging to the *Labiatæ*, comprising nearly a hundred species, widely dispersed throughout the world, but abounding chiefly in the northern temperate and subtropical regions of the Eastern Hemisphere. Their flowers have a five-toothed calyx, either with the teeth all equal or the upper one much broader; a short-tubed corolla, with the four upper lobes short erect or bent forwards, and nearly equal, and the lower ones much larger, spreading and often concave; four stamens in two pairs, projecting between the two uppermost lobes of the corolla, the lowermost pair being the longest; and a style divided at the apex into two nearly equal prongs. The nuts forming the fruit are netted or wrinkled, and attached near the base of their inner sides.

Several species of *Teucrium* were formerly reputed to possess medicinal virtues, and found a place in the Materia Medica, but they are now discarded by all except rustic practitioners. There are three British species :— *T. Chamædrys*, the Common or Wall Germander, at one time employed in gout and rheumatism, and also as a febrifuge; *T. Scordium*, the Water Germander, a creeping marsh-plant with a disagreeable garlic-like odour when bruised, once highly esteemed as an antidote for poisons, and as an antiseptic and anthelmintic; and *T. Scorodonia*, the Wood Germander or Wood Sage, an extremely bitter plant, with the smell and taste of hops, for which it is said to be substituted in Jersey. Of the other species, *T. Marum*, or Cat Thyme, causes sneezing, and was formerly included in the London Pharmacopœia, and employed in the preparation of compound powder of Asarabacca, but lavender-flowers are now generally substituted for it. [A. S.]

TEYL-TREE. *Tilia europæa.*

TEYSMANNIA *altifrons*, the sole representative of this genus of palms, is a native of the interior of the island of Sumatra, where it was discovered in 1855 by M. Teijsmann, the director of the Botanic Garden at Buitenzorg in Java, after whom it is named. In appearance it is very distinct from the generality of palms, its leaves bearing more resemblance in shape to those of the plantain-tree than to either of the ordinary forms of palm-leaves. It has scarcely any stem above-ground, but forms horizontal ones underground, with the growing end turned upwards and bearing a crown of leaves; these being, in this particular palm, of a simple somewhat rhomboid form, rounded at the top and narrowed to the base, measuring between six and seven feet long by nearly one-and-a-half wide, longitudinally plaited like a fan, and upon stalks upwards of a yard long, furnished with hooked spines along the edges. The inhabitants of Sumatra call this palm Beluwan or Belawan, and use its leaves for thatching their houses, for which, from their large size and entire form, they are admirably adapted. As a genus it is closely allied to *Corypha*, from which, indeed, it differs mainly in habit; its technical characters, with the exception of some slight differences in the seed, being almost identical with those of that genus. [A. S.]

THALAMIFLORÆ. One of the four large classes into which Decandolle and others divide dicotyledonous plants, including all those orders in which the majority of genera have distinct petals, inserted with the stamens on the receptacle, under or immediately around the ovary.

THALAMIFLORAL, THALAMIFLOROUS. Having the stamens arising immediately from the thalamus.

THALAMIUM. A hollow case containing spores in algals; also the disk or *lamina prolifera* of lichens, and a form of the hymenium in fungals.

THALAMUS. The receptacle of a flower; the part on which the carpels are placed.

THALASSIA. A small genus of marine plants found in the Red Sea and also on the shores of some of the West Indian Islands, belonging to the *Zosteraceæ*, and closely allied to the well-known Seawrack or Grass-weed of our own shores. They have thin narrow very blunt entire or fringe-toothed leaves, with sheathing bases, in tufts at the top of the stems; and flower-stalks arising from the centre of the leaves, and bearing a terminal spathe consisting of a single split leaf, the two sexes being produced on different plants. The male flowers are surrounded by three scales, and have nine stalkless conniving anthers shorter than the scales. The female flowers are undescribed. [A. S.]

THALASSICUS. Seagreen.

THALASSIOPHYLLUM. A most remarkable genus of *Algæ* belonging to the same group as *Laminaria*, distinguished by the frond being spirally wound round the stem, like the network of *Dictyurus*, or the frond of *Riella*. The following description is taken from a translation of Merten's memoir as given in Hooker's Bota-

nical Miscellany :—'The ocean hardly boasts a more beautiful production than this; it is generally about the height of a man, very bushy and branched, each branch bearing a broad leaf at its extremity, which unfolds spirally, and by this gradual development produces the stem with its branches and lateral divisions. A spiral border wound round the stem indicates the growth of the frond. The frond presents a convex bent lamina without nerves; or to a certain degree a leaf of which one half is wanting, for the stem may be considered as an excentric nerve. A number of long rather narrow perforations, arranged in a radiate form, give the frond the appearance of a cut fan; these perforations being coëval with its formation, and apparently not owing to inequalities of substance. At first these perforations, which are situated near the stem, and where the frond is bent in, are round, and have their margins turned outwards; but by the subsequent growth of the frond they become longer, and their margins disappear. In the middle of the frond they are like true clefts; but nearer the margins, from the greater development of the leafy substance, they are more contracted in their breadth, and therefore seem round. The frond has a complete and entire margin, but is frequently torn; its substance is coriaceous. The root resembles that of the larger *Laminariæ*, but is more woody.' *T. Clathrus* is abundant on the shores of Russian America in the Bay of Illuluk, which it clothes like a thick hedge for a space of sixty or eighty feet from the land.   [M. J. B.]

THALASSIOPHYTA. A name used by Lamouroux for *Algæ*, but inapplicable from its being too restricted, and excluding all fresh-water species.   [M. J. B.]

THALAY, THAULAY. Indian names for the fibre of *Pandanus odoratissimus*.

THALIA. A genus of *Marantaceæ*, comprising certain herbaceous plants, natives of Tropical and Extratropical America. The leaves are stalked, and covered with powdery bloom like that on a plum. The flowers are borne on a stalked panicle, and are concealed between two bracts. The calyx has three segments, the corolla six; the three outer of these nearly equal, the three inner unequal; one having a slight stalk, another two thread-like processes at the base, and the intermediate one or lip hooded and semicircular. The single thread-like stamen is attached to the inner petal, that has the two processes at the base. The ovary is inferior one-celled, and contains a single ovule, attached to its base. The style is thick, twisted spirally, and the stigma is somewhat two-lipped.

T. dealbata is an elegant aquatic plant, native of South Carolina. Its fine glaucous foliage and elegant panicles of purple flowers render it a very desirable plant for aquaria. It will even resist our winters. The structure of the leafstalk in this plant is curious, and has not been described fully. In the interior are a number of air canals having at intervals horizontal partitions, consisting of beautiful star-shaped cells. Traversing the air-canals, and passing between the rays of the star-like cells, are bundles of woody tissue, which may be seen even by the naked eye. Under the microscope these wood-cells or fibres are seen to be here and there marked by little tubercles, apparently the remains of cellular tissue ruptured by the disproportionately rapid growth of the two kinds of tissue, cellular and woody.   [M. T. M.]

THALICTRUM. A well-marked genus of herbaceous plants belonging to the *Ranunculaceæ*, distinguished among its allies by the absence of petals and of appendages to the fruit. Amongst the best-known species is *T. aquilegifolium*, the Feather Columbine (*Pigamon à feuilles d'Angelie* or *Columbine plumeuse* of the French), a robust bushy herbaceous plant, with glaucous leaves tinged with purple, and large panicles of flowers, which though destitute of petals are rendered conspicuous by the numerous stamens with long slender filaments and large sulphur-coloured anthers. It is a native of the Alps, and is commonly grown in shrubberies and old-fashioned gardens. *T. glaucum*, a yet more robust plant of similar habit, is a native of Spain, and is also a handsome plant.

There are three British species: *T. flavum*, the Common Meadow-Rue, a tall plant with glaucous bipinnate leaves, and compact panicles of erect flowers, conspicuous by their yellow stamens, frequent in moist meadows and by the banks of rivers; *T. minus*, with leaves three to four times pinnate, and diffuse panicles of drooping flowers, mostly found in chalky or magnesian thickets; and *T. alpinum*, from ten to twelve inches high, with twice ternate glaucous leaves, and simple stems bearing a raceme composed of a few drooping flowers. Among the numerous exotic species, besides those mentioned, several are to be met with in English gardens, the foliage of all of which more or less resembles in character that of the Common Columbine. French : *Rue des prés*; German : *Wiesenraute*.   [C. A. J.]

THALLODES. Of or belonging to or proceeding from a thallus.

THALLOGENS. A name applied by Lindley and others to comprise those cryptogams which are extremely simple in their structure, and exhibit nothing like the green leaves of phænogams. In the few cases in which there are leaf-like expansions they are not arranged symmetrically round a stem, and are destitute of all trace of stomates and breathing pores. In a very few cases only is there anything like trachese, and then only as local organs and constituting no part of the general mass; while in those lichens or *Algæ* whose stems are of long duration, though there may be something like centrifugal growth indicated by zones, it is of a totally different nature from that of acrogens. The most definite point of distinction,

however, consists in the fact that the spore of sacrogens when germinating produce either a cellular mass or plant, in which bodies called archegonia are formed, which by impregnation produce from an embryonic cell either a new plant or a spore-bearing capsule, while in thallogens no bodies corresponding to archegonia are ever produced. The spores of *Pucciniæi* and *Æcidiacei* indeed produce a sort of preparatory organism described above under the name of PROTOSPORE, but it has nothing homologous with the prothallus of acrogens, arising as it does from the mycelium of the fungus, and not from the immediate germination of the spores. The only apparent exception amongst acrogens is that of *Characeæ*, but the infant state of the nuclei has not at present been accurately observed.

Thallogens then include the two vast tribes of algals and fungals, of which the latter are divisible into two main divisions FUNGI and LICHENS, to which heads, together with that of ALGÆ, we must refer for particulars.　　　[M. J. B.]

THALLOPHYTES. Thallogens.

THALLUS. A fusion of root stem and leaves into one general mass. This term, also used to express the part of thallogens immediately bearing the fructification, is applied more particularly to the cellular mass in which the perithecia are inclosed in *Hypoxylon*, which is however more frequently called stroma, or still more especially to the whole vegetative system of lichens. This consists of several distinct strata, which it is of much consequence to distinguish in the description of lichens. The external or cortical layers consist of closely-packed often cartilaginous cells, formed by the anastomosing of the tips of the central branched threads; next to this, in the more typical lichens, is a layer consisting of globose green bodies called gonidia, generated from the free tips of some of the same threads which produce the cortical stratum. In *collemals* these globules form little necklaces, are quadripartite as in *Omphalaria*, or fissiparous-produced that is by repeated vertical division, as in *Synalyssa* and *Paulia*. This stratum is called the gonimic. Next to this comes the filamentous medullary stratum, which gives rise to all the others, and from which alone the fruit is produced. This consists of a mass of threads spreading in every direction, and constituting the essential part of the lichen. After this follows occasionally a second gonimic stratum, and then one similar to the cortical, giving out fibrous processes or flocci. These however may be absent, the medullary stratum resting without any especial condensation upon the matrix. The medullary stratum may be clearly traced, giving rise to the two first, and also to the condensed tissue which immediately bears the asci or threads of the spermatia. Though the walls of the apothecia or spermogonia may be confluent above with the cuticle, from which they differ very little in struc-

ture and often in substance, they may be distinctly traced below to the medullary threads. In *Coccocarpia*, if indeed it be not a mere parasite as Tulasne suggests, there is no excipulum; but the fructifying mass is at first inclosed in the medullary stratum, through which it at length bursts. Our own observations accord, as far as the materials which we have had at our disposal go, with Tulasne's, and we believe all the genera of the natural order of Coccocarpei to be parasitical, and the entire order anomalous. The whole plant, in fact, appears to consist of fruit without any especial thallus, though spermogonia exist as well as in other lichens. In *Cænogonium*, which is apparently allied to *Biatora*, the medullary stratum is free, and expanded like the mycelium of a fungus, with an almost total suppression of the upper stratum. Whether this is the effect of peculiar conditions or a normal structure, as is most probable, remains to be seen. A *Biatora* has however been found in Switzerland, which suggests doubts. In some abnormal forms, as *Lepraria*, the gonimic stratum is predominant, while in *L. latebrarum* the threads of the medullary stratum are still evident.　　　[M. J. B.]

THAMNIUM. The branched bush-like thallus of lichens.

THAMNOMYCES. A genus of *Fungi* allied to *Sphæria* and *Hypoxylon*, in which the common thallus or stroma is branched or much elongated, and the perithecia are formed of the medullary substance coated with the bark. Most of the species, which are very curious, are tropical; but one, *T. hippotrichoides*, is not uncommon in England in cellars or damp rooms, on old matting made of *Scirpus lacustris*, or on hemp sacks. The plant is about the thickness of a horsehair, much branched, and bearing ovate fruit scattered over the stem or branches. As far as this species is concerned, the genus seems the same with *Rhizomorpha* as defined by Fries. The asci are at length absorbed, and the dark elliptic sporidia seem naked.　　[M. J. B.]

THAMNOPTERIS. A genus of asplenioid ferns, with thick erect caudices, and simple coriaceous fronds, remarkable in the aspleniöid group for the submarginal vein, which unites the apices of the parallel forked oblique veins, and by the long narrow linear crowded indusiate sori. The typical species is often called the Bird's-nest Fern, and has been severally called *Asplenium Nidus* and *Neottopteris vulgaris*; it is represented growing on a *Ficus*, in Plate 10, fig. *f*. The species are few in number, and chiefly Eastern, their head-quarters being India, the Indian Archipelago, the Pacific Islands, Australia, &c. One of the finest is *T. Musæfolia*, a native of the Philippine Islands. [T. M.]

THAPSIA. The plants belonging to this genus of *Umbelliferæ* were in very ancient times celebrated for their medicinal products—the Cyrenean Silphium or Laser Cyrenaicum being generally supposed to have been the produce of one of them. The species are herbaceous perennials, with the lower leaves once twice or thrice pinnated, or sometimes even more highly divided, and the upper ones reduced to the sheathing stalk only. Their flowers are disposed in large compound many-rayed umbels, with few or no involucral leaves, and they have the rim of their calyx five-toothed, and the points of their elliptic yellow-coloured petals turned in. Their fruits are flattened from the back; each half having five primary and four secondary ribs, the two side ones of the latter being expanded into thin entire wings. About a dozen species have been described, but half of them are now referred to other genera.

The true species of *Thapsia* are all natives of the countries bordering on the Mediterranean. *T. garganica* is a native of Southern Europe from Spain to Greece, and also of Algeria, where it is called Drias, and is considered by the natives to be a specific

Thapsia garganica.

against pains of all kinds, every part of the plant being held to be of equal efficacy. To camels, however, it is a deadly poison. Its root is purgative. *T. Silphion*, often regarded as a variety of the foregoing, is found on the mountains in the neighbourhood of the site of the ancient Cyrene, and is supposed to have formerly produced the gum-resin known to the ancients as Laser Cyreniacum, sometimes called Asa-dulcis to distinguish it from Asa-fœtida, both of these being included by the Greeks under the name Silphion, as also were other umbellifers. Representations of it occur on the coins of Cyrene. [A. S.]

THASPIUM. A genus of North American orthospermous *Umbelliferæ*, consisting of perennial herbs, with ternately or biternately divided leaves, the radical ones sometimes undivided, and the umbels terminal or opposite the leaves, without an involucre, and with three-leaved and one-sided involucels. The calyx-limb is minutely toothed; the elliptical petals are prolonged into a long inflexed point; the styles are slender, as long as the ovary, and

somewhat divergent, the elliptical fruit is not contracted at the sides, and the convex carpels have five equidistant winged ribs, while the intervals contain single vittæ, and the commissure has two. The genus differs from *Zizia* only in the structure of the fruit. Its popular American name is Meadow Parsnip. [W. C.]

THATCH. *Calyptronoma Swartzii*, and *Copernicia tectorum*. —, PALMETTO. *Thrinax parviflora*. —, SILVER. *Thrinax argentea*.

THATCH-TREE. A name applied to palms generally in the West Indies.

THAULAY. See THALAY.

THÉ. (Fr.) The name given to various plants of which tea-like infusions are made. — À FOULON. *Psoralea glandulosa*. — BOU. *Thea Bohea*. — D'AMÉRIQUE. *Capraria biflora*. — D'EUROPE. *Veronica officinalis*. — DE LA MARTINIQUE. *Capraria biflora*. — DE LA MER DU SUD. *Leptospernum scoparium*. — DE LA NOUVELLE HOLLANDE. *Smilax glycyphylla*. — DE LA NOUVELLE JERSEY. *Ceanothus americanus*. — D'OSWEGO. *Monarda didyma*. — DE SANTÉ. *Capraria biflora*. — DE SIMON PAULI. *Myrica Gale*. — DES ANTILLES. *Capraria biflora*. — DES APALACHES. *Prinos glaber*, also *Viburnum cassinoides*. — DES JÉSUITES. *Psoralea americana*; also *Ambrina ambrosioides*. — DU LABRADOR. *Ledum latifolium*. — DU MEXIQUE. *Ambrina ambrosioides*. — DU PARAGUAY. *Ilex paraguayensis*.

THEACEÆ. Mirbel's name for the *Ternströmiaceæ*.

THEA. A genus of *Ternströmiaceæ*. A few modern botanists combine the two well-known genera, *Thea* and *Camellia*, adopting for the genus the name *Camellia*, which is the oldest of the two; but as they have from the time of Linnæus downwards been regarded by the majority as distinct, we shall here consider them so, more especially too as improved and better-marked characters for their distinction have lately been pointed out. *Thea*, as now defined, is characterised by the calyx consisting of five persistent sepals with bracts at the base, by the inner or free series of stamens agreeing in number with the petals (viz., five, seven, or eight), and by having only three styles; while *Camellia* has numerous deciduous sepals, double as many free stamens as petals, and normally five styles, though these are sometimes reduced to four or even three. Another distinction consists in the flowers of *Thea* being turned downwards, whilst those of *Camellia* are erect. The fruit of *Thea* is three-celled, usually with only one seed in each cell, and splits at maturity through the cells into three valves, each of which has a partition down its middle. The genus is confined to Upper India, China, and Japan; and, in addition to the well-known Tea-plant cultivated in all these countries, it contains five other species, none of which, however, are employed in the manufacture of tea. All are evergreens, and either shrubs or small trees, with shining leathery leaves and white or rose-coloured flowers, either solitary or in clusters in the leaf-axils.

The native country of the Tea-plant, like that of many others which have been long cultivated by man, is uncertain. Hitherto the only country in which it has been found in a really wild state is Upper Assam; but China, where it has for so many centuries been most extensively cultivated, has not yet received so thorough an exploration by botanical travellers as to warrant the assertion that it is not indigenous to any

Thea viridis.

part of that vast empire. A Japanese tradition, however, which ascribes its introduction to China to an Indian Buddhist priest who visited that country in the sixth century, favours the supposition of its Indian origin.

It was at one time commonly supposed that the two well-marked sorts of Tea, Black and Green, were the produce of distinct species; but Mr. Fortune has proved that the Chinese manufacture the different kinds indiscriminately from the same plant; and botanists are now pretty generally agreed that the two supposed Chinese species, called *T. Bohea* and *T. viridis*, are nothing more than varieties of one and the same species, for which Linnæus' name, *T. chinensis*, is adopted, and of which the Assam Tea-plant (sometimes called *T. assamica*) is merely a third variety, or perhaps, indeed, the wild type.

Though the produce of the same variety of the Tea-plant, the Black and Green Teas prepared for exportation are mainly the growth of different districts of China, the Black Tea district being situated in the provinces of Fokien and Kiangsi, and the Green in Chekiang and Nganwhi; but the two kinds may be produced in either district, the difference being caused solely by the diverse methods of preparation. For the manufacture of Black Tea the freshly-gathered leaves, freed from

extraneous moisture by a short exposure in the open air, are thrown in small quantities at a time into round flat iron pans, and exposed to gentle fire-heat for about five minutes, which renders them soft and pliant, and causes them to give off a large quantity of moisture. After this they are emptied out into bamboo sieves, and whilst still hot repeatedly squeezed and rolled in the hands to give them their twist or curl. They are next shaken out on large screens, and placed in the open air in the shade for two or three days; and finally exposed in iron pans to a slow and steady fire-heat until completely dried, care being taken to keep them in constant motion to prevent burning. The chief difference in the manufacture of genuine Green Tea consists in the leaves being so long exposed to the air after rolling that fermentation does not take place, and in not being subjected to such a high temperature in the final drying; but the greater part, if not the whole, of the Green Tea consumed in Europe and America is coloured artificially by the Chinese to suit foreign trade. The Chinese distinguish a great number of varieties of Tea, some of which sell for as much as 50s. per lb.; but these fine kinds will not bear a sea-voyage, and are used only by the wealthier classes in China and Russia, to which country they are carried overland. In ordinary commerce four kinds of Black and six of Green Tea are recognised, but the difference between them consists chiefly in size, the several kinds being obtained by sifting. The principal Black Teas are— *Bohea,* the coarsest kind, but now seldom if ever imported, *Congou,* which forms the bulk of our tea; *Souchong* and *Pekoe,* both finer and dearer kinds; while the Green Teas are *Hyson Skin, Twankay Hyson, Young Hyson, Imperial,* and *Gunpowder*—the latter being the smallest, closest curled, and generally the youngest leaves, and the *Hyson Skin* the largest, least curled, and oldest.

Tea was introduced into Europe by the Dutch East India Company some time in the first half of the seventeenth century, but it does not appear to have made its way into England before A.D. 1660; and although the English East India Company turned their attention to the tea-trade in 1678, when they imported 4,713 lbs., it was still a rarity at the close of the seventeenth century. The official trade accounts commence in 1725, in which year 370,323 lbs. were consumed in the United Kingdom. Half a century later the quantity had risen to 5,648,188 lbs. In the first year of the present century the quantity entered for home consumption was 23,730,150 lbs.; while in 1861 it was no less than 77,949,464 lbs., the revenue derived from this latter quantity amounting to 5,521,320l., the duty being 1s. 5d. per pound. In 1863 upwards of 136,000,000 lbs. were imported, of which 85,206,779 lbs. were entered for home consumption. At present the duty is 6d. per lb.

Physiologists are not thoroughly agreed as to the effects of tea upon the human system. Its most active principles are *theine* and a *volatile oil*, to which latter its flavour and odour are due, and which possesses narcotic and intoxicating properties; but it also contains fifteen per cent. of gluten or nutritious matter, and more than twenty-five per cent. of tannin. The late Professor Johnstone endeavoured to explain its action by stating that the *theine* lessened the waste of the body, and consequently lessened the necessity for and thus stood in the place of food, while the gluten actually nourished the body; but Dr. Edward Smith has recently shown these statements to be fallacious, only a trifling proportion of the gluten being taken up by boiling-water, and the *theine* promoting instead of retarding vital action, thereby increasing the bodily waste. He sums up its action thus :—' It increases the assimilation of food, both of the flesh and heat-forming kinds; and with abundance of food it must promote nutrition, whilst in the absence of sufficient food it increases the waste of the body.' [A. S.]

THECÆ. A term sometimes used for the capsules of mosses, or for the asci of fungi and lichens, but now generally exploded as unnecessary. [M. J. B.]

THECAPHORE. The stalk of an ovary.

THEET-SEE, or THITSEE. *Melanorrhœa usitatissima*, which yields the varnish of Martaban.

THEINE. A crystalline principle found in tea and a few other vegetable substances. It is considered identical, or nearly so, with the *caffeine* of coffee, and the *guaranine* of guarana. See **THEA.**

THEKEL. A Chilian name for the purgative diuretic infusion of the leaves of *Chæradodia chilensis.*

THELEOPHYTON. A genus of *Chenopodiaceæ*, from the sandy coast of Tasmania. They are smooth herbs covered with watery papillæ, the stems prostrate, bearing monœcious flowers—the females axillary, the males at the extremity of the branches. They differ from *Atriplex* in habit, in the five-lobed calyx of the male flowers, and in the urceolate two-lobed calyx (bracts of some authors) which encloses the fruit. [J. T. S.]

THELEPHORA. A genus of *Fungi*, which was formerly almost of the same extent as the natural order *Auricularini*, but is now confined to those species whose hymenium shows slight traces of papillæ or veins, and is confluent with the pileus, which has no cuticle and is of a fibrous texture. The veins and papillæ, it should be observed, are not distinct growths, as in the lower *Agaricini* or *Hydnei*, but depend entirely upon the structure of the pileus. The more highly developed species have a central stem, with a regular pileus. To these succeed others, in which the pileus is variously divided, still retaining a stem; and then, through a series of lateral-stemmed or stemless species, we arrive at those which are totally resupinate. Amongst the latter we have one or two which are injurious to fabricated timber, especially *T. puteana*, which is extremely hygrometric. They may, however, readily be destroyed by a strong solution of corrosive sublimate. The species occur in all parts of the world, and are especially abundant and prominent in the United States; but the finest, amongst which is *T. dendritica* (which without sufficient reason has been erected into a distinct genus, because it exhibits the typical characters of *Thelephora* more perfectly than others), are essentially tropical. We possess, however, some beautiful representatives, amongst which *T. caryophyllœa*, with its funnel-shaped or variously incised pileus, is the most interesting. *T. laciniata* is perhaps the most common, and is abundant everywhere in heathy pinewoods, attaining often a considerable size. Some of the species are unpleasantly distinguished by their disagreeable smell. The best-known is *T. palmata*, but this is far surpassed by *T. fastidiosa*: both are British species. [M. J. B.]

THELESPERMA. A genus of *Compositæ*, comprising a Brazilian perennial, with much-divided leaves and terminal flower-heads, surrounded by a double involucre, whose outer series of scales are shorter than the inner, which are somewhat united together. The receptacle is covered with membranous scales, white at their margins, and bears a number of yellow tubular five-toothed florets. The fruits are somewhat compressed, and surmounted by a two-awned pappus. [M. T. M.]

THELYGONUM. A genus of *Chenopodiaceæ*, which however is referred by some authors to *Urticaceæ*, on account of the presence of stipules. It consists of a smooth somewhat succulent herb, inhabiting the Mediterranean region, with stalked oval leaves, the lower ones opposite, the upper alternate. The flowers are sessile axillary and monœcious; the males two or three together, bractless, with a two-leaved perigone, and twelve to twenty stamens; and the females one to three, with numerous bracts. The capsule is leathery, indehiscent, with a single horse-shoe-shaped seed. *T. Cynocrambe* is subacrid and slightly purgative, but is sometimes used as a potherb. [J. T. S.]

THELYMITRA. A rather extensive genus of terrestrial orchids, belonging to the *Neotteæ.* The perianth is regular, spreading, and the labellum sessile, spurless. They are herbs, with fascicled or tuberous roots; while the stems have one sheathing leaf, and bear the blue white pink or yellow flowers in loose spikes. This genus may be recognised from all others by having the segments of the perianth and of the labellum nearly equal, and the hood-shaped column enclosing the suberect anther. All the described species, with the exception of one, *T. javanica*, which is found in the mountains of Java, are from Australia and New Zealand. The name is derived from the Greek words *thelus* 'a woman' and *mitru* ' a cap,' in allusion to the hood-shaped column. *Macdonaldia* is generally referred to this genus.   [W. B. H.]

THELYPTERIS. *Lastrea.*

THEOBROMA. This genus is named from the Greek words *theos* 'god' and *broma* 'food,' in consequence of the well-known Cacao or Chocolate being the produce of its seeds. It is a group of tropical American *Byttneriaceæ*, consisting of eight or ten species of small trees, with large entire leaves, and solitary or clustered flowers growing from the sides of the old branches and stems, and producing large five-celled more or less pentagonal fruits, with a thick tough almost woody rind, each cell containing numerous seeds embedded in pulp. The seeds are destitute of albumen, and have large thick crumpled oily cotyledons. The flowers have a deeply five-parted calyx; five hooded petals terminated by spatula-shaped or roundish appendages; ten stamens united together at the bottom, five being sterile and alternate with the petals, and five fertile and opposite or enclosed in them, each of the latter bearing two double-celled anthers; and a five-cleft style.

T. Cacao was the first-known species of the genus, and the Cacao or Cocoa of commerce is now usually said to be produced by it, though it is probable that several of the other species afford a considerable

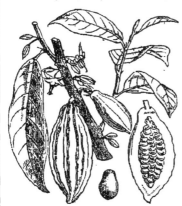

Theobroma Cacao.

portion. It is a small tree, seldom more than sixteen or eighteen feet high; and has large oblong taper-pointed leaves, and clusters of flowers with a rose-coloured calyx and yellowish petals. Its fruits vary from six to ten inches in length and three to five in breadth, and are oblong, blunt, and marked with ten elevated ribs running lengthways. Each fruit contains between fifty and a hundred seeds, and it is from

these that the Cacao is prepared. When ripe the fruits turn yellow outside; and they are then gathered by hand, and afterwards split open and the seeds removed. These are then made to undergo a slight amount of fermentation or sweating, lasting from one to two days, for the purpose of developing their colour; and are afterwards exposed to the sun daily for about three weeks, or until they are thoroughly dry, when they are packed for exportation.

The cultivation of the Cacao-tree is spread over the greater part of Tropical America; but the bulk of the Cacao-seeds brought to England comes from our West Indian Colonies, principally from Trinidad and Grenada. In 1863 our imports amounted to 9,502,965 lbs., but only 4,106,463 lbs. were for home consumption, the remainder being re-exported. An import duty of one penny per pound is charged upon them. To prepare them for use the seeds are roasted in revolving metal cylinders, then bruised to loosen their skins (which are removed by fanning), and the cotyledons, commonly called ' cocoa-nibs,' afterwards crushed and ground between heated rollers, which softens the oily matter, and reduces them to an uniform pasty consistence. This is then mixed with variable amounts of sugar and starch to form the different kinds of cocoa, or sweetened and flavoured with vanilla or other substances for the formation of chocolate.

As an article of food cocoa is exceedingly valuable, from the large amount of nutritive matter it contains; but as a refreshing beverage it is much inferior to either tea or coffee, owing to the large amount (50 per cent.) of fat which it contains, and also to the fact that the whole of the substance is taken into the stomach, while with tea or coffee only an infusion is drunk. It contains a peculiar principle, which is called *theobromine*. The European consumption of Cacao-seeds is estimated at nearly forty millions of pounds, the Spaniards being the largest consumers.   [A. S.]

THEOBROMINE. The peculiar principle of cocoa.

THEO-METL. *Agave Theometl.*

THEOPHRASTACEÆ. A small order proposed by Alphonse Decandolle for *Theophrasta* and a few allied small genera, which differ from other *Myrsinaceæ* chiefly in the presence of scales in the throat of the corolla, alternating with its lobes. It is more frequently reduced to a tribe of *Myrsinaceæ.*

THEOPHRASTA. This genus of *Myrsinaceæ* comprises a few noble-looking shrubs, with unbranched stems, bearing at the top tufts of long rigid spiny holly-like leaves, from the axils of some of which the racemes of flowers are produced. The calyx is deeply five-cleft; the corolla somewhat bell-shaped, five-lobed, with five fleshy scales in its throat, alternating with the lobes of the corolla and with the five stamens; the anthers converge into a cone, their connectives being also prolonged in the form of a sharp point ; the ovary is one-celled, with a central placenta ; and the fruit is succulent. It is said that a kind of bread is made from the seeds of *T. Jussiæi* in San Domingo, where the plant is known as Le petit Coco. From their handsome foliage this and other species are very ornamental in hothouses in this country.   [M. T. M.]

THEOPYXIS. The name of a perennial herb, with leafy stem and umbellate flowers, belonging to the *Primulaceæ.* The calyx is five to six-parted, its segments glandular ; the corolla is not described ; the style is undivided ; the capsule five to six-valved ; and the seeds furnished with three wings. The single species of this genus is a native of Chili.   [M. T. M.]

THERESA. A genus of *Labiatæ* containing a single species from Chili, a plant nearly related to *Scutellaria*, differing chiefly in having the limb of the corolla almost entire.   [W. C.]

THERESIA. A genus of *Liliaceæ* proposed by Koch to receive the *Fritillaria persica*, which has the scaly bulb and much of the habit of the true lilies. It differs from both *Fritillaria* and *Lilium* in the hypogynous insertion of the stamens, and the inconspicuous stigma. *T. persica* is a tallish glaucous plant, with the leaves obliquely twisted (somewhat as in those of *Alströmeria*), and a terminal raceme of drooping green and purplish flowers. It is a native of Mount Ararat, and a second species, which has the fetid odour of the crown-imperial, has been lately added from the district between Beyrout and Damascus.   [J. T. S.]

THERMOPSIS. A genus of papilionaceous *Leguminosæ*, comprising a number of North Asiatic and American herbs, with palmate downy leaves, and yellow flowers in terminal clusters. The calyx is irregularly five-cleft ; the standard is roundish, notched, reflected at the sides, as large as the wings ; the stamens are ten in number, and distinct ; the ovary many-ovuled ; the stigma terminal. The fruit is a linear or curved compressed legume. *T. fabacea* from North America, *T. lanceolata* from Siberia, and other species are cultivated in gardens in this country.   [M. T. M.]

THESIUM. A genus of unpretending herbaceous plants belonging to the *Santalaceæ*, among which they are distinguished by the following characters :—Perianth four to five-cleft, persistent ; stamens with a small tuft of hair at the base ; stigma simple ; fruit crowned by the perianth. The genus is represented in Britain by *T. linophyllum*, the Bastard Toadflax, a humble spreading plant, with very narrow alternate leaves, and simple or branched leafy racemes of minute white flowers, which are stalked, and furnished each with three bracts. It is a plant of uncommon occurrence, growing in high chalky pastures. None of the foreign species possess attractive properties.   [C. A. J.]

THESPESIA. A small genus of entire-leaved tropical trees belonging to the *Malvaceæ*, characterised by its flowers having an entire-rimmed calyx, surrounded by an outer calyx or involucre of three leaves, which soon falls off ; by its simple style, furrowed towards the thickened top and bearing five distinct stigmas ; and by its hard, almost woody, and generally unopening five-celled fruits, the cells of which contain several large obovoid seeds.

T. populnea, the best-known species, is an extremely common tree on the seashores of most eastern tropical countries, and also in Western Africa, the West Indies, South America, and the Pacific Islands. It forms a tree forty or fifty feet high, and has a dense head of foliage, on account of which it is called the Umbrella-tree in some countries, and is planted in many tropical districts for the sake of its shade, and for forming avenues. Its leaves are large roundish heart-shaped and pointed ; and its flowers, which like those of many mallowworts are large and showy, are at first yellow with a purple central spot, but change altogether to purple before they die off in the evening. Several parts of the tree are applied to useful purposes. The inner bark of the young branches yields a tough fibre, fit for cordage, and used in Demerara for making coffee-bags, and the finer pieces of it for cigar envelopes. The wood is considered almost indestructible under water, and is therefore used for boatbuilding ; besides which its hardness and durability render it valuable for cabinetmaking and building purposes, while in Ceylon it is employed for gunstocks. The flower-buds and unripe fruits yield a viscid yellow juice, useful as a dye, and a thick deep red-coloured oil is expressed from the seeds.   [A. S.]

THESPIS. A genus of *Asteraceæ* or *Compositæ*, comprising certain Indian herbs, with toothed leaves, and axillary or terminal flower-stalks, bearing small flower-heads, surrounded by involucres of numerous oblong scales. The receptacle is flat, and bears a number of tubular florets, the outer of which are female, the central male. The fruits are surmounted by a short pappus of seven or eight whitish or reddish hairs.   [M. T. M.]

THEVETIA. An American genus of *Apocynaceæ*, formerly combined with the Asiatic genus *Cerbera*, from which its single two-celled ovary and winged seeds distinguish it. The half-dozen species belonging to it are shrubs or small trees, inhabiting the West Indian Islands and Tropical America from Mexico to Brazil and Peru. Their leaves are alternate, and their flower-cymes terminal or lateral. The flowers have a five-parted calyx, with numerous glands at the base inside ; a salver-shaped corolla, with the tube enlarging upwards, and closed in above them by five scales, and a two-celled ovary surrounded by a ring-like five-notched disk. The fruits are slightly fleshy, and contain a hard stone, divided into two cells, each cell containing two slightly winged seeds. *T. neriifolia* has large saffron-coloured flowers three inches in length, and is commonly cultivated in Tropical America as an ornamental garden shrub, or for making hedges. Its bark is reputed to possess powerful febrifugal properties, while its milky juice is a dangerous poison, and its fruits are likewise regarded as noxious, though, according to Dr. Seemann, a gentleman in Panama ate four of them when a boy, without injury. [A. S.]

THEYA. An Indian name for *Shorea robusta,*

THIBAUDIA. A beautiful genus of vacciniaceous shrubs, chiefly found in Peru and New Grenada, though the species of one group, forming the genus *Agapetes* of some authors, are met with in India, Java, and Madagascar. They have leathery evergreen leaves, and axillary racemes (sometimes collected in great fascicles at the ends of the shoots) of very handsome tubular flowers, the colour of which is frequently scarlet, sometimes tipped with green or yellow. The calyx-tube is connate with the ovary, its limb four-toothed; the corolla is conically tubulose, with a five-toothed limb; the stamens are ten in number, the anthers two-horned at the apex; and the ovary is five-celled, with numerous ovules in each cell. The globose berry is crowned by the limb of the calyx. Some of the species are to be met with in the hothouses of this country. [T. M.]

THINOGETON. A genus of *Atropaceæ* (*Solanaceæ*) comprising an herbaceous plant, native of the seashores of Columbia. The calyx is five-toothed; the corolla-funnel or bell-shaped; the stamens five, of unequal length, the anthers opening longitudinally; and the ovary two-celled, surmounted by a style, which is dilated at the top. The fruit is berry-like, and enclosed in the enlarged calyx. The generic name is derived from the Greek words *thin* 'the seashore' and *geiton* 'near to,' in reference to the habitat of the plant. [M. T. M.]

THISANTHA. A small group of plants formerly included in and forming a section of *Crassula*, the type of the order of houseleeks. It is entirely confined to South Africa, and is composed of little annual succulent herbs, with forking stems, opposite leaves, and small flowers—the lower ones solitary in the forks of the stems, and the upper clustered. They have a five-cut calyx, a five-parted corolla, five stamens alternate with and shorter than the corolla segments, and five free ovaries (without scales) ripening into as many follicles, each containing not more than two seeds. [A. S.]

THISMIA. A small leafless erect herb from the Tenasserim coast, the place of the leaves occupied by small scales; the flowers few, in a terminal raceme, rather large for the plant, of a yellow colour variegated with red. It forms a genus of *Burmanniaceæ*, distinguished by its regu-

lar campanulate perianth, with six lobes, of which five are produced into long tails; by its six stamens; and by its one-celled ovary, with three parietal placentas.

THISTLE. *Carduus.* —, BLESSED. *Cnicus benedictus.* —, CARLINE. *Carlina.* —, COTTON. *Onopordon Acanthium.* —, CREEPING. *Cirsium arvense.* —, DISTAFF. *Carthamus lanatus.* —, FISHBONE. *Chamæpeuce Casabonæ.* —, FULLER'S. *Dipsacus Fullonum.* —, GLOBE. *Echinops.* —, GOLDEN. *Scolymus*; also *Protea Scolymus.* —, HOLY. *Carduus (Silybum) marianus.* —, HORSE. *Cirsium.* —, JERSEY. *Centaurea Isnardi.* —, MELON. *Melocactus.* —, MEXICAN. *Erythrolæna conspicua.* —, MILK. *Silybum* (or *Carduus*) *marianum.* —, MUSK. *Carduus nutans.* —, OUR LADY'S. *Silybum marianum.* —, PLUME. *Cirsium*; also applied to *Carduus lanceolatus*, and some other species having a feathery pappus. —, SAFFRON. *Carthamus tinctorius.* —, ST. BARNABY'S. *Centaurea solstitialis.* —, SCOTTISH. *Onopordon Acanthium*, one of the plants considered to be the emblem of Scotland. —, SOW. *Sonchus.* —, SPEAR. *Carduus lanceolatus*, generally regarded as the national emblem of Scotland. —, STAR. *Centaurea Calcitrapa.* —, SYRIAN. *Notobasis syriaca.* —, TORCH. *Cereus.* —, YELLOW *Argemone mexicana.*

THITSEE. *Melanorrhœa usitatissima,* the Varnish-tree of Burmah.

THLADIANTHA *dubia* is the representative of a genus of *Cucurbitaceæ* from China and India, forming a tall scrambling pale-green pubescent branched climber, with simple tendrils, broadly ovate-cordate irregularly toothed leaves, and bright-yellow axillary flowers, which are diœcious. The males are dimorphous, with a campanulate calyx-tube, and large complanate sepals—the larger flowers with the petals nearly free erect, forming a campanulate corolla longer than the sepals, and the smaller ones having the petals shorter than the sepals; the anthers are five, one-celled. The females have the calyx and corolla of the males, with their short style terminated by reniform capitate stigmas. The fruit is oblong, very succulent, with about twelve longitudinal ribs connected by network, between which the surface is hollowed. The fruit is eaten by the natives of the Himalayas. [T. M.]

THLASPI. A genus of unpretending herbaceous plants giving name to the tribe *Thlaspideæ* of cruciferous plants. The characters are:—Pouch laterally compressed, notched, valves winged at the back; cells two to eight-seeded. *T. arvense,* the Field Penny Cress or Mithridate Mustard, occurs as a weed in cornfields, in some places in great abundance. It grows to the height of from ten to twelve inches, with bright-green oblong leaves, which are toothed, and at the base arrow-shaped; the stems are slender, and bear numerous minute white flowers, which are succeeded by very large orbicular pouches, rendering the plant conspicuous, when it often perhaps but for them would remain unnoticed among other weeds. *T. perfoliatum*, a rare species occasionally found in chalky pastures, is best distinguished by its pouches, which are inversely heart-shaped. French: *Bourse de Pasteur*; German: *Hirtentasche*. [C. A. J.]

THLASPI BLANC VIVACE. (Fr.) *Iberis sempervirens*. — DE LA PETITE ESPÈCE. *Iberis amara*. — DES JARDINIERS. *Iberis umbellata*. — JAUNE. *Alyssum saxatile*. — VIVACE. *Iberis semperflorens*.

THLIPSOCARPUS. A genus of *Compositæ*, whose species have a similar habit and form of leaf to those of *Taraxacum*. The involucre consists of two rows of organs—the inner of numerous erect scales, the outer of eight or nine spreading bracts; the corollas are all strap-shaped, yellow above, purplish below; the outer fruits are compressed, rough, marked on one side by two or three ridges, the inner more slender, cylindrical, tapering towards the top; the pappus is uniform, and consists of two rows—the inner row of five long scales, prolonged at the apex into a rough hair; the outer row of numerous rough hairs, shorter than the inner series. The plant is a native of Gibraltar and the adjacent parts of Spain. The generic name refers apparently to the roughness of the fruit: it is derived from *thlibo* 'to rub against.' [M. T. M.]

THOMASIA. The name of a genus of shrubs, natives of the south-western districts of Australia, and belonging to the *Byttneriaceæ*. The leaves are covered with star-shaped hairs, and provided with permanent stipules; the flowers are borne in clusters, opposite the leaves, and have each a tripartite bract at the base of the petaloid bell-shaped five-parted calyx; a corolla with five small scale-like petals, or none; ten stamens, five of them sterile, the filaments awl-shaped, distinct or united; a three-celled ovary; and a capsular fruit, with few seeds, provided with a little strophiole or crest. Five or six of the species are valued in this country as elegant greenhouse plants. The flowers are white or purple, and the plants have very much the general appearance of some species of *Solanum*. [M. T. M.]

THOMASSINIA. A small genus established to include several perennial umbelliferous herbs, which differ from *Angelica* in the want of general or partial involucres; in the free calyx, with five ovate acuminate teeth; in the roundish fruit, with five equidistant ribs; and in the acutely carinated commissure of the carpels. The three species are natives of the Mediterranean region. [W. C.]

THOMPSONIA. A shrub, native of Madagascar, has been considered to form a separate genus of *Passifloraceæ*, under the above name. It has unequally pinnate leaves, axillary tendrils, and flower-stalks bearing five flowers. These latter have four sepals, four smaller petals, a corona of fine threads arranged in one row, and eight stamens. By these characters it may be distinguished. [M. T. M.]

THONNINGIA. A genus of *Balanophoraceæ*, comprising a fleshy parasitical leafless plant growing on the roots of trees in Western Tropical Africa. The rootstock is brown, and sends up flower-stalks clothed with red scales; the stamens are united together into a solid column, which is garnished with a few scales towards its base. [M. T. M.]

THORA. *Ranunculus Thora*.

THORN. A common name for various thorn-bearing trees, especially applied in this country to the *Cratægus Oxyacantha*. —, BLACK. *Prunus spinosa*. —, BUCK. *Rhamnus*. —, BUFFALO. *Acacia latronum*. —, CAMEL'S. *Alhagi Camelorum*. —, CHRIST'S. *Paliurus aculeatus*. —, EGYPTIAN. *Acacia vera*. —, ELEPHANT. *Acacia tomentosa*. —, EVERGREEN. *Cratægus Pyracantha*. —, GLASTONBURY. *Cratægus Oxyacantha præcox*. —, GOAT'S. *Astragalus Tragacantha*. —, HAW. *Cratægus Oxyacantha*. —, JERUSALEM. *Parkinsonia aculeata*. —, LILY. *Catesbæa spinosa*. —, MOUSE. *Centaurea myacantha*. —, ORANGE. *Citriobatus*. —, SALLOW. *Hippophaë rhamnoides*. —, THIRSTY. *Acacia Seyal*. —, WASHINGTON. *Cratægus cordata*. —, WHITE. *Cratægus Oxyacantha*; also *Cratægus punctata*, the hardwood of which is used in Canada for engraving. —, of West Indies. *Macromerium jamaicense*. —, WILLOW. *Hippophaë rhamnoides*.

THORN-APPLE. *Datura Stramonium*.

THORN-BROOM. *Ulex europæus*.

THOROUGH-WAX, or THOROW-WAX. *Bupleurum rotundifolium*.

THOROUGHWORT. *Eupatorium perfoliatum*.

THOTTEA. A tropical Asiatic shrub, constituting a genus of *Aristolochiaceæ*. The stem is wavy, jointed, swollen at the joints; the leaves entire; the flowers very large, in clusters opposite the leaves; the perianth has a four-sided tube, which expands above into a bell-shaped coloured and three-cleft limb, downy within, and somewhat prickly without; the stamens are from thirty to forty in number, adherent to a disk surmounting the ovary, and confluent with the style; stigma depressed, radiate; fruit rod-like, quadrangular, two-celled. [M. T. M.]

THOUINIA. Under this name was formerly included several genera belonging to different natural orders, but it is now exclusively applied to a genus of *Sapindaceæ*, consisting of trees or shrubs, frequently of climbing habit, and natives of Brazil and of Tropical Australia. The leaves are sometimes simple, but usually pinnate; and the flowers grow in axillary racemes, occasionally replaced by tendrils. The sepals and petals are four or five in number; stamens eight, inserted within a thick disk; ovary three-lobed, with a single ovule in each of its three compartments; fruit a three-winged samara. *T. pinnata* is cultivated as a stove-plant in this country. The genus is named in honour of M. Thouin, Professor of Agriculture at Paris. [M. T. M.]

THREE-CLEFT, THREE-PARTED. Split into three parts or divisions, deeper than when three-lobed.

THREE-EDGED. Having three acute angles with concave faces, as the stems of many plants.

THREE-LOBED. Divided into three lobes or segments.

THREE-VALVED. Applied to capsules which open by three valves or divisions.

THRELKELDIA. An Australian genus of *Chenopodiaceæ*, comprising a smooth branched undershrub, with alternate semiterete leaves, and solitary sessile axillary flowers, which have an urceolate perigone with three membranous scales within the margin; three stamens, opposite the scales; and an utricle enclosed in the enlarged fleshy perigone, with a single vertical seed. [J. T. S.]

THRIFT. *Armeria vulgaris.* —; PRICK-LY. *Acantholimon.*

THRINAX. A small and principally West Indian genus of Fan Palms (*Palmaceæ*), distinguished from its congeners by its flowers having a deeply six-cut calyx; no corolla; six nine or twelve stamens joined together at the bottom; and a simple ovary containing a single erect ovule, and terminated by a hollow one-sided funnel-shaped stigma. Six or eight species are known, all comparatively low-growing palms, seldom exceeding twenty feet in height, and frequently not more than ten; having their trunks clothed with the persistent bases of old leaves or marked with circular scars, and bearing a crown of much-cut fan-shaped leaves. Their flower-spikes grow from the axils of the leaves, and have their stalks sheathed with numerous spathes; the flowers being of a greenish or greenish-yellow colour, and producing little round one-seeded fruits. In Jamaica these palms are commonly known by the name of Thatch-palms, from their leaves being used for thatching, for which some of them are admirably adapted. One of them, *T. argentea*, the Silver Thatch-palm, is usually said to yield the young unexpanded palm-leaves imported from the West Indies under the name of Palmetto Thatch, and extensively employed for making palm-chip hats, baskets, and other fancy articles; but it is more than probable that the leaves are gathered from several species, while in the United States those of the allied genus *Sabal* are substituted. The tough leafstalks are also split into strips and woven into serviceable baskets, and the undeveloped leaves or cabbage forms an excellent vegetable. *T. argentea* is likewise a native of Panama, where it is called Palma de escoba, or Broom-palm, its leaves being there made into brooms. [A. S.]

THRINCIA. A genus of stemless herbaceous plants, with rough leaves, and solitary yellow flowers, belonging to the tribe *Cichoraceæ* of compound flowers. The characters are :—Involucre unequally imbricated; pappus of the outer florets short and scaly, of the inner plumose; receptacle naked. *T. hirta*, the only British species, is a common plant on gravelly pastures and commons, sending out from the crown of the root a few horizontal or ascending lanceolate often runcinate leaves, and slender scapes bearing each a solitary yellow flower. The fruit of the inner florets is beautifully striated and marked with raised dots. The foreign species possess no attractive properties which render them worthy of cultivation. [C. A. J.]

THROAT. The orifice of a monopetalous flower.

THROATWORT. *Trachelium*; also *Campanula Cervicaria* and *Digitalis purpurea.* —; GREAT. *Campanula Trachelium.*

THRUMWORT. *Actinocarpus*; also *Amaranthus caudatus.*

THRYALLIS. A genus of *Malpighiaceæ*, consisting of Brazilian climbing shrubs, whose young branches and inflorescence are covered with star-shaped hairs. The calyx is five-parted, without glands; the corolla yellow, of five stalked petals; stamens ten, all fertile, the filaments united at the base; ovary three-celled; styles three; fruit surrounded by the enlarged calyx, and consisting of three indehiscent carpels. One or two species are in cultivation as stove-climbing plants. [M. T. M.]

THRYPTOMENE. The name of a shrub belonging to the *Chamælauciaceæ*, and native of South-western Australia. The leaves are somewhat cylindrical, spine-pointed; and the flower-stalks axillary solitary, one-flowered, shorter than the leaves. The calyx-tube is marked with ten ridges, its limb divided into five petaloid segments; petals five; stamens ten, all fertile, the anthers roundish, with a small terminal gland; ovary one-celled, with one or two ovules; fruit capsular. [M. T. M.]

THUIA. (Fr.) *Thuja orientalis.* — THÉRIACAL. *Thuja occidentalis.*

THUJA. The derivation of this name is said to be from *thyon* 'sacrifice,' the resin of some of these plants having been used instead of incense. The genus is included in the cupressineous division of *Coniferæ*, and consists of evergreen trees natives of North America. One species is very common in English gardens under the name of Arbor Vitæ, the origin of which designation is uncertain. The branches are very numerous, the smaller ones arranged in two rows, and covered with small closelypreased lozenge-shaped leaves arranged in four ranks. Students are apt to mistake the small branches and consider them as leaves, by overlooking the minute closely-pressed true leaves. The male flowers are borne in small ovoid lateral catkins; the stamens themselves are in four rows, the anther-scales having on their under-surface four pollen-sacs bursting lengthwise. The female cones, borne on the same plant as the male ones, are solitary and terminal; each consists of eight to twelve opposite woody scales, mucronate at the apex—the outer ones with two winged seeds, the inner ones sterile.

T. occidentalis is the American Arbor Vitæ, a hardy evergreen shrub, which thrives well in almost any situation. The plant is everywhere pervaded by a powerful aromatic odour, and the leaves have been used as a remedy for rheumatism, on account of their sudorific properties. In America the wood of the tree, which there attains a much greater height than with us, is used for posts and other similar purposes. *T. orientalis*, the Chinese Arbor Vitæ, is sometimes put into a distinct genus on account of its roundish cones, more numerous scales, and wingless seeds [see BIOTA]. It is a native of Japan and China, and has long been cultivated in this country. It is of a closer habit, has its branches directed more vertically upwards, and its leaves are smaller and more dense-ly packed than in the American species. This plant has a pungent aromatic odour; the young branches are said to be used for a yellow dye, and the wood is made use of where something is required to with-stand humidity. [M. T. M.]

THUJÆCARPUS. *Juniperus.*

THUJOPSIS. A genus of cupressineous *Coniferæ*, consisting of Japanese trees, with whorled pendent branches, the smaller twigs being very numerous and two-rank-ed. The leaves are opposite, overlapping, or sickle-shaped and sharply pointed. The

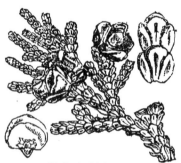

Thujopsis dolabrata.

flowers are monœcious . the males in soli-tary cylindrical catkins, with anther-scales having three to five pollen-sacs on their

under-surface; and the females succeeded by terminal cones, which are somewha globular when ripe, the scales woody im-bricated and five-seeded, the seeds being winged. *T. dolabrata*, a recently introduced shrub from Japan, is a noble-looking plant, and promises to bear our climate. *T. lævi-virens* has foliage resembling that of a *Sela-ginella. T. pygmæa* and *T. prostrata* are re-markable for their peculiar dwarf depress-ed habit of growth. [M. T. M.]

THUNBERGIA. A considerable genus of *Acanthaceæ*, containing a number of climbing herbaceous plants from Africa and Tropical Asia, with large coloured flowers. The calyx is very short, truncate or toothed, and concealed between two large bractlets, the five corolla-lobes are nearly equal and spreading; the four sta-mens have parallel-celled ciliate anthers; the stigma is shortly bilobed; the cap-sule is globose and seed-bearing at the base, and terminates in a flattened beak, two-celled with one or generally two seeds in each cell. The seeds are globular, hol-lowed out on the inner face, and inserted on a cupular expansion of the placenta The members of this genus are extensively cultivated on account of the beauty of their flowers. [W. C.]

THUNDER-DIRT. The name in New Zealand for the gelatinous volva of *Ileodic-tyon*, which is or was formerly eaten by the natives. [M. J. B.]

THUNDER-PLANT. *Sempervivum tec-torum.*

THUNDER-STROKE. See BRONTESIA.

THUNIA. A genus of orchids, consist-ing of one species from Tropical Asia for-merly referred to *Phajus*. It is an herba-ceous plant, with distant oblong strongly-veined leaves, whose sheathing bases clothe the stem : the flowers are six or eight together, in a pendulous raceme furnished with large deciduous bracts; sepals and petals nearly equal, white; lip shorter, the sides involute, the extremity spreading fringed, white with lines of purple hairs. [W. B. H.]

THURBERIA. A genus of *Malvaceæ*, comprising a tall handsome smooth her-baceous plant, native of Texas. The leaves are tripartite; and the flowers white or red, with scattered black dots. The outer calyx has three persistent leaves; the inner or true calyx is cup-shaped; the stamens are united into a column, sur-rounding or enclosing the undivided style; the ovary is three-celled, each compart-ment being partially subdivided into two, and containing six to eight ovules; the stigma is club-shaped; the fruit capsular three-celled three-valved, the valves with hairy margins. [M. T. M.]

THUS. Frankincense, a resinous exuda-tion from *Abies excelsa.*

THYLACIUM. A genus of the *Cappa-ridaceæ*, comprising certain shrubs, natives of South-eastern Africa. The calyx is in shape like a pod, and opens transversely by a lid, the corolla is absent; stamens numerous; ovary one-celled, stalked; stigma sessile; fruit one-celled, with numerous seeds. The name of the genus is derived from the Greek *thulax* 'a pod,' in allusion to the peculiar calyx. [M. T. M.]

THYM. (Fr.) *Thymus.* — DE CRÈTE. *Thymus capitatus.*

THYMBRA. A genus of *Labiatæ*, containing a single species, a native of the eastern regions of the Mediterranean. It is a low rigid shrubby plant, with narrow linear-ciliate leaves, and many-flowered whorls, more or less approximated at the ends of the axillary branches. The oblong calyx is two-lipped, and the throat is villose; the upper lip of the corolla is erect and emarginate, and the lower is spreading and trifid, the four stamens have glabrous filaments; the style is bifid, with subulate lobes, and a minute terminal stigma. [W. C.]

THYME. *Thymus.* —, BASIL. *Calamintha Acinos.* —, CAT. *Teucrium Marum.* —, COMMON. *Thymus vulgaris.* —, HORSE. *Calamintha;* also *Clinopodium.* —, LEMON. *Thymus citriodorus.* —, WATER. *Anacharis Alsinastrum.* —, WILD. *Thymus Serpyllum.*

THYMELACEÆ. An order of apetalous dicotyledons, consisting chiefly of shrubs or small trees, or rarely undershrubs or herbs, remarkable for the great tenacity of their inner bark. The leaves are entire, without stipules; the flowers usually sessile, in heads or spikes, or solitary, often sweet-scented. The order is chiefly characterised by a tubular perianth, with four or five lobes, and bearing either as many or twice as many stamens in its tube, and often small scales at the mouth; and by a simple ovary within the perianth-tube, with a short simple style, and a single pendulous ovule. There are about forty genera, a few of them dispersed over the temperate regions of the Northern Hemisphere, rather more common within the tropics, but most abundant in South Africa and Australia. The most important are *Daphne* in the Northern Hemisphere, *Gnidium* and *Struthiola* in South Africa, and *Pimelea* in Australia.

THYMÉLÉE DES ALPES. (Fr.) *Daphne Cneorum.*

THYMOPSIS. This name has been given to a much-branched shrub, native of Asia Minor, and belonging to the order *Hypericaceæ.* The flowering branches are erect, tufted; the leaves are linear revolute, dotted; and the flowers have a bell-shaped five-cleft persistent calyx, whose segments are unequal, five petals, withering stamens, united into three parcels; and an ovoid ovary with three furrows, three compartments, and three filiform styles. The fruit is capsular, three-valved. [M. T. M.]

THYMUS. The Thyme genus, of which the well-known Wild Thyme of our banks and dry pastures is a familiar example, belongs to the *Labiatæ*; and is widely dispersed over Europe, Northern Africa, and Central Asia, but is most abundant in the Mediterranean region. Between forty and fifty species of it are described, all low much-branched spreading or decumbent shrubby herbs, frequently covered with hoary hairs; and having small entire leaves, often with their edges turned in, and dense terminal leafy heads or loose spikes of purple or rarely white flowers.

The Wild Thyme, *T. Serpyllum*, is common throughout Temperate Europe and Asia, and Northern Africa. It has procumbent stems, with numerous short ascending branches, ending in short loose leafy whorled flower-spikes; the leaves being egg-shaped and narrow, and more or less fringed towards the bottom, those of the flower-spikes being similar but smaller. There are two varieties—*vulgaris*, with smaller strongly-veined leaves, and *montana*, with larger leaves and longer more erect branches. The Lemon Thyme of the gardens, frequently called *T. citriodorus*, is a cultivated form of the first variety.

The Common or Garden Thyme, *T. vulgaris*, grows more erect than the Wild Thyme, is clothed with hoary down, and has the edges of its leaves turned in; its flowerwhorls are in loose terminal heads, or some of the lower ones are remote from the others; the leaves of the whorls are blunt, while the ordinary ones are sharppointed. In the South of France an essential oil distilled from it is imported into this country and sold as marjoramoil, for which it is substituted. [A. S.]

The Common Thyme, a native of Spain and Italy, is recorded as having been introduced into this country about A.D. 1548, or perhaps earlier. Its uses are well known. The leaves, both in a green or dried state, are employed for seasoning soups, stews, sauces, and stuffings, to which they give an agreeable and highly aromatic flavour. Before the introduction of the Eastern species this plant was in great repute. According to Evelyn, it was extensively cultivated in the neighbourhood of Sandwich and Deal for medicinal purposes. It yields a species of camphor by distillation with water, and in Spain they infuse it in the pickle with which they preserve their olives. The Romans were well acquainted with Thyme, which was one of the plants recommended to be grown for the sake of bees.

The Lemon-scented Thyme is a hardy very dwarf trailing evergreen, possessing the most agreeable perfume of any of its genus. It has been long cultivated in this country. The plant is very distinct from the Common Thyme, the branches being diffuse, and striking root at every joint as they trail on the ground. It is used for the same purposes as the other species, and is found to attain the greatest perfection when grown in a dry light sandy soil. [W. B. B.]

THYRSACANTHUS. A genus of *Acan-*

thaceæ, containing a number of species of shrubs or herbs, natives of Tropical America. They have large leaves, and red fascicled or cymose flowers in a long terminal raceme. The calyx is divided to the middle into five equal short lobes, the corolla is tubular and incurved, with a five-lobed or two-lipped spreading limb; and the two fertile stamens are usually included, and have parallel anther-cells blunt at the base. The upper portion of the capsule is without seeds, while the lower portion, being swollen, gives it a spathulate form; it contains only four (sometimes two) seeds.   [W. C.]

THYRSANTHUS. A genus established for the reception of *Lysimachia thyrsiflora*, which differs from the other members of the genus by the corolla being divided to its base into narrow segments, each separated from the other by a minute tooth, and by the absence of the alternating sterile filaments. This name has also been applied to a genus of *Primulaceæ* now called *Naumbergia*.   [W. C.]

THYRSE (adj. THYRSIFORM). A panicle whose principal diameter is in the middle, between the base and apex.

THYRSEFLOWER. *Thyrsacanthus.*

THYRSODIUM. A genus of *Amyridaceæ*, consisting of trees, natives of Brazil, Guiana, etc. The flowers are diœcious or polygamous. The male flowers have a bell-shaped calyx, with five sharply-pointed segments, five petals inserted into the tube of the calyx, and a rudimentary ovary with a two-lobed stigma. The female flowers and fruit are not known.   [M. T. M.]

THYRSOID. Thyrse-like.

THYRSOPTERIS. A very handsome Juan Fernandez plant, belonging to the tribe *Cyatheineæ* of *Polypodiaceæ*. It is a curious large-leaved fern of herbaceous habit, with large supradecompound fronds, elevated on stipes four to five feet long, and as thick as a walking-stick; the leafy portion being four to five feet long, and the lowest pinnæ about two feet. They are remarkable for producing, on the same frond, distinct contracted fertile and leafy barren portions, the fertile parts being entirely reduced to rachiform segments, each terminating in a large globose spongy receptacle, surrounded by a globose involucre, and so placed that they form thyrsiform panicles. The veins are free. Among cyatheaceous ferns it is at once known by the distinct character of the sterile and fertile portions of the frond.   [T. M.]

THYRSULA. The little cyme which is borne by the greater part of labiates in the axils of their leaves.

THYSANELLA. A genus of *Polygonaceæ* founded on *Polygonum fimbriatum*, a native of Georgia. It is a smooth branched herb, with erect rod-like stems, and narrowly linear elongate acute sessile leaves; the ochreæ truncate, with long hairs. The flowers are polygamo-diœcious, in spikes arranged in a panicle, with densely imbricated ochreate bracts, which are obliquely truncate with an awn-like point. The perianth is five-leaved, with scarious and fringed margins, the two outer leaves between heart-shaped and arrow-shaped, enlarged after flowering; stamens eight; styles three, with simple stigmas.   [J. T. S.]

THYSANOCARPUS. A genus of *Cruciferæ* allied to *Tauscheria*, but the pouch is not concavo-convex, the margin is much more broadly winged, and in most of the species the extremity is not prolonged into a beak. The obovate or orbicular pouch, and the white or violet flowers distinguish it from *Isatis*. They are natives of Northwestern America, and consist of small annuals, with the pouch winged, plano-convex, or wingless and lenticular. [J. T. S.]

THYSANOSPERMUM. A genus of *Rubiaceæ*, comprising a climbing shrub with opposite leaves. The calyx and corolla are both five-parted, the latter white with a slender tube, its lobes overlapping one another in the bud; fruit capsular; seeds numerous, winged. The species is a native of Hong-Kong. The generic name is derived from the Greek *thusanoi* 'fringe,' in allusion to the winged seeds. [M. T. M.]

THYSANOTUS. A genus of Australian *Liliaceæ*, with narrowly linear leaves, and terminal umbels of purple flowers, green on the exterior. The perianth consists of six divisions, of which the inner three are broader, and fringed at the margin; stamens six (rarely three), with glabrous filaments; ovary three-celled, with two ovules in each cell.   [J. T. S.]

TIA. A Chinese name for *Sageretia theezans*.

TIAKLOU. An Indian name for *Berberis tinctoria*.

TIARELLA. A small genus of North American *Saxifragaceæ* allied to *Heuchera* and *Mitella*, but differing from the former in having ten stamens, and from the latter in the calyx being almost free from the slender ovary, as well as in the entire petals. They are perennial herbs, with simple or trifoliolate incised and serrated leaves, and a leafless scape bearing a raceme, or a leafy stem with a panicle of white flowers. Calyx bell-shaped, nearly free from the ovary, five-parted; petals five, small; styles two; capsule one-celled, with two unequal valves; seeds few, subglobose. The most common species of this genus, *T. cordifolia*, is met with in the regions extending from Canada to Virginia.   [J. T. S.]

TIARIDIUM. A genus of *Ehretiaceæ* found in Tropical America and Asia, and having the habit of *Heliotropium*, from which it differs in the angular tube of the corolla, with a contracted five-rayed orifice, and in the two-celled mitre-shaped nuts. *T. indicum* is an astringent, and is used to allay inflammation; it is also said to be beneficial in cleansing ulcers. [J. T. S.]

TIBISIRI. A Guiana name for the fibre of the Ita Palm, *Mauritia flexuosa*.

TICKSEED. *Corispermum*; also *Coreopsis*.

TICOREA. A genus of *Rutaceæ*, consisting of tropical and subtropical South American trees or shrubs, with white flowers speckled with glandular dots, and arranged in a branched inflorescence. The calyx is five-toothed; the corolla funnel-shaped, its limb five-parted; the stamens five to eight, some of them sterile; the ovaries five, surrounded by a disk, free, or united by their inner corners; and the fruit capsular, of five carpels. The bark of *T. febrifuga* is bitter, astringent, and used in Brazil in fevers. The leaves of *T. jasminiflora* are also used medicinally in Brazil. [M. T. M.]

TIEDMANNIA. A genus of North American orthospermous *Umbelliferæ* established on a single glabrous herb, with a fistulose stem, and leaves reduced to terete nodose petioles. The involucres and involucels are composed of from four to six subulate leaves; the calyx-limb is five-toothed; the petals broadly ovate, with a narrow inflexed point; the obovate fruit much compressed dorsally; and the carpels with five somewhat carinate equal ribs, the lateral ones being dilated into a membranaceous margin nearly as broad as the dorsal disk, and the furrows having a single large vitta in each, the commissure having two. [W. C.]

TIEUTÉ. *Strychnos Tieuté*.

TIGAREA. *Tetracera Tigarea*.

TIGELLATE. Having a short stalk, as the plumule of a bean.

TIGER-FLOWER. *Tigridia*.

TIGER-LILY. *Lilium tigrinum*.

TIGER-WOOD. The heartwood of *Machærium Schomburgkii*, valuable for cabinetmaking, obtained from British Guiana.

TIGRIDIA. A genus of Mexican bulbous herbs of the order *Iridaceæ*, having ensiform plaited leaves, and flowers of great beauty, but of a very evanescent character. The perianth has a short tube, and a six-parted spreading limb, the outer segments of which are larger, and the smaller inner ones subpanduriform; there are three stamens, continuous with the tube of the perianth, their filaments connate into a long tube; the ovary is three-celled, with a filiform style as long as the staminal tube, and three filiform bifid stigmas; and the capsule is membranaceous, with numerous seeds. The flowers are orange or yellow, richly spotted, whence the name Tiger-flower. [T. M]

TIKOOR, TIKUL. Indian names for *Garcinia pedunculata*.

TIKOR. An Indian name for the tubers of *Curcuma leucorrhiza*; also for a kind of arrowroot prepared from the tubers.

TIL, or TEEL. *Sesamum orientale* and *S. indicum*, the seeds of which are commonly known as Til-seed. The black-seeded variety is called Kala-til in India, the white seeded Suffed-til. — BLACK. *Guizotia oleifera*.

TIL-TREE. *Tilia*. —, CANARY ISLAND. The stinking-wooded *Oreodaphne fœtens*.

TILE-ROOT. *Geissorhiza*.

TILIACEÆ (*Elæocarpeæ, Lindenblooms*). An order of polypetalous dicotyledons, consisting of trees or shrubs or very rarely herbs, with alternate stipulate leaves, and usually cymose flowers. They are chiefly characterised by a valvate calyx, indefinite hypogynous stamens, and a free ovary divided into several cells, with the placentas in the axis. The calyx connects the order with *Malvaceæ* and *Sterculiaceæ*, from which it is chiefly distinguished by the stamens. The species are numerous, especially within the tropics; some are natives of the temperate regions, both of the Northern and Southern Hemispheres, but none extend into the Arctic Circle, or ascend to great mountain elevations. The genera, about forty in number, have been distributed into two suborders or independent orders, *Tilieæ* and *Elæocarpeæ*, upon characters which have failed in so many instances that they have been rearranged in seven tribes, viz—*Brownlowieæ, Grewieæ, Tilieæ, Apeibeæ, Prockieæ, Sloanieæ*, and *Elæocarpeæ*. The most important genera are—*Brownlowia, Grewia, Triumfetta, Corchorus, Liihea, Tilia, Apeiba, Prockia, Sloanea*, and *Elæocarpus*.

TILIA. The typical genus of *Tiliaceæ*, well known through the Common Lime, so frequently planted as an ornamental tree. It consists of very few species, though a considerable number of supposed ones have been described; and is entirely confined to the temperate countries of the Northern Hemisphere, the Limes being the only European representatives of the order. All the species are large trees, with alternate more or less heart-shaped deciduous leaves, and small yellowish highly fragrant flowers borne in axillary cymes, which have a curious long leaf-like bract attached to their stalks. The flowers have five sepals, as many petals, numerous stamens, and a globular five-celled ovary, each cell containing two ovules; but four cells are abortive, so that the fruit is only one-celled, and two (frequently only one) seeded.

The Common Lime or Linden, *T. europæa*, attains a height of from sixty to a hundred and twenty feet. It is met with generally throughout Europe, except in the extreme North; one variety of it, the small-leaved Lime, is indigenous to Britain, but the large-leaved variety which is commonly planted, is a native of the South of Europe. Various parts are applied to useful purposes. The white soft but close-grained wood is used by carvers and turners, and by musical instrument-makers for sounding-boards. The tough inner bark, called Bass or Bast, is the material of which the Russian mats used by gardeners and upholsterers are made; and the Russian peasants make shoes, ropes, nets, and other articles of it. The sap yields sugar, and the flowers an abundance of honey, of which bees are excessively fond. [A. S.]

TILIACORA. Drs. Hooker and Thomson write of this genus of *Menispermaceæ* as one easily distinguishable from the rest of the tribe *Cocculeæ*, by the mottled albumen of the seeds, and the numerous ovaries. The species are climbing shrubs, with ovate-acuminate leaves, and yellow flowers in axillary clusters. They are indigenous throughout India and Java. [M. T. M.]

TILL. The Lentil, *Ervum Lens.*

TILLÆA. A minute succulent plant belonging to the *Crassulaceæ*, among which it is distinguished by its three and sometimes four-cleft flowers. It rarely exceeds two inches in height, and bears procumbent or ascending stems, with opposite oblong blunt fleshy leaves, and minute axillary flowers, of which the petals are white tipped with rose-colour. It grows on moist barren heaths, principally in the eastern counties of England, and sometimes makes itself a troublesome weed in garden-walks. [C. A. J.]

TILLANDSIA. A genus of *Bromeliaceæ*, consisting of tropical and extratropical American herbaceous plants, growing frequently on trees, and covered with scurfy scales. The sepals are spirally twisted; the petals rolled into a tube below, concealing the six hypogynous stamens; ovules attached in two rows to the inner angles of the three compartments of the ovary, which latter is free, or detached from the calyx. Fruit capsular, bursting by three valves; seeds surrounded by fine hairs, by means of which they are diffused and enabled to become deposited on the branches of trees.

Some of these plants serve as reservoirs for water, which flows down the channelled leaves; these are dilated at the base, so as to form a bottle-like cavity capable of containing a pint or more. Travellers tap these vegetable pitchers for the sake of the grateful fluid they contain. *T. utriculata*, a native of Jamaica, and many others have this desirable property of storing water. Dr. Gardner, in his *Travels in Brazil*, relates that a certain species of *Utricularia* grows only in the water collected in the bottom of the leaves of a large *Tillandsia*. The aquatic plant throws out runners, which direct themselves to the nearest *Tillandsia*, and there form new plants. In this way no less than six *Tillandsias* may sometimes be seen connected together.

T. usneoides, a native of the West Indies, the Southern States, and Central America, hangs down from the trees like a tuft of long grey hair, much in the same way as certain lichens (*Usnea*) do in European pine-forests. The trees in some parts of Central America,

have a strange gaunt appearance, from the profusion of this plant growing from their branches. The plant is collected, and steeped in water in order to remove the outer cellular portion, the fibrous part being used in place of horsehair to stuff cushions, mattresses, &c. Powdered and mixed with lard, the plant is medicinally employed as an application to piles. *T. recurvata* is used in a similar manner in Peru. Several species are grown in stoves in this country, as air-plants. Their flowers are white blue purple or pink. [M. T. M.]

TILLEUL. (Fr.) *Tilia.*

TILLY. The seed of *Croton Pavana.*

TIL-SEED. The seeds of *Sesamum orientale* and *S. indicum.*

TIL-TREE. *Tilia europæa.*

TIL-WOOD. The timber of *Oreodaphne fœtens*, which has an atrocious smell.

TIMANDRA. A genus of Brazilian shrubs of the family *Euphorbiaceæ*. The species are much-branched, and have small stipulate entire leaves, covered with star-shaped hairs, and marked with pellucid spots. The flowers are monœcious: the males in clusters, with a four-cleft bell-shaped calyx, four petals, and eight stamens; the females solitary, axillary, with a five-parted calyx, no corolla, and a three-lobed ovary with three divided stigmas. Fruit capsular; seeds three. [M. T. M.]

TIMMIA. A fine genus of mosses, consisting of two European species only, having somewhat the habit of *Polytrichum*, but more closely allied to *Mnium*. It differs from other nearly related genera in the inner peristome consisting of a transparent membrane, divided more than halfway into about sixty-four thread-shaped cilia, at first more or less united at the apex. *T. austriaca* occurs in this country, though rarely, and never with fruit. [M. J. B.]

TIN. The Arabic name for the Fig.

TINÆA *intacta* is the only known representative of a genus of terrestrial orchids spread over parts of Asia Africa and Europe, including Ireland. Two peculiarities characterise the genus. The plate seen between the anther-cells is not equivalent to the *processus rostelaris* of our common European *Ophrydeæ*, but comes nearer to that of the *Habenarieæ* of the other continents. It bears the caudiculæ conjointly in two channels; and the glandules are formed out of its own substance, so that there is either an impressed aperture, or an aperture with an outward slit. The second peculiarity is that the shanks of the stigma, which alone are developed, have the shape of two semicylindrical erect elevations; they are either united or quite distinct. The lower lip of the rostellum is undeveloped. The generic name has been changed into NEOTINEA (which see), because there is already a genus *Tinea* in zoology. *T. intacta* (or *Neotinea intacta*) has many synonyms—among them

Aceras secundiflora, *Orchis intacta*, and *Peristylus maculatus*, the structure of the flowers having been for a long time misunderstood. The plant has a tuberous root, a stem from two to twelve inches high, three or four oblong leaves arranged in a rosette, and with brown spots on the upper surface. The flowers are whitish and spotted, very minute, and arranged in a dense cylindrical spike.   [B. S.]

TINANTIA. The name of a Mexican herbaceous plant, of somewhat shrubby habit, which constitutes a genus of *Nyctaginaceæ*. The flowers are spiked, and have a tubular or funnel-shaped perianth, the lower part of which is persistent, while the limb is plicated and deciduous; the three to five stamens project from the corolla; and the fruit is pendulous and distended.   [M. T. M.]

TINDER, GERMAN. The soft Amadou, *Polyporus fomentarius.*

TINE-TARE. *Ervum hirsutum;* also *Lathyrus tuberosus.*

TINGUY. A Brazilian name for the leaves of *Magonia pubescens* and *M. glabrata.*

TINIER. (Fr.) *Pinus Cembra.*

TINKAR'S-ROOT. The roots of *Triosteum perfoliatum.*

TINOSPORA. The species of this genus of *Menispermaceæ* were formerly included under *Menispermum*. They are all climbing shrubs, natives of India, with thickened jointed leafstalks, and long axillary or terminal clusters of flowers. The more technical characters are the presence of six free stamens in the male flowers, the curved ovules, peltate albuminous seeds, and spreading cotyledons. Dr. Thomson thus remarks on the extreme vitality of these plants: 'When the main trunk is cut across or broken, a rootlet is speedily sent down from above, which continues to grow till it reaches the ground, and restores the connection.' A bitter principle, *calumbine*, pervades the plants of this genus, many of which have tonic and emetic properties. An extract called Galuncha is prepared from *T. cordifolia* and *T. crispa*. It is considered to be a specific for the bites of poisonous insects and for ulcers. It is administered as a diuretic and tonic in cases of fever, and is also employed in snake-bites. The young shoots of *T. cordifolia* are used as emetics.   [M. T. M.]

TINTEREE. An Indian name for the Tamarind-tree.

TIPILIE. An Indian name for Long Pepper.

TI-PLANT *Cordyline Ti*, which is doubtfully identified with *Dracæna terminalis.*

TIPUANA. Three large Brazilian and Bolivian trees have recently been separated from *Machærium* and formed into a genus under this name, which is derived from Tipu, the vernacular name of the Bolivian species (*T. speciosa*): one of the valleys of the province of Parana, where the best gold is found, being also called Tipuana, from the presence of these trees. It is distinguished from *Machærium* by its flowers having the calyx top-shaped or sharp towards the base instead of rounded, and the petals smooth, not downy; and also by its pods containing frequently two or three seeds in the lower swollen part, separated from each other by woody partitions, and terminating upwards in a thin wing traversed by arched parallel veins, and having the thickened style along one edge of it. The three species have unequally pinnate leaves, with alternate leaflets, and loose-branching terminal panicles of showy yellow or pale-purple flowers. *T. heteroptera* furnishes a wood known to the timber-dealers at Rio Janeiro by the name of Angelim. It is, however, very scarce, being seldom met with in the forests. The name Angelim is likewise given by the Brazilians to several species of *Andira*, a genus belonging to the same tribe, *Dalbergieæ*.   [A. S.]

TIPULARIA. A terrestrial genus of orchids belonging to the *Vandeæ*. They are herbs with tuberous roots, producing small green blossoms tinged with purple, in a many-flowered raceme; and a single ovate plaited leaf, on a slender petiole, after flowering. The sepals and petals are spreading; the lip prolonged below into a slender ascending spur, about twice the length of the flower, three-lobed; the middle lobe linear, as long as the petals, the lateral lobes short and triangular. Only one species is known, *T. discolor*, a native of North America. The genus is named from the supposed resemblance of the flowers to insects belonging to the genus *Tipula*.   [W. B. H.]

TIRASSE. (Fr.) *Polygonum aviculare.*

TIRESIAS. A synonym of *Œdogonium*, which is worthy of being mentioned here, because a species of *Tiresias* is one of the *Algæ* in which a spiral structure in the cell-walls has been observed by Mr. Bowerbank, like that in the well-known *Conferva Melagonium*.   [M. J. B.]

TIRITE. *Ischnosiphon Arouma.*

TISANE. A drink prepared in France from the dried flowers of *Malva sylvestris.*

TISI. An Indian name for Linseed.

TISSUE. The material out of which the elementary organs of plants are constructed.

TITHONIA. A genus of Mexican perennials belonging to the *Compositæ*. The leaves are triplinerved and serrate; the flower-heads solitary at the ends of the branches, each surrounded by an involucre consisting of two or three rows of scales, furrowed within at the base, dilated and leafy at the apex; receptacle convex, with numerous scales sheathing round the fruits. The outer florets are strap-shaped and neuter, the inner ones tubular five-toothed and perfect. The stigmas are longer than the tube, awl-shaped, hairy, revolute. The outer fruits are compressed, with a very short pappus; the central ones somewhat four-cornered, surmounted by a pappus of numerous small-toothed scales. *T. tagetiflora* is cultivated in this country for the sake of its orange-coloured flowers. [M. T. M.]

TITHYMALE. (Fr.) *Euphorbia Cyparissias.* —, PETITE. *Euphorbia exigua.*

TITHYMALUS. *Euphorbia.*

TITTMANNIA. A genus of *Scrophulariaceæ*, generally however considered as a section of *Vandellia*, containing the species with very short appendages to the filaments of the anterior stamens, and globular fruit included in the calyx. [W. C.]

TIWAJ. An Indian name for *Wrightia antidysenterica.*

TJETTEK. A Javanese name for the virulent poison prepared from *Strychnos Tieuté.*

TMESIPTERIS. A genus of club-mosses, distinguished at once by its peculiar habit, consisting of a single species only, which is found in the Southern Hemisphere, and from thence extending from the Pacific Islands up to California. The plant is pendulous, and frequently grows on tree-ferns in New Zealand, Australia, and Tasmania. The stem is angular and branched; the leaves are alternate vertical and coriaceous, the fertile ones two-lobed or didymous, plane, ribbed but nerveless, obtuse or mucronate (often in the same specimen), and decurrent at the base; capsules large oblong two-lobed, the lobes divaricate and acute, opening with a vertical fissure, and containing a quantity of very minute curved spores. The germination has at present not been ascertained. Two species, depending upon the acute and truncate leaves, have been proposed, but the examination of a good series of specimens shows that they are untenable. [M. J. B.]

TOADFLAX. *Linaria.* —, BASTARD. *Thesium linophyllum*; also an American name for *Comandra.* —, IVY-LEAVED. *Linaria Cymbalaria.*

TOADSTOOLS. The common name of agarics and *Boleti*, which, according to the notion of older herbalists, derived their origin from toads, as puffballs derived theirs from wolves, or deerballs (*Elaphomyces*) from deer. [M. J. B.]

TOBACCO. *Nicotiana.* —, AMERICAN. *Nicotiana Tabacum* and its varieties. —, INDIAN. *Lobelia inflata*; also *Cannabis indica.* —, MOUNTAIN. *Arnica montana.* —, PERSIAN, or SHIRAZ. *Nicotiana persica.* —, RIVERSIDE. *Pluchea odorata.* —, SYRIAN. *Nicotiana rustica.*

TOBACCO-ROOT. The root of *Lewisia rediviva.*

TOBAGO-CANES. A name under which the slender trunks of *Bactris minor* are

sometimes imported into Europe, to be made into walking-sticks.

TOCOCA. A name used by the natives of Guiana, and applied botanically to a genus of *Melastomaceæ*, consisting of Brazilian shrubs, whose leafstalks have very generally attached to them a kind of bladder, divided longitudinally into two compartments. The ants avail themselves of these cavities as nests. The flowers are solitary or in clusters; each has a five-toothed calyx, five white or pink petals, ten equal stamens, and a five or six-celled ovary ripening into a fleshy many-seeded fruit. The stigma is convex. *T. guianensis* is in cultivation in this country; in its native habitat its fruits are edible, and their juice is sometimes used as ink. [M. T. M.]

TOCOYENA. A vernacular name latinised, and applied to a genus of *Cinchonaceæ*, consisting of tropical American shrubs having yellowish flowers in terminal corymbs. The calyx is five-toothed; the corolla funnel-shaped, with a very long tube dilated at the throat, and a limb of five blunt lobes; anthers five, inserted at the throat of the corolla; style filiform, hairy at the top; fruit succulent two-celled, surmounted by the calyx. Seeds numerous. Some of the species are in cultivation as stove-plants. [M. T. M.]

TOCUSSO. An Abyssinian corn-plant or millet, *Eleusine Tocusso.*

TODDALIA. A small genus of *Xanthoxylaceæ*, confined to the tropics of Asia and Africa, and consisting of shrubs, with alternate trifoliolate leaves marked with pellucid dots, and small unisexual flowers, borne in axillary or terminal panicles; they have four or five (rarely three) sepals and as many petals; the males containing a similar number of stamens, and a rudimentary quinquangular pistil; and the females sterile stamens with a nearly globular five-celled ovary, bearing a broad peltate lobed stigma. Their fruits are globular fleshy berries marked with dots.

T. aculeata is very widely dispersed through Tropical Asia, and extends to as far south as Mauritius. It is a shrub of moderate size, with weak or flexuose smooth branches, usually armed with small prickles having their points bent backwards, and bearing trifoliolate leaves composed of oblong or oval-oblong leaflets, the leafstalks and also the midribs of the leaflets being generally prickly. The native Indian physicians ascribe stimulating powers to all parts of this plant, and prescribe the fresh bark of its roots as a remedy for the kind of remittent fever known as 'hill-fever,' from its being contracted in the jungles of the Indian hills. On the Malabar Coast the plant is called Kaka Toddali, whence the generic name adopted by botanists. [A. S.]

TODDY. Palm-wine. The juice which flows from the incised spathes of *Borassus flabelliformis*, *Raphia vinifera*, *Mauritia vinifera*, *Arenga saccharifera*, the cocoa-nut, date, and other palms. It forms a delicious beverage when fresh, and is employed in India by bakers, instead of yeast, in the preparation of bread; it is also extensively distilled into a spirituous liquor generally drunk by the natives, among whom it is known by the name of Bowra.

TODEA. A small genus of ferns related to *Osmunda*, and distinguished from it by their dorsal instead of panicled fructifications. They occur in South Africa, New Holland, and New Zealand, and form two groups: one with coriaceous fronds and dense lines of spore-cases; the other with pellucid fronds and sparse lines of spore-cases. The latter some botanists separate under the name of *Leptopteris*. They have an erect sometimes elongated caudex, and bipinnate fronds, which in the true *Todeas*, represented by *T. barbara* alias *africana*, are thick and firm in texture, and bear oblong or linear forked sori, crowded with spore-cases; and in the group *Leptopteris* are pellucid-membranaceous, with oblong or linear oligocarpous sori. These latter are natives of New Zealand. The spore-cases, as in *Osmunda*, are pedicellate, with a rudimentary ring, represented by a few parallel striæ near the apex, eventually bursting into two equal hemispherical valves. [T. M.]

TODS'-TAILS. A Scotch name for the common Highland Clubmosses.

TOFFS. The fragrant flowers of the North African *Rhaponticum acaule*.

TOFIELDIA. A genus of *Melanthaceæ*, consisting of a few perennial plants, natives of the colder parts of Europe, North America, and the regions of the Andes. The roots are somewhat tuberous, the leaves grass-like, and the flowers inconspicuous in terminal clusters, each one with a six-parted perianth, surrounded by a three-parted involucre. The anthers are introrse, and the fruit three-celled and dehiscent. *T. palustris* is found in boggy places in the North of England, and in Scotland. Its leaves are in tufts close to the ground, and the flower-stems bear a cluster of small yellow blossoms. [M. T. M.]

TOGGRY. *Cajania indica*.

TOKO-PAT. An Assam name for *Livistona Jenkinsiana*.

TOL. (Fr.) A common name for several kinds of *Aloë*.

TOLILOLO. (Fr.) *Mentha Pulegium*.

TOLMENEER, or TOLMEINER. The Sweetwilliam, *Dianthus barbatus*.

TOLOSA-WOOD. *Pittosporum bicolor*.

TOLPIS. A genus of favourite garden annuals, natives of the South of Europe, belonging to the tribe *Cichoraceæ* of compound flowers. They are marked by a number of long awl-shaped bracts clothing the flower-stalk and base of the involucre; and the pappus of the outer florets is toothed that of the inner florets armed

with two or four awns. *T. barbata* and *T. umbellata* have yellow flower-heads with a purple eye, and *T. altissima* has flower-heads entirely yellow. [C. A. J.]

TOMATE. (Fr.) *Lycopersicum esculentum*.

TOMATO. *Lycopersicum esculentum*. —, CANNIBAL'S. *Solanum anthropophagorum*.

TOM-BONTRIN'S-BUSH. *Picramnia Antidesma*.

TOMENTOSE. Covered with dense rather rigid short hairs, so as to be sensibly perceptible to the touch.

TOMENTUM. The down which produces the tomentose character.

TONALCHILE. (Fr.) Guinea-pepper.

TONCHAT. *Maranta Tonchat*.

TONGA-BEAN. *Dipterix odorata*; also called Tonka-bean or Tonquin-bean.

TONGA-BEAN WOOD. *Alyxia buxifolia*.

TONGO. A Pacific Island name for the Mangrove.

TONGUEA. *Pachypodium*.

TONGUE-SHAPED. Long, fleshy, plano-convex, obtuse; as the leaves of some *Aloës*.

TONTELEA. A genus of *Hippocrateaceæ*, consisting of tropical American shrubs or small trees, with opposite short-stalked entire or serrated leaves, and panicles of greenish or yellowish flowers, the stamens of which, like those of *Hippocratea*, have single-celled anthers bursting transversely—the genus being thus distinguished from *Salacia*, which has double-celled anthers bursting longitudinally. From *Hippocratea* it differs in the character of the fruit; that of *Tontelea* being a fleshy two or three-celled roundish berry, containing a solitary wingless seed, covered with pulp, in each cell; while that of *Hippocratea* consists of several separate pieces, each of which splits open when ripe, and contains usually several winged seeds.

The berries of *T. scabra*, the Guiana species, are edible, as also are those of several Brazilian species called Saputa by the inhabitants; they are sweet and mucilaginous. The West African plant with a large richly flavoured fruit, called *Tontelea pyriformis* by some authors, is a species of *Salacia*. [A. S.]

TOOLA-LODH. A Bengalee name for the bark of *Wendlandia tinctoria*.

TOOLSI, TULASI. Indian names for species of Basil.

TOOMA. A species of *Mimosa* used for tanning in India.

TOOMBISAI. An Indian name for the fruit of *Diospyros Embryopteris*.

TOON, TOONA. Indian names for the Toon-tree, *Cedrela Toona*.

TOOROO. A South American palm.

TOOTHACHE-TREE. *Xanthoxylon fraxineum.*

TOOTHED. Dentate; having any kind of small divisions.

TOOTHWORT. *Dentaria*; also *Lathræa.*

TOOT-PLANT. A poisonous New Zealand shrub, *Coriaria ruscifolia.*

TOPANA. A Greek name for the edible tubers of *Bunium ferulaceum.*

TOPINAMBOUR. (Fr.) *Helianthus tuberosus.*

TOP-SHAPED. Inversely conical, with a contraction towards the point; as the fruit of some roses.

TOQUE. (Fr.) *Scutellaria.*

TORCHE-PIN. (Fr) *Pinus Pumilio.*

TORCHES. *Verbascum Thapsus.*

TORCHWOOD. *Cereus heptagonus*; also *Thiodia serrata*. —, MOUNTAIN. *Amyris balsamifera.*

TORDYLIOPSIS. A genus of herbaceous *Umbelliferæ*, founded on a single species from Nepal. It is a hairy plant, with much-divided leaves, and six to eight-rayed terminal umbels, with many-leaved general and partial involucres. The calyx-teeth are acute, the outer larger with a dilated base; and the petals on the outer margin are large obcordate bilobed, the others smaller cuspidate or rarely somewhat bilobed. The mature fruit is unknown, but in its young state it is hairy. The genus requires further examination.   [W. C.]

TORDYLIUM. A small genus of herbaceous *Umbelliferæ*, chiefly from the Mediterranean region, with pinnatisect leaves which have ovate segments, and compound umbels with general and partial involucres. The calyx consists of five subulate teeth; the petals are obcordate, with an inflexed lobe, the outer ones being often large and radiant; the flat fruit has a broad thick wrinkled margin; and the carpels have scarcely visible ribs: the three dorsal equidistant, and the two distant lateral ones close to the thickened margin, while there are one or three vittæ in the interstices. The genus has been divided into two sections—*Eutordylium*, with a single vitta in the interstices and two in the commissure; and *Condylocarpus*, with three vittæ in the interstices and many in the commissure.
The plants of this genus have the general appearance of *Caucalis*, but they are readily distinguished by the flat fruit. One species, *T. maximum*, is included in the British Flora; it occurs very rarely on waste ground in Middlesex and the adjoining counties.   [W. C.]

TORENIA. A genus of *Scrophulariaceæ*, containing several species of herbs, with opposite leaves, and short few-flowered racemes. They are scattered over the tropical regions of the Old World, one species being found also in America. The tubular calyx is plicate or winged, and five-toothed or two-lipped; and the upper lip of the open-mouthed corolla is emarginate or bifid, and the lower trifid. The capsule is oblong, included within the calyx.   [W C.]

TORFACEOUS. Growing in bogs or mosses.

TORIA. An Eastern name for *Sinapis glauca*, extensively cultivated in India for the oil obtained from its seed.

TORILIS. A genus of *Umbelliferæ*, comprising herbaceous mostly annual plants, with much-divided leaves covered with short adpressed hairs. The general involucre is one to five-leaved, and the involucel many-leaved. The calyx has five triangular-lanceolate acute persistent teeth; and the petals are obcordate, with an inflexed point, the outer ones radiant and bifid. The fruit is laterally compressed, the carpels having five bristly primary ridges, and four intermediate ones occupying the whole of the interstices, and covered with numerous prickles. The species are indigenous to Europe, Asia, and North Africa.   [W. C.]

TORMENTIL, TORMENTILLA. The *Potentilla Tormentilla*, a species in which the petals are four instead of five in number.

TORONJA. A Spanish name for the Citron.

TORONJIL. A Spanish name for *Citrus decumana.*

TOROSE, TORULOSE. A cylindrical body, swollen out here and there.

TORREYA. A genus of *Taxaceæ*, to which the name of Stinking Yews has been given, on account of the leaves and wood emitting a disagreeable odour when bruised or burned. They are small evergreen trees of North America, China, or Japan, and grow from twenty to fifty feet high; the linear or lanceolate leaves are more or less distinctly two-ranked, and the flowers diœcious, the males solitary and the females erect, in twos or threes. The fruits are drupaceous, each with a single seed, which has a ruminated albumen covered by a hard bony shell. The timber of *T. taxifolia* and *T. myristica* is heavy and close-grained, but has an unpleasant smell. The kernels of the seeds of *T. nucifera* yield an oil, which is used for culinary purposes, though the kernel is too astringent to be eaten.   [T. M.]

TORRONTES. A kind of white grape grown in Spain.

TORROO. A Guiana palm.

TORSIVE. Twisted spirally. The same as Contorted, except that there is no obliquity in the form or insertion of the pieces as in the petals of *Oxalis.*

TORTELLE. (Fr.) *Sisymbrium offici-nale.*

TORTILIS. Susceptible of twisting.

TORTILLARD. (Fr.) *Ulmus campes-tris.*

TORTOISE-PLANT. *Testudinaria ele-phantipes.*

TORTOISE-WOOD. A variety of Zebra-wood.

TORTOZON. A large Spanish grape.

TORTULA. A large genus of acrocar-pous mosses, distinguished by the thirty-two thread-shaped teeth of the peristome being twisted into a common fascicle. Several of the species are extremely common on mudwalls, exposed pastures, roofs of houses, &c. *T. ruralis* is one of our finest species, forming large tufts, which are peculiarly conspicuous and indeed ob-noxious on slate roofs and thatch, from the broad hair-pointed leaves and abun-dant fruit. Most of the species are peren-nial. The genus belongs to the natural order *Trichostomeæ.*   [M. J. B.]

TORTUOUS. Having an irregular bend-ing and turning direction.

TORULACEI. A natural order of naked-spored *Fungi* belonging to the division *Coniomycetes.* The mycelium is very slightly developed if at all apparent, and the whole plant seems to consist of a mass of variously constituted simple or septate naked spores, generally united together in chains. In the typical plants the spores are almost always of a dark dingy hue. The coloured species must be carefully examined and compared with *Oidium* and other genera which bear spores in chains. In *Sporidesmium* the whole plant through various modifications is reduced to single spores. The higher forms of *Pucciniæi,* as *Aregma* and *Xenodo-chus,* whose species are confined to the leaves of roseworts, are sometimes referred here, but they have little in common ex-cept the analogy presented by their long many-celled spores. The most extraordi-nary genus perhaps is *Sporoschisma,* which consists of a central thread breaking up into jointed spores contained in a common tube, exactly after the fashion of many *Oscillatoriæ.* It is to be observed that in those cases in which there is apparently no mycelium, a microscopic examination of the tissues of the plant on which the fungus grows will always detect it. In-deed, it is obvious that no true fungus in its perfect state can be propagated without previous mycelium.   [M. J. B.]

TORUS. The same as Thalamus.

TOUCH-ME-NOT. *Impatiens Noli-tan-gere.*

TOUCHWOOD. A name given to the soft white substance into which wood is converted by the action of *Fungi,* of which ash, especially under the influence of *Poly-porus squamosus,* affords good examples.

Occasionally, when highly impregnated with mycelium, it has been observed to be luminous. It derives its name from its property of burning for many hours like tinder when once ignited. This is some-times confounded with the powdery snuff-coloured mass into which wood is some-times converted without the agency of *Fungi* by a process of chemical combus-tion distinguished by the name of Erema-causis, and is not to be distinguished from wood affected by dry-rot, except from the absence of fungous spawn. When wood is damp, or placed in an atmosphere charged with moisture, the oxygen of the air com-bines with the hydrogen, and carbonic acid is given off from the residue; and as this action constantly recurs, the texture of the wood is destroyed and the whole is reduced into a crumbling mass, which con-tains a proportionally larger amount of carbon than the original wood. Two par-ticles of hydrogen and two of oxygen being abstracted for one of carbon, it is clear that more carbon will be left behind in proportion than either hydrogen or oxygen. It is this evolution of carbonic acid in a damp atmosphere when in contact with wood which makes such situations preju-dicial to health. This kind of decay, which often takes place in trees where no fungus is present, and which spreads from within outwards like a putrefactive ferment, con-taminates the sound tissues which sur-round it. There is reason, moreover, for believing that the brown condition so com-mon to diseased vegetable cells has a simi-lar origin. The name of Touchwood is also given to *Polyporus igniarius.*   [M. J. B.]

TOULICIA. The name of a tree of Guiana, which constitutes a genus of *Sa-pindaceæ.* The leaves are pinnate; and the flowers in dense terminal clusters, each flower with a five-parted calyx, five petals provided internally with a cleft hairy scale, a five-lobed disk, eight sta-mens inserted on the disk, a three-celled ovary (each cell with a single ovule), and a short three-cleft style. The fruit is a three-winged samara.   [M. T. M.]

TOUMBEKI. A Turkish name for Persian or Shiraz Tobacco.

TOUPOLE. (Fr.) *Polygonatum offici-nale.*

TOURBETTE. (Fr.) *Sphagnum.*

TOURNEFORTIA. A genus of *Ehretia-ceæ,* inhabiting the tropics of both hemi-spheres, extending as far north as the Canaries and Central Russia. They consist of erect or twining shrubs, with scabrous or downy leaves, and flowers arranged as in *Heliotropium;* but the fruit is composed of two carpels, and is in the form of a drupe enclosing two nuts, which are some-times deeply divided so as to resemble four; each nut has two seeds. *T. heliotropioides,* from Buenos Ayres, with pale lilac flowers, is one of the prettiest species. Another is shown in Plate 7, figs. c and f. [J. T. S.]

TOURNESOL. (Fr.) *Heliotropium eu-*

ropæum. — EN DRAPEAUX. A dye obtained from *Crozophora tinctoria.* —, NAIN. A species of *Rudbeckia.*

TOURRETIA. A weedy creeper found in most parts of Tropical America, and belonging to the *Pedaliaceæ* rather than the *Bignoniaceæ,* with which it has sometimes been associated. We only know one species, *T. lappacea,* so called from its fruit somewhat resembling the flower-heads of *Lappa.* It has a quadrangular climbing stem, opposite ternate leaves (the petioles of which gradually merge into tendrils), and racemose flowers, resembling those of *Castilleja vulgaris,* having scarlet bracts. The calyx is two-parted, the corolla irregular and tubular, the stamens didynamous, and the capsule covered with spines, two-celled, opening with two valves, whilst the seeds are numerous and winged. [B. S.]

TOURRETTE. (Fr.) The name of several species of *Arabis.*

TOUS-LES-MOIS. A kind of arrowroot obtained from the tubers of some species of South American *Canna—C. glauca, C. coccinea, C. Achiras,* and *C. edulis;* the latter, a native of Peru, is believed to furnish the chief portion of that sold in the shops.

TOUT-BLANC. (Fr.) *Narcissus polyanthos.*

TOUTE-BONNE. (Fr.) *Blitum Bonus-Henricus;* also *Salvia Sclarea.* — DES PRES. *Salvia pratensis.*

TOUTE-ÉPICE. (Fr.) The seeds of *Nigella sativa;* also the berries of *Eugenia Pimenta.*

TOUTE-SAINE. (Fr.) *Hypericum Androsæmum.*

TOUT-VENU. (Fr.) *Senecio vulgaris.*

TOUZELLE. (Fr.) A *Triticum.*

TOVARIA. The name of a Peruvian herb, forming a genus of *Capparidaceæ.* The leaves are ternate; the flowers grow in a terminal drooping cluster, having a calyx of eight overlapping sepals, eight petals, inserted on the margin of a convex receptacle, their stalks densely hairy; eight stamens; a sessile ovary with eight parietal placentæ, and a radiate stigma. Fruit one-celled. [M. T. M.]

TOVOMITA. In a recent monograph of the order of *Clusiaceæ,* twenty-one well-authenticated and three doubtful species are referred to this genus, all of them being natives of Tropical South America and the West Indian Islands, and varying in size from shrubs six or eight feet high to large trees. They have smooth feather-veined leaves, and cymes of partly unisexual and partly perfect flowers, producing four-celled fruits, which split in four valves, and contain a solitary seed in each cell; the seed being destitute of a true aril, but having its outer coat developed into a fleshy pellucid aril-like covering traversed by veins. The flowers have two or four sepals, the outer two being largest and completely shutting in the other floral organs in the bud; four or eight petals; indefinite stamens, with thickened filaments; and a four-celled ovary containing a solitary ovule in each cell, and bearing four short styles crowned with concave or cushion-formed stigmas. All the species abound more or less in a resinous juice, which exudes from them when wounded, and hardens into resin. The bark of *T. fructipendula,* an arboreous species native of Chicaplaya in the Peruvian Andes, is used by the inhabitants for dyeing a reddish-purple colour, and also for medicinal purposes. [A. S.]

TOW-COCK. *Dolichos sinensis.*

TOWERWORT. *Turritis.*

TOWNSENDIA. The name of a North American herbaceous plant, constituting a genus of *Compositæ.* The leaves are tufted, linear, entire, and woolly. The head of flowers is sessile, surrounded by an involucre of overlapping linear scales; the receptacle is naked, pitted; the outer florets strap-shaped, involute at the margins, and the central ones tubular, five-toothed. The fruits are hairy, and the pappus is in one row, scaly in the outer, hairy in the inner fruits. [M. T. M.]

TOWRANEERO, TURANIRA. Names for the Bastard Bully-tree of Guiana.

TOXICODENDRON. *Rhus Toxicodendron.*

TOXICOPHLÆA. A genus of *Apocynaceæ,* containing a single species, a tree from the Cape of Good Hope. It has opposite elliptic smooth leaves, and numerous crowded flowers in the axils of the leaves. The calyx is five-parted; the base of the corolla is tubular, gradually widening upwards, the throat and upper surfaces of the limb being villose, and the limb divided into five short ovate-acute lobes; the stamens are inserted below the mouth of the tube, and have very short filaments and ovate anthers; and the ovary is two-celled, with a single ovule in each cell. The bark of this tree is poisonous, and is used by the Hottentots as an ordeal. [W. C.]

TOYO. A fragrant plant of British Guiana, an infusion and syrup of the leaves and stems of which are employed as a remedy in chronic coughs.

TOYWORT. *Capsella Bursa-pastoris.*

TOZZIA. A genus of *Scrophulariaceæ* containing a single species, a small branching glabrous herb from the mountains of Central Europe. The leaves are opposite and sessile, and the flowers are in short pedicels in the axils of the leaves, forming a lax raceme. The calyx is campanulate membranous and unequally four-toothed; the corolla-tube is exserted, the upper lip of the limb slightly concave and two-lobed; and the one-seeded globose capsule is subdrupaceous. [W. C.]

TRABECULA (adj. TRABECULATE.) A cross-bar; as in the teeth of many mosses.

TRACHEÆ. Spiral vessels ; air-tubes, containing a spiral thread of considerable toughness and elasticity.

TRACHELANTHUS. A genus of *Boragineæ*, founded on *Solenanthus cerinthoides* a native of Northern Persia. It has the corolla of *Cerinthe*, being tubular, with a five-lobed limb about one-third the depth of the whole ; the lobes have two bulges at the base ; the scales in the throat are lanceolate from a triangular base ; the colour is red, margined with yellow. The fruit is similar to that of *Cynoglossum*, a smooth glaucous plant, with the stem corymbose paniculately branched at the top, the leaves rigid and leathery, with small tubercles beneath.   [J. T. S.]

TRACHELIUM. A genus of *Campanulaceæ*, containing a few species of perennial plants, with alternate ovate-acute deeply serrated leaves, and violet blossoms in a many-flowered terminal corymb. The calyx has five subulate divisions ; the corolla has a long slender tube, and a spreading five-lobed limb ; the filaments of the stamens are filiform throughout their length, and free at their base ; and the apex of the exserted style is thickened, and densely covered with hairs. The species are found in the Mediterranean region. [W. C.]

TRACHYDIUM. A genus of *Umbelliferæ* founded on a single species from the mountains of Northern India. It is an annual or biennial, sending out from the crown of the root, both leaves, and numerous cæspitose simple stems. The leaves are petiolate and tripinnatisect, the opposite divisions being bipinnatisect, and the lobes lanceolate acute. The segments of the involucre are similar to but smaller than the ordinary leaves, and those of the involucels are more or less united and membranaceous. The calyx has five small teeth ; the petals are lanceolate, with incurved acuminate apices ; the fruit is compressed at the side ; and the carpels have five muricated ribs, the furrows with a single vitta in each, while the commissure has two. The carpophore is divided.   [W. C.]

TRACHYLOBIUM. A genus of leguminous plants very closely allied to and by some botanists combined with *Hymenæa*. The principal distinctions between the two genera consists in the petals of *Trachylobium* being only three in number, nearly equal and long-stalked, the ovary being elevated on a stalk and bearded with hairs, and the pods covered with wart-like excrescences ; while *Hymenæa* has five stalkless unequal petals, a stalkless smooth ovary, and a pod without warts. The species are all large trees, bearing panicles of white flowers, and having leaves composed of a pair of leaflets. They are natives of Brazil and Madagascar.

T. Martianum is, according to Martius, one of the trees from which the resin known as Brazilian Copal is obtained ; but it is doubtful whether any of this kind of Copal comes to this country, our principal supply of that article being derived from Eastern and Western Africa.   [A. S.]

TRACHYMENE. A genus of orthospermous *Umbelliferæ*, containing several species of herbs or undershrubs, with compound many-rayed umbels. The calyx-tube is compressed, and the limb five-toothed ; the petals are elliptic and entire ; the style is divergent ; the tuberculated fruit is compressed and contracted at the sides, separating into two semi-ovate gibbous carpels ; and the carpophore is entire. The genus has been divided by Decandolle into two sections—*Platymene*, including the herbaceous species, with compressed stem and small divided leaves ; and *Dendromene*, comprising the shrubby species with entire leaves.   [W. C.]

TRADESCANTIA. A genus of lily-like plants belonging to the *Commelynaceæ*, well marked by their three sepals, three petals, three-celled capsule, and filaments clothed with jointed hairs. *T. virginica* is the Common Spiderwort of gardens, a pretty plant twelve to eighteen inches high, with numerous branched jointed succulent stems, linear-lanceolate glossy leaves, and dense umbels of flowers conspicuous by their three spreading bright-blue petals. Varieties are also cultivated with purple white and double flowers. *T. rosea* from Carolina is like the preceding, but smaller and more delicate. *T. discolor* is so called from the colour of its leaves, which are green above, purple below ; the flowers, which are white, issue from a purple single-leaved spathe. This is a hothouse plant. Other species are cultivated, all more or less resembling the above French : *Éphémérine*.   [G. A. J.]

TRAGACANTH. A kind of gum obtained from *Astragalus verus*, *A. creticus*, *A. aristatus*, *A. gummifer*, and *A. strobiliferus*. —, SENEGAL. The produce of *Sterculia Tragacantha*.

TRAGANTHUS. The name of a genus of *Euphorbiaceæ*, comprising certain tropical American herbaceous plants, the flowers of which are monœcious, arranged in axillary spikes. The male flowers have a four-parted calyx, enclosing four stamens ; and the females have also a small four-parted calyx, girt at the base by large overlapping scales arranged in four rows, a hairy three-celled ovary, and six curved styles. The fruit consists of three carpels, which separate one from the other, each bearing the two persistent styles at the summit. In the centre, between the carpels, is a winged column, from which the former separate when ripe.   [M. T. M.]

TRAGIA. A genus named in honour of Tragus, an ancient German botanist, who, according to the fashion of the times, assumed a classical title, his true name having been Hieronymus Bock. The genus is included among the *Euphorbiaceæ*, and consists of herbs or undershrubs, widely distributed in the subtropical regions of the Old and New Worlds. Some of them are of climbing habit, and have serrated or lobed leaves, axillary flowers, the females few in number, situated at the base of the racemes, the males more numerous, all provided with entire or three-cleft bracts. The male flowers have a tarpartite calyx, enclosing three stamens; the females a six-parted calyx, with persistent occasionally divided segments, a three-celled ovary with one ovule in each compartment, a three-cleft style, and capsular fruit. Some of the species have medicinal virtues. Thus an infusion of the root of *T. cannabina* is employed as a diaphoretic and alterative in India, where also the juice of *T. Chamælea*, mixed with wine or oil, is esteemed astringent and tonic. The root of *T. involucrata* is employed in India as a tonic and alterative in syphilitic maladies. The caustic juice of *T volubilis* is likewise used as an application to ulcers. The species possess little beauty.　　　[M. P. M.]

TRAGOPOGON. A genus of *Compositæ*, inhabiting Europe and the temperate parts of Asia, and consisting of biennial or perennial herbs, having simple or branched stems, narrow grass-like leaves, and distinct terminal flower-heads of a yellow or purple colour. The heads are many-flowered, and the florets all ligulate and perfect, containing both stamens and ovary. The involucre has from eight to sixteen leaves, in one row, connected at the base; and the receptacle is naked or nearly so, and deeply indented. The fruits are all of the same form, having a long beak, a lateral areole, and the feathery pappus or seed-down in many rows,—that of the external row of fruits being interwoven.

Among the species of this genus is the culinary vegetable called Salsafy, *T. porrifolius*, a biennial indigenous to Britain and the Continent of Europe. It is distinguished by its smooth long narrow tapering acuminated leaves; by its peduncles being much thickened, and hollow at the apex; by its eight-leaved involucre, which is usually longer than the florets; and by its rose-coloured or purple flowers.

Salsafy has a long fusiform root full of milky juice, on which its salutary qualities depend. In colour it resembles the parsnip, of which it has also nearly the flavour, but is more agreeable. It ranks as one of the most salubrious of culinary vegetables, being antibilious, cooling, deobstruent, and slightly aperient; but although it is deservedly esteemed as an esculent, it is nevertheless decidedly inferior to *Scorzonera* in these properties; nor does it keep so well when taken out of the ground, as it soon becomes hardened, insipid, and difficult to cook properly. When taken by the invalid as a remedy for indigestion, it is important to know that the precautions necessary in cooking it are the same as with Scorzonera (which see), it being borne in mind that Salsafy usually requires a rather longer time boiling. It grows more freely than *Scorzonera*, and when fresh from the garden it is perhaps inferior only to that vegetable in its medicinal properties.　　　[B. C.]

TRAGOPYRUM. A genus of *Polygonaceæ*, natives of Russia and Siberia, consisting of shrubs with divaricate branches, sometimes spinous at the point, furnished with oblong or elliptical entire leathery leaves on short stalks, and racemose flowers on nodding pedicels. They have a coloured five-leaved perianth, the inner three segments larger than the rest, eight stamens, three very short styles with capitate stigmas, and a three-edged nut inclosed in the three inner perianth-leaves, the two outer ones being reflexed.　　　[J. T. S.]

TRAGUS. A genus of grasses of the tribe *Paniseæ*, now included in *Lappago*.

TRAILING Of an elongated prostrate habit of growth.

TRAILLIA. A genus of *Cruciferæ* from Mesopotamia. It consists of an annual with the habit of *Vella annua*, having rigid hairy branches, with few oblong leaves decurrent into the petioles, and small yellow flowers. The pouch is indehiscent, rough and one-seeded, crowned by the broad rigid leaf-like style.　　　[J. T. S.]

TRAINASSE. (Fr.) *Polygonum aviculare*; also *Agrostis stolonifera*.

TRAMA. A name given in mycology to the substance which separates the two surfaces of the gills of an *Agaricus*, or of two contiguous pores in *Polyporus*. It varies much in structure, and affords good definitions of genera. In *Agaricus*, for example, it is filamentous; in *Russula* and *Lactarius* vesicular. In some cases it is of the same substance with that of the pileus, as in *Trametes*; in others it is different, as in such *Polypori* as *P. destructor*. In *Schizophyllum* it is completely exposed by the splitting of the gills along their edge into two plates.　　　[M. J. B.]

TRAMETES. A genus separated by Fries from *Polyporus*, originally intended to receive those species in which the substance of the walls of the pores (or trama, as it is called by botanists) is continued immediately from the pileus without any change. So limited, the best-known British species is *T. suaveolens*, which grows occasionally in this country on the dead trunks of willows and limes, and is at once known by its larger pores from *T. odora*, which has the same strong smell of aniseed. Fries has, however, of late proposed a different definition of the genus. In a large portion of *Polyporus*, including such common species as *P. versicolor*, the trama though narrow is of the same substance as the flesh of the pileus. They differ, however, from typical species of *Trametes* in the fact that the pores, which are developed in a centrifugal direction, are perpendicular to the fibrillose stratum above the portion in connection with the trama, whereas in *Trametes* the whole pileus and trama are of the same substance. The species are placed in a genus named *Polystictus*, while *Polyporus* is confined to those in which the trama and substance from which it springs are different in texture. These distinctions, though at first apparently too refined, are founded on an extensive examination of species, and will probably prove tenable. [M. J. B.]

TRANSVERSE. Broader than long.

TRAPA. The very singular four-horned fruits of the European species of *Trapa* (*T. natans*), which was the only one formerly known, have been compared to the spiked iron instruments called caltrops, employed in ancient warfare for strewing on the ground to impede the progress of cavalry; and, from the plant growing in water, it is commonly called the Water Caltrops. The genus belongs to the *Haloragaceæ*. Its flowers have a four-parted calyx with the tube adhering to the ovary; four petals, and as many stamens; and a two-celled ovary, with a cylindrical style and hemispherical flat-headed stigma. After flowering, the lobes of the calyx harden and form two or four more or less conspicuous horns at the top of the fruit; the latter being one-celled hard and unopening, and containing a solitary large pendulous seed, with very unequal cotyledons. Besides the European species, there are five or six others, natives of India, China, and Japan. All are floating plants, with long-jointed rootstocks, having tufts of hair-like roots (sometimes regarded as submerged leaves) at the joints, and surmounted by a radiating cluster of triangular toothed leaves, with swollen float-like stalks which serve to buoy them up.

The seeds of all these plants abound in starch, and are much eaten as food. Those of *T natans*—called Jesuit's nuts at Venice, and Chataigne d'Eau by the French—are ground into flour and made into bread in some parts of Southern Europe. In Kashmir those of *T bispinosa*, the Singhara of the natives, feed 30,000 persons for five

Trapa bicornis.

months in the year, and are so extensively collected that the celebrated Runjeet Singh of Lahore derived a revenue of 12,000*l.* per annum from them. *T. bicornis*, the Ling of the Chinese, has a fruit like a bull's head; the seeds of this plant also form a considerable article of food. [A. S.]

TRAPEZIFORM, TRAPEZOID. Having four sides, those which are opposite not being parallel; scarcely different from Rhomboid.

TRAP-TREE. A species of *Artocarpus*, which furnishes a gutta or glutinous gum, used as birdlime in Singapore.

TRASI. (Fr.). *Cyperus esculentus.*

TRATTINICKIA. A genus of trees belonging to the *Amyridaceæ*. The species are natives of Brazil, and have large branching panicles of small reddish flowers. Calyx cup-shaped, of three segments; corolla bell-shaped, three-cleft; stamens six, with very short filaments; ovary globose; style short. The trees abound in resinous juice. [M. T. M.]

TRAVELLER'S-JOY. *Clematis Vitalba.*

TRAVELLER'S-TREE. *Urania speciosa.*

TREACLE, COUNTRYMAN'S. *Ruta graveolens.*

TREAD-SOFTLY. *Cnidoscolus stimulans.*

TREASURE-FLOWER. *Gazania.*

TRECULIA. A genus of *Artocarpaceæ*, named in honour of M. Trécul, an eminent French vegetable anatomist. The species are trees, natives of Senegambia, having male and female flowers crowded together in the same head. The male flowers have a tubular three-cleft perianth; the females a perianth of three leaves, and an ovary with a pendulous ovule. The genus is closely related to *Artocarpus*, but may be distinguished by the characters just mentioned. [M. T. M.]

TREE. Any woody plant of perennial duration which rises from the ground with a trunk.

TREE-BEARD. A South American name for *Tillandsia usneoides.*

TREE-FERN. See FILICES.

TREE-HAIR. A name sometimes given to the dark wiry pendulous entangled masses of a lichen, *Cornicularia jubata*, which is not uncommon on trees in subalpine woods. [M. J. B.]

TREE-LIKE. Resembling a tree, but very small. The same as Dendroid.

TREE OF CHASTITY. *Vitex Agnus-castus.*

TREE OF HEAVEN. *Ailantus.*

TREE OF LONG LIFE. *Glaphyria nitida.*

TREE OF SADNESS. *Nyctanthes arbor-tristis.*

TREE OF THE MAGICIANS. A Chilian name for *Lycioplesium pubiflorum.*

TREE OF THE SUN. A Japanese name for *Retinospora obtusa.*

TRÈFLE. (Fr.) *Trifolium.* — BITUMINEUX. *Psoralea bituminosa.* — D'EAU. *Menyanthes trifoliata.* — DE BOKHARA. *Melilotus alba (leucantha).* — DE HOLLANDE. *Trifolium pratense.* — DE VIRGINIE. *Ptelea trifoliata.* — ÉPINEUX DE CANDIE. *Fagonia cretica.* — HÉMORROÏDAL. *Lotus hirsutus.* — JAUNE. *Lotus corniculatus.* — JAUNE DES SABLES. *Anthyllis Vulneraria.* — JAUNE PETIT. *Medicago lupulina.* — NOIR. *Medicago lupulina.* — ODORANT. *Meli-*

lotus cœruleus. — ROUGE DU ROUSSIL-
LON Trifolium incarnatum.

TREFOIL. Trifolium ; also Medicago
lupulina, and Stylosanthes procumbens. —,
BIRD'S-FOOT. Lotus. —, HOP Trifolium procumbens. —, MARSH. Menyanthes trifoliata. —, MOON Medicago arborea. —, SHRUBBY. Ptelea trifoliata. —.
TICK. Desmodium.

TREMANDRACEÆ. (Foreworts.) A
small order of polypetalous dicotyledons,
consisting of heath-like shrubs, all Australian, with small entire leaves often verticillate, and red blue or rarely white flowers on slender axillary pedicels. They are
chiefly characterised by regular flowers,
with four or five valvate sepals, as many
spreading petals, twice as many free hypogynous stamens, anthers opening in terminal pores, and a free ovary, usually two-
celled, with one two or rarely three pendulous ovules in each. The order, although
small, is perfectly distinct in habit and
character, and, though having some affinity
with Polygalaceæ, is at once distinguished
by its regular flowers ; it has, however, a
more remote analogy with the tribe Lasiopetaleæ of Sterculiaceæ.

TREMANDRA. A genus of Tremandraceæ, conferring its name on the order to
which it belongs, and composed of two
species inhabiting Western Australia.
They are delicate shrubs, covered with a
stellate down , and have opposite ovate
leaves, axillary purple flowers, a five-cleft
calyx, a corolla composed of five petals,
ten stamens, two-celled anthers, and a two-
celled ovary.   [B. S.]

TREMBLE. (Fr.) Populus tremula.

TREMBLIN. (Fr.) Briza minor.

TREMBLING-TREE. Populus trepida.

TREMELLA. The typical genus of the
natural order of Fungi called Tremellini,
distinguished by its tremulous gelatinous
generally more or less waved and sinuated
mass, having an even hymenium without
any definite upper or under side, and free
from papillæ or tubercles. The species
vary greatly in colour, being white bright
or pale-yellow, rose-coloured, chocolate,
brown, purple, &c. Their form is as varied
as their colour, sometimes yielding sinuated plates, sometimes brain-like masses,
sometimes club-shaped processes, and sometimes orbicular bodies or uniform resupinate strata. Occasionally they grow on
living trees, but more frequently on dead
branches, while two occur on the naked
ground or amongst grass. T. mesenterica,
which is conspicuous in every dead hedge
in winter from its orange tint, produces
occasionally myriads of conidia. [M. J B.]

TREMELLINI. A natural order of
hymenomycetous Fungi, distinguished by
their gelatinous texture, their hymenium,
in the more typical forms, covering the
whole surface without any definite upper
or under side ; the sporophores, which are
often lobed or quadripartite, not being

packed into a regular hymenium but placed
at very different heights, and the spicules
being much elongated. The spores moreover, which are either simple or septate,
produce occasionally little offsets at the
sides, which may either be secondary spores
or spermatia. If secondary spores, the
primary must be considered as protospores,
analogous to those of Puccinici. This
opinion is, however, at present merely
theoretical. Tremellini occasionally contain a nucleus which is not gelatinous, and
which has sometimes a cretaceous texture.
The species occur almost exclusively on
decayed wood, either naked or bursting
through the bark. Two species only have
at present been described with a terrestrial
habit. When dry many of the species
shrink up very much, but they recover
their original condition perfectly when
moistened. Hirneola has several representatives in tropical climates besides the
common Jew's Ear, which seems universally distributed , but the greater part of
the order is peculiar to temperate climes
of either hemisphere.   [M. J. B.]

TREMÈNE. (Fr.) Trifolium pratense.

TREMME. (Fr.) Agrostis stolonifera.

TRENTANELLE. (Fr.) Rhus Cotinus.

TREVESIA. A genus of Araliaceæ, containing a single species from India, a
prickly shrub or tree, with large round
pinnatisect leaves, and whitish-green
flowers in terminal paniculate umbels.
The calyx-limb is unequally toothed ; the
petals are from four to seven, and the stamens from six to nine (generally seven),
with cordate anthers. The ovary is five to
eight-celled, covered with a large epigynous disk ; the styles are the same in number as the cells, but united into a single
pyramid at the apex, and surmounted by
a bilobed stigma ; the fruit is fleshy, with
five to eight one-seeded cells.   [W. C.]

TREWIACEÆ. An order formerly proposed by Lindley for the genus Trewia,
which he has since, with other botanists,
referred to Euphorbiaceæ.

TREWIA. The name of a genus of Euphorbiaceæ, comprising a tree, native of
India, with triplinerved leaves, and diœcious flowers—the males in racemes, the
females in pairs on a branched peduncle.
The male flowers have a membranous two-
leaved calyx, ultimately reflected ; within
this are numerous stamens, placed on a
convex receptacle. The female flowers have
a calyx of one membranous sheathing leaf,
ultimately falling off ; and a four-celled
sessile ovary, with the style divided into
four feathery stigmas. The fruit is fleshy,
with four one-seeded stones.   [M. T. M.]

TRI. In compound words = three ; as
tricostata, having three ribs ; tricornis,
having three horns.

TRIADELPHOUS. Having the stamens
collected into three parcels.

TRIAKENIUM. That kind of fruit

called a Cremocarp, in which the number of carpels is three.

TRIANGULAR. Three-cornered.

TRIANOSPERMA. A genus of *Cucurbitaceæ*, nearly allied to *Bryonia*, but distinguished by the presence of three seeds only in the fruit. The species are chiefly Brazilian and West Indian, and have thick fleshy roots, climbing stems with branched tendrils, and palmate leaves. The flowers are monœcious, borne in loose panicles. The male flowers have three stamens, united by means of their curved anthers, but free as to their filaments. In the female flower the ovary is three-celled, with three erect ovules, and terminated by a short style, which divides into three stigmas. The fruit is globular and somewhat fleshy. The root of *T Tayuya* is used in Brazil in small doses as an emetic, in larger ones as a drastic. *T. ficifolia* is a purgative and purifier of the blood. Some of the species have been introduced into the Paris gardens. [M, T M.]

TRIANTHEMA. A genus of *Tetragoniaceæ*, having a very wide geographical distribution, three or four species being natives of India, as many of the Cape of Good Hope; while one is confined to Arabia, and one spread over Tropical America and the West Indian Islands. They are usually prostrate more or less fleshy herbs, sometimes with their stems woody towards the base; they have opposite entire leaves, with the stalks enlarged into sheaths, one of each pair of leaves being often larger than the other; and their flowers are produced, either solitary or in clusters, in the leaf-axils. The flowers have a five parted calyx, coloured inside, with the divisions mucronate below the top; no petals; five ten or twenty stamens rising from the calyx-tube, and one two or rarely three styles. The fruit is either one-celled, or divided into two by a spurious partition, and when ripe separates crossways near the bottom into two pieces; the upper of largest piece, called the lid, being thick and having the seeds attached to one side, and the lower thin and having the seeds attached to the opposite side. The bitterish rather nauseous-tasted roots of *T. obcordata*, one of the Indian species—a perennial with spreading prostrate stems, the tender tops of which, together with the leaves, are collected by the natives and eaten as a potherb—are sold in the bazaars, and employed by the native doctors as a cathartic in combination with ginger. [A. S.]

TRIANTHUS. A Patagonian perennial plant, of the family *Compositæ*, has been so named, as the heads of flowers consist each of three florets. The plant is branched; its leaves awl-shaped, spreading; and the heads of flowers solitary on the ends of the branches, each surrounded by an involucre of two rows of scales—the outer ovate lanceolate acuminate prickly, the inner flat linear acuminate; the receptacle small, and naked. The corollas are two-lipped, white and perfect; and the fruits

inversely pyramidal, beakless, crowned by a pappus of three to five linear deciduous scales, hairy at the margins. [M. T. M.]

TRIAS. An unimportant genus of orchids referred to the *Malaxideæ*, and inhabiting Tropical Asia. Two species have been described. They are small herbs, with roundish glabrous one-leaved pseudobulbs forming dense tufts, small coriaceous veinless leaves, erect radical one-flowered peduncles shorter than the leaves, and rather large dark-green flowers. [W. B. H.]

TRIASPIS. A genus of *Malpighiaceæ*, comprising shrubs, natives of the Cape of Good Hope and of Tropical Asia. The flowers are rose-coloured, and have a five-parted glandless calyx, five stalked fringed unequal petals, ten stamens, all fertile of unequal lengths; three ovaries, each with two hairy sinuous wings; three styles, long slender and dilated at the top; and a winged one-seeded fruit. The generic name is derived from the Greek, and signifies 'three shields,' probably in allusion to the winged ovaries. [M. T M.]

TRIBE. One of the subdivisions of a Natural Order. Thus *Leptospermeæ* and *Myrteæ* are tribes of the order *Myrtaceæ*. These minor groups are sometimes themselves divided into one or more series of lesser groups, according to the number of genera, their diversities of structure, &c.

TRIBRACHIA. A genus of *Cinchonaceæ*, including a semiparasitical shrub, native of Sumatra. The flowers are white, arranged in groups of three, in a compact head. The tube of the calyx is somewhat globular, its limb entire or slightly toothed; the corolla has a short tube, and a limb divided into three lance-shaped three-sided segments; the stamens are five in number, and inserted into the throat of the corolla by means of very short filaments; and the ovary is two-celled, surmounted by a fleshy disk, and having a cylindrical style, terminated by an undivided stigma. The fruit is fleshy, [M. T M.]

TRIBULE AQUATIQUE. (Fr.) *Trapa natans.*

TRIBULOPSIS. A small genus of *Zygophyllaceæ*, consisting of prostrate annual herbs, with alternate leaves. It is nearly allied to *Tribulus*, but the nuts are single-seeded. Three species have been described from Australia. [W. C.]

TRIBULUS. A genus of *Zygophyllaceæ*, consisting of procumbent herbs, with opposite bistipulate and abruptly pinnate leaves, and one-flowered peduncles springing from the axils of the leaves. The caducous calyx has five sepals, and the corolla five petals; of the ten stamens those opposite to the sepals have a gland at their base; the style is very short or absent, and the stigma hemispherical and five-rayed, as in the poppy. The flattened pentagonal fruit is composed of five carpels, which are spinous or tubercular on the back. At maturity the fruit breaks up into five indehiscent cells, which are transversely divided into from two to four single-seeded compartments. Albumen is but sparingly present in the embryos of this order, but in *Tribulus* it is altogether wanting. The species are generally distributed within the tropics of the Old World, and extend into the warmer temperate countries, one species only being found in the South of Europe. [W. C.]

TRICA. A button-like shield belonging to the genus *Gyrophora*.

TRICALYSIA. A genus of *Cinchonaceæ*, comprising a shrub native of Western Tropical Africa, with hairy flowers, closely crowded in the axils of the leaves. The flowers have, outside the true calyx, a double epicalyx, each portion with four teeth, while the true calyx has a five to six-toothed limb; the corolla has a short tube, and its five or six-parted limb is divided into five or six narrow spreading divisions; stamens five to six, inserted on to the throat of the corolla, beyond which they project; ovary two-celled; stigmas two, linear. [M. T. M.]

TRICERA. A genus of West Indian shrubs of the family *Euphorbiaceæ*. The flowers are monœcious, disposed in racemes—the male flowers being below, the females solitary at the apex of the raceme. The males have a perianth of four segments, enclosing four stamens; the females a five-leaved perianth, and three styles, ultimately dividing into six stigmatic branches. The fruit consists of three two-seeded carpels, separating one from the other when ripe. [M. T. M.]

TRICERANDRA. A supposed genus found in Manchuria, now referred to *Chloranthus*.

TRICERASTES. A genus of *Datiscaceæ*, consisting of an erect annual herb from California, with alternate tripartite serrated leaves, having the central lobe pinnatifid, and axillary heads of small green hermaphrodite flowers. The calyx-tube is connate with the ovary, with a minute three-toothed limb; there is no corolla; three stamens alternate with the calycine teeth; and the ovary is inferior, one-celled, with three parietal placentas and numerous ovules, and three bipartite styles opposite the calycine teeth. The capsule is three-valved at the apex. [T. M.]

TRICEROS. A little-known genus of Loureiro's, apparently terebinthaceous. The original species from Cochin China is the only one referred to it. It is a small tree, with spreading branches, and imparipinnate and bijugate leaves. The calyx and corolla have each five spreading divisions; the five stamens have slender filaments, and ovate two-celled anthers; there are three short styles; and the berry is round below, but is furnished above with three horns, and has three one-seeded cells. [W. C.]

TRICHADENIA. A genus of *Pangiaceæ*,

of which only one species, *T. zeylanica*, is known. This is a very large Cingalese tree, called Tettigaha or Tettigass by the natives; its wood, however, is of little or no value. It has alternate oblong leaves, and short axillary panicles of small pale-green unisexual flowers, the two sexes being borne on separate trees. The female flowers produce roundish fleshy fruits, about an inch in diameter, containing from one to three bony-shelled seeds, from which the Cingalese extract an oil, useful for burning, and as a remedy for diseases of the skin in children. Both kinds of flowers have an entire calyx, which ultimately breaks away irregularly at the bottom, and falls away in a single cup-like piece; and five overlapping petals, with fleshy hairy scales attached to them along the middle on the inside. The males contain five stamens, with thick filaments, spirally twisted in the bud, and oblong anthers; and the females a free one-celled ovary, with three ovules attached to the sides, and bearing three styles with broad kidney-shaped stigmas. [A. S.]

TRICHÆTA. *Trisetum*.

TRICHANTHERA. A genus of *Zygophyllaceæ*, containing a single species—a small and slender plant from Arabia, with alternate stipulate setaceous leaves. The five-cleft calyx is persistent; the corolla consists of five linear petals; the five stamens have flattened filaments and slender anthers; the style has five deep furrows, and a capitate stigma; and the ovate and stipitate capsule is obtusely five-sided, and has five many-seeded cells. The single series of stamens is not sufficient to separate this plant from *Zygophyllaceæ*, with which order it otherwise altogether agrees; the stipitate ovary being found also in *Guaiacum*. [W. C.]

TRICHIA. A genus of myxogastrous *Fungi*, remarkable from the threads which accompany the spores having a spiral structure. Some controversy exists as to the real nature of these bodies. An attentive examination, however, of the threads when branched (which is sometimes the case) shows, we think, that the spiral appearance does not arise from a mere twisting, but from the formation of one or more threads of a spiral form within a tube, with which they afterwards become intimately incorporated—the threads passing into the branch exactly like those of true spiral vessels in phænogams, when the vessels are branched. The species are very widely diffused, and occur in various parts of the world. The threads and spores often exhibit bright colours, as deep tawny, scarlet, golden-yellow, buff, &c. The spores are mostly smooth but sometimes rough, with little points. Most of them occur in Great Britain. [M. J. B.]

TRICHIDIUM. A hair which bears the spores of such fungals as *Geastrum*.

TRICHILIA. A number of Indian and Australian species were formerly comprised under this genus of *Meliaceæ*, but they are now referred to other genera, as also are several of the American species; and *Trichilia* is restricted to two or three African and a dozen or more American and West Indian species, some of which are trees, and others erect or climbing shrubs. Their leaves are unequally pinnate, or rarely trifoliolate; and their flowers, which are borne in axillary panicles, have a four or five-cut calyx, as many egg-shaped or oblong overlapping petals, an eight or tenparted stamen-tube, with narrow blunt segments bearing terminal anthers, and a three-celled ovary containing two ovules side by side in each cell. Their fruit is a three-celled capsule, which when ripe splits into three valves, each of which has a partition down the middle, with a seed, covered with a pulpy aril, on either side of it. *T. emetica*, the Roka of the Arabs, is a large tree with pinnate leaves composed of four pairs of smooth elliptical leaflets and an odd one, and dense panicles of whitish flowers like those of the citron. In an Arabic work, quoted by Forskahl, the fruits are called ' Djouz elkai,' and are said to possess emetic properties. The Arabian women mix them with the perfumes used for washing their hair; while the ripe seeds are made into an ointment with sesamum-oil, and used as a remedy for the itch.   [A. S.]

TRICHINIUM. A genus of *Amaranthaceæ*, consisting of annual or perennial herbs, natives of Tropical and Extratropical New Holland. The flowers are in terminal heads, or spikes provided with three shining bracts to each flower; the perianth consists of five linear segments; stamens five, coherent at the base; ovary one-celled, with one erect ovule; style simple; fruit utricular, included within the perianth. Some of the species are extremely ornamental.   [M. T. M.]

TRICHOCARYA. This genus of *Chrysobalanaceæ* includes a number of trees or shrubs growing in the islands of the Indian Archipelago. The leaves are feather-veined, and the flowers grow in clusters. The calyx has a long cylindrical or angular tube, expanding above into a somewhat cup-shaped limb, which is divided into five triangular segments; the petals are ovate, acute, shorter than the sepals; the stamens numerous, perigynous; and the ovary is enclosed by the tube of the calyx, one-celled, with a single ovule, and a basilar style. Fruit succulent externally, bony within, globose above, constricted and three-sided below: the stone is one-seeded, and very hairy in the interior. From this latter circumstance the genus takes its name, derived from the Greek *thrix* ' a hair,' and *karua* ' a nut.'   [M. T. M.]

TRICHOCENTRUM. A genus of orchids, belonging to the tribe *Vandeæ*, inhabiting South and Central America. They are epiphytal stemless herbs, with broad prominently-veined leaves, and axillary flowers. The sepals and petals are spreading,

free, equal; the lip sessile, connate with the base of the column, furnished with a long spur, two-lobed. It comes near *Cycocladus*, from which it differs in its lip being united at the base with the column, and in the latter being furnished with two ears or wings.   [W. B. H.]

TRICHOCLADUS. A genus of *Hamamelidaceæ*, containing four species of villose shrubs, with shortly petiolate and entire leaves, and flowers in axillary or terminal pedunculate heads. The flowers are dioecious from the abortion of parts. The calyx-tube is connate with the ovary below, but divides into five lobes above; the epigynous corolla has five long linear petals; the five stamens are inserted on the petals, and have very short filaments; the ovary is two-celled, with a single ovule in each cell; and there are two distinct styles. The species are natives of the Cape of Good Hope.   [W. C.]

TRICHOCLINE. A genus of *Compositæ*, consisting of Brazilian perennial herbaceous plants, with leaves clustered near the bases of the simple stems. The head of flowers is terminal and solitary, surrounded by an involucre which is bell-shaped, consisting of an outer row of leafy scales, and an inner series of membranous ones. The receptacle is covered with fine fringe-like hairs. The corollas are two-lipped, the central ones equally so, the outer with the exterior lip largest. Achenes top-shaped, surmounted by a pappus of numerous scaly serrated hairs.   [M. T. M.]

TRICHOCORONIS. By this name is designated a genus of *Compositæ*, consisting of herbs growing in marshes and moist places in Texas. The stems are creeping at the base; the branches sticky; the leaves amplexicaul; the flower-stalks slender, naked, solitary or corymbose; the flowers rosy or purple, surrounded by an involucre of ten or twelve membranous scales; and the receptacle conical, naked. The corollas are more or less glandular, tubular below, expanding above into a bell-shaped five-toothed limb; branches of the style projecting, linear, flattened. Achenes pentagonal, surmounted by a short crown-like pappus.   [M. T. M.]

TRICHODESMA. A genus of *Boraginaceæ*, from India, Egypt, and South Africa. They are strigose annuals, with the habit of *Borago* or *Cynoglossum*. The corolla is subrotate, with a naked throat; anthers exserted, with pointed awns, furnished with two rows of hairs on the back, by which they adhere together; nuts half immersed in pits in the central column.   [J. T. S.]

TRICHODESMIUM. A genus of *Algæ* belonging to the *Oscillatoriæ*, distinguished by their short threads being collected in little fascicles, which float freely, forming a scum upon the surface of the sea. Instead, however, of occurring in circumscribed patches, it covers, without any intermission, oceanic tracts many miles in extent, distinguished by a peculiar red-brown tint, and resembling at first, when closely examined, minute fragments of chopped hay. It was, we believe, in more recent times first noticed, particularly, in Osbeck's voyage; but there is some reason to believe that the phenomenon was known to ancient mariners, and that the Red Sea; where it has been lately observed, derived its name from it. One circumstance which has more especially attracted the notice of navigators is, that while sailing through the scum, not only a disagreeable pungent smell has been perceived, but the mucous membrane of the eyes and nose have been affected, inflammation of the eyes and severe sneezing being induced by it. It is not, indeed, the only plant of the same natural order that has noxious properties, some of the common species of *Oscillatoriæ* emitting an odour like that of *Chara*, which in certain cases is strong enough to produce headache.   [M. J. B.]

TRICHODIUM. The three species which were formerly described under this genus of grasses, are now placed in *Agrostis* by Steudel and others.   [D. M.]

TRICHOGASTRES. A natural order of gasteromycetous *Fungi*, comprising those genera which have in an early stage a sinuous complicated crumb-like hymenium, enclosed in a common peridium consisting of one or more distinct coats, and at maturity breaking up into a dusty mass of spores mixed with threads. It is closely connected with *Podaxinei* through the genus *Polyplocium*, which is equally dusty when mature, though retaining traces of the walls of the hymenium. The most familiar instances are the common puffballs, which are found in almost every part of the world. *Batarrea* is connected with the phalloid fungi by its gelatinous volva. The species love open exposed situations, though a few are always found in the shade. One or two are esculent.   [M. J. B.]

TRICHOGLOTTIS. A small genus of orchids, belonging to the *Vandeæ*. They are epiphytal herbs, with linear or linear-lanceolate coriaceous or fleshy leaves, and flowers on short lateral or leaf-opposed few or one-flowered peduncles. It comes near *Phalænopsis*, but the inflorescence is sufficient to distinguish it. The species described are from Tropical Asia. [W. B. H.]

TRICHOGYNE. The name of a genus of undershrubs or herbs, natives of the Cape of Good Hope and of the Mediterranean region, and belonging to the family *Compositæ*. The leaves are sessile, membranous, densely woolly; the flower-heads in terminal tufts, rarely in axillary whorls. The involucre consists of a small number of loosely imbricated scales; the receptacle is scaly at the margin, elsewhere naked; and the pappus of the female flowers is absent, that of the male flowers consisting of one row of hairs, which are feathery at their points.   [M. T. M.]

TRICHOLÆNA. The species which were formerly described under this genus of grasses, along with a few others, form the section *Tricholæna* of the great genus *Panicum*, in Steudel's *Synopsis*.   [D. M.]

TRICHOLEPIS. A genus of Indian herbaceous plants, of the family *Compositæ*. The leaves are narrow, serrated and sessile. The involucre consists of very numerous overlapping scales, which are hair-like, and recurved at the points. The receptacle has a number of small scales terminating in fine hairs; and the pappus is various, either of one or of more rows of rough scales, confluent below or disunited, or sometimes altogether wanting.   [M. T. M.]

. TRICHOLOBUS. A genus of *Connaraceæ*, consisting of trees, natives of the islands of the Indian Archipelago. The flowers have five lance-shaped sepals, and as many petals; ten stamens, alternately long and short, united together below; a sessile one-celled ovary, containing two ovules, and surmounted by a short style, and a dilated stigma. The capsule is sessile, and opens by two valves. [M. T. M.]

TRICHOLOMA. *Glossostigma.*

TRICHOMA. The filamentous thallus of algals, as *Conferva.*

TRICHOMANES. A very extensive and also a very varied and beautiful genus of ferns, typical of the tribe *Trichomanineæ* of the *Polypodiaceæ*. It belongs to the series with free veins and urn-shaped or tubular involucres, and is distinguished from *Loxsoma* by its pellucid texture, and from *Ftea* by its monomorphous fronds. The fronds are either simple pinnate or decompound, usually membranaceous in texture, and pellucid. The sori are seated in extrorse-

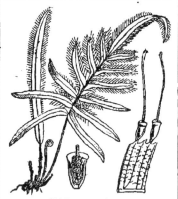

Trichomanes pinnatum.

marginal cups, either sunk in or free on the margins of the fronds: the veins being continued into filiform exserted sometimes capitulate receptacles, free within the cups, and bearing the sessile lenticular sporecases near their base. The involucres or cups are funnel-shaped or shortly bell-shaped, truncate at the mouth, entire with a straight or spreading margin, or more or less distinctly two-lipped. The species are most abundant in the moist shady woods

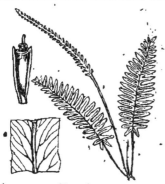

Féea spicata.

of the tropics both of the Old and New World. One of them, *T. radicans* or *specio-sum*, occurs in Madeira and on the coast of Ireland; this species was formerly found sparingly in Yorkshire. There are two tolerably distinct groups—*Eutrichomanes*, with the involucres truncate, spreading or not at the mouth; and *Didymoglossum*, with the involucres two-lipped. They are distinguished from *Féea* by the much-contracted fertile fronds of the latter. [T. M.]

TRICHONEMA. A genus of *Iridaceæ*, occurring chiefly in South Africa and in the Mediterranean region; and consisting of small bulb-tuberous plants, with narrow leaves, and short terete scapes bearing solitary crocus-like flowers. It is closely related to *Crocus*, and differs chiefly from that familiar genus in the short tube of the perianth, and in having three bifid stigmas with slender lobes. [T. M.]

TRICHOPETALUM. A small genus of *Liliaceæ* from Chili, with fasciculate roots, linear-ensiform grass-like leaves, and sub-solitary racemose or spicate-paniculate white flowers, green on the outside of the hexapetaloid perianth, the segments of which are recurved, the three inner fringed at the margins. There are six stamens, with glabrous filaments; and the capsule is oblong three-celled, with numerous kidney-shaped compressed seeds having a hard black seed-coat. *Anthericum plumosum* is to be referred to this genus, and is now known as *T. stellatum*. [J. T. S.]

TRICHOPHORUM. The stipe of certain fungals.

TRICHOPILIA. A beautiful though small genus of epiphytal orchids, belonging to the *Vandeæ*. They are natives of Tropical America and the West Indian Islands, and consist of herbs with curi-ously sheathed fleshy pseudobulbs, having but one coriaceous leaf, and solitary axillary brilliantly-coloured flowers. The sepals and petals are equal, long narrow, in some species twisted; and the lip somewhat three-lobed, convolute, naked within. It differs from *Maxillaria* in the column not being reclinate on the ovary, in the spreading sepals and petals, and especially in the singular column terminated by three little plume-like lobes, which unite at their base into a sort of hood that covers a remarkably compressed anther. [W. B. H.]

TRICHOPODIUM. A genus of Indian herbaceous plants, of the family *Aristolochiaceæ*. The leaves are lanceolate or linear; the female flowers, which alone are described, have a perianth which is tubular at the base and has a six-cleft limb; there are six sterile stamens, inserted in as many pits, and three cleft stigmas. The fruit is triangular, with wings at the angles, three-celled and indehiscent; and there are one or two seeds in each cell. [M. T. M.]

TRICHOPTERIS. *Amphidesmium.*

TRICHOS. In Greek compounds = hair-like, or hairy.

TRICHOSACME. A Mexican genus of *Asclepiadaceæ*, consisting of a solitary species, *T. lanata*, an erect shrub covered all over with white wool. It is characterised by the corolla having a very short flattened tube, and egg-shaped segments, slightly notched at the apex, and marked outside with a bearded nerve, which is prolonged a considerable distance beyond the apex of the segment, and forms a slender appendage, densely covered upwards with long jointed hairs, resembling a pencil-brush: the generic name, derived from *trichos* 'hair' and *acme* 'a point,' referring to this appendage. The staminal corona is shortly urceolate or ring-like, the rim being divided into five short teeth, each of which is slightly notched; the anthers have no terminal appendages; and the pollen-masses are pendulous. [A. S.]

TRICHOSANDRA. A genus of asclepiads, containing a single species, *T. borbonica*, a twining shrub, native of the island of Bourbon, with smooth leaves shining on the upper side, and solitary many-flowered cymes on short stalks beyond the leaf-axils. It is allied to *Gymnema*, from which it is technically distinguished by the gynostegium, which is nearly as long as the calyx-tube, being naked; and by the anthers terminating in a white irregularly torn hairy membrane. Its flowers have a corolla approaching a bell-shaped form, with five erect segments, and naked at the orifice; and its fruits are smooth and woody, and contain seeds furnished with hair-tufts. [A. S.]

TRICHOSANTHES. A genus of *Cucurbitaceæ*, named from two Greek words signifying 'hairy flowers,' in allusion to the blossoms being beautifully fringed. It consists of about thirty (mostly Asiatic) species of trailing or climbing plants, with simple or twice or thrice divided tendrils, heart-shaped entire or three to five-lobed leaves, and flowers of separate sexes, but usually borne on the same plant—the males being generally in racemes, and the females solitary. These produce very long or roundish fleshy fruits, containing flat irregular-shaped seeds embedded in pulp.

T. cucumerina, the Doonmaala, a common Cingalese and South Indian plant, is much valued by the native doctors in Ceylon as a remedy for fevers; and, from experiments made in the hospital at Badulla, it would seem to possess considerable efficacy. It contains tannic acid; and the infusion of it, which is the form used, is very bitter. *T. colubrina*, the Serpent Cucumber or Viper Gourd, is so called from the remarkable snake-like appearance of its fruits, which are frequently six or more feet long, and at first striped with different shades of green, but ultimately change to a bright orange-colour. It is a native of Central America. Another species, *T. anguina*, a native of India and China, is called the Snake Gourd, but its fruits are seldom more than half as long as the above. [A. S.]

TRICHOSMA. A section of *Eria*, with terete two-leaved stems, smooth glabrous leaves, and terminal few-flowered spikes. It is represented by *E. suavis*. [T. M.]

TRICHOSPERMUM. A genus of *Tiliaceæ*, of which only two species are known—one inhabiting Java, the other the Feejees. They are middle-sized trees, with entire ovate leaves, and small cymose flowers. The sepals are distinct, and like the petals are five in number; whilst the stamens are numerous, free, all of them bearing anthers. The capsule is two-valved, somewhat wedge-shaped, containing numerous seeds. The Feejean species, *T. Richii*, yields a useful timber. [B. S.]

TRICHOSPORANGIA. See OOSPORANGIA.

TRICHOSTEMMA. A genus of *Labiatæ*, natives of North America, consisting of low annuals with entire leaves, and mostly solitary one-flowered pedicels terminating the branches. The oblique bell-shaped calyx is deeply five-cleft, its three upper teeth long and partly united, and the two lower ones very short; the corolla is divided into five nearly equal oblong lobes, the three lower of which are more or less united; and the four stamens have very long capillary filaments, exserted considerably beyond the corolla. [W. C.]

TRICHOSTOMEI. A natural order of acrocarpous mosses distinguished by a peristome with thirty thread-shaped teeth, frequently disposed in pairs, and sometimes spirally twisted. It abounds in species which are principally European, and some of which ascend to very high latitudes, the only three mosses in lat. 64° 57′ S. belonging to this order. It is worthy of remark, that when the teeth are spiral, the cells of the lid which immediately covers them

follow the same arrangement. The typical genus *Trichostomum*, of which we have nine species, differs from *Tortula* only in the straight teeth; and even this character fails in *Trichostomum rigidulum*, which is perhaps our most common species. *T. glaucescens*, a very rare plant, is remarkable for its glaucous hue, which depends upon some extraneous substance whose nature has not at present been ascertained. A similar appearance occurs also in *Bartramia*. [M. J. B.]

TRICHOTHECIUM. A genus of thread-moulds (*Hyphomycetes*) formerly proposed on erroneous characters, and, so far as *T. roseum* is concerned (about which alone we wish to speak), identical with *Dactylium*. This *T. roseum* consists of a creeping mycelium, from which arise short erect threads, crowned above with a few obovate uniseptate spores. The mass is at first white, but at length acquires a pale rose-colour, by which it is readily distinguished. The plant grows very abundantly on various objects, whether dead or living; and is sometimes highly destructive to cucumber-plants, forming broad patches on the leaves and stem. It occurs also not unfrequently in closed cavities, as in nuts, to which it must have made its way from without, through the tissues. Hoffmann has observed a second form of fruit in the shape of globose granules which he calls spermatia; these bodies germinate, and have apparently nothing to do with impregnation. As in the case of bunt, and some other *Fungi* which occur in the tissues of plants, it is possible that the germination of these minute bodies may facilitate the entrance of the mycelium into the plant. A solution of bisulphite of soda, or indeed anything which contains sulphurous acid, properly applied, may facilitate the destruction of the mould, when requisite. [M. J. B.]

TRICHOTOMOUS. Having the divisions always in threes.

TRICOCCÆ. A name under which Klotzsch and some others have designated the large order *Euphorbiaceæ*, taken in its most enlarged sense.

TRICOCCUS. A fruit consisting of three cocci, or elastically dehiscing shells.

TRICOLOR. The garden name for *Amaranthus tricolor*.

TRICOLOR. Consisting of three colours.

TRICOMARIA. A shrub, native of Chili, constituting a genus of *Malpighiaceæ*. The leaves clasp the stem; the branches are spiny; and the flowers are orange-coloured. The calyx is five-parted, the four outer segments having each two glands at the base; the petals are five, stalked, hairy on the outer surface; there are ten stamens, all fertile, three filaments united at the base; the ovary is tri-lobed three-celled, each with a single ovule, and there are three styles. The fruit is succulent, three-celled, and hairy on the outer surface. [M. T. M.]

TRICOSTATE. Having three ribs.

TRICYCLA. This name has been given to a tree, native of Brazil, which constitutes a genus of *Nyctaginaceæ*. Some of the branches are spiny; the leaves are alternate and tufted; and the flowers are solitary, on short stalks from the base of the tufts of leaves. The involucre consists of three coloured leaves. The perianth is petaloid, tubular, constricted in the middle, its limb having five lobes; stamens five, free; ovary one-celled, with a single ovule; fruit angular, enclosed within the hardened base of the perianth, and surrounded by the persistent involucre.   [M. T. M.]

TRICYRTIS. A genus of *Melanthaceæ*, from Nepal and Japan. It consists of erect woolly herbs, with alternate ovate-cordate amplexicaul leaves, and a leafy terminal panicle of flowers; these have a six-leaved perianth, the segments connivent in a ball, and narrowed into claws, the three outer bulging at the base; six stamens; a three-cleft style, with six stigmas; and seeds with rough black seed-coats.   [J. T. S.]

TRIDAX. The name of a genus of *Compositæ*, comprising a Central American herbaceous plant, with stalked ovate leaves, borne on procumbent stems. The flower-heads are surrounded by an involucre of two rows of bracts, the outer (six or eight in number) ovate leafy hairy externally, the inner membranous and very smooth; the receptacle is covered with lanceolate scales. The fruits are compressed, hairy, each surmounted by a pappus of fifteen or sixteen branched scales.   [M. T. M.]

TRIDENTATE. When the point is truncated, and has three indentations.

TRIDENTIA. One of the subdivisions of *Stapelia*, proposed by Haworth. It has the outer staminal crown five-parted, the divisions in the form of three teeth, and the inner bifid, the innermost horn being longer than the others.   [T. M.]

TRIDESMIS. A genus of trees or shrubs of the family *Hypericaceæ*. The species are natives of the Moluccas, and have angular branches, bearing on their extremities a terminal bud, consisting of membranous wavy dotted scales. The flower-stalks originate from the axils of the scars of the fallen leaves. The calyx is five-parted, persistent; petals five, provided in the interior with a trilobed linear appendage; stamens five, in three parcels, alternating with which are three small awl-shaped scales; ovary three-celled, ovules numerous, styles three; fruit capsular. The name is derived from the Greek *treis* 'three' and *desme* 'a bundle,' in allusion to the number of stamens. [M. T. M.]

TRIEDER. Having three sides.

TRIENNIAL, TRIENNIS. Lasting for three years.

TRIENTALIS. A small genus of *Primulaceæ*, the species of which are found in Europe and North America. They are low and smooth perennials, having an erect stem, which bears some alternate usually minute and scale-like leaves below, and a single whorl of large leaves at the top, from which spring one or more single-flowered peduncles. The calyx is five to seven-parted; the corolla rotate, with a short tube, and as many deep flat divisions as the calyx; there are five to seven stamens, inserted at the base of the corolla; the capsule is many-seeded, and opens to the base with five to nine recurved fugacious valves; and the seeds are inverted, and have a reticulated tunic.   [W. C.]

TRIFARIAM, TRIFARIOUS. In three rows.

TRIFID. Split halfway into three parts.

TRIFOLIATE, TRIFOLIOLATE. Bearing three leaflets from the same point; as in those of the clover.

TRIFOLIUM. A genus of papilionaceous *Leguminosæ*, distinguished by trifoliate leaves, with stipules adhering to the leafstalk. The number of British species is variously estimated at from fifteen to twenty; of those about half may be called meadow or pasture herbs, and the remainder weeds.

The agrarian species of Clover or Trefoil may be grouped as follows :— RED : *T. pratense*, Red or Broad-leaved Clover ; *T. medium*, Zigzag Clover ; *T. incarnatum*, Carnation Clover. PINKISH OR WHITE : *T. hybridum*, Alsike Clover ; *T. repens*, White or Dutch Clover. YELLOW : *T. procumbens* ; *T. filiforme*.

The Broad-leaved Red Clover is found in most fertile meadows, and is extensively employed as a shifting crop, either by itself, or in mixtures which the farmer calls 'seeds.' Its arable form is much larger than the wilder varieties; it is, indeed, so much an induced plant, that it has become difficult to make it hold to some lands so perfectly as it formerly did, in which cases the soil is described as 'clover-sick.' The Zigzag Clover is so called from the angular bends at each joint of its stalk. Its leaflets are more pointed than those of *T. pratense*, and usually without the white spot, but this character is not constant. It is a lover of sandy soils, whereas the *T. pratense* is not so well adapted for light land; and being a large species it appears to have been introduced to cultivation as a good cropper where the commoner clover had failed. Some ten years ago *T. medium* could be obtained of the seedsman, but at present its place is supplied by what is labelled *T. pratense perenne*, and commonly called 'Cow-grass.' The solution of this mystery appears to be that the two forms here mentioned are but varieties of the Broad-leaved Clover, the sand-clover in cultivation so rapidly assuming the characters of Broad Clover, that, however different they may originally have been, their distinctive characters cannot with certainty be maintained in their growth as crop-plants. Hence the disputes which are so constant between farmers and

4 F

seedsmen, for not sending the true Cow-grass, are exceedingly difficult to settle.

The Carnation or Crimson Clover, as a crop-plant, appears to have been introduced from the Continent. It is an annual species, much used (especially in the upland soils in the neighbourhood of London) upon the white-crop stubble sown in autumn, in which case even a heavier crop than that of the Broad-leaved Clover can be cleared away the following summer in time for a late sowing of turnips. Several varieties of its seed can now be obtained, among which the *T. incarnatum 'tardif rouge'* and *T. incarnatum 'tardif blanc'* of Vilmorin are red and white forms, coming in about a fortnight later than the usual variety, and so have been recommended for succession.

The Alsike Clover is also of foreign origin, being much grown on the Continent. It has got the name of 'hybrid clover' from its apparently possessing characters intermediate between the common red and Dutch clovers, but its hybridity is not admitted by botanists. Its flowers, which grow in compact heads like those of the red clover, are of a pinkish blush. Its shoots trail along the ground without rooting, as in the Dutch Clover. It is a good pasture plant, deserving of more attention than it has yet received in this country.

The Dutch Clover, or Shamrock of Ireland, is a valuable feeding plant in dry and thin soils; and in laying down permanent pastures, unless in strong land, it should be always pretty freely employed. Its spontaneous growth in the meadow is always hailed as a sign of improved condition. It must not in that case be confounded with the *T. fragiferum*, called Strawberry-headed Clover from the fruitlike aspect of its calyces, which expand and take on a reddish colour after the flowers fade—this latter peculiarity being indicative of stiff clays.

The Procumbent or Hop Trefoil of the botanist is readily distinguished from the other species by its bunch of yellow flowers, withering to the bright-brown of a strobile of hops, which it is not unlike in general aspect, and hence its common name. This must not be confounded with the Hop Trefoil of the farmer, which is the *Medicago lupulina.* They may be readily distinguished thus :—The ripened fruits of the *Medicago lupulina* are arranged in a bunch of black twisted seed-pods. The pods of the *T. procumbens* are straight, and always covered with the persistent dried hop-like flowers. This latter has been used for farm purposes, but is of little value. The small Yellow or Suckling Clover is more diminutive in all its parts than the preceding. It has been recommended as a mixture in light pasture herbage, but is scarcely worth consideration.

A four-leaved Shamrock or other clover is greatly esteemed as being lucky, perhaps upon the principle that it is thought by some to be fortunate to get anything rare ; four-leaved (even-leaved) clovers are, however, not unfrequently met with. [J. B.]

TRIFOLIUM DES JARDINIERS. (Fr.) *Cytisus sessilifolius.*

TRIFURCATE. Having a fork with three tines, as some hairs.

TRIGLANS. Containing three nuts (glans) within an involucre ; as the Spanish chestnut.

TRIGLOCHIN. Marsh-herbs with very narrow radical leaves, and slender spikes of inconspicuous green flowers, belonging to the order *Juncaginaceæ.* The flower is composed of six concave deciduous leaves, six stamens, three to six plumose stigmas, and as many combined one-seeded capsules. There are two British species, which agree in having grass-like but fleshy leaves, grooved throughout and sheathing at the base. The flowers, which are very small, are only remarkable for their feathery stigmas. *T. palustre,* the Marsh Arrow-grass, is common in wet meadows and in marshy situations generally. In this species the stigmas are three, and the three capsules form a linear column. *T. maritimum* is a somewhat more robust plant, and is sufficiently distinguished by its six capsules, so combined as to be broadly elliptical or almost globose in form. In general habit both species bear some resemblance to a *Plantago,* but the spike is much more lax. [O. A. J.]

TRIGONANTHUS. *Ceratostylis.*

TRIGONELLA. A rather extensive genus of herbaceous leguminous plants, widely spread over Southern Europe, Western and Central Asia, Northern Africa, and occurring more sparingly in Australia, all the species possessing a heavy penetrating odour. Their leaves are composed of three leaflets, the middle one being stalked ; and their flowers are disposed in axillary umbel-like heads, or are produced, either solitary or in clusters of two or three, in the leaf-axils. They are succeeded by straight or slightly curved flattened or cylindrical many-seeded pods, which are longer than the calyx, and split into two valves at maturity.

T. Fœnum græcum, the Fenugreek or Fenugræc, is an erect annual plant about two feet high, a native of the Mediterranean region, but cultivated in India and other warm countries, and occasionally in England, though our climate is scarcely suitable to it. The seeds of Fenugreek were held in high repute among the ancient Egyptians, Greeks, and Romans, for medicinal and culinary purposes, but at the present day their use in medicine is with us confined to veterinary practice—Fenugreek powder being the principal ingredient in most of the quack nostrums which find so much favour amongst ignorant grooms and horsekeepers. They have a powerful odour of *coumarine,* and are largely used for flavouring the so-called concentrated cattle-foods, and for rendering damaged hay palatable. [A. S.]

TRIGONIA, TRIGONIACEÆ. The genus *Trigonia,* consisting of tropical American trees, with opposite stipulate leaves (white underneath) and paniculate flowers, presents so many anomalies, that it has been proposed to consider it as a distinct order of polypetalous dicotyledons under the name of *Trigoniaceæ*. It had been referred to *Polygalaceæ*, chiefly on account of its irregular flowers and the long hairs of its seeds; but it has little else in common with them, and the position of the petals and insertion of the stamens is quite different.

As the irregularity of the flower is of the same nature as in *Leguminosæ*—i.e., it has one petal, which is of quite a different shape from the others, placed uppermost or next the stem from which it springs—it disagrees with the *Polygalaceæ*, which have not this characteristic, and should therefore be regarded as a distinct family, or (what is perhaps more advisable) placed as a section of *Leguminosæ*. The irregularity of the stamens is also of the same nature as in *Leguminosæ*, the fissure or vacant space being opposite the enlarged upper petal. Some good authorities think that the real affinities of the genus or order lie probably in the direction of *Vochyaceæ*, through the medium of *Lightia*.   [B. C.]

TRIGONIDIUM. A small but curious genus of orchids from Tropical America, belonging to the tribe *Vandeæ*. They are epiphytal herbs, with creeping stems, bearing pseudobulbs, few coriaceous leaves, and solitary flowers on erect radical peduncles clothed with sheathing bracts. The sepals are equal, somewhat herbaceous, cohering at the base, spreading at the apex, about twice the size of the petals. The remarkable flowers of this genus distinguish it from all others.   [W. B. H.]

TRIGONOSTEMON. A genus of *Euphorbiaceæ*, comprising a Javanese shrub, with acuminate whorled leaves, hairy on the under-surface. Flowers monœcious, crowded on axillary racemes; calyx five-parted; petals five, inclining inwards, alternating with five glands; stamens three, united below, free above, the anther-lobes divergent. In the female flowers the three cells of the ovary have each one ovule, and the fruit is capsular.   [M. T. M.]

TRIGONOUS. Having three angles and three plane faces; as the stem of *Carex acuta*.

TRIHILATE. Having three apertures, as some sorts of pollen-grains.

TRIJUGOUS. When the petiole of a pinnated leaf bears three pairs of leaflets.

TRILATERAL. A prism of three sides.

TRILIX. *Prockia.*

TRILLIACEÆ. A small order of monocotyledons, sometimes considered as a suborder of *Smilaceæ* or of *Liliaceæ*. It is distinguished by simple stems, bearing a whorl of netted-veined leaves, and a single terminal flower, with usually three herbaceous sepals, three larger petals, six to ten stamens with linear anthers, a free

ovary with three to five cells and as many distinct styles, and a succulent fruit. The species are all natives of the temperate regions of the Northern Hemisphere, and are distributed into five or six genera, of which the most important are *Trillium* and *Paris*.

TRILLIDIUM. A genus of *Trilliaceæ* from India, containing the *Trillium Govenianum* of Wallich, which is somewhat intermediate between *Trillium* and *Paris*, having the same ternary arrangement of the flower which occurs in the former, from which it differs in the leaves of the perianth being all similar (coloured), the anthers extrorse after flowering, and the stigmas subulate. It is a herb with a horizontal creeping rhizome, and an erect stem, terminated by a whorl of three stalked five-nerved leaves, in the centre of which there is a single erect flower.   [J. T. S.]

TRILLIE. (Fr.) *Trillium.*

TRILLIUM. An exclusively North American genus, referred by some botanists to *Smilaceæ*, while others consider it the type of a distinct order called *Trilliaceæ*. It is distinguished from its congeners by its flowers having three green persistent sepals, and three larger coloured and withering petals, six stamens with anthers bursting inwards, and a six-sided three-celled ovary, with numerous ovules in several rows in each cell, and bearing three distinct or very rarely cohering styles. The plants belonging to it are perennial smooth herbs, with tufted tuberous roots or creeping rootstocks, and simple stems bearing at the summit three broad stalkless or short-stalked thin leaves arranged in a whorl, and a solitary flower either with or without a stalk in the middle. Seventeen species, spread over the Continent of America from Georgia to the Arctic regions, are described.

The fleshy roots of *T. erectum* (sometimes called *T. pendulum*), under the name of Beth-root, form one of the numerous drugs prepared for sale in the United States by some of the societies of the religious sect called Shakers. They are esteemed astringent, tonic and antiseptic, and are employed in spitting of blood and several other complaints. The plant is also called Indian Balm or Lamb's Quarters. It has an erect stem a foot or more high, bearing three broad almost rhomboid leaves, and drooping fetid flowers, with green sepals striped with purple, and deep purple petals.   [A. S.]

TRILOBED, TRILOBUS. Three-lobed, as in the leaf of *Anemone Hepatica*.

TRIMERIA. The name of a South African tree constituting a genus of *Homaliaceæ*. The leaves are alternate three-nerved, and the flowers grow in axillary spikes; the calyx consists of three sepals, the corolla of three concave petals larger than the sepals; there are nine stamens, aggregated together in three bundles, placed opposite to the petals, and alternating with as many large glands; ovary free, with three parietal placentas, each bearing a single ovule; styles three; fruit one-celled, three-valved; seeds three or one. This genus derives its name from the Greek words *treis* 'three' and *meros* 'a part,' indicating the ternary arrangement of the parts of the flower; in this one particular, but in no other, the genus shows a resemblance to endogens. [M. T. M.]

TRIMERIS. A shrub of St. Helena, constituting a genus of *Lobeliaceæ*. The flowers are in axillary racemes; the calyx is five-cleft, the segments being provided with a thick dorsal nerve; the corolla consists of five petals, two upper ones free linear, the lower three united into an erect three-lobed lip; and the five stamens are inserted with the corolla on to the upper part of the tube of the calyx, the anthers united so as to form a tube, the two lower ones hairy. The ovary is two-celled, the stigma two-lobed; and the fruit capsular, bursting from above downwards into two valves. [M. T. M.]

TRIMESTRIS. Existing for three months.

TRIMUS. Lasting for three years.

TRINCOMALEE-WOOD. The timber of *Berrya Amonilla*.

TRINERVED, TRINERVIS. Having three ribs, all proceeding from the base.

TRINIA. A genus of *Umbelliferæ*, consisting of biennial branching herbs, with angular stems, and bipinnatisect leaves, the divisions of which are triternate, and the lobes linear. The numerous many-rayed umbels are paniculate or thyrsoid, and without involucres. The flowers are diœcious, or rarely monœcious. The calyx-limb is absent; the petals of the staminal flowers are lanceolate and produced into a slender appendage, which is rolled inwards; the pistilloid flowers have oval petals, with a short appendage, the point of which is bent inwards. The oval fruit is compressed at the side, and the carpels have five filiform equal ribs, the intervals being without vittæ, or having but a single one. The genus is indigenous to Central and Southern Europe, Asia Minor, and the Cape of Good Hope. [W. C.]

TRINODAL. Having three nodes only.

TRINRAGAN. An Eastern name of the Palmyra Palm.

TRIODIA. A genus of grasses belonging to the tribe *Aveneæ*. The inflorescence is in simple contracted spike-like panicles, the spikelets of which are few-flowered and awnless; outer glumes two, nearly equal; flowering glumes with three small teeth at the top. Steudel describes eleven species, which are all natives of the Southern Hemisphere, save *T. decumbens*, a British representative of the genus, which is a common grass growing on spongy wet cold soils, and not of much agricultural importance. [D. M.]

TRIŒCIOUS, TRIOICUS. Having male flowers on one individual, female on another, and hermaphrodite on a third. Its sign is ♂ ☿ ♀.

TRIOLET. (Fr.) *Trifolium repens*; also *Medicago lupulina*.

TRIONUM. *Hibiscus Trionum*.

TRIOPTERYS. A genus of trailing shrubs, indigenous to Tropical America. Their flowers are purple or violet, in axillary or terminal clusters. Calyx five-parted, four of the segments having two glands at the base; petals five, stalked, entire; stamens ten, all fertile, alternately long and short, the filaments united at the base; ovary three-lobed, each of the lobes having three crest-like ridges on the outer surface, and each containing a single pendulous ovule; styles three; fruit with three wings-on each lobe, whence the name of the genus, from *treis* 'three' and *pteron* 'wing.' One or two species are cultivated as stove-climbers in this country. [M. T. M.]

TRIOSTEUM. A genus of *Caprifoliaceæ*, consisting of several species of coarse hairy perennial herbs, with large entire leaves tapering to the base but connate round the simple stem; and sessile axillary flowers, solitary or in clusters. The leaf-like lobes of the calyx are linear-lanceolate and persistent; the corolla is tubular, swollen-at the base, and five-lobed; there are five stamens; the ovary is generally three-celled; and the fruit is a rather dry triangular drupe, with three-ribbed one-seeded bony nutlets. The species are natives of North America and the mountains of Central Asia. [W. C.]

TRIPALEOLATE. Consisting of three pales or paleæ, as the flower of a bamboo.

TRIPARDE, or TRIPARELLE. (Fr.) A kind of Olive.

TRIPARTED, TRIPARTITE. Parted to the base in three divisions.

TRIPARTIBLE. Partible into three.

TRIPE DE ROCHE. This name, or that of Rock Tripe, is given in North America, in consequence of the blistered thallus, to several species of lichens belonging to *Gyrophora* and *Umbilicaria*, but especially to the latter, which afford a coarse food, whose nutritive qualities are, however, much impaired by the presence of a bitter principle which is apt to cause serious diarrhœa. Bad, however, as it is, it has proved of the most material service to some of our Arctic voyagers, especially to the expeditions under the lamented Sir John Franklin, though from constitutional peculiarities it is not available to all. In no case, however, did it completely appease the pangs of hunger, probably from its not containing in the proper proportions all the constituents necessary to compose a truly nutritious article of food. Some of these lichens, of large size, have been found on the northernmost Arctic land which has yet been explored. [M. J. B.]

TRIPETALOID. Consisting of six parts, of which three resemble petals, and three are green and small.

TRIPETALOIDEÆ. One of the Linnæan natural orders, which included *Butomus, Sagittaria*, and their allies.

TRIPHASIA. Four species have been described as belonging to this genus of *Aurantiaceæ*, but one of them is now referred to *Atalantia*, and two others are imperfectly known; so that the genus is practically confined to a single species, *T. trifoliata*, that on which it was originally founded by Loureiro. This is a spiny shrub, having leaves composed of three egg-shaped leaflets, notched at the top; its flowers are white and sweet-scented, and usually grow singly in the leaf-axils: producing one to three-celled berries, containing a single seed surrounded with pulp in each cell. They have a trilobed calyx, as many petals, six distinct stamens, and an ovary elevated on a short stalk, and ending in a longish thick style, which ultimately falls away. It is a native of Southern China, but it is now naturalised in many parts of the East Indies, and is also cultivated in the West Indies. Its fruits are about as large as hazel-nuts, and have a red skin. When ripe they have an agreeable sweet taste, but if gathered green they have a strong flavour of turpentine, and the pulp is very sticky. They are sometimes preserved whole in syrup, and occasionally sent to this country from Manilla as lime-berries.   [A. S.]

TRIPHYLLOUS. Having the leaves in a whorl of three ; also, having only three leaves.

TRIPINNARIA. *Colea.*

TRIPINNATE. When the leaflets of a bipinnate leaf become themselves pinnate.

TRIPINNATIFID. Three times divided in a pinnatifid manner.

TRIPINNATISECT. Parted to the base in a tripinnate manner.

TRIPLANDRON. A tree of Columbia, forming a genus of *Clusiaceæ*. The short recurved flower-stalks are arranged in groups of three. The flowers are diœcious: the males having two small bracts, placed beneath the four-leaved calyx; four roundish spreading petals, reflected at the margins; and numerous stamens in three rows, combined together into a convex four-sided mass, with thick filaments, and terminal anthers. In the females the barren stamens are combined into a fleshy four-cornered cup, surrounding the globose four-cornered many-celled ovary, and there are nine sessile radiating stigmas.   [M. T. M.]

TRIPLARIS. A genus of *Polygonaceæ* from Tropical South America, remarkable for the great development of the three outer lobes of the limb of the fruiting perianth, which somewhat resemble the wings of the maple fruit. They are trees or shrubs, with alternate shortly stalked entire leaves, accompanied by extremely short obliquely truncate ochreæ, and bearing racemose bracteated unisexual flowers, of which the males are six or eight-parted. The nut is three-edged, with winged angles, and the embryo similar in shape to the nut, not six-lobed as in *Ruprechtia*. Schomburgk describes the *T. Schomburgkiana*, which he found in Guiana, as having the trunk and branches hollow between the nodes, and serving as the habitation of very venomous ants.   [J. T. S.]

TRIPLE-NERVED, TRIPLINERVED, TRIPLINERVIS. The same as Triple-ribbed.

TRIPLE-RIBBED. When of three ribs the two lateral ones emerge from the middle one a little above its base.

TRIPLICATO-PINNATE. The same as Triplnnate.

TRIPLICI. Thrice repeated.

TRIPLO. Thrice.

TRIP-MADAM. *Sedum reflexum.*

TRIPOLI POWDER. A pulverous substance which is imported from Germany, and used as a material for polishing steel. It consists entirely of the flinty integuments of several species of *Diatomaceæ*, divested of everything except the silex. Several of the species of which it is composed, are found to be identical with those which are at the present day contributing to form a sediment on the Victoria Barrier, in the Antarctic regions, hundreds of miles in length. Ehrenberg even asserts that in beds of fossil *Diatomaceæ*, which are occasionally several feet in depth, species are still in the process of propagation, but this is doubtless a mere fancy. The Phonolite stones of the Rhine also abound in the remains of these minute *Algæ*. [M. J. B.]

TRIPOLIUM. A genus of *Compositæ*, very closely allied to *Aster*, and hardly to be distinguished from it except by the involucre, which consists of a number of bract-like scales, disposed along the upper part of the flower-stalk, or somewhat biseriate. The ligulate florets are longer and narrower than in *Aster*. The species are somewhat fleshy, and inhabit salt-marshy districts throughout Europe and North America. *T. vulgare*, frequently called *Aster Tripolium*, is not unfrequent on muddy seashores or salt-marshes in this country ; its ray-florets are purple, or sometimes absent. The somewhat fleshy leaves of this plant are occasionally gathered, with those of *Salicornia*, to make a kind of pickle.   [M. T. M.]

TRIPSACUM. A genus of grasses belonging to the tribe *Rotlboelliceæ.* The inflorescence is in spikes, either solitary or three together—the upper male, the lower female ; male glume two-flowered, the outer male, the inner neuter ; female glume one-flowered; styles two. The few species are natives of the Southern States of America. The Buffalo-grass, *T. dactyloides*, is considered a good forage species there. It is rather too tender for the climate of Britain, where it is either killed or much hurt during severe winters. ● [D. M.]

TRIPTERIS. A genus of herbs or undershrubs of the family *Compositæ*, natives of Arabia and the Cape of Good Hope. The plants are frequently dotted over with glands, secreting an odoriferous substance, like that of the common marigold. The heads of flowers are at the ends of the branches, and are surrounded by an involucre of one or two rows of scales, that are frequently membranous at their margins. The receptacle is naked, flat, or somewhat convex. The florets of the ray are strap-shaped, yellow white or purplish; those of the disk tubular, yellow. The fruits of the central or disk-florets are abortive, those of the ray three-sided and winged at the angles, provided with a hollow beak, closed by a thin membrane; at other times the fruits are wingless, and have a solid beak. The pappus is always absent. The name is given in allusion to the winged fruit. [M. T. M.]

TRIPTEROCOCCUS. A genus of Australian and Tasmanian herbaceous plants, of the family *Stackhousiaceæ*. The branches are somewhat four-sided; the leaves very narrow, with two stipules; and the flowers in terminal spikes; calyx with a distended tube, its limb five-parted; petals five, their claws cohering so as to form a tube, and their limbs spreading; stamens five, inserted with the petals into the throat of the calyx; ovary three-lobed three-celled, each cell with a single erect ovule; style cylindrical; fruit of three winged indehiscent carpels, ultimately separating from a central column. The generic name alludes to the three winged fruits. [M. T. M.]

TRIPTEROUS. Three-winged.

TRIPTILION. A genus of Chilian herbs of the family *Compositæ*. The leaves are rigid, membranous, pinnately divided, and spiny; and the flower-heads are aggregated in tufts, each one surrounded by an involucre of two rows of bracts, the outer of which are spreading leathery and spine-pointed, and the inner erect and membranous. The receptacle is covered with fringed hairy scales; corollas two-lipped, the outer lip three-toothed, much wider than the inner one; fruits angular, smooth or hairy; pappus of three to five-parted fringed scales, recurved at the points. The flowers are white or blue. Some of the species are grown as annuals for the sake of their pretty flowers. The generic name is derived from *treis* 'three' and *ptilon* 'a wing,' in allusion to the pappus. [M. T. M.]

TRIPTOLEMÆA. In his recent synopsis of the *Dalbergieæ* (*Leguminosæ*), Mr. Bentham has combined the genus *Triptolemæa*, originally founded upon a group of exclusively Brazilian plants, with *Dalbergia*, an extensive genus common to the tropics of both hemispheres. As a section of this latter genus, the *Triptolemæas* are characterised by their cymes of numerous extremely small flowers, which, by imperfection, are of one sex only, and have the calyx-teeth blunt and the petals furnished with short claws, their ten stamens being united into a sheath slit on the upper side, and their ovary containing only one ovule; and also by their pods being hardened, and strongly marked with netted veins at the seed-bearing part. Nine species have been described, but they are now reduced to three. These are trees or woody climbers, with alternate unequally pinnate leaves, composed of a variable number (five to twenty-five) of oblong leathery leaflets, usually shining, and marked with netted veins on the upper surface. The true Rosewood of commerce, that imported from Brazil, was for a long time supposed to be the produce of this genus, upon the authority of the French traveller and botanist Guillemin, who brought from Brazil specimens of two species of *Triptolemæa* as the true rosewood plant; but according to Dr. Allemão of Rio Janeiro, the greater part of the best kind of rosewood sent to Europe is the timber of *Dalbergia nigra*, while other qualities are the produce of species of *Machærium*. [A. S.]

TRIQUE-MADAME. (Fr.) *Sedum album*; also *S. acre*.

TRIQUETER, TRIQUETROUS. Three-edged, or three-cornered.

TRISECTED. Cut deeply into three parts.

TRISERIAL. In three rows. Instead of 'serial,' the word *fariam* is generally affixed to a Latin numeral; thus, *trifariam* (*trifarious*), in three rows.

TRISETARIA. A genus of grasses belonging to the tribe *Aveneæ*, which contained one species, *T. linearis*, now included in *Trisetum*. [D. M.]

TRISETUM. A genus of grasses belonging to the tribe *Aveneæ*. The inflorescence is panicled; spikelets two to four-flowered; glumes two, membranous and pointed, rarely awned; lower pales with two short bristles, awned at the back; the upper keeled with a twisted awn; stamens three; styles two; ovary smooth. This genus is nearly allied to the oat-grass, and includes nearly seventy species. These are widely distributed over the different quarters of the globe. They are chiefly natives of the temperate zones, where some of them are useful pasture grasses. The British representatives of the genus are *T. pubescens* and *T. flavescens*, both superior kinds and useful for agricultural purposes, particularly the latter, which generally forms a portion of all productive meadows. [D. M.]

TRISPORIC. Applied to bodies composed of three spores.

TRISTACHYA. A genus of grasses belonging to the tribe *Aveneæ*. The inflorescence is panicled; spikelets two-flowered, the inferior male or neuter, the superior stalked hermaphrodite, bearded at the base; glumes two, lance-shaped three-nerved, channeled and herbaceous, the upper slightly the longest; pales two, herbaceous and pointed. Steudel describes seven species, which are natives of South America and South Africa. [D. M.]

TRISTANIA. A genus of Australian shrubs, of the myrtle family. They have linearleaves, and yellow flowers in corymbs; calyx five-cleft; petals five; stamens arranged in five parcels, opposite the petals; fruit capsular, many-seeded; seeds without wings. Some of the species are grown as pretty greenhouse plants. [M. T. M.]

TRISTEMMA. This genus of *Melastomaceæ* consists of certain tropical African shrubs with four-sided stems, and flowers in heads surrounded by involucres. The calyx is provided with a projecting rim or rings near to its four or five-lobed limb; the petals are stalked; the stamens eight to ten, equal, their anthers opening by one pore, the ovary is confluent with the tube of the calyx, and contains four or five compartments, which open at the hairy apex when ripe. [M. T. M.]

TRISTICHA. A genus of *Podostemaceæ*, comprising species which grow in wet places in Brazil, Southern Africa, and Madagascar. They are little moss-like plants, with much-branched slender annual stems. The perianth is membranous and three-parted, concealing a single stamen, and a stalked three-celled ovary surmounted by three stigmas. The fruit is three-celled, three-valved, and marked by nine ribs. [M. T. M.]

TRISTICHOUS. In three rows.

TRISTIS. Dull-coloured.

TRITELEIA. A small genus of *Liliaceæ*, from Western North America and Buenos Ayres. It has a salver-shaped perianth, with a six-parted limb, six stamens in two rows, a trilobed stigma, and a many-seeded ovary. The leaves are linear, and the scapes bear involucrate umbels of white or blue flowers, or in some of the species simple peduncles bear solitary flowers. *T. laxa*, a native of California, has glaucous leaves, and a many-flowered umbel of deep-blue flowers. *T. uniflora* is a very handsome white-flowered species. [J. T. S.]

TRITERNATE. When a common petiole divides into three secondary petioles, which are each subdivided into three tertiary petioles, each bearing three leaflets.

TRITHRINAX. A genus of *Palmaceæ*, of which three species are described :—*T. brasiliensis*, that upon which the genus was founded, a native of Rio Grande, the most southern province of Brazil; *T. aculeata*, a native of Western Mexico; and *T. mauritiæformis*, of New Granada. They are all low-growing palms, with the lower part of their trunks marked by close circular scars, and the upper clad with the persistent bases of old leafstalks. They have deeply-cut fan-shaped prickly-stalked leaves, with threads hanging from between the segments; and much-branched spikes of greenish-yellow flowers, which are either perfect or (by abortion) of one sex only. The perfect ones contain six free or slightly connected stamens, rising from the bottom of the corolla, and three distinct ovaries with narrow tapering styles and simple stigmas. Only one of the ovaries comes to maturity, forming a one-seeded fruit, the seed having the embryo placed at the back near the top. [A. S.]

TRITICUM. A genus of grasses of the tribe *Hordeæ*, which includes, among other species—*T. vulgare*, or Common Wheat; *T. repens*, the Creeping Couch or Cooch; and *T. caninum*. *T. vulgare* is an annual cereal or corn-grass, which under the name of Wheat is well-known to every one. Its varieties, though endless, may perhaps be all comprehended under the following heads, of each of which we may have varieties, with more or less hairiness on the chaff-scales, &c.:—*T. vulgare muticum* (*T. hybernum*, Linn.), the awnless or Beardless Wheat; *T. vulgare barbatum* (*T. æstivum*, Linn.); and *T. Spelta*, the grains in which are more or less adherent to the chaff-scales.

The native country and origin of Wheat has ever been a curious subject of speculation. We think, however, that M. Fabre's experiments, detailed in the *Journal of the Royal Agricultural Society*, afford very strong presumptive evidence that this cereal is derived from a wild grass of Southern Europe and Western Asia, known to the botanist as Ægilops: which see. It is true that a specimen of this genus would at first sight appear to be very different from wheat, but it is really not so on a minute examination of its parts, and under cultivation it soon affords a very respectable grain; its green herbage, too, emits the peculiar smell on being bruised which belongs to wheat, and, as we know from experiment, it is subject to the same epiphytes or attacks of 'blight' as wheat. That a plant very dissimilar from wheat, in fact a wild useless grass, should yet in cultivation become so changed as to afford a useful grain, is so far fortunate in that we might expect, from this amount of adaptability to circumstances, that it would be capable of easily affording a large variety of sorts. Such we know to be the case, and hence no plant is so easily adapted to variations of climate, soil, and management as wheat.

Our wild species of the genus are perennial grasses. *T. repens*, the Couch, is by far too well and unfavourably known to merit our dwelling upon it at great length. This has been split up into several species by some botanists, which has arisen from its capabilities of changing from circumstances; for, like its cultivated ally, it is bearded or beardless, and can adapt itself to all positions. *T. caninum* differs from it mainly in the absence of the running underground stems (rhizomes). It has, however, the same pungent flavour which belongs to all the *Tritici*, due probably to the presence of some kind of essential oil, in virtue of which it would appear to be capable of exerting powerful emetic action, at least on dogs, as we have seen these animals vomit most violently in a few seconds after eating two or three blades of the common Couch.   [J. B.]

TRITOMA. This genus of *Liliaceæ* is closely allied to *Aloë*, but in place of fleshy leaves it has long linear grass-like root-leaves, from the midst of which is thrown up a scape, bearing at its summit an ovoid or elongated spike of scarlet or yellow flowers. The perianth is tubular or bell shaped, and six-parted; from its orifice project six stamens; the style is thread-like, and terminated by a three-lobed stigma; the capsule is three-celled, and splits through the sutures into three valves. The species are natives of the Cape of Good Hope. Three or four are in cultivation as hardy plants, throwing up their splendid flowers late in autumn to a height of three or four feet or more. Few plants are so effective when placed on a lawn or in front of a shrubbery. The old name, *Kniphofia*, has of late been sometimes revived for them.   [M. T. M.]

TRITOMA #AUX-ALOES. (Fr.) *Tritoma Uvaria.*

TRITOMODON. A Japanese shrub, of the family *Vacciniaceæ*. Its stem is much-branched; the leaves clustered towards the ends of the branches, wedge-shaped, hairy on the midrib and leafstalk; and the flowers grow in hairy racemes. The calyx is five-parted, hairy; the corolla membranous white, bell-shaped, its limb divided into five three-toothed segments; stamens ten, awl-shaped, the filaments with a narrow wing, and the anthers ending in a reflexed point, ovary free, five-celled. The generic name was given in allusion to the three-toothed lobes of the corolla.   [M. T. M.]

TRITONIA. A genus of Cape herbs, with bulb-tuberous rhizomes, ensate leaves, and a spicate inflorescence. They belong to the *Iridaceæ*, and are allied to *Ixia*. They have a two-valved spathe; tubular flowers, with a six-parted nearly regular limb; three stamens, three spreading stigmas; and a many-seeded capsule, the seeds being neither winged nor berried. Many of them are very handsome.   [T. M.]

TRIUMFETTA. The numerous species of this genus of *Tiliaceæ* are widely dispersed over the tropics of both hemispheres; and are either annuals or perennial shrubby herbs, or rarely shrubs, more or less clothed with star-shaped hairs. Their leaves are alternate entire or palmately lobed; and their yellow flowers are solitary or in clusters in the leaf-axils, succeeded by nearly globular unopening fruits thickly beset with slender hooked prickles, like the burrs of the burdock. The flowers have five coloured sepals; as many petals, or rarely none; indefinite or sometimes ten (rarely only five) free stamens, rising from a short disk bearing five glands opposite the petals; and a two to five-celled ovary bearing a slender style,

each cell containing two ovules separated by a spurious partition.

All the species possess more or less of the mucilaginous property of the order, and several of them are on that account employed medicinally in the tropics. In Jamaica the name Paroquet Burr is commonly given to them, on account of the green paroquets feeding on their ripe fruits or burrs. The inner bark of some species, particularly *T. angulata* and *T. semitriloba*, afford very good fibre, resembling jute both in regard to appearance and quality. The first of these is extremely common in Tropical Asia, and is an annual plant, with an erect branching stem becoming woody at the base, and usually producing broad three-lobed leaves on long stalks; while the latter is more generally distributed over the tropics of both hemispheres, and is a shrub of about five or six feet in height.   [A. S.]

TRIURIDACEÆ. An order of monocotyledons, consisting of small slender colourless herbs, often almost transparent, without any other leaves than small scales, and small flowers either solitary or in terminal racemes. In their usually six-parted perianth, hypogynous stamens, distinct carpels, and apparently homogeneous embryo, they are connected with *Alismaceæ*, from which they differ chiefly in the divisions of the perianth being always valvate in a single series, and in their embryo not being curved. These curious little plants are generally found, like the smaller *Burmanniaceæ*, on rotten leaves or other decaying vegetable matter in the moist tropical forests of both the New and the Old World. They are distributed into five or six genera, of which the principal are *Triuris* and *Sciaphila.*

TRIURIS. A genus of *Triuridaceæ*, distinguished by diœcious flowers, a perianth with only three lobes ending in long filiform tails, three stamens, and styles arising from the base of the carpels. There is but a single species known, a little Brazilian leafless herb, with a slender stem a few inches high, and a rather large terminal flower.

TRIXAGO. A genus of *Scrophulariaceæ*, containing a single species found all over the world. It is intermediate between *Eufragia* and *Bartsia*, differing from both however in its fleshy ovate-globose capsule, and in its thick trifid placenta.   [W. C.]

TRIXIS. The name of a genus of composite plants, consisting of herbs or shrubs sometimes of twining habit, and natives of the East Indies and the eastern shores of South America. The heads of flowers are in loose corymbs or panicles, and each is surrounded by a tubular involucre, consisting of one or two rows of scales, the innermost of which are the longest; the receptacle is either naked, or provided with fine fringe-like hairs. The fruits are striated hairy oblong, surmounted by a large disk; and the pappus is in two or more rows, scaly or somewhat feathery.

One or two species, with white flowers, are grown in this country. [M. T. M.]

TRIZEUXIS. An epiphytal genus of orchids, belonging to the tribe *Vandeæ*, containing one species, an inhabitant of Tropical America and Trinidad. It bears distichous recurved acute laterally compressed fleshy leaves, which are grooved at the base; and small greenish flowers, in a panicle arising from the axils of the lower leaves, collected into heads at the extremities of the branches of the panicle. The genus is remarkable in having the lip superior—that is, with the parts of the flower in their proper position, the ovary not being twisted as in the generality of orchids. [W. B. H.]

TROCHETIA. The name of a genus of small shrubs, natives of Bourbon and Madagascar. They are covered with brown scales, and have entire feather-veined leaves, and axillary flower-stalks. The calyx is five-parted; petals five, deciduous; stamens numerous, combined below into a tube, some of them sterile, strap-shaped, entire or cleft, alternating with the fertile ones; ovary sessile, five-celled, the style thread-like; fruit capsular five-celled five-valved, the valves bearing numerous roundish seeds on their centre. [M. T. M.]

TROCHLEAR. The same as Pulley-shaped.

TROCHOCARPA. New Holland shrubs or small trees of the family *Epacridaceæ*. The leaves are on short stalks, the flowers white or yellow, placed on terminal or axillary spikes. At the base of the five-cleft calyx are two small bracts; the corolla is funnel-shaped, its limb divided into five spreading hairy segments; the stamens are concealed within the corolla, the anthers being pendulous; and a five-lobed cup-like disk surrounds the ten-celled ovary, in each compartment of which is a single seed. The fruit is succulent, with ten one-seeded stones, which ultimately fall away one from the other. The name is derived from the Greek *trochos* 'a wheel' and *karpos* 'fruit,' indicating the radiated arrangement of the cells of the fruit. *T. laurina* is a very handsome greenhouse shrub. [M. T. M.]

TROCHODENDRON. A genus of *Magnoliaceæ*, comprising a Japanese tree, whose leaves are described as being arranged in whorls, and as lasting green for three years, each whorl being separated by a rather long interval from its neighbour. On this space the perulæ or bud-scales remain, and do not, as in ordinary cases, fall off. The leaves themselves are stalked, somewhat rhomb-shaped, cuspidate, and of a thick texture. The clusters of flowers are terminal, and the pedicels are provided with a small linear bract at the base. The flowers themselves have no calyx or corolla, but a crowd of deciduous stamens, a five to eight-celled ovary with several ovules in each cell, and five to six styles. The fruit is capsular, surmounted by the persistent styles, dividing when ripe into five to eight valves; seeds pendulous. The name is derived from the Greek *trochos* 'a wheel' and *dendron* 'tree,' in allusion to the whorls of leaves. [M. T. M.]

TROCHOPTERIS *elegans* is a small but remarkable Brazilian fern, closely resembling a rosulate lichen in the habit of growth, the fronds being scarcely an inch long, spreading horizontally, subround pilose and five-lobed; the two basal lobes are somewhat contracted, and bear the sporangia—which have the many-rayed apical ring characteristic of the *Schizæineæ*, to which they belong. It is free-veined, allied to *Anemia* by the fructification being borne on flat rachiform lobes, but distinguished as well by habit as by the lobes being scarcely contracted, and lying flat in the plane of the fronds, so that they do not resemble panicles. [T. M.]

TROCHOSTIGMA. Five species of Japanese plants were formed into a genus under this name by the Dutch botanists Siebold and Zuccarini; but four of them have since been referred to the older genus *Actinidia*, placed by some systematists in the order *Dilleniaceæ*, and by others in *Ternströmiaceæ*; while the fifth has been found to belong to the genus *Sphærostemma*, one of the *Schizandraceæ*. [A. S.]

TROÈNE. (Fr.) *Ligustrum*, — D'É-GYPTE. *Lawsonia alba.*

TROLLE. (Fr.) *Trollius.*

TROLL-FLOWER. *Trollius.*

TROLLIUS. A genus of herbaceous perennials belonging to the *Ranunculaceæ*, distinguished by the following characters:—Sepals petal-like; petals very narrow, numerous; stamens and ovaries numerous. The genus is represented in Britain by *T. europæus*, the Globe-flower or Globe-Ranunculus, frequent in mountain-pastures in Scotland, Wales, Ireland, and the North of England. It is a handsome plant, with deeply five-lobed leaves, which are again cut and serrated; and large pale-yellow flowers, which before full expansion are nearly globose. This species is often cultivated as a border flower, as are also *T. asiaticus* and *T. caucasicus*, plants of similar habit. French : *Trolle globuleux*; German : *Kugelranunkel*. [C. A. J.]

TROMOTRICHE. A name given by Haworth to some species of *Stapelia*.

TROMPETTE DU JUGEMENT. (Fr.) *Datura suaveolens* and *D. arborea.*

TROMPHE D'ÉLÉPHANT. (Fr.) *Rhinanthus Elephas.*

TRONG. The Malayan name for the Egg-plant.

TROPÆOLACEÆ. An order established for the genus *Tropæolum*, which, formerly placed in *Geraniaceæ*, has been repeatedly separated therefrom, but is again reunited, especially on account of the close affinity the structure of its flowers bears to that of *Pelargonium*. The genus *Magallana*, usually added to *Tropæolaceæ*, is founded on a mistake.

TROPÆOLUM. An extensive genus of herbs, mostly of climbing habit, representing the group or order *Tropæolaceæ*. Many of the species, which are all South American, are in cultivation, and are of a very ornamental character. The genus is known by its irregular flowers, with five sepals produced into a spur behind, and five petals (fewer by abortion), of which the two upper are more or less dissimilar from the rest; and by its equal free stamens, its sessile tri-lobed three-celled ovary, and its subcarnose indehiscent one-seeded carpels. The leaves are alternate peltate or palmate, angulate lobate or dissected; and the flowers solitary and axillary, orange-red or yellow, rarely blue or purple. [T. M.]

The *Tropæolums* are remarkable for possessing an acrid taste, similar to that which exists among the *Cruciferæ*. The only species grown for culinary purposes are *T. majus* and *T. minus*.

T. majus, the great Indian Cress or Nasturtium, is a hardy annual, a native of Peru, from whence it was introduced in A.D. 1686. The plant is of a trailing habit, but when its succulent stems can obtain any bush for support, they will attach themselves by means of the long twining petioles, and attain a considerable height. The leaves are alternate entire, nearly round, and somewhat undulated or lobed, with the stalk inserted towards the centre instead of at the margin. The flowers, which are borne on long footstalks, are large and showy, being of a rich orange colour, and having the two upper petals marked with deep reddish-brown. The seeds consist of three conjoined berries or nuts, with grooved wrinkled gibbous husks, which become fungous when dry. The flowers and young leaves are frequently used to mix in salads. They have a warm taste, not unlike that of the common cress, from which circumstance the plant has obtained the name of Nasturtium. The flowers are also used to garnish dishes, and have an excellent effect when tastefully arranged with other flowers of a complementary colour. The berries are gathered when young and quite green, and, without the aid of spice, make an agreeable pickle, which, as well as the green leaves steeped in vinegar, is accounted a good antiscorbutic, and is also an excellent substitute for capers.

It is worthy of remark that, in certain conditions of the atmosphere, the flowers, like those of the *Dictamnus Fraxinella*, have the power of emitting electric sparks towards evening—a circumstance first observed by the daughter of the great Linnæus.

The small Indian Cress or Nasturtium, *T. minus*, is a hardy annual, a native of Peru, and has been cultivated in this country since A.D. 1596. It is very similar in appearance to *T. majus*, already noticed, but is of a different habit, being much smaller in every respect, and of dwarf weak growth. The seed-pods are also small, on which account alone they are considered preferable to those of *T. majus* for pickling as a substitute for capers. [W. B. B.]

TROPHIS. Under this name is designated a genus of *Artocarpaceæ*, consisting of certain milky-juiced trees with entire leaves, and diœcious flowers arranged in axillary clusters. In the male flowers the four stamens are placed in front of the four segments of the perianth; in the female flowers the ovate ovary contains a single ovule attached to its inner surface near the top, and the stigma is bifid. The fruit is succulent, with one globular pendent seed; the cotyledons fleshy, and of unequal size. The species are natives of Tropical Asia and America. The leaves of *T. aspera* are used in the East Indies to polish wood, while those of *T. americana*, a West Indian species, are said to be occasionally used as fodder for cattle. [M. T. M.]

TROPHYWORT. *Tropæolum*.

TROPIDOCARPUM. A small genus of *Cruciferæ*, inhabiting North-western America, and consisting of annuals with pinnatifid leaves, and small yellow flowers in leafy racemes. The pod is linear or lanceolate-linear, compressed contrary to the septum, the valves somewhat keeled, the septum narrow often incomplete, and the seeds oblong, compressed. [J. T. S.]

TROPIS. In Greek compounds=the keel of a papilionaceous flower, or any part resembling it.

TROSCART. (Fr.) *Triglochin*.

TROTTLES. An old name for *Symphytum asperrimum*.

TROXIMON. A genus of perennial *Compositæ*, the species of which are natives of North America. The lower leaves are lobed, the upper entire, sheathing. The flower-heads are each surrounded by an involucre of two rows of bracts; the corollas are ligulate, yellow; and the fruits are quadrangular, surmounted by a pappus arranged in two rows—the outer row of numerous very short persistent scales, the inner of deciduous hairs. [M. T. M.]

TRUBS, or TRUBBES. Truffles.

TRUE-LOVE. *Paris quadrifolia*: more correctly written Trulove, according to Dr. Prior.

TRUFFE. (Fr.) *Tuber melanosporum*. — D'EAU. *Trapa natans*.

TRUFFLE. *Tuber*. —, AFRICAN. *Terfezia*. —, ENGLISH. *Tuber æstivum*. —, FALSE. A name sometimes applied to species of *Elaphomyces* and *Scleroderma*, of which the former is really allied to *Tuber*, the latter to the puffballs. It is also given occasionally to the fungi noticed under *Hypogæi*. —, FRENCH. *Tuber melanosporum*. —, HARTS. *Elaphomyces*. —, PIEDMONTESE. *Tuber magnatum*. —,

RED. *Melanogaster variegatus.* — , WHITE. *Chœromyces.*

Applied generally, the name Truffle (or Trubs) comprises all the *Fungi* which belong to the natural orders *Hypogœi* and *Tuberacei.* We shall, however, treat it here as confined to the Truffles, properly so called, belonging to the typical genus *Tuber*, and the closely allied genera *Chœromyces* and *Terfezia.*

The Truffles of commerce all belong to the genus *Tuber*, of which several species are edible; the English Truffles belonging principally to *T. œstivum*, and the best French Truffles to *T. melanosporum.* These are black and warty externally, with the flesh variously marbled. The Piedmontese Truffles, on the contrary (which bear a high

Tuber æstivum.

price, and are highly esteemed), are smooth, and within white more or less tinged with pink. Truffles are in this country sought for almost exclusively by dogs of a particular breed, but on the Continent sows are used for the same purpose, and they are raked up by persons who have a peculiar knack in recognising the spots where they

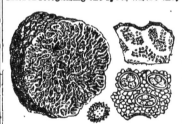

Tuber æstivum (section).

are likely to grow. In Poitou it is a common practice to enclose a space upon the downs, sowing it with acorns, and when the oaks attain size enough to shade the ground, there is sure to be a crop of truffles. All attempts have failed at cultivating them in the same way as mushrooms. In the South of France, indeed, truffles have been procured in woods by watering the ground previously prepared with water in which the parings had been steeped; but no one has yet been able to prepare spawn for sale in a form similar to that of mush-

room-spawn. We believe, however, that this will some time or other be accomplished. The late Mr. Disney made a serious attempt at cultivation, but, unfortunately, the truffles on which he experimented were the refuse of an oil-shop, and were in slices which had been dried by artificial heat. Notwithstanding this, something like spawn appeared, and it is to be regretted that he did not continue his experiments with better materials. Our English truffles have not the fine aroma of the best French truffles, but when properly ripened they are by no means to be despised, and they always command a high price in our markets.

Truffles require a calcareous soil, and where that condition exists they are, we believe, much more common than is usually supposed. Without the assistance of a dog we have collected a couple of pounds in a few minutes, in a locality where truffles have never yet been sought for as objects of merchandise. They are by no means, as is usually supposed, confined to beech-woods; but are found in England sometimes amongst oaks without any admixture of beech, and they do not dislike the neighbourhood of a few conifers. In Somersetshire we have seen them so near the surface as to be cut off by the scythe every time the lawn was mowed. Besides the edible truffles, which receive different names from collectors according to their degree of ripeness, there are several strongly-scented or minute species, mostly with an even bark, which are either not esculent or too small to attract general notice. The large White Truffle belonging to the genus *Chœromyces* is too rare in England to be of much consequence, but it is a poor article of food. The African Truffle (*Terfezia*), is a much better esculent than the white truffle, but is not equal to the *Tuber œstivum*, though it has of late attracted notice in Algiers from its abundance. We have received numerous specimens of this kind from Mogadore. A species of *Hydnotrya* is sold abundantly in the market of Prague. The Red Truffle of the Bath market is a *Melanogaster*, and therefore belongs to *Hypogœi*, not *Tuberacei.*   [M. J. B.]

TRULOVE. *Paris quadrifolia.*

TRUMPET-FLOWER. A name applied to various large tubular flowers, as those of *Bignonia, Tecoma, Catalpa, Brunsfelsia, Solandra*, &c.

TRUMPET HONEYSUCKLE. *Caprifolium sempervirens.*

TRUMPET SHAPED. Hollow, and dilated at one extremity, like the end of a trumpet; as the corolla of *Caprifolium sempervirens.*

TRUMPET-TREE, or TRUMPET-WOOD. *Cecropia peltata.*

TRUMPET-WEED. The name of a seaweed, *Ecklonia buccinalis*, belonging to the natural order *Laminariaceæ*, and very common and well-known at the Cape of Good Hope. The stem is often twenty feet high, and is crowned at the top by a fan-shaped cluster of leaves, ten feet or more in length. The stem of this seaweed, says Dr. Harvey, which is hollow in the upper portion, is when dried often used in the colony as a siphon, and by the native herdsmen is formed into a trumpet for collecting the cattle in the evening. A very long-necked variety of the common bottle-gourd is used in a similar manner for drawing wine from casks in Hungary, exactly after the fashion of the glass hebers which are used for taking whisky-toddy from the quaighs. The name is also applied in America to *Eupatorium purpureum.*   [M. J. B.]

TRUNCATE. Terminating very abruptly as if a piece had been cut off; as the leaf of the tulip-tree.

TRUNCUS, or TRUNK. The bole or principal stem of a tree.

TRYMA. An inferior drupe, with a two-valved separable flesh; as the walnut.

TRYMALIUM. A genus of *Rhamnaceæ,* whose component species are shrubs, natives of South-western Australia. The leaves are feather-veined, smooth above, and covered below with star-shaped hairs. The flowers are hairy, in panicles or cymose heads. Calyx with a hemispherical tube, connate with the base of the ovary, its limb divided into five spreading, ovate acute, internally coloured segments; petals five, inserted into a lobed fleshy disk; stamens five, inserted with the petals, with which they alternate; ovary partly adherent to the tube of the calyx, its free portion hairy, two to four-celled, each cell containing a single erect ovule; style two to four parted; fruit indehiscent, of four woody carpels, ultimately separating one from the other.   [M. T. M.]

TRYPETHELIUM. A fine genus of lichens distinguished by the thallus producing a number of distinct pustules arising from the medullary stratum, though often more highly coloured, in which numerous perithecia are immersed, containing a gelatinous nucleus producing asci and highly-developed sporidia. It bears almost the same relation to the genus *Verrucaria* that *Hypoxylon* does to *Sphæria.* Indeed, the resemblance of particular species to *Hypoxylon* is so close that it requires a minute examination of the crust from whence the tubercles spring to distinguish them. The species are all tropical or subtropical, extending northwards as far as South Carolina, while a single obscure species occurs in New Zealand. [M. J. B.]

TRYSLE, TRYSSIL. A native bark of Demerara used for tanning, and also as an emetic and fish-poison.

TSADA. *Eleusine coracana.*

TSAN-TJAN. *Fucus cartilaginosus.*

TSCHUDYA. A small genus of *Melastomaceæ,* differing from *Clidemia* by a few artificial characters merely, and consisting of erect shrubs indigenous to Guiana and

Brazil. They have ovate-lanceolate serrated leaves, terminal panicles, a campanulate calyx with a few obscure teeth, a five-petaled corolla, ten stamens, and a five-celled berry containing numerous angular seeds.   [B. S.]

TSHERIVELLO. A Telinga name for *Oldenlandia umbellata.*

TSHETTIK, TJETTIK. Eastern names for *Strychnos Tieuté.*

TSIN-Y. A Chinese name for *Magnolia Yulan.*

TSJAMPAC. *Michelia Champaca.*

TUALIKA. An Indian name for *Schmidelia serrata.*

TUARI, or TAUARÉ. The bast of *Lecythis Ollaria* and other species, used by the Brazilians as wrappers for cigarettes.

TUBÆFORM, TUBATE. The same as Trumpet-shaped.

TUBE. The part of a monosepalous calyx, or monopetalous corolla, formed by the union of the edges of the sepals or petals; also applied to adhesions of stamens.

TUBE-FLOWER. *Clerodendron Siphonanthus.*

TUBER. See TRUFFLES and TUBERACEI.

TUBER (adj. TUBEROUS). A roundish underground succulent stem, covered with buds, from which new plants or tubers are produced; as the potato. A receptacle of vegetable food.

TUBERACEI. A natural order of *Fungi* strictly analogous, amongst the sporidiferous kind, with the *Hypogæi* amongst the sporiferous. All the genera, with a single exception, are strictly subterraneous, and they are generally remarkable for the high development of the sporidia, which have mostly a cellular coat, either smooth, or rough with bristles. Hofmeister has observed that the threads which give rise to the fruit-bearing sacs or asci produce lateral branchlets, the tips of which become amalgamated with the walls of the sac, like the tips of the pollen-tubes with the embryo-sac in phænogams, and sometimes penetrate it like the similar branchlets in *Saprolegniæ.* He has, however, seen no active molecules in these branchlets, and therefore is unable to speak positively about their functions.

Tuberacei differ much in the complication of their hymenial surface. In some it simply lines a cavity like that of a closed *Peziza*; in others this cavity is slightly convolute, the walls still remaining distinct, and following all the sinuosities of the hymenia; in others the sinuosities are so frequent and so involved, that there appears merely to be mucedinous veins between the confluent hymenial surfaces, the whole mass being contained in a smooth or warty bark; while in others, again, all outer bark is wanting, and in one genus the hymenial surface is, as it were, turned inside out and completely exposed. Many *Tuberacei* are remarkable for their strong scent, and several are esteemed as great delicacies. No plants more amply repay a close examination, but from their subterranean habit they require much tact and patience in searching after them. Europe appears to present a maximum of species, which increase as we go southward; but a good many have been discovered in this country, principally by Messrs. Broome and Thwaites. Of exotic species we can say little, as they have not at present attracted much attention.   [M. J. B.]

TUBERCLE. Any small warty excrescence.

TUBERCLED. Covered with little excrescences or warts.

TUBERCULARIA. A spurious genus of *Fungi*, but worthy of note here on account of the extremely common occurrence of one of the supposed species, *T. vulgaris*, on dead stems of currant, gooseberry, sycamore, &c. in gardens. Though apparently perfect, as the little bright rose-coloured pustules, which burst through the bark, bear a multitude of minute spores on delicate branched threads, forming a somewhat gelatinous mass when moist on the firmer base, they are not really so ; these granules being merely conidia, and the production when fully developed bears a stratum of scarlet granulated cysts, and is then *Nectria cinnabarina*. The other *Tuberculariæ* produce species either of *Nectria*, *Hyponea*, or *Sphæria*.   [M. J. B.]

TUBERCULATED. The same as Tubercled.

TUBERCULE. Simple roots which acquire a succulent condition, become reservoirs of vegetable food, and serve for propagation, in consequence of being terminated by a bud. A little tuber.

TUBERCULUM. A wart-like shield, such as is found in the genus *Verrucaria*.

TUBÉREUSE. (Fr.) *Polianthes.* — BLEUE. *Agapanthus umbellatus.* — DES JARDINS. *Polianthes tuberosa.*

TUBERIFORM. Tuber-like.

TUBEROSE. *Polianthes tuberosa.*

TUBEROSTYLIS. The name of a genus of *Compositæ*, comprising a dwarfish herb, growing parasitically on the roots of the mangrove-trees in Darien. The heads consist of numerous perfect flowers, surrounded by an involucre of many rows of bracts—the inner ones oblong concave, the outer much shorter ovate and flat. Receptacle convex, naked : corolla tubular, five-toothed ; style arising from a thick spongy mass ; stigmas elongated, recurved, extending beyond the corollas ; fruit inversely conical, curved furrowed and rough, surmounted by a thick obscurely-toothed margin. The generic name expresses the peculiarity of the style.   [M. T. M.]

TUBEROUS. Having the succulent enlarged condition of a tuber.

TUBI, TUBULE. The pores of certain fungals ; also ringed tubes found in the globule of a *Chara*.

TUBU. The Malay name for the Sugarcane.

TUBULAR, TUBULATE, TUBULOSE. Approaching a cylindrical figure, and hollow.

. TUBULIFLORE. One of the three large suborders into which Decandolle divides the *Compositæ*. It comprises the *Corymbiferæ* and *Cynarocephalæ* of Jussieu, including those genera which have all or at least the central florets of each head regular and tubular.

TUBURCINIA. A genus of naked-spored moulds presumed to belong to the section *Ustilaginei*, with the spores or protospores either globose or conchiform, made up of minute cells. The species are, in fact, very similar to *Sporidesmia*, differing, in the typical species, in their subterranean habit, and, if they be really *Ustilaginei*, in the nature of their reproductive bodies. The scab in potatoes arises from one of the species, and another occurs in the swollen base of the stems of *Orobanche*. This is not uncommon in France, but it has not yet been detected in England. We have, however, a very distinct species, which is developed on the leaves of *Trientalis europæa*, differing from the others in its not being subterranean.   [M. J. B.]

TUCKAHOO. The America-Indian name for a curious tuberous production, which is dug out of the ground in several parts of the United States, and which has been referred by Fries to the genus *Pachyma*. Like *Sclerotium*, however, *Pachyma* has no fruit, and there is some reason to doubt whether it has any pretensions to be classed with *Fungi* at all. It is composed almost entirely of pectic acid, and it is very probable that it is a peculiar condition of some root, though of what plant has not at present been ascertained. One similar production at least has been found in China, where it is supposed to possess medicinal virtues; and there is reason to believe that another exists there, attaining a diameter of several inches, like the American Tuckahoo. As may be supposed from its chemical constitution, it affords a nutritive article of food, for which purpose it is dug up by the natives like the *Mylitta* or Native Bread of Tasmania, with which, however, it does not correspond in character. It is also employed occasionally as a material for making jelly, for which it is well adapted, the pectic acid of currants and other fruits being the principle which disposes their juice when boiled to form a jelly-like mass. The principal objection which is brought forward against the supposed phænogamous origin of the production, is the absence of all trace of vascular or cellular structure like that of phænogams, or of bark except such as may be supposed to arise from mere contact with the soil; but the dissimilarity between its structure and that of *Fungi* is quite as great, and the conversion of a fungus into pectic acid would be more surprising. [M. J. B.]

TUCKERMANNIA. A name applied to a succulent Californian herb, of the family *Compositæ.* The leaves are finely and pinnatedly divided; the involucre is double—the outer of six to eight scales, the inner of eight to ten; the receptacle is flat, scaly; the florets of the ray ligulate, three-toothed, those of the disk cylindrical, five-toothed; the stigmas hairy, surmounted by a short cone; and the fruits elliptical, winged, smooth, without pappus. [M. T. M.]

TUCUM. *Astrocaryum vulgare,* cultivated in Brazil for the fibre of its young leaves.

TUCUMA. *Astrocaryum Tucuma,* the fruit of which is eaten by the Indians of the Upper Amazon.

TUE-CHIEN. (Fr.) *Colchicum autumnale.*

TUFTED. Growing in tufts, or close dense cushion-like or tussock-like masses.

TULA. Under this name is described a little-known Peruvian herb, supposed to constitute a genus of *Cinchonaceæ.* The limb of the corolla is five-cleft, its segments toothed and crisped; anthers included; fruit capsular, two-celled, many-seeded. [M. T. M.]

TULASI. *Michelia Champaça.*

TULASNEA. A small genus of *Melastomaceæ,* consisting of herbs, probably annuals, confined to Brazil. Their stem is simple, thread-like, and either erect or ascending; the leaves are small, ovate, and obscurely serrated; and the flowers terminal, and either solitary or in panicles. The calyx is four-toothed, the corolla tetrapetalous; the number of stamens four; the capsule two-celled, two-valved, and many-seeded. [B. S.]

TULIP. *Tulipa.*

TULIPACEÆ. A name sometimes given to the whole or a portion of the order *Liliaceæ.*

TULIPA. A well-known genus of liliaceous plants; distinguished by the erect position of the anthers, and by having the stigma sessile on the ovary. *T. Gesneriana,* the Tulip of gardens, has been a favourite object of the florist's care for three centuries. Gesner, who first made it known by a botanical description and figure, saw it in A.D. 1559 at Augsburg, the seeds having been brought from the Levant. It was at that time known in Italy under the name of *tulipa,* given to it on account of its resembling a turban, 'tulbent.' In the middle of the seventeenth century, Tulips became the object of a trade such as is not to be met with again in the history of commerce, and by which their price rose above that of the most precious metals. It is a mistake, however, to suppose that the high prices paid for bulbs, amounting in some instances to 2,500 and even 4,600 florins, represented the estimated value of a root, since these large sums often changed hands without any transfer of property. Bulbs were bought and sold without being seen, without even being in existence. In fact, they were the subject of a speculation not unlike that of railway scrip in this country at no very distant date. The tulip however was, and still is, extensively cultivated, there being many hundreds of named varieties. *T. sylvestris* is considered by some botanists to be a distinct species, by others to have been derived from useless roots of *T. Gesneriana,* discarded from gardens soon after its introduction, and reverted to its natural condition. It grows wild in the South of France and other countries of Europe, and *is found,* also in a wild state, in chalk-pits in England. The flowers are yellow and fragrant; and the leaves much narrower than in any of the cultivated varieties. [C. A. J.]

TULIPE. (Fr.) *Tulipa.* — DES FLEURISTES. *Tulipa Gesneriana.* — DU CAP. *Hæmanthus.*

TULIPIER. (Fr.) *Liriodendron.* — DE VIRGINIE. *Liriodendron tulipifera.*

TULIP-TREE. *Liriodendron tulipifera;* also *Paritium elatum.* —, QUEENSLAND. *Stenocarpus Cunninghami.*

TULIP-WOOD. The striped rose-coloured wood of *Physocalymma floribunda.* —, AUSTRALIAN, or QUEENSLAND. *Cupania (Harpulia) pendula.*

TULOSTOMA. A genus of puffballs, distinguished by its paper-like peridium distinct from the tall stem, at first covered with a scaly or powdery coat or veil which soon falls away, and opening with a determinate orifice, filled with spores mixed with a few threads adherent to the peridium. The species are few, and occur in either hemisphere. *T. mammosum* is the only British species, but it is local, though not unfrequent on the tops of old mossy walls about London. In Sweden this species occurs only on vast sandy tracts, while *T. fimbriatum,* distinguished by its fringed mouth, grows on decayed heaps of seaweeds. The other species belong to Africa, Cuba, or the islands of the South Pacific Ocean. [M. J. B.]

TUM. A kind of Mastic obtained from *Pistacia atlantica.*

TUMBEKY. The narcotic leaf of a species of *Lobelia.*

TUMBO. The African name for *Welwitschia;* applied also to other plants.

TUMTUM. An Arabian name for Sumach, *Rhus Coriaria.*

TUNA. The Spanish-American name for several *Opuntias,* but adopted by botanists as the scientific designation of one of the Prickly Pears, *Opuntia Tuna.*

TUN-HOOF. *Nepeta Glechoma.*

TUNICA. A genus of *Caryophyllaceæ*, intermediate between *Dianthus* and *Gypsophila*, having the peltate seeds and straight embryo of the former, and the short few-nerved calyx of the latter. The species are natives of Europe and the Mediterranean region, and also of Central Asia. [J. T. S.]

TUNICA (adj. TUNICATE). The skin of a seed; any loose membranous skin not formed from epidermis.

TUNNA. An Indian name for the Toontree, *Cedrela Toona.*

TUPA. One of the genera of *Lobeliaceæ*, consisting of tall herbaceous plants or undershrubs, with unbranched stems, alternate lance-shaped leaves, and many-flowered leafy racemes. The calyx is five-lobed, the corolla persistent, its tube slit on the upper side, its limb bent downwards, and consisting of five petals irregularly united together—the two lateral ones spreading, all ultimately crowded together after flowering; stamens five, united together, some or all of the anthers hairy; capsule two-valved.

These plants are natives of Peru, Chili, and the West Indies. *T. Feuillei* yields an acrid poison in Chili, where the root is chewed to relieve the pain of decaying teeth. So acrid is this plant, that Feuillee says that even the odour of the flowers will cause excessive vomiting, and if taken internally, or even applied to the skin, violent inflammation and pain are produced, sometimes resulting in death. Some of these plants are grown in this country for their handsome purple scarlet yellow or greenish flowers. [M. T. M.]

TUPELO-TREE. *Nyssa.*

TUPISTRA. A genus of the group called *Aspidistreæ*, which is usually regarded as belonging to *Liliaceæ*, though differing in habit from most of the order. They are natives of India, and have thick tuberous rhizomes winged by the bases of the leaves, which are two-ranked, and resemble those of the *Zingiberaceæ*. The flowers are on a scape, dingy purple or green, with a bell-shaped six or eight-cleft perianth, having six or eight stamens inserted on the sides of its tube, and the stigma radiating and four-lobed. [J. T. S]

TURANIRA-WOOD. The timber of the Bastard Bully-tree of Guiana.

TURBINATE. The same as Top-shaped.

TURBITH. A genus of *Umbelliferæ*, containing a single species, an herbaceous plant with tripartite decompound leaves, the segments of which are very narrow and linear; and terminal umbels, which have deciduous involucres, and many-leated involucels. The calyx-tube is five-toothed and deciduous; and the petals are obovate, with an inflexed appendage. The fruit is contracted at the side, and the carpels have five obtuse equal ribs, with one vitta in the intervals and two in the commissure. The carpophore divides into two. The species is a native of the mountains of Carnia and Piedmont. [W. C.]

TURBITH BLANC. (Fr.) *Globularia Alypum.*

TURCZANINOWIA. This latinised version of the name of a celebrated Russian botanist is applied to a genus of *Compositæ*. The species is a perennial plant, native of Dahurian marshes. The leaves are entire, the flower-heads borne in a many-headed corymb, each surrounded by an involucre of linear scales; the outer florets are ligulate, entire, female, white; the central ones tubular, five-toothed, perfect and yellow; the achenes compressed, and surmounted by a pappus of silky hairs. [M. T. M.]

TURGENIA. A genus of *Umbelliferæ*, consisting of herbs, with pinnatisect leaves, and few-rayed umbels, and with the general and partial involucres having three to five leaves. The sepals are setaceous. The fruit is contracted laterally and subdidymamous; the carpels have five primary ridges with a single row of prickles, and four large secondary ones with two or three rows of prickles. In other respects the characters of the genus are as in *Caucalis*, of which it is by many considered only a section. The species are natives of the Mediterranean region. [W. C.]

TURIO. A scaly sucker, which afterwards becomes a stem; as in asparagus.

TURKEY-BERRY. A West Indian name for *Solanum torvum* and *S. mammosum.*

TURKEY-BERRY TREE. *Cordia Collococca.*

TURKEY-BLOSSOM. A West Indian name for *Tribulus cistoides.*

TURKEY-FEATHER LAVER. The common name of *Padina pavonia.*

TURK'S-CAP. *Melocactus communis*; also *Lilium Martagon.*

TURK'S-HEAD. *Melocactus communis.*

TURMERIC. A medicinal and tinctorial substance obtained from the root of *Curcuma longa.* It forms one of the chief ingredients in the preparation of Indian curry-stuff or curry-powder, to which it imparts its yellowish hue.

TURMERIC-TREE. A species of *Zieria.*

TURNEP. *Brassica Rapa.*

TURNERACEÆ. (*Turnerads*). A small order of polypetalous dicotyledons, consisting of tropical herbs or undershrubs, chiefly American or African, with alternate leaves, and yellowish or blue axillary flowers. They agree with *Passifloraceæ*, *Homaliaceæ*, and some others in their petals alternating with the lobes of a campanulate or tubular calyx, and in their one-celled ovary with three parietal placentas; and are chiefly remarkable for their forked styles. It is doubtful whether the two or three small genera associated with *Turnera* in the order, should not be rather treated as sections only of that genus, which has a considerable number of species chiefly Brazilian, but mostly of a weedy aspect.

TURNERA. This genus gives its name to the order *Turneraceæ*, and consists of herbs or undershrubs inhabiting the West Indies and South America. The leaves are notched or sometimes more deeply cleft, and provided with two small glands at the base. The flowers arise singly from the axils of the leaves, and are either sessile or stalked, in which latter case the flower-stalk is often adherent to the leaf-stalk. Very rarely the flowers are in terminal racemes. The calyx is coloured and five-parted; the petals and stamens five, attached to the calyx; ovary free, one-celled, with three parietal placentas; styles three; stigmas three, fan-shaped; capsule one-celled, bursting into three pieces.

Several species are in cultivation in greenhouses, and have for the most part yellow flowers. An infusion of the leaves of *T. opifera* is employed as an astringent by the natives of Brazil. *T. ulmifolia* is also considered to have tonic and expectorant properties.   [M. T. M.]

TURNIP. *Brassica Rapa.* —, DEVIL'S. *Bryonia dioica.* —, FRENCH. A variety of *Brassica Napus.* —, INDIAN. *Arisæma atrorubens*; also applied to the tubers of *Psoralea esculenta.* —, LION'S. The tuberous roots of *Leontice.* —, PRAIRIE. The tubers of *Psoralea esculenta.* —, ST. ANTHONY'S. *Ranunculus bulbosus.* —, SWEDISH. *Brassica campestris rutabaga.*

TURNIP-RADISH. A variety of *Raphanus sativus.*

TURNIP-SHAPED. Napiform.

TURNIP-TOPS. The young green leaves of the common or Swedish turnips, eaten as a vegetable by the working classes.

TURNSOLE. A purple dye-drug, the inspissated juice of *Crozophora tinctoria*; also an old name for *Euphorbia helioscopia.*

TURPENTINE. A resinous exudation, which flows from incisions made in the stem of trees of the pine family. —, BOSTON. American Turpentine, obtained from *Pinus palustris* and *P. Tæda.* —, BOURDEAUX. A resin obtained from *Pinus Pinaster.* —, CHIO, SCIO, or CYPRUS. The limpid fragrant balsamic resin of *Pistacia Terebinthus.* —, STRASBURGH. A resin obtained from *Abies pectinata.* —, VENETIAN. An oleo-resin obtained from *Abies Larix*, the common Larch.

TURPENTINE-TREE. *Pistacia Terebinthus*; also *Bursera gummifera.* —, AUSTRALIAN. *Tristania albicans.*

TURPENTINE VESSELS. Tubes formed in the interstices of tissue, into which turpentine, or such secretions, are naturally drained during the growth of a plant. They are common in conifers.

TURPINIA. This genus of *Staphyleaceæ*, named in compliment to M. Turpin, a well-known French naturalist and artist, consists of certain West Indian and tropical Asiatic trees or shrubs, bearing white flowers in terminal panicles. These have a coloured five-parted calyx; five petals, inserted upon a ten-lobed disk, as also are the five flattened awl-shaped filaments of the stamens; a sessile three-lobed ovary, with numerous ovules in the inner corner of each compartment; three styles, and a succulent three-celled fruit, with two or three seeds in each cell. The fruit of some of these plants is edible. [M. T. M.]

TURQUETTE. (Fr.) *Herniaria glabra.*

TURQUOISE. (Fr.) A kind of Olive.

TURRÆA. A genus of *Meliaceæ*, the species of which belong exclusively to the Old World, and are nearly all tropical. They are either shrubs or trees, sometimes of large size; and have entire or bluntly-lobed leaves, and usually large flowers, variously disposed on lateral stalks. The flowers have a five-toothed calyx; five long strap-like petals, twisted round each other previous to expanding; a long cylindrical stamen-tube, slit into ten at the top and having the anthers inside, opposite the slits, each anther being tipped by a single or double strap-like prolongation; and a five ten or twenty-celled ovary bearing a slender style, and a club-shaped or round stigma.   [A. S.]

TURRITIS. The plants of this genus of *Cruciferæ* are closely allied to *Arabis*, from which they mainly differ in having their seeds arranged in two rows in a linear pod. The species are unimportant weeds, with clasping leaves, somewhat arrow-shaped at the base, and elongated racemes of white or sulphur-coloured flowers. *T. glabra*, or Tower Mustard, is a plant of wide distribution, being a native throughout Europe in dry exposed situations, on banks and by roadsides in many parts of Britain, and of North America from Hudson's Bay to the Rocky Mountains. It grows from one to two feet high, and has glaucous leaves (of which the radical ones are toothed at the base, the upper arrow-shaped), and yellowish-white flowers. There are several other species. French: *Tourrette*; German: *Thurnkraut.*   [C. A. J.]

TURTLE-HEAD. *Chelone.*

TURUNJABINS. An Indian name for the Manna of the desert, obtained from the Camel's Thorn, *Alhagi Camelorum.*

TURWAR. A tanning bark obtained in India from *Cassia auriculata.*

TUSO SO. The Japanese name for *Stauntonia.*

TUSSILAGE. (Fr.) *Tussilago.*

TUSSILAGO. The Coltsfoot, a common and in many places a troublesome weed, the existence of which indicates a clayey soil. *T. Farfara*, the only British species, sends up very early in spring a short erect flower-stalk four to six inches high, imbricated with scales, and bearing at its summit a single large bright-yellow radiated flower-head; as this dies away the stalk elongates, and finally bears a head of white serrated pappus-hairs, much employed by goldfinches in lining their nests. The leaves, which appear after the flowers, are all radical, broadly heart-shaped, angular, and toothed: beneath they are thickly clothed with white cottony down, which was formerly used (being previously dipped in a solution of saltpetre) as tinder. The leaves themselves are still employed in rural districts as a remedy for asthma, either smoked or in the form of an infusion. There are several foreign species, which in habit resemble *T. Farfara*. The Butter Bur, formerly called *T. Petasites*, is now sometimes placed in a distinct genus, PETASITES: which see. [C. A. J.]

TUTSAN. *Androsæmum officinale.*

TUTSANS. Lindley's name for the order *Hypericaceæ.*

TUTUMA. An American name for *Crescentia Cujete.*

TUWAK. A Malay name for the toddy obtained from *Arenga saccharifera.*

TUYE. (Fr.) *Ulex europæus.*

TUZELLE BLANCHE DE PROVENCE. (Fr.) A kind of Wheat.

TWAYBLADE. *Listera.*

TWEEDIA. Twining shrubs, natives of Chili, and belonging to the family *Asclepiadaceæ.* They have very pointed fleshy leaves, and handsome blue flowers, arranged in umbels. The corolla is large bell-shaped five-cleft, hairy externally, and with five fleshy appendages within; the anthers have a membranous wing at their summits; and the stigma is pointed and cleft. *T. cærulea* and *T. versicolor* are in cultivation in this country. [M. T. M.]

TWICE-WRITHEN. *Polygonum Bistorta.*

TWIGGY. Consisting of numerous small slender branchlets.

TWIG-RUSH. *Cladium Mariscus.*

TWIN DIGITATO-PINNATE. When the secondary petioles, on the sides of which the leaflets are arranged, proceed in twos from the summit of a common petiole; as in *Mimosa purpurea.*

TWIN-FLOWER. An American name for *Linnæa.*

TWINING. Ascending by means of spiral convolutions around a supporting body.

TWIN-LEAF. *Jeffersonia.*

TWISTED-STALK. *Streptopus.*

TWO-LIPPED. When a tubular body, as a calyx and corolla, is parted at the mouth so as to form two divisions.

TYDÆA. A genus of herbaceous plants belonging to the *Gesneraceæ*, and inhabiting the mountains of New Grenada. We are at present acquainted with only four species, all inmates of our gardens, where they are better known under their old name of *Achimenes*, the most widely diffused being *T. picta* (*Achimenes picta*). They are erect robust herbs, with fine blotched leaves, and axillary bright-coloured flowers. The calyx is connate with the ovary, the corolla almost funnel-shaped and five-lobed; the stamens are included, the ovary surrounded by five glands, the stigma five-cleft, and the fruit a capsule. [B. S.]

TYLE-BERRY. *Jatropha multifida.*

TYLOCHILUS. *Cyrtopodium.*

TYLOPHORA. A considerable genus of *Asclepiadaceæ*, confined to the tropical and warm regions of the Old World; and consisting of twining mostly thin-leaved herbs or shrubs, bearing slender flower-stalks proceeding from between the leaves, and having umbels of small flowers disposed alternately along them. It is characterised by the staminal corona consisting of five simple acuminate fleshy leaflets, more or less united to the gynostegium, and usually shorter than it; by the pollen-masses, which are very small and swollen (hence the name, from *tylos* 'a swelling,' and *phoreo* 'to bear'), being transverse subascending or erect; and by the pointless stigma. The fruits are smooth, compressed, and attenuated at the apex.

T. asthmatica, a twining shrubby species with slender branches, native of the Indian Peninsula, Ceylon, and the Moluccas, yields a strong white silky fibre resembling that of the yercum (*Calotropis gigantea*). Its roots also possess valuable medicinal properties, acting in large doses as an emetic (in consequence of which they are substituted in India for Ipecacuanha), and in smaller doses, as a cathartic. They have been successfully employed in epidemic dysentery, and are said to have a good effect in humoral asthma. The Cingalese call the plant Binooga, and the natives of Madras Koorinja. Two varieties are distinguished by botanists: one being everywhere covered, except upon the upper surface of the leaves, with soft close-pressed down, and the other quite free of down in every part. [A. S.]

TYMPANANTHE. *Dictyanthus.*

TYMPANUM. A membrane which stretches across the mouth of the spore-case of some urn-mosses.

TYPHACEÆ. (*Typhæ, Typhineæ, Typhoids*). An order of monocotyledons, consisting of reed-like herbs growing in marshes ditches or shallow water, with long narrow parallel veined leaves, and small flowers densely packed in cylindrical spikes or globular heads. In structure they come near to *Aracea*. The flowers are monœcious, without any perianth, unless the small scales or tufts of hairs intermixed with the stamens and ovaries be regarded as such. The ovary tapers into a slender simple style, and ripens into a small nut with a single pendulous seed: the embryo is straight, lying in copious albumen. There are very few species, but some of them are dispersed over nearly all parts of the globe. They form two genera, *Typha* and *Sparganium*.

TYPHA. Tall herbaceous aquatics giving name to the order *Typhaceæ*, and distinguished by bearing the stamens and pistils in separate flowers but on the same plant; either forming a continuous spike or spadix shaped like a constable's mace, with the barren flowers in the upper part, or an interrupted spadix with the barren flowers above, the fertile below, the point of interruption. There are two British species, *T. latifolia* and *T. angustifolia*—often popularly but erroneously called Bulrush, which name properly belongs to the genus *Scirpus* — common, especially the former, on the borders of ponds and lakes, where with their singular large terminal spikes (called from their form Cat's-tail, or Reed-mace), they present a most picturesque appearance, and are often selected by artists to indicate the presence of water. *T. latifolia* grows to the height of five or six feet; its spikes are continuous, leaves very long linear and nearly plane. In the other species, which is smaller, the spike is interrupted, and the leaves are grooved. French : *Massette* ; German : *Rohrkolbe*.　　　[C. A. J.]

TYPHONIUM. This name is applied to a genus of *Araceæ*, differing from *Arum* principally in having a single erect ovule, arising from the base of the ovary. The upper part of the spadix too is more sharply pointed than in *Arum*. The species of this genus are Indian herbs, with perennial fleshy rootstocks, and petiolate heart-shaped leaves whose sheathing stalks encircle the base of the long-peduncled spadix. The spathe is uniform in colour, and not spotted. The rootstocks of *T. orixense* are very acrid, and are used in India as an application to scirrhous tumours.　　[M. T. M.]

TYRIA. A genus of Peruvian shrubs of the family *Vacciniaceæ*. The leaves are scattered, and thick in texture; the flowers grow in tufts. The tube of the calyx is marked by ten ribs, its limb five-parted, the segments lance-shaped, withering ; the corolla is cylindrical, five-cleft ; stamens ten, within the corolla, the filaments combined below into a shallow cup; and the anthers two-celled below, one-celled above, opening by a pore at the top ; ovary ten-ribbed, with five compartments.　　[M. T. M.]

TZONTECOMATL. A Mexican cosmetic prepared from the seeds of *Swietenia Mahagoni* mixed with oil.

UBI. The Malay name for Yam. — BUNGALA. The Potato.

UBRIDI. A Guiana name for the astringent bark of the Wild Cashew-tree.

UDIKA-BREAD. *Irvingia Barteri*.

UDORA. M. Caspary, in a recent monograph of the order *Hydrocharidaceæ*, combines the present genus with *Anacharis*, and restores the old name *Elodea*, which

Nuttall changed to *Udora*, in consequence of his incorrectly supposing that *Elodea* had previously been assigned by Adanson to a genus of tutsans. Ten species of *Elodea* (otherwise *Udora*) are described by Caspary—all aquatic perennial plants growing below the surface of the water, and inhabiting fresh-water rivers and lakes in various parts of both North and South America. *Elodea canadensis* of Richard includes, amongst others, the plant called *Udora canadensis* by Nuttall in America, and *Anacharis Alsinastrum* by Babington in England. It proves to be a great pest in still waters, choking up the stream by its rapid growth, and impeding navigation. See ANACHARIS.　　　[A. S.]

UFYOON. An Arabic name for Opium.

UGENA. *Lygodium.*

UGNI. A genus founded on a single Chilian species, which was at first referred to *Myrtus* (from which it differs in the structure of the embryo) and afterwards to *Eugenia*, to which it is so nearly allied that there seems no good reason for separating it. The calyx has four linear divisions, not five as Turczaninow makes it; there are five roundish obovate petals ; the numerous stamens have flattened filaments and two-celled anthers ; the subulate style has the apex incurved, and surmounted by an acute stigma. The berry, crowned with the persistent calyx, has four cells, each nearly subdivided by the projecting placenta, and containing six to eight seeds having a hard testa, and a curved exalbuminous embryo, with the cotyledons and short radicle blended into a solid mass. The species *Eugenia Ugni* has very agreeably-flavoured aromatic fruit, and some attempts have been made to introduce it into general cultivation. [W. C.]

UGOORO. An Indian name for Eaglewood and Aloes-wood.

UHDEA. A Mexican genus of *Compositæ*, comprising an undershrub, with much-divided hairy leaves, and yellow capitulate flowers, the heads arranged in a definite corymb at the ends of the branches. The genus is most nearly allied to *Actinomeris*, from which, however, it differs in habit, and in the ovary, which is destitute of pappus.　　　[M. T. M.]

ULANTHA. *Chloræa.*

ULE. A tree from which Caoutchouc is obtained : supposed to be *Castilloa elastica*.

ULEX. A genus of prickly shrubs belonging to the order *Leguminosæ*, distinguished by their two-parted calyx bearing two minute bracts at the base, and their turgid few-seeded legume. *U. europæus*, the Common Furze, Whin, or Gorse, is one of the few British social plants sufficiently important to give a name to the localities on which it fixes, a ' Furze-brake' being a characteristic feature of English landscape. Harsh and rugged though Furze be in appearance, it has by no means a wide geographical range. Even in North Britain it dwindles in size, and in the more exposed regions is hardly known. In Russia and Sweden it occurs only as a greenhouse plant, and even in the South of England an unseasonably severe frost nips the flowers or sometimes destroys all the exposed part of the plant. Unlike the spines of *Prunus* and *Mespilus*, which are modifications of branches, and the prickles of *Rubus* and *Rosa*, which are simply extensions of the cuticle, the thorns of Furze represent leaves. The true leaves are minute, situated at the base of the thorns, and most observable in young seedlings.

U. europæus is distinguished by the two bracts at the base of the calyx being ovate concave and somewhat spreading. The double-flowered Furze of gardens is a variety of this species, as is also the Irish Furze, distinguished by the softness of its upright branches. *U. nana*, the Dwarf Furze, called also French Furze, is a much smaller plant, specifically distinguished by its minute adpressed bracts. The flowers are of a deeper yellow, and expand in the greatest profusion at the season when heath is in blossom, with which it harmonises beautifully in colouring. French: *Ajonc*: German: *Stechginster*. [O. A. J.]

U. europæus, the young leaves of which are trifoliolate, like so many others of the order, has been much recommended for cultivation, and especially on soils almost too poor to grow anything else. In the *Cyclopædia of Agriculture* we find it thus noticed: 'When regularly cut down every year, the annual shoots, mown as wanted, and bruised to deaden the prickles, supply a green food throughout the winter, which all animals, and especially horses, are particularly fond of. When cultivated the seeds sown are either collected from the wild plants, or from a variety which, by successive cultivation, has become rather more succulent and productive.' Our own observations on the use of both the wild and the cultivated Furze as food for cattle, lead to the conclusion that its feeding properties are too low to render its gathering and preparation at all a remunerative matter: still less does its value at all warrant the purchase of crushing machinery, which has been invented for bruising the prickly plant. [J. B.]

ULIGINOSE. Growing in swampy places.

ULLAT-KUMU. An Indian name for *Abroma augusta.*

ULLPU. A drink obtained from the farina of the seeds of *Milium nigricans.*

ULLUCO. The Peruvian name of *Ullucus tuberosus.*

ULLUCUS. A genus of *Basellaceæ,* synonymous with **MELLOCA**: which see. Ulluco and Melloca are native names for the best-known species, which is a fleshy Peruvian herb, with a stem throwing out thread-like branches, which when they enter the earth produce edible tubers. The plant is extensively cultivated for these tubers in the Andes of Peru and Bolivia, under the name of Oca-quina. They are

about the size of a hazel-nut, waxy, and of a yellow colour. When the failure of the potato was dreaded, this plant was one of the substitutes proposed; but the tubers proved far less agreeable to British palates than might have been supposed from the de-

Ullucus tuberosus.

mand for them in South America, where they are used by the Indians in the preparation of Chuña, a starchy substance obtained by alternately freezing and steeping them. A second species, *U. peruvianus,* is possibly not distinct from *U. tuberosus.* [J. T. S.]

ULMACEÆ. (*Celtideæ, Elmworts.*) A small order of apetalous dicotyledons, considered by some botanists as a suborder of *Urticaceæ* but differing from them in their hermaphrodite flowers; by others the two groups are widely separated. They are all trees or shrubs, with rough alternate leaves, furnished with stipules, and small green or brown flowers in loose clusters or cymes. They have a small calyx-like often irregular perianth, definite stamens, and a free ovary, either one or two-celled, but always with two styles or stigmas. They consist of two tribes, raised by some botanists to the rank of natural orders: the *Ulmeæ* proper, with a two-celled ovary—including *Ulmus* and four or five other genera, dispersed over the temperate regions of the Northern Hemisphere, and often very valuable timber-trees; and the *Celtideæ*, with a one-celled ovary, many of them tropical, comprising four or five genera, of which the most extensive are *Celtis* and *Sponia.*

ULMAIRE. (Fr.) *Spiræa Ulmaria.*

ULMUS. A genus of lofty trees giving name to the order *Ulmaceæ*, to be distinguished among other British trees in March and April by their purplish-brown flowers, which, though small, are so numerous as to tinge the whole tree; in April by their green membranous leaf-like seed-vessels; and all the summer by their harsh serrated pointed simple leaves, which are unequal at the base. Much difference of opinion exists among botanists as to which of the Elms should be considered species, and which varieties.

The Common Elm, *U. campestris*, is the most generally diffused species, though said to have been introduced into Britain by the Crusaders. It is a lofty upright tree, composed of many tiers of spreading branches, which often hang in graceful festoons at the extremities; the winged seed-vessel (samara) is deeply cleft; the leaves are rough to the touch, and taper to a point. The young twigs are downy, and sometimes slightly corky. The Cornish Elm has its flower-buds arranged more

Ulmus campestris.

regularly on the twigs than the last; the leaves are much smaller, more evenly notched, and nearly smooth; the branches are generally rigid erect and compact. The Wych Elm, *U. montana*, is well distinguished from the preceding by its numerous spreading branches, which frequently droop so as to conceal the main trunk; its flowers are in looser tufts than those of the common elm, and the seed-vessel differs materially in being only slightly notched. The leaves are much larger, tapering to a sharp point, and nearly equal at the base. The Cork-barked Elm is in habit intermediate between the common and wych elms, being more spreading than the former, but not so much so as the latter. The leaves are large, but the best distinctive character is afforded by the branches, which when one year old are very hairy, and in the second year are thickly coated with a cracked corky excrescence, from which the tree derives its name.

The Elm was held in high estimation by the ancients, partly for the sake of its leaves, which were dried and employed as fodder, and partly for the use to which the tree itself was applied, namely, as a prop for vines. The former custom still obtains in some parts of the Continent; but the Elm is now principally valued for its timber, which is not only tough, but remarkable for its durability under water. Hence it is employed in naval architecture. It was formerly much used in making water-pipes, but of late years it has been superseded by cast-iron pipes. The Elm, growing in a forest and in good soil, arrives

at perfection in 150 years, but it will live for 500 or even 600 years. It retains its foliage till late in the autumn, the leaves assuming a rich yellowish hue some time before they fall from the tree. The Common and Cornish Elms are considered to afford the best timber. The American Elm was introduced into England in A.D. 1752. It is distinguished by its seed-vessel being fringed at the edge with hairs. French: *Orme*; German: *Ulme*.   [C. A. J.]

The Elm, though one of our commonest trees, is nevertheless a doubtful native; for, in the language of old Aubrey:—'I never did see an elme that grew spontaneously in a wood, as oakes, ashes, beeches, &c., which consideration made me reflect that they are exotique; but by whom were they brought into this island? Not by the Saxons; for upon enquiry I am informed that there are none in Saxony, nor in Denmarke, nor yet in France, spontaneous; but in Italy they are naturall—e.g. in Lombardie, &c. Wherefore I am induced to believe that they were brought hither out of Italy by the Romans, who were cultivators of their colonies. The Saxons understood not nor cared for such improvements, nor yet had hardly leisure if they would.'—Aubrey's *Wiltshire*, cap. ix.

As regards the species of Elm, authors are by no means agreed. We are, however, inclined to think that the two following may stand at the head of two groups, about which the many forms which occur in our estates and shrubberies may be ranged as varieties. These are *U. campestris*, the English Elm, distinguished by its aspiring method of growth; and *U. montana*, the Scotch Elm, a shorter tree with more or

Ulmus montana.

less pendent branches. Both of these kinds occasionally attain to enormous dimensions, rivalling even the oak in size, and both have warm admirers as contributing to the beauty of forest scenery. As timber-trees both the English and Scotch Elms are employed extensively, but the former is the favourite in this respect, and we think it decidedly more profitable to grow for timber.

Before we possessed our *Gardener's Chro-*

nicles, to point out to us the garden operations for each month, the budding of the
Elm was a matter for the gardener to note
warily; for, as say the old rhymes :—

> 'When the Elmen leaf is as big as a farding
> 'Tis time to sow kidney-beans in the garding.'.
> When the Elmen leaf is as big as a penny
> You must sow kidney-beans if you aim to have
> any.'

So the farmer derived a lesson from the
Elm-leaf, as thus :—

> 'When the Elmen leaf is as big as a mouse's ear
> Then to sow barley never fear.'
> 'When the Elmen leaf is as big as an ox's eye
> Then say I, High boys, high!'

The *Ulmus montana* is often called the
Wych Elm and Witch Hazle, probably
from the similarity of its leaves to those of
the hazel-nut; and hence, like it, its twigs
were formerly employed as riding-switches
to ensure good luck on the journey. Had
Tam O'Shanter but possessed this, he
could not possibly have lost his horse's
tail! Forked branches of Wych Elm, as
of hazel, were used as divining-rods, and
formed the *virgula divinitoria* of the ex-
perts. A more practical use for its branches was that of converting them into long
bows, the archer esteeming the elm next to
the yew for that purpose. [J. B.]

ULNA (adj. ULNARIS). The average
length of a man's arm; about twenty-four
inches.

ULSEE. An Indian name for Flax.

ULVACEÆ. A natural order of green-
spored *Algæ*, characterised by their flat or
tubular green or rarely purple membranous frond, which never throws out rootlets at the base, consisting of cells which
are divided both vertically and horizontally,
and generally in fours. The fruit consists
of zoospores furnished with two or four
lash-shaped appendages. In some species
both these kinds of spores occur. Thuret
has observed both germinating, but Robin
believes that these with two cilia have
the office of impregnation. In *Prasiola*
and *Bangia* the frond is very narrow and
sometimes filiform, but there is every
gradation, from threads with a single row
of quaternate cells to the large frond of
Ulva latissima. In *Tetraspora* the gelatinous element predominates so much that
we have a close approach to the palmelloid
Algæ. Ulvaceæ are distributed all over the
globe, occurring both in salt and fresh water, and a few grow on the damp ground or
on rocks, where they are occasionally dry.
No *Algæ* are more thoroughly citizens of
the world. [M. J. B.]

ULVA. The typical genus of the natural
order *Ulvaceæ*. It is distinguished from
Porphyra principally by its green colour,
and from *Enteromorpha* by its flat frond.
In one or two species, however, the frond
is shaped like a sac when young and becomes flat by the rupture of the apex, and
some states of *U. Linza* come very near to
Enteromorpha intestinalis. Ulva is sometimes divided into two genera: *Ulva*
proper, in which the frond consists of a
single stratum of cells, and *Phycoseris*, in
which there are two strata. Most of the
species are marine and very widely diffused, but *U. bullosa* (so-called from its being
swollen out with bubbles of oxygen disengaged from its frond) and one or two
more grow in fresh water, and are very
nearly related to *Tetraspora*. The most
familiar species is probably *U. Lactuca*,
which from its being frequently attached
to oysters is called Oyster-Green. This and
U. latissima are sometimes eaten like the
true Laver, under the name of Green Laver.
It is also used occasionally in Scotland as
a sort of water-dressing bound round the
temples, and is considered efficacious as
a remedy for headache. [M. J. B.]

ULVE MARINE. (Fr.) *Ulva Lactuca* and
other seaweeds.

UMBAREE. An Indian name for the
fibre of *Hibiscus cannabinus*; also for inferior hemp.

UMBEL. An inflorescence in which the
stalks radiate from a common point, and
the expansion of the flowers is centripetal.

UMBELLATÆ. The Linnæan name for
the *Umbelliferæ*.

UMBELLATE. Arranged in an umbel.

UMBELLIFERÆ. See APIACEÆ. This
is one of the most natural and, consequently, one of the most easily recognised
of the orders of plants, but one of the most
difficult to divide into well-defined genera.
It consists of herbs, often strongly scented,
with small flowers, usually in a simple or
compound umbel, which has given the
name to the order, although this umbel is
sometimes contracted into a dense head,
while in a very few species this normal
inflorescence is departed from. The ovary
is two-celled, with a single pendulous ovule
in each cell, and is crowned by two styles
on the top of the disk. The fruit always
separates into two dry one-seeded carpels
or mericarps, resembling seeds, as they
are popularly but erroneously called. The
real seed is inside, closely adhering to the
outer pericarp; it has a minute embryo in
the base of the horny albumen. The mericarps are furnished with a definite number
of raised longitudinal ribs, and underneath the intervening channels are frequently placed elongated receptacles for
essential oil, called vittæ, remarkably constant in each species in their number and
position. It is chiefly from the arrangement of these ribs and vittæ, and from
the shape of the enclosed albumen, that
modern botanists have derived the characters by which the numerous genera of
Umbelliferæ are distinguished.

Though mostly herbs, these plants sometimes attain gigantic size, as in some species of *Heracleum*, and the *Angelica* represented in Plate 16. Dr. Welwitsch, moreover, mentions having found in Tropical
Africa, in the region of Golungo Alto, an
arboreous umbellifer, with a stem one to

one-and-a-half foot thick, which is prized highly by the natives for its medicinal properties and its value as a timber-tree. This, so far as is at present known, is the most gigantic plant of the order.

UMBELLIFEROUS. Bearing umbels.

UMBELLULE. A partial umbel; an umbel formed at the end of one of the rays of a general umbel.

UMBER-BROWN. Nearly the same as deep brown,

UMBILICAL CORD. A thread by which seeds are sometimes attached to their placenta.

UMBILICARIA. See TRIPE DE ROCHE and GYROPHORA. *Umbilicaria* is, in fact, a *Gyrophora* without the convolute disks of that genus. [M. J. B.]

UMBILICATE. The same as Peltate.

UMBILICUS. The hilum of a seed; the scar formed by its separation from the placenta.

UMBILICUS. Herbs, indigenous to the South of Europe and the Levant, belonging to the order *Crassulaceæ*. The characters are—Calyx five-parted; corolla bell-shaped, with five acute lobes; stamens ten, inserted in the corolla: nectariferous scales five, obtuse; carpels five, tapering to a point. Some of the species have the radical leaves rosulate, or disposed like the petals in the flower of a double rose; others have them alternate on the stalk; in all they are fleshy; and the flowers, which are either white or yellow, grow in simple or branched racemes. They principally affect dry stony places, on which account they are often employed in the decoration of artificial rockeries. [C. A. J.]

UMBONATE. Round, with a projecting point in the centre, like the boss or *umbo* of an ancient shield; as the pileus of many species of *Agaricus*.

UMBONULATE. Terminated by a very small boss or nipple.

UMBRACULIFORM. Umbrella-shaped; that is to say, hemispherical, with rays or plaits proceeding from a common centre; resembling an expanded umbrella; as the stigma of *Sarracenia*.

UMBRACULUM. A convex body, which in *Marchantia* terminates the seta, and bears the reproductive bodies on the underside; also any similar body.

UMBRELLA-LEAF. *Diphylleia cymosa.*

UMBRELLA-SHAPED. The same as Umbraculiform.

UMBRELLA-TREE. *Magnolia Umbrella* and *M. tripetala*; also *Thespesia populnea* and *Pandanus odoratissimus.* —, GUINEA. *Paritium guineense.*

UMBRELLAWORT. *Oxybaphus.*

UMBRINUS. Umber-brown.

UMBROSUS. Growing in shady places.

UMIRI. A Brazilian name for *Humirium floribundum.*

UMLEE, or UMLI. Indian names for the Tamarind.

UMRITI. An Indian name for the Emblic Myrobalan, *Emblica officinalis.*

UNARMED. Having no spines, prickles, or other sharp hard projections. It sometimes means pointless.

UNCARIA. This generic name was first given to a group of Indian and American climbing plants with hooked spines, belonging to the *Cinchonaceæ*, one of which affords the astringent masticating or tanning material called Gambir or Terra Japonica; but as these plants agree in their principal technical characters with

Uncaria Gambir.

the older Linnæan genus *Nauclea*, they are combined with it by most botanists. They, however, form a well-marked section of that genus, characterised by their climbing habit, and by their old or barren flower-stalks being converted into hard woody spines, directed downwards so as to form hooks. Their flower-heads also are not so dense, and their fruits are narrowed or stalked at the base. See NAUCLEA.

The name *Uncaria*, being thus disengaged, was afterwards given to a South African plant, *U. procumbens*, the sole representative of a genus of *Pedaliaceæ*, commonly known as the Grapple-plant at the Cape of Good Hope and in other parts of South Africa, on account of its very curious fruits being furnished on all sides with strong-branched very sharp hooks, by means of which they lay hold of the clothes of travellers or the skin of animals, and adhere so tenaciously that they are difficult to remove. Dr. Livingstone says that when these fruits happen to lay hold of the mouth of an ox, the animal stands and roars with pain and a sense of helplessness. The plant was first described by Burchell, and named *Uncaria* from the Latin word *uncus* ' a hook '; but Decandolle, who retained the name *Uncaria* for the cinchonal genus above alluded to, afterwards changed it to *Harpagophytum*, from the Greek *arpax* ' to seize ' and *phyton* ' a plant.' It is a prostrate herb, with opposite five-nerved hand-shaped leaves, and purple flowers borne singly on short stalks rising from the leaf-axils. The flowers have a small persistent five-parted calyx, with narrow lobes, one of which is shorter than the rest : a tubular or funnel-shaped corolla, not puffed out at the base, with a nearly equal five-lobed limb: four stamens, in two pairs of different lengths; and a stigma formed of two plates. The fruit contains an indefinite number of angular wrinkled seeds. [A. S.]

UNCATE, UNCIFORM, UNCINATE. Hooked ; curved suddenly back at the point.

UNCI. Hooked hairs ; any kind of hook.

UNCIA (adj. UNCIALIS). An inch.

UNCINIA. A genus of cyperaceous plants belonging to the tribe *Caricinæ*. The spikes of inflorescence are solitary terminal erect, simple androgynous, the upper male, the lower female ; scales one-flowered, imbricated ; stamens three : styles three, rarely two-cleft ; achenes convex or triangular. Steudel describes twenty-nine species, mostly natives of the Southern Hemisphere. [D. M.]

UNCTUOUS. Having a surface which, though not actually greasy, feels so.

UNDERSHRUB. A woody plant of small size, the ends of whose branches perish every year. See SUFFRUTEX.

UNDULATE, UNDULATING. Wavy ; having an uneven alternately convex and concave margin or surface.

UNDULATO-STRIATE. Having elevated lines with a wavy direction.

UNEQUAL-SIDED. The same as Oblique.

UNGERIA. This genus, named in compliment to the Professor of Botany at Vienna, includes a tree, native of Norfolk Island, having thick entire leaves, shining above, and covered below with stellate downy hairs, the stipules deciduous. The flowers are rose-coloured, growing in terminal panicles ; the calyx club-shaped or bell-shaped, its limb five-cleft, somewhat two-lipped ; the petals five, stalked, longer than the calyx, their limb spreading and destitute of scales ; the stamens united into a tube, adherent below to the stalk supporting the ovary, dilated above, five-cleft, each segment bearing within three anthers ; the ovary stalked five-lobed five-celled, each cell with a single ovule. Fruit capsular, five-valved, five-seeded. The genus is included in *Sterculiaceæ*. [M. T. M.]

UNGEROOT. An Arabic name for Gum Sarcocol.

UNGNADIA. The name of a genus of *Sapindaceæ*, consisting of a North American tree related to *Æsculus*, with unequally pinnate leaves, and lateral racemes of flowers. The flowers are polygamous : each has a five-parted calyx, three stalked unequal petals, whose stalks are provided with a little crest ; nine stamens adhering to the stalk of the ovary, and to a sheathing scale-like process originating from the thalamus ; and a stalked three-celled ovary, with two ascending ovules in each cell. The fruit is unknown. [M. T. M.]

UNGOOR. A Persian name for a kind of Grape.

UNGOOZEH. A Persian name for Asafœtida.

UNGUICULATE. A term exclusively applied to petals which have an unguis or stalk.

UNGUIS. Half-an-inch, or the length of the nail of the little finger ; also the stalk of a petal.

UNHA DE BOY. A Brazilian name for the mucilaginous leaves of *Caulotretus microstachyus*.

UNI. In Latin compounds = one : as *unialatus*, having one wing ; *unicalcaratus*; one spur ; *unicapsularis*, one capsule, and so on.

UNICOLOR. Uniformly of one and the same colour.

UNICORN-PLANT. *Martynia*.

UNICORN-ROOT. The root of *Helonias dioica*, used in North America as an anthelmintic.

UNICORN'S-HORN. *Helonias dioica*.

UNICUS. Growing singly.

UNIFOLIATE, UNIFOLIOLATE. When a compound leaf consists of one leaflet only ; as in the orange-tree.

UNIJUGATE, UNIJUGUS. Having one pair of leaflets. See CONJUGATE.

UNILATERAL. One-sided.

UNINERVATE, UNINERVIS. One-ribbed.

UNINTERRUPTED. Consisting of regularly increasing or diminishing parts, or of parts all of the same size. See CONTINUOUS.

UNIOLA. A genus of grasses belonging to the tribe *Festuceæ*. The inflorescence is in panicles or racemes ; spikelets three to twenty-flowered, the florets more or less imbricated. The parts of the flower are inconstant in the species, some being monandrous, whilst others are triandrous ; and some have the florets mostly sterile, while others are nearly all hermaphrodite. They are natives principally of North and South America, and several species are sufficiently hardy to survive the winters in Great Britain. *U. stricta* and *U. spicata* are two handsome hardy grasses. [D. M.]

UNIPAROUS. Having but one peduncle.

UNISEPTATE. Having but one septum or partition.

UNISEXUAL. Of one sex only.

UNJEER. The Indian name of the Garden Fig.

UNONA. A great number of American and African plants have at one time or other been placed under this genus of *Anonaceæ*, but they are now referred to other genera, *Unona* being restricted to about a dozen Asiatic species, characterised by their flowers having three sepals, six longish thin flat petals in a double row (or sometimes only three, the inner row being suppressed); numerous four-sided stamens with rather distant anthers, the connecting portion prolonged into a nearly round or flattened process; and numerous hairy ovaries, each containing several ovules in a single row, and bearing an oval or oblong recurved style, with a furrow down its inner face. Two species are climbing shrubs, and the rest upright shrubs or trees, with simple pellucid dotted leaves, and rather large flowers, usually borne singly on stalks, growing from the sides of the branches at or near the leaf-axils; the petals also have pellucid dots, and increase in size after expanding. The fruits consist of numerous long distinct carpels, usually constricted between the seeds, and thus divided into several one-seeded joints.

One of the commonest species, *U.discolor,* found throughout most parts of India, Ceylon, Malacca, Java, and Southern China, is a small tree with smooth or hairy very variable-shaped leaves from two to eight inches long, dirty green or yellow flowers, and purple fruits with joints about the size of peas. The Chinese at Hongkong obtain a fine purple dye from the unripe fruits. See also HABZELIA. [A. S.]

UNSTEETLA. A Cherokee name for *Spigelia marilandica.*

UNTAMOL. A vernacular name for Indian Ipecacuanha, the dried roots of *Tylophora asthmatica.*

UNUNTAMUL. An Indian name for the roots of *Hemidesmus indicus.*

UNXIA. The name applied to a genus of *Compositæ,* native of Guiana. The species are branched herbs, with entire hairy leaves, and axillary flower-heads on short stalks, each one surrounded by a somewhat globose involucre of five ovate scales. The outer florets are ligulate and female, the central ones tubular five-toothed and male. The fruits are compressed, smooth, without pappus. Some of the species have a smell of camphor. [M. T. M.]

UOLIN. (Fr.) *Pimelea.*

UPAS ANTIAR. A Javanese name for a poison composed of a black gum-resin-

ous mass, formed of the concrete juice of *Antiaris toxicaria.* — RADJA, or TIEUTÉ. A Javanese name for the frightful poison obtained from the bark of the root of *Strychnos Tieuté.*

UPAS-TREE. *Antiaris toxicaria.*

UPSTART. *Colchicum autumnale.*

URA. In Greek compounds = tail or tail-like process, or even a tail-like inflorescence.

URACHNE. A genus of grasses of the tribe *Stipeæ,* synonymous with *Piptatherum.* The inflorescence is in ramose diffuse panicles, the spikelets one-flowered; glumes two, membranaceous muticous; pales two, subcoriaceous, the lower convex the upper awned; scales three; stamens three, the anther-lobes often bearded at the top; styles two, with plumose stigmas. The few species are mostly natives of Southern Europe and Northern Africa. [T. M.]

URALEPIS. A genus of grasses belonging to the tribe *Festuceæ.* The inflorescence is panicled or racemose; spikelets many-flowered, the florets distichous; glumes two unequal, half keel-shaped and awned; pales two, membranaceous, the lower concave three-nerved, two to four-cleft, with small awns between the clefts, the upper two-keeled; stamens one to three. There are nineteen species, mostly natives of South America and Africa. [D. M.]

URALIER. (Fr.) *Anthocercis.*

URANDRA. One of the genera of the order *Icacinaceæ.* It includes a large Cingalese tree, with leathery ovate acuminate stalked leaves, and perfect flowers, which have a cup-shaped five-toothed persistent calyx, alternating with the teeth of which are five purple petals, greenish at their tips. The stamens alternate with the petals, their filaments being densely covered with long club-shaped hairs at their upper portion; the ovary is surrounded by a small glandular ring-like disk; and the fruit is oblong one-seeded, fleshy externally fibrous and woody within. [M. T. M.]

URANIA *speciosa* (or *Ravenala madagascariensis*—its older and more correct name) represents a magnificent palm-like genus of *Musaceæ,* confined to Madagascar, where it is called the Traveller's Tree, because the leaves when cut yield an abundant and refreshing juice, with which travellers allay their thirst. The plant is occasionally cultivated in our hothouses, but not unfrequently *Strelitzia augusta,* which it somewhat resembles in habit, goes under that name. The plant does not seem indigenous to Mauritius, as stated by some, but whole groves of it have been planted in the botanic gardens of that island. The leaves are of gigantic size, somewhat like those of *Musa Ensete,* but arranged in two rows on opposite sides of the arboreous stem. The flowers are small in comparison to the gigantic foliage, and are aggregated in the axils of the leaves. The arillus surrounding the bean-like seeds is of a most beautiful ultramarine colour, and yields an essential oil. A dye is extracted from the capsules. An American species, referred by some authors to this genus (*U. guianensis*) properly belongs to *Phenacospermum*.　　[B. S.]

URARI. The Ourari or Wourali poison of *Strychnos toxifera*.

URBUREE. *Cicer arietinum*, also called Chenna.

URCEOLA. The single species of this genus of *Apocynaceæ*, called *U.elastica*, is a large climbing milky-juiced shrub or tree, frequently with a trunk as thick as a man's body. It is confined to Borneo Sumatra and other islands of the Eastern Archipelago, where its milky juice, collected by making incisions in its soft thick rugged bark, or by cutting the trunk into junks, forms one of the kinds of Caoutchouc called Juita-

Urceola elastica.

wan; but, owing principally to want of care in its preparation, this Eastern caoutchouc is inferior in quality to the South American, the milk being simply coagulated by mixing with saltwater, instead of being gradually inspissated in layers on a mould. The plant has sharp ovate-oblong opposite leaves, roughish on the upper and hairy on the under surface; and bears many-flowered terminal cymes of small greenish blossoms, which produce double fruits, consisting of two large roundish apricot-coloured rough leathery-skinned pieces about the size of oranges, containing numerous kidney-shaped seeds nestling in a copious tawny-coloured pulp, which is much relished both by natives and European residents, and is said to taste like well-bletted medlars. The flowers have a five-cleft calyx; a pitcher-shaped hairy corolla with five short erect teeth; five stamens, rising from the base of the corolla, and having very short filaments and arrowhead-shaped anthers, with tufts

of white hairs in the centre and pollen-bearing at the top; and an entire disk surrounding two flat-topped ovaries, bearing a short style and egg-like stigma divided by a circular line into two differently coloured halves.　　[A. S.]

URCEOLATE. Pitcher-shaped, that is, similar to Campanulate, but more contracted at the orifice, with a small limb.

URCEOLINA. A genus of *Amaryllidaceæ*, the two or three species of which as yet known are found in Peru. They have roundish bulbs, broad oval petiolated leaves growing up with the flowers, and a tall scape supporting an umbel of several (five to eight) pendulous flowers, two inches long or more. The tube has a straight slender cylindrical green base an inch long, and a yellow ventricosely bell-shaped upper portion, which is contracted at the mouth, with short reflexed green segments; there are six stamens inserted in the tube, and joined at the base by a membrane (an abbreviated corona); the style is erect filiform, with an obtuse three-cornered stigma; and the capsule is cordiform, three-cornered three-furrowed three-celled, and many-seeded. They are handsome plants.　　[T. M.]

URCEOLUS. The two confluent bracts of *Carex*; any flask-shaped or cup-shaped anomalous organ.

URCHILLA. A Spanish name for the Orchella-weed.

URCHIN. (Fr.) *Hydnum*.

UREDINEI. A section of *Pucciniæi*, a natural order of *Fungi* including those genera, whose protospores (except in one case, where there are two forms of fruit) are not septate and disposed in regular sort. All were formerly included in one genus, *Uredo*, but this has been gradually divided, till the group so named contains comparatively few species. Some are undoubtedly merely the secondary fruit of other *Fungi*, but many, so far as is at present known, are true species. In *Uredo* proper the little heaps of brown or yellow protospores are composed of several layers of cells, each of which encloses a spore. The stroma which supports them is composed of little irregular cells. Of the brown species, *Uredo Circææ* on enchanter's nightshade may be quoted as one of the most common; and of those with yellow spores *U. confluens*,which abounds in spring on *Mercurialis perennis. Trichobasis*—most of whose species are referrible as a secondary form of fruit to different *Pucciniæ*, which they often accompany—has free caducous protospores attached to a short stalk; *Uromyces*, of which *U. Ficariæ*, found on the lesser celandine, is a good example, has stalked protospores which are not caducous. *Coleosporium* has two kinds of protospores, the one consisting of short strings with deciduous joints, the other of obtuse clavate three to four septate bodies, while a third form, with the terminal spore polygonal (as figured in Berkeley's *Intro-*

duction to *Cryptogamic Botany*, p. 10), constitutes the genus *Physonema* of Bonorden. *C. Tussilaginis* and *C. pingue* are common everywhere, the one on coltsfoot, the other on roses. *Lecythea* is distinguished by its elongated abortive protospores surrounding those which are fertile. The species, however, are mere conditions of *Melampsora*, so common on willows spurge and poplars, and distinguished by its wedge-shaped closely-compacted protospores. *Cystopus* alone remains, which is remarkable for its white protospores, disposed in short necklaces. The mycelium in this genus is strongly developed, and consists of coarse branched threads.

Uredinei have been considered by some authors, as for example Unger, as mere transformations of the cellular tissue of plants. The researches, however, of Tulasne and others, show that they possess a far more complicated structure than has been usually assigned to them, and are decisive against such an opinion. [M. J. B.]

UREDO. See *Uredinei*.

URENA. A genus of *Malvaceæ*, distinguished from its congeners by its flowers having a five-cleft involucre outside and alternate with the true calyx, which is likewise five-cleft, and a style divided at the top into ten branches; and also by its fruits, which consist of five unopening carpels, being covered with prickles, divided at the top into numerous radiating hooks, the carpels ultimately separating from each other. It consists of a few extremely variable species, very extensively distributed over the tropics of both hemispheres: but, owing to their great variability and wide dispersion, numerous spurious species have been described. They are woody annuals or perennial shrubby plants, with entire or more or less deeply-lobed leaves, usually furnished at the base with one to three slit glands on the underside of the principal nerves; and their flowers are yellow red or rose coloured, and either solitary or clustered towards the points of the branches. *U. lobata* and *U. sinuata* are both common tropical weeds. They possess mucilaginous properties, for which they are used medicinally; and their inner bark affords an abundance of fibre, resembling jute rather than flax or hemp. [A. S.]

URENS. Stinging.

URERA. This genus of *Urticaceæ* is sometimes merged in *Urtica* by botanical writers, from which, however, it is known by its alternate not opposite leaves, and by the obliquely ovate fruit, included within the inner succulent leaves of the perianth. In the genus *Urtica* the perianth leaves do not become succulent as the fruit ripens. See *Urtica*. [M. T. M.]

URGERÃO. *Stachytarpha jamaicensis.*

URGINEA. A genus of *Liliaceæ*, very closely allied to *Scilla*, but differing in the more widely-spreading segments of the perianth, and in the greater number of

seeds. The species are natives of the Mediterranean region, and have large bulbs, whence proceed the leaves and long-stalked racemes of flowers, the latter however being produced first.

The bulbs of *U. maritima*, the old *Scilla maritima*, are known in medicine as Squills. These bulbs are of large size, covered on the outside with thin brownish layers, which enclose a large number of thick fleshy scales. They are imported from Malta and elsewhere, some having the scales white, while others are of a darker colour; the lighter sort is preferred by druggists. It has been supposed that the Red Squills are the produce of another species, *U. Pancration*, but this seems doubtful. Fresh squills are very acrid, causing irritation and even vesication of the skin; the drug is, however, usually imported in the dried state, when its acridity is in great measure dissipated. The bitter taste of squills is due to a substance called *scillitin*. Squills are used in medicine as a diuretic in certain forms of dropsy, and as an expectorant in coughs. In large doses it causes vomiting, and in extreme quantity it acts as an acrid poison. [M. T. M.]

URHUR. An Indian name for the peas of *Cajanus indicus*.

URJOON. An Indian name for *Terminalia alata*.

URKAN. The Arabian name for *Lawsonia alba*.

URN. The spore-case of urn-mosses.

URN-MOSSES. An English name for the *Bryaceæ* or true Mosses.

UROCARPUS. A genus of *Rutaceæ*, comprising a West Australian shrub, covered with scale-like hairs, having ovate leaves, and white flowers arranged on the ends of the branches, in an umbellate manner. The calyx is minute, five-toothed; petals five spreading, much longer than the calyx; stamens ten, all fertile; ovaries two, united by their inner angles, elsewhere distinct; styles two, connate; stigma thickened, two-lobed; fruit of two horned valves, from which the inner cartilaginous lining separates with elasticity; seed solitary by abortion. The generic name is derived from the Greek *oura* 'a tail,' in allusion to the horned fruit. [M. T. M.]

UROCHLÆNA. A genus of grasses belonging to the tribe *Festuceæ*. The inflorescence forms terminal ovate spikes; spikelets many-flowered; glumes herbaceous, five-nerved; lower pales seven to nine-nerved, hairy at the base, the upper slightly bidentate or toothed; stamens three; styles short and distant. Only one species has been described, viz. *U. pusilla*, which is annual and a native of South Africa. [D. M.]

UROCHLOA. *Panicum.*

UROOS. An Indian name for *Adhatoda vasica*.

UROPEDIUM. A terrestrial genus of

orchids belonging to the *Cypripedeæ*, comprising one very handsome species, *U. Lindeni*, a native of New Grenada, growing at an elevation of 8,500 feet above the sea-level. It is closely related to *Cypripedium*,

Uropedium Lindeni.

from which it differs in its broader flattened lip, and extremely long-tailed petals. The leaves are about a foot long, oblique at the extremity, shining and fleshy in texture. The flowers are solitary, on long peduncles ; sepals ovate-lanceolate, yellow, streaked with orange ; petals linear-lanceolate, extended into a long narrow tail, a foot or more in length, purple-orange at the base.   [W. B. H.]

UROPETALUM. A genus of bulbous *Liliaceæ*, from the Cape of Good Hope and the Mediterranean region. They have a simple scape, bearing a raceme of green or green-and-orange flowers, which have a deeply six-cleft perianth, between funnel-shaped and bell-shaped ; the filaments of the six stamens are dilated at the base ; the capsule is three-edged many-seeded ; the seeds horizontal, compressed, with a hard black seed-coat, over a spongy inner covering. *U. serotinum* occurs in many places in the South of Europe.   [J. T. S.]

UROPHYLLUM. A genus of shrubs, natives of Southern India, and included in the order *Cinchonaceæ*. The leaves have a very long tail-like point, while the flower-stalks are short, and bear greenish flowers in whorled heads, surrounded by numerous bracts. The limb of the calyx is short, bell-shaped ; the corolla is funnel-shaped, hairy at the throat, and with its limb divided into five ovate lobes ; stamens five ; ovary surmounted by a glandular disk, and having five compartments, each containing numerous ovules ; stigma five-lobed ; fruit small succulent globular, crowned by the calyx-limb, and having pores. The name is derived from the Greek *oura* 'a tail' and *phyllon* 'leaf.'   [M. T. M.]

UROSKINNERA *spectabilis* is the sole representative of a Central American genus of *Scrophulariaceæ*, named in honour of Mr. G. Ure Skinner, to whom our gardens are indebted for so many new plants. It is an undershrub, somewhat resembling in habit certain *Gesneraceæ*, and covered in all parts with soft hairs. The leaves are oblong toothed, the flowers arranged in terminal crowded panicles, and supported by filiform bracts. The corolla is infundibuliform, and its five lobes are ranged in two lips ; it is of a pale-violet colour outside, and nearly white inside.   [B. S.]

UROSPERMUM. The name of a genus of *Compositæ*, consisting of Mediterranean annual plants, with alternate amplexicaul divided leaves, and flower-heads on long stalks surrounded by an involucre of eight bracts, arranged in one series. The receptacle is somewhat convex, destitute of scales ; the corollas all ligulate and yellow ; the achenes tubercled, provided with a long empty beak distended below ; and a feathery pappus in one row. The generic name is from the Greek *ouros* 'a tail' and *spermum* 'a seed,' in allusion to the long beak above described.   [M. T. M.]

UROSTIGMA. One of the genera into which Miquel has proposed to divide the large Linnæan genus *Ficus*, but which are more conveniently considered as sections or subgenera. It comprises the greater number of the tropical species with coriaceous laurel-like leaves, and is distinguished chiefly by the long three-cleft perianth with a single stamen of the male flowers, and by the usually elongated stigma of the females. In habit the numerous species do not differ from some of those retained in *Ficus*.

URTICACEÆ. (*Urticeæ, Nettleworts*). A large order of apetalous dicotyledons, consisting of trees shrubs or herbs from almost every part of the globe, with alternate or opposite leaves furnished with stipules, and small unisexual flowers usually in cymes or in heads, not in catkins. The small calyx-like perianth has from one to five divisions, with as many stamens opposite to the segments. The free ovary has one cell containing a single ovule, and a simple terminal style or stigma.

Taken in an extended sense the order includes *Artocarpaceæ*, with pendulous ovules and no albumen in the seed, and *Moraceæ*, with pendulous ovules and albuminous seeds ; but it is more frequently confined to *Urticeæ* proper, which have erect ovules and albuminous seeds. These are also remarkable for the causticity of their limpid juice ; their stipules are not convolute, and they are frequently herbaceous, many species yielding exceedingly tenacious fibres. The order thus restricted still comprises about forty genera, amongst which the most important are *Urtica, Pilea, Böhmeria, Procris, Forskolea*, &c.

URTICA. This genus gives its name to the order *Urticeæ*, and consists for the most part of erect herbaceous plants, covered with stinging hairs, and having opposite leaves, and monœcious or diœcious flowers in axillary clusters or spikes. The fruit is an achene enclosed in the perianth; seed erect, conjoined with the wall of the fruit.

The species are numerous, and some of them are very widely distributed. Two are commonly found wild in this country, while a third, *U. pilulifera*, a native of Southern Europe, is occasionally found in the neighbourhood of villages. *U. dioica*, the Common Nettle, is a perennial plant, with stems two to three feet high, dark-green heart-shaped leaves, coarsely toothed, and the flowers in branched spikes. *U. urens*, the Small Nettle, is a much smaller more delicate-looking plant, with its male and female flowers intermixed in small loose nearly sessile clusters. *U. pilulifera*, commonly called the Roman Nettle, is also an annual plant, intermediate in size between the foregoing; its male flowers are in loose spikes, the females in stalked globular heads.

Although the species are for the most part herbaceous, some are more or less shrubby; while one, *U. Gigas*, a native of New South Wales, is described as a 'formidable tree.' We are indebted to Bennett's *Wanderings of a Naturalist in Australia* for the following account of it:—

'A specimen seen by Sir William MacArthur, still in full vigour, rises from its base by a series of buttresses of singularly regular outline, gradually tapering without a branch to the height of 120 to 140 feet; the trunk then divides into a regularly-formed wide-spreading head, which excites admiration by its extraordinary size: but the ordinary elevation of this tree is from twenty-five to fifty feet, with a circumference of twelve to twenty feet. The leaves, when young and in vigorous growth, attain a breadth of from twelve to fifteen inches, and are of a beautiful dark-green colour. As may be expected, the poisonous fluid secreted from the foliage is very powerful, particularly in the younger leaves; and their sting is exceedingly virulent, producing great suffering, not unattended with danger. It is found in the northern part of New South Wales, and is a great impediment to the traveller.'

The stinging property just referred to is also met with to a slight extent in our English nettles. Some of the Indian species seem to be particularly powerful in this respect, especially *U. crenulata* and *U. stimulans*. Both these, however, are exceeded by *U. urentissima*, a native of Timor, where it is called by the natives the Devil's-leaf; its effects are so violent as to last for twelve months, and even to produce death. The sting of the nettle has a bulbous base, which serves as a reservoir for the acrid fluid. From this extends a long sharply-pointed tubular hair. When the hand touches the nettle the point of the sting enters the skin and breaks off, allowing the passage of the caustic fluid from the reservoir, through

the tube, into the wound; but if, in accordance with the old precept, the nettle be grasped forcibly, the hair is broken off below the point, which then does not penetrate, and the fluid is poured out on the skin, not beneath it. In the case of the more noxious species it would, we imagine, make little difference whether the poison were on the skin or beneath it, except in rapidity of action.

Some of the Nettles are considered to have medicinal properties: thus *U. baccifera* in the West Indies is used as an aperient; the root of *U. pilulifera* is astringent and diuretic; and Nettle-tea, an infusion of the leaves of *U. dioica*, is much used by the peasantry in this country to purify the blood. The herbage and seeds of *U. membranacea*, an Egyptian plant, are used in Egypt medicinally. The tubers of *U. tuberosa*, according to Roxburgh, are eaten, raw boiled or roasted, by the natives of India. Among the miscellaneous uses of these plants, it may be mentioned that, in Java, the leaves of *U. stimulans* are or were employed to excite and goad bulls in their combats with tigers.

The Nettles, taking the name in the wide sense, are remarkable for the excellent fibre they produce. *U. argentea* is employed in the Sandwich Islands for making ropes, as is *U. baccifera* in the West Indies. *U. cannabina*, or Kentucky Hemp, yields abundance of useful fibre; so also do *U. heterophylla*, *U. Puya*, *U. tenacissima*, and *U. nivea*—species severally referred to URERA, BOHMERIA, and GIRARDINIA: which see.

The Stinging Nettle of our hedges and roadsides, *U. dioica*, is a very ancient textile plant, its inner bark affording a tough fibre suitable for many purposes, and used by the inhabitants in many parts of Europe for making cordage, fishing-lines, coarse cloth, &c. Nettles have been from ancient times used externally as stimulants in cases of paralysis. The young tops of nettles are eaten as a vegetable, and may easily be forced for that purpose, if nothing better is to be had; but in our experience they are always gritty, probably from the abundance of crystalloid matter contained in the cells of the epidermis (*cystolithes*). These tender tops are much more commonly employed in this way throughout Germany, Belgium, and other parts of the Continent than with us. According to Sir Walter Scott, the Nettle was at one time cultivated as a pot-herb in Scotland. Cattle will eat the leaves in a dried state for forage; and in some places the fresh tops are given to pigs, and when chopped up, to fowls and young turkeys. Both the dried leaves and seeds are given to fowls in the winter-time, to make them lay eggs. In Holland, and also in Egypt, it is said that the horse-dealers mix the seeds of nettles with oats or other food, in order to give the animals a sleek coat. A yellow colouring-matter, employed in domestic dyeing, is obtained by boiling the roots with alum; and a decoction of the plant mixed with salt coagulates milk. The seeds yield oil when pressed. The generic name is derived from the

Latin *uro* 'to burn,' in allusion to the stinging hairs. [M. T. M.]

URUCURI, URUCURI-IBA. Brazilian names, respectively, for *Attalea excelsa* and *Cocos coronata*.

URVILLEA. A genus of *Sapindaceæ*, distinguished from its allies by the three unopening pieces of which its fruits are composed being winged along the back, somewhat inflated in the middle, and at length separating from each other and from the central axis; each piece contains a single roundish seed, partly enveloped in an aril, and having thick fleshy straightish cotyledons or seed-leaves. The few species belonging to it are all climbing shrubs, natives of Tropical America and the West Indies, and have leaves consisting of three leaflets, and racemes of whitish flowers with two tendrils near the top of the main stalk. [A. S.]

USEREKEE. An Indian name for the Emblic Myrobalan, *Emblica officinalis*.

USHOKA. The Bengalee name of *Jonesia Asoca*.

USNEA. A genus of lichens belonging to the order *Parmeliaceæ*, being the typical genus of the division *Usneacei*, in which the disk is open from the first, and the thallus mostly vertical and shrubby, without any hypothallus. The thallus of *Usnea* itself is rounded branched and generally pendulous, with a central thread; occasionally in very old specimens the thread vanishes, and is replaced by a cavity. The apothecia are terminal orbicular and peltate, formed of the substance of the thallus and nearly of the same colour, the circumference mostly without a border and generally ciliated. The species grow on rocks or trunks of trees, from which latter circumstance they are often called Tree Moss or Tree Hair, and seem to be what Milton had in mind when he talks of

> th' humble shrub
> And bush with frizzled hair implicit.

We have three species in Great Britain, which are also widely distributed over the world. Some of the Southern species, as *U. melaxantha*, are magnificent. In the stem of this (which attains a considerable size) concentric zones of *growth have* been observed by Dr. Hooker. We have not, however, been able to verify this, but, on the contrary, we have observed radiating wedges, which present another analogy in their resemblance to the medullary rays of exogens. [M. J. B.]

USTERIA. A genus of *Loganiaceæ*, comprising a shrub with terminal panicles of flowers on hairy pedicels; calyx short, fourcleft, the anterior division largest, petallike; corolla salver-shaped, its tube distended below, the limb unequally fourparted; stamen one, on the corolla; ovary two-celled; ovules numerous, placed on placentas ascending from the base of the compartments; style short; fruit capsular; seeds numerous winged, on placentas that

are ultimately detached from the walls of the capsule. [M. T. M.]

USTILAGINEI. A section of *Fungi* of the natural order *Pucciniæi*, in which group the protospores are not disposed in orbicular or elliptic sori, but, except in one or two instances, form irregular profusely dusty masses. Where there is anything like sori they are much elongated, as in *U. longissima*, so common on *Glyceria aquatica*. The protospores of *Ustilaginei* are either produced from very delicate branched tissue or from closely-packed cells. In *Polycystis*, e. g. those of the meadow-saffron and violet, they are irregular, and composed of a few cells; in *Tilletia*, the common bunt, globose with a minutely cellular cuticle; in *Tuburcinia* very irregular in form, and either subglobose or conchiform, consisting of minute cells; and in *Ustilago*, which is the typical genus, simple with a simple coat. To this genus *Ustilago* belong the various kinds of smut, which are so injurious to corn and grasses. A large species occurs on the common reed, the spores of which are very troublesome to the labourers employed in the reed-beds, causing severe headaches. The largest of the genus is the maize smut, which is often many inches in diameter. The protospores are mostly black or brown, but occasionally they are claret-coloured, violet, &c. In *Thecaphora*, of which no species has yet been gathered in Great Britain, they have a foxy tint, and have a few straight septa. The species of this genus occur amongst the tissues of seeds. [M. J. B.]

USTILAGO. Smut, a disease in which the natural tissue is replaced by black powder. Also the typical genus of USTILAGINEI: which see.

USTORUK. An Indian name for Storax.

USULSOOS. An Arabic name for Liquorice-root.

UTARASHA. An Indian name for *Adhatoda vasica*.

UTERUS. The volva or receptacle of certain fungals.

UTR. An Eastern name for the essential oil or attar of roses.

UTRICLE, UTRICULUS. A seed-vessel consisting of a very thin loose pericarp, enclosing a single seed: any thin bottle-like body; the two confluent glumes of *Carex*.

UTRICULAR, UTRICULOSE. Bearing many utricles.

UTRICULARIA. A genus of aquatic plants belonging to the order *Lentibulariaceæ*, with a two-lipped spurred corolla, and two-parted calyx of which the upper segment is entire. There are three British species of Bladderwort, which agree in having finely-divided capillary leaves, and delicate yellow flowers, rising above the surface of the water, the rest of the plant remaining submersed. Their roots stems and leaves are furnished with numerous membranaceous vesicles or small bladders, which during the early stage of the plant are filled with water, but when the flowers are ready to expand become filled with air. After the season of blossoming, the vesicles become again filled with water, and the plant descends to ripen its seeds at the bottom. There are many foreign species, some of which are highly ornamental to the watery places in which they grow, but they are rarely if ever cultivated. The flowers are of delicate structure, and turn black in drying. French : *Utriculaire* ; German : *Wasserschlauch.* [C. A. J.]

UTRICULIFORM. Having the shape of a bottle.

UVA DE GUANCHES. *Sempervivum uviferum.* — **DEL MONTE.** *Chondodendron convolvulaceum.* — **MARITIMA.** *Ephedra distachya.* — **URSI.** *Arctostaphylos uva-ursi.*

UVARIA. This name, derived from the Latin *uva* 'a grape,' is applied to a genus of *Anonaceæ*, in consequence of the resemblance presented by the fruit of some of the species to a bunch of grapes. The species are numerous, all climbing plants, covered with star-shaped hairs. They occur in the tropical and subtropical districts of the Old World, from Western Africa to the Philippine Islands. The principal characters by which the genus may be recognised are the following :—Flowers hermaphrodite, with the petals equal, overlapping one another in the bud, and the flattened stamens arranged on a flat receptacle, which bears also a number of linear-cylindrical ovaries, each with a very short style.

The roots of *U. Narum* are fragrant and aromatic, and are used medicinally in India, in intermittent fevers and liver complaints; bruised in saltwater they are employed as an application in certain skin-diseases : by distillation they yield a fragrant greenish oil. The bark of *U. tripetaloidea* yields by incision a fragrant gum. *U. triloba* is said to contain a powerful acid; its leaves are used as an application to boils and abscesses, while its seeds are emetic. *U. febrifuga* is so called from the febrifugal properties ascribed to the flowers by the Indians on the Orinoco. The fruits of *U. zeylanica* and *U. cordata* are edible. Several of the species have very fragrant flowers; and in Bourbon an oil is extracted from those of *U. longifolia*, which is used as a perfume. [M. T. M.]

UVETTE. (Fr.) *Ephedra.*

UVULARIA. A genus of *Melanthaceæ*, the type of the suborder *Uvulareæ*, which is intermediate between the true *Melanthaceæ* and the *Liliaceæ*. They have sessile or amplexicaul leaves, and solitary drooping flowers, in which points they have considerable resemblance to *Polygonatum*. They, however, have the style more or less deeply three-cleft, the anthers with their faces turned outwards, and the fruit is a dry three-celled pod. The perianth is narrowly bell-shaped, usually pale-yellow, with spa-

thulate-lanceolate segments having a honey-pore at the narrow base of each. The greater number of species inhabit North America, but some occur in the mountains of India ; they are astringent, and the bruised leaves of *U. grandiflora* are considered in the United States as a remedy for the bite of the rattlesnake. [J. T. S.]

VACCARIA. A genus of *Caryophyllaceæ* scarcely distinct from *Saponaria*, the chief points of difference being that the calyx is pentangular, and much enlarged after flowering. From *Gypsophila* it differs in the calyx, which is narrowed at the top, and in the petals, which have their claws connivent at the throat. They are annuals, with smooth connate leaves, and dichotomous cymes of rose-coloured flowers. [J. T. S.]

VACCINIACEÆ. (*Vacciniæ, Cranberries*). An order of monopetalous dicotyledons, closely allied to *Ericaceæ* in their stamens being free from the corolla, in the peculiar form of their anthers, as well as in most other characters, but separated by almost all botanists on account of their constantly inferior ovary and fruit. They consist of much-branched shrubs or small trees, often evergreen, with alternate undivided leaves, without stipules. The flowers, growing solitary or in racemes, are often richly coloured ; and the fruit, usually a berry, is frequently edible. The species are numerous in the temperate and colder parts of the world, especially in swamps or subalpine countries, as well as in high mountain-chains within the tropics ; and many of them are known as garden shrubs. They are distributed into about fifteen genera, the greater number of species being included in *Vaccinium* and *Thibaudia.*

VACCINIUM. A name used by classical writers to designate some now-unknown plant, and applied in modern botany to a genus of low-growing heath-like shrubs, which are found dispersed through a very wide area in both the Old and New World, and generally in mountainous districts or moist heathy places. The genus is the type of the order *Vacciniaceæ.* The leaves are alternate, and are generally evergreen, and the flowers are solitary or clustered. The calyx is adherent to the ovary below, while its upper portion is divided into four or five small teeth ; the corolla is generally urn-shaped or bell-shaped, four or five-toothed at the free edge, concealing eight or ten stamens ; the anthers have each of them two horns, and open by pores at the summit ; the fruit is a globular four or five-celled berry, with several seeds in each compartment, at least in the young state. Three species are natives of Great Britain. *V. Myrtillus* is the Whortleberry or Bilberry ; this is an erect little shrub, with angular branches, and deciduous leaves of a bright-green colour, but which turn red in autumn ; the flowers are globular, pinkish, with two-awned anthers ; and the globular fruit is of a bluish-black colour. The fruits are frequently made into preserves, syrups, puddings, tarts, &c.; and they are said to be used on the Continent for colouring wine. *V. uliginosum*, a less common plant than the preceding, has roundish branches and small deciduous entire leaves. *V. Vitis idæa*, the Cowberry, has short procumbent stems and evergreen leaves; its flowers are of a pale-pink, and arranged in terminal drooping clusters; and its fruits are of a reddish colour, and edible, and are frequently sold as cranberries. The leaves and stems are used for dyeing yellow; the former, moreover, are sometimes mixed with those of the bearberry, *Arctostaphylus uva-ursi*, from which, however, they may be distinguished by the dots on their lower surface. The fruits of several other species are gathered for table use in America, and some of them are useful on account of their astringency, or from their yielding a blue dye. Several species are grown in this country as ornamental shrubs.

The true cranberry, *Oxycoccus*, is distinguished from *Vaccinium* by the corolla being split into four linear segments. See OXYCOCCUS.   [M, T. M.]

VACH. The Sanscrit name for the Sweet Flag, *Acorus Calamus*.

VACHELLIA. This genus was established by Drs. Wight and Arnott upon the well-known *Acacia Farnesiana* (see ACACIA, but the characters relied upon for distinguishing it from Acacia—viz., the pods being swollen and nearly cylindrical, filled with pulp, and not opening when ripe —are common to numerous American and African acacias; and many botanists consequently reunite them, or retain the group merely as a section of that extensive genus, including the gum-arabic tree (*Acacia arabica*) and other gum-producing

Vachellia (Acacia) Farnesiana.

species. The flowers of *Vachellia* (or *Acacia*) *Farnesiana*, like those of so many other acacias, grow in little globular heads; they form the Cassie-flowers of the perfumers, who extract their fine violet-like odour by macerating them in purified fat or the finest olive-oil, which they use in the preparation of various *bouquets*, or for

mixing with violet perfumes to increase their strength. This species is a large shrub or low tree, and has bipinnate leaves composed of from four to eight pairs of pinnæ, each with from ten to twenty pairs of little narrow blunt leaflets. Originally it appears to have been confined to the tropics of the Western Hemisphere, but it is now common in nearly all tropical countries, and also in many parts of the South of Europe, where it was introduced early in the seventeenth century, and from whence the perfumers derive their supply of the flowers. Large quantities of gum, resembling inferior gum-arabic, exudes from its trunk and branches.   [A. S.]

VACIER, or VACIET. (Fr.) *Vaccinium Myrtillus*.

VACILLANS. Swinging, as the anthers of grasses, which oscillate lightly from the end of their filament.

VACONA. (Fr.) *Pandanus utilis*.

VACUOUS. Empty; a term applied to cases when an organ does not contain what usually belongs to it. Bracts which usually support flowers are said to be vacuous when they have no flower in their axils.

VADARI. An Indian name for *Zizyphus Jujuba*.

VAGARIA. A name given by Herbert to a plant which he afterwards ascertained to be *Lapiedra Plaçiana*.

VAGIFORM. Having no certain figure.

VAGINA (adj. VAGINANS, VAGINATE). A sheath; a petiole rolled round a stem, as in grasses; or any part which sheaths some other part.

VAGINERVOSE. Having the veins arranged without any order.

VAGINULA. A sheath that surrounds the base of the seta in urn-mosses.

VAGUS. Having no particular direction.

VAHEA. Nearly the whole of the large quantities of Caoutchouc or India-rubber consumed by our manufacturers is obtained from a spurgewort (*Siphonia brasiliensis*) and a fig (*Ficus elastica*); but the milky juice of numerous plants belonging to the Apocynaceæ likewise contain it, such as various species of the genera *Urceola, Cameraria, Collophora, Willughbeia,* and the present genus *Vahea,* although, with the exception of the first-named, it is not collected from them for commercial purposes. *Vahea* contains four species, three from Madagascar and the neighbouring islands, and one from Western Tropical Africa; and two of these—viz., *V. madagascariensis,* the Voua-Here of the natives, and *V. gummifera*—both Madagascar species, are known to afford an abundance of caoutchouc, which will probably at no distant date form an article of export from that magnificent island. These plants are tall climbing shrubs or trees, with opposite smooth more or less elliptical blunt leaves, and dense terminal cymes of rather large white flowers, producing pear-shaped or round fruits filled with granular pulp, in which the bean-like seeds pestle.' Their calyx is five-parted, without glands; their corolla has a five-cleft limb and a cylindrical tube, hairy inside, but destitute of scales at the mouth, and somewhat bulged out at the base, where the stamens are inserted; and their single two-celled ovary is seated within a cup-shaped disk, and bears a short thick style and long conical stigma, tipped with two narrow erect lobes. [A. S.]

VAHLIA. A genus of *Saxifragaceæ* from Africa and Asia. They are subdichotomous herbs, often more or less woolly, with opposite linear or lanceolate leaves, and thin axillary white shortly-stalked flowers, which have the calyx-tube adherent to the ovary, and the limb five-parted, the petals spreading, the stamens five, the styles two, and the capsule one-celled, opening between the styles. *V. capensis* has the aspect of a *Silene*.　　　[J. T. S.]

VAILLANTIA. A genus of *Galiaceæ*, containing two species of annual branching herbs indigenous to Southern Europe. It is nearly allied to *Galium*, from which it differs in having a campanulate corolla, and in the flowers being arranged in threes, of which the central one is perfect and four-cleft, while the lateral are barren and three-cleft. French: *Vaillantie*. [W. C.]

VAINGA. An Indian name for the gum-resin of *Pterocarpus Marsupium.*

VALBRICK. The Danish name for the Maple.

VALDIVIA. A genus of *Saxifragaceæ*, consisting of a single species of ornamental aspect, *V. Gayana*, a native of Chili. It is distinguished by the following among other peculiarities:—Calyx-tube connate with the ovary, the limb five-cleft; corolla of five to seven perigynous converging petals; stamens five to seven, with subulate filaments, and oblong anthers dehiscing longitudinally; ovary inferior three-celled, with two placentas in each cell affixed to the central angle; style simple, persistent; stigma capitate, three-furrowed; capsule three-celled, inferior, crowned by the persistent calyx-limb; seeds numerous. The species is an evergreen herbaceous perennial, with rather large spathulate oblong rugose serrated radical leaves, and short erect pyramidal panicles of pretty rose-coloured flowers, the tube-like portion of which is angular, and the tips of the petals recurved; the flowers are three-quarters of an inch long. The plant is now an inmate of our gardens.　[T. M.]

VALENTINIA. A genus of *Sapindaceæ*, comprising a West Indian shrub, with sessile rigid leaves, wavy and spiny at the margins like those of the holly, and flowers placed in umbel-like groups at the ends of the branches. The calyx is five-parted, scarlet, spreading, persistent; corolla none; stamens eight; ovary free, roundish; style thick; capsule somewhat pulpy, dividing into three or four revolute valves, white at

first but becoming scarlet; seeds three or four, embedded in yellow pulp. [M. T. M.]

VALERIAN. *Valeriana.* —, GREEK. *Polemonium cæruleum.* —, RED. *Centranthus ruber.*

VALERIANACEÆ. (*Valerianeæ, Valerianworts.*) An order of monopetalous dicotyledons, consisting of herbs usually strong-scented or aromatic (especially their roots), with radical or opposite entire or pinnately-divided leaves, and rather small but often elegant flowers, in terminal cymes or panicles, rarely contracted into heads. They agree with *Compositæ* and *Dipsaceæ* in their inferior one-celled ovary with a single ovule, in their calyx being often reduced to a membrane or feathery pappus bordering the top of the ovary, and in the insertion of the stamens, in the corolla-tube alternating with its lobes: but the flowers are not collected into heads resembling a single blossom, the anthers are free, the ovule is pendulous, and the seed has no albumen. The corolla is sometimes irregular, with the stamens fewer than its lobes, and the ovary has occasionally two additional empty cells. There are about 150 species known, natives of temperate climates, chiefly of the mountains of the Northern Hemisphere or of South America, ascending sometimes to great elevations. They are distributed into about a dozen genera, *Valeriana*, *Centranthus*, and *Valerianella* being the most familiar examples.

VALERIANA. An extensive genus of herbaceous plants, the type of the order *Valerianaceæ*. The species are widely distributed over Tropical and Extratropical America, India, and Central Europe, and more sparingly in North America. For the most part they especially affect mountainous districts, although by no means confined to such localities. They have a perennial rootstock, with a tuft of leaves at its top, from amid which the erect flowering stem is thrown up. The form of the leaves is frequently very different even on the same plant, the lowermost being entire, while the upper ones are more or less pinnatedly divided. The flowers are white or red, generally numerous, and arranged in terminal panicles or heads. The limb of the calyx at the time of flowering is entire and rolled inwards, but as the fruit ripens it gradually unrolls, and forms a bell-shaped feathery pappus, consisting of numerous finely-branched hairs. The corolla has a short tube, without a spur. Fruit small, indehiscent, one-celled, one-seeded when ripe.

Many of the species of this genus are or have been employed in medicine, on account of their highly stimulant and antispasmodic properties. That now most used is the Wild Valerian, common in marshy and wet places in this country and Central Europe, the roots of which are collected for medicinal purposes; they have a warm aromatic slightly bitter taste, and, when dry a peculiar fetid odour, which seems to be especially agreeable to cats, who become, as it were, intoxicated with it. This odour seems to be due to the presence of valerianic acid. It is stated that rat-catchers avail themselves of this root as a means of attracting their prey. What is known to chemists as volatile oil of Valerian seems not to exist naturally in the plant, but to be developed by the agency of water. Valerian is used in medicine as a powerful stimulant to the nervous system in hysteria, and even in epilepsy. On the Continent it is likewise used as a febrifuge.

V. celtica is supposed to be the Saliunca of ancient writers. Its perfume is highly prized by Eastern nations, for the purpose of aromatising their baths. The roots are collected by the Styrian peasants with no slight difficulty and labour, and are exported by way of Trieste to Turkey and Egypt, whence they are conveyed to India and Ethiopia. *V. montana, V. Phu, V. pyrenaica, V. supina,* and *V. paniculata* (a native of Peru), all possess similar properties. *V. sitchensis,* a native of North-western America, is considered by the Russians as the most powerful species. *V. Dioscoridis* is stated by Dr. Sibthorp to have been the 'Phu' of Dioscorides: it has a much more aromatic and a less nauseous odour than the British species.

Two Valerians are natives of this country, and a third is now well-established in certain parts of Scotland and Western England. *V. officinalis,* the most common species, has erect stems two to four feet high, irregularly pinnated leaves, and small white or pink flowers in broad terminal corymbs. This plant is usually found in moist hedgerows or on the banks of ditches and streams. *V. dioica,* a native of bogs and marshes, has stems not attaining to a height of more than six to eight inches; the lower leaves are ovate entire, the upper ones pinnate, with one large segment at the end; the flowers are small, unisexual. *V. pyrenaica,* occasionally found wild, is a larger plant than the common Valerian, from which also it may be known by its broad heart-shaped toothed leaves. Several other species are grown in gardens, many of them handsome flowering plants.

The generic name is derived from the Latin *valere* 'to heal,' in allusion to the curative properties of the plants; but some derive it from Valerius, who is supposed to have been the first to employ them medicinally.   [M. T. M.]

VALÉRIANE. (Fr.) *Valeriana.* — DES JARDINS. *Valeriana Phu.* — DES MARAIS. *Valeriana dioica.* — GRANDE. *Valeriana Phu.* — GRECQUE. *Polemonium cæruleum.* — ROUGE. *Centranthus ruber.*

VALERIANELLA. Common herbs belonging to the order *Valerianaceæ,* and allied to *Valeriana,* from which they are distinguished by having the fruit crowned with several unequal teeth, and not with a feathery pappus. Several species are indigenous to Britain, of which the most frequent is *V. olitoria* (the common Lamb's Lettuce), a weak succulent herb, six to twelve inches high, with repeatedly forked stems, oblong blunt leaves, and numerous bluish-white semitransparent flowers, some of which are solitary in the forks of the stems, and others crowded into leafy heads at their summits. This species is often cultivated as a salad, not so much on account of its flavour, which is insipid, as because it is in perfection early in the year. There are several other native species, which are discriminated mainly by minute differences in the fruit. The foreign species resemble *V. olitoria,* and may also be cultivated as salad. French : *Mâche* ; German : *Ackersalat.*   [C. A. J.]

VALERIANWORTS. The plants of the order *Valerianaceæ.*

VALISALOO. An Indian name for Ram-til oil.

VALLEA. The name of a genus of Peruvian trees of the family *Tiliaceæ.* The leaves are entire heart-shaped, provided with large leafy stipules ; and the flower-stalks are axillary and terminal, two to three-flowered. Calyx of five lanceolate coloured segments, valvate in the bud ; petals five, overlapping, three-lobed ; stamens numerous, in two rows, the anthers opening by pores at the top ; ovary sessile, surrounded by a disk at the base, and containing two ovules in each of its compartments ; fruit capsular, muricate, three to five-valved, the valves spreading, and each bearing two seeds, attached along its centre.   [M. T. M.]

VALLECULÆ. The channels or furrows lying between the ridges upon the fruit of umbellifers.

VALLESIA. A genus of *Apocynaceæ,* containing several shrubs or trees from Tropical America, with alternate ovate and petiolate leaves, and white flowers in cymes opposite to the leaves. The calyx is five-parted ; the corolla salver-shaped ; the tube slightly inflated both above and below ; the stamens included, their ovate anthers supported on short slender filaments ; and the two ovate compressed ovaries contain four ovules. One of the drupes is sometimes averted.   [W. C.]

VALLISNERIACEÆ. A name under which it has been proposed to separate as a distinct order, *Vallisneria, Elodea,* and a few other *Hydrocharidaceæ* which have a one-celled ovary. They are, however, more generally considered as a tribe only of the latter order.

VALLISNERIA. This genus, so remarkable on account of the extremely curious manner in which the process of fertilisation is effected, belongs to the order *Hydrocharidaceæ,* and consists of two species, one of which is confined to Australia, while the other is widely dispersed over the tropical and warm regions of the earth —both of them, however, inhabiting only fresh-water rivers or lakes. *V. spiralis* the best-known species, and the one commonly grown in aquaria in this country is found wild in many parts of Southern Europe. It is a perennial herb, and has a very short stem, bearing a tuft of thin narrow green grass-like leaves, hardly a quarter of an inch broad, but often a yard or more long, with their apices finely saw-toothed: the stem also sending off suckers from its sides, which ultimately take root and produce new plants. The two-sexes are borne on separate plants. The male flowers are extremely minute, white, and of a globular form, without special stalks, but seated upon and entirely covering a short general stalk of a conical form; the whole being enclosed while young in a very short-stalked spathe, which splits into two or three valves at maturity, when also the little flowers become severally detached from the general stalk, and rise by their natural buoyancy to the surface of the water, where their three-parted calyx expands and permits of the escape of the pollen from the anthers. The stamens vary from one to three in number, and alternate with several rudimentary ones. The female flowers are altogether different from the males. They have a cylindrical ovary, bearing three small spreading calyx-lobes at the top, and contain three rudimentary stamens, and three large oval often split stigmas. Each flower is enclosed in a tubular spathe, borne singly at the end of a very long slender spirally-twisted stalk, which uncoils more or less according to the depth of the water, so as to allow the flower to float upon the surface, where it expands and is fertilised by its stigmas coming in contact with the

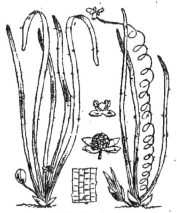

Vallisneria spiralis.

pollen of one or more of the very numerous detached male flowers floating about. After this latter process has taken place, the spiral stalk coils up again, and by that means conveys the flower to the bottom of the water, where it produces a cylindrical berry varying from half-an-inch

to two inches in length, and containing numerous cylindrical seeds marked with longitudinal ridges.

The leaves of this plant form an exceedingly beautiful object under the microscope, the extreme tenuity and transparency of their cellular tissue allowing the observer to watch the movement of the fluid contents of the cells.   [A. S.]

VALLOTA. A genus of *Amaryllidaceæ*, much cultivated for the beauty of its rich scarlet flowers. There is but one

Vallota purpurea.

species, *V. purpurea*, of which some varieties occur. This is a stoutish bulb, with lorate leaves, and a scape supporting several large erect flowers, which have a straight tube, a funnel-shaped limb, conniving filaments adhering by one side only to the tube, and a declinate style. It is closely allied to *Cyrtanthus*.   [T. M.]

VALONIA. A commercial name for the large capsules or acorn-cups of *Quercus Ægilops*.

VALONIACEÆ. A natural order of green-spored *Algæ*, characterised by the rooting variously-shaped frond, made up of large bladder-like cells filled with a green watery endochrome. In *Anadyomene* the cells are disposed in a fan-shaped membrane; in *Chamædoris* the stem is annulated: in *Penicillus* there is a spongy stem formed of interwoven filaments. In both these genera it is terminated by a brush-like head. *Valonia* forms irregular masses of large cells or sacs repeatedly constricted, resembling the membranous eggs of some mollusc. In *Dictyosphæria*, which consists of an irregular membrane, the surface is marked with the outlines of hexagonal cells, indicative of strong dissepiments within. In *Blodgettia*, which has exactly the habit of a large *Cladophora*, the walls are formed of two or three membranes, the innermost of which is veined and reticulated, a free vein in each mesh of the network being terminated by a short necklace of spores. They are all natives of warm seas, not a single species. occurring on our coasts, though a few are found on the shores of the Mediterranean. [M. J. B.]

VALORADIA. A small genus of *Plumbaginaceæ*, natives of Abyssinia and China. They are branching undershrubs, with alternate ciliate leaves, and flowers in terminal fascicles. The calyx and corolla are five-parted; the five stamens have linear anthers; the ovary is one-celled, with a single ovule; and the filiform style terminates in five acute stigmas. [W. C.]

VALVARIS, VALVATE. United by the margins only; as the sepals of rhamnads, or the valves of a capsule.

VALVES. The doors by which various bodies open; as the separable sides or face of anthers, the carpels or parts of carpels of fruits.

VALVULÆ, VALVULES. The bracts of sedges.

VANCOUVERIA. A genus of *Berberidaceæ*, consisting of a stemless herb from North-western America. The rhizome is slender and horizontal; the leaves all radical, twice or thrice ternate; and the scape simple, bearing a slightly compound raceme of white flowers on nodding pedicels. The six sepals are caducous membranous, with three to nine much smaller bracteoles at the base; the six petals are reflexed, and there are six stamens. The fruit is follicular, with numerous seeds. [J. T. S.]

VANDA. A magnificent genus of epiphytal orchids from Tropical Asia, containing upwards of a score of species, most of which attain a considerable size, and are amongst the largest found in the Old World. The leaves are distichous, coriaceous, from a few inches to two feet in length, oblique at the point. The flowers are large, beautifully coloured, in lateral erect or pendulous racemes; the perianth spreading, the sepals and petals similar, the lip saccate, more or less three-lobed, with the central lobe fleshy. The species of this genus are, on account of their size and the great beauty of their flowers, among the most conspicuous of epiphytes cultivated in the hothouses of Europe. The following are some of the better kinds—*V. suavis, Batemanni, gigantea, cærulea, Lowii,* and *tricolor.* In India the crushed leaves and stems of *V. spathulata* are mixed with oil, and used in the preparation of an ointment for skin-diseases; the powdered leaves are also taken internally in cases of diarrhœa, &c. [W. B. H.]

VANDELLIA. A genus of herbaceous plants of the family *Scrophulariaceæ.* They have axillary tufted flowers; a nearly equal tubular or bell-shaped five-toothed calyx; a five-cleft and two-lipped corolla, the upper lip being the shortest of the two; four stamens, all fertile, the filaments of which have a tooth-like appendage at the base; and the anthers are coherent, the cells diverging below. The fruit is a globose two-celled two-valved capsule, containing

numerous seeds. Some of these plants have emetic and purgative properties. A decoction of *V. diffusa* is employed medicinally in Guiana in fevers and disorders of the liver. The species are natives of the East Indies, China, Burmah, and South America. Some of them are grown in this country. The generic name commemorates a Professor of Botany at Lisbon. [M. T. M.]

VANELLE. (Fr.) *Stylidium.*

VANGLO. A West Indian name for Tilseed, *Sesamum orientale.*

VANGUERIA. A genus of *Cinchonaceæ*, comprising certain shrubs which are natives of Madagascar and India. The flowers have a minutely five-toothed calyx-limb, a white bell-shaped corolla with a hairy throat, to which the five stamens are attached by very short filaments. The fruit is succulent, in shape like an apple, having on the top an irregular scar, and containing five stones. The fruits of *V. edulis* and also those of *V. Commersoni* are eaten in Madagascar, under the name of Voa-vanga or Von-vanguer, which latter word has been adapted to serve as the designation of the genus. In the Mauritius, where these plants are naturalised, the Creoles employ the leaves in dysentery, and as external applications in strangulated hernia. Two or three species are in cultivation as stove plants. [M. T. M.]

VANILLACEÆ. A name under which it was formerly proposed to separate *Vanilla* from the bulk of the *Orchidaceæ.*

VANILLA. A small genus of climbing orchids belonging to the *Arethuseæ*, natives of Tropical Asia and America. Their leaves are oblong, somewhat succulent, cor-

Vanilla aromatica.

date at the base, and articulated with the stem; and their flowers are thick fleshy and dull-coloured, the sepals and petals being nearly equal spreading, and the lip entire, attached to the column, and bearded. The fruit is linear-oblong and fleshy. The climbing habit of this genus is sufficient to distinguish it from most others.

This is, perhaps, the most important

genus of the whole family, and the only one which possesses any economical value. The fruit of several species is largely employed by confectioners to flavour chocolates creams and liqueurs, under the name by which it is botanically known. The best Vanilla is the produce of *V. planifolia*, a native of Mexico, but several other South American species are also used. About five or six cwts. are annually imported into this country. See Plate 14, fig *b*. [W. B. H.]

VANILLA. The thin pod-like capsule of *Vanilla planifolia* and other species,

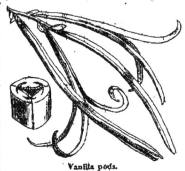

Vanilla pods.

much used for flavouring purposes. —, CHICA. The Panama name for the fruit of a species of *Sobralia*. —, CUBA. *Critonia Dalea*.

VANILLOES. A sort of bastard Vanilla obtained from *Vanilla Pompona*.

VANTANEA. The name of a tree, native of Guiana, constituting a genus of *Tiliaceæ*. The leaves are entire alternate, and the flowers in terminal corymbs. Calyx five-cleft; petals five, inserted on a very short disk; stamens numerous, inserted with the petals; ovary surrounded by a disk; style filiform. The fruit is undescribed. [M. T. M.]

VANZEY. An Abyssinian name for *Cordia abyssinica*.

VAQUETTE. (Fr.) *Arum maculatum*.

VARAGOO. The Tamil name for Millet, *Panicum miliaceum*.

VARAIRE. (Fr.) *Veratrum*.

VARANA. An Indian name for the Garlic Pear, *Cratæva Tapia*.

VARANGOO. An Indian name for *Paspalum frumentaceum*.

VAREC. (Fr.) *Fucus*.

VAREOA. The name of a Cingalese plant of which little is known, except of the fruit, which is a six-sided one-celled berry, placed upon a six-lobed disk, and surmounted by a short spine. The genus is referred to *Passifloraceæ*. [M. T. M.]

VARIABILIS, VARIANS. Not being constant in appearance.

VARIEGATED. Having colour disposed in various irregular spaces.

VARIEGATIO. A diseased condition of plants, in consequence of which the leaves become partially white, from a total suppression or modification of the chlorophyll; it is distinguished from chlorosis by its being more or less permanent, and not materially affecting health, much less ending in destruction. It is indeed said that planting in a rich soil and free exposure to light will sometimes cause the variegation to cease. In some cases, however, of this kind chlorosis may be confounded with variegation, and in others the affection has been produced by external causes, as in that of Meyen's beech, which had been eaten down the first year by snails and in the second by deer, and which then for a season or two produced variegated leaves, which, however, entirely disappeared after two or three seasons. Individual shoots, indeed, will often revert to the original condition in variegated plants, and these probably if propagated would remain true. The cause of this disease is completely unknown. It may take place originally in a seedling, but more frequently it occurs in some particular shoot of a tree, from whence it is propagated by cuttings or grafts. Occasionally variegated plants have a tendency to revert to their original condition, but this is not usually the case. Variegated grafts sometimes affect the stock, and, on the contrary, grafts may contract the disease from the stock. Variegated plants have also been obtained by crossing, as in the vine. [M. J. B.]

VARIETY. A term indicating a lower grade of subdivision, next to the species; as the different sorts of pears or apples.

VARIOLÆ. Pustular shields, such as are found in the genus *Variolaria*.

VARIOLARIA. A spurious genus of *Fungi*, arising from *Porina pertusa*, the soridia being multiplied at the expense of the fruit, and often to such an extent as to obliterate the crust altogether. In very old specimens the crust quite vanishes, and the productions are then referred to *Lepraria*. [M. J. B.]

VARIUS. Liable to change—of colour.

VARNISH-TREE, BLACK. *Melanorrhœa usitatissima*. —, FALSE. *Ailantus glandulosa*. —, JAPAN. *Rhus vernicifera*. —, MARTABAN. *Melanorrhœa usitatissima*. —, NEW GRENADA. *Elæagia utilis*. —, SYLHET. *Semecarpus Anacardium*.

VARRONIA. A genus of *Boraginaceæ*, consisting of three species, two of which are found in Tropical America, and one in Africa. *V. rotundifolia* is one of the chief features of the Peruvian deserts, and produces a fleshy fruit, which fattens poultry. The *Varronias* are bushes or small trees, with simple ovate or nearly orbicular leaves, and terminal panicles bearing highly ornamental white or yellow flowers. The calyx is five-toothed striate and nearly bell-shaped; the corolla funnel-shaped; the stamens are five in number and exserted; and the fruit a fleshy drupe, including a two-to four-celled nut, each cell containing one seed.   [B. S.]

VARSAR. A Sanscrit name for the aromatic seeds of *Cleome pentaphylla.*

VASA. The tubes which occur in the interior of plants, and serve for the conveyance of sap or air. *V. laticis* and *propria* are names given to the milk-vessels or cinenchyma; *V. spiralia, chymifera,* and *spiroidea* are spiral vessels; *V. scalariformia, annulata,* and *moniliformia* are modified spiral vessels or ducts; *V. porosa* and *punctata* are the dotted vessels which constitute bothrenchyma; and *V. exhalantia* are the stomates.

VASCOA. The two South African plants to which this generic name was given by M. De Candolle are now by most botanists referred to *Rafnia,* of which they are allowed to form a section, characterised by the flowers having the lower or keel-petals blunt instead of beaked as in the true *Rafnias,* and by their leaves clasping the stem. Both species are shrubs from two to five feet high, with simple roundish heart-shaped leaves, placed alternately upon the lower parts of the branches and oppositely upon the upper; the latter bearing clusters of yellow pea-shaped flowers in their axils—the genus belonging to the peaflowered section of *Leguminosæ.*

The Dutch colonists at the Cape of Good Hope call *V. amplexicaulis* Zoethout-boschje or Liquorice-bush, on account of its roots tasting like liquorice, for which they are a good substitute. A decoction of them is also used as a demulcent in catarrh and disorders of the chest; while a similar preparation of the other species (*V. perfoliata*) acts as a powerful diuretic, and is considered serviceable in various forms of dropsy.   [A. S.]

VASCULAR, VASCULOSE. Containing spiral vessels or their modifications.

VASCULAR SYSTEM. All that part of the interior structure of a plant into whose composition spiral vessels or their modifications enter.

VASCULUM. A pitcher-shaped leaf. Also a case in which botanists place their freshly-gathered specimens, when on a journey.

VASE-SHAPED. Formed like a flower-pot.

VASIFORM TISSUE. Ducts, that is tubes having the appearance of spiral vessels and bothrenchyma.

VATAIREA. The name of a tree of the papilionaceous subdivision of the *Leguminosæ,* having the leaves unequally pinnate, and grey beneath; and the pod leathery roundish compressed, brown, grooved at the margins, indehiscent, and containing a large flattened seed. The flower is not described. The seeds of *V. guianensis* are said to be pounded and mixed with lard, as an ointment in cases of ringworm and other skin-diseases. The tree is, as its name implies, a native of Guiana.   [M. T. M.]

VATERIA. One of the genera of the *Dipterocarpaceæ,* comprising certain Indian trees, whose flowers are of a whitish colour, and borne on terminal or axillary panicles. They have a five-parted calyx (the segments of which occasionally enlarge as the fruit ripens), five petals, numerous stamens, and a three-valved somewhat spongy fruit containing a single seed, and partially invested by the reflexed calyx.

V. indica yields a useful gum-resin, called Indian Copal, Piney Varnish, White Dammer, or Gum-anine. The resin is procured by cutting a notch in the tree, so that the juice may flow out and become hardened by exposure to the air. It is employed in India as a varnish for carriages, pictures, &c. On the Malabar Coast it is made use of in the manufacture of candles, which burn with a clear light and an agreeable fragrance, and do not require snuffing. The Portuguese employ the resin instead of incense. Ornaments are fashioned from it under the name of amber. Medicinally it is employed in rheumatic and other affections. The seeds are used to obviate nausea; while the timber is in request for building purposes. [M. T. M.]

VATICA. A genus nearly allied in botanical structure and other points to *Vateria.* It consists of Indian trees, abounding in resin. The flowers are yellow, in terminal or axillary panicles. The five segments of the calyx become ultimately enlarged and leaf-like, and surmount the leathery or woody fruit, which contains a single seed, and opens partially by two valves. *V. Tumbugaia* yields a large quantity of resin, and its timber, like that of some allied species, is valued for constructive purposes.   [M. T. M.]

VAUBIER. (Fr.) *Hakea.*

VAUCHERIA. A genus of green-spored *Algæ,* named after the celebrated Genevan botanist Vaucher, belonging to the natural order *Siphoneæ,* characterised by simple or slightly and irregularly-branched threads producing short lateral curved antheridia, which yield a multitude of minute spermatozoids (which move about by means of two long cilia), and cysts in which a single zoospore variously ciliate is formed after impregnation. The species occur on mud or stones in salt or fresh water, forming generally dense spongy dark-green tufts, or upon the naked soil in fields and gardens, where they present a web of matted threads. One or two are very troublesome in greenhouses, by running over the soil in pots which contain delicate seedlings. The changes in the spores produced by impregnation, and the consequent formation of a surrounding membrane, have been closely observed by Pringsheim, whose observations should be compared with those of Thuret on the impregnation of the spores in *Fucus*. Little is known of exotic species, as it is scarcely possible to recognise them from dried specimens, which lose all their distinctive characteristics.   [M. J. B.]

VAUQUELINIA. A genus of *Rosaceæ*, comprising a Mexican tree, with entire saw-toothed leaves, and corymbs of white flowers. The tube of the calyx is hemispherical, its limb five-parted; petals five; stamens fifteen to twenty, inserted with the petals into the throat of the calyx; ovary five-celled; styles five, distinct; stigmas capitate; fruit capsular five-valved, surrounded by the persistent calyx; seeds ten, winged above.   [M. T. M.]

VAUTHIERA. A genus of cyperaceous plants belonging to the tribe *Rhynchosporeæ*. Inflorescence in crowded spikelets; scales imbricated spathe-like one-flowered, the exterior ones empty; stamens three; nut bluntly triquetrous. *V. australis*, a native of New Zealand, is the only species described.   [D. M.]

VAUVAN. *Abelmoschus esculentus*.

VAVÆA. A genus of *Meliaceæ*, peculiar to the Tonga and Feejee Islands, and consisting of two species, both trees of middle size, having alternate and (unlike most *Meliaceæ*) simple leaves. The flowers are paniculate and white; the calyx is four to seven-cleft; the petals short free, and four to seven in number; the fruit a round three to four-celled berry.   [B. S.]

VEGETABLE. Of the nature of a plant. Also applied in a special sense to any esculent plant.

VEGETABLE BRIMSTONE. Lycopodium powder.

VEGETABLE GOLD. An acid extracted from the roots of *Trixis Pipizahuac*.

VEGETABLE HAIR. *Tillandsia usneoides*.

VEGETABLE IVORY. The albumen of the nut of *Phytelephas macrocarpa*.

VEGETABLE KINGDOM. That division of organic nature which comprises plants.

VEGETABLE LEATHER. *Euphorbia punicea*.

VEGETABLE MARROW. The Succade Gourd, a variety of *Cucurbita Pepo*; also *Persea gratissima*.

VEGETABLE SHEEP. *Raoulia eximia*.

VEGETABLE SILK. A cotton-like material obtained from the seed-pods of *Chorisia speciosa*.

VEGETABLE TALLOW. A fatty substance obtained from *Stillingia sebifera*, *Vateria indica*, and other plants.

VEGETABLE WAX. A ceraceous excretion obtained from different parts of various plants, as the coating on the fruits of *Myrica cerifera*.

VEGETATE. To grow, after the manner of a plant.

VEGETATION. A term applied to plants in general.

VEILED. The same as Velate.

VEILLEUSE. (Fr.) *Colchicum autumnale*.

VEINED. Traversed by veins, as the parenchyma of a leaf.

VEINING. The arrangement of veins.

VEINLESS. Having no veins.

VEINLETS. Veins of the smallest size.

VEINS. The fibrovascular tissue of leaves, through which sap is carried into the parenchyma. *Costal* or *primary veins* are such as spring from the midrib; *external veins* are those next the edge.

VEITCHIA. This name was originally proposed by Herbert for *Barbacenia squamata*. It has since been applied by Dr. Lindley to a curious Japanese conifer, of which imperfect specimens only were available for examination; but this has now been shown by Professor Oliver to be nothing, but a monstrous condition of some Japanese conifer, the name of which has not been yet ascertained.   [T. M.]

VELAME DO CAMPO. *Croton campestris*.

VELAR. (Fr.) *Erysimum*.

VELARET. (Fr.) *Sisymbrium Irio*.

VELATE. Partially concealed from view; veiled.

VELEZIA. A small genus of *Caryophyllaceæ*, from the Mediterranean region. It is nearly allied to *Tunica*, but has a more slender calyx, and almost always only five stamens. They are annuals, with squarrosely and dichotomously-branching stems, linear subulate opposite leaves, and solitary axillary red flowers on short rigid peduncles.   [J. T. S.]

VELLA. A genus of *Cruciferæ*, from the western part of the Mediterranean region, consisting of erect pilose shrubs, with obovate leaves, and erect subterminal racemes of yellow flowers. The pouch is two-valved ovate compressed, crowned by the persistent style; seeds one or two in each cell.   [J. T. S.]

VELLANGA. An Indian name for the Wood Apple, *Feronia elephantum*.

VELLEJA. A genus of Australian herbs, belonging to the *Goodeniaceæ*, and distinguished by their three to four-leaved unequal calyx, by the corolla-tube being split at the end with a two-lipped limb, by the distinct anthers and undivided stigma, and by the presence of a gland between the two front stamens. They are nearly related to *Euthales*.   [T. M.]

VELLOMARDOO. An Indian wood, *Terminalia alata*.

VELLOZIA. A genus of *Hæmodoraceæ*, chiefly Brazilian, having leafy dichotomously-branched stems, bearing linear or linear-lanceolate leaves, arranged either spirally or in three rows, rarely in a distichous manner. The flowers are large, white blue or violet, and solitary. The perianth-tube isconnate with the ovary, its limb six-parted and campanulate; the stamens are sometimes six in number free, sometimes indefinite and collected in clusters. The ovary is inferior three-celled, the style triquetrous and tripartite, and the stigma

Vellozia compacta.

capitately trigonous. The capsule is subglobose, with numerous seeds. There are two groups included in the genus : *Xerophyta*, which are those with six free stamens; and *Vellozia* proper, in which the stamens are twelve, fifteen, eighteen, or twenty-four, in three or six phalanges, naked or coalescent with scales at the base. These plants are so abundant as to give a character to the dry mountain regions of Brazil. *V. compacta* is a fair representative of the family.   [T. M.]

VELLUS. The stipe of certain fungals.

VELONIA. The acorns of *Quercus Ægilops.*

VELOTE. (Fr.) *Dillwynia.*

VELTHEIMIA. A genus of *Liliaceæ* from the Cape of Good Hope. It comprises bulbous herbs, with lanceolate undulated leaves, and a scape bearing a raceme of nodding flowers, usually fawn-coloured and white or green. The perianth is cylindrical tubular, with a very short six-toothed limb. The capsule is three-winged, the seeds subsolitary in each cell, with a hard black seed-coat. *V. viridifolia* and *V. glauca* are sometimes cultivated, and are tolerably hardy.   [J. T. S.]

VELUM. The annulus of certain fungals.

VELUMEN. The velvety coating formed over some leaves, by short soft hairs.

VELUTINOUS. Velvety; having a hairy surface, which in texture resembles velvet, as in *Rochea coccinea.*

VELVET-BUR. *Priva echinata.*

VELVET-FLOWER. *Amaranthus caudatus.*

VELVET-LEAF. *Cissampelos Pareira*; also *Sida Abutilon* and *Lavatera arborea.*

VELVET-SEED. *Guettarda elliptica.*

VELVETY. The same as Velutinous.

VELVOTE FAUSSE. (Fr.) *Linaria spuria.* —VRAIE. *Linaria Elatine.*

VENÆ. The veins of plants.

VENATICA, or VINATICO. One of the shipbuilding woods recognised at Lloyds ; a coarse kind of mahogany obtained in Madeira from *Persea indica.*

VENATION. The arrangement of veins in a leaf or other organ.

VENEFICIUM. Plants like animals are liable to be affected by poisonous substances, whether in a liquid or gaseous form, and it often becomes a matter of considerable importance on civil trials to be able to give accurate information on the subject. Where poisons in a solid form are liable to rapid dissolution, where a strong solution is present, or the atmosphere highly impregnated with gaseous elements, rapid destruction will take place; but a more gradual decay may be produced by the constant presence of noxious matter, as evidenced by the condition of trees in large towns, or in the neighbourhood of extensive gas or other chemical works. The taint may be communicated immediately, by admission of the noxious air, through the breathing pores of the leaves, or by absorption from the soil. In some cases, as in subjection to the fumes of ignited brimstone, death is almost immediate.

Poisons sometimes affect the irritability of plants, as in the repression of the curious motions of the leaves of the sensitive plant. Fungi are in some cases unaffected by poisons which would destroy phænogams. They appear, for instance, in tan-pits, where no phænogam could exist, and many moulds are developed in solutions of poisonous metallic salts, as of copper arsenic and mercury. The metal is sometimes deposited on the threads in a solid form by a sort of electrotyping. Plants also are sometimes injured by substances which are essential to the existence of others. Rhododendrons, for instance, have an antipathy to lime, as is sometimes curiously evidenced in Wales, in districts where geological formations abounding in or destitute of lime happen to be contiguous. [M. J. B.]

VENGAY. An Indian name for the astringent gum-resin of *Pterocarpus Marsupium.*

VENIDIUM. A genus of Cape herbs, of the family *Compositæ.* The leaves are generally somewhat woolly ; the involucre is bell-shaped, and consists of numerous leafy scales outside, the inner ones being membranous; the receptacle is flat, usually destitute of scales; the corollas of the ray ligulate, female, those of the disk tubular, perfect. The achenes are smooth, each with three dorsal wings, the two side ones with infolded margins, and larger than the central one, which is straight. Pappus none, or of four small scales. [M. T. M.]

VENIVEL. *Coscinium fenestratum.*

VENOSE. Having many branched veins, as in reticulated leaves. *Indirectly venose* is when lateral veins are combined within the margin, and emit other little veins.

VENTENATIA. The only known species of this genus of *Ternstræmiaceæ* is a native of Benin, on the coast of Western Tropical Africa. It forms a small tree, and has egg-shaped taper-pointed stalked glaucous leaves, and large scarlet flowers, having a trilobed calyx, eleven or twelve spreading oblong petals blunt at the top and tapering to the base, numerous free stamens, a five-celled ovary containing numerous ascending ovules attached to the central angle, and a simple long style bearing a somewhat five-lobed stigma. [A. S.]

VENTILAGO. A name, derived from the Latin words *ventilo* 'to blow' and *ago* 'to drive away,' given to a small genus of *Rhamnaceæ*, in consequence of its fruits terminating in an oblong flat thin wing, by means of which they are scattered by the wind. These fruits are one-seeded woody nuts, seated upon or surrounded by the persistent base of the calyx. The species all belong to the tropics of the Eastern Hemisphere, and are tall climbing shrubs with stiff woody branches, and alternate short-stalked leathery feather-veined leaves, which are marked on the upper side with close transverse veinlets. The flowers grow in small axillary or terminal panicles, and have a spreading five-cleft calyx, five petals, as many stamens, and a two-celled ovary immersed in the flat fleshy disk, and terminating upwards in two short conical styles or stigmas.

V. maderaspatana, a common plant in Ceylon and the Indian Peninsula, and found also in Tenasserim, is employed by the native dyers of Mysore for producing an orange-red dye. Another Indian species, *V. calyculata*, a native of the central and northern parts of India, has until recently been confounded with *V. madera-patana*, and is probably equally serviceable for dyeing purposes.　　　　　　　[A. S.]

VENTRAL. Belonging to the anterior surface of anything, as a vertical section, which is the line running down the front of a carpel on the side next the axis.

VENTRICOSE. Swelling unequally on one side, as the corolla of many labiate and personate plants.

VENULÆ PROPRIÆ. The veinlets which first leave the costal or primary veins.

VENUS' BATH. *Dipsacus sylvestris*: so named from water collecting in the connate bases of the opposite leaves.

VENUS' COMB. *Scandix Pecten-veneris.*

VENUS' FLYTRAP. *Dionæa muscipula.*

VENUS' HAIR. *Adiantum Capillus-veneris.*

VENUS' LOOKING-GLASS. *Specularia Speculum.*

VENUS' NAVELWORT. *Omphalodes linifolia.*

VEPRIS. A genus of *Rutaceæ*, comprising a small tree native of the Mauritius. The flowers are of a whitish colour, the males and females on the ends of different branches. The calyx is short, four-parted; petals four, longer than the calyx, spreading. In the males are eight stamens, those opposite to the petals being dwarfer than the rest, all inserted on a short stalk supporting the four rudimentary ovaries. In the females the ovaries are placed on a short gland-like eight-lobed stalk, or gynophore surrounded by eight minute scales. The fruit is fleshy dotted, four-furrowed and four-celled. The generic name is derived from the Greek *vepres*, a 'briar' or 'bramble.'　　　　　　[M. T. M.]

VERATRIA, or VERATRINE. An acrid alkaline principle found in *Veratrum* and *Asagræa*.

VERATRUM. A genus of perennial herbs, natives of mountainous regions of Europe and North America. The genus is included in the order *Melanthaceæ*, and comprises plants with creeping roots, erect stalks, ovate pointed leaves, and panicles of polygamous flowers. The perianth has

Veratrum album.

six spreading lobes and a very short tube; there are six stamens, inserted into the base of the segments, the anthers opening transversely; and the capsule is three-horned. These plants are remarkable for their powerfully acrid properties. The one best known is *V. album*, called White Hellebore, although it has little in common with the true hellebore (*Helleborus*) except acridity. The rootstocks of *V. album* are collected in the Alps and the Pyrenees for medicinal purposes. They are extremely acrid, and in poisonous doses produce inflammation of the stomach and bowels, and finally insensibility and death. The drug is rarely employed in this country. Its effects seem to be due to the presence of *veratria*, an acrid alkaline substance (see ASAGRÆA). Gardeners make use of *V. album* powdered to destroy caterpillars. *V. viride*, a North American species, is used for similar purposes, but seems rather less powerful than the European plant. Besides those above mentioned, other species are in cultivation, many of them handsome objects when in bloom. Although containing so powerful a poison, slugs and snails seem to be particularly fond of the leaves of these plants.   [M. T. M.]

VERBACHINA. The Mexican name of *Phytolacca octandra*.

VERBASCUM. The Mullein genus is distinguished from its congeners in the tribe *Verbasceæ*, and indeed from almost the entire order of *Scrophulariaceæ*, by having five fertile stamens. Its flowers have a deeply five-cleft or five-parted calyx, a very short-tubed corolla with five broad rounded slightly unequal lobes, stamens with all the filaments woolly or the two lower ones smooth, and a thickish style flattened towards the point. The genus is widely dispersed over Europe, Western and Central Asia, and Northern Africa. An immense number of species have been described, but many of them are, according to Mr. Bentham, merely varieties, though he himself enumerates no fewer than eighty-three true species and nine doubtful ones. Six are indigenous to Great Britain. They are tall erect strong-growing herbs, usually lasting for two years, and are frequently covered all over with thick wool. Their leaves are alternate coarse and more or less toothed, the root-leaves very large and stalked, while those of the stem become gradually smaller towards the summit, and have no distinct stalks. The yellow brown purple or rarely white flowers are of short duration, and are succeeded by globular or egg-shaped fruits, which split through the partition into two valves.

The thick woolly leaves of *V. Thapsus*, the Great Mullein, have a mucilaginous bitterish taste, and a decoction of them is employed in domestic practice in catarrhs and diarrhœa. They are also used as emollient applications to hard tumours, and in pulmonary complaints in cattle—hence one of its popular names is Bullock's Lungwort. The ancient Greeks are said to have used the leaves as lamp-wieks, while the Romans, who called the plant 'candelaria,' dipped its stalks in suet to burn at fune-

rals. The English name, Hig-taper or High-taper, appears to allude to a similar use. This was a famous plant with the witches of old, whence it has sometimes been called Hag-taper.   [A. S.]

VERBENACEÆ. (*Vitices, Verbenæ*). An order of monopetalous dicotyledons, consisting of trees shrubs or herbs, with the leaves (at least the lower ones) usually opposite without stipules, and flowers in terminal spikes heads or panicles, or in opposite cymes or clusters. They closely resemble *Labiatæ* in their tubular or campanulate calyx, in their corolla being for the most part irregularly five-lobed, in their stamens being either two or four in pairs, and in their two or four ovules being enclosed in as many cells; but they differ in their ovary, which is not lobed, and has a terminal style. They also rarely have the aromatic properties of *Labiatæ*, the upper leaves are occasionally alternate, the ovules are not always erect, and the fruit rarely separates into distinct seed-like nuts.

The species are numerous, mostly tropical or from the temperate regions of the Southern Hemisphere, very few being found in Europe, Northern Asia, or North America. They are distributed into above forty genera, arranged in three principal tribes:—1. *Verbeneæ*, with a racemose spicate or capitate inflorescence and erect ovules; sixteen genera, of which *Verbena*, *Lippia*, and *Lantana* are the most numerous in species. To this tribe should also be referred *Phryma*, a curious North American and Asiatic herb which, on account of the convolute cotyledons of its seeds, some botanists separate into an order by itself called *Phrymaceæ.*—2. *Viteæ*, with a cymose inflorescence and laterally-attached ovules; this comprises twenty genera, amongst which the most important are *Tectona*, *Callicarpa*, *Clerodendron*, and *Vitex.*—3. *Avicennieæ*, with pendulous ovules, confined usually to the genus *Avicennia*, but which might well include the *Myoporaceæ*, which most botanists regard as a distinct order.

VERBENA. A genus of *Verbenaceæ*, consisting of numerous species of herbs or shrubs scattered over the tropical and subtropical regions of the world, being specially abundant in America and rarer in Asia. They have opposite leaves, and sessile bracteated flowers, in single or often panicled axillary or terminal spikes. The calyx is tubular and five-toothed, with one of the teeth often shorter than the rest; the corolla also tubular, straight or more generally curved, with a spreading limb, somewhat unequally five-cleft; the stamens included, the upper pair sometimes without anthers; the style slender, and the stigma capitate. The ripe fruit splits into two or four seed-like nutlets, each containing a single seed.   [W. C.]

Various species of this genus and innumerable varieties are extensively cultivated for their fragrance and beauty; but the remarkable virtues which the common Verbena was in olden times reputed to possess are apparently imaginary. The common name of *V. officinalis*, Vervain or Vervein, our only native species, is derived from the Celtic *ferfean*, from *fer* ' to drive away ' and *faen* ' a stone,'—the herb having been much used in affections of the bladder, and particularly in calculus, perhaps for no better reason than that it is usually found growing amongst rubbish or in stony places. The flowers were formerly held in great repute, like those of the *Euphrasia* or eyebright, as a remedy for defective vision; in both cases the pretty bright-eyed corolla was supposed to point to their uses.

Vervein has ever been held to be ' an herb of grace,' and so highly was it esteemed that people are said to have worn it about the person—a correspondent in *Notes and Queries* says, as a remedy against blasts, but we have been taught also for general good luck ; though to make it properly effective, so says the correspondent just referred to,—

' When they gather it for this purpose, firste they crosse the herbe with their hand, and then they blesse it thus :

Hallowed be thou, Vervein
  As thou growest on the ground,
For in the Mount of Calvary,
  There thou was first found.
Thou healedst our Saviour Jesus Christ,
  And staunchedst His bleeding wound ;
In the name of Father, Son, and Holy Ghost,
  I take thee from the ground ! '

We doubt whether botanists will agree as to the locality just given for Vervein, but in America are several species from which the infinite varieties of our garden Verbenas have been derived.   [J. B.]

VERBENA. The *Aloysia citriodora* is the Lemon-scented Verbena of the gardens. The Verbena of the perfumers, so much prized for its lemon-like scent, is the lemon-grass, *Andropogon Schœnanthus* or *A. citratum*, from which the ' oil of verbena ' is extracted.

VERBESINA. A rather extensive American genus of *Compositœ*, the type of one of the divisions (*Verbesineœ*) of the large tribe *Senecionideœ*. It is characterised by its flower-heads being surrounded by an involucre composed of two or more series of scales, the florets being seated on a flat or convex chaffy disk or receptacle ; by the style-branches being fringed towards the top, and ending in conical appendages ; and also by the fruits or achenes being flattened and generally winged at the edges, and furnished with two stiff awns at the top. The species vary from herbs to shrubs or even small trees, sometimes growing as high as twenty feet ; and have toothed or pinnately-lobed opposite or alternate leaves, and yellow or rarely white flowers ; sometimes the ray florets are white, and the rest pale-yellow. Very few possess any interest beyond the botanical characters. The Ram-til of India was formerly referred to this genus, and is frequently found mentioned under the name *V. sativa* in modern botanical works,

though long ago separated under the name of *Guizotia oleifera*. The Mexicans use a decoction of the Capitaneja (*V. Capitaneja*), as a vulnerary, applying it to the sores caused by the saddle on the backs of horses and mules. See GUIZOTIA. [A. S.]

VERDAN. (Fr.) A kind of Olive.

VERDIAN. (Fr.) *Salix monandra*.

VERDIGRIS-GREEN. Deep green, with a mixture of blue.

VERDOLE. (Fr.) A kind of Olive.

VERDURE DE MER. (Fr.) *Pyrola rotundifolia*.

VERGE DE JACOB. (Fr.) *Asphodelus tuberosus*. — DE PASTEUR. *Dipsacus pilosus*. — D'OR. *Solidago virga aurea*. — SANGUINE. *Cornus sanguinea*.

VERGERETTE, or VERGEROLLE. (Fr.) *Erigeron*.

VERGNÉ, or VERNE. (Fr.) *Alnus glutinosa*.

VERMICULAR. Worm-shaped ; thick, and almost cylindrical, but bent in different places, as the roots of *Polygonum Bistorta* and the spadix of *Anthurium Scherzerianum*.

VERMILLON-PLANTE. (Fr.) *Phytolacca*.

VERNALIS, VERNUS. Appearing in the spring of the year.

VERNATION. The manner in which leaves are arranged within the leaf-bud.

VERNICOSE. Covered with a natural varnish.

VERNIMBOK. (Fr.) The Pernambuco dyewood.

VERNIS DU CANADA. (Fr.) *Rhus radicans*. — DU JAPON. *Ailantus glandulosus*. — DE LA CHINE. *Calophyllum Augia*.

VERNIX. *Thuja articulata*.

VERNONELLA. A somewhat shrubby herbaceous plant of the *Compositœ*. It is a native of Natal, and has linear sessile leaves, solitary terminal heads of flowers, surrounded by a hemispherical involucre of numerous membranous coloured scales, the outer of which are oblong, irregularly notched, the inner more lanceolate. The receptacle is somewhat convex scaleless, pitted; corolla regularly five-cleft ; branches of the style awl-shaped, hispid ; fruits cylindrical, hairy ; pappus in two rows, the outer serrated, the inner feathery. [M.T.M.]

VERNONIACEÆ. One of the large tribes of *Compositœ*, characterised, with few exceptions, by alternate leaves, rayless flower-heads, and long subulate stigmatic branches to the style. The species are numerous in America, with a few others dispersed over the warmer regions of the Old World.

VERNONIA. One of the most extensive genera of the large order *Compositœ*, and the type of the tribe *Vernoniaceæ*, characterised by having a cylindrical style, with tapering branches covered all over with bristles. It has a wide geographical range, its representatives occurring in most parts of the warm regions of the world, but abounding in the greatest number in the Western Hemisphere. Upwards of 400 species are described, differing greatly in habit and general appearance, some being annual and others perennial herbs, and some erect and others climbing shrubs, while a few attain the size of small trees. Their leaves are alternate; and their flower-heads usually in terminal cymes or panicles, each head consisting of numerous (or rarely of only a few) tubular equal perfect florets, generally of a purplish or blue colour. The achenes are angular rarely cylindrical, mostly marked with parallel longitudinal raised lines, and crowned with a usually double pappus, consisting of an inner series of hair-like bristles surrounded by very much shorter scaly ones. Very few of these plants appear to be applied to any useful purpose. In Southern India a solid green-coloured oil, or fat, is obtained by pressure from the seeds of *V. anthelmintica*, an annual species common in many parts of that country. *V. cinerea* is employed medicinally by Hindoo doctors, a decoction of it being used in intermittent fevers.   [A. S.]

VERONICA. A large genus of *Scrophulariaceæ*, comprising herbs or undershrubs widely distributed through the temperate and colder regions of the globe. The leaves are opposite or whorled; and the flowers grow in axillary or terminal spikes or racemes, the corolla having a very short tube, and a rotate four-cleft limb; the stamens are only two in number; and the capsule is flattened.

The species are numerous and ornamental, the British ones being all herbaceous. Among them may be mentioned *V. spicata*, with terminal spikes of blue flowers, often cultivated in gardens. *V. Anagallis* grows in ditches, and has lance-shaped leaves, and axillary clusters of flowers; and *V. Beccabunga* is also found in moist places, and has rather fleshy blunt leaves, which are considered to be antiscorbutic. The curious name of this plant seems to be derived from the old word *beck* 'a rill or ditch,' and *bung* 'a purse.' *V. Chamædrys*, the Germander Speedwell, one of the loveliest of our wild flowers, has coarsely-toothed leaves and axillary clusters of large deep-blue blossoms. The cultivated species are numerous, many of them being handsome hardy border plants. Some of the New Zealand shrubby kinds (as *V. salicifolia*, *speciosa*, *Hulkeana*, &c.) are particularly handsome as greenhouse plants. [M. T. M.]

VÉRONIQUE. (Fr.) *Veronica.* — DES JARDINIERS. *Lychnis Flos-cuculi.* — FEMELLE, or PETIT CHÊNE. *Veronica Chamædrys.* — GERMANDRÉE. *Veronica Teucrium.*

VERPA. A genus of *Fungi*, closely allied

to *Morchella*, but distinguished by the cap being hollow or inflated below, and equally depressed all round. The surface is nearly even or wrinkled, but never pitted as in the morels. The species are few in number, and two only have been gathered in this country. Of these we once gathered *V. digitaliformis* in abundance, but for the last twenty-five years we have visited the original spot annually without finding a single specimen. Nothing is said of its esculent qualities, but it is probably as wholesome as morels.   [M. J. B.]

VERRUCÆ. Warts; sessile elevations of a glandular nature.

VERRUCÆFORM. Shaped like a wart.

VERRUCARIÆI. A natural order of lichens belonging to the division whose fruit is in the form of perithecia (*Angiocarpi*). These are scattered and immersed in the thallus, which is continuous, and not furnished with any distinct fertile pustules as in *Trypethelea*. They are mostly inhabitants of the trunks of trees, though sometimes they grow on the hardest rocks, and occasionally on pebbles constantly immersed in water. The typical genus *Verrucaria* is distinguished from *Sphæriacei* merely by the thin crust producing gonidia. In cases where the crust has vanished or is abortive, it is sometimes difficult to distinguish them. Species of this order occur in all parts of the world, but the finest are inhabitants of the Tropics, where the perithecia sometimes acquire a considerable size. Those who wish for information respecting British species should consult Leighton's work on *Angiocarpous Lichens*, published by the Ray Society. It should be observed that the genus *Endothia*, distinguished from *Verrucaria* by its naked spores, consists merely of the pycnidia or spermogonia of different sporidiferous lichens.   [M. J. B.]

VERRUCOSE. Covered with warts; the same as Tubercled.

VERRUCULARIA. The name of a Brazilian shrub of the family *Malpighiaceæ*. The stipules are combined into a sheath surrounding the stem; and the flowers are arranged in terminal panicles, and are of a yellowish colour. The calyx is deeply five-cleft, and has ten glands: the petals are five, stalked unequal; stamens ten, all fertile, the anthers provided with a wart-like appendage near the top; ovary three-lobed, with three styles; fruit bursting into six valves. The name of the genus is derived from the wart-like excrescences on the anthers.   [M. T. M.]

VERRUCULOSE. Covered with little warts.

VERSATILE. Swinging freely, as the oscillating anthers of grasses.

VERSCHAFFELTIA. A genus of *Palmaceæ*, comprising a very handsome species, recently introduced into Europe from the island of Seychelles, and at first distinguished by the temporary name of *Regelia* *majestica.* The fruit is globose drupaceous, with the scar of the stigma basilar; the endocarp is woody and rugose; the seed erect, with vertical furrows; the albumen densely and profoundly anastomosanti-ruminate; and the embryo basilar, erect. The species, called *V. splendida*, has a simple erect stem, clothed with spreading black needle-shaped spines; and the fronds are broad and entire, with the apex bifid, and the edges serrated.　　[T. M.]

VERTEBRATE. Contracted at intervals, like the vertebra of animals, there being an articulation at each contraction, as in some leaves.

VERTEX. The summit of any part.

VERTICAL. Placed in a direction from the base to the apex.

VERTICIL. A whorl; a ring of organs on the same plane. A *spurious verticil* is the same as a Verticillaster.

VERTICILLARIA. The name of a Peruvian tree, constituting a genus of *Clusiaceæ.* The leaves are acuminate; the flowers perfect; calyx of two coloured sepals; petals four; stamens numerous, in many rows; ovary sessile, three-celled; stigma three-lobed, concave; fruit capsular, three-valved, three-seeded. This tree yields an abundance of balsamic resin.　[M. T. M.]

VERTICILLASTER. A false whorl formed in labiate plants by the presence of short-stalked or sessile cymes in the axils of opposite leaves.

VERTICILLATÆ. A Linnæan natural order equivalent to the more modern *Labiatæ.*

VERTICILLATE. When several bodies form a ring round a common axis, as leaves round a stem, or the sepals petals and stamens round an ovary.

VERTICORDIA. A genus of *Chamælauciaceæ,* consisting of shrubs, natives of South-western Australia. Their leaves are generally crowded small heath-like; and the flowers are white pink or yellow, in terminal corymbs, each flower protected by two concave bracts, which ultimately become spreading, and sometimes fall off. Calyx adherent to the ovary, its limb five-lobed, the lobes palmately-divided and feathery; petals five, entire or palmately-divided; stamens twenty, ten fertile, ten sterile alternating with the fertile, and having strap-shaped or three-cleft filaments; ovary one-celled; style filiform; fruit dry one-celled, one-seeded, indehiscent.　　[M. T. M.]

VERVAIN. *Verbena.* —, BASTARD. *Stachytarpha.*

VERVEINE. (Fr.) *Verbena.* — À BOUQUET or DE MIQUELON. *Verbena Aubletia.* — CITRONNELLE. *Aloysia citriodora.* — PUANTE. *Petiveria alliacea,* —, DE ST. DOMINGUE. *Heliotropium.*

VESALEA. A genus of *Caprifoliaceæ,* scarcely if at all differing from *Abelia,* to which the few species have been recently referred. See ABELIA.　　[W. C.]

VESCE. (Fr.) *Vicia.* — BLANCHE, or DU CANADA. *Vicia sativa.* — EN ÉPI. *Vicia Cracca.* — SAUVAGE. *Vicia sepium.*

VESCERON. (Fr.) *Vicia Cracca.*

VESI. *Afzelia bijuga,* one of the sacred trees of the Feejeans.

VESICARIA. A genus of *Cruciferæ,* natives of the Northern Hemisphere, distinguished by the globose or ovoid inflated pouch, with hemispherical valves, and numerous seeds (generally four to six in each cell). They are herbs, sometimes shrubby at the base, with oblong or linear entire or expand leaves, and terminal racemes of yellow flowers. *V. utriculata* is generally distributed throughout Southern Europe; it has bladder-like pouches, somewhat larger than a pea.　　[J. T. S.]

VESICLE. A little cell or bladder, one of the ultimate atoms of which the bulk of vegetable tissue is built up.

VESICULA. An air-cavity.

VESICULÆFORM, VESICULAR, VESICULATE. Inflated, bladdery.

VESICULIFERI. A synonym of *Physomycetes,* descriptive of those moulds which have their spores inclosed at first in a little globose transparent sac, as *Mucor* and *Ascophora.*　　[M. J. B.]

VESICULOSE. The same as Vesiculæform, &c.

VESPERTINUS. Appearing in the evening.

VESSE-LOUP. (Fr.) *Lycoperdon Bovista.*

VESSELS. See VASA.

VESTIA. A genus of *Solanaceæ,* containing a single species from Chili, an erect branching shrub, having the appearance of and nearly related to *Cestrum,* from which it differs chiefly in the fruit being a dry capsule, and not a berry.　[W. C.]

VETCH. *Vicia sativa.* —, BASTARD. *Phaca.* —, BASTARD HATCHET. *Biserrula Pelecinus.* —, BITTER. *Orobus;* also *Ervum Ervilia.* —, BLADDER. *Phaca.* —, COMMON. *Vicia sativa.* —, CHICKLING. *Lathyrus sativa.* —, GRASS. *Lathyrus Nissolia.* —, HATCHET. *Biserrula.* —, HORSESHOE. *Hippocrepis comosa.* —, KIDNEY. *Anthyllis Vulneraria.* — MILK. *Astragalus.* —, SENSITIVE JOINT. *Æschynomene.* —, TARE. *Ervum hirsutum.*

VETCHLING. *Lathyrus.*

VETIVER, or VETIVERT. (Fr.) The Khus-khus grass, *Andropogon muricatus.*

VETTILEI. An Indian name for *Chavica Betle.*

VEUVE. (Fr.) *Scabiosa purpurea.*

VEXILLARY. An æstivation in which one piece is much larger than the others, and is folded over them, they being arranged face to face, as in papilionaceous flowers.

VEXILLUM. The standard or fifth petal placed at the back of a papilionaceous corolla.

VIBORGIA. This name commemorates a Danish botanist, and is applied to a genus of *Leguminosæ*. The species are natives of the Cape of Good Hope, and have shrubby stems, somewhat spiny branches, palmate leaves, and yellow papilionaceous flowers. The calyx is bell-shaped, five-toothed; the vexillum deflected, the wings shorter than the keel, the stamens ten, monadelphous, the ovary stalked, with six ovules, and a thread-like style; and the pod stalked compressed winged, leathery or membranous, one or two-seeded. [M. T. M.]

VIBRISSEA. A small genus of *Fungi* closely allied to *Peziza*, but remarkable for the asci and thread-shaped sporidia bursting from the hymenium, though still remaining attached to it so as to render it velvety. The only well-known species, *V. truncorum*, is of a golden-yellow colour, and grows upon sticks or wood in water. It is very rare in this country. The genus derives its name from the vibrating of the sporidia and asci on the hymenium. When taken from the water it is perfectly smooth, but when exposed to the air and sun it is soon covered with threads, which are shot out of the hymenium, and wave to and fro with an oscillating motion. This very singular process is sometimes continued for several hours. [M. J. B.]

VIBURNUM. An extensive genus of *Caprifoliaceæ*, consisting of shrubs, natives of Europe, Asia, and North America, but not found in tropical regions. The leaves are opposite, and the flowers numerous, in large terminal cymes. Each flower has a minutely five-toothed calyx; a rotate or bell-shaped corolla, which is five-lobed at the edge; five stamens; two or three nearly sessile stigmas; and an ovary possessing in the young state two or three cells, but becoming one-celled and one-seeded as it ripens into the berry. The name of the genus is said to be derived from *vieo* 'to tie.' The ancients made use of the word *viburna* to signify any pliant branched plant, that could be used for tying or binding.

Two of the species grow wild in Britain, *V. Lantana* and *V. Opulus*. The former, commonly known by the name of the Wayfaring-tree, is a large shrub generally found growing in hedges or woods. Its leaves are broad, toothed, downy beneath, its flowers all perfect, and its berries flattened, first red, then black. The leaves and berries are astringent. The latter are used in Switzerland in the manufacture of ink, while the former yield with alum a yellow dye. The wood is white and hard, and useful for turnery

purposes. The rind of the root is used to make birdlime.

The other British species, *V. Opulus*, the Gueldres Rose, has smooth three to five-lobed leaves, and the outermost flowers are destitute of stamens, while by way of compensation the corolla is much enlarged. In the cultivated variety of *V. Opulus* all the flowers are affected in this way, so that the inflorescence becomes globular—whence the name Snowball-tree, by which it is frequently known. The red fruit is very ornamental in autumn. It is eaten in Norway and Sweden with honey and flour. A spirit is also distilled from it. The branches yield a yellow dye. The wood is used in Norway for making weavers' combs, shoemakers' pegs, tobacco-pipes, &c.

Many other kinds are grown in gardens, especially *V Tinus*, the Common Laurestine, a native of the South of Europe, &c. In Corsica it forms large woods. Its leaves are oblong permanent, hairy beneath, its flowers pinkish or white, appearing in winter, its berries dark-blue. This is a very valuable shrub, from its dense evergreen foliage and cheerful flowers. There are several varieties in cultivation. When grown as a standard for hall or conservatory decoration, the Laurestine rivals the bay in the beauty of its foliage and excels it in its flowers. [M T M.]

VICENI. Growing in twenties.

VICIA. A large genus of papilionaceous *Leguminosæ*, whose species are distributed throughout the temperate regions of the globe, and are occasionally found in mountainous districts in the Tropics, but have not hitherto been met with in Australia. They are weak plants, generally of climbing habit, with pinnate leaves, which latter terminate in tendrils, and have at their base lunate stipules. The flowers are solitary tufted or in stalked clusters. The style is cylindrical, with a tuft of hairs on the under-side, or with a slight downy ring around the stigma.

V. Faba, the common Field Bean, differs in habit from the rest of the genus in being erect; its tendrils are very minute, and its leaves somewhat fleshy. The flowers are large; white with a black spot, and very fragrant. The pod is leathery, tumid, spongy. It is sometimes considered as the representative of a distinct genus, FABA: which see. Mr. Church has recently shown that there exists at the base of the ripe pod, on the lower surface, a minute aperture, through which an evaporation of water takes place, so that the seeds become dry before the dehiscing of the pod. The plant is a native of Persia and the borders of the Caspian Sea, but is cultivated extensively in almost every quarter of the globe. Its roots are diuretic, while its seeds, in spite of their nutritious qualities, are not wholly destitute of poisonous ingredients. In this country the ripe seeds, or beans, are used in enormous quantities for feeding horses, and although largely cultivated here for that purpose, yet a considerable bulk is imported from Egypt.

In an unripe condition they are served up at our own tables.

V. sativa is the Tare or Vetch of our farmers, and is extensively grown as fodder for cattle. It is distinguished from most of the species growing in this country, either wild or cultivated, by its sessile solitary rarely twin flowers, and by its smooth seeds. *V. angustifolia* and *V. Bobartii* are merely narrow-leaved varieties of it. Several species besides the last-named are natives of this country. One of the commonest and most beautiful is *V. Cracca*, the Tufted Vetch, which has narrow tendril-bearing leaves, entire stipules, and stalked clusters of blue flowers. *V. sylvatica* is not so common; its flowers are white or pink, and streaked with purple veins. *V. Orobus* is an erect plant without tendrils, bearing flowers in stalked clusters. The other species growing wild in this country are less common. See also ERVUM. [M. T. M.]

VICTORIA. This truly royal genus of the *Nymphæaceæ* or Waterlily family includes one or (as some think) three species, of the highest interest from their beauty and curious conformation. They are aquatic plants, with thick fleshy rootstocks, marked with the scars of former leaves, and sending upwards numerous long cylindrical leafstalks, which are traversed in the interior by several air-canals, the larger of them arranged with much regularity, and are thickly covered on the outside by stout conical prickles. These prickles have spiral vessels and a small cavity in their interior, opening by a little pore at the top. From the under-surface of the base of the leafstalks numerous adventitious roots are given out. The blade of the leaf is peltate, circular in outline, and, when fully developed six to twelve feet in diameter, its margin uniformly turned upwards to the extent of two or three inches, so that the leaves when floating have the appearance of so many large shallow trays. The upper surface of the leaf is of a rich green colour, and studded with little boss-like prominences. The lower surface is of a deep-purple or violet hue, and traversed by several very prominent nerves, which radiate from the centre to the margin of the leaf, and are connected one with another by smaller nerves running transversely, so that the whole of the under-surface is divided by compartments into a number of irregularly quadrangular spaces or cells. The nerves themselves are permeated by air-canals, and covered by strong spines. Thus the enormous leaves are well adapted to float on the water, and the extent of surface exposed is so great, that a considerable weight can be supported without submerging them. Even a child of twelve years of age, may be borne up, if the precaution be taken of first placing on the leaf a small piece of board, to prevent the feet from tearing and slipping through its substance.

The flower-stalk has a similar outward appearance to that of the leaf, but is stouter, and its air-canals are arranged in a different manner. The flower-bud before expansion is pear-shaped. The calyx is adherent below to the ovary, and is here covered with prickles; its limb, however, is destitute of these appendages, and is divided into four ovate deciduous sepals, of a rich purple tint externally, whitish internally. The petals are very numerous, in several rows, and (as in our common waterlily) exhibit a gradual transition in their form to that of the stamens, so that it is somewhat difficult in all cases to decide where the one set of parts ceases, and the others begin. The outer petals are rather larger than the sepals or lobes of the calyx, oblong concave and white, the inner ones gradually becoming narrower, more pointed, and of a beautiful deep rose-colour. When fully expanded the outer petals are bent downwards, while the central rose-coloured ones, with the stamens, remain erect; and thus a noble appearance is presented, as of a central rose-coloured crown supported by a series of pure white and most gracefully-curved petals. The stamens are numerous, the outer ones somewhat lance-shaped, gracefully curved, of a fine rose-colour, and having two linear anther-cells on the inner face, near but not quite extending to the top. Within these fertile stamens are other sterile ones, smaller in size, less highly-coloured, arching over the stigmas, to which they approximate also in colour and form. The ovary is adherent to the calyx-tube, somewhat globular or top-shaped, its upper portion hollowed like a cup, and presenting in the centre a little rounded or conical knob. Along the upper margin of the cup are placed the stigmas, fleshy pointed bodies, somewhat flattened at the sides, and bent in the middle, so that their points project over the cup towards the centre. Each stigma has a prominent line along its upper surface, running down to the central knob, which is thus the focus of a series of ridges, radiating towards the stigmas. The interior of the ovary contains numerous cavities corresponding to the stigmas, and each containing several ovules. The fruit when ripe is a sort of globular berry, thickly beset with formidable prickles. The seeds escape by the rotting of the outer portions of the fruit.

These noble plants inhabit the tranquil rivers of South America, especially those which are tributary to the Amazon. They, differ in the size of the seeds and other particulars, but when it is remembered how variable aquatic plants are, it is better, for the present at least, to consider them as forms of one rather than as distinct species.

Generically *Victoria* is most nearly allied to *Euryale*, but it is distinguished by the deciduous sepals, by the gradual transition in the form of the petals to that of the stamens, by the more numerous cavities of the ovary, and other particulars. The leaf of *Euryale* is, however, an exact miniature copy of that of the *Victoria*, save that it is not turned up at the margin.

The earliest traveller who discovered this

plant was Hænke, in A.D. 1801. Bonpland subsequently met with it, but M. D'Orbigny was the first to send home specimens to Paris in 1828: they were, however, neglected or overlooked. In a work published some few years after this time, M. D'Orbigny mentions having discovered the plant in the River Parana in Guiana. It was known, he says, to the natives by the name of Irupé, in allusion to the shape of the leaves, which resembles that of the broad dishes used in the country. The Spaniards call the plant Water Maize, as they collect the seeds, and eat them roasted. In 1832 a German traveller found it in some tributaries of the Amazon; but it was not until the late Sir Robert Schomburgk discovered it in the Berbice River, in British Guiana, in the year 1837, that public attention was drawn to the magnificent plant. Sir Robert, in a letter to the Royal Geographical Society, describes the largest specimen he met with as having leaves six feet five inches in diameter, with a rim five to six inches high, and flowers a foot and a quarter across. The *Victoria* has now for some years been introduced to this country, and has delighted and astonished thousands, by the size of its leaves and the beauty and fragrance of its flowers. At Chatsworth, at Syon, at Kew, at Oxford and elsewhere, it has been grown to even larger size than it attains in its native rivers. The late Sir William Hooker published an account of it, splendidly illustrated, from which much of the above information has been derived.   [M. T. M.]

VICTORIALE. (Fr.) *Allium Victorialis.* — RONDE. *Gladiolus communis.*

VICTORIPERREA. An undescribed genus of *Pandanaceæ*, the sole species of which, *V. impavida*, is named and figured in Hombron and Jacquinot's *Voyage au pôle Sud*; but neither its native country, nor the characters upon which it is founded, are mentioned.   [A. S.]

VICUIBA. *Myristica Bicuhyba.*

VIDIMARAM. An Indian name for *Cordia Myxa.*

VIEUSSEUXIA. A genus of tuberous-rooted *Iridaceæ*, natives of the Cape of Good Hope, and named in honour of a Swiss physician. The species have narrow sword-shaped leaves, and a cylindrical branched stem, bearing stalked flowers originating from the axils of spathes. The perianth is six-parted: the three outer segments narrowed at the base into a sort of stalk, and clothed with hairs, the three inner portions much smaller, awl-shaped, or with three terminal points; the filaments are coherent so as to form a tube, and are inserted below into a disk surmounting the ovary; the style is short, and surmounted by three petaloid stigmas. The flowers of many of the species are very ornamental, on which account they are cultivated in this country, though frequently confounded with the closely-related *Moræa*.   [M. T. M.]

VIGNA. This is one of the genera founded upon plants originally referred to the old Linnæan genus *Dolichos*, belonging to the papilionaceous division of the *Leguminosæ*. It is distinguished by its pods being nearly cylindrical, instead of flattened as in *Dolichos*, and constricted between the seeds, which are separated from each other by thin spurious partitions. Its flowers have a bell-shaped four-cut calyx; a pea-like corolla having a roundish upper petal, with two ear-like appendages at the base; one free and nine united stamens; and a hairy-topped style, with the stigma on one side. The species, upwards of thirty of which are described, are dispersed over the tropics of both hemispheres, most numerously, however, on the American continent; and are herbs with twining or prostrate annual stems, trifoliate leaves, and axillary flower-stalks, having the flowers, which are usually yellow or purplish, disposed in short racemes or collected into heads.

V. sinensis is very extensively cultivated in the East, particularly in India, where its pulse is called Chowice, and forms, in conjunction with rice, a considerable part of the food of the Hindoos, the large amount of nutritive matter it contains compensating for the smaller quantity in the rice, which is so largely consumed by them. The Chinese, who call the plant Tow-Cok, cook and eat the green pods as we do kidney-beans. When ripe the pods are frequently as much as a yard long, and contain about twenty seeds, of variable colour and diversely marked. A variety of this plant (the *Dolichos melanophthalmus* of some authors) is cultivated in Italy and other parts of Southern Europe under the name of Fagiolo del Occhio.   [A. S.]

VIGNE. (Fr.) *Vitis.* — BLANCHE *Bryonia.* — DE JUDÉE. *Solanum Dulcamara.* — DE SALOMON. *Clematis mauritiana.* — DE VIERGE. *Ampelopsis hederacea.* — DU MONT IDA. *Vaccinium Vitis idœa.* — DU NORD. *Humulus Lupulus.* — ÉLÉPHANTÉ. *Cissus glauca.* — MALGACHE. *Buddlea madagascariensis.* — NOIRE SAUVAGE. *Tamus communis.* — SAUVAGE. *Vitis Labrusca.*

VIGNEAU. (Fr.) *Ulex europœus.*

VIGNETTE. (Fr.) *Spiræa Ulmaria*; also *Clematis*, and *Mercurialis annua.*

VIGNOLDIA. A little-known genus of *Cinchonaceæ*, comprising certain Abyssinian shrubs, with white or purple flowers. One of the sepals of the calyx exceeds the others in size. The fruit is capsular, two-celled, dehiscing from above downwards by two valves.   [M. T. M.]

VIGUIERA. A genus of *Compositæ*, whose species are natives of Tropical South America. The stems are herbaceous, branched, the leaves triplinerved, and the flower-heads in loose corymbs; involucre somewhat globose, of one or two rows of leafy scales; receptacle flat, studded over with scales that sheath round the fruits; florets strap-shaped at the outside, tubular in the centre of the head, all yellow; stig-mus awl-shaped, hairy; fruits compressed, hairy; pappus of four ovate and two linear scales. [M. T. M.]

VIJUCO DEL GUACO. *Mikania Guaco.*

VILFA. A genus of grasses belonging to the tribe *Agrostideæ*. They have the inflorescence in panicles; spikelets one-flowered; glumes membranous, unequal, not exceeding the pale; pales membranous, unarmed; stamens three; styles two, with feathery stigmas. Under this genus Steudel describes 123 species, which have an extensive geographical range, from Mexico through the Southern Hemisphere to New Holland. Some of the annual species are pretty, and are cultivated in gardens on that account. [D. M.]

VILLARESIA. This name is employed to designate a genus of trees of the family *Aquifoliaceæ*, and inhabiting Chili. The leaves are evergreen, shining, entire or spiny at the margin; and the flowers small, white, arranged in panicled heads. The calyx is five-parted, persistent; the petals are five, each with a prominent rib on the inner side; the stamens five, with flattened awl-shaped filaments; ovary sessile, partially two-celled; ovules two; stigma oblique; drupe globose, with a woody stone and a single seed. [M. T. M.]

VILLARSIA. A genus of *Gentianaceæ*, comprising aquatic species, natives of Central Europe, North America, the Cape of Good Hope, Australia, and Tropical Asia. The leaves are entire or toothed, marked with small spots on the under-surface. The flowers are in axillary umbels or terminal panicles, usually of a yellow colour, and fringed with fine hair-like processes. The distinctive features of the genus reside in the presence of five glands beneath the ovary, and in the capsule, which opens by two cleft valves. These plants partake of the bitter principle so prevalent in the order to which they belong. *V. indica* is used medicinally in India, and is given internally to persons bitten by the cobra. Some of the species are in cultivation for the sake of their elegant blossoms. A rare British plant formerly included in this genus is now separated, and placed under *Limnanthemum.* [M. T. M.]

VILLOSITY, VILLUS (adj. **VILLOSE, VILLOUS**). Shagginess; a coating of long weak hairs.

VILMORINIA. A genus so named in compliment to M. Vilmorin, a well-known Parisian cultivator. The genus is included among the papilionaceous *Leguminosæ*; and comprises a West Indian shrub, with pinnate leaves, recurved stipules, axillary racemes shorter than the leaves, and purple flowers. The calyx is somewhat four-toothed and two-lipped; the standard oblong, the wings shorter than the keel; stamens ten, diadelphous, pod stalked, lanceolate, narrowed below, flattened, thread-like at the point; seeds twelve to sixteen. *V. multiflora* is in cultivation as a stove shrub. [M. T. M.]

VIMINARIA. The name of a genus of papilionaceous *Leguminosæ*, comprising a shrub native of Eastern Australia and Tasmania, with slender twig-like branches, the older ones destitute of leaves, the younger with compound leaves, and the flowers growing in racemes. Calyx bell-shaped, five-toothed; vexillum broadly ovate; wings and keel oblong; stamens ten, distinct; ovary sessile, with two ovules; style thread-like, curved; stigma minute; pod ovate, indehiscent. Two species with yellow flowers are in cultivation as greenhouse plants. The generic name is derived from *vimen* 'a twig,' in allusion to the branches. [M. T. M.]

VIMINEOUS. Having long flexible shoots, as many osiers.

VINAGRILLO. A South American name for *Oxalis Acetosella*, used as a salad plant. It is also applied in Chili to dried cakes of pounded oxalis-leaves, which are infused in water to make an acid drink.

VINAIGRIER. (Fr.) *Rhus glabra.*

VINATICO. A coarse mahogany obtained in Madeira from *Persea indica.*

VINCA. A genus of *Apocynaceæ*, containing several species of woody herbaceous plants, with opposite entire shining leaves, and blue purple or white flowers, seated on solitary axillary alternate peduncles. The calyx is five-parted; the corolla salver-shaped, with the tube longer than the calyx; and the throat bearded, the limb flat, and divided into five oblique truncate lobes; the five stamens included; the two follicles erect, and containing many naked seeds. The species are confined to the Old World, growing in shady places. Two occur in Britain. [W. C.]

VINCETOXICUM. Many of the plants now included in this genus of *Asclepiadaceæ* were formerly referred, by Linnæus and others, to *Asclepias*, and afterwards by Brown to a section of *Cynanchum*. Between twenty and thirty species are described, the greater part of them natives of the Old World, and chiefly of Western and Central Asia; a few, however, are European, one extending as far north as Denmark and Sweden. They are either perennial herbs or undershrubs, and either of an erect or of a somewhat twining habit; and their leaves are mostly opposite, though occasionally alternate or in whorls of four. Their flowers, which are very small and disposed in flat-topped heads, have a five-parted calyx, a wheel-shaped deeply five-lobed corolla, a fleshy saucer-shaped staminal corona, divided into five or ten round or obscurely-pointed lobes, anthers terminated by a membrane, pendulous pollen-masses swollen on one side and fixed beneath their apices, and a stigma furnished with a very short entire point. The fruits consist of two spreading smooth follicles, irregularly swollen on one side, and of a parchment-like texture.

The root of *V. officinale* or Swallowwort, which is the common North European species, possesses drastic and emetic properties, and was formerly in some repute as a medicine; being employed in scrofula and skin-diseases, and also, particularly in Germany, as an antidote to poisons—whence it has been named Contrayerva Germanorum and Taine-poison. When fresh it has a disagreeable odour, and an acrid bitter taste.   [A. S.]

VIN D'AULNÉE. (Fr.) A preparation of *Inula Helenium*.

VINE. *Vitis.* —. BEAN. *Phaseolus diversifolius.* —, GRAPE. *Vitis vinifera.* —, KANGURU. *Cissus antarctica.* —, PEPPER. *Ampelopsis bipinnata.* —, POISON. *Rhus radicans.* —, POTATO. *Ipomœa pandurata*, called also Man of the Earth. —, RED-BEAD. *Abrus precatorius.* —, SCRUB. An Australian name for *Cassytha.* —, SEVEN-YEAR. *Ipomœa tuberosa.* —, SORREL. *Cissus acida.* —, SPANISH ARBOUR. *Ipomœa tuberosa.* —, STRAINER. *Luffa acutangula.* —, WATER. *Phytocrene*; also *Doliocarpus Calinea.* —, WHITE. *Clematis Vitalba.* —, WILD. *Vitis Labrusca.* —, WHITE WILD. *Bryonia dioica.*

VINE. See VITICULA.

VINEALIS. Growing wild in vineyards.

VINE-BOWER. *Clematis Viticella.*

VINEGAR. An acid liquor manufactured by fermenting vegetable juices, such as an infusion of malt, inferior wines, or a solution of sugar, or from alcohol, toddy, &c.

VINEGAR-PLANT. During the process of acetous fermentation of liquids a coat of greater or less thickness, consisting of many layers separable the one from the other, is formed on the surface. This under the microscope is found to consist of interlaced delicate branched threads, which, if placed in circumstances favourable to their development, give rise to a crop of *Penicillium glaucum*, a universally-distributed mould belonging to the mucedinous order *Hyphomycetes*. If a portion of this coat is placed in a solution of sugar and water, kept in a proper temperature, the whole is converted into vinegar far more rapidly than it would be without the presence of the fungous mass. It is therefore called the Vinegar-plant, and is much used in the manufacture of vinegar. The exact mode in which the Vinegar-plant operates on the solution is not known, but it is supposed that it acts in the same way as the yeast-plant, though a much less surface is presented to the decomposible flu'd. *Rhus typhina* also is sometimes called Vinegar-plant.   [M. J. B.]

VINE MILDEW. Shortly after the first observed occurrence of the potato-murrain in England, a disease broke out in several parts of Kent amongst the vines, characterised by the appearance of a white mould on the leaves and young bunches of grapes, and producing either complete abortion in the fruit, or dwarfill-shaped juiceless berries, cracking in every direction and exposing their numerous seeds, or where a little pulp was formed rapidly reducing the whole into a state of decomposition. The mould was studied at Margate, and ascertained to belong to the genus *Oidium*: and as Mr. Tucker, an intelligent gardener there, had paid great attention to the subject, and had completely conquered it by the application of sulphur, it was named by Mr. Berkeley *Oidium Tuckeri*. Subsequent observations have confirmed a suspicion, which was before entertained, that the *Oidia* of this group are merely a peculiar condition of different species of *Erysiphe*, and it is generally allowed that such is the case with the vine-mildew, though it has never been observed to make any further advance than the production of those peculiar cysts which accompany the true fruit of *Erysiphe*, known under the name of pycnidia. The disease has since spread in every direction, European vines suffering from it in America, though American vines, both in the United States and in Europe, remain free from the malady. Many remedies have been proposed for this evil, but, while others have failed to a greater or less extent, the application of sublimed sulphur (on account, probably, of its being always accompanied by a certain amount of sulphurous acid) has been, when properly and perseveringly applied, almost uniformly efficacious. In extremely hot districts, as in Spain and Portugal, possibly from the sulphur being simply ground and not sublimed, more benefit has been derived from its ignition, care being taken that the consequent vapour be made to pass so rapidly through the vineyard that the leaves may not be withered by its action being continued too long or in too great strength. In artificial cultivation sulphur is a sure remedy, but if its fumes are employed at all, the sulphur should merely be melted, and that cautiously, without suffering it to ignite, the consequence of which would be the substitution of sulphuric for sulphurous acid.   [M. J. B.]

VINETTE DE BREBIS. (Fr.) *Rumex Acetosella.*

VINETTIER. (Fr.) *Berberis.*

VINEWORTS. A name given by Lindley to the order *Vitaceæ*.

VINSONIA. This is one of several undescribed genera of *Pandanaceæ*, named and figured by Gaudichaud in the botanical portion of the *Voyage de la Bonite*. No less than ten species of this genus are indicated by names, but none of them are described.   [A. S.]

VIOLACEÆ. (*Violarieæ, Violettworts*), An order of polypetalous dicotyledons, consisting of herbs or shrubs, with usually alternate and simple leaves furnished with stipules, and axillary flowers, either solitary or in cymes racemes or panicles. They have the one-celled free ovary with parietal placentas (usually three) of *Dixaceæ* and their allies, but are distinguished by their stamens being almost always five in number, with very short filaments and comparatively large anthers, erect and often connate in a ring round the pistil—their connective often very broad, and produced into an appendage at the top, with the cells opening inside the ring. The flowers, when irregular, are often large and showy, and the capsule in the greater number of genera opens in three very elastic valves. There are between two and three hundred species known, dispersed over nearly all parts of the globe, and distributed into twenty-one genera forming four tribes:—1. *Violeæ*, with irregular flowers, the lower petal often spurred, containing seven genera, of which *Viola* in temperate climates, and *Ionidium* within the tropics are the most important; 2. *Paypayroleæ*, three small tropical genera, with slightly irregular long-clawed petals; 3. *Alsodeieæ*, shrubby and chiefly tropical, with small nearly regular flowers, comprising *Alsodeia* and six other small genera; and 4. *Sauvagesieæ*, remarkable for the variously-formed staminodia which surround their perfect stamens; the capsule also differs from that of other tribes in opening along the placentas and not between them, and the tribe is often raised to the rank of a distinct order. It contains *Sauvagesia* and three other small genera, all tropical: see SAUVAGESIACEÆ.

VIOLA. A genus of very varied and interesting plants, giving name to the order *Violaceæ*. They have a calyx of five leaves, which from their extension at the base are apparently joined by their sides; and the corolla is of five unequal petals, the lower of which is spurred. To the botanist this is a somewhat perplexing family, as scarcely two agree as to their specific differences, and yet the general observer is so well acquainted with their nature and habits that the Violet scarcely needs a detailed description. Our native species may be referred to two groups—the stemless Violets, with solitary flowers, growing apparently from the crown of the plant, and including *V. odorata* the Sweet Violet, and its varieties; and those with the stems evident, and solitary flowers springing from the axils of the leaves, which are alternate, on more or less branched stems—the latter group including *V. canina* the Dog Violet, and *V. tricolor* the Pansy.

The scented Violets are very variable in colour, the flowers being sometimes blue—

> Violets blue as Juno's eyes
> And sweet as Cytherea's breath,

as Shakspere hath it; while sometimes they are white or lilac, and double varieties of them are cultivated. We can, however, make out no valid characters by which to distinguish them, and our experiments in their cultivation lead us to the conclusion that it is easy to produce all three from the seed of either the White or Blue Violet. The hairy scentless *V. hirta*, we are also inclined, after long examination study and

experiment, to think is a mere inodorous variety. It is remarkable that the Sweet Blue Violet, which is mostly held in such reverence as the type of all that is loving and lovely, should yet in some districts be denied admission to the cottage. We have frequently been told, in parts of Gloucestershire, that the Blue Violet was 'unlucky to have in the house;' and upon pressing for a reason, we were once informed that these flowers 'certainly brought in fleas.' Probably the warmer weather of spring, which ushers in the Violet—said to be 'a stinking flower' by the foxhunter—is just that which causes the troublesome little insects in question to be hatched.

Dog Violets are perhaps so called from their want of scent, on the same principle that the large mushroom, which is so detested by those who have never eaten it, is dedicated to the horse, and called the horse-mushroom. [J. B.]

The endless varieties of Heartsease, or Pansy, are all derived from the cornfield weed *V. tricolor*, and the allied species *V. altaica* from Tartary, and *V. grandiflora* from Switzerland. The Neapolitan Violet is stated by Loudon to be a variety of *V. odorata*, and the 'Tree Violets' of the conservatory are merely double varieties of the same species, which have been subjected to particular treatment. *V odorata* is known under some form or other throughout Europe, and in many parts of Asia; but the *Viola* of classic authors is supposed to have been the Stock Gilliflower of modern gardens. French: *Violette*; German: *Märgveilchen*. [C. A. J.]

VIOLET. *Viola.* —, CORN. *Specularia hybrida* —, DAME'S, or DAMASK. *Hesperis matronalis*. —, DOG. *Viola canina*. —, DOG'S-TOOTH. *Erythronium*. —, FRINGED, of New Holland. *Thysanotus*. —, GREEN. *Solea*. —, MERCURY'S. *Campanula urticæfolia*. —, NEAPOLITAN. A double-flowered variety of *Viola odorata*. —, ROCK. *Chroolepus Iolithus*. —, SPURLESS. *Erpetion*. —, SWEET. *Viola odorata*. —, TOOTH. *Dentaria bulbifera*. —, TREE. A variety of *Viola odorata*. —, WATER. *Hottonia palustris*.

VIOLETTE. (Fr.) *Viola*. — À ODEUR D'AIL. *Erysimum Alliaria*. — AQUATIQUE. *Hottonia palustris*. — BLEUE. *Browallia elata*. — DE MARIE. *Campanula Medium*. — DE MARS. *Viola odorata*. — DES SORCIERS. *Vinca minor*.

VIOLET-WOOD. Kingwood, supposed to be derived from a species of *Triptolomœa*. Also applied to the wood of *Acacia pendula*, and to a wood of Guiana, the produce of *Andira violacea*.

VIOLETWORTS. A name for the order *Violaceæ*.

VIOLIER. (Fr.) *Cheiranthus incanus*. — D'ÉTÉ. *Cheiranthus annuus*. — D'HIVER. *Galanthus nivalis*. — DES DAMES. *Hesperis matronalis*. — JAUNE. *Cheiranthus Cheiri*.

VIORNE. (Fr.) *Viburnum*. — À MAN-

CHETTE. *Viburnum Lentago.* — D'AMÉRIQUE. *Lantana Camara.* — LAURIER-TIN. *Viburnum Tinus.*

VIOULTE. (Fr.) *Erythronium.*

VIPER-GOURD. *Trichosanthes colubrina.*

VIPÉRINE. (Fr.) *Echium.* — DE CRÊTE. *Onosma simplicissima.* — DE VIRGINIE. *Aristolochia Serpentaria.*

VIRECTA. A genus of tropical African herbs belonging to the *Cinchonaceæ.* The flowers are white, in dense corymbs. The calyx-limb is divided into five linear hairy divisions; the corolla funnel-shaped, its limb parted into five linear ciliated segments; and the capsule somewhat globular, two-celled, two valved.   [M. T. M.]

VIRENS, VIRESCENS. A shade of clear green, but not so bright as grass-green.

VIREYA. A name proposed for several species of *Rhododendron,* characterised by the minuteness of the calyx, and the distinct insertion of the stamens and corolla; but as these features occur in the most typical species of the original genus, the name has been dropped.   [W. C.]

VIRGATE. Twiggy; producing many weak branchlets or twigs.

VIRGILIA. The type of this genus of *Leguminosæ,* which was dedicated by the French botanist Lamarck to the well-known ancient poet, is called *V. capensis,* a small tree native of the Cape of Good Hope, with imparipinnate leaves, and bearing dense racemes of pink flowers. Several other plants, however, have at different times been referred to it, but most of them are now placed under the genera *Cladrastis* and *Calpurnia.* The genus is characterised by its flowers having a broad bell-shaped unequally five-toothed calyx; a pea-like corolla, with the two lower or keel-petals combined along the back from the middle to the top, where they are curved inwards like a beak; ten free stamens, and a sessile hairy ovary. Its pods are oblong flattened unopening, and of a leathery texture.

V. capensis is a handsome tree with a rough black bark, attaining a height of fifteen or twenty feet, and is called Keurboom by the Dutch in Cape Colony, where its soft light wood, which is very plentiful, though liable to be wormeaten, is used for yokes, spars &c.   [A. S.]

VIRGILIER À BOIS-JAUNE. (Fr.) *Cladrastis tinctoria.*

VIRGINIAN CREEPER. *Ampelopsis hederacea.*

VIRGINIAN POKE. *Phytolacca decandra.*

VIRGINIAN SILK. *Periploca græca.*

VIRGIN'S-BOWER. *Clematis Vitalba.*

VIRGIN'S-MILK. A cosmetic in which benzoin is employed.

VIRGIN-TREE. *Sassafras Parthenoxylon.*

VIRGULTUM. A young slender branch.

VIRIDESCENS. The same as Virens.

VIRIDIS, VIRIDULUS. A clear full green; any kind of greenness.

VIROLA. Aublet, in his work on the plants of Guiana, established this genus upon one of the American Nutmegs, named by him *V. sebifera;* but modern botanists regard it and its allies, of which six or seven have been discovered since Aublet's time, as forming one of the sections of the large genus *Myristica,* characterised by the long narrow anthers, usually six or three in number, adhering by their backs throughout nearly the whole length of the thick cylindrical stamen-column, the naked portion of the column being very short. All the species belonging to the section *Virola* are confined to Tropical South America; and are large trees, with simple entire leaves, having their side-veins usually more distant than in other sections of American Nutmegs, and also more curved, and uniting by cross-veins at a greater distance from the margin.

V. sebifera forms a tree sixty feet high, and has egg-shaped leaves from six inches to a foot long by two to four inches broad, heart-shaped at the base, and covered with rust-coloured tomentum on the under-surface. It is common in the forests of Guiana and North Brazil, and is also found as far north as Panama, where it is called Malagueto de montana. A solid oil or fat, obtained by macerating the seeds in hot water, is used in Guiana for making candles. An acrid red juice, employed medicinally by the Brazilians, exudes from wounds made in the bark.   [A. S.]

VIROSE. Having a disagreeable nauseous smell.

VISCACEÆ. A name under which Miers proposed to separate *Viscum* and a few other genera from the remainder of *Loranthaceæ,* as being in the structure of their ovary more nearly allied to *Santalaceæ* than to other loranthaceous genera. In all other respects, however, the retention of the latter order in the limits usually assigned to it, seems a more natural arrangement.

VISCARIA. A section of the genus *Lychnis,* differing from the typical species in the capsule being imperfectly five-celled at the base, and opening loculicidally. *L. Viscaria* and *L. alpina* are British species of this section.   [J. T. S.]

VISCID, VISCOSE, VISCOUS. Glutinous, clammy.

VISCUM. This genus has been proposed as the type of a separate order, but Professor Oliver, the most recent investigator of these plants, retains it under *Loranthaceæ.* He divides the species into two groups, according to the presence or absence of leaves. The leafless group comprises species which are found in the Indian Archipelago, as well as in Mauritius, Bourbon, and Australia. The leafy series, consists of species natives of Europe, Southern Asia, and Southern Africa. The flowers are always unisexual, either monœcious or diœcious. The male flowers have a four-parted perianth, the lobes of which are either deciduous or persistent; the anthers are adherent to the segments of the perianth, and open by a number of pores, so that the surface of the anther resembles a honeycomb. The female flowers have a perianth like that of the male flower, adherent to the ovary, which latter is surmounted by a sessile stigma. When the ovary is cut across, no cavity is apparent, owing to the adhesion of the inside of the ovary to the seed. Not unfrequently two embryos are contained in the same seed.

V. album, the Mistleto, is the only species to which any considerable interest attaches. It is a parasitical shrub, whose root (or what corresponds to a root) is firmly embedded in the substance of the tree on which it grows. The stem, when full-grown, attains the thickness of a broomstick; it repeatedly divides and subdivides, in a regularly-forked manner, each joint or articulation being marked by a prominent ring. The leaves are opposite stalkless, oblong or somewhat lance-shaped, leathery, and of a yellowish-green colour. The male flowers are in clusters of four or five in the forks of the branches; the female flowers are sessile like the males, and solitary or nearly so. The fruit forms a small white berry.

The mode of attachment of the Mistleto to the nourishing plant has been made the subject of an elaborate paper by Dr John Harley, in the *Transactions of the Linnæan Society* (xxiv. p. 175). The roots of the mistleto come in contact especially with the new wood inside the bark, where the descending sap is richest and most abundant, and are prolonged inwards in a direction parallel to that of the medullary rays. The cellular systems of the two plants thus come into contact, but no direct communication takes place between their vessels. As growth goes on, and annual rings of wood are added to the stock, similar rings are formed in the mistleto, and so the woody layers of the two plants become coincident. The parasite slowly but surely involves the destruction of the branch upon which it is growing, by inducing an overflow of sap, and consequent exhaustion, or by preventing the due flow of sap. In either case it seals its own fate with that of its supporter. The corroded and contorted appearance of old stumps killed by the mistleto is very singular.

The Mistleto may be made to grow on the apple and other trees, by cutting a notch in the bark on the under-surface of a branch, and carefully inserting the seed therein. Two precautions are especially needed—one is to place the seed in such a position that the embryo shall be directed towards the trunk of the tree, and the other is to avoid crushing the seed. The apple is the tree on which the mistleto grows most abundantly. The orchards in Herefordshire are greatly infested with this parasite, which, however, has a value of its own, for it appears that upwards of one hundred tons of mistleto are annually forwarded to London and other large towns from that county alone, for Christmas decorations. Some sorts of apples are preferred to others for its growth, and, singularly enough, it is rarely if ever found on the pear-tree. Next in frequency to the apple the mistleto prefers the poplars, though it is not found on the Lombardy poplar. Hawthorns, limes, maples, and the mountain-ash are all favourite habitats for the plant. It has been found on the Cedar of Lebanon and on the larch, but rarely upon the oak. Dr. Bull, in a paper in the *Journal of Botany* (ii. 273), only mentions seven authentic instances of the growth of mistleto on the oak in this country.

Space will permit us only to allude to the many mythological legends respecting the mistleto and its use in Druidical rites—how it was cut with a golden sickle by a priest in white robes, amid the sacrifice of victims and the fasting of the devotees, and how, once procured, the plant acted as a heal-all, and a charm against disasters. Balder, one of the heroes of Icelandic romance, is said to have met his death from a dart of mistleto. According to the story, it was prophesied that Balder would die, to avert which fate his mother exacted a vow from all things on earth that they would not injure him. One of his enemies, knowing that the mistleto had not taken the vow, as it did not grow on the earth but on trees, made a dart of its wood, and with it killed the hero. The origin of the modern custom connected with mistleto is not very clear. Like many other customs, its original significance is only guessed at. If known, perhaps the innocent merriment now associated with the plant would be exchanged for a feeling of stern disapproval, and the mistleto would be banished from our homes. In such a case, however, ignorance is bliss. Mistleto-leaves are still considered as tonics for animals, but the ancient medicinal reputation of the plant has not survived.　　　[M. T. M.]

The Mistleto is well-known, especially in the orchards of cider-making counties, for its winter dress of olive-green leaves and shining white berries, so different from the branches of the trees upon which it fastens itself. The mistleto is remarkable for the many species of trees upon which it is found. It is occasionally seen on the oak, but so rarely that with some it has been doubted whether it occurs upon this tree at all. We have seen two examples—one at Eastnor Park, near Ledbury, Herefordshire, the other at Frampton-on-Severn, Gloucestershire. The magnificence of the oak on the one hand, and the rarity of the mistleto upon it on the other, are probable reasons for the greater reverence paid to the parasite when found on this tree.

That Mistleto was a special object of worship with the ancient Britons, and that many important rites were performed with it by the Druids or priests, is certain, and hence we may trace its use among ourselves in Christmas decoration. The curious basket of garland with which 'Jack-in-the-Green' is occasionally even now invested on May-day, is said to be a relic of a similar garb assumed by the Druidical assistants when about to hunt for the mistleto, which when they had found they danced round the oak, to the tune of 'Hey derry down, down down derry!' which literally signified, '*In a circle move we round the oak.*' What gives countenance to this is, that some oakwoods in Herefordshire are called 'the derry,' and the following line from Ovid shows that the Druids did sing beneath the oak:—

Ad viscum Druidæ cantare solebant

Having found mistleto in the oak, or in the next sacred tree, the apple, the priest cut the branches with a golden sickle, and distributed portions to the people; and it is suggested by Fosbrooke, that 'as the Druids had an extraordinary veneration for the number three, and as the berries of the mistleto may be often found clustered in threes, this may probably have enhanced their esteem for the *celestial plant.*'

The Mistleto has been highly extolled for its medicinal virtues from a very remote antiquity. The older writers seem to have held it in esteem as ministering to fertility, deriving the notion, in all probability, from the multitude of berries which grow on the plant, a notion which may have something to do with some of our Christmas observances. The mistleto of the oak had such repute for 'helping' in the diseases incidental to infirmity and old age, that it was called *Lignum Sanctæ Crucis*, Wood of the Holy Cross; and as the parasite is the same on one tree as on another, we may infer that the robust nature of the oak was supposed to impart to it, strengthening properties. Ray is, perhaps, the latest writer who has greatly extolled mistleto. He mentions it as a specific in epilepsy, and as useful in apoplexy and giddiness. It is easy to see that what gave countenance to this idea has been the fact that the parasite grows, from the under-part of the foster-parent, with its head downwards. Alas for a plant of such reputed powers—it is now excluded from the Pharmacopœias!   [J. B.]

VISH, or VISHA. *Aconitum ferox.*

VISHALA. An Indian name for the Colocynth or Bitter Apple.

VISHANIA. *Ligustrum.*

VISMIA. With the exception of one or two tropical West African plants, this genus of *Hypericaceæ*, of which upwards of twenty species are described, is confined to the tropics of America. They are trees or shrubs, with four-sided branches, opposite often glandular dotted entire leaves, and terminal panicles or cymes of yellow or greenish flowers. These latter have five or sometimes only four sepals; as many petals clothed with hairs inside, and dotted with black glands; an indefinite number of stamens collected into five hairy bundles, and placed opposite the petals, alternating with as many scales; and five distinct styles. The genus is, however, best characterised by its fruit, which is a roundish five-celled berry with numerous seeds in each cell.

The yellow resinous juice common to the order exists in greater abundance in the plants belonging to this genus than in any of its congeners, and possesses more powerful purgative properties, resembling in that respect, and likewise in its appearance, the gamboge of the Old World—so much so indeed, that that collected from *V. guianensis*, a species found in Guiana Brazil Surinam and Mexico, is called American Gamboge. Other species, however, such as the *V. sessiliflora* and *V. cayennensis* of Guiana, and the *V. micrantha* and *V. longifolia* of Brazil, also yield a similar resin, to which the name American Gamboge is equally applicable.   [A. S.]

VISNAGE. (Fr.) *Ammi Visnaga.*

VISNEA. The sole species of this genus of *Ternströmiaceæ* was named *Mocanera* by Linnæus on account of its fruit, being supposed by some authors to have been the Mocan, which was made into a kind of syrup and much used, both with their daily food and medicinally, by the Guanches, the aboriginal inhabitants of the Canaries, in which islands alone the plant is found. Other authors, however, attribute the Mocan to the Carob-tree (*Ceratonia Siliqua*) or to the *Myrica Faya*. The plant is a shrub with smooth branches and leaves, the latter being alternate elliptic or lance-shaped, the upper ones producing from their axils two short recurved stalks, each bearing a solitary flower. These have a deeply five-parted calyx, with a couple of bracts, five spreading petals coalescing at the base and bearing twenty free stamens shorter than the petals, and with long taper-pointed anthers fixed by their broad bases, a three-celled obscurely ten-angled hairy ovary, with two pendulous ovules in each cell, and three slender styles. [A. S.]

VITACEÆ. (*Vites, Ampelideæ, Sarmentaceæ, Leeaceæ, Vineworts.*) A small order of polypetalous dicotyledons, nearly allied in character to *Celastraceæ* and *Rhamnaceæ*, but at once distinguished from the former by their stamens being opposite the petals, and from the latter by their valvate petals; and from both by their habit. With the exception of the small genus *Leea*, they are tall climbers, remarkable for the anomalous structure of their wood. The lower leaves are often opposite, the remainder alternate, but opposite to them is either a cyme or raceme of small green flowers, or a branching tendril. Besides the great genus *Vitis*, which is now made to include all the species of *Cissus* and *Ampelopsis*, whether natives of the New or of the Old World, the order comprises only the small genus *Pterisanthes*, with a remarkable flat flower-stalk, and the slightly anomalous *Leea*, both confined to the Old World.

VITELLINUS. Dull yellow, just turning to red ; the colour of the yolk of egg.

VITELLUS. The sac of the amnios in a thickened state, and forming a case, within which lies the embryo.

VITELOTTE. (Fr.) A kind of long red Potato.

VITEX. A genus of *Verbenaceæ*, containing a large number of woody plants scattered over the tropical regions of both hemispheres, a few reaching as far north as the Mediterranean. They have ternate digitate or rarely simple leaves, and axillary or terminal and paniculate cymes. The short calyx is five-toothed; the corolla two-lipped, the upper lip being two-lobed and the lower three-lobed; the didynamous stamens exserted; the ovary four-celled, with one ovule in each cell; and the stigma bifid, with pointed lobes. The drupe is four-celled, or by abortion two-celled. The plants of this genus are very aromatic, and many of the fruits are very acrid. The leaves bark and fruit of different species are used medicinally by the natives of India.   [W. C.]

VITICES. See VERBENACEÆ.

VITICULA. A trailing or scrambling stem, like that of the vine, gourd, cucumber, &c. The same as Vine.

VITICULOSE. Furnished with trailing stems or viticulæ.

VITIS. The genus *Vitis* is composed of a considerable number of species, including the well-known Grape-Vine, which is its most familiar and, in an economic point of view, most important representative. It has a wide geographical range, but is principally found in the Northern Hemisphere, the majority of its species being natives of Tropical and Temperate Asia to as far north as Japan, and also of North America, while none are indigenous to Europe. All the species are climbers, furnished with tendrils opposite the leaves, as in the Grape-Vine; the leaves of some being simple and either undivided or variously lobed, and of others compound. Their small greenish flowers are disposed in panicles set opposite the leaves, the Eastern species having complete flowers, and the Western usually incomplete ones, the two sexes very frequently on different plants. The genus belongs to the *Viteæ* section of the order *Vitaceæ*, having distinct stamens, and a two-celled ovary with two ovules in each cell ; and is characterised by its five petals being distinct at the bottom but cohering at the top, falling off without separating, and by its berries containing four or by abortion only two seeds.

It may be observed that the petals are slightly attached to the disk at the base of the ovary, but they cohere at the top, forming a sort of cap, which is usually thrown off by the stamens as they elongate and expand. Sometimes, however, the cap is not thrown off, and the stigma is consequently not exposed to the pollen; as a consequence the berries, if they form at all, are without seeds.

The most important products of the Grape-Vine are Wine (derived from the Celtic *gwin*) and Vinegar—the one obtained by vinous and the other by acetous fermentation of the juice of the fruit ; Brandy, a product of distillation ; and Currants (Corinths) and Raisins, both of which are the dried fruits—the former being those of a particular small variety, the culture of which is chiefly confined to the Ionian Islands. These severally form very important articles of commerce throughout the civilised world. The total computed real value of the four principal ones in our home-trade amounted in 1861 to 6,291,189*l.*, and the revenue derived from them to 2,371,714*l.*   [A. S.]

The Grape-Vine is a native of the southern shores of the Caspian Sea, and of Armenia and Caramania. Associated with the fig, it follows the shores of the Black Sea, through Pontus Mingrelia and Colchis, and it has also been found in the Crimea. Alphonse De Candolle states that it grows spontaneously throughout the lower region of the Caucasus, in the north but more especially in the southern parts of that chain ; in Armenia, and on the southern shores of the Caspian Sea; and he adds, 'there can be no doubt, from historical testimony and that of botanists, that this was the original country of the vine. But no species of *Vitis* is wild in Europe.'

The cultivation of the Vine dates soon after the Flood : 'Noah began to be an husbandman, and he planted a vineyard.' From Asia, according to Humboldt, the vine passed into Greece, and thence into Sicily. It was early carried into France by the Phocæans, when those Ionian colonists fled from the power of Cyrus, and founded the city of Marseilles, about 540 B.C. From Greece or from Sicily it could have been easily introduced into Italy. The Romans planted it on the banks of the Rhine, and even, it is said, in Britain. But Tacitus mentions, B.C. 55, that our climate was thought unpropitious to the vine, which failed to mature its fruit owing to the moist atmosphere of our island. It would appear from this that its cultivation had been attempted, for otherwise its failure could not have been asserted. The same author states that it was not known when Agricola commanded the island. Domitian restricted the cultivation of the vine, wishing rather to encourage that of grain; but in A.D. 278, permission to plant the vine was given by the Emperor Probus. Being free from restriction, its cultivation throughout the provinces, including Britain, would of course extend ; and before the Roman power had so far declined as to permit the Saxon invasion, vineyards must have existed in this country. They are mentioned in the earliest Saxon charters, and those vineyards must have existed previously ; for, as authors have remarked, the combating invaders could neither have had the time, nor probably the skill, to plant them. The monks in A.D. 1140 planted a vineyard at Edmondsbury in Suffolk, and William of Malmesbury says that vineyards were possessed by barons as well as by monks. 'Winton, afterwards named by the Saxons Winchester, or the City of Wine, was so called because there was the best vintage in Britain.' (Johnson, *On the Grape Vine.*)

There is abundant evidence to prove that vineyards were formerly plentiful in many parts of this country, and that considerable quantities of wine were made in good seasons. But although our land is rich enough for the nourishment of the vine, and indeed over rich, causing too much luxuriance for the climate, the cultivation of the grape for wine must always be attended with comparatively unprofitable results. This will evidently appear from the following extract from *Reports of Her Majesty's Secretaries of Embassy and Legation on the Effect of the Vine Disease* (1859):—' A proprietor of an extensive vineyard at Huesca, in the province of Aragon, assured me that the drought last summer was so great, and the vintage so plentiful, that it would have been easier for him to irrigate his vineyards with wine than with water. He also stated that in order to make room for the new wine, he offered to sell that of a former vintage at about five-pence English for a little less than four gallons, but finding that he could not even get one halfpenny the gallon, and there being a scarcity of wine-jars or vats, he was obliged to throw away the whole of that year's vintage. It is not, however, the province of Aragon alone that produces such a superabundance of wine; many of the wine-districts of old Castille are equally prolific. At Aranda del Duero, for instance, wine appears to be at times as cheap, and water as scarce as at Huesca; for I was informed by an English gentleman that, on passing through that town a few years ago, he saw some bricklayers at work mixing their mortar with wine instead of water, and he stated that this was not an unusual occurrence.'

When we take these facts into consideration, and reflect on the immense quantities of wine that can be produced at an exceedingly low price in those countries that have a climate suitable for the vine, we must readily come to the conclusion that any attempt to cultivate the grape for wine in this country must be very unprofitable, as compared with other crops for which our climate is better adapted. We are without the limits assigned by the illustrious Humboldt for the successful cultivation of the vine; these limits comprise a belt, or zone, between the latitudes of 36° and 48°, or where the mean temperature of summer is not below 66° or 68°. Farther north than latitude 50° it is too cold, and farther south than 36° it is too hot. Its cultivation may, however, be successfully carried on in a zone nearly 1,000 miles in width from north to south in the Northern, and likewise in a similar zone in the Southern Hemisphere.

The Vine accommodates itself remarkably well to artificial treatment—so much so, that in countries so cold that its berries do not ripen, nor even colour, scarcely indeed form in their warmest seasons, they can be produced by the aid of fire-heat and glass, at all times of the year in abundance by those who are inclined to incur the expense. The cost in winter, is of course very considerable; but in the season naturally the most favourable, when the ordinary climate requires but a little assistance, the expense of ensuring a plentiful supply of grapes for several months is comparatively trifling, especially if proper varieties are employed. These are exceedingly numerous. That which may be most successfully cultivated in this way with the greatest ease, by aid of the most ordinary skill, and which will yield the most acceptable produce, is the Black Hamburg or Frankenthal.

Some varieties of the grape are cultivated specially for the production of Raisins. There is also the Black Corinth or Zante grape, which furnishes the Currants of the shops. This is stoneless or without seeds, except that occasionally there are amongst the produce from the same plant larger berries (these being such as have been fertilised) containing one or more seeds. The variety itself does not differ materially in appearance and foliage from other vines, and has often fruited in the garden of the Royal Horticultural Society at Chiswick. It is, indeed, only a variety of *V. vinifera*, and not a distinct species as some have supposed. It has even been stated that it will only succeed in Greece, and that elsewhere it degenerates and becomes like an ordinary grape; but the fact is that in some places out of Greece it thrives so much better that it forms its seeds and produces its fruit in perfection, to the depreciation of its value in commerce, which is owing to its imperfection—the absence of seeds, this being its general condition when grown in the islands of Greece.

There are various kinds of grapes, which grow wild and bear abundantly in North America, but they are very inferior to the varieties of *V. vinifera*. They belong to *V. Labrusca, V. cordifolia*, and others, and are called Fox-grapes from their foxy perfume; their pulp is slimy and disagreeable. Of late years the vine has been subject to the vine-disease, or vine-mildew, caused by a parasitic fungus called *Oidium Tuckeri*, and which in some cases has completely destroyed the crop. Sulphur has proved the best preventive. [R. T.]

VITI-VERT, VITTIE-VAYR, or **VITTI-VAER.** Indian names for the Khus-khus Grass, *Andropogon muricatus.*

VITTADINIA. A genus of *Compositæ*, consisting of perennial plants, natives of New Zealand and South-eastern Australia. The flower-heads are placed on the ends of the branches, and are surrounded by an involucre of one or two rows of linear somewhat membranous scales; the outer florets are strap-shaped, female, white or purple; the central ones tubular, five-toothed, yellow. The achenes are elongated striated, surmounted by a pappus of one row of rough crowded hairs.　[M. T. M.]

VITTÆ. Narrow fistulæ or channels lodged in the coat of the fruit of umbellifers, and containing oil.

VITTARIA. A genus of polypodiaceous ferns constituting the group *Vittarieæ*. They are found in tropical countries both of the Old and New World, and consist of herbaceous plants, with simple narrow almost grass-like fronds, bearing a close resemblance to those of *Tæniopsis*, but distinguished by having the linear continuous sori placed, not dorsally, that is at the back of the frond, but in an extrorse-marginal furrow.　[T. M.]

VITTATE. Striped lengthwise.

VIVIANIACEÆ. The small Brazilian and Chilian genus *Viviania*, including *Cæsarea*, *Cissarobryon*, and *Linostigma*, forming a tribe of *Geraniaceæ*, has by many botanists been considered as a distinct natural order, under the above name.

VIVIANIA. This genus gives its name to the order *Vivianiaceæ*, maintained by some botanists. The species are Chilian undershrubs, with opposite egg-shaped leaves, covered with white down on the undersurface, and bearing white pink or purple flowers in terminal panicles. Calyx bell-shaped, persistent, its tube marked by ten ridges, its limb five-toothed; petals five, stalked; stamens ten, five short opposite the petals, the others opposite five hypogynous glands; ovary sessile three-celled, with two ovules in the inner angle of each compartment; stigmas three, thread-like; fruit capsular.　[M. T. M.]

VOANDZEIA. So called from Voandzou, the name given by the natives of Madagascar to the only known representative of this genus of *Leguminosæ*, the *V. subterranea* of botanists, a creeping annual, with long-stalked leaves composed of three leaflets, the centre one of which is stalked. The specific name, *subterranea*, has been given to it because its flower-stalks, like those of the *Arachis hypogæa*, bend down after flowering and increase in length, so that the young pods are pushed into the earth, beneath which they ripen. Its flowers are partly unisexual, and partly perfect; they have a bell-shaped calyx, a yellow papilionaceous corolla with horizontal wing or side-petals, one free and nine united stamens, and a two-ovuled ovary ending in a short style and hooked stigma—the female flowers being destitute of both corolla and stamens. It is a native of Africa, and is extensively cultivated in many parts of that continent, from Bambarra and the coast of Guinea to Natal, its esculent pods and seeds forming common articles of food among the inhabitants of those regions. Although the plant is not indigenous to the Western Hemisphere, it is commonly found in many parts of South America, such as Brazil and Surinam, whither it has

been carried by the negro slaves, and has now become naturalised. The pods are sometimes called Bambarra Ground-nuts; in Natal the natives call them Igiuhluba; while in Brazil they are known by the name of Mandubi d'Angola (showing their African origin), and in Surinam by that of Gobbe.　[A. S.]

VOANDZOU. The Malagassy name of a genus of *Leguminosæ*, called after it *Voandzeia*.

VOA-VANGA, or VOA-VANGUER. Malagassy names for the fruits of *Vangueria Commersoni* and *V. edulis*.

VOCHYACEÆ. (*Vochysiaceæ*, *Vochysieæ*). An order of polypetalous dicotyledons, consisting of trees or shrubs from tropical America, often of great beauty, with opposite entire leaves, accompanied by stipules or glands at the base, and yellow white pink or purple flowers (usually very showy) in terminal racemes or panicles. The order is chiefly characterised by irregular flowers, four or five sepals, as many petals and stamens or more frequently fewer, the stamens especially being often reduced to one, and always perigynous; and by a three-celled ovary, free or more or less inferior, the seeds usually without albumen. There are nine or ten genera, amongst which *Vochysia* and *Qualea* are most conspicuous for the beauty of their flowering panicles; *Erisma* for its inferior ovary and curious fruit; and *Lightia* for its more symmetrical flowers, connecting the order with *Trigonia*. Little is known of the properties of these trees, beyond the hardness of the timber which some of them supply, and the position of the order in the natural system is as yet unsettled.

VOCHYSIA. The type of the order *Vochyaceæ*, constituting a genus of trees inhabiting tropical American forests, and when in bloom presenting a magnificent spectacle, accompanied by a penetrating often violet-like odour. The leaves are simple, opposite or verticillate, ovate and entire. The calyx is five-cleft, four of the lobes being very small, but the fifth large and developed into a spur; the petals are three in number, two of them being smaller than the other; there are three stamens, and the capsule is triangular and three-celled, each cell containing one winged seed. The flowers are arranged in highly ornamental panicles, and are generally of a yellow or bright-orange colour. They are all used as timber, and the Copal-ye-wood of Guiana is derived from *V. guianensis*.　[B. S.]

VOGELIA. A genus of *Plumbaginaceæ*, founded on a single plant from the Cape of Good Hope. It is a shrub, with slender branches, obcordate alternate leaves, and flowers in densely imbricated spikes. The five sepals are broadly ovate; the corolla-tube is slender, and the limb is five-lobed; the stamens are included; the ovary is one-celled, containing a single ovule; and the style is filiform, terminating in five acute stigmas.　[W. C.]

VOIREUSE. (Fr) *Mercurialis annua.*

VOLA. A Sanscrit name for Myrrh.

VOLANT D'EAU (Fr) *Myriophyllum spicatum.*

VOLKAMERIA. A genus of *Verbenaceæ* closely allied to *Clerodendron*, but distinguished from it by its fleshy or corky fruits, containing only two stones instead of four as in *Clerodendron*, each stone also being two-celled, and containing a single seed in each cell. There are two well-authenticated species, besides several doubtful ones—*V. aculeata* a native of Tropical America, and *V. Acerbiana* a native of Nubia ; both of them shrubs with simple opposite leaves, and cymes of white flowers, having salver-shaped corollas, with the limb divided into five segments, the two upper of which are larger than the rest, and diverge from each other. [A. S.]

VOLUBILIS. Having the property of twisting round some other body.

VOLUBILIS, or V. DES JARDINIERS. (Fr.) *Pharbitis hispida.*

VOLUTE. Rolled up in any way.

VOLVA. A membrane, usually of a tough texture, in which a fungal is sometimes enclosed when young, and which is burst open as the latter grows.

VOLVARIA. A beautiful subgenus of rose-spored agarics, distinguished by its well-developed volva. The gills, moreover, are perfectly free and rose-coloured. The only common species is *Agaricus pusillus*, which abounds in pastures in autumn, and is conspicuous (though small) from its perfect volva, and its white silky pileus contrasting with the pink gills. *A. volvaceus* occurs sometimes abundantly in stoves, but not so frequently as formerly, when tan was more used for heating. A closely-allied species is raised artificially in Italy, on spent coffee-grounds, and is employed as food. We are not aware that any of the remaining species are esculent. [M. J. B.]

VOMIER. (Fr) *Eriostemon.*

VOMIQUE. (Fr.) *Strychnos.*

VOMIQUIER. (Fr.) The seed of *Ignatia amara.*

VOOGINOOS. The Abyssinian name of *Brucea antidysenterica.*

VORGE. (Fr.) *Lolium temulentum.*

VORTANQUI. The Spanish name for Sappan-wood.

VOSAKAN (Fr.) *Helianthus annuus.*

VOSSIA. A genus of grasses belonging to the tribe *Rottboelliæ*. Spikes of inflorescence compressed jointed; spikelets two-flowered; the lower male, the upper hermaphrodite, glumes two, unequal—the exterior thick and hard, terminating in a sharp point, the inner thin and paper-like ; males two ; stamens three ; styles two. *V. cuspidata* is the only species, and is a native of the West Indies. [D. M.]

VOTOMITA. A little-known genus of Aublet's, founded on a single species from French Guiana, and doubtfully referred to *Cornaceæ*. It is a shrub, with opposite entire leaves on short petioles, and few-flowered axillary corymbs. The calyx is connate with the ovary, and the limb has four short teeth ; the corolla consists of four oblong-acuminate petals, the four stamens have short filaments, and oblong anthers united into a tube, through which the filiform style passes ; there are four oblong stigmas ; and the drupe is one-celled and one-seeded. [W. C.]

VOUA-HÉRÉ. The Malagassy name for *Vahea madagascariensis.*

VOUAPA. A genus of papilionaceous *Leguminosæ*, consisting of trees, natives of Guiana, and having pinnated leaves, and clusters of flowers. On the pedicels are two small leathery bracts ; the calyx is four-parted and membranous ; the corolla consists of a single petal, which is curved in the bud, the remaining four petals being suppressed ; stamens three ; ovary stalked, with one or two ovules ; style very long, curled up spirally ; pod compressed. The generic name is adapted from that given by the natives to these plants. *V. bifolia* is in cultivation as a stove-plant ; its flowers are of a violet hue. [M. T. M.]

VOUÈDE. (Fr.) *Isatis tinctoria.*

VOUÉN POUÉN. A native name in Madagascar for *Cratæva excelsa.*

VOULOU. (Fr.) *Bambusa.*

VOYRA. A genus of tropical American herbs of the *Gentianaceæ*, and connecting that order with the *Orobanchaceæ*, inasmuch as the species are parasitical on the trunks of old trees, and have only minute scale-like leaves. The flowers are terminal, either solitary or in panicles. They have a five-cleft calyx ; a salver-shaped corolla, which withers on the plant before it falls off, its tube swollen at the base, and its limb divided into five spreading segments ; stamens five, concealed within the corolla ; fruit capsular, partially two-celled, bursting by two valves ; seeds numerous, minute. The tuberous roots of *V. rosea* are of a reddish colour externally, and white within ; they are baked and eaten in Guiana like potatoes. [M. T. M.]

VRIESIA. A genus of *Bromeliaceæ*, so named in honour of the late Professor De Vriese, a Dutch botanist of eminence. The species have flat leaves, and bear the flowers in spikes, protected by large handsomely-coloured bracts. The sepals are three, convolute, equal ; petals rolled round at the point, each one with two scales attached to it ; stamens six, projecting, three inserted into the petals, three between them, ovary partly inferior ; stigma with three coiled hairy divisions. One or two species are in cultivation as ornamental stove-plants. *V. speciosa*, a Brazilian herb, is particularly handsome. [M. T. M.]

VRILLÉE. (Fr.) *Convolvulus arvensis.* —

BÂTARDE. *Polygonum Convolvulus.* — BÂTARDE GRANDE. *Polygonum dumetorum.*

VRONCELLE. (Fr.) *Convolvulus arvensis.*

VULNERA. Plants are, like animals, subject to injury from outward agents, and the wounds produced are more or less injurious according to their severity or the nature of the plant. In the case of large trees, wounds are injurious by exposing the wood to the immediate decomposing agency of moisture and other atmospheric conditions. The object in such cases is to diminish the surface as much as possible, which must be done by pruning off all inequalities with a sharp knife, and then to exclude the air by some plaister or covering which will not injure the tree, but permit the overlapping of the surface by the new bark, without any injurious decay. One of the best applications is Forsyth's mixture, consisting of one portion of fresh cowdung, mixed with half the quantity of lime-rubbish, the same amount of wood-ashes, and one-sixteenth of river-sand finely sifted. A powder of wood-ashes mixed with burnt bones, in the proportion of one-sixth of the latter to five-sixths of the former, is then applied with a dredger till the plaister is covered, allowing it to remain half an hour to absorb the moisture. More powder is then rubbed on with the hand, till the surface becomes smooth. Where the bark has been knocked off, new wood may be generated from the medullary rays, if the surface is protected from drought by a suitable covering. In this case, however, the alburnum must remain free from contact with any strange matter. Trees, again, are often injured by rabbits, mice, and other animals. In such cases, as they often gnaw round the tree, immediate steps must be taken, or the injury will be past remedy. Some substance must be applied which the animals will not touch, but which at the same time will not injure the tree. An application of soot and sulphur mixed with water, in which a small quantity of size has been dissolved, is perhaps as good as any. Gas-tar, which is sometimes used, is too strong for such a purpose. [M. J. B.]

VULNÉRAIRE. (Fr.) *Anthyllis Vulneraria.*

VULPIA. A genus of grasses belonging to the tribe *Festuceæ*, now included in *Festuca*. The species are mostly annuals, some (as *Festuca bromoides* and *F. myurus*) being natives of Britain. [D. M.]

VULPIN. (Fr.) *Alopecurus.*

VULVAIRE. (Fr.) *Chenopodium Vulvaria.*

VUSHIRA. An Indian name for *Pothos officinalis.*

VUTSUNAB. The deadly *Lagenandra toxicaria.*

WAAK. The bark of *Sida Abutilon.*

WACHENDORFIA. A genus belonging to the tribe *Wachendorfeæ*, which is by some botanists referred to *Liliaceæ*, but by others to *Hæmodoraceæ*. They are Cape herbs, often hairy, with tuberous rhizomes, and narrowly elliptical radical leaves, sheathing at the base, and usually nerved and plaited, in some of the species resembling those of *Plantago lanceolata*. The stem is round, with very small leaves, and a terminal panicle of purple red or yellow flowers, with large bracts. The perianth is rough exteriorly, six-cleft, irregular, with three of the segments more spreading than the others—the posterior one spurred at the base, the spur generally adnate to the pedicel; stamens six, three of them sterile or absent, ovary free, three-edged. [J. T. S.]

WADADURI. A Guiana name for *Lecythis grandiflora.*

WAGEN-BOOM. The wood of *Protea grandiflora.*

WAGENERIA. One of the numerous genera into which Klotzsch has divided the old well-marked genus *Begonia*. The species of the present group are trailing undershrubs, natives of Tropical America. Their chief distinguishing characteristic lies in the male flowers, which have four petals, while the females have five; the filaments are free, attached to a cushion-like receptacle, and bear oblong anthers; the style is persistent, covered with pimples, and surmounted by a stigma, whose two lobes are twisted spirally. The capsule is winged, dehiscent, and contains an entire stalked placenta. [M. T. M.]

WAGWANT. *Briza media.*

WAHAHÉ. The Maori name of *Hartighsea spectabilis.*

WAHLENBERGIA. An extensive genus of *Campanulaceæ*, abounding in the Cape Colony and throughout the Southern Hemisphere, and found also (though more rarely) in extratropical regions. It differs from *Campanula* only in the capsule, which is somewhat globose and half-superior, the free portion opening by three to five valves within the persistent segments of the calyx. [W. C.]

WAHOO. A North-west Indian name for *Euonymus atropurpureus.*

WAIATUMA. A name given by the Indians of Rio Negro to the edible fruits of *Salacia dulcis.*

WAIE. (Fr.) *Chamædorea.*

WAI-FA, or WAI-HWA. Chinese names for the unexpanded flower-buds of *Sophora japonica*, used for dyeing the silk garments of the mandarins a yellow colour, &c. See SOPHORA.

WAILESIA. A genus of epiphytal orchids, belonging to the tribe *Vandeæ*. The plants have the habit of *Vanda*, with distichous coriaceous channelled three-ribbed leaves, a foot or more in length; and from nine to twelve flowers, in an erect raceme, about an inch and a half in diameter, yellow spotted with crimson. They are related to *Trichoglottis*; but the latter differs in having a distinct appendage within the sac of the lip, and the flowers in short lateral spikes. The only species, *W. picta*, is a native of Malacca. [W. B. H.]

WAITZIA. A genus of *Compositæ*, comprising certain Australian herbs, whose stems bear heads of flowers arranged in corymbs. The heads are hemispherical, each surrounded by an involucre of many rows of dry coloured stalked scales, provided with a radiating petaloid appendage. The receptacle is flat, pitted, destitute of scales; the corollas hermaphrodite tubular slender, five-toothed at the apex; the branches of the style have little knobs at the ends; the achenes are flattened, ovate, prolonged at the top into a beak; pappus of one row of serrated rough setæ. The species furnish some of the very beautiful 'everlasting' flowers of our gardens. [M. T. M.]

WAKE-PINTLE. *Arum maculatum.*

WAKE-ROBIN. *Arum maculatum*; also *Trillium cernuum*; also *Anthurium* and *Philodendron.*

WALDSTEINIA. A genus of *Rosaceæ*, comprising certain herbaceous plants, with the aspect of some of the *Potentillas*. The leaves are palmately divided; and the flowers yellow, in terminal corymbs. The calyx is double, consisting of an outer row of five small segments, and an inner tubular whorl, whose limb is five-parted, and whose throat has a thickened lobed rim running around it; petals five, sessile; stamens numerous, inserted on the calyx with the petals; ovaries two to six, at the base of the calyx, each with a single ovule; styles terminal. The species are natives of Hungary, and derive their generic name from Count Waldstein, a writer on Hungarian plants. *W. geoides* is an old-fashioned but pretty hardy perennial. [M. T. M.]

WALEWORT, or WALLWORT. *Sambucus Ebulus.*

WALKERA. The name applied to a tree found in various parts of Tropical Asia, and constituting a genus of *Ochnaceæ*. The leaves are serrated, the flowers are in clusters; the calyx has five persistent lance-shaped sepals; the corolla has as many persistent petals, longer than the sepals; stamens five, shorter than the sepals; style single, as long as the stamens; fruit of five kidney-shaped drupes, placed on a small spongy receptacle. In Western India a decoction of the roots or of the leaves is used as a tonic and stomachic. The genus is named in honour of Dr. Walker, the founder of the Botanic Garden at Cambridge. *W. serrata* is in cultivation as a stove-plant. [M. T. M.]

WALLABA-TREE. *Eperua falcata.*

WALLENIA. A genus of tropical American shrubs, of the family *Myrsinaceæ*.

The leathery leaves are entire, and the flowers grow in terminal panicles. The calyx is bell-shaped, four-toothed; the corolla tubular, with a four-parted limb; stamens four, filaments thick, cohering below; fruit fleshy, globular. [M. T. M.]

WALLERIA. A genus of *Liliaceæ*, from East Tropical Africa, distinguished in the conantherous group by having the ovary free and the stamens equal, the ovary being semiadherent in the rest of the group; while the stamens are equal in *Conanthera*, *Cumingia*, and their allies, and unequal in *Zephyra* and *Cyanella*. Dr. Kirk describes them as leafy herbs, with linear-lanceolate leaves, and solitary axillary flowers, which have a six-parted perianth, with very short tube and equal spreading limb; six equal stamens, with short filaments and elongated anthers, which are two-celled, opening by pores; and a free three-celled ovary, containing numerous ovules. The two described species were found on the Manganja Hills. The genus is named after Mr. Horace Waller, one of the few survivors of the ill-fated Mission to Central Africa. [T. M.]

WALLFLOWER. *Cheiranthus Cheiri.* —, WESTERN. *Erysimum arkansanum.*

WALL GERMANDER. *Teucrium Chamædrys.*

WALLICHIA. A genus of palms, named in honour of the late Dr. Wallich, a celebrated Danish botanist, and author of several valuable works on Indian plants. It consists of about eight species, natives of Northern and Eastern India, Siam, Java, and the Philippine Islands, growing in tufts, and either without stems or with short reed-like ones. Their leaves are pinnate, and rise from a mass of coarse fibres, the leaflets being entire and wedge-shaped at the base, and variously-lobed toothed or irregularly jagged in the upper part, and whitish underneath. The species belonging to the section *Harina* bear both male and female flower-spikes on the same plant, while those of the section *Orania* have them on distinct plants, the spikes in either case having numerous overlapping spathes on their stalks. The male flowers have a more or less deeply tripartite calyx, three valvate petals, and six or an indefinite number of stamens; while the females have a tripartite calyx and corolla, and a two or rarely three-celled ovary. The fruits are olive-shaped, purple or whitish in colour, and contain an acrid stinging juice. [A. S.]

WALLINIA. A genus of *Chenopodiaceæ* from the Cape of Good Hope, comprising an erect branched herb, with alternate entire fleshy leaves, and minute clustered sessile flowers, in simple leafless spikes at the extremity of the branches. The flowers have three bracts; a calyx of five sepals, which are unchanged in fruit; five stamens, and four styles. The fruit is ellipsoidal, eight-ribbed, with an herbaceous pericarp adhering to the bony coat of the seed. [J. T. S.]

WALNUT. *Juglans regia.* —, BELGAUM, COUNTRY, or INDIAN. *Aleurites triloba.* —, JAMAICA. *Picrodendron Juglans.* —, OTAHEITE. *Aleurites triloba.*

WALPERSIA. The name of a genus of heath-like Cape shrubs of the family *Rhamnaceæ*, bearing the flowers in heads. The calyx is woolly, with a short tube adherent to the ovary, its limb divided into five narrow erect three-sided segments; petals five, small, with incurved hairy points; stamens five, opposite the petals, the anthers one-celled; ovary with a single erect basal ovule in each of its three compartments; style short; fruit partly adherent to the calyx, ultimately separating into three one-seeded carpels. [M. T. Me]

WALTHERIA. A widely distributed tropical genus of *Byttneriaceæ*, comprising herbs or shrubs with serrated leaves, covered with hairs, some of which are star-shaped. The flowers are borne in axillary or terminal heads; the calyx is persistent, bell-shaped, five-cleft; petals five, stalked, the stalks adherent to the tube formed by the union of the lower parts of the filaments; ovary sessile oblique one-celled, with two ovules; style somewhat lateral; stigma fringed or tubercled; fruit capsular, surmounted by the style. *W. americana* is employed as a febrifuge in Surinam, and *W. Douradinha* is used for diseases of the chest and other complaints in Brazil. The genus is named in honour of Prof. Walther of Leipsic. [M. T. M.]

WAMARA. A native name for the Brown Ebony of Demerara.

WAMPEE. The Chinese name for the fruits of *Cookia punctata*, highly esteemed in China and the Indian Archipelago.

WANGALA, WANGLO. Guiana names for the seeds of *Sesamum orientale.*

WANGHEE, WHANGHEE. The names given to some Eastern canes imported for walking-sticks, and supposed to be furnished by the narrow-leaved Bamboo.

WANZEY. An Abyssinian name for *Cordia abyssinica.*

WARANANA. A large timber-tree of British Guiana, called the Wild Orange, the wood of which is much used in the colony for oars and staves.

WARATÁH. *Telopea speciosissima.* Also a name applied to certain anemone-flowered varieties of *Camellia japonica.*

WARE. A general name for Seaweed.

WAREA. A genus of *Cruciferæ* from the Southern States of North America. They are glabrous annuals, with entire leaves, and corymbose purple or white flowers; while the fruits are slender compressed pods, supported on long stipes. [J. T. S.]

WARENCE. *Rubia tinctorum.*

WARIALEE. An Indian name for Fennel-seed.

WARRACOORI. A native Demerara name for the wood of the White Cedar, *Icica altissima.*

WARREA. A terrestrial genus of orchids, belonging to the tribe *Vandeæ.* They are herbs, with small or no pseudobulbs, reed-like strongly-veined leaves, and nearly regular racemose showy flowers. Several species have been described as belonging to this genus, but some of them have been separated under the name of *Warscewiczella.* *W. cyanea* is remarkable for the deep-blue colour of its lip, pure blue being rarely found among orchids. The species are natives of Tropical America. [W. B. H.]

WARREE. An Indian name for *Panicum miliaceum.*

WARRI-WARRI. A kind of Indian fan made by the natives of Guiana, from the leaves of the Acuyuru Palm, *Astrocaryum aculeatum.*

WARSCEWICZELLA. A small genus of tropical American orchids, very nearly related to *Warrea.* They are terrestrial herbs, destitute of pseudobulbs; the leaves linear or linear-lanceolate, coriaceous, equitant at the base; and the flowers large and showy, solitary on radical peduncles, which are furnished with a few sheathing bracts. Sepals and petals spreading, nearly equal; lip large, with a square appendage at its base, the sides involute. [W. B. H.]

WARSCEWICZIA. The gardens of Europe owe the introduction of numerous beautiful and interesting plants to M. Warscewicz. The genus which commemorates his name belongs to the *Cinchonaceæ*, and comprises certain trees and shrubs, natives of Tropical America, closely allied in the structure of the flowers to *Calycophyllum.* The difference consists in the five-toothed calyx, in the throat of the corolla being devoid of hairs, in the attachment of the stamens to the base of the tube of the corolla, and in other minor points. As in *Mussænda* and several allied genera, one of the sepals is larger than the rest, and resembles a coloured leaf. [M. T. M.]

WART-HERB. *Rhynchosia minima.*

WARTS (adj. WARTY). Hard or firm excrescences. See EXOSTOSIS.

WART-SHAPED. The same as Verrucæform.

WARTWORT. *Euphorbia helioscopia.*

WASHIBA. A strong hard durable and elastic wood of Guiana, much used by the Indians for making bows.

WASHINGTONIA. A name given by the Americans to *Sequoia Wellingtonia.*

WATER-BLINKS. *Montia fontana.*

WATER-BUCKLER. *Hydropeltis.*

WATER-CAN. *Nuphar lutea.*

WATERCRESS. *Nasturtium officinale.*

WATER-FIRE. *Bergia ammannioides.*

WATER-GLADIOLE. A name given by Gerarde to the Flowering Rush, *Butomus.*

WATER-LEAF. *Hydrophyllum;* also *Rhodomenia palmata.*

WATER-LETTUCE. The West Indian name of *Pistia Stratiotes.*

WATER-LILIES. A general name for the *Nymphæaceæ.*

WATER-LILY. *Nymphæa.* —, ROYAL. *Victoria regia.* —, WHITE. *Nymphæa alba.* —, YELLOW. *Nuphar.*

WATER-NYMPH. *Nymphæa.*

WATER-PEPPERS. The English name for the *Elatinaceæ.*

WATER-PLANT. An aquatic plant, *i.e.* one growing in water not in earth (terrestrial), or air (aërial).

WATER-PLATTER. *Victoria regia.*

WATERSHIELD. *Brasenia.*

WATERSHIELDS. An English name for the *Cabombaceæ.*

WATER-SOLDIER. *Stratiotes.*

WATER-SPIKE. *Potamogeton.*

WATER-TORCH. *Typha latifolia.*

WATER-TREE. *Tetracera potatoria.* —, RED. *Erythrophleum.*

WATER-WEED. *Anacharis Alsinastrum,* also called *Udora.* —, NEW GRENADA. *Marathrium utile.*

WATER-WITHE. *Vitis caribæa.*

WATER-WOOD. *Chimarrhis cymosa.*

WATERWORT. *Elatine.*

WATSONIA. A rather numerous genus of Cape *Iridaceæ,* resembling and formerly combined with *Gladiolus.* They are herbaceous plants, with bulbous or tuberous rootstocks, very narrow or broad sword-shaped leaves, and loose spikes of large often brightly-coloured flowers, or dense spikes of smaller ones. The flowers rise from a stiff two-valved spathe, and have a coloured short-tubed calyx with a six-parted limb, the segments being either nearly equal or bilabiate; three stamens, which rise from below the throat of the calyx, and are either erect or somewhat one-sided, with versatile anthers: and a three-celled ovary, bearing a slender style ending in three two-parted narrow stigmas, and containing numerous ovules. All the species are confined to the Cape of Good Hope. [A. S.]

WATTLE-TREE. An Australian name for *Acacia.* —, BLACK. *Acacia affinis;* also *A. mollissima.* —, RASPBERRY JAM. A West Australian species of *Acacia.* —, SAVANNAH. *Citharexylon quadrangulare* and *C. cinereum.* —, SILVER. *Acacia mollissima.* —, —, of Tasmania. *Acacia dealbata.*

WATTLE-WOOD. *Lætia Thamnia.*

WAVY. The same as Undulate.

WAW-WAW. *Rajania pleioneura.*

WAX, CARNAUBA. The produce of the young leaves of the Wax Palm of Brazil, *Copernicia cerifera,* used for making candles. —, VEGETABLE. A kind of wax obtained from the berries of several species of *Myrica,* especially *M. cerifera.* It is sometimes called Myrtle Wax, from the name of Candleberry Myrtle applied to *Myrica.*

WAXCLUSTER. *Gaultheria hispida.*

WAX-TREE. *Vismia.* —, JAPAN. *Rhus succedaneum.* —, NEW GRENADA. *Elæagia utilis.*

WAXWORK. *Celastrus scandens.*

WAXY. Having the texture and colour of new wax.

WAYAKA. A Feejean name for *Pachyrhizus angulatus.*

WAY-BENNET, or WAY-BENT. *Hordeum murinum.*

WAYBREAD. *Plantago major.*

WAYFARING-TREE. *Viburnum Lantana.*

WAYTHORN. *Rhamnus catharticus.*

WEASEL-SNOUT. *Galeobdolon luteum.*

WEBBIA. A genus of somewhat shrubby *Compositæ,* natives of Tropical Africa, as well as of the Cape of Good Hope. The leaves are entire, smooth above, hairy below. The flower-heads are surrounded by an involucre of two or three rows of overlapping scales; the receptacle is pitted; the flowers are unisexual and diœcious—the males with a tubular corolla, concealing the anthers and the style; the females more deeply divided, rather fleshy, the style protruding beyond the corolla, and the stigmas elongated and hairy. The achenes are cylindrical, striated, with very hairy ridges, and glandular furrows; pappus hairy, in many rows. [M. T. M.]

WEDDELINA. The merits of a French botanist and traveller are intended to be commemorated by this name, which is applied to a genus of *Podostemaceæ,* comprising a small herbaceous plant, native of Guiana. It has a linear rootstock, which divides into a number of thick branches closely intertwined, rounded on one surface and hollowed on the other. The leaves are divided into numerous linear segments. The flowers have a thin membranous perianth of five pieces, each traversed by a thick midrib, which remains in the form of a stiff thread, after the cellular part has rotted away; the stamens are six to ten, hypogynous; style terminal; stigma capitate. [M. T. M.]

WEDELIA. A genus of *Compositæ,* consisting of herbs or undershrubs, most abundant in Tropical and Subtropical America, but also found in Asia and Australia. The leaves are serrated or three-cleft; and the flower-stalks solitary in the forks of the branches, rarely in the axils of the leaves. The involucre consists of two or three rows of scales, the outer of which are leafy, the inner membranous, the receptacle convex, the outer florets ligulate, the central ones tubular, both kinds yellow; stigmas conical. The achenes are compressed, surmounted by a pappus of toothed or hairy scales. Some of the species are in cultivation.　　[M. T. M.]

WEDGE-SHAPED. The same as Cuneate.

WEED. Any plant which obtrusively occupies cultivated or dressed ground, to the exclusion or injury of some particular crop intended to be grown. Thus, even the most useful plants may become weeds if they appear out of their proper place. The term is sometimes applied to any insignificant-looking or unprofitable plants which grow profusely in a state of nature; also to any noxious or useless plant.

WEEMBY. An East African name for *Eleusine coracana*.

WEENONG. A Javanese name for *Tetrameles*.

WEIGELA. A handsome genus of *Caprifoliaceæ* from China and Japan, some species of which are amongst the finest shrubby ornaments of our gardens in early summer. The flowers are produced in short cymes at the ends of the young shoots, and have a five-lobed subequal calyx with a linear pentagonal tube adnate below to the ovary, beyond which it is produced; a funnel-shaped regular corolla, equal-sided at the base, and widened at the throat, with a spreading five-parted limb; five stamens; a filiform exserted style with a peltate-capitate stigma; a free epigynous gland; and an inferior ovary cut into four false cells by the projection of a pair of double placentæ, which do not unite in the axis. The genus is nearly allied to *Diervilla*, and is united with it by some botanists; but Dr. Lindley has pointed out that the seed-vessel is crustaceous not membranaceous, and the seeds winged instead of wingless.　　[T. M.]

WEIGELTIA. The name of a shrub native of Surinam, and forming a genus of *Myrsinaceæ*. The leaves are entire, with pellucid dots; and the flowers grow in axillary spreading racemes; calyx and corolla each four-parted; stamens four, opposite to the lobes of the corolla; anthers short, style short, acuminate. The plant is but imperfectly known.　　[M. T. M.]

WEINMANNIA. The plants belonging to this genus of *Cunoniaceæ* are found in various parts of South America both in the tropical and temperate regions, in Southern Africa, Madagascar and the neighbouring islands, and also in New Zealand. They are evergreen shrubs or trees, with simple or compound opposite leaves, and racemes of smallish usually tufted flowers,

which have a persistent four-parted calyx with the segments overlapping, four overlapping petals, eight long stamens (alternating with as many glands or with the lobes of a disk), and a two-celled ovary bearing two distinct styles. The fruit is a leathery capsule splitting when ripe through the partition into two boat-shaped sharp-pointed pieces, and containing several very small hairy seeds.

The tree species of *Weinmannia* mostly afford a soft light wood, useful in common carpentry and cabinet-making purposes, though obtainable only in planks of small size. The astringent bark of one of the Peruvian species is used for tanning leather, and in Bourbon *W. tinctoria* is employed for dyeing red.　　[A. S.]

WEISSIEI. A natural order of pterocarpous mosses, with an erect equal capsule, an obsolete peristome (or one with sixteen teeth often united at the base), a dimidiate veil, and the texture of the leaves close. The true *Gymnostoma* differ only from *Weissia* in the want of a peristome. Several species of the latter genus occur in Great Britain, but they are mostly small and obscure plants. *W. cirrhata* is one of the prettiest, and is not uncommon in woods, on posts and rails, where it is recognised at once by its peculiar habit. *Gymnostomum curvirostrum*, whose stem is beset with rooting fibres nearly to the top, is used in the Arctic regions for lampwicks.　　[M. J. B.]

WELCOME-TO-OUR-HOUSE. *Euphorbia Cyparissias.*

WELD. *Reseda Luteola.*

WELDENIA. A genus containing a Mexican herb, which is probably to be referred to *Melanthaceæ*. It has imbricated linear-lanceolate smooth root-leaves, and numerous subsessile white flowers, enclosed in spathes, which split open longitudinally. The perianth is coloured, salver-shaped, with a very long narrow tube, and a three-cleft limb; stamens six; ovary free; style filiform, with a three-sided capitate stigma; fruit subglobose, with five or six seeds in each of the three (or four) cells.　　[J. T. S.]

WELDWORTS. A name proposed by Lindley for the order *Resedaceæ*.

WELLINGTONIA. English botanists, in their desire to do honour to a British hero, seem to have committed an oversight in separating the *Wellingtonia gigantea* of our gardens from SEQUOIA, to which the reader is referred.　　[M. T. M.]

WELWITSCHIA. A low woody plant, most singular in shape structure and mode of growth, recently brought by Dr. Welwitsch from the dry sandy country of Mossamedes, in Western Africa. It was first designated by the name of *Tumboa*, which was believed to be that by which it is known to the natives; but this word, it appears, is applied generally to all plants which have a short thick woody trunk or rhizome, and it has therefore been named after its discoverer by Dr. Hooker, who has shown that, notwithstanding the anomalies by which it is characterised, it forms a genus of the order *Gnetaceæ*. In its first youth its two original cotyledonary leaves appear to grow considerably, and extend horizontally in opposite directions, raised but little above the surface of the sand; whilst the intervening stock thickens and hardens, assuming an obconical shape, flattish at top, and rapidly tapering below into the descending root. As years go on, the original pair of leaves, having attained their full size and a hard tough fibrous consistence, do not die away, but gradually split up into shreds; the woody mass which bears them rises very little higher, but increases horizontally both above and below the insertion of the leaves, so as to clasp their base in a deep marginal slit or cavity; and every year, from the upper side at the base of the leaf, are developed several short flowering-stalks. These are erect dichotomously-branched jointed stems, six inches to a foot high, bearing a pair of small opposite scales at each fork or joint, and each branch terminated by an oblong cone, under the scales of which are the flowers and seeds. The result is that the country is studded with these misshapen table-like or anvil-like masses of wood, whose flat tops, pitted with the scars of old flowering-stems, never rise above a foot from the ground, but vary according to age in a horizontal diameter of from a few inches to five or six feet; those of about eighteen inches diameter, being supposed to be already above a hundred years old, still retaining their leaves, ragged indeed and shortened by the injuries of time, but which in their full vigour extend to a length of six feet. The flowers appear to be of two kinds—females, with naked ovules like those of *Gnetum*; and hermaphrodites, showing a higher and more complex type of structure, connecting gymnospermous with angiospermous dicotyledons. (See *Transactions of the Linnean Society*, xxiv. 1, plate 1—14.)

Dr. Welwitsch found these misshapen monsters, deeply sunk in the soil with their middle-sized roots, in considerable quantities at Cabro Negro (15° 40′ south lat.), on the dry plateau of the coast of Benguela, which is covered with loose sandy rough rubble, and is from 300 to 400 feet above the level of the sea. A little north of this place, at Mossamedes, in the neighbourhood of the Nicolas River, on the little Fishbay (at 14° 20′ south lat.), Herr Monteiro found it at a later period in a perfectly similar situation on quartzose schistose soil; and Mr. Baines and Mr. Anderson in Damara-land, between 22° and 23° south latitude, in the neighbourhood of Whalefish Bay, in a district in which not a drop of rain ever falls. The distribution of this remarkable plant, which calls to mind some vegetable relic of a creation long since past, falls between the fourteenth and twenty-third degrees of south latitude, as far as at present ascertained. It is well known to the natives. The crown, when divested of its leaves, resembles so closely the cracked surface of an old *Polyporus igniarius* that it might, on a superficial view, be taken for a fungus.

WENDLANDIA. A genus of *Cinchonaceæ*, consisting of trees or shrubs, natives of the East Indies. The flowers, which are small and white, are borne in terminal panicles. The calyx-tube is nearly globular, striated, its limb minutely five-toothed; the corolla has a cylindrical tube, expanding into a five-cleft limb; stamens five, projecting; ovary surmounted by a fleshy disk; style projecting; fruit capsular, bursting from above by two valves. The genus is named in honour of M. Wendland, a Hanoverian botanist. [M. T. M.]

WENDTIA. A genus of *Oxalidaceæ* from Chili, consisting of erect or prostrate shrubs with the habit of *Potentilla*. They have opposite shortly-stalked wedge-shaped silky leaves, more or less deeply three or more lobed, no stipules, and terminal one-flowered peduncles, bearing yellow flowers with bracteated five-sepaled calyces, and five petals, ten stamens, and a globose three-celled ovary, having twin ovules in each cell, and a sessile stigma of which the three lobes are petaloid. [J. T. S.]

WENIWEL. *Coscinium fenestratum*.

WERNERIA. A genus of *Compositæ*, consisting of low-growing tufted herbaceous plants, natives of mountainous regions in Equatorial America. The leaves are long and woolly; and the flower-heads solitary, each with a bell-shaped involucre of one row of scales, and naked receptacle. Outer florets strap-shaped, yellow or white, the central ones tubular, yellow; stigmas blunt at the points, feathered; fruits top-shaped, hairy; pappus hairy, in several rows. *W. rigida*, a native of Quito, is in cultivation as an herbaceous perennial. The genus is named in honour of Werner, the celebrated mineralogist. [M. T. M.]

WESTRINGIA. A genus of Australian shrubs belonging to the *Labiatæ*, and containing several species. They have verticillate entire evergreen leaves, and solitary subsessile axillary flowers. The calyx is campanulate costate and five-toothed; the upper lip of the corolla two-lobed; and the four stamens included, the upper ones only being fertile, and furnished with dimidiate anthers. [W. C.]

WETTINIA. A genus formerly associated with screw-pines, but recently found to be a genuine member of the great natural order of Palms, and closely allied to *Iriartea*: indeed, so much do the species resemble in habit even some *Iriarteas*, that the Peruvians often mistake their leaves for those of the former, when collecting them during Lent for cabbage; but on boiling them they soon find out their mistake, the leaves of *Wettinia*, like those of the genus *Socratea*, being very bitter and unfit to eat, whilst those of *Iriartea* are sweet and good eating. There are two species of *Weltinia*, both inhabiting the eastern slopes of the Andes, about 3,500 feet above the sea-level— *W. augusta*, originally discovered by Pavon, and collected more recently by Pöppig on the banks of the Tocache; and *W. maynensis*, called Pullo-corota and Shullu-choura by the natives, inhabiting those of the R.ver Mayo. Their stems are from thirty to forty feet high, unarmed, and (like some species of *Iriartea*) borne on stilt-like aërial roots covered with prickles. The leaves are terminal and pinnatisect, the segments truncate and erose on their apex. The spadix is developed below the crown of the leaves; the flowers are diœcious, and the fruit is a one-seeded dry berry.   [B. S.]

WHAMPEE.   *Cookia punctata.*

WHANGHEE.   See WANGEE.

WHARRE.   The Crab, *Pyrus Malus.*

WHEAT.   The grain-bearing *Triticum vulgare*, of which two forms are distinguished, *T. æstivum* and *T. hybernum.* —, BUCK. *Fagopyrum.* —, COW. *Melampyrum.* —, GOATS. *Tragopyrum.* —, GUINEA. *Zea Mays.* —, SPELT. *Triticum Spelta.* —, TURKEY. *Zea Mays.*

WHEEL-SHAPED.   Rotate.

WHICKEN.   *Pyrus Aucuparia.*

WHIN.   *Ulex europæus.* —, MOOR, or NEEDLE. *Genista anglica.* —, PETTY. *Genista anglica*; also *Ononis arvensis.*

WHIN-BERRY.   *Vaccinium.*

WHIP-SHAPED.   Flagelliform.

WHIP-TONGUE.   *Galium Mollugo.*

WHIRLING PLANT.   *Desmodium gyrans.*

WHISKY.   A spirituous liquor distilled from the fermented worts of malt or grain.

WHITE-BEAM.   *Pyrus Aria.*

WHITE-BEN.   *Silene inflata.*

WHITE-BLOW.   *Draba verna*; also *Saxifraga tridactylites.*

WHITE-BOTTLE.   *Silene inflata.*

WHITE-CAPS.   A name employed sometimes to indicate *Agaricus arvensis*, which is more commonly known under the designation of Horse Mushroom.   [M. J. B.]

WHITE DEAL.   The timber of *Abies excelsa.*

WHITE DAMMER.   A gum-resin produced by *Vateria indica.*

WHITE-HEAD.   *Parthenium Hysterophorus.*

WHITE HOOP.   A Jamaica name for *Tournefortia bicolor.*

WHITE-HORSE.   *Portlandia grandiflora.*

WHITE-POTHERB.   *Valerianella olitoria.*

WHITE-ROOT.   *Polygonatum officinale.*

WHITE-ROT.   *Hydrocotyle vulgaris*; also *Pinguicula vulgaris.*

WHITE-THORN.   *Cratægus Oxyacantha.*

WHITE-TREE.   *Melaleuca Leucadendron.*

WHITE-WOOD.   *Tilia americana*; also *Liriodendron tulipifera*, *Oreodaphne Leucoxylon*, *Nectandra leucantha*, *Tecoma Leucoxylon*, and *Tecoma pentaphylla.* — of Australia. *Lagunaria Patersoni.* — of Tasmania. *Pittosporum bicolor.*

WHITEWORT.   *Matricaria Chamomilla*; also *Polygonatum officinale.*

WHITFIELDIA.   A genus of tropical African shrubs belonging to the order *Acanthaceæ.* The technical distinguishing peculiarities are to be sought in the presence of two bracts at the base of the four or five-parted calyx, both bracts and calyx being of a reddish hue. Additional characteristics are—the funnel-shaped two-lipped corolla, twice the length of the calyx; the ovary with four ovules; and the four large discoid seeds, which are provided with little hook-like appendages. *W. lateritia*, an ornamental evergreen stove-shrub, was brought from Sierra Leone by Mr. T. Whitfield, after whom the genus is named. The branches bear terminal clusters of rather large brick-red flowers. Another species is a native of Fernando Po.   [M. T. M.]

WHITIA.   A genus belonging to the *Cyrtandreæ* tribe of *Gesneraceæ*, and to the small section of that tribe characterised by having a berry-like unopening fruit. It differs from *Cyrtandra* in the calyx being divided to the base into five equal segments; in its stamens, only two out of five of which are fertile, projecting beyond the funnel-shaped tube of the corolla; in the insertion of the anthers being unequal, not parallel; and in the funnel-shaped form of the stigma. Two species are known, both climbing shrubs of Java, having opposite unequal pairs of leaves, and axillary fascicles of flowers.   [A. S.]

WHITLAVIA.   A genus of *Hydrophyllaceæ*, containing two handsome species, with large flowers, natives of California. It is allied in general habit, as well as in the form of the leaves and the glandular hairs, to *Eutoca*; but the great size and the tubular-campanulate form of the corolla, as well as the scales at the base of the filaments, easily distinguish it.   [W. C.]

WHITLEYA.   *Anisodus.*

WHITLOW-GRASS.   *Draba.*

WHITLOW WORT.   *Paronychia.*

WHITTEN-TREE.   *Viburnum Opulus.*

WHORL.   A ring of organs all on the same plane. The same as Verticil.

WHORLED.   Verticillate; collected into a ring-like series.

WHORT, or WHURT.   *Vaccinium Myrtillus.*

WHORTLEBERRY.   *Vaccinium*; especially applied in this country to the fruit of *Vaccinium Myrtillus*; sometimes also applied to the fruit of *Oxycoccus*. —, RED or MOUNT IDA. *Vaccinium Vitis idœa.*

WI. The Feejean name for *Spondias dulcis.*

WIBELIA. *Davallia.*

WICHURÆA. A genus of Australian shrubs of the family *Rhamneæ.* The branches are somewhat spiny; the leaves linear, somewhat tufted; the stipules membranous, persistent; and the flowers nearly sessile at the ends of the branches, surrounded by dry membranous bracts. The calyx-tube is dilated, its limb divided into five triangular acute segments; petals five, stalked; stamens five; disk five-lobed, hairy, the lobes overhanging the semiadherent three-celled ovary; style distinct; stigma three-toothed; capsule surrounded by the persistent calyx and corolla, surmounted by the style, and girt at the base by the disk, when ripe dividing into three valves; seeds three. It is by some included in *Cryptandra.* [M. T. M.]

WICKSTRÖMIA. This genus of *Thymelaceæ* consists of about twenty species, scattered over Tropical and Subtropical Asia Australia and the Pacific Islands, some of them being small trees, and others shrubs. It is distinguished from *Daphne* by its usually opposite always deciduous leaves, and by its flowers having four small narrow scales below the ovary. The flowers are disposed in short terminal or axillary racemes or spikes, and have a tubular coloured calyx with four spreading lobes, without any scales in the orifice; eight stamens, with scarcely any filaments, in two rows near the top of the calyx-tube; and an ovary ending in a short style, and round-headed stigma. The fruits are small single-seeded berries, at first enclosed in the calyx but ultimately free, the calyx splitting open and falling away. *W. indica* is a large tree-like shrub, common on the sea-shores of Tropical Eastern Australia, the Feejee, Society, and other Polynesian islands, where the natives use its bark (which, like that of other daphnads, contains an extremely tough and easily-separable fibre) for making fishing-nets and lines, ropes, &c. The Feejeans, who call the plant Sinu Mataivi, also employ it medicinally, using the bark and leaves as a remedy for coughs, and the bark alone as an application to sores. It has oval or lanceolate-oblong net-veined leaves about two inches in length. [A. S.]

WIDDELILAM. An Indian name for Peppermint.

WIDDRINGTONIA. Formerly included in the genus *Thuja*, but now constituting a distinct group of the cupressineous division of *Coniferæ*. The species consist of trees, natives of the Cape of Good Hope, and have crowded alternate leaves (not opposite as in *Thuja*). These leaves in the young plant are linear and spreading, while in the older plant they are scale-like, and closely pressed up against the stem. The flowers are diœcious; the males in terminal catkins, the stamens numerous, and arranged in four rows, each stamen having a two-celled anther; the females in solitary terminal cones, each consisting of four scales, connate at their edges, and each bearing five to ten winged seeds. In the ripe state the cones are globular and woody, with comparatively few seeds. *W. cupressoides*, better known as *Thuja cupressoides*, is cultivated in this country as a greenhouse shrub. [M. T. M.]

WIDOW-WAIL. *Cneorum.*

WIEDEMANNIA. A small genus of plants, natives of Australia, nearly related both in habit and structure to *Lamium*, but differing in the tubular corolla, which is two-lipped, the upper lip being lanceolate and the lower bifid, with all the teeth rigid and very acute. [W. C.]

WIEGMANNIA. The name of a genus of *Cinchonaceæ* which includes a small shrub, native of the Sandwich Islands. The purple flowers are borne on contracted cymes, surrounded by a kind of involucre, formed by the stipules of the upper leaves. The tube of the calyx is marked by eight ridges, and its limb divided into four rather large leafy segments; the corolla is funnel-shaped, the limb four-lobed; the stamens four, concealed within the corolla, the anthers nearly sessile; the ovary surmounted by a fleshy disk. The fruit is a two-celled eight-ribbed berry, crowned by the leafy limb of the calyx. In each of its cells is a single ovule. [M. T. M.]

WIGANDIA. A genus of *Hydroleaceæ*, containing several species of hispid large-leaved herbs, natives of Tropical and Subtropical America. The flowers are borne in gyrate bibracteated branched spicate racemes; the calyx is five-parted; the corolla rotate; the stamens exserted; and the capsule two-valved with two parietal placentas, the revolute margins of which are entirely covered with seeds. [W. C.]

WIGHTIA. A genus referred by Bentham to *Scrophulariaceæ*. It is founded on a single species, a climbing shrub from Nepal. The calyx is coriaceous and campanulate, with two to five short lobes; the corolla is funnel-shaped, the limb two-lipped, the upper lip being erect and bi-lobed, and the lower patent and trifid; the four stamens are inserted in the tube of the corolla, and there is no trace of a fifth; the two cells of the anthers are equal and parallel; the ovary is two-celled, with numerous ovules; and the capsule is oblong, and dehisces septicidally with two valves, and contains numerous oblong seeds furnished with linear wings. [W. C.]

WIG-TREE. *Rhus Cotinus.*

WILD. Growing in a state of nature. Sometimes applied in depreciation of plants inferior to others to which they bear more or less resemblance.

WILD-BOAR'S TREE. A San Domingo name for *Hedwigia balsamifera*.

WILD CINCHONA. *Mussænda frondosa*.

WILDE PRUIME. The fruit of *Pappea capensis*, or the Wild Plum.

WILDING. The Crab, *Pyrus Malus*.

WILD SPANIARD. *Aciphylla squarrosa* and *A. Colensoi*.

WILLDENOWIA. An ill-defined genus of *Restiaceæ*, consisting of Cape herbaceous plants, with branched rush-like leafless stems, provided here and there with membranous sheaths. The flowers are diœcious, the males in racemes at the ends of the branches, each raceme having at its base a large sheathing bract, and the pedicels also being each provided with a very long membranous bract: the flowers themselves consisting of a membranous four to five-parted perianth the segments of which are narrow, nearly equal in size, and of three distinct stamens with one-celled anthers. The female flowers are in spikes at the ends of the branches, each spike provided with a sheathing deciduous bract; the perianth is placed upon a thick six-lobed cup-like disk and consists of six nearly equal segments in two rows; stigmas two; fruit indehiscent. Some of the species have a very elegant appearance : two of them are in cultivation, *W. teres* and *W. striata*. At the Cape the small wiry stems are used for making brooms. [M. T. M.]

WILLEMETIA. This name has been applied to several genera of various orders, but is now exclusively adopted for a Central European mountain plant, of the family *Compositæ*. The leaves are entire ; and the flower-heads few in number, each surrounded by an involucre of numerous overlapping scales; the receptacle is flat, scaleless, pitted ; the corollas all strap-shaped ; the achenes uniform, beaked ; and the pappus hairy, in one row. [M. T. M.]

WILL-O'-THE-WISP. *Tremella Nostoc.*

WILLOW. *Salix*. —, CRACK. *Salix fragilis*. —, FRENCH. *Epilobium angustifolium*. —, GOAT. *Salix Capræa*, the badge of the Cummings. —, GOLDEN. A Madeira name for *Genista scoparia*. —, HUNTINGDON, or WHITE. *Salix alba*. —, PERSIAN. *Epilobium angustifolium*. —, PRIMROSE. A West Indian name for *Œnothera*. —, ROSE. *Salix purpurea*. —, SWEET. *Myrica Gale*. —, WEEPING. *Salix babylonica*.

WILLOW-HERB. *Epilobium angustifolium*. —, HOODED. *Scutellaria*.

WILLOW-WEED. *Lythrum Salicaria*; also *Polygonum lapathifolium*.

WILLOWWORTS. A name proposed by Lindley for the *Salicaceæ*.

WILLUGHBEIA. A genus of *Apocynaceæ*, containing several climbing shrubs from Southern Asia. They are milky, and have entire opposite leaves and tendrils,

and axillary and terminal cymes. The calyx is five-parted ; the corolla salver-shaped and five-cleft, with oblong lobes ; the ovate-acute anthers are longer than the filaments ; the ovary is one-celled, with numerous ovules attached to two parietal placentas ; the baccate fruit is about the size and shape of an orange, and the numerous seeds are buried in the pulp. [W. C.]

WILSONIA. A genus of *Convolvulaceæ*, containing one or two species, undershrubs from Australia. The calyx is five-toothed, and the corolla funnel-shaped ; the single style has a capitate stigma ; and the small ovary contains two ovules. [W. C.]

WILTED. The same as Flaccid.

WIMMERIA. A genus of Mexican shrubs, similar in general appearance to the species of *Celastrus*, and belonging to the same family. The leaves are entire, and the flower-stalks cymose; calyx five-lobed ; petals five, spreading, inserted with the five stamens into a lobed fleshy perigynous disk ; ovary three-celled, with several ovules in each cell; style short, stigma three-lobed ; fruit indehiscent, three-winged. [M. T. M.]

WINCHIA. A genus of *Apocynaceæ*, containing a single woody plant from Martaban, with ternate or quaternate oblong leaves, and terminal flower-panicles. The calyx is cut into five roundish lobes ; the corolla is salver-shaped, its limb is divided into five oblong divisions, externally downy and hairy on the inside; the five stamens have very short filaments, and lanceolate acute anthers ; and the ovary is two-celled, with numerous ovules. [W. C.]

WIND-FLOWER. *Gentiana Pneumonanthe*; also *Anemone*. —, BASTARD. *Gentiana Pseudo-Pneumonanthe*.

WINDLE-STRAW. *Agrostis Spica venti*; also *Cynosurus cristatus*.

WIND-SHAKE. See ANEMOSIS.

WINE. The fermented juice of various fruits prepared with sugar, as grape-wine, orange-wine, &c.; also the sap of certain plants, as palm-wine. There are besides various medicinal preparations in the form of wine, such as quinine-wine, taraxacum-wine, &c.

WINEBERRY. *Vaccinium Myrtillus*; also *Ribes rubrum*. —, NEW ZEALAND. A name given by the colonists to *Coriaria sarmentosa*.

WINGED. Furnished with any kind of membranous or thin expansion.

WING-POINT. *Pterostigma*.

WINGS. The two lateral petals of a papilionaceous flower; any kind of membranous expansion.

WINNA. An Indian name for layers of the dried bark of *Lecythis Ollaria*, used in Guiana as wrappers for cigarettes.

WINTER-BERRY. *Prinos*, also *Ilex montana*.

WINTERGREEN. *Pyrola*; also *Trientalis*, and *Gaultheria procumbens*. —, AROMATIC. *Gaultheria*. —, CHICKWEED. *Trientalis*. —, FALSE. *Pyrola*. —, SPOTTED. *Chimaphila maculata*. —, SPRING. *Gaultheria procumbens*.

WINTERLEIN. A German name for *Linum usitatissimum*.

WINTER'S BARK. *Drimys Winteri*.

WINTER-SWEET. *Origanum*.

WINTER-WEED. *Veronica hederæfolia*.

WIRE-BENT. *Nardus stricta*.

WIRTGENIA. *Spondias*.

WISLIZENIA. A genus of *Cruciferæ*, comprising an annual species, native of New Mexico. The leaves are ternate, and the flowers, which are borne in racemes, are yellow. The stamens are very long; the ovary stalked globose two-celled, surmounted by an awl-shaped style and a globular stigma. [M. T. M.]

WISTARIA. A genus of climbing shrubs of the *Leguminosæ*, natives of North America, Japan, and the northern provinces of China. They have pinnate leaves, with small deciduous stipules, and flowers in axillary and terminal racemes. The calyx is provided with two small bracts, and is somewhat bell-shaped, its limb being slightly two-lipped and five-toothed; the standard is roundish, with two small hardened prominences at the base; stamens ten, diadelphous; ovary stalked, with numerous ovules; pod linear woody or leathery, many-seeded.

Two well-known species are largely grown in this country for the sake of their elegant racemes of lilac flowers, which are produced in great profusion on a south wall or other sheltered spot.

W. chinensis, the Chinese species, has larger and paler flowers than those of *W. frutescens*, the American kind, whose flowers, moreover, are slightly scented, and have a greenish spot at the base of the standard. The generic name is in honour of Caspar Wistar, a professor of anatomy at Pennsylvania. [M. T. M.]

WITCH-BALLS. Interwoven rollermasses of the stems of herbaceous plants, often met with in the steppes of Tartary.

WITCHEN. The Rowan-tree, *Pyrus Aucuparia*.

WITCHES' BESOMS. This name is given to the tufted bunches of branches, altered from their original form, which are developed on the Silver Fir in consequence of the attack of *Peridermium elatinum*, a fungus belonging to the natural order *Æcidiacei*. The leaves as well as branches are altered in form from their first appearance, and soon fall, a new crop of infested foliage being produced each year from the buds. The fungus is apparently confined to the besoms. Specimens occurred a few years since at Hastings, but we have not heard of them elsewhere in Eng-

land. They are abundant in Germany, where they are called HexenBesen. [M.J.B.]

WITCHES' BUTTER. The vulgar name of *Exidia glandulosa*, a dark-brown or black jelly-like fungus studded above with little glandular points, and below rough like crape. Some of the dark species of *Tremella* are probably confounded under the same name. [M. J. B.]

WITCHES' THIMBLE. *Silene maritima*.

WITHERINGIA. A genus of *Solanaceæ*, so named in compliment to Dr. Withering, an eminent physician and writer on British botany in the last century. The species are of a shrubby habit, with flowers in umbels or clusters, and white yellow rose greenish or bluish in colour. The calyx is bell-shaped, four to five-cleft; the corolla wheel-shaped, four to five-cleft; stamens four to five, the anthers converging, opening lengthwise: fruit berry-like, two-celled. These plants are indigenous in Peru, Mexico, and South Africa. The Peruvian Indians are stated to employ the roots of *W. montana* in soups. [M.T.M.]

WITHE-ROD. *Viburnum nudum*.

WITHWIND. The Woodbine; also *Convolvulus arvensis*.

WITHY. *Laserpitium Siler*; also a common name for Willow. —, GREY. *Salix Caprea*. —, HOOP. *Rivina octandra*.

WITSENIA. A genus of Cape plants belonging to the *Iridaceæ*, and having a similar habit to the species of *Iris*: having like them also a thick fleshy stock, terminated by a tuft of sword-shaped leaves, which are arranged in two rows. The flowers are borne on simple or branched scapes; each one has a regular six-parted tubular perianth, to the throat of which are attached three very short stamens. The ovary is inferior or nearly so, three-celled, with numerous ovules; the style is simple, and is terminated by a three-toothed stigma; the fruit is a three-valved capsule. *W. corymbosa* is an old inhabitant of our greenhouses, where its fine purplish-blue flowers still render it a favourite. 'The stem' of *W. Maura* is said to abound in saccharine juice.' [M. T. M.]

WITTEDENIA. A garden misnomer for *Vittadenia*.

WOAD. *Isatis tinctoria*, also called Dyer's Woad. —, WILD. *Reseda Luteola*.

WOADWAXEN. *Genista tinctoria*.

WOLF-BERRY. *Symphoricarpos occidentalis*.

WOLFSBANE. *Aconitum Lycoctonum*; also *Arnica montana*.

WOLF'S-CLAW. *Lycopodium clavatum*.

WOLF'S-MILK. *Euphorbia*.

WOLLASTONIA. Under this name is described a genus of *Compositæ*, consisting of undershrubs or herbs, natives of India, the Moluccas, and Australia. The leaves are entire, often hairy, triplinerved, and the flower-heads surrounded by an involucre, the outer scales of which are leafy, the inner smaller and membranous. The receptacle is flat and scaly; the outer florets are ligulate and female, the central ones tubular and perfect; the stigmas are conical; the fruits are compressed or topshaped, with or without a pappus. When present, the pappus consists either of one or of five deciduous slender awns. [M. T. M.]

WOLLUT COMUL. A Bengalee name of *Abroma augusta*.

WOLVEBOON. The South African *Hyenanche capensis*, the poisonous seeds of which are used to destroy hyænas.

WONDER OF THE WORLD. *Panax Schinseng.*

WOOD. The hard part of a stem, formed chiefly of woody tissue or pleurenchyma.

WOOD-APPLE. *Feronia Elephantum.*

WOODBINE. *Caprifolium Periclymenum*; also *Polygonum Convolvulus.* —, SPANISH. *Ipomæa tuberosa.*

WOOD, COOPER'S. *Alphitonia excelsa.*

WOOD OF THE HOLY CROSS. The Mistleto of the Oak.

WOODROOF, or WOODRUFF. *Asperula odorata.* —, QUINSY. *Asperula cynanchica.* —, SWEET. *Asperula odorata.*

WOODROW, or WOODROWEL. *Asperula odorata.*

WOODSIA. A small genus of polypodiaceous ferns, widely dispersed in temperate latitudes, two of its species occurring wild in Great Britain. They are small ferns of herbaceous texture, with pinnate or bipinnate fronds, free veins, and punctiform sori, the peculiarity of which is that they are placed within involucres, which however assume several distinct forms. In some species the involucre is soft membranous saucer-shaped, and fringed with long hairs; in others more cup-shaped, with the edge broken into a few distinct broad lobes; and in others, again, subglobose with the mouth contracted. North America, Mexico, Peru, India, the Caucasus, and even the British Isles all furnish their quota of species. [T. M.]

WOODVILLEA. A name applied to a Californian herb of the family *Compositæ*, having much the appearance of some *Calendula.* The involucre is bell-shaped, and consists of linear scales in two or three rows; the receptacle is naked; the florets of the ray are ligulate and neuter, while those of the disk are tubular and perfect; achenes hairy, those at the outside linear sterile, those of the disk oblong compressed; pappus in many rows, finely hairy. [M. T. M.]

WOODVINE, YELLOW. *Morus calcar galli.*

WOODWARDIA. A genus of polypodiaceous ferns, remarkable for their indu-

slatelinear-oblong or sublunate sori, placed near the costa, the receptacles being formed of transverse arcuately anastomosing veins, which form one or more series of elongated costal areoles. There are two minor groups included—namely, *Woodwardia* proper, in which the sori are immersed, and the indusia vaulted and straight; and *Doodia*, in which the sori are superficial, the indusia convex and sublunate—the former series found principally in Madeira India and Japan, the latter in New Holland, New Zealand, and the Pacific Isles. The fronds vary considerably in size in the two groups. [T. M.]

WOOGINOOS. An Abyssinian name for *Brucea antidysenterica.*

WOOL. A term sometimes applied to fine vegetable fibres, such as cotton.

WOOLLEN. *Verbascum Thapsus.*

WOOLLY. Of the nature or appearance of wool.

WOOLLY-BUTT. An Australian name for a large timber-tree, a species of *Eucalyptus.*

WOO-PEI-TZE. The large Chinese galls, found, it is said, on *Rhus semialata*, or on *Distylium racemosum.*

WOORALI, or WOORARI. A virulent poison made by the Indians of Guiana from *Strychnos toxifera.*

WORM-GRASS. *Spigelia*; also *Sedum album.*

WORMIA. Eight species of this genus of *Dilleniaceæ* are known—three natives of the Malayan Peninsula, two of Ceylon, one of India, one of Tropical Australia, and one of Madagascar. They are all trees, sometimes growing to a very large size; and have large thickish entire or toothed leaves, smooth above, and with stipules growing to their stalks, though quickly falling away. Their flowers are showy, generally yellow, but sometimes white, and produced in few or many-flowered racemes; or rarely solitary, opposite the leaves at the summit of the branches. They have five thick sepals and as many petals; numerous stamens, either all equal in length, or the inner ones longer and curved outwards, with narrow anthers opening by holes at the top; and five to ten ovaries, scarcely cohering together, each containing numerous ovules and ending in a long style. Their fruits consist of as many carpels as ovaries, which usually burst open, when ripe, along their inner edge.

W. excelsa is a very large forest-tree, native of Java and the Malayan Peninsula, where it is called Kayu Sipur by the Malays, and is valued for its excellent timber, which bears some resemblance to oak. It has oval sharply-toothed leaves, from four inches to a foot long; and simple or rarely branched racemes of about the same length, bearing numerous showy yellow flowers between three and four inches across. [A. S.]

WORMSEED. *Ambrina anthelmintica*; also *Erysimum cheiranthoides, Artemisia*

Vahliana, and *A. judaica*. The name is applied in herb-shops to *Semen contra*, the produce of several species of *Artemisia*. —, AMERICAN. *Ambrina anthelmintica*. —, BARBARY, or LEVANT. One of the forms of *Semen contra*. —, SPANISH. *Halogeton tamariscifolium*.

WORM-SHAPED. The same as Vermicular.

WORMSKIOLDIA. The two species of this genus of *Turneraceæ* are both African, one being a native of the tropics of the western coast, and the other of Abyssinia. They are branching annuals, with erect hairy stems, bearing so strong a resemblance to the radish genus that one species was formerly referred to it. Their flowers have a tubular five-toothed slightly coloured calyx; five narrow yellow petals, inserted above the base of the calyx-tube, together with as many stamens, which project a short distance out of the tube; a one-celled ovary, with the ovules attached to the sides in three rows; and three slender undivided styles, bearing somewhat fringed stigmas. Their fruits are tapering irregularly swollen capsules, which split lengthways into three narrow valves, bearing the seeds attached to their centres. [A, S.]

The same name is given to a genus of rose-spored *Algæ*, framed by Agardh to receive the beautiful ash-leaved seaweed which is such an ornament to our coasts and such a favourite with collectors, from its lovely colour and delicately-veined fronds. It belongs to the natural order *Rhodymeniaceæ*, from most of which it differs in the nerved leaves being of definite form and a delicately membranous areolated substance. It differs at once from *Delesseria* (with which it was formerly associated) in the repeated division of the endochrome of the fruit-bearing cells. Both the tetraspores and capsules are contained in minute leaves (sporophylla) distinct from the frond. It is possible that the plant brought by Dr. Hooker from Cape Horn may be distinct. [M. J. B.]

WORMWOOD. *Artemisia Absinthium*. —, ROMAN. *Ambrosia artemisiæfolia*; also *Artemisia pontica*. —, WILD. *Parthenium Hysterophorus*.

WORT. A term applied to plants generally, and sometimes especially to those of herbaceous habit. Also used to designate a sweet infusion of malt or grain.

WORTES. Chaucer's name for cultivated plants generally.

WORTS. *Vaccinium Myrtillus*.

WOUNDS. See VULNERA.

WOUNDWORT. *Anthyllis Vulneraria*. —, CLOWN'S. *Stachys palustris*. —, KNIGHT'S WATER. *Stratiotes aloides*. —, MARSH. *Stachys palustris*.

WOUNDWORTH. *Liabum Brownei*.

WOURALI. The Woorari, Ourari, or Urari, an arrow-poison prepared by the South American Indians from *Strychnos toxifera*.

WRACK. Seaweed thrown ashore. —, GRASS or SEA. *Zostera marina*.

WREATH, PURPLE. *Petrea volubilis*.

WRIGHTIA. A genus of *Apocynaceæ*, consisting of shrubs, or small sometimes scandent and aerial rooting trees, with opposite smooth or downy leaves, and terminal cymes of white yellow or red flowers. They are confined to the Eastern Hemisphere, ranging from Silhet and Nepal to Western Australia. Their flowers have a five-parted calyx, furnished with five glandular scales; and a tubular five-lobed corolla, closed at the throat by a coronal appendage; the stamens rising from the middle or top of the tube and protruding, their anthers adhering to the stigma in the middle, and their slender style thickened towards the top and bearing a blunt sometimes bifid stigma. The fruits consist of two long distinct or cohering follicles, containing numerous seeds furnished with a tuft of silky hairs at their lower ends.

An inferior kind of indigo, prepared from the leaves of *W. tinctoria* in some parts of Southern India, is called Pala Indigo, from Pala or Palay, the Tamil name for this and some allied milky trees. The wood of the Palay is beautifully white close-grained and ivory-like, and is commonly used in India for making toys. It is well adapted for turning carving and inlaying, and has been tried for engraving as a substitute for boxwood, but found unsuitable for that purpose. The wood of *W. antidysenterica* has also been made the subject of a similar experiment without success. It is very hard in the centre, and is used in India for posts and rice-beaters. The bark is the Conessi-bark of the Materia Medica, and is valued as a tonic and febrifuge, and as a remedy for dysentery. The oat-like seeds also are reputed to possess valuable medicinal properties. [A. S.]

WRINKLED. The same as Rugose.

WUCKOONAR. A Travancore name for the fibre of *Crotalaria juncea*.

WUKKUM. An Indian name for the brownish-red wood furnished by *Cæsalpinia Sappan*.

WULFENIA. A genus of *Scrophulariaceæ*, containing three species of perennial herbs, natives of the mountains of Central Europe and Asia. The calyx is five-parted; the corolla is tubular, with a spreading limb; there are two stamens, with diverging anther-cells; the style is terminated by a simple capitate stigma; the acute capsule is four-valved; and the ovoid seeds are convex behind and concave in front. [W. C.]

WULFFIA. A genus of South American herbs, belonging to the *Compositæ*. The stems are erect, the leaves ovate serrate somewhat triplinerved, and the flower-heads stalked terminal or axillary; the florets yellow—those of the ray ligulate and neuter, those of the disk perfect and tubular. The involucre is hemispherical, consisting of numerous loosely imbricated lanceolate scales; the receptacle is flat, and has persistent lance-shaped paleæ; the branches of the style are surmounted by a cone. The achenes of the ray are abortive, those of the disk thick four-sided fleshy, smooth or hairy at the summit.   [M. T. M.]

WULLUT CUMAL. A Bengalee name of *Abroma augusta*.

WURD. An Arab name for *Rosa centifolia*.

WURRUS. A brick-red dye-powder, somewhat resembling dragon's-blood, collected from the seed-vessels of *Rottlera tinctoria*.

WYDLERIA. A genus of *Umbelliferæ* from the Caribbees, containing a single species, a glabrous herb, with an erect branching stem, and ternately-divided leaves, having the divisions multifid and the lobes cuneate. The involucres are absent or only one-leaved, while the involucels are many-leaved. The ovate-lanceolate petals have a long incurved apex. The ovate fruit is a little contracted at the side, and slightly didymous; while the carpels have five thickish obtuse ribs, with a single vitta in the intervals, and two in the commissure; the carpophore is bifid. [W. C.]

WYMOTE. *Althæa officinalis.*

WYTH. The White Hoop, or Basket Wyth of Jamaica, *Tournefortia bicolor*.

XANTHIUM. A genus of annuals placed in the group *Ambrosieæ* of the *Compositæ*, and remarkable chiefly for the anomalous structure of their flowers, which are monœcious; the barren ones consisting of obovate sessile corollas, collected into numerous heads, each enclosed by an involucre of a few scales. In the fertile flower the involucre is single, prickly, with two beaks, entirely closing in two flowers. *X. Strumarium*, or Burweed, is thus described by Hooker and Arnott: 'A rank weed-like plant, remarkable for the curious structure of its flowers, and the prickly involucres which surround the fertile ones enlarging and becoming part of the fruit. It is scarcely naturalised, and rarely ripens seed in the South of England.' The foreign species are of similar habit. French: *Lampourd*; German: *Spitzklette*. [C. A. J.]

XANTHO. In Greek compounds = such yellow as gamboge.

XANTHO. A Californian genus of *Compositæ*, the only species of which, better known as *Lasthenia glabrata*, has linear leaves, and solitary flower-heads on the ends of the branches. The involucre is flattened, bell-shaped, divided above into from ten to fifteen oblong acute segments; receptacle conical, tubercled; outer florets strap-shaped, female; central ones tubular, hermaphrodite, the tube dilated above into

a bell-shaped five-cleft limb; branches of the style linear, studded with little pimples, those of the disk-florets longer than those of the ray, dilated at the apex, triangular; achenes oblong, surmounted by a thick entire rim, without pappus. The plant has yellow flowers, and is grown as an annual in the flower-border. [M. T. M.]

XANTHOCEPHALUM. A genus of Mexican herbs of the family *Compositæ*. The leaves are narrow and toothed, and the heads of flowers terminal. The involucre is bell-shaped, and consists of a few overlapping scales; the receptacle slightly convex, destitute of scales; the outer florets ligulate female, the central ones tubular perfect. Achenes compressed, smooth; pappus very short, membranous, irregularly toothed. The florets, both of the ray and of the disk, are yellow—whence the name, from *xanthos* 'yellow' and *kephale* 'head.'   [M. T. M.]

XANTHOCERAS. A low-growing tree, native of the mountains of Northern China, belonging to the *Sapindaceæ*. The leaves are pinnate; the flowers white, in terminal clusters, each with a calyx of five segments; five petals, hairy at the base; five glands, alternating with the petals, and reflexed; eight stamens, with glandular anthers; a globose three-celled ovary, each compartment of which contains eight ovules; a thick style, and three-lobed stigma; fruit capsular, three-celled; seeds numerous, large.   [M. T. M.]

XANTHOCHRYSUM. A genus of *Compositæ* allied to *Helichrysum*. The involucre consists of many rows of scarious scales, each of which has an elliptical golden-coloured appendage. The flowers are all hermaphrodite: each has a double pappus, the outer of short entire truncated hairs, the inner of larger unequal serrated hairs, united below into a ring. These 'everlasting' plants are natives of Australia. The generic name refers to the golden-yellow colour of the involucre. [M. T. M.]

XANTHOCHYMUS. A genus of arboreous *Clusiaceæ*, the name of which is derived from the two Greek words *xanthos* 'yellow' and *chymos* 'juice,' alluding to the yellow resinous juice which exudes from their trunks. The genus consists of three tropical Asiatic species, and a doubtful one from Madagascar—all trees with thick opposite leaves, and bearing clusters of polygamous flowers. It is characterised by having five sepals, as many petals, stamens collected into five bundles placed opposite the petals and alternating with five large glands, and a five-celled ovary narrowed upwards into a short style bearing a five-rayed stigma. Its fruit is a five (or by abortion fewer) celled berry, containing in each cell a solitary seed enveloped in pulp. Of the three Asiatic species, *X. ovalifolia* is confined to Ceylon, and was at one time supposed to be the tree which afforded the Gamboge of that island; but this is now known to be the produce of *Garcinia Morella*, the juice of *X. ovalifolia* being value

less. *X. pictorius*, a native of the mountains of Northern India, and *X. dulcis*, found in the islands of the Indian Archipelago, both yield edible pleasant-tasted fruits of a beautiful bright shining-yellow colour, and of a nearly globular form, about as large as apricots, but pointed with the remains of the style, which is generally at one side, owing to one or more of the cells being imperfect.   [A. S.]

XANTHOCOMA. The name of a Mexican herbaceous plant, of the family *Compositæ*. The leaves are linear, entire; the flower-heads solitary, terminal, surrounded by an involucre of overlapping scales, somewhat leafy at the points; the outer florets strap-shaped female, the central ones tubular perfect; fruits compressed, destitute of pappus. The florets of the ray and of the disk are alike tubular.   [M. T. M.]

XANTHOGALUM. A subdivision of the genus *Galium*, comprising the perennial species, that have six to ten stamens in a whorl, and all the flowers perfect, of a yellow colour, and arranged in a panicle. The common *G. verum* belongs to this section.   [W. C.]

XANTHOPHYLL. The yellow colouring-matter of plants.

XANTHORRHIZA. A genus of *Ranunculaceæ*, consisting of an undershrub, *X. apiifolia*, inhabiting the Southern States of North America. It has clustered stems, stalked pinnate or bipinnate leaves with cut leaflets, and small dull purple flowers in axillary branched racemes. The flowers are often polygamous by abortion; they have five deciduous sepals, five petals much smaller than the sepals, five or ten stamens, and from five to fifteen ovaries with two or three ovules in each. The follicles are small, usually one-seeded. The generic name is composed of the two Greek words *xanthos* 'yellow', and *rhiza* 'root'; and is given to this plant on account of its long roots and rootstock being of a bright-yellow colour, whence also it is commonly called Yellow-root in the United States. Its inner bark wood and pith are also of the same colour. The plant was formerly employed by the American aborigines for dyeing yellow; and the American physicians of the present day use it medicinally as a tonic, all parts of it having a pure intensely bitter taste.   [J. T. S.]

XANTHORRHŒA. The Black-boy or Grass Gum-trees of the Australian Colonies form a most remarkable genus of *Liliaceæ*, differing widely in general appearance from the other genera of that order; most of the species having thick trunks like those of palms, covered with a dense coating formed of the persistent bases of old leaves glued together by the yellow or red resin with which these plants abound, and usually burnt and blackened outside by bush-fires. In some, however, the trunk is extremely short. Their leaves are long wiry and grass-like, and are borne in a dense tuft at the top of the stem, and hang down gracefully all round it; their long flower-stalks rising out of the centre, and sometimes growing as high as fifteen or twenty feet, bearing at the top a dense cylindrical flower-spike, resembling that of the *Typha*, made up of a mass of scales out of which the flowers protrude. These have a calyx of six pieces conniving at the bottom, where the six stamens are inserted, the latter having long projecting filaments and loose swinging anthers; and their three-celled ovary bears a long straight style, and ripens into a woody capsule, which splits when ripe into three valves, and contains a few black seeds.

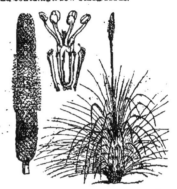

Xanthorrhœa hastilis.

The tall-growing species, *X. arborea*, *X. hastilis*, &c., form conspicuous features in some Australian landscapes; and when denuded of leaves have been compared to or even mistaken for black men holding spears—hence their common colonial name. Their leaves afford good fodder for cattle, while the natives eat the tender white centre of the top of the stem. Two kinds of fragrant resin—one of a yellow colour, called Botany Bay or Acaroid resin, and the other red like Dragon's-blood, and called Black-boy Gum—are obtained from them. For *X. hastilis*, see Plate 5 b.   [A. S.]

XANTHOSOMA. A genus of *Araceæ*, comprising certain West Indian plants, with erect rootstocks, arrow-shaped leaves, and a yellow spathe rolled round at the base. The spadix is covered with flowers of both sexes; the anthers adhere one to another, by means of their conical dilated connectives; the anther-lobes open by a transverse chink at the top; the ovaries are numerous, crowded, and have very thick styles, terminated by large lobed depressed yellow stigmas—whence the name of the genus, from *xanthos* 'yellow' and *soma* 'body.' Starch is obtained from the rootstocks of *X. sagittifolia*. One or two species are in cultivation as hothouse plants.   [M. T. M.]

XANTHOXYLACEÆ, or **XANTHOXY-**

LEÆ. A tribe of *Rutaceæ*, raised by some botanists to the rank of a natural order; and distinguished from other *Rutaceæ* chiefly by having unisexual flowers with small spreading petals, a lobed ovary with two ovules in each cell, and lateral or basal styles often united at the top only, the fruit usually separating into two to five distinct cocci. Seventeen genera, consisting chiefly of tropical trees or shrubs, have been referred to the group.

XANTHOXYLON. The type of the *Xanthoxylaceæ*, and a rather extensive genus, possessing a wide geographical range, having representatives in most of the tropical countries of the world, and in some parts of the temperate regions—one reaching as far north as Canada in the Western, and several as far as Japan in the Eastern Hemisphere. The species differ considerably in appearance, some being very large trees, while others are erect or climbing shrubs; and they are often furnished with prickles on their branches and leafstalks. Their leaves are alternate and compound, either pinnate (with or without an odd terminal leaflet), trifoliate, or rarely reduced to a single leaflet, the leaflets being usually marked with pellucid dots. Their flowers are small, unisexual, and disposed in variously-formed axillary or terminal panicles. They have four or five (or rarely three) sepals and petals, both overlapping in the bud; the males containing as many stamens as sepals and a rudimentary pistil, and the females either no stamens at all or imperfect ones; and from one to five carpels, free or cohering at the base, each ending in a style, which is either distinct or united with the others at the top. The ripe carpels or fruits split into two pieces, and contain one or two shining-black seeds.

The fruits of most of the species have an aromatic pungent taste like pepper. Those of *X. piperitum*, a Japanese species, are called Japan-pepper; and those of *X. hastile* are the Tej-bul of Northern India, where they are used for intoxicating fish. The popular name of Toothache-tree is applied to several American species (especially *X. fraxineum*) in consequence of their bark and fruits being employed as a remedy for toothache. *X. caribæum* a West Indian, and *X. nitidum* a Chinese species, are reputed to be febrifugal; while the young prickly stems of *X. clava-Herculis* are commonly made into walking-sticks in the West Indies. [A. S.]

XAVERIA. *Anemonopsis*.

XENODOCHUS. A fine genus of parasitic *Fungi* closely allied to *Aregma*, and distinguished by the necklace-like chains of multiseptate protospores breaking up at the joints; whereas in *Aregma* the articulations are scarcely moniliform, and remain attached to each other. The only species which is at present known, occurs on the leaves of the larger burnet in meadows, but is not common. The ulterior development of the protospores has not yet been observed. [M. J. B.]

XERAMPELINUS. Dull red, with a strong mixture of brown.

XERANTHEMUM. Showy annuals belonging to the order *Compositæ*, thus characterised :— Receptacle chaffy; pappus chaffy and bristly; involucre imbricated, radiated, the ray coloured. The leaves are cottony and whitish beneath, and the terminal heads of flowers, which are either purple or white, are of the peculiar *texture*, which is commonly called 'everlasting.' They are consequently very durable, and even when their colour fades it may be revived by the vapour of acid. There are three species, natives of the South of Europe and of the Levant. French : *Immortelle*, German : *Strohblume*. [C. A. J.]

XERINGUE. A South American name for the caoutchouc-yielding *Siphonia* and *Micrandra*.

XEROBOTRYS. A name under which Nuttall proposed to separate the *Arctostaphylos* (or *Arbutus*) *tomentosa* and another species, both Californian, from the rest of the genus, on account of the nuts of the drupe being divided into two one-seeded cells, instead of containing only one seed altogether.

XEROCARPUS. The name of a Senegambian trailing herbaceous plant, which constitutes a genus of the papilionaceous subdivision of the order *Leguminosæ*. The whole plant is densely hairy; the leaves ternate; the flowers rose-coloured, in axillary and terminal racemes. The calyx is divided into five nearly equal segments; the vexillum or standard *is* oblong, the wings curved, the keel straight; the ten stamens are monadelphous; the ovary contains many ovules; the style is thread-like straight; and the pod scimetar-shaped, membranous, many-seeded. [M. T. M.]

XEROCOCCUS. The name of a genus of *Cinchonaceæ*, comprising a semi-parasitical shrub, whose flowers have a tubular corolla, with a limb divided into four erect concave petals; ovate anthers; and a stigma divided into two thick fleshy lobes. Fruit dry, whence the name of the genus, from the Greek *œêros* 'dry.' The plant is a native of Costa Rica. [M. T. M.]

XEROPETALON. A genus of trees, natives of Tropical and Subtropical Africa, and belonging to the *Byttneriaceæ*. The flowers are rose-coloured and borne on corymbs, often expanding before the leaves. They have each a five-parted calyx, which, like the five petals, is persistent; stamens twenty, united below into a cup, which is attached to the calyx—some of them being sterile, others fertile; ovary three to five-celled; style terminal, three to five-parted; fruit capsular, with one seed in each compartment. The generic name is derived from the Greek *xêros* 'dry,' in allusion to the persistent petals, which ultimately become dry and membranous. [M. T. M.]

XEROPHYLLUM. A genus of *Melanthaceæ* from North America, containing an herb with the habit of an asphodel, bearing a dense tuft of wiry dry rough-edged root-leaves, and an erect stem clothed with needle-like leaves, and terminated by a compact raceme of white flowers. These have oval sessile spreading distinct segments; six stamens, with short kidney-shaped two-celled anthers; three thread-like styles; a globular loculicidal pod, with two triangular seeds in each cell. The nut is margined with a membranous seed-coat. *X. asphodeloides* is common in the pine-barrens of North America, from New Jersey and Oregon, southward. [J. T. S.]

XEROTES. A genus referred to *Juncaceæ*. It consists of dry rigid rush-like or sedge-like herbs, natives of the coast of Australia, and having linear grass-like leaves, with dilated bases and occasionally toothed points. The flowers are diœcious, racemose spicate or capitate, with scarious imbricated bracts when sessile, or bractless when stalked. The male flowers have a six-parted somewhat coloured perianth, with the inner or all the segments cohering at the base, and six stamens; and the female flowers have the segments free and persistent, the ovary three-celled, with three styles. The capsule is cartilaginous, almost berry-like. [J. T. S.]

XESTÆA. A genus of *Gentianaceæ*, comprising an herbaceous species, native of damp places in Venezuela. The flowers have a four-cleft calyx, whose segments are keeled at the back; a funnel-shaped corolla, with a contracted tube and a dilated throat, expanding into a four-parted limb; four stamens, inserted into the base of the corolla-tube, the unchanged anthers concealed within the corolla; ovary partly two-celled, with a deciduous style, and a stigma divided into two plates. The fruit is a two-valved capsule, containing numerous seeds. [M. T. M.]

XIMENESIA. A genus of *Compositæ*, consisting of annual plants, with more or less divided hairy leaves, and flower-heads in loose corymbs. The scales of the involucre are arranged in two rows, and are leafy, narrow and equal in shape; the florets of the ray are ligulate, those of the disk tubular. The achenes of the ray-florets are flattened, winged, notched, and two-awned. The species, which are natives of Mexico, have yellow flowers, not unlike those of *Coreopsis*. [M. T. M.]

XIMENIA. One species of this genus of *Olacaceæ* is widely dispersed over the tropics of both the Old and New World, while the others are restricted to their respective localities in either hemisphere. The genus is characterised by its flowers having a very small calyx, which does not finally become enlarged; four distinct petals, very hairy inside, conniving at the bottom and curved back at the top; twice as many free stamens, all fertile; and a free four-celled ovary, with a single ovule in each cell. The three or four species are either large shrubs or small trees, fre-

quently armed with spines; and having smooth leathery entire leaves, and axillary few-flowered racemes or clusters of flowers, producing fleshy fruits containing a one-seeded stone.

X. americana produces oblong yellow fruits about an inch in length, which are eaten by the natives in various parts of the tropics. They have an acid-sweet aromatic taste, with some degree of austerity. Its flowers are very fragrant, smelling something like cloves; and its wood is also odoriferous, and is used in Western India as a substitute for sandal-wood, but it is obtainable only in pieces of small size. *X. elliptica* is a native of the Feejees and other islands of the Pacific Ocean, and bears round orange-coloured fruits, of which the natives are very fond, though they are rather tart: before they are ripe they possess a powerful odour of essential oil of almonds. It also produces an extremely hard wood. [A. S.]

XIPHIDIUM. A genus of *Liliaceæ*, inhabiting Tropical America. They have simple stems, leafy at the base; the leaves ensiform, equitant, and entire or subserrulate: and the flowers panicled, subsecund, nodding, with a six-leaved coloured spreading perianth; stamens three; style filiform, with a capitate threelobed stigma; seeds numerous. [J. T. S.]

XIPHOPTERIS. A small genus of polypodiaceous ferns belonging to the *Pleurogrammeæ*. It is found chiefly in South America and the West Indies, but is reported also from Tropical Western Africa. The fronds are small fasciculate erect, sterile and deeply-toothed below, dilated and soriferous above, where they are often longitudinally folded. The veins

Xiphopteris serrulata.

are simple from a central costa and free, the receptacle of the naked sori coalescent with the costa, and sometimes more or less continued up the basal part of the veins. Hence these plants have sometimes been regarded as grammitoid rather than pleurogrammous. The most common species is *X. serrulata*. [T. M.]

XYLARIA. An important genus of sphæriaceous *Fungi*, characterised by its stipitate clavate or branched stroma. The species in which the stem is obsolete border closely on *Hypoxylon*. The genus is far more abundant in tropical countries (where the species sometimes attain a large size), than in Great Britain. We have, however, several indigenous ones, of which three occur in most countries. *X. Hypoxylon*, the commonest of all, and which therefore appears under endless forms, may be found at the foot of many a gate-post or pea-stick, and is common on stumps in woods, looking like the snuff of a candle, and in its young state mealy and white with conidia. *X. polymorpha*, as the name implies, is variable in form, but not much-branched or compressed like the last. It is a coarse species, and occurs generally on stumps. *X. digitata*, which is far neater and very much tufted, and frequently spindle-shaped, occurs principally if not exclusively on fabricated wood. *X. carpophila*, a more delicate species than the others mentioned above, is common on beech-mast in woods, but is very rarely found in a fertile state. [M. J. B.]

XYLIA. An Indian tree, with bipinnate leaves, and axillary racemes of flowers, has been so named, and constitutes a genus of *Leguminosæ*. The calyx is tubular five-toothed, the petals five free membranous, the stamens ten, the pod sessile oblong sickle-shaped compressed woody, with partitions between the seeds, which latter are attached to the pod by a thick fleshy funicle. [M. T. M.]

XYLOCARPUS. A genus of trees, natives of the Molucca Isles, belonging to the order *Meliaceæ*. The flowers are borne in axillary panicles; they have a cup-shaped calyx, whose limb is divided into four segments; four petals; stamens united into a tube, with eight divisions, notched at their margins, and eight anthers; ovary on a disk, four-furrowed, four-celled, each cell with two to five ovules; style short; fruit fleshy, one-celled by the obliteration of the partitions, containing many large seeds, and bursting by four valves. Some of these trees have bitter properties. [M. T. M.]

XYLODIUM. One of the names of the Achene.

XYLOMELUM. A genus of New Holland *Proteaceæ*, consisting of trees with opposite entire leaves, and flowers in axillary spikes. The perianth is regular; attached to it and projecting beyond it are four stamens; there are four glands at the base of the one-celled ovary; the style is thread-like and deciduous, the stigma blunt; the fruit is a hard woody follicle, with two winged seeds. The name of the genus, signifying 'woody pear,' is derived from the nature of the fruit, which is inversely pear-shaped and very thick and woody; ultimately it splits more or less completely and equally into two parts. *X. pyriforme* is in cultivation. [M. T. M.]

XYLOPHYLLA. A genus of *Euphorbiaceæ* or (as some regard it) a section of *Phyllanthus*, consisting of shrubs, without leaves, but whose branches are flattened out and leaf-like, bearing the flowers in tufts in the notches of the margin. The flowers are unisexual, provided with persistent bracts. The male flowers have a five to six-parted calyx, and three or five

Xylophylla latifolia.

stamens, united to a glandular disk. The female flowers have a three-celled ovary, placed in a five to six-lobed disk; styles three; stigmas six; fruit capsular. These plants are natives of the West Indies and other tropical countries, and receive their generic name from the singular appearance of their leaf-like branches, as well exemplified in *X. latifolia*. See PHYLLANTHUS. [M. T. M.]

XYLOPIA. A genus of *Anonaceæ*, so named from the Greek words *xulon* 'wood' and *picros* 'bitter,' in allusion to the properties of the wood. The species are trees or shrubs, and are indigenous in Brazil and other warm districts of South America, and also in the West Indies. The flowers have a three to five-lobed calyx, with ovate leathery segments; six petals, the three outermost of which are largest; and numerous stamens on a globular receptacle, which also bears two to fifteen carpels, each containing one or two seeds.

The species of this genus are noted for the bitterness of their wood, and the aromatic properties of their fruit and seeds. *X. frutescens*, a native of Cayenne, yields seeds which are eaten by the natives in lieu of spices. The bark is also employed in the manufacture of cordage. *X. grandiflora*, a Brazilian species, is valued on account of its carminative fruits, which are also esteemed for their febrifugal properties. The Bitter-wood of the West Indies is the timber of *X. glabra*. Sugar placed in hogsheads made of this wood becomes so highly impregnated with the bitter flavour as to be useless, and even cockroaches will not touch the casks. The bark and fruits are said to taste like orange-seeds. *X. aromatica*, a native of South America, furnishes fruits used by the natives instead of pepper—hence they are sometimes spoken of under the name of Ethiopian Pepper. *X. sericea*, a native of Brazil, supplies aromatic pepper-like berries, which may be used as a substitute for that condiment. The tough bark of this tree is in esteem, owing to the excellent cordage that is manufactured from its fibres. Some of the Javanese species, according to Blume, are not altogether free from noxious properties, for if too often or too largely partaken of they give rise to vertigo, and hæmorrhage. Two or three of them are grown in this country as stove-shrubs. Some of the species are often referred to HABZELIA; which see. [M. T. M.]

XYLOSMA*(including *Hisingera*, *Myroxylon*, *Roumea*, and *Cræpaloprumnon*) is a genus at one time placed under *Euphorbiaceæ*, but now more correctly ranked amongst the *Flacourtiaceæ*. It consists of about twenty-five species, dispersed over the tropical regions. They are either shrubs or trees, often spiny, having ovate generally dentate leaves, insignificant whitish or greenish flowers, and small berries. The calyx consists of from four to six scaly sepals, the corolla is entirely wanting, the stamens are numerous, the placentas from two to six in number, the style either long or wanting, and the stigma entire or from two to six-lobed. [B. S.]

XYLOSTEUM. A section of the Honeysuckle genus (*Lonicera*) in which the plants are twining or erect, and the flowers axillary. Also the Fly Honeysuckle.

XYLOTHECA *Kraussiana*, a native of Natal, and the sole representative of a genus of *Flacourtiaceæ*, is a tall shrub with obovate oblong smooth net-veined leaves, fringed at the edges, and showy yellow unisexual flowers, the males having a three-parted deciduous calyx with concave overlapping segments, nine spreading petals, and numerous stamens. Its fruits are of an oval form, woody and one-celled, and contain numerous seeds covered with pulp, attached to the inside in three or four rows. [A. S.]

XYRIDACEÆ. An order of monocotyledons, consisting of rush-like or sedge-like herbs, with fibrous roots, and long narrow radical leaves, the yellow flowers in heads enclosed in imbricated scales, at the top of leafless scapes. The perianth consists of three outer segments, of which one is more petal-like than the others, or of that one only, and either three or two inner petal-like segments. There are three stamens. The ovary is free, with three parietal placentas; and the capsule opens in three valves, containing numerous small albuminous seeds. The species are almost all tropical, dispersed over both the New and Old Worlds, and comprised in the two genera *Xyris* and *Abolboda*, to

which some botanists add *Philydrum*, raised by others to the rank of a distinct order.

XYRIDANTHE. The name of a genus of *Compositæ*, consisting of an herbaceous species, native of Swan River. The leaves are narrow entire membranous, and the branches erect and destitute of leaves, but bearing a terminal head of flowers of a shining-brown colour, like those of *Xyris*. The outer scales of the involucre are concave, overlapping; the inner spreading, provided with a small white petaloid appendage; the corollas are tubular; and the anthers have numerous filamentous hairs. The achenes are woolly, surmounted by long feathery pappus-hairs. [M. T. M.]

XYRIS. A genus of *Xyridaceæ*, the principal one of the order, and comprising above fifty species chiefly American, but some also natives of Tropical Asia and Africa. They are all sedge-like herbs, with narrow radical leaves, and small flower-heads terminating the simple scapes, the yellow petals very fugacious. None of them are of any special interest.

XYSMALOBIUM. This genus is distinguished from *Gomphocarpus*, and other genera of *Asclepiadeæ* to which it is allied, by the staminal corona being seated at the top of the tube of the filaments, and consisting of ten parts in a single series; the five parts opposite the anthers being egg-shaped or roundish, fleshy, and without hairs or other appendages inside, and the other five much smaller. With the exception of one found in Senegambia and another in Angola, the eight or nine known species are confined to the Cape Colony. All are erect perennial herbs, and bear umbels of largish flowers between the leaf-stalks; the flowers having a bell-shaped corolla, with five spreading segments, which are sometimes bearded at the top. The genus is named from the Greek words *xysma* 'a shaving' and *lobos* 'a pod,' in consequence of the fruits being covered with scales, or ramenta. The Senegambian species, *X. Heudelotianum*, produces a watery turnip-shaped root, called Yakhop by the negroes, by whom it is eaten. [A. S.]

YACCA WOOD. The ornamental timber of *Podocarpus coriacea*, which yields an ornamental wood, used in the West Indies for cabinet-work.

YAKA. A Fecjean name for *Pachyrhizus angulatus*.

YAKHOP. The Senegambian name of *Xysmalobium Heudelotianum*.

YAM. *Dioscorea*. —, CHINESE, *Dioscorea Batatas*. —, COMMON, or CULTIVATED, *Dioscorea sativa*. —, GRENADA, or GUINEA, *Dioscorea bulbifera*. —, INDIAN, *Dioscorea trifida*. —, JAPANESE, *Dioscorea Batatas*. —, NEGRO-COUNTRY, *Dioscorea alata*. —, PORT MONIZ, *Tamus edulis*. —, RED, *Dioscorea alata*. —, WATER, *Ouvirandra fenestralis*. —, WHITE, *Dioscorea alata*. —,

WILD. *Cissus sicyoices* and *Rajania pleio-neura.*

YAMADOU. An oil expressed from the seeds of *Myristica sebifera.*

YAMS. Lindley's name for the *Dioscoreaceæ.*

YANGUA. A name given by Spruce to a Brazilian plant now referred to CYBISTAX; which see.

YAN-SOUN. The Egyptian name for Anise.

YAOBA. A Caribbean name for *Sauvagesia erecta.*

YAPON. The South Sea Tea, *Ilex vomitoria.*

YARI-YARI. A Guiana name for the strong elastic wood of *Duguetia quitarensis.*

YARR. A Scotch name for *Spergula arvensis.*

YARRAWARA. An aboriginal name for the Black Butt, one of the largest of the *Eucalypti* of New South Wales.

YARROW. *Achillea Millefolium.*

YARURI. A Demerara name for Paddlewood, the strong but light and elastic timber of *Aspidosperma excelsum.*

YAW-WEED. *Morinda Royoc.*

YEAST. See YEAST-PLANT.

YEAST-PLANT. It has long been known that the particles of which Yeast is composed germinate, and are multiplied with extraordinary rapidity when placed in a solution of sugar kept at a proper temperature. It was therefore at once allowed that the substance was organised, whether belonging to the Animal or vegetable kingdom; and while some pronounced it an alga, others as confidently asserted that it was a fungus. Dr. Hassall and others observed that a particular mould grew pretty uniformly on a solution of malt; but we believe that Mr. Hoffmann, in union with Mr. Berkeley, first watched the growth of single yeast-globules in a drop of water surrounded by air enclosed in a glass cell, and ascertained that a *Penicillium* and a *Mucor* grew immediately from the globules. They were also convinced that these were not the only moulds to which the yeast-globules gave rise. It was clear, then, that yeast consists of a mixture of different moulds in a peculiar condition due to their development in a fluid, and that when a fit opportunity offers, these globules are capable of being developed into their ordinary form. The globules, however, preserve their character without developing their perfect forms when the fluid in which they float is drained away, and in this condition the mass is called German Yeast—a substance largely imported into this country, and on account of its freedom from the bitter principle of hops, and some peculiarities in its action on fermentable substances, often preferred to ordinary fluid yeast. It is a singular fact respecting yeast in this condition, that a sudden fall from a great

height will sometimes completely destroy its power of vegetating.

Yeast is of very different qualities, according to the nature of the liquor in which it is generated; and though there is little difference, if any, to the naked eye, the yeast-merchants distinguish several varieties, which, according to their respective energy and activity, are employed for different purposes. It has not yet been ascertained whether these different varieties are composed of the germs of different species of *Fungi*, or of the same species in different proportions.

It is often said that yeast works by catalysis, but this is merely the substitution of a technical phrase for the simple fact that yeast promotes fermentation. There is no doubt, however, that it acts partly by presenting a large surface over which the fluid is spread, and thus favouring the disengagement of the carbonic acid gas, formed in the process of fermentation, exactly as that gas is set free when a lump of sugar or a piece of bread-crumb is placed in a glass of effervescent wine which apparently has previously parted with all the gas which it contained. It is moreover conjectured, that as chemical action always takes place when there is an interchange of two fluids of different densities separated by a membrane, the decomposition of a fermentable fluid containing yeast is favoured by this interchange, which is known to chemists and physiologists under the names of endosmose and exosmose.

Substances which are hostile to the growth of fungi, generally, are hostile to fermentation. Hence a mixture of sulphites of soda, or the ignition of sulphur, are used to arrest the process where it is necessary.

In the manufacture of wine we have observed occasionally a species of *Mucor* (*M. clavatus*) to be developed in large fleecy clouds, to the great improvement of its quality.   [M. J. B.]

YEBLE. (Fr.) *Sambucus Ebulus.*

YELANGA. An Indian name for the Wood-apple, *Feronia Elephantum.*

YELLOW. The colour of gamboge.

YELLOW-BERRIES. The dried unripe berries of *Rhamnus infectorius,* imported in large quantities from the South of Europe and the Levant for the use of dyers.

YELLOW HERCULES. *Xanthoxylon clava-Herculis.*

YELLOWNESS. A disease in plants, in which the green parts assume a yellowish colour. The same as Flavedo.

YELLOW-ROOT. *Xanthorrhiza apiifolia;* also *Hydrastis canadensis.*

YELLOW-WEED. *Reseda luteola.*

YELLOW-WOOD. *Xanthoxylon;* also *Tobinia.* —, CAPE. *Podocarpus Thunbergii.* —, EAST INDIAN. *Chloroxylon Swietenia.* —, QUEENSLAND. *Oxleya Xanthoxyla.* —, PRICKLY. *Xanthoxylon clava-Her-*

culis. —, SOUTH AFRICAN. *Podocarpus elongata.* —, WEST INDIAN. *Xanthoxylon clava-Herculis.*

YELLOWWORT. *Chlora.*

YEMANEH. An Indian name for *Gmelina arborea.*

YERBA DE LA PURGACION. *Boerhaavia tuberosa.* — DE ST. MARTIN. *Sauvagesia erecta.*

YERBAL. A forest or wild grove of *Ilex paraguayensis.*

YERBA-MATE, YERVA-MATE, or YERVA DE PALOS. *Ilex paraguayensis.*

YERCUM. *Calotropis gigantea* and *C. Hamiltoni.*

YEROS. A Spanish name for *Ervum Lens.*

YEUSE. (Fr.) *Quercus Ilex.*

YEUX DE BOURIQUE. (Fr.) *Mucuna urens.* — DE L'ENFANT JESUS. *Myosotis palustris.* — DE PEUPLE. The buds of the Poplar.

YEVERING BELLS. *Pyrola secunda.*

YEW, or YEUGH. *Taxus baccata.* —, STINKING. *Torreya.*

YOKE-ELM. *Carpinus Betulus.*

YOKEWOOD, JAMAICA. *Catappa longissima.*

YOUNGIA. A genus of herbaceous plants, belonging to the *Compositæ.* The leaves are long, variously-divided, membranous; and the flower-heads small, each surrounded by a cylindrical involucre of about eight scales, with an outer row of five smaller scales; florets ligulate; fruits oblong compressed striated, surmounted by a white thread-like pappus. The species are natives of India, Japan, China, and the Mauritius. [M. T. M.]

YOUPON. The South Sea Tea, *Ilex vomitoria.*

YOUTHWORT. *Drosera rotundifolia.*

YPADU. A Peruvian name for the leaves of *Erythroxylon Coca.*

YPRÉAU. (Fr.) *Populus alba.*

YQUETAIA. A Brazilian name for a *Scrophularia,* probably *S. aquatica.*

YRUPÉ. A Guiana name for *Victoria regia.*

YSANO. A Bolivian name for *Tropæolum tuberosum.*

YUCA. A name in the Spanish-American States for the Cassava.

YUCCA. A genus of *Liliaceæ,* sometimes assuming an arborescent habit, producing a crown of linear-lanceolate more or less rigid leaves, and from the centre of each crown an erect panicle of showy whitish flowers. They are chiefly found in the Southern States of America and in Mexico, one or two extending to Tropical America.

The flowers have a six-leaved perianth, which is bell-shaped; six stamens, the filaments flattened and broadest at top; a three-celled ovary, with three sessile stigmas; and an oblong bluntly hexagonal three-valved capsule containing many seeds. They are very handsome garden plants, most of them nearly or quite hardy. In *Y. gloriosa,* one of the stateliest of the species, the crown of leaves becomes elevated on a stout stem, and the panicle is three feet or more in length, branching out

Yucca gloriosa.

on every side. In some, as *Y. filamentosa,* the leaves give off from their margin thread-like bodies, which hang loosely; and in one tender species, *A. schidigera,* these bodies are so large and broad as to resemble carpenter's shavings. The leaves, treated like hemp and flax, afford a fibre which may be used in the manufacture of cloth or cordage; and the macerated stems deposit a feculent matter, from which starch may be obtained. At Carthagena a starch or glue of this kind is made from the stem of *Y. gloriosa.* These plants are popularly called Adam's-needle. [T. M.]

YULAN. *Magnolia conspicua.*

YVRAIE. (Fr.) *Lolium.*

ZACHUN. A fixed oil, expressed from the seeds of *Balanites ægyptiaca.*

ZACYNTHA. A genus of *Compositæ,* so called because first discovered in the island of Zante, the ancient Zacinthus. The species is an annual, with divided leaves, and both terminal and lateral heads of flowers. The involucre is ultimately fleshy, its inner scales folded, the outer ones membranous spreading; receptacle flat, without scales; florets all ligulate; achenes slightly curved, flattened, wingless; pappus hairy, in one row. *Z. verrucosa* is sometimes grown as an annual. [M. T. M.]

ZADD. An Abyssinian name for *Juniperus procera*.

ZADWAR. The Arab name of *Curcuma Zedoaria*.

ZAFRAN. The Indian name for *Crocus sativus*, whence our name Saffron.

ZAHINA. A kind of Tare grown in Spain.

ZAKKOUM. An oil obtained in Palestine from *Elæagnus hortensis angustifolia*.

ZALACCA. One of the genera belonging to the *Calameæ* or scaly-fruited section of the order of Palms. It is composed of six or seven species, natives of Assam and the coast of Burmah and Malacca, mostly growing in large masses, in wet places, and forming dense tufts, rendering the jungles almost impassable. None of the species have stems; and their leaves, which are pinnate and usually have tufted leaflets, are without the long tail-like ends so conspicuous in many genera of the same section; but their sheathing stalks are armed with spines arranged in rows. The two sexes of flowers are borne on separate plants, the flower-spikes having numerous spathes at the bottom, and one round each of the catkin-like branches: the male catkins being made up of numerous pairs of flowers within woolly cup-like bracts, and the females of single flowers similarly placed within bracts, and sometimes having a barren flower at their side. Their fruits, like those of the rest of the section, are covered with overlapping scales arranged like plates of mail; and contain one, two or three seeds, enveloped in a thin fleshy coat, and having horny solid albumen with a hole or pit at the top, and the embryo at the bottom.

The fleshy substance surrounding the seeds of this genus is edible, though usually very acid, particularly in *Z. conferta*, a common species in the fresh-water marshes of Sumatra, called Palumbei, or Assam-pnya (*i.e.* hog-acid), by the Malays, who use the pulp as a condiment with their food, and the leaves in the manufacture of resin-torches. Strips of the leaf-stalks of *Z. macrostachya* are also used at Malacca for tying on thatch, and for weaving into baskets.　　　[A. S.]

ZALUZANIA. A Polish botanist is commemorated by this name, which designates a genus of *Compositæ*, including a Mexican perennial plant, with divided leaves, and corymbose or panicled heads of flowers. The involucre has two rows of scales, the inner of which are three-lobed, as also are the scales on the receptacle. The florets of the ray are ligulate, and female; those of the disk tubular, hispid and perfect; stigmas hairy; outermost fruits somewhat triangular hispid, those of the centre smooth compressed; pappus absent. *Z. triloba* is in cultivation.　　　[M. T. M.]

ZAMBARONE. A Sicilian name for the fibre of the *Agave*, used for making cordage and mats.

ZAMIA. A genus of *Cycadeaceæ*, consisting of moderate-sized trees, having much of the appearance of palms, and in some particulars of ferns. They have stout generally unbranched stems, terminated by tufts of thick pinnated leaves, often spiny at the margins or points. The male and female flowers are borne in cones, composed of woody scales, with a truncated six-sided summit; and each scale of the female flower has two seeds.

The species are natives of Central America, the West Indies, the Cape of Good Hope, and South-eastern Africa, where they frequently constitute a conspicuous feature in the vegetation. One species, native of Panama, is described as growing on the trunks of other trees. The stems

Zamia furfuracea.

of these plants contain an abundance of starchy matter, which is sometimes collected and used as arrowroot. *Z. tenuis* and *Z. furfuracea* are employed for this purpose in the Bahamas.

Several species are known in cultivation, their stiff prickly foliage and palm-like stems rendering them objects of much interest. A noble collection of these and nearly-allied plants may be seen in the great Palm-house in Kew Gardens. There is abundant evidence to suggest that in former ages some of these cycads grew in this country, as fossilised stems of plants apparently belonging to this or to a closely-allied genus are found in abundance in some of the oolitic strata in the Isle of Portland, where they are known to the workmen as fossil birds'-nests, or sometimes as fossil pineapples. The trunks are found, apparently as they grew, marked with the scars of fallen leaves, but it is singular that but few traces of perfect leaves have yet been discovered. [M. T. M.]

ZANNICHELLIA. A submerged aquatic belonging to the order *Naiadaceæ*, distinguished from the allied genera *Ruppia* and *Potamogeton* by having its minute flowers imperfect and axillary, and its membranous stigma dilated into a disk. *Z. palustris*, the Horned Pondweed, resembles in habit some of the smaller *Potamogetons*. The stems are long and cord-like; and the leaves opposite, very narrow, and bearing the flowers at their base enclosed in a membranous sheath, the barren consisting of a single stamen, the fertile of four or sometimes more ovaries, each surmounted by a peltate stigma. [C. A. J.]

ZANONIA. A genus of Indian climbing plants of the family *Cucurbitaceæ*. The species have entire heart-shaped leaves, axillary tendrils, and diœcious flowers, borne in axillary clusters. In the male flower the calyx is three-lobed; the corolla is wheel-shaped spreading five-parted; and there are five stamens with flat filaments united at the base, and one-celled anthers. In the females the calyx is adherent to the three-celled ovary, and its limb is five-parted; styles three spreading branched; fruit fleshy, three-celled, with two or more winged seeds in each cell. The leaves of *Z. indica* are used in baths for the relief of nervous complaints, and beaten up with butter they form a liniment which is used for similar purposes. [M. T. M.]

ZANORA. *Iriartea exorrhiza.*

ZANTEDESCHIA. *Richardia.*

ZANTEDESQUE. (Fr.) *Richardia.*

ZANTE-WOOD. *Rhus Cotinus*; also *Chloroxylon Swietenia.*

ZANTHORHIZA. *Xanthorrhiza.*

ZANTHOXYLON. *Xanthoxylon.*

ZAPANIA. A name applied to that section of the genus *Lippia*, in which are placed those species which have a flattened calyx and capitate flowers. [W. C.]

ZARA. A Spanish name for Maize.

ZAROLLE. (Fr.) *Goodenia.*

ZASMIDIUM. An imperfectly-characterised genus of *Fungi*, belonging to the tribe *Physomycetes*, which is known by the brittle carbonaceous sporangia filled with simple spores, and springing from a mass of equal threads. *Z. cellare* is commonly known as hanging down from the roofs of cellars in large masses, or covering corks, bottles, and other matters. It sometimes even penetrates the tissue of the corks, but does not seem to injure the wine like some of the white mycelia. Indeed the wine-merchant encourages its growth, as he thinks it an ornament to his vaults, and an indication to customers who visit them that his wine is old.

While on the subject of cellar fungi, which are sometimes so injurious, it may be well to state that if sawdust is used at all for packing the bottles, it should be previously soaked in a solution of some mineral salt, which does not readily absorb moisture, after which, being thoroughly dried, there is little fear of any fungus appearing. The lathes, moreover, should be kyanised, and the corks themselves sealed, after being washed carefully with a solution of corrosive sublimate, none being allowed to extend beyond the part of the cork which is exposed. If, however, fungus has once attacked the corks, they should be carefully removed, and the wine recorked, or there will certainly be mischief. This sometimes is indicated by an unpleasant odour, and sometimes the whole strength of the wine is appropriated, and the fluid becomes almost a *caput mortuum*. [M. J. B.]

ZAUSCHNERIA. A handsome decumbent Californian plant, of herbaceous character, belonging to the *Onagraceæ*. It is much-branched, bearing linear-lanceolate greyish leaves, and large racemose spikes of fuchsia-like flowers, of which the calyx-tube is elongated four-angled and coloured, and its limb four-parted, the corolla of four petals, the stamens eight in two rows, and the ovary four-celled inferior, with a filiform exserted style, and capitate stigma. *Z. californica* is a showy species, with the flowers of a bright red colour. [T. M.]

ZEA. A genus of grasses belonging to the tribe *Phalarideæ*. They are monœcious plants, with the male flowers in terminal racemes; spikelets two-flowered; glumes nearly equal, herbaceous, terminating in sharp points; pales two, wedge-shaped fleshy oblique and truncate; stamens three. The females are axillary, in the sheathes of the leaves. There are five species described by Steudel in his *Synopsis*, all natives of South America. *Z. Mays*, or Maize, is the well-known and important

Zea Mays.

cereal so largely grown in the United States of America, where it generally bears the name of Indian-corn. Though not now found in a wild state, there is little doubt about America being the native region of the plant, the Indians throughout that continent having been found engaged in its cultivation at the period when the New World was discovered. Some of the varieties are considered to be in a truly wild state as they are found growing in some of the West Indian islands.

Maize is largely cultivated throughout most of the warmer-temperate regions of the globe, and probably ranks next to rice as the grain which affords nutriment to the largest number of human beings. It has many qualities to recommend it for culture where the climate is sufficiently warm to ripen the grain properly, growing as it does freely in very different kinds of soil, as well as under dissimilar states of moisture and dryness. The crop is easily saved,

Zea Mays (cobs).

and with ordinary care the grain is as easily preserved. Some of the finest samples which have reached Britain in the cob or ear have been grown in Australia, where the climate is very favourable for producing Indian-corn. It is also extensively consumed in many parts of Africa. In India likewise Maize is extensively cultivated, and in the principal towns or their neighbourhood the cobs are roasted and sold in the public thoroughfares, much in the same way that roasted chestnuts are hawked in this country. The immature cobs are sometimes boiled as a vegetable. Latterly a fine flour, called Maizenn, has been prepared from the grain, which is getting into repute as an ingredient for light puddings in our hotels and restaurants.

Nearly three millions of quarters of Indian-corn were imported into this country in 1863, of which the greater portion was entered for home consumption. The computed value was 4,042,908l.　[D. M.]

ZEBRA-PLANT. *Calathea zebrina.*

ZEBRA-WOOD. A beautiful furniture-wood, obtained in Demerara from *Omphalobium Lamberti.* The name is also applied to the wood of a variety of *Eugenia fragrans* called *cuneata*; and, according to some, to *Guettarda speciosa.*

ZEBRINA. A name proposed for *Cyanotis vittata* alias *C. zebrina*, also known in gardens as *Tradescantia zebrina.*

ZÉDOAIRE. (Fr.) *Kæmpferia.*

ZEDOARY. *Curcuma Zerumbet*, the Long Zedoary of the shops. —, ROUND. *Curcuma Zedoaria.*

ZEHNERIA. A genus of *Cucurbitaceæ*, comprising certain perennial herbaceous

species, with toothed or lobed leaves, simple tendrils, and axillary flowers. The male flowers are in clusters, the females either solitary or aggregated together. The calyx is bell-shaped; five-toothed; the corolla spreading five-parted, hairy within; stamens three, the anthers with linear lobes. The female flowers have an adherent three-celled ovary, with numerous ovules; style cylindrical, terminated by a three to four-cleft stigma, and encircled at the base by a three-lobed gland; berry ovate, with numerous seeds, thickened at the margin. The species are natives of the warmer parts of Asia and Africa.　[M. T. M.]

ZELKONA-TREE. *Planera Richardi.*

ZENKERIA. A genus of papilionaceous trees, of the family *Leguminosæ.* The species are natives of Brazil, and have pinnate leaves, and white flowers in tufts at the base of the young branches, expanding before the leaves. The calyx is divided into three equal reflexed segments; petals three; stamens three; ovary stalked compressed, with two ovules; style short, thick. The genus is imperfectly known, but has lately been referred to *Apuleia.* [M. T. M.]

ZENOBIA. A name proposed by Don for some species of *Andromeda*, but generally used to denote a section of that genus in which the anthers are tipped with four long tubular awns. The filaments are very short, and dilated at the base. The calyx is five-toothed; the corolla campanulate, with a five-lobed revolute limb; and the stigma is truncate. They are evergreen shrubs, natives of North America, with few often toothed leaves, and numerous flowers in racemes.　　　[W. C.]

ZEPHYRA. A genus of *Liliaceæ* from Peru, with blue paniculate salver-shaped flowers, having the lower part of the tube adherent to the base of the ovary; stamens six, two sterile and longer, the anthers free, one cell produced at the base, the apex opening by twin-pores.　[J. T. S.]

ZEPHYRANTHES. A small genus of *Amaryllidaceæ*, found in Chili, Buenos Ayres, Mexico, and other parts of America and the West Indies, and by some botanists regarded as a section of *Amaryllis.* They have linear leaves, produced in spring along with or rather earlier than the flowers. The scapes support one or sometimes two showy blossoms, the perianth of which is erect funnel-shaped and equal; the six stamens inserted in the base of the limb, one often separate, the faucial membrane inconspicuous, the style declinate with a trifid stigma, and the capsule trilobed. They are very pretty dwarf bulbs, with white or rose-coloured blossoms. [T. M.]

ZERUMBET. *Zingiber Zerumbet* and *Curcuma Zerumbet*; also *Alpinia nutans.*

ZEUGITES. A genus of grasses belonging to the tribe *Andropogoneæ.* Inflorescence in panicles; spikelets three to four-flowered, the lower flower female and sessile, the male stalked; glumes two, the exterior broader and concave, the interior narrower and keeled; pales two, nearly equal; stamens three, in the male flowers; styles two, in the female. There are two species described. [D. M.]

ZEUXINE. A genus of small-flowered terrestrial orchids from Tropical Asia, belonging to the *Neotteæ.* They are stemless herbs, with linearleaves; and the flowering spike is terminal, and sessile amongst the leaves. The flowers are, as in *Goodyera,* red white or yellow. It differs from *Monochilus,* a nearly-allied genus, in its undivided lip, and from *Chloidia* in its simple inflorescence. [W B. H.]

ZEYHERIA *montana* is the only representative of a bignoniaceous genus, peculiar to Brazil. It is a large tree, with digitate leaves, an irregularly-splitting calyx, a tubular corolla, four fertile and one sterile stamen, glabrous anthers, and a nearly round very prickly capsule, the valves of which are placed in a contrary direction to the partition dividing the fruit into two cells. The plant is common, and imparts, by its stately growth and rich golden panicles, a distinctive feature to Brazilian scenery. [B. S.]

ZEYSOUM. An Egyptian name for the flower-heads of *Santolina fragrantissima,* a substitute for chamomiles.

ZEZEGANY. *Sesamum orientale.*

ZICHYA. A genus of climbing shrubs, natives of Swan River, and belonging to the family of papilionaceous *Leguminosæ.* The leaves are ternate, and the flower-stalks axillary, bearing numerous flowers arranged umbel-wise. The calyx is bell-shaped, its limb five-toothed and two-lipped; the vexillum or standard is roundish notched stalked reflexed, longer than the wings, which adhere to the curved shortened keel; stamens diadelphous; ovary many-celled; style short; pod oblong linear compressed leathery, incompletely divided by cellular partitions into numerous compartments. One or two species are grown as ornamental greenhouse plants in this country. The generic name is derived from that of the Austrian Countess Zichy, who was an ardent lover of botany. [M. T. M.]

ZIERIA. With the exception of *Z. lanceolata,* which is found also in Tasmania, the whole of the dozen or more species belonging to this genus of *Rutaceæ* are confined to the continent of Australia, and chiefly to the eastern coast, extending to as far as the tropics. They are small trees or shrubs, with opposite simple or trifoliate leaves, full of pellucid dots; and usually axillary few or many-flowered panicles of white flowers, having a four-parted calyx, four petals, as many stamens with smooth filaments inserted into a deeply-lobed disk, and four single-celled ovaries, with a short simple style rising from between them, and ending in a four-lobed stigma; the ripe fruit consisting of four, (or sometimes fewer) single-seeded pieces, each ultimately splitting into two valves.

The Tasmanian species, *Z. lanceolata,* is a shrub, and is called Stinkwood by the colonists, on account of its fetid smell. One common at Illawarra, and there called Turmeric-tree, has a very yellow inner bark, suitable for dyeing, and also a yellow close-grained hard wood, which is valuable for ornamental purposes, and might probably be used for engraving. [A. S.]

ZIETENIA. A section of the genus *Stachys,* containing several undershrubs, natives of the Mediterranean region. They are glabrous, or more generally covered with a soft white wool. [W. C.]

ZIGZAG. The same as Flexuose.

ZILLA. A genus of *Cruciferæ* from Northern Africa, consisting of smooth glaucous undershrubs, with numerous stiff divaricate spinescent branches, the younger ones leafy, the racemes spinescent at the apex, with few distant violet flowers. The pouch is two-celled indehiscent ovateglobose corky, with a thick conical persistent style forming a beak; seed solitary in each cell, with folded leafy cotyledons enclosing the embryo. [J. T. S.]

ZIMMT. The German name for Cinnamon.

ZINGIBERACEÆ. (*Scitamineæ* taken in a restricted sense, *Canneæ, Amomeæ, Alpiniaceæ, Gingerworts.*) An order of monocotyledons, considered by some as a suborder of *Scitamineæ,* distinguished from both *Musaceæ* and *Marantaceæ* by the stamens (of which one only is perfect) bearing a two-celled anther. This stamen belongs to the inner whorl, the two others of the same series being always abortive or rudimentary; whilst the three belonging to the outer whorl are converted into petals, one of them (called the labellum) usually very large, the two others smaller or sometimes wanting. The species are all tropical, more or less aromatic, having the rootstock usually creeping; and the leaves large, simple, with pinnate or diverging veins. The flowers, often handsome, arise from among membranous bracts and form a dense spike or raceme, or sometimes a branched panicle; the inflorescence being either sessile amongst the radical leaves, or terminating a scape or leafy stem. There are above thirty genera, including *Zingiber, Curcuma, Amomum, Alpinia, Costus,* &c.

ZINGIBER. The Greeks applied this name to the article we now call Ginger. Botanically, it is adopted to designate a genus of *Zingiberaceæ,* consisting of herbaceous Indian plants, with creeping jointed woody rootstocks, from which are sent up, every year, stems surrounded by sheathing leaves arranged in two ranks. The flowers are borne on cone-shaped spikes, thrown up from the rootstock, and protected by bracts. The distinguishing features of the flowers are that the lateral inner lobes of the corolla are absent, and that the filament is prolonged beyond the anther in the form of a long beak.

The most important species of this genus is *Z. officinale*, whose rhizomes furnish the well-known spice called Ginger. The plant is largely cultivated both in the East and West Indies, as well as in Africa and China. It is supposed that there are two varieties, one producing darker-coloured rhizomes than the other, this difference in colour being independent of the mode of preparation, to be hereafter mentioned. The young rhizomes preserved in syrup are imported from the West Indies and China, and form the delicious conserve known as 'preserved ginger'—that imported from

Zingiber officinale.

the West Indies being preferred to the Chinese kind.

The rhizomes (or, as they are called in commerce, races) are prepared for use in the West Indies when the plants are about a year old. They are dug up, cleansed, scraped, and dried in the sun, and in this state form the uncoated ginger of the shops; but when the outer skin is not thus removed, the ginger is called 'coated,' and has a dirty appearance. The softer kinds of ginger are preferred to the merchants, the hard shrivelled inferior kinds being used for grinding. The darker kinds of ginger are sometimes bleached by exposure to the fumes of chloride of lime or burning sulphur. East Indian gingers are not so largely imported or so highly esteemed as the West Indian kinds, as the latter are less liable than the former to the attacks of worms. This tendency seems partly due to the system of cultivation employed in Malabar. African ginger is imported in small quantities from Sierra Leone, while China only exports the preserved ginger already mentioned.

Ginger, when broken across, shows a number of little fibres embedded in floury tissue. It has a well-known hot pungent taste, due to the presence of a volatile oil. It also contains a large quantity of starch and yellow colouring-matter, enclosed in large cells. According to Dr. Hassall, the ground ginger of the shops is adulterated with sago-meal, potato-flour, wheat-flour, ground rice, cayenne-pepper, mustard husks, and turmeric powder blended in varying proportions.

Ginger is an aromatic stimulant, used chiefly as a condiment, but is also serviceable in certain forms of weak digestion, or in spasms. It is also employed externally as a plaister in headache. In the Mauritius it is used as a poultice to promote the removal of thorns, needles, &c. from the skin. The irritation set up by the poultice tends to bring the needle or other foreign substance near to the surface, when it can be removed by a slight incision.

An infusion of ginger, under the name of Ginger-tea, is generally sold in military cantonments in India. In this country it is employed in the preparation of cordials, by mixing with brandy, wine, and other liquors, and is also largely consumed in the manufacture of Gingerade or Gingerbeer, an almost universal summer beverage.

The root known as Zedoary-root was considered at one time to be the produce of *Z. Cassumunar*, but it is now referred to certain species of *Curcuma*—*C. Zerumbet* and *C. Zedoaria*. A few of the gingers are grown as objects of curiosity in hothouses.　　　　　　　　　　[M. T. M.]

ZINNIA. Handsome annuals belonging to the tribe *Corymbiferæ* of compound flowers, distinguished by having the fruit crowned by two erect awns, and by the ray being composed of five persistent florets. There are several species, all American. *Z. multiflora* bears numerous flower-heads, of which the disk is yellow, the ray scarlet, the latter preserving both form and colour until the seeds ripen; but the species most frequently grown is *Z. elegans*, a plant of stiff formal habit, but justly prized for the brilliancy of its scarlet crimson rose-coloured buff or white flower-heads, which like the last have the advantage of retaining their beauty for a long time.　　[C. A. J.]

ZINZEYD. A Persian name for the fruit of *Elæagnus orientalis*, an article of dessert.

ZIPPELIA. The name of a genus of *Piperaceæ*, comprising an undershrub, native of Java. It has a creeping underground stem, with erect herbaceous knotted branches, alternate palminerved leaves, and long-stalked clusters of flowers, each flower being perfect, borne on a short stalk, protected by a hollow bract. There are six stamens, with short thick filaments, adnate to the base of the germen, which latter is globular, and contains a single erect ovule springing from its base; stigmas four, ultimately reflexed. The fruits are dry, covered with small hooked spines, and without taste.　　　　[M. T. M.]

ZIRBELNUSSE. A German name for the pignous or seeds of *Pinus Cembra*.

ZIT-SI. An Indian name for *Melanorrhœa usitatissima*.

ZITWERSAMEN. A German name for Wormseed.

ZIZANIA. A genus of grasses belonging to the tribe *Oryzeæ*. Spikelets one-flowered, the males above, the females beneath in the same panicle. Glumes of the male flowers small, roundish, and membranaceous; pales two, membranaceous: the inferior sharp-pointed and five-nerved, the superior shorter acute and three-nerved. The glumes are wanting in the female flowers; pales two, membranaceous, the lower oblong keeled awned seven-

Zizania aquatica.

nerved, the upper scarcely shorter, three-nerved, bluntly three-keeled on back.

Steudel describes four species, exclusive of *Z. aquatica* (figured above), for which see HYDROPYRUM. [D. M.]

ZIZIA. A genus of North American orthospermous *Umbelliferæ*, consisting of smooth perennial herbs, with ternately or biternately-divided leaves, the segments of which are oblong or ovate. There is no involucre, and the involucels are few-leaved. The limb of the calyx is obsolete, or has five very short teeth; the petals are oblong, with a lengthened inflexed point; the roundish fruit is contracted laterally; the carpels have five more or less prominent (but not winged) ribs, the intervals containing one to three vittæ, and the commissure having two to four; the carpophore splits into two; and the seed is very convex on the back and flat in front This genus, vulgarly called Golden Alexanders, has the aspect and characters of *Thaspium*, with the exception of the fruit. [W. C.]

ZIZYPHORA. A genus of *Labiatæ*, containing several small thyme-like herbs or undershrubs, natives of Southern Europe and Central Asia. They have square stems, opposite leaves, and flowers in rather scanty whorls at the ends of the branches. The calyx is striated with thirteen nerves, and the throat is bearded; the corolla is two-lipped, the upper lip being reflexed, while the lower is trifid and spreading; and the two lower stamens are fertile, very slight rudiments only of the upper ones existing. [W. C.]

ZIZYPHUS. The Jujube or Lotus genus of *Rhamnaceæ* is a rather extensive one, and has a wide geographical range, abounding, however, principally on the borders of the tropics in the Old World. Its flowers have a spreading five-cleft calyx, five small hood-shaped petals, with as many stamens opposite and at first enclosed in them; and a flat somewhat five-angled disk, with the two or three-celled ovary buried in it; but the genus is chiefly characterised by having a fleshy berry-like fruit, containing a one two or three-celled stone with a single flattened seed in each. The species are mostly stiff shrubs or sometimes small trees, with more or less spiny branches, their alternate three-nerved leaves being furnished with one or two thorny stipules.

The fruits of several species of this genus have an agreeable flavour. Those of *Z. vulgaris* are commonly eaten, both in a fresh and dried state, in the countries bordering on the Mediterranean, and afford the Jujubes of the shops; they are rather acid when fresh, but the dried fruits are more agreeably tasting, and are given to allay cough. The lozenges sold as Jujubes are commonly but erroneously said to be flavoured with them. *Z. Jujuba*, an Indian species, yields an excellent dessert-fruit, and is largely cultivated by the Chinese, who recognise a great number of varieties, differing in the shape colour and size of the fruits. Those of one variety are called Chinese Dates from their resemblance to that fruit. *Z. Lotus* is one of the plants supposed to have yielded the seductive sweet fruits from which the ancient Lotophagi took their name. Another African species, *Z. Baclei*, is the Lotus mentioned by Mungo Park as being used for making into bread, tasting like gingerbread, and also for the preparation of a pleasant beverage. *Z. spina-Christi* is supposed by some to have furnished the crown of thorns put on Our Saviour's head. [A. S.]

ZOADULÆ. The locomotive spores of some confervæ.

ZŒGEA. A genus of *Compositæ* allied to *Centaurea*, and comprising a number of annual herbs, the lower leaves of which are lobed, the upper ones being narrow and entire. The scales of the involucre have a membranous toothed appendage to their summit; the outer florets are large subligulate and neuter, the central ones fertile and tubular; the fruits are compressed, and surmounted by a three-rowed pappus—the outer series consisting of overlapping scales, the middle set of very long hairy ones, and the innermost hairy and very short. [M. T. M.]

ZOLLIKOFERIA. A genus of Mediterranean herbs of the family *Compositæ*. The leaves are pinnately-lobed, the lobes becoming ultimately white and hard at the points. The scales of the involucre are ovate oblong, membranaceous at the edges; corollas ligulate; fruits cylindrical, slightly striated, provided at the base with four little horns, bent downwards; pappus soft, hairy, in many rows.   [M. T. M.]

ZOLLINGERIA. A genus of *Compositæ;* nearly allied to *Artemisia,* but distinguished therefrom by the fruits, which are ovate, with a short stout beak. *Z. scandens* is a Japanese shrub. [M. T. M.]

ZONARIA. A genus of dark-spored *Algæ* belonging to the natural order *Dictyotaceæ,* with fan-shaped vertically-cleft fronds, and roundish scattered spots of spores. The root is coated with woolly hairs. The frond is opaque, and not distinctly zoned as in *Padina,* but only obscurely marked. Under a lens, says Dr. Harvey, the surface appears to be finely striated longitudinally, an appearance caused by the superficial cellules which are ranged in lines proceeding from the base, slightly diverging from one another, and admitting the introduction of new series of cells between each original row as the frond advances in growth. The genus is essentially one of warm countries. We have in Great Britain only *Z. parvula,* a doubtful *Zonaria,* and *Z. collaris,* sometimes washed ashore in Jersey. [M. J. B.]

ZONATE, ZONED. Marked with concentric bands of colour.

ZOOCARPS, ZOOSPERMATA. The locomotive spores of some *confervæ.*

ZOOSPORES. A name given to the active spores of *Algæ,* belonging both to the green and dark-spored series. Their activity depends either on a general coat of short cilia on a circle at one extremity, or on two or more lash-like cilia variously disposed. The occurrence of spores endowed with apparently voluntary motion was formerly considered so surprising, that it was either rejected as unworthy of credit, or the organisms which produced them were considered as animals. It is now, however, generally allowed that there is no essential difference between animal and vegetable life, and that therefore the usual indications of either are not to be regarded as decisive of the especial kingdom to which a being belongs in which they are manifested. Zoospores so long as they are free have indeed a great likeness to *Infusoria,* but as soon as they have found a fit resting-place all traces of motion cease, and their offspring comports itself as a vegetable. Zoospores occur both in the dark and green-spored series of *Algæ,* and if *Saprolegnia* be fungoid, they occur also among *Fungi.* The peculiar zoosporic sporelings of the myxogastric *Fungi,* consisting, as it is said, of the animal substance called sarcode which exists in similar *Infusoria,* have been noticed. [M. J. B.]

ZOOSPORIC. Having the characters of zoospores.

ZOPILOTL. A Mexican cosmetic prepared from the seeds of *Swietenia Mahagoni* mixed with oil.

ZORILLE. (Fr.) *Gompholobium.*

ZORZOLINA. An Italian name for Sesame-seed.

ZOSTERACEÆ. A small order of monocotyledons, or a tribe of *Naiadaceæ,* consisting of marine plants resembling seaweeds and living among them, but bearing long grass-like sheathing leaves, and perfect flowers. These latter are enclosed in the sheathing bases of the leaves, have no perianth, and are always unisexual, the sessile anthers and ovaries mixed in the same sheath or separated in different ones. The ovary has a single pendulous ovule, and terminates in a cleft style. The seed is remarkable for the very large two-lobed radicle folded over a highly-developed plumule. These plants are found abundantly in the seas which border Europe, Asia, and North Africa, and also in the West Indies and Australia. They consist of the genus *Zostera,* and four or five small ones separated from it.

ZOSTERA. In consequence of their extremely low organisation, this genus and its allies have been separated from *Naiadaceæ,* to which many botanists have referred them, and formed into an order—*Zosteraceæ.* Several species have from time to time been described, but a few of them have since been referred to other genera, and the rest reduced to two. These are marine herbs, usually growing in shallow water near the edges of the sea, their long rooting stems creeping along in the sand or mud, and sending up slender erect branches, bearing long narrow grass-like alternate leaves, sometimes forming such dense masses as to impede the passage of boats. Their flowers are of separate sexes, either upon the same or different plants; and are arranged in two rows on one side of a leaf-like stalk, which is enclosed in a sheath formed of the enlarged base of short leaves, differing only in length from the ordinary leaves. They have neither calyx nor corolla: the males consisting of a single stalkless anther, containing conferva-like pollen; and the females of an egg-shaped one-celled ovary, containing a solitary ovule, and tapering into a slender style bearing two long stigmas. Both species are indigenous to Britain, but are also found in most other parts of the world, from Iceland southward to the Cape of Good Hope, Tasmania, and New Zealand.

Z. marina, the common Seawrack, Grass-wrack, or Grass-weed, has leaves varying from one to several feet in length, and rarely more than a quarter of an inch broad. These are commonly used for packing, and by upholsterers for stuffing mattresses and cushions, being sold for that purpose under the names of Ulva marina or Alva marina. They contain a small amount of iodine, and a considerable quantity of potash. [A. S.]

ZOSTEROSTYLIS. *Cryptostylis.*

ZOYSIA. A genus of grasses belonging to the tribe *Andropogoneæ.* The inflorescence is in simple raceme-like spikes; spikelets consisting of one sessile flower; lower glumes often wanting, upper with short awns; pales two, membranaceous and hair-pointed, the upper one-nerved, the lower nerveless; stamens three; styles two. The three species described are natives of the East Indies and Japan.   [D. M.]

ZOZIMIA. A genus of *Umbelliferæ*, containing two species of herbs, with decompound leaves, compound umbels, and many-leaved involucres and involucels. The calyx-limb is five-toothed; the petals obovate and emarginate, with an inflexed apex; the hairy fruits flattened dorsally; the carpels with five ribs; the commissure with two vittæ; and the carpophore bipartite.   [W. C.]

ZUCCA. Under this name has been mentioned, rather than described, a plant of the *Cucurbitaceæ*, with lateral tendrils, and solitary axillary flowers, concealed by a large bract. The calyx has five coloured sepals; and the male flowers have five stamens. Little else is known of this genus.   [M. T. M.]

ZUCKER WURZEL. The German name for the Skirret root.

ZURLOA. The plant upon which this genus of *Meliaceæ* was established by Tenore found its way into some of the Continental gardens, but its native country and history are unknown. It is an evergreen tree, with unequally pinnate smooth shining leaves, and large terminal panicles of white and rose-coloured flowers, which have a small five-toothed calyx, five roundish or elliptical petals (the edges of which meet without overlapping in the bud) a ten-toothed stamen-tube with as many elliptical anthers inside, and a five-furrowed ovary bearing a conical style and flat cup-shaped stigma. Its fruits are top-shaped five-angled capsules, having five single-seeded cells, and splitting open into as many valves when ripe, the seeds being black and as large as chestnuts.   [A. S.]

ZURRUT. An Arab name for *Sorghum vulgare.*

ZYGADENUS. A genus of *Melanthaceæ* from North America. It consists of smooth somewhat glaucous herbs, with creeping rhizomes or coated bulbs, grass-like leaves, and panicles of rather large greenish-white flowers, which are perfect with a withering spreading perianth of six leaves, sessile or slightly clawed at the base, where there are one or two glands; sometimes the bases adhere to the ovary; stamens six; styles short subulate; capsule tripartible at the top, with six or eight margined or slightly-winged seeds in each cell.   [J. T. S.]

ZYGIA. A genus of trees or shrubs, of the *Mimoseæ* division of *Leguminosæ.* The species are natives of Tropical America and Africa, and also of the Cape of Good Hope. They have bipinnate leaves, and flowers in panicles or in spiked heads; calyx tubular, five-toothed; corolla funnel-shaped, five-cleft; stamens numerous, the filaments combined into a spirally-twisted tube, projecting far beyond the petals; style longer than the stamens; pod flattened, membranous, divided by cellular partitions into several compartments; seeds numerous.   [M. T. M.]

ZYGNEMACEÆ. A natural order of green-spored *Algæ*, characterised by floating (rarely attached) jointed threads, with a spiral or figured endochrome, propagated by large zoospores formed from the union of the two contiguous endochromes in the same or neighbouring threads, or by the bisection of a single endochrome. They abound in fresh water, and have been much studied on account of the curious structure of the endochrome, and the phenomena attending the formation of the zoospores. In some genera (as *Zygnema*, *Mougeotia*, and *Tyndaridia*) union between contiguous threads is effected either by simple contact and subsequent amalgamation, or by means of lateral tubes. The spermatozoids are either derived immediately from the cells, or from antheridia produced from the cells as in *Œdogonium.* The endochrome is sometimes stellate, sometimes marked with a line of globules or with the globules symmetrically arranged, or is disposed in one or more spirals. When the latter are numerous, the similarity to the spiral vessels of phænogams is very striking. *Œdogonium* is in several respects anomalous; but though the threads are attached, and there is no union of threads, added to the peculiarities of the impregnation, it is more readily referred here than to any other order, unless a new order is proposed for its reception. In *Thwaitesia* and (according to Mr. Thwaites) in *Mesocarpus* and *Staurocarpus* the mass arising from the endochrome of two contiguous joints is ultimately resolved into four zoospores. Exotic species are but little known, but there is no doubt, from the example of India, that they are frequent in hot as well as in temperate countries. [M. J. B.]

ZYGODESMUS. A genus which, according to the degree of condensation of the creeping threads which constitute the principal mass of the fungus, may be assigned with almost equal propriety to *Auricularini* and *Mucedinei.* The peculiar characteristic consists in these threads being suddenly bent in such a manner, that on one side there is a little swelling or knuckle, and on the other an indentation occupying about two-thirds of their diameter, and looking like a septum, the thread then resuming its original course. The commonest species is *Z. fuscus*, which occurs on sticks and decayed timber in woods. Its spores are globose and rough with little points.   [M. J. B.]

ZYGODONTEI. A small natural order of acrocarpous mosses proposed by Dr. Montagne. They have a striated pear-shaped capsule, an abortive single or double peristome, and a dimidiate smooth veil. The habit is that of the true *Gymnostoma.* They are related to *Orthotrichei*, differing principally in the smooth dimidiate calyptra. A few species of *Zygodon* occur in Great Britain, but the only one which is at all common is *Z. viridissimus,* and that seldom bears fruit, as it is diœcious. *Z. cónoideus,* another of our species, occurs also in Tasmania. A few are sprinkled about in hot as well as in temperate or equable climates. [M. J. B.]

ZYGOLEPIS. A tree, native of the Philippine Islands, and the representative of a genus of *Sapindaceœ,* has received this name, in allusion to the scales on the petals. The leaves are pinnate, and the flowers in axillary panicles; the parts of the flower arranged in rows of five, each petal having a two-lobed scale in front of it; and the ovary having a short style. By these marks the genus may be distinguished from its nearest allies. [M. T. M.]

ZYGOPETALUM. A rather extensive genus of showy terrestrial orchids, referred to the *Vandeœ,* inhabiting Tropical America. The leaves are distichous large and plicate; and the flowers on a long scape, furnished with large boat-shaped bracts. The union of the petals at the base and the curious structure of the anther characterise this genus. Several species are cultivated in our gardens on account of their great beauty. [W. B. H.]

ZYGOPHYLLACEÆ. (*Beancapers.*) An order of polypetalous dicotyledons closely allied to *Rutaceœ, Simarubaceœ,* and *Geraniaceœ,* and difficult sometimes to separate from those orders by positive characters, although generally recognised by habit. They are shrubs or herbs, with more or less jointed stems; the leaves usually opposite and compound, with one pair or several pinnate leaflets, and with persistent stipules, sometimes converted into prickles; the flowers white red or yellow, very rarely blue, on axillary peduncles. There are five or rarely four sepals and petals; as many or twice as many stamens inserted on a fleshy disk; an angular or winged several-celled ovary, with two or more ovules in each cell; a dry fruit, often separating into distinct cocci; and pendulous seeds, with a small quantity of albumen. The species are widely dispersed over the tropical and warmer parts of the globe, but few occur in temperate climates; and they are distributed into seventeen genera, including *Tribulus, Zygophyllum, Fagonia, Guaiacum,* and others.

ZYGOPHYLLUM. A genus of trees and shrubs, giving its name to the order *Zygophyllaceœ.* The species are natives of the Cape of Good Hope, the Cape de Verd Isles, and the Levant. The leaves are opposite, and consist of two leaflets, either flat or cylindrical, and sometimes fleshy; and the flowers are solitary stalked axillary, with an unequally five-parted calyx, five-stalked white red or yellow petals, ten stamens each with a scale at the base, and a short stalked ovary ripening into a five-sided capsule, which has five compartments opening by as many valves, each containing a single seed. *Z. Fabago* has vermifuge properties, and its flower-buds are used instead of capers. The leaves of *Z. simpl..* are employed by the Arabs in diseases of the eye. The smell of this plant is so detestable that no animal will eat the foliage. *Z. coccineum* has aromatic seeds, employed by the Arabs in place of pepper. Several species are grown as greenhouse plants their flowers being handsome. The generic name is derived from *zugon* 'a yoke' and *phyllon* 'a leaf,' in allusion to the pairs of leaflets borne by these plants. [M. T. M.]

ZYGOSTATES. A small genus of epiphytal orchids belonging to the tribe *Vandeœ,* and inhabiting the forests of South America. The sepals and petals are membranaceous, similar; and the lip boat-shaped, with an incurved appendage at the base. They form stemless herbs, destitute of pseudobulbs; and with few narrow fleshy leaves, and small flowers in pendulous racemes. They are distinguished from *Ornithocephalus* by having a linear horizontal arm on each side of the column at its base, and a fleshy incurved process at the base of the lip, standing between the arms. [W. B. H.]

ZYGOSTIGMA. A name expressive of a peculiarity in the stigmas of the genus of *Gentianaceœ* to which it is applied. The species are herbaceous plants of little interest, natives of Brazil. The corolla is funnel-shaped, the anthers revolute, the ovary partly two-celled, and surmounted by two stigmas, which are branched, the branches being adherent one to another. The fruit is capsular. [M. T. M.]